SUPPORT FOR LEARNING THE CONCEPTS

old nephew suggested that Kasner call this number a googol. If you are looking for a number that is even larger than a googol, try a googolplex, which is 10^{googol}, or $10^{10^{100}}$.

Order of Operations

To evaluate an expression or to check the solution to an equation, we need to know the *order of operations* to follow. For example, suppose we want to evaluate the expression $2 + 3x$ when $x = 4$. Substituting 4 for x, we obtain $2 + 3 \cdot 4$. What is the value of $2 + 3 \cdot 4$? Does it equal 20, or does it equal 14? Some standard rules, called the order of operations, have been developed to ensure that there is only one correct answer. In mathematics, unless parentheses indicate otherwise, always perform multiplication before addition. Thus, the correct answer is 14.

$$2 + 3 \cdot 4 = 2 + (3 \cdot 4) = 2 + 12 = 14$$

The order of operations for evaluating an expression is as follows.

TIMELY TIP

Some students use the phrase "*Please Excuse My Dear Aunt Sally*" or the word "PEMDAS" (*Parentheses, Exponents, Multiplication, Division, Addition, Subtraction*) to remind them of the order of operations. Remember: Multiplication and division are of the same order, and addition and subtraction are of the same order.

PROCEDURE ORDER OF OPERATIONS

1. First, perform all operations within parentheses or other grouping symbols (according to the following order).
2. Next, perform all exponential operations (that is, raising to powers or finding roots).
3. Next, perform all multiplications and divisions from left to right.
4. Finally, perform all additions and subtractions from left to right.

Timely Tips appear where appropriate to give quick study tips and extra support for learning the topic.

Procedures are set apart from the text for easy reference when doing homework or preparing for tests.

NEW! Warm Up Exercises now begin each exercise set with fill-in-the-blank problems to ensure a firm grasp of the section's fundamental concepts.

SECTION 2.1 *Exercises*

Warm Up Exercises

In Exercises 1–12, fill in the blank with an appropriate word, phrase, or symbol(s).

1. A collection of objects is called a(n) _____.
2. Three dots placed in a set to show that the set continues in the same manner is called a(n) _____.
3. The three ways a set can be written are _____, _____, and _____.
4. A set that contain no elements or the number of elements in the set is a natural number is called a(n) _____ set.
5. A a set that is not finite is called a(n) _____. set.
6. Two sets that contain the same elements are called _____ sets.
7. Two sets that contain the same number of elements are called _____ sets.
8. The number of elements in a set is called the _____ number.
9. The set that contains no elements is called the _____ set.
10. The two ways to indicate an empty set are _____ and _____.
11. A set that contains all the elements for any specific discussion is called a(n) _____ set.
12. Two sets that have the same cardinal number can be placed in a(n) _____ correspondence.

CHAPTER 3 *Summary*

Important Facts and Concepts | **Examples**

Section 3.1
Quantifiers

Form of Statement	Form of Negation
All are.	Some are not.
None are.	Some are.
Some are.	None are.
Some are not.	All are.

Example 1, page 96

Summary of Connectives

Formal Name	Symbol	Read	Symbolic Form
Negation	~	not	$\sim p$
Conjunction	$\wedge$	and	$p \wedge q$
Disjunction	$\vee$	or	$p \vee q$
Conditional	$\rightarrow$	if-then	$p \rightarrow q$
Biconditional	$\leftrightarrow$	if and only if	$p \leftrightarrow q$

Examples 2–8, pages 97–101

Section 3.2 & Section 3.3
Basic Truth Tables

Negation		Conjunction	Disjunction	Conditional	Biconditional
p	$\sim p$	p	q	$p \wedge q$	$p \vee q$	$p \rightarrow q$	$p \leftrightarrow q$

p	$\sim p$	p	q	$p \wedge q$	$p \vee q$	$p \rightarrow q$	$p \leftrightarrow q$
T	F	T	T	T	T	T	T
F	T	T	F	F	T	F	F
		F	T	F	T	T	F
		F	F	F	F	T	T

Examples 1–10, pages 107–114
Examples 1–10, pages 118–124

Section 3.4
De Morgan's Laws

$$\sim(p \wedge q) \Leftrightarrow \sim p \vee \sim q$$
$$\sim(p \vee q) \Leftrightarrow \sim p \wedge \sim q$$

Examples 4–6, pages 130–131

NEW! Chapter Summaries are redesigned in a chart format for easier study and review. For each concept, definition, or idea listed, page references point to where in the text the item is discussed.

ANNOTATED INSTRUCTOR'S EDITION

9TH EDITION

A Survey of

Mathematics

with Applications

ALLEN R. ANGEL
Monroe Community College

CHRISTINE D. ABBOTT
Monroe Community College

DENNIS C. RUNDE
State College of Florida

PEARSON

Boston   Columbus   Indianapolis   New York   San Francisco   Upper Saddle River
Amsterdam   Cape Town   Dubai   London   Madrid   Milan   Munich   Paris   Montreal   Toronto
Delhi   Mexico City   Sao Paulo   Sydney   Hong Kong   Seoul   Singapore   Taipei   Tokyo

Editor in Chief: Anne Kelly
Acquisitions Editor: Marnie Greenhut
Senior Content Editor: Chere Bemelmans
Assistant Editor: Elle Driska
Associate Managing Editor: Tamela Ambush
Senior Production Project Manager: Peggy McMahon
Associate Director of Design, USHE North and West: Andrea Nix
Art Director, Cover and Interior: Beth Paquin
Cover Designer: Rokusek Design
Image Manager: Rachel Youdelman
Photo Research: PreMedia Global USA, Inc.
Media Producer: Tracy Menoza
Software Development: Bob Carroll and Mary Durnwald
Executive Marketing Manager: Roxanne McCarley
Marketing Assistant: Caitlin Crain
Senior Author Support/Technology Specialist: Joe Vetere
Permissions Project Supervisor: Michael Joyce
Procurement Manager: Evelyn Beaton
Procurement Specialist: Debbie Rossi
Text Design, Production Coordination, Illustrations, and Composition: Cenveo Publisher Services/Nesbitt Graphics, Inc.

For permission to use copyrighted material, grateful acknowledgment has been made to the copyright holders on page C-1 in the back of the book, which is hereby made part of this copyright page.

Many of the designations used by manufacturers and sellers to distinguish their products are claimed as trademarks. Where those designations appear in this book, and Pearson was aware of a trademark claim, the designations have been printed in initial caps or all caps.

The Library of Congress has cataloged the Student Edition of this title as follows:

Library of Congress Cataloging-in-Publication Data

Angel, Allen R., 1942–
 A survey of mathematics with applications / Allen R. Angel, Christine
D. Abbott, Dennis C. Runde.--9th ed.
   p. cm.
 Includes index.
 ISBN 0-321-75966-4
 1. Mathematics--Textbooks. I. Abbott, Christine D. II. Runde, Dennis
C. III. Title.
 QA39.3.A54 2012
 510--dc23
                                        2011042964

3 4 5 6 7 8 9 10—V011—15

www.pearsonhighered.com

ISBN-10: 0-321-63928-6
ISBN-13: 978-0-321-63928-8

To my wife, Kathy Angel (photo on page 56)
A. R. A.

To the memory of my parents, Ed and June Dunn
C. D. A.

To my parents, Bud and Tina Runde
D. C. R.

Contents

Mathematics is an exciting, living study. Its applications shape the world around you and influence your everyday life. We hope that as you read this book you will realize just how important mathematics is and gain an appreciation of both its usefulness and its beauty. We also hope to teach you some practical mathematics that you can use every day and that will prepare you for further mathematics courses.

The primary purpose of this text is to provide material that you can read, understand, and enjoy. To this end, we have used straightforward language and tried to relate the mathematical concepts to everyday experiences. We have also provided many detailed examples for you to follow.

The concepts, definitions, and formulas that deserve special attention are in boxes or are set in boldface, italics, or color type. In the exercise sets, within each category, the exercises are graded, with more difficult problems appearing at the end. At the end of most exercise sets are Challenge Problems/Group Activities Exercises that contain challenging or exploratory exercises. At the end of each chapter are Group Projects that reinforce the material learned or provide related material.

Be sure to read the chapter summary, work the review exercises, and take the chapter test at the end of each chapter. The answers to the odd-numbered exercises, all review exercises, and all chapter test exercises appear in the answer section in the back of the text. You should, however, use the answers only to check your work. The answers to all Recreational Mathematics exercises are provided in either the Recreational Mathematics boxes themselves, or in the back of the book.

It is difficult to learn mathematics without becoming involved. To be successful, we suggest that you read the text carefully *and work each exercise in each assignment in detail*. Check with your instructor to determine which supplements are available for your use.

We welcome your suggestions and your comments. You may contact us at the following address:

Allen Angel
c/o Marketing
Mathematics and Statistics
Pearson
75 Arlington St., Suite 300
Boston, MA 02116

or by email at:

math@pearson.com

Subject: for Allen Angel

Good luck with your adventure in mathematics!

Allen R. Angel
Christine D. Abbott
Dennis C. Runde

We present *A Survey of Mathematics with Applications*, Ninth Edition, with the vision in mind that we use mathematics every day. In this edition, we stress how mathematics is used in our daily lives and why it is important. Our primary goal is to give students a text they can read, understand, and enjoy while learning how mathematics affects the world around them. Numerous real-life applications are used to motivate topics. A variety of interesting and useful exercises demonstrate the real-life nature of mathematics and its importance in students' lives.

The text is intended for students who require a broad-based general overview of mathematics, especially those majoring in the liberal arts, elementary education, the social sciences, business, nursing, and allied health fields. It is particularly suitable for those courses that satisfy the minimum competency requirement in mathematics for graduation or transfer.

New to This Edition

- Why This Is Important is a new concept woven throughout the book to help students make the connection between their lives and the mathematics they're learning. Why This Is Important notes can be found in all chapter and section openers as well as the Mathematics Today features.
- Many chapter and section openers contain new, interesting, and motivational information and applications to introduce the section and illustrate the real-world nature of the material in that section. For example, Section 2.3 introduces Venn diagrams and set operations with the experience of purchasing a laptop computer. The Chapter 3 opener indicates how logic has become important in electronic devices such as cell phones and digital cameras.
- Recreational Mathematics boxes added throughout the book show various ways that math can be fun!
- Approximately 40% of the examples and exercises in the book are changed. We updated many examples and exercises to reflect current data and topics of interest to students.
- Exercise sets now begin with fill-in-the-blank Warm Up Exercises.
- We revised and greatly expanded the chapter summaries into a chart format for easier studying.
- All chapter tests have been reorganized to include exactly 20 questions for consistency in length while thoroughly covering the content presented in the chapter.

Content Revision

In this edition, we have revised and expanded certain topics to introduce new material and to increase understanding.

Chapter 1 "Critical Thinking Skills," includes exciting and current examples and exercises.

Chapter 2 "Sets," includes many new applications of sets pertaining to a greater variety of topics, such as the sales of iPods and other electronic devices.

Chapter 3 "Logic," contains new exercises, as well as a greater variety of exercises. We include several puzzles, sudoku and kakuro, as Recreational Mathematics exercises. Also, we now show an alternative method to work truth tables.

Chapter 4 "Systems of Numeration," contains information on the bases 2, 8, and 16, which have many applications in modern devices such as smart phones, cameras, and high-definition televisions.

Chapter 5 "Number Theory and the Real Number System," has updated information regarding the largest prime number found and the most calculated digits of pi. We updated exercise sets to reflect current economic numbers involving the national debt, the gross domestic product, population growth and so on.

Chapter 6 "Algebra, Graphs, and Functions," has updated examples and exercises dealing with real-life situations. We moved material on exponential equations from Section 6.3 to Section 6.10 and updated it to include examples and exercises on population growth.

Chapter 7 "Systems of Linear Equations and Inequalities," contains many updated examples and exercises.

Chapter 8 "The Metric System," has many new up-to-date examples, exercises, and photographs of real-life metric use throughout the world.

Chapter 9 "Geometry," includes many updated examples and exercises, and we rewrote several topics for greater clarity.

Chapter 10 "Mathematical Systems," has many new examples, exercises, and real-life applications to modern technology.

Chapter 11 "Consumer Mathematics," contains updated interest rates involving a variety of loans and investments. We rewrote much of the material clearly and concisely. We now calculate monthly payments on installment loans and principal and interest for a mortgage payment, using a formula in addition to a table.

Chapter 12 "Probability," has updated examples and exercises that deal with real-life applications, including video games, smart phones, and Facebook.

Chapter 13 In "Statistics," the authors combined Sections 13.3 and 13.4 to emphasize the relationship between frequency distributions and statistical graphs. We rewrote material in Section 13.7, The Normal Curve, for greater clarity, and we updated many examples and exercises with real-life applications.

Chapter 14 "Graph Theory," involves many new applications of graphs to a variety of topics, including maps, social networks (such as Facebook), and other real-world applications.

Chapter 15 "Voting and Apportionment," includes many updated examples and exercises about voting and apportionment. We rewrote some of this material for greater clarity.

Continuing and Revised Features

- **Chapter Openers** Interesting and motivational applications introduce each chapter, which includes the Why This Is Important section, and illustrate the real-world nature of the chapter topics.

- **Problem Solving** Beginning in Chapter 1, students are introduced to problem solving and critical thinking. We continue the theme of problem solving throughout the text and present special problem-solving exercises in the exercise sets.
- **Critical Thinking Skills** In addition to a focus on problem solving, this book also features sections on inductive and deductive reasoning, estimation, and dimensional analysis.
- **Profiles in Mathematics** Brief historical sketches and vignettes present stories of people who have advanced the discipline of mathematics.
- **Did You Know?** The colorful, engaging, and lively Did You Know? boxes highlight the connections of mathematics to history, the arts and sciences, technology, and a broad variety of disciplines.
- **Mathematics Today** These boxes discuss current real-life uses of the mathematical concepts in the chapter. Each box ends with Why This Is Important.
- **Technology Tips** The material in these boxes explains how students can use calculators, Excel, or other technologies to work certain types of application problems.
- **Timely Tips** These easy-to-identify boxes offer helpful information to make the material under discussion more understandable.
- **Boxed Material** Important definitions, formulas, and procedures are boxed, making key information easy to identify for students.
- **Group Projects** At the end of each chapter are suggested group projects that instructors can use to encourage students to work together. Instructors can also assign these projects to individual students.
- **Chapter Summaries, Review Exercises, and Chapter Tests** The end-of-chapter Summaries, now in chart format, provide an easier study experience by directing students to the location in the text where specific concepts are discussed. Review Exercises and Chapter Tests also help students review material and prepare for exams.

Online Homework Systems

MyMathLab® Online Course (access code required)

MyMathLab delivers **proven results** in helping individual students succeed. It provides **engaging experiences** that personalize, stimulate, and measure learning for each student. And it comes from a **trusted partner** with educational expertise and an eye on the future.

To learn more about how MyMathLab combines proven learning applications with powerful assessment, visit **www.mymathlab.com** or contact your Pearson representative.

MyMathLab® Ready to Go Course (access code required)

These new Ready to Go courses provide students with all the same great MyMathLab features that you're used to, but make it easier for instructors to get started. Each course includes pre-assigned homeworks and quizzes to make creating your course even simpler. Ask your Pearson representative about the details for this particular course or to see a copy of this course.

MathXL® Online Course (access code required)

Math XL® is the homework and assessment engine that runs MyMathLab. (MyMathLab is MathXL plus a learning management system.) With MathXL, instructors can:

- Create, edit, and assign online homework and tests using algorithmically generated exercises correlated at the objective level to the textbook.
- Create and assign their own online exercises and import TestGen tests for added flexibility.
- Maintain records of all student work tracked in MathXL's online gradebook.

With MathXL, students can:

- Take chapter tests in MathXL and receive personalized study plans and/or personalized homework assignments based on their test results.
- Use the study plan and/or the homework to link directly to tutorial exercises for the objectives they need to study.
- Access supplemental animations and video clips directly from selected exercises.

MathXL is available to qualified adopters. For more information, visit our website at www.mathxl.com, or contact your Pearson representative.

Student's Solutions Manual
ISBN 13: 978-0-321-63931-8; ISBN 10: 0-321-63931-6
by Tamsen Herrick of Butte College

This for-sale manual contains solutions to all odd-numbered exercises and to all Review and Chapter Test exercises.

Video Resources

These digitized videos review chapter content for student use at home or on the go. They are ideal for distance learning and supplemental instruction.

Annotated Instructor's Edition
ISBN 13: 978-0-321-63928-8; ISBN 10: 0-321-63928-6

This special edition of the text includes answers next to the exercises, for quick reference. Answers that do not fit next to the exercise are placed in a separate section in the back of the book. Answers to all text exercises are included.

Online Supplements

Online supplements are available for download only at **www.pearsonhighered.com/irc.**

Instructor's Solutions Manual
by Tamsen Herrick of Butte College

This manual contains solutions to all exercises in the text and answers to Group Projects.

Instructor's Testing Manual

This manual includes three alternate tests per chapter.

Insider's Guide

This manual includes resources and helpful section-specific teaching tips designed to assist both new and adjunct faculty with course preparation.

PowerPoint Lecture Presentation

These fully editable lecture slides include definitions, key concepts, and examples for use in a lecture setting and are available for each section of the text.

TestGen®

TestGen enables instructors to build, edit, print, and administer tests using a computerized bank of questions developed to cover all the objectives of the text. TestGen is algorithmically based, allowing instructors to create multiple but equivalent versions of the same question or test with the click of a button. Instructors can also modify test bank questions or add new questions. Tests can be printed or administered online. The software and testbank are available for download from Pearson Education's online catalog.

Acknowledgments

We thank our spouses, Kathy Angel, Jason Abbott, and Kris Runde, for their support and encouragement throughout the project. They helped us in a great many ways, including proofreading, typing, and offering valuable suggestions. We are grateful for their wonderful support and understanding while we worked on the book.

We also thank our children: Robert and Steven Angel; Matthew and Jake Abbott; and Alex, Nick, and Max Runde. They also gave us support and encouragement and were very understanding when we could not spend as much time with them as we wished because of book deadlines. Without the support and understanding of our families, this book would not be a reality.

We thank Patricia Nelson of the University of Wisconsin–LaCrosse and James Lapp for their conscientious job of checking the text and answers for accuracy. We also thank Sherry Tornwall of the University of Florida for continually making valuable suggestions for improving the book. And thanks to Becky Troutman for preparing the Index of Applications.

Many people at Pearson deserve thanks, including all those listed on the copyright page. In particular, we thank Anne Kelly, Editor in Chief; Marnie Greenhut, Acquisitions Editor; Chere Bemelmans, Senior Content Editor; Elle Driska, Assistant Editor; Peggy McMahon, Senior Production Project Manager; Roxanne McCarley, Executive Marketing Manager; Caitlin Crain, Marketing Assistant; Tracy Menoza, Media Producer; and Beth Paquin, Senior Designer. We also thank Judith Bucci of Nesbitt Graphics, Inc., for her assistance as Project Manager for this edition.

Tamsen Herrick of Butte College also deserves our thanks for the excellent work she did on the *Student's* and *Instructor's Solutions Manuals*.

Finally, we thank the reviewers from all editions of the book and all the students who have offered suggestions for improving it. A list of reviewers for all editions of this book follows. Thanks to you all for helping make *A Survey of Mathematics with Applications* the most successful liberal arts mathematics textbook in the country.

Allen R. Angel

Christine D. Abbott

Dennis C. Runde

Reviewers for This and Previous Editions

*Marilyn Ahrens, Missouri Valley College

*David Allen, Iona College

Mary Anne Anthony-Smith, Santa Ana College

Frank Asta, College of DuPage

Robin L. Ayers, Western Kentucky University

Hughette Bach, California State University–Sacramento

Madeline Bates, Bronx Community College

Rebecca Baum, Lincoln Land Community College

Vivian Baxter, Fort Hays State University

Una Bray, Skidmore College

David H. Buckley, Polk State College

Robert C. Bueker, Western Kentucky University

Carl Carlson, Moorhead State University

Kent Carlson, St. Cloud State University

Donald Catheart, Salisbury State College

Yungchen Cheng, Southwest Missouri State University

Joseph Cleary, Massasoit Community College

Donald Cohen, SUNY College of Agriculture & Technology at Cobleskill

David Dean, Santa Fe College

*John Diamantopoulos, Northeastern State University

*Greg Dietrich, Florida State College at Jacksonville

Charles Downey, University of Nebraska

*Jeffrey Downs, Western Nevada College

Annie Droullard, Polk State College

Ruth Ediden, Morgan State University

Lee Erker, Tri-County Community College

*Nancy Eschen, Florida State College at Jacksonville

Karen Estes, St. Petersburg College

Teklay Fessanaye, Santa Fe College

Kurtis Fink, Northwest Missouri State University

Raymond Flagg, McPherson College

Penelope Fowler, Tennessee Wesleyan College

Gilberto Garza, El Paso Community College

Judith L. Gersting, Indiana University–Purdue University at Indianapolis

*Patricia Granfield, George Mason University

Lucille Groenke, Mesa Community College

*Kaylinda Holton, Tallahassee Community College

John Hornsby, University of New Orleans

*Judith Ink, Regent University

Nancy Johnson, Broward College

*Phyllis H. Jore, Valencia College

*Heidi Kiley, Suffolk County Community College

Daniel Kimborowicz, Massasoit Community College

Mary Lois King, Tallahassee Community College

*Harriet H. Kiser, Georgia Highlands College

*Julia Ledet, Louisiana State University

David Lehmann, Southwest Missouri State University

Peter Lindstrom, North Lake College

James Magliano, Union College

Yash Manchanda, East Los Angeles College & Fullerton College

*Richard Marchand, Slippery Rock University

Don Marsian, Hillsborough Community College

Marilyn Mays, North Lake College

*Susan McCourt, Bristol Community College

Robert McGuigan, Westfield State College

Wallace H. Memmer, Brookdale Community College

Maurice Monahan, South Dakota State University

Julie Monte, Daytona State College

Karen Mosely, Alabama Southern Community College

*Kathleen Offenholley, Brookdale Community College

Edwin Owens, Pennsylvania College of Technology

Wing Park, College of Lake County

Bettye Parnham, Daytona State College

Joanne Peeples, El Paso Community College

*Traci M. Reed, St. John's River Community College

Nelson Rich, Nazareth College

Kenneth Ross, University of Oregon

Ronald Ruemmler, Middlesex County College

Rosa Rusinek, Queensborough Community College

Len Ruth, Sinclair Community College

John Samoylo, Delaware County Community College

Sandra Savage, Orange Coast College

Gerald Schultz, Southern Connecticut State University

Richard Schwartz, College of Staten Island

Kara Shavo, Mercer County Community College

Minnie Shuler, Chipola College

Paula R. Stickles, University of Southern Indiana

Kristin Stoley, Blinn College–Bryan

Steve Sworder, Saddleback College

Shirley Thompson, Moorhead College

Alvin D. Tinsley, Central Missouri State University

*Sherry Tornwall, University of Florida

William Trotter, University of South Carolina

Zia Uddin, Lock Haven University of Pennsylvania

*Michael Vislocky, University of Cincinnati

Sandra Welch, Stephen F. Austin State University

Joyce Wellington, Southeastern Community College

Sue Welsch, Sierra Nevada College

Robert F. Wheeler, Northern Illinois University

Susan Wirth, Indian River State College

James Wooland, Florida State University

*Judith B. Wood, Central Florida Community College

Jean Woody, Tulsa Community College

Michael A. Zwick, Monroe Community College

*Denotes reviewers for ninth edition.

1

Critical Thinking Skills

Life constantly presents new problems. The more sophisticated our society becomes, the more complex the problems. We as individuals are constantly solving problems. For example, when we consider ways to reduce our expenses or when we plan a trip, we make problem-solving decisions. We also have to make problem-solving decisions when we figure out how to divide our time between studying, friends, family, work, and recreational activities. Additionally, businesses are constantly trying to solve problems that involve making a profit for the company and keeping customers satisfied.

The goal of this chapter is to help you master the skills of reasoning, estimating, and problem solving. These skills will aid you in solving problems in the remainder of this book as well as those you will encounter in everyday life.

◄ *Planning a trip uses critical thinking skills to stay within a budget while visiting exciting new places.*

SECTION 1.1 Inductive Reasoning

▲ *A device like this can be used to gain access to your computer.*

Thus far, no two people have been found to have the same fingerprints or DNA. So fingerprints and DNA have become forms of identification. As technology improves, so do identification techniques. Computerized fingerprint scanners are now showing up in police stations, in high-tech security buildings, and with personal computers. You can purchase a personal USB fingerprint scanner that requires your distinctive fingerprint to gain access to your computer. The belief that no two people have the same finger size, shape, and density is based on a type of reasoning we will discuss in this section.

Why *This is Important* As you will see in this section, we use a type of reasoning, called *inductive reasoning*, every day when we make decisions based on past experiences.

Inductive Reasoning

Before looking at some examples of inductive reasoning and problem solving, let us first review a few facts about certain numbers. The *natural numbers* or *counting numbers* are the numbers 1, 2, 3, 4, 5, 6, 7, 8, ... The three dots, called an *ellipsis*, mean that 8 is not the last number but that the numbers continue in the same manner. A word that we sometimes use when discussing the counting numbers is "divisible." If $a \div b$ has a remainder of zero, then *a is divisible by b*. The counting numbers that are divisible by 2 are 2, 4, 6, 8,.... These numbers are called the *even counting numbers*. The counting numbers that are not divisible by 2 are 1, 3, 5, 7, 9,.... These numbers are the *odd counting numbers*. When we refer to *odd numbers* or *even numbers*, we mean odd or even counting numbers.

Recognizing patterns is sometimes helpful in solving problems, as Examples 1 and 2 illustrate.

Example 1 *The Product of Two Even Numbers*

If two even numbers are multiplied together, will the product always be an even number?

Solution To answer this question, we will examine the products of several pairs of even numbers to see if there is a pattern.

$2 \times 2 = 4$	$4 \times 6 = 24$	$6 \times 8 = 48$
$2 \times 4 = 8$	$4 \times 8 = 32$	$6 \times 10 = 60$
$2 \times 6 = 12$	$4 \times 10 = 40$	$6 \times 12 = 72$
$2 \times 8 = 16$	$4 \times 12 = 48$	$6 \times 14 = 84$

All the products are even numbers. Thus, we might predict from these examples that the product of any two even numbers is an even number. ∎

Example 2 *The Sum of an Odd Number and an Even Number*

If an odd number and an even number are added, will the sum be an odd number or an even number?

Solution Let's look at a few examples in which one number is odd and the other number is even.

$$3 + 4 = 7 \qquad 9 + 6 = 15 \qquad 23 + 18 = 41$$
$$5 + 12 = 17 \qquad 5 + 14 = 19 \qquad 81 + 32 = 113$$

All these sums are odd numbers. Therefore, we might predict that the sum of an odd number and an even number is an odd number. ∎

In Examples 1 and 2, we cannot conclude that the results are true for all counting numbers. From the patterns developed, however, we can make predictions. This type of reasoning process, arriving at a general conclusion from specific observations or examples, is called *inductive reasoning*, or *induction*.

Definition: Inductive Reasoning

Inductive reasoning is the process of reasoning to a general conclusion through observations of specific cases.

Induction often involves observing a pattern and from that pattern predicting a conclusion. Imagine an endless row of dominoes. You knock down the first, which knocks down the second, which knocks down the third, and so on. Assuming the pattern will continue uninterrupted, you conclude that any one domino that you select in the row will eventually fall, even though you may not witness the event.

Inductive reasoning is often used by mathematicians and scientists to predict answers to complicated problems. For this reason, inductive reasoning is part of the *scientific method*. When a scientist or mathematician makes a prediction based on specific observations, it is called a *hypothesis* or *conjecture*. After looking at the products in Example 1, we might conjecture that the product of two even numbers will be an even number. After looking at the sums in Example 2, we might conjecture that the sum of an odd number and an even number is an odd number.

Examples 3 and 4 illustrate how we arrive at a conclusion using inductive reasoning.

Example 3 *Fingerprints and DNA*

What reasoning process has led to the conclusion that no two people have the same fingerprints or DNA? This conclusion has resulted in the use of fingerprints and DNA in courts of law as evidence to convict persons of crimes.

Solution In millions of tests, no two people have been found to have the same fingerprints or DNA. By induction, then, we believe that fingerprints and DNA provide a unique identification and can therefore be used in a court of law as evidence. Is it possible that sometime in the future two people will be found who do have exactly the same fingerprints or DNA? ∎

Example 4 *Divisibility by 3*

Consider the following conjecture: "If the sum of the digits of a number is divisible by 3, then the number itself is divisible by 3." We will test several numbers to see if the conjecture appears to be true or false.

Solution Let's look at some numbers whose sum of the digits is divisible by 3.

Number	Sum of the Digits	Is the Sum of the Digits Divisible by 3?	Is the Number Divisible by 3?
243	$2 + 4 + 3 = 9$	Yes; $9 \div 3 = 3$	Yes; $243 \div 3 = 81$
2088	$2 + 0 + 8 + 8 = 18$	Yes; $18 \div 3 = 6$	Yes; $2088 \div 3 = 696$
6783	$6 + 7 + 8 + 3 = 24$	Yes; $24 \div 3 = 8$	Yes; $6783 \div 3 = 2261$
49,116	$4 + 9 + 1 + 1 + 6 = 21$	Yes; $21 \div 3 = 7$	Yes; $49,116 \div 3 = 16,372$

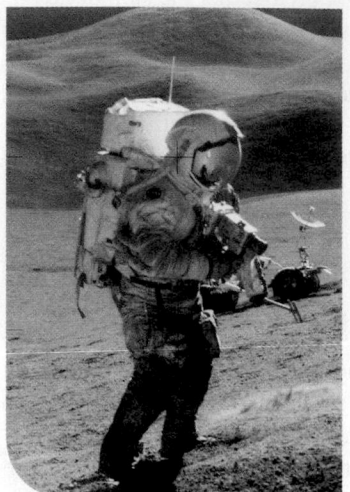
In each case, we find that if the sum of the digits of a number is divisible by 3, then the number itself is divisible by 3. From these examples, we might be tempted to generalize that the conjecture "If the sum of the digits of a number is divisible by 3, then the number itself is divisible by 3"* is true. ∎

Example 5 *Pick a Number, Any Number*

Pick any number, multiply the number by 4, add 2 to the product, divide the sum by 2, and subtract 1 from the quotient. Repeat this procedure for several different numbers and then make a conjecture about the relationship between the original number and the final number.

Solution Let's go through this one together.

Pick a number:	say, 5
Multiply the number by 4:	$4 \times 5 = 20$
Add 2 to the product:	$20 + 2 = 22$
Divide the sum by 2:	$22 \div 2 = 11$
Subtract 1 from the quotient:	$11 - 1 = 10$

Note that we started with the number 5 and finished with the number 10. If you start with the number 2, you will end with the number 4. Starting with 3 would result in a final number of 6, 4 would result in 8, and so on. On the basis of these few examples, we may conjecture that when you follow the given procedure, the number you end with will always be twice the original number. ∎

The result reached by inductive reasoning is often correct for the specific cases studied but not correct for all cases. History has shown that not all conclusions arrived at by inductive reasoning are correct. For example, Aristotle (384–322 B.C.) reasoned inductively that heavy objects fall at a faster rate than light objects. About 2000 years later, Galileo (1564–1642) dropped two pieces of metal—one 10 times heavier than the other—from the Leaning Tower of Pisa in Italy. He found that both hit the ground at exactly the same moment, so they must have traveled at the same rate.

When forming a general conclusion using inductive reasoning, you should test it with several special cases to see whether the conclusion appears correct. If a special case is found that satisfies the conditions of the conjecture but produces a different result, such a case is called a *counterexample*. A counterexample proves that the conjecture is false because only one exception is needed to show that a conjecture is not valid. Galileo's counterexample disproved Aristotle's conjecture. If a counterexample cannot be found, the conjecture is neither proven nor disproven.

Deductive Reasoning

A second type of reasoning process is called *deductive reasoning*, or *deduction*. Mathematicians use deductive reasoning to *prove* conjectures true or false.

Definition: Deductive Reasoning
Deductive reasoning is the process of reasoning to a specific conclusion from a general statement.

Example 6 *Pick a Number, n*

Prove, using deductive reasoning, that the procedure in Example 5 will always result in twice the original number selected.

---

*This statement is in fact true, as is discussed in Section 5.1.

Solution To use deductive reasoning, we begin with the *general* case rather than specific examples. In Example 5, specific cases were used. Let's select the letter n to represent *any number*.

Pick any number:	n
Multiply the number by 4:	$4n$ $\quad$ 4n means 4 times n
Add 2 to the product:	$4n + 2$
Divide the sum by 2:	$\dfrac{4n + 2}{2} = \dfrac{\overset{2}{4n}}{\underset{1}{2}} + \dfrac{\overset{1}{2}}{\underset{1}{2}} = 2n + 1$
Subtract 1 from the quotient:	$2n + 1 - 1 = 2n$

Note that for any number n selected, the result is $2n$, or twice the original number selected. ∎

In Example 5, you may have *conjectured*, using specific examples and inductive reasoning, that the result would be twice the original number selected. In Example 6, we *proved*, using deductive reasoning, that the result will always be twice the original number selected.

SECTION 1.1 *Exercises*

Warm Up Exercises

In Exercises 1–8, fill in the blank with an appropriate word, phrase, or symbol(s).

1. Another name for the natural numbers is the _____ numbers. Counting

2. If $a \div b$ has a remainder of 0, then a is _____ by b. Divisible

3. A belief based on specific observations that has not been proven or disproven is called a conjecture or _____. Hypothesis

4. A specific case that satisfies the conditions of a conjecture but shows the conjecture is false is called a _____. Counterexample

5. The process of reasoning to a general conclusion through observation of specific cases is called _____ reasoning. Inductive

6. The process of reasoning to a specific conclusion from a general statement is called _____ reasoning. Deductive

7. The type of reasoning used to prove a conjecture is called _____ reasoning. Deductive

8. The type of reasoning generally used to arrive at a conjecture is called _____ reasoning. Inductive

9. While logging on to your computer, you type in your username followed by what you believe is your password. The computer indicates that a mistake has been made and asks you to try again. You retype your username and the same password. Again, the computer indicates a mistake has been made. You decide not to try again, reasoning you will get the same error message from the computer. What type of reasoning did you use? Explain. Inductive reasoning; a general conclusion is obtained from observation of specific cases.

10. You have purchased one lottery ticket each week for many months and have not won more than $5.00. You decide, based on your past experience, that you are not going to win the grand prize and so you stop playing the lottery. What type of reasoning did you use? Explain. Inductive reasoning; a general conclusion is obtained from observation of specific cases.

Practice the Skills

In Exercises 11–14, use inductive reasoning to predict the next line in the pattern.

11. $1 \times 5 = 5$
    $2 \times 5 = 10$
    $3 \times 5 = 15$
    $4 \times 5 = 20$ $\quad 5 \times 5 = 25$

12. $12 \times 10 = 120$
    $12 \times 11 = 132$
    $12 \times 12 = 144$
    $12 \times 13 = 156$ $\quad 12 \times 14 = 168$

13.
```
        1
      1   1
    1   2   1
  1   3   3   1
1   4   6   4   1    1 5 10 10 5 1
```

14. $10 = 10^1$
    $100 = 10^2$
    $1000 = 10^3$
    $10,000 = 10^4$ $\quad 100,000 = 10^5$

In Exercises 15–18, draw the next figure in the pattern (or sequence).

15. △, ▢, ⬠ *

16. 😊😠😊😠😊😐, ... *

17. △▢⬠⬡, ... *

18. 😊, ⊙⊙, 😊, ⊙⊙, ⊙⊙, ... *

In Exercises 19–28, use inductive reasoning to predict the next three numbers in the pattern (or sequence).

19. 2, 4, 6, 8, ... 10, 12, 14

20. 3, 7, 11, 15, ... 19, 23, 27

21. 3, −3, 3, −3, ... 3, −3, 3

22. 5, 3, 1, −1, ... −3, −5, −7

23. 1, $\frac{1}{2}$, $\frac{1}{3}$, $\frac{1}{4}$, ... $\frac{1}{5}$, $\frac{1}{6}$, $\frac{1}{7}$

24. 4, −20, 100, −500, ... 2500, −12,500, 62,500

25. 1, 4, 9, 16, 25, ... 36, 49, 64

26. 0, 1, 3, 6, 10, 15, ... 21, 28, 36

27. 1, 1, 2, 3, 5, 8, 13, 21, ... 34, 55, 89

28. 3, $-\frac{9}{4}$, $\frac{27}{16}$, $-\frac{81}{64}$, ... $\frac{243}{256}$, $\frac{-729}{1024}$, $\frac{2187}{4096}$

Problem Solving

29. Find the letter that is the 118th entry in the following sequence. Explain how you determined your answer. Y

Y, R, R, Y, R, R, Y, R, R, Y, R, R, Y, R, R, ...

30. a) Select a variety of one- and two-digit numbers between 1 and 99 and multiply each by 9. Record your results. Answers will vary.
b) Find the sum of the digits in each of your products in part (a). If the sum is not a one-digit number, find the sum of the digits again until you obtain a one-digit number. The sum is 9.
c) Make a conjecture about the sum of the digits when a one- or two-digit number is multiplied by 9. The sum of the digits in the product when a one- or two-digit number is multiplied by 9 is 9.

31. *A Square Pattern* The ancient Greeks labeled certain numbers as **square numbers**. The numbers 1, 4, 9, 16, 25, and so on are square numbers.

1   4   9   16   25

a) Determine the next three square numbers. 36, 49, 64

b) Describe a procedure to determine the next five square numbers without drawing the figures. Square 6, 7, 8, 9 and 10

c) Is 72 a square number? Explain how you determined your answer. No, 72 is between 8^2 and 9^2, so it is not a square number.

32. *A Triangular Pattern* The ancient Greeks labeled certain numbers as *triangular numbers*. The numbers 1, 3, 6, 10, 15, 21, and so on are triangular numbers.

1   3   6   10   15   21

a) Can you determine the next two triangular numbers? 28, 36

b) Describe a procedure to determine the next five triangular numbers without drawing the figures. *

c) Is 72 a triangular number? Explain how you determined your answer. No

33. *Quilt Design* The pattern shown is taken from a quilt design known as a triple Irish chain. Complete the color pattern by indicating the color assigned to each square.

Blue: 1, 5, 7, 10, 12; Purple: 2, 4, 6, 9, 11; Yellow: 3, 8

34. *Triangles in a Triangle* Four rows of a triangular figure are shown.

a) If you added six additional rows to the bottom of this triangle, using the same pattern displayed, how many triangles would appear in the 10th row? 19

b) If the triangles in all 10 rows were added, how many triangles would appear in the entire figure? 100

35. *Airline Revenues* The graph at the top of page 7 shows the annual operating revenues, in millions of dollars, for U.S. passenger and cargo airlines from 2002 through 2008.

a) Assuming this trend continues, use the graph to predict the annual operating revenue, in millions of dollars, for U.S. passenger and cargo airlines in 2009. ≈ $200,000

*See Instructor Answer Appendix

b) Explain how you are using inductive reasoning to determine your answer. We are using specific cases to make a prediction.

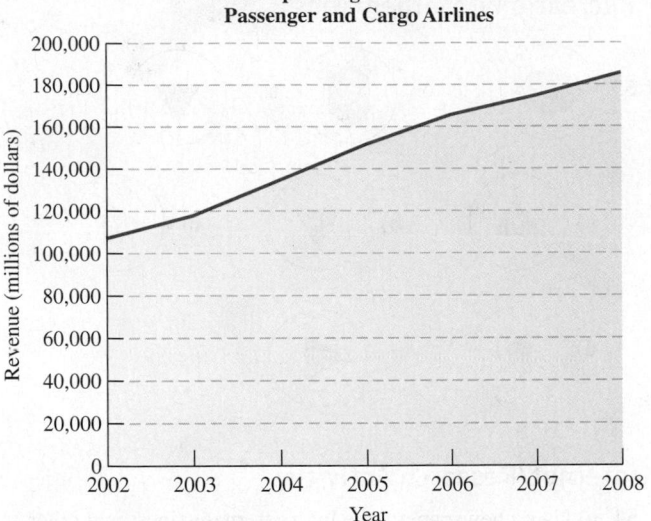

Annual Operating Revenues for U.S. Passenger and Cargo Airlines

Source: Air Transport Association of America

36. *Government Spending* The graph shows the amount of money spent, in trillions of dollars, by the U.S. government each year from 2000 through 2008.

a) Assuming this trend continues, use the graph to predict the amount of money the U.S. government will spend in 2014. ≈$3.7 trillion

b) Explain how you are using inductive reasoning to determine your answer. We are using specific cases to make a prediction.

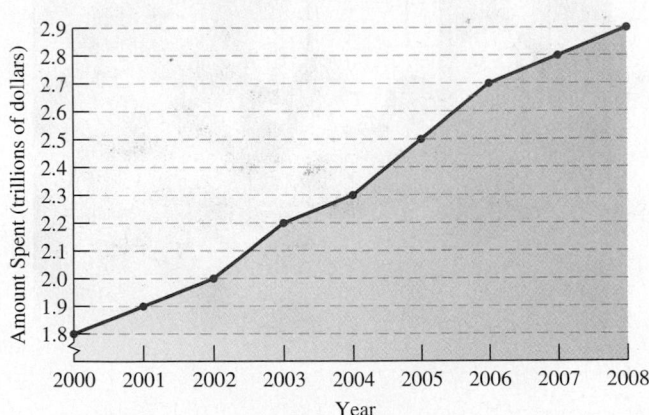

U.S. Government Spending

Source: U.S. Department of Treasury

In Exercises 37 and 38, draw the next diagram in the pattern (or sequence).

37.   **38.**

39. Pick any number, multiply the number by 4, add 12 to the product, divide the sum by 4, and subtract 3 from the quotient. See Example 5.

a) What is the relationship between the number you started with and the final number? You should obtain the original number.

b) Arbitrarily select some different numbers and repeat the process, recording the original number and the result. You should obtain the original number.

c) Can you make a conjecture about the relationship between the original number and the final number? The result is the original number.

d) Try to prove, using deductive reasoning, the conjecture you made in part (c). See Example 6. $n, 4n, 4n + 12, \frac{4n + 12}{4} = n + 3, n + 3 - 3 = n$

40. Pick any number and multiply the number by 4. Add 6 to the product. Divide the sum by 2 and subtract 3 from the quotient.

a) What is the relationship between the number you started with and the final answer? You should obtain twice the original number.

b) Arbitrarily select some different numbers and repeat the process, recording the original number and the results. You should obtain twice the original number.

c) Can you make a conjecture about the relationship between the original number and the final number? The result is always twice the original number.

d) Try to prove, using deductive reasoning, the conjecture you made in part (c). $n, 4n, 4n + 6, \frac{4n + 6}{2} = 2n + 3, 2n + 3 - 3 = 2n$

41. Pick any number and add 1 to it. Find the sum of the new number and the original number. Add 9 to the sum. Divide the sum by 2 and subtract the original number from the quotient.

a) What is the final number? 5

b) Arbitrarily select some different numbers and repeat the process. Record the results. You should obtain the number 5.

c) Can you make a conjecture about the final number? The result is always the number 5.

d) Try to prove, using deductive reasoning, the conjecture you made in part (c). *

42. Pick any number and add 10 to the number. Divide the sum by 5. Multiply the quotient by 5. Subtract 10 from the product. Then subtract your original number.

a) What is the result? You should obtain 0.

b) Arbitrarily select some different numbers and repeat the process, recording the original number and the result. You should obtain 0.

c) Can you make a conjecture regarding the result when this process is followed? The result is always 0.

d) Try to prove, using deductive reasoning, the conjecture you made in part (c). *

*See Instructor Answer Appendix

In Exercises 43–48, find a counterexample to show that each statement is incorrect.

43. The difference between two odd numbers is an odd number. $7 - 5 = 2$, which is not an odd number.

44. The quotient of any two counting numbers is a counting number. $5 \div 2 = 2\frac{1}{2}$, which is not a counting number.

45. When a counting number is added to 3 and the sum is divided by 2, the quotient will be an even number.
$(3 + 2)/2 = 5/2$, which is not an even number.

46. The product of any two three-digit numbers is a five-digit number. $900 \times 900 = 810,000$, which is not a five-digit number.

47. The difference of any two counting numbers will be a counting number. $1 - 2 = -1$, which is not a counting number.

48. The sum of any two odd numbers is divisible by 4. .
$1 + 5 = 6$, which is not divisible by 4

49. *Interior Angles of a Triangle*
   a) Construct a triangle and measure the three interior angles with a protractor. What is the sum of the measures? The sum of the measures of the interior angles should be 180°.
   b) Construct three other triangles, measure the angles, and record the sums. Are your answers the same? Yes, the sum of the measures of the interior angles should be 180°.
   c) Make a conjecture about the sum of the measures of the three interior angles of a triangle. The sum of the measures of the interior angles of a triangle is 180°.

50. *Interior Angles of a Quadrilateral*
   a) Construct a quadrilateral (a four-sided figure) and measure the four interior angles with a protractor. What is the sum of the measures?. The sum of the measures of the interior angles should be 360°
   b) Construct three other quadrilaterals, measure the angles, and record the sums. Are your answers the same? Yes, the sum of the measures of the interior angles should be 360°.
   c) Make a conjecture about the sum of the measures of the four interior angles of a quadrilateral. The sum of the measures of the interior angles of a quadrilateral is 360°.

Challenge Problems/Group Activities

51. Complete the following square of numbers. Explain how you determined your answer.

1	2	3	4
2	5	10	17
3	10	25	52
4	17	52	?

129, the numbers in positions are found as follows:

a	b
c	a + b + c

52. Find the next three numbers in the sequence.

1, 8, 11, 88, 101, 111, 181, 808, 818, 888, 1001, 1111, ...
1881, 8008, 8118

Recreational Mathematics

53. 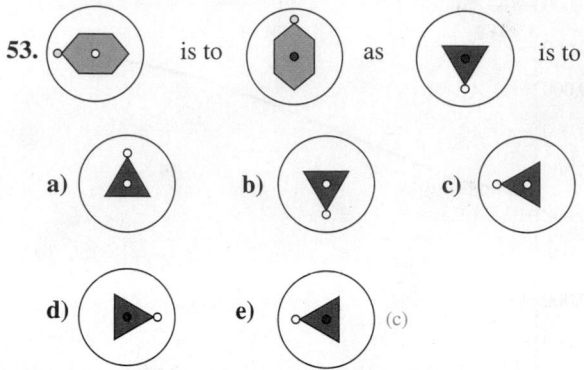 is to ___ as ___ is to

a) ___ b) ___ c) ___

d) ___ e) ___ (c)

Internet/Research Activities

54. a) Using newspapers, the Internet, magazines, and other sources, find examples of conclusions arrived at by inductive reasoning.

   b) Explain how inductive reasoning was used in arriving at the conclusion.

55. When a jury decides whether or not a defendant is guilty, do the jurors collectively use primarily inductive reasoning, deductive reasoning, or an equal amount of each? Write a brief report supporting your answer.

SECTION 1.2   Estimation

▲ *Estimate the sales tax on a $10,000 motorcycle if the sales tax rate is 8%.*

What is the approximate sales tax on a $10,000 motorcycle if the sales tax rate is 8%? What is the approximate cost to purchase 52 forty-four-cent stamps? In this section, we will introduce a technique for arriving at an approximate answer to a question.

Why *This is Important* Estimation is a technique we use every day for determining whether an answer is reasonable.

An important step in solving mathematical problems—or, in fact, *any* problem—is to make sure that the answer you've arrived at makes sense. One technique for determining whether an answer is reasonable is to estimate. *Estimation* is the process of arriving at an approximate answer to a question. This section demonstrates several estimation methods.

To estimate, or approximate, an answer, we often round numbers, as illustrated in the following examples. The symbol ≈ means *is approximately equal to.*

Example 1 *Estimating the Cost of Bagels*

Sandy Mendez decides to purchase bagels for her colleagues. Estimate her cost if she purchases 29 bagels at $1.99 each.

Solution We may round the amounts as follows to obtain an estimate.

Number	Number Rounded
29	30
× $1.99	× $2.00
	$60.00

Thus, the 29 bagels would cost approximately $60.00, written ≈ $60.00   ■

In Example 1, the true cost is $1.99 × 29, or $57.71. *Estimates are not meant to give exact values for answers but are a means of determining whether your answer is reasonable.* If you calculated an answer of $57.71 and then did a quick estimate to check it, you would know that the answer is reasonable because it is close to your estimated answer.

Example 2 *Two Ways to Estimate*

At a local office supply store, Karen Bowlby purchased pens for $15.89, a calendar for $7.19, a ruler for $1.94, index cards for $1.49, legal pads for $8.29, scissors for $10.79, and paper clips for $0.82. The cashier said the total bill was $55.41. Use estimation to determine whether this amount is reasonable.

Solution The most expensive item is $15.89, and the least expensive is $0.82. How should we estimate? We will estimate two different ways. First, we will round the cost of each item to the nearest 10 cents. For the second method, we will round the cost of each item to the nearest dollar. Rounding to the nearest 10 cents is more accurate. To determine whether the total bill is reasonable, however, we may need to round only to the nearest dollar.

	Round to the Nearest 10 Cents		**Round to the Nearest Dollar**	
Pens	$15.89 →	$15.90	$15.89 →	$16.00
Calendar	7.19 →	7.20	7.19 →	7.00
Ruler	1.94 →	1.90	1.94 →	2.00
Index cards	1.49 →	1.50	1.49 →	1.00
Legal pads	8.29 →	8.30	8.29 →	8.00
Scissors	10.79 →	10.80	10.79 →	11.00
Paper clips	0.82 →	0.80	0.82 →	1.00
		$46.40		$46.00

Using either estimate, we find that the bill of $55.41 is quite high. Therefore, Karen should check the bill carefully before paying it. Adding the prices of all seven items gives the true cost of $46.41.   ∎

Example 3 *Select the Best Estimate*

The number of bushels of grapes produced at a vineyard are 71,309 Cabernet Sauvignon, 123,879 French Colombard, 106,490 Chenin Blanc, 5960 Charbono, and 12,104 Chardonnay. Select the best estimate of the total number of bushels produced by the vineyard.

a) 500,000   b) 30,000   c) 300,000   d) 5,000,000

Solution Following are suggested roundings. On the left, the numbers are rounded to thousands. For a less accurate estimate, round to ten thousands, as illustrated on the right.

Round to the Nearest Thousand		**Round to the Nearest Ten Thousand**	
71,309 →	71,000	71,309 →	70,000
123,879 →	124,000	123,879 →	120,000
106,490 →	106,000	106,490 →	110,000
5,960 →	6,000	5,960 →	10,000
12,104 →	12,000	12,104 →	10,000
	319,000		320,000

Either rounding procedure indicates that the best estimate is (c), or 300,000.   ∎

Example 4 *Using Estimation in Calculations*

The Martellos traveled 1276 miles from their home in Springfield, Missouri, to Yellowstone National Park.

a) If their trip took 19.9 hours of driving time, estimate the average speed in miles per hour, that their car traveled.

b) If their car used 52 gallons of gasoline, estimate the average gas mileage of their car, in miles per gallon.

c) If the cost of gasoline averaged $3.51 per gallon, estimate the total cost of the gasoline used.

Solution

a) To estimate the average miles per hour, divide the number of miles by the number of hours.

$$\frac{1276}{19.9}$$

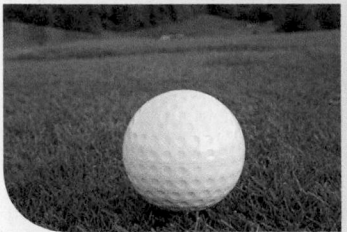
Round these numbers to obtain an estimate.

$$\frac{1300}{20} = 65$$

Therefore, the car averaged about 65 miles per hour.

b) To estimate the average gas mileage, divide the number of miles by the number of gallons.

$$\frac{1276}{52}$$

Round these numbers to obtain an estimate.

$$\frac{1300}{50} = 26$$

Therefore, the car averaged about 26 miles per gallon.

c) To estimate the total cost of gasoline, multiply the price per gallon by the number of gallons. Round the number of gallons of gasoline to 50 gallons and the price of the gasoline to $3.50 per gallon. The cost of the gasoline is about 50 × $3.50, or $175. ∎

Now let's look at some different types of estimation problems.

Example 5 *Estimating Distances on Trails to the West*

In the mid-1800s, thousands of settlers followed trails to the West to gain cheap, fertile land and a chance to make a fortune. One of the main trails to the West was the Oregon Trail, which ran from Independence, Missouri, to the Oregon Territory. Another trail, the California Trail, ran from Fort Hall on the Oregon Trail to Sacramento, California. A map of the Oregon Trail and the California Trail is shown below.

Trails West, 1850

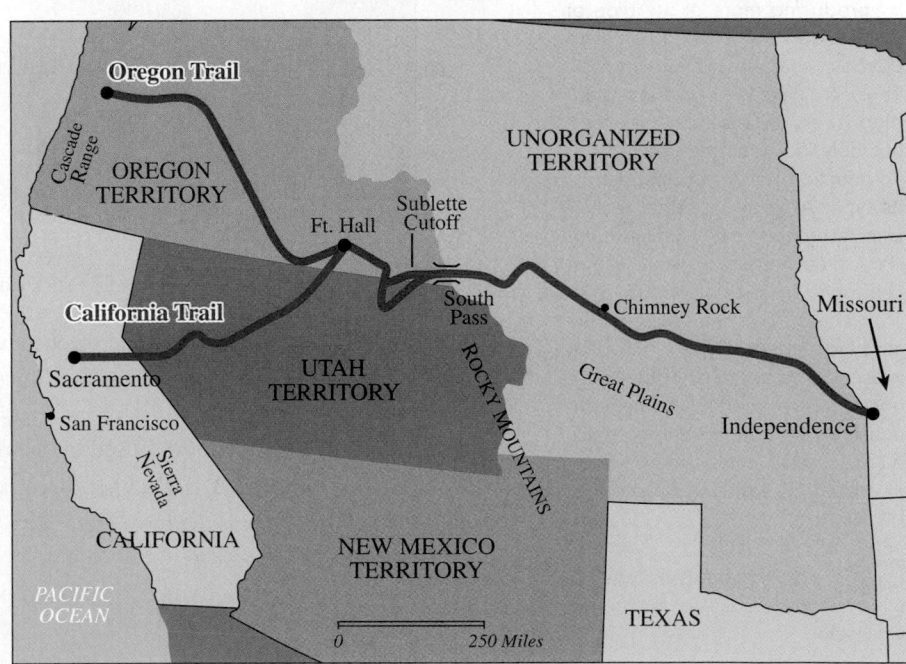

a) Using the Oregon Trail, estimate the distance from Independence, Missouri, to Fort Hall in the Oregon Territory.

b) Using the California Trail, estimate the distance from Fort Hall in the Oregon Territory to Sacramento, California.

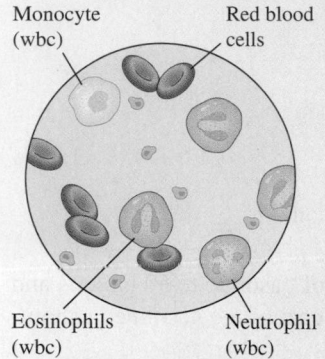
Solution

a) Using a ruler and the scale given on the map, we can determine that approximately $\frac{3}{4}$-inch represents 250 miles (mi). One way to determine the distance from Independence, Missouri, to Fort Hall in the Oregon Territory is to mark off $\frac{3}{4}$-inch intervals along the Oregon Trail. If you do so, you should obtain approximately 4 intervals. Thus, the distance is about 4×250 mi, or about 1000 mi.

Sometimes on a map like this one, it may be difficult to get an accurate estimate because of the curves on the map. To get a more accurate estimate, you may want to use a piece of string. Place the beginning of the string at Independence, Missouri, and, using tape or pins, align the string with the road. Indicate on the string the point represented by Fort Hall. Then remove the string and make $\frac{3}{4}$-inch interval markings on the string (or measure the length of string you marked off). If, for example, your string from Independence, Missouri, to Fort. Hall measures $3\frac{1}{4}$ inch, then the distance is about 1083 mi.

b) Using the procedure discussed in part (a), we estimate that the distance from Fort Hall in the Oregon Territory to Sacramento, California, is about $1\frac{5}{8}$ inch, or about 2.2 three-quarter-inch intervals. Thus, the distance from Fort Hall in the Oregon Territory to Sacramento, California, is about 2.2×250 mi, or about 550 mi. ■

Example 6 *Estimated Energy Use*

Some utility bills contain graphs illustrating the amount of electricity and natural gas used. The following graphs show gas and electric use at a specific residence for a period of 13 months, starting in November 2010 and going through November 2011 (the month of the current bill). Also shown, in red, is the bill for the average residential customer for November 2011. Using these graphs, answer the following questions.

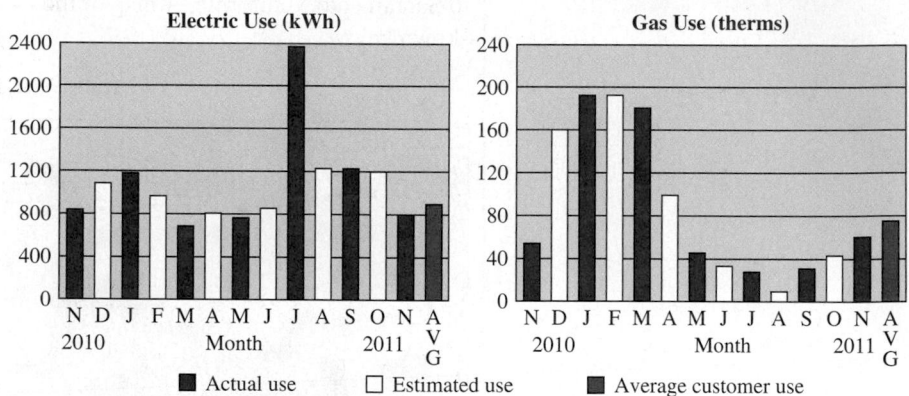

a) How often were actual gas and electric readings made?

b) Estimate the number of therms of gas used by the average residential customer in November 2011.

c) Estimate the amount of gas used by the resident in November 2011.

d) If the cost of gas is $1.12295 per therm, estimate the gas bill in March 2011.

e) In which month was the most electricity used? How many kilowatt-hours (kWh) of electricity were used in this month?

f) If the cost of electricity is 8.1716 cents per kWh, estimate the cost of the electricity in January 2011.

Solution

a) Actual readings were made every other month, in November 2010, January 2011, March 2011, May 2011, July 2011, September 2011, and November 2011. Thus, actual readings were made 7 times.

Did You Know?

Early Estimation

The ancient Egyptians and Greeks used sticks to estimate heights. To measure height, a person held a stick in his or her outstretched arm until it just covered the height of the object. The person then turned the stick through a right angle. Measuring the distance the stick appeared to cover on the ground provided an estimate of the object's height.

b) In November 2011, approximately 75 therms were used by the average residential customer, as shown by the height of the red bar.

c) In November 2011, approximately 60 therms were used by the resident.

d) In March 2011, about 180 therms were used. The rate is $1.12295 per therm. To get a rough approximation, round the rate to $1.12 per therm.

$$1.12 \times 180 = \$201.60$$

Thus, the cost of gas used was about $201.60.

e) The most electricity was used in July 2011. Approximately 2400 kWh of electricity were used.

f) In January 2011, about 1200 kWh were used. Write 8.1716 cents as $0.081716. Rounding the rate to $0.08 per kWh and multiplying by 1200 yields an estimate of $96.

$$0.08 \times 1200 = \$96$$

Thus, the cost of electricity in January 2011 was about $96. ∎

Example 7 *Estimating the Number of Corn Kernels in a Photo*

Estimate the number of corn kernels in the top layer in the accompanying photograph.

Solution To estimate the number of kernels, we can divide the photograph into rectangles with equal areas and then select one area that appears to be representative of all the areas. Estimate (or count) the number of kernels in this single area and then multiply this number by the number of equal areas.

Let's divide the photo into 20 approximately equal areas. We will select the left region in the top row as the representative region. We enlarge this region and count the kernels in it. If half a kernel is in the region, we count it (see enlargement on page 14). There are about 18 kernels in this region. Multiplying by 20 gives $18 \times 20 = 360$. Thus, there are about 360 kernels in the photo.

In problems similar to that in Example 7, the number of regions or areas into which you choose to divide the total area is arbitrary. Generally, the more regions, the better the approximation, as long as the region selected is representative of the other regions in the map, diagram, or photo.

When you estimate an answer, the amount that your approximation differs from the actual answer will depend on how you round the numbers. For example, in estimating the product of 196,000 × 0.02520, using the rounded values 195,000 × 0.025 would yield an estimate much closer to the true answer than using the rounded values 200,000 × 0.03. Without a calculator, however, the product of 195,000 × 0.025 might be more difficult to find than 200,000 × 0.03. When estimating, you need to determine the accuracy desired in your estimate and round the numbers accordingly.

SECTION 1.2   *Exercises*

Warm Up Exercises

In Exercises 1–2, fill in the blank with an appropriate word, phrase, or symbol(s).

1. The process of arriving at an approximate answer to a question is called _____. Estimation

2. The symbol ≈ means is approximately _____ to.
Equal

Practice the Skills

In Exercises 3–57, your answers may vary from the answers given in the back of the text, depending on how you round your answers.

In Exercises 3–12, estimate the answer. There is no one correct estimate. Your answer, however, should be something near the answer given.

3. 261 + 127.4 + 273.9 + 16.2 + 81.5 760

4. 2.57 + 212.6 + 176.2 + 83 470

5. 198,600 × 3.072 600,000

6. 1854 × 0.0096 19

7. $\dfrac{405}{0.049}$ 8000

8. 0.63 × 1523 900

9. 51,608 × 6981 350,000,000

10. 11% of 8221 800

11. 18% of 1576 320

12. 296.3 ÷ 0.0096 30,000

Problem Solving

In Exercises 13–22, estimate the answer.

13. The cost of one pen if a box of 5 pens costs $10.49 $2

14. The cost of a dozen clams if 20 dozen clams cost $37.80 $2

15. The amount of money Rick spends on gasoline in a year if the average amount he spends per month is $120.80. $1440

16. An 8% sales tax on a car that costs $11,250 $880

17. One third of an annual profit of $8795 $3000

18. The cost of 5 items purchased at a hardware store if the items cost $1.29, $6.86, $12.43, $25.62, and $8.99 $55

19. The total weight of three people on an elevator if their weights are 95 lb, 127 lb, and 210 lb. 400 lb

20. The weight of one pork chop in a package of six pork chops if the weight of the package is 3.25 lb 0.5 lb

21. A 15% tip on a meal that costs $26.32 $3.90

22. The number of months needed to save $400 if you save $23 each month 16

23. *Utility Bill* Joe Kuby pays $114.99 per month for the Verizon Fios Triple Play Offer. This package includes unlimited local and long-distance telephone, cable TV, and Internet service. His previous monthly costs for these services were $65.99, $49.99, and $49.95, respectively. Estimate the amount of money Joe saves per month with the Triple Play Offer. $51

24. *Estimating Weights* In a tug of war, the weight of the members of the two three-person teams is given below. Estimate the difference in the weights of the teams. 30 lb

Team A	Team B
189	183
172	229
191	167

25. *Picking Strawberries* Chuck Chase hires 11 people to pick strawberries from his field. He agrees to pay them $1.50 for each quart they pick. Estimate the total amount of money he will have to pay if each person picks 8 quarts. $120

26. *Estimating Time* Donna Burke is a long-distance runner whose average time per mile in marathons is 6 minutes, 25 seconds. Estimate the time it will take her to complete a 26-mile, 385-yard (or ≈ 26.2-mile) marathon. 4 hours

27. *Currency* Estimate the difference in the value of 50 U.S. dollars and 100 Mexican pesos. Assume that one Mexican peso is about 0.083 U.S. dollar. $42

28. *The Cost of a Vacation* The Kleins are planning a vacation in the Great Smoky Mountains National Park. Their round-trip airfare from Houston, Texas, to Knoxville, Tennessee, totals $973. Car rental is $61 per day and lodging is a total of $97 per day, and they estimate a total of $200 per day for food, gas, and other miscellaneous items. If they are planning to stay six full days and nights, estimate their total expenses. $3130

29. *The Pacific Coast Highway* Above and to the right is a map of California's scenic Pacific Coast Highway. Using the scale on the map, estimate the distance between Pfeiffer Big Sur State Park and Hearst Castle. ≈ 60 mi

▲ *Hearst Castle*

30. *The Olympic Peninsula* Below is a map of the Olympic Peninsula in the state of Washington. Using the scale on the map, estimate the distance of the route shown in red, starting at Port Angeles and ending at Forks, passing through Sappho. ≈ 55 mi

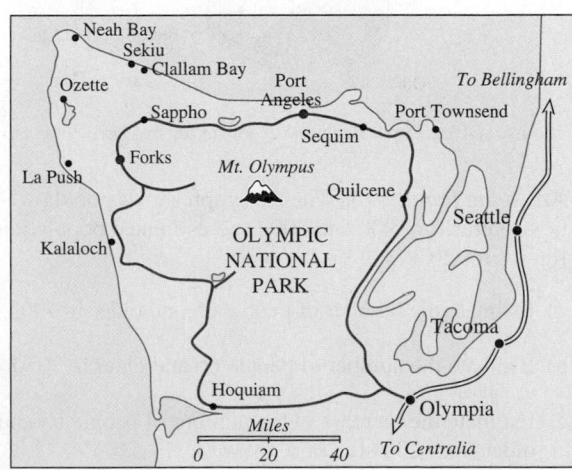

31. *Health Club Membership*   The circle graph below shows the percent of health club memberships, by age, in the United States in 2011. *Fit for Life* health club had 700 members in 2011. Assuming this graph applies to the *Fit for Life* membership,

a) estimate the number of *Fit for Life* health club members who were between the ages of 18 and 34. 210

b) estimate the number of *Fit for Life* health club members who were age 17 and younger. 70

c) estimate the number of *Fit for Life* health club members who were age 55 or older. 175

Health Club Membership by Age in 2011

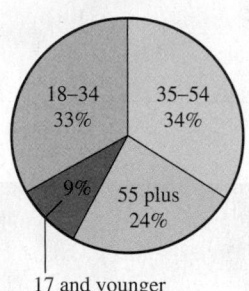

17 and younger

32. *Dream Jobs*   The circle graph below shows the kind of job parents of children ages 5 to 17 hope their children will grow up to have. The survey involved 504 parents.

a) Estimate the number of parents who hope their child will become a doctor. 100

b) Estimate the number of parents who hope their child will become a professional athlete. 50

c) Estimate the number of parents who hope their child will start a successful new business. 125

Jobs That Parents Hope Their Children Will Have

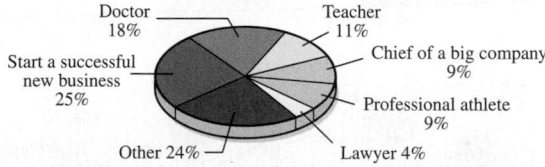

Source: Office Depot Back-to-School survey by Harris Interactive

33. *An Aging Population*   The bar graph shows population figures for 1900 and 2000 and estimated population figures for 2050.

a) Estimate the number of people 65 and older in 1900. 5 million

b) Estimate the number of people 65 and older in 2050. 98 million

c) Estimate the increase in the number of people 65 and older from 2000 to 2050. 65 million

d) Estimate the total U.S. population in 2000 by adding the five categories. 280 million

Population by Age

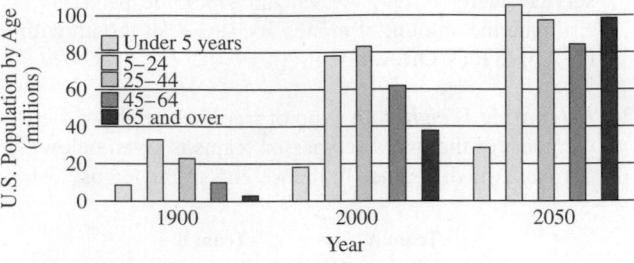

Source: U.S. Census Bureau

34. *Gaining Weight*   The graph shows that as a society we tend to get heavier as we grow older. Also, with age, the amount of muscle tends to drop, and fat accounts for a greater percentage of weight.

a) Estimate the average percent of body fat for a woman, age 18 to 25. 19%

b) Estimate the average percent of body fat for a man, age 56+. 25%

c) Greg, an average 40-year-old man, weighs 179 lb. Estimate the number of pounds of body fat he has. 36 lb

Getting Older Usually Means Getting Fatter

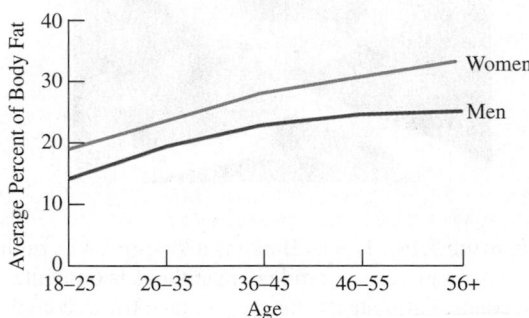

35. *Land Ownership by the Federal Government*   The federal government owns a great deal of land in the United States. The graph at the top of page 17 shows the percent of land owned by the federal government in the 12 states in which the federal government owns the greatest percentage of a state's land.

a) Estimate the percent of land owned by the federal government in Nevada. 85%

b) Estimate the difference between Alaska and Oregon in the percent of land owned by the federal government. 15%

c) Nevada has a total area of 70,264,320 acres. Estimate the number of acres owned by the federal government in Nevada. 59,500,000 acres

d) By just looking at the graph, is it possible to determine whether the federal government owns more land in Nevada or Utah? Explain.

No, since we are not given the area of each state

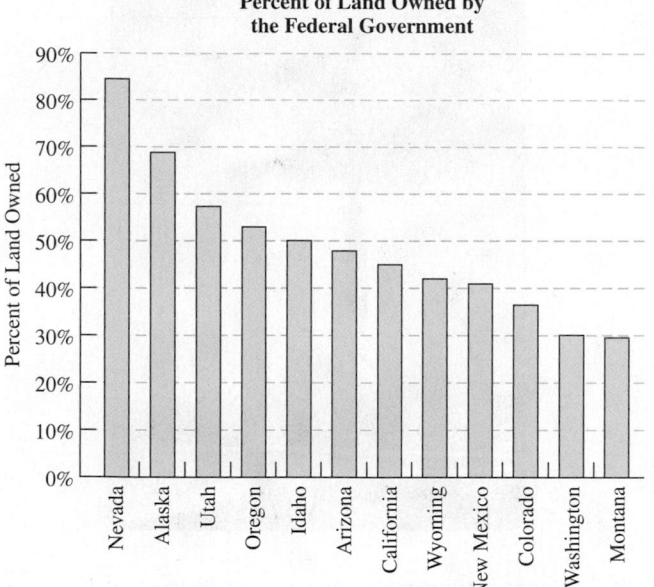

Percent of Land Owned by the Federal Government

Source: Office of Governmentwide Policy, General Services Administration

36. *Calories and Exercise* The chart shows the calories burned per hour for an average person who weighs 150 lb.

a) Estimate the number of calories Phyllis Nye, who weighs 150 lb, burns in a week if she stair-climbs for 2 hours each week and jogs at 5 miles per hour for 4 hours each week. 3000 calories

b) Estimate the difference in the calories Phyllis will burn each week if she runs for 4 hours at 8 miles per hour rather than does casual bike riding for 4 hours. 2500 calories

c) Assume Phyllis jogs at 5 miles per hour for 3 hours and bicycles at 13 miles per hour for 3 hours each week. Estimate the number of calories she will burn in a year from these exercises. 150,000 calories

Activity	Calories* per Hour
Running, 8 mph	920
Bicycling, 13 mph	545
Jogging, 5 mph	545
Air-walking	480
Stair-climbing	410
Weight-lifting	410
Walking, 4 mph	330
Casual bike riding	300

*For a 150-lb person.

In Exercises 37 and 38, estimate the maximum number of smaller figures (at left) that can be placed in the larger figure (at right) without the small figures overlapping.

37.   20

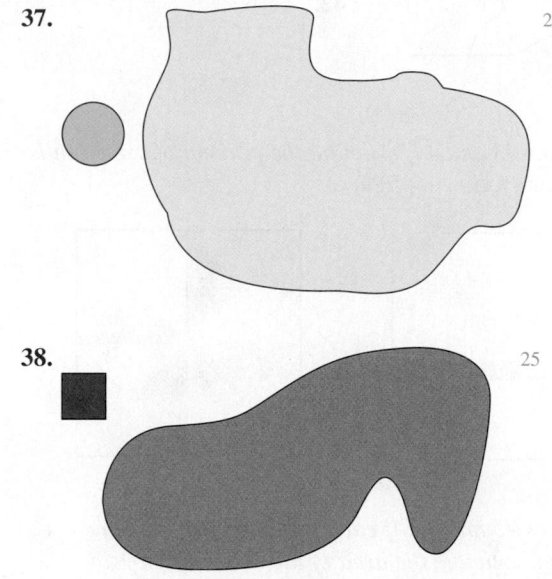

38.   25

39. Estimate the number of bananas shown in the photo.
≈ 120 bananas

40. Estimate the number of berries shown in the photo.
≈ 160 berries

In Exercises 41 and 42, estimate, in degrees, the measure of the angles depicted. For comparison purposes a right angle, ⌐, measures 90°.

41.   150° **42.** 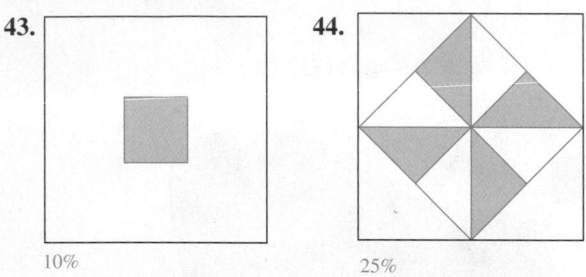 315°

In Exercises 43 and 44, estimate the percent of area that is shaded in the following figures.

43. **44.**

10%   25%

In Exercises 45 and 46, if each square represents one square unit, estimate the area of the shaded figure in square units.

45. **46.**

9 square units   12 square units

47. Statue of Liberty The length of the torch of the Statue of Liberty, from the tip of the flame to the bottom of the torch's baton, is 29 feet. Estimate the height of the Statue of Liberty from the top of the base to the top of the torch (the statue itself). 150 feet

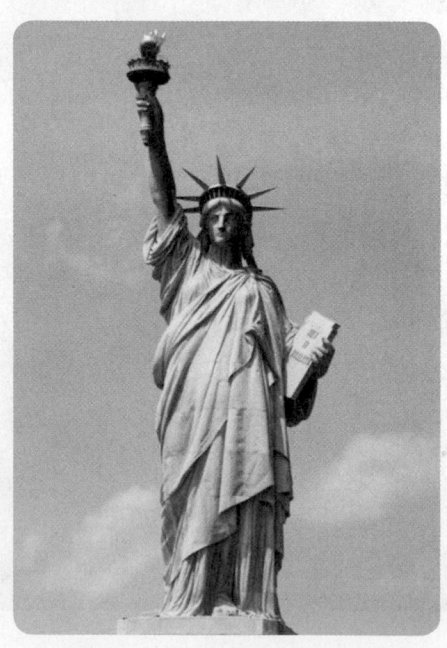

48. Estimating Heights If the height of the woman in the photo is 62 in. tall, estimate the height of the tree. 240 inches or 20 ft.

49. Distance Estimate, without a ruler, a distance of 12 in. Measure the distance. How good was your estimate? Answers will vary.

50. Weight In a bag, place objects that you believe have a total weight of 10 lb. Weigh the bag to determine the accuracy of your estimate. Answers will vary.

51. Phone Call Estimate the number of times the phone will ring in 1 minute if unanswered. Have a classmate phone you so that you can count the rings and thus test your estimate. Answers will vary.

52. Temperature Fill a glass with water and estimate the water's temperature. Then use a thermometer to measure the temperature and check your estimate. Answers will vary.

53. Pennies Estimate the number of pennies that will fill a 3-ounce (oz) paper cup. Then actually fill a 3-oz paper cup with pennies, counting them to determine the accuracy of your estimate. Answers will vary.

54. Height Estimate the ratio of your height to your waist size. Then have a friend measure your height and waist size. Determine the stated ratio and check the accuracy of your estimate. Answers will vary.

55. Walking Speed Estimate how fast you can walk 60 ft. Then mark off a distance of 60 ft and use a watch with a second hand to time yourself walking it. Determine the accuracy of your estimate. Answers will vary.

Challenge Problems/Group Activities

56. Shopping Make a shopping list of 20 items you use regularly that can be purchased at a supermarket. Beside each item write down what you estimate to be its price. Add these price guesses to estimate the total cost of the

20 items. Next, make a trip to your local supermarket and record the actual price of each item. Add these prices to determine the actual total cost. How close was your estimate? (Don't forget to add tax on the taxable items.) Answers will vary.

57. *A Ski Vacation* Two friends, Tiffany Connolly and Ana Pott, are planning a skiing vacation in the Rockies. They plan to purchase round-trip airline tickets from Atlanta, Georgia, to Denver, Colorado. They will fly into Denver on a Friday morning, rent a midsize car, and drive to Aspen that same day. They will stay at the Holiday Inn in Aspen. They will begin skiing at the Buttermilk Ski Area on Saturday, ski up to and including Wednesday, drive back to Denver on Thursday, and fly out of Denver Thursday evening.

a) Estimate the total cost of the vacation for the two friends. Do not forget items such as food, tips, gas, and other incidentals. Answers will vary.

b) Using informational sources, including the Internet, determine the airfare cost, hotel cost, cost of ski tickets, cost of a car rental, and so forth. You will need to make an estimate for food and other incidentals. Answers will vary.

c) How close was your estimate in part (a) to the amount you found in part (b)? Was your estimate in part (a) lower or higher than the amount obtained in part (b)? Answers will vary.

Recreational Mathematics

58. *A Dime* Look at a dime. Around the edge of a dime are many lines. Estimate the number of lines there are around the edge of a dime. There are 118 ridges around the edge.

59. *A Million Dollars*

a) Estimate the time it would take, in days, to spend $1 million if you spent $1 a second until the $1 million is used up. Answers will vary.

b) Calculate the actual time it would take, in days, to spend $1 million if you spent $1 a second. How close was your estimate? 11.6 days

Internet/Research Activities

60. *Water Usage*

a) About how much water does your household use per day? Use the following data to estimate your household's daily water usage.

Activity	Typical Use
Running clothes washer	40 gal
Bath	35 gal
5-minute shower	25 gal
Doing dishes in sink, water running	20 gal
Running dishwasher	11 gal
Flushing toilet	4 gal
Brushing teeth, water running	2 gal

Source: U.S. Environmental Protection Agency

b) Determine from your water department (or company) your household's average daily usage by obtaining the total number of gallons used per year and dividing that amount by 365. How close was your estimate in part (a)?

c) Current records indicate that the average household uses about 300 gal of water per day (the average daily usage is 110 gal per person). Based on the number of people in your household, do you believe your household uses more or less than the average amount of water? Explain your answer.

61. Develop a monthly budget by estimating your monthly income and your monthly expenditures. Your monthly income should equal your monthly expenditures.

62. Identify three ways that you use estimation in your daily life. Discuss each of them briefly and give examples.

▲ *Getting the most for your money while purchasing pizza involves problem solving.*

To maximize their profits, businesses try to keep their expenses down. We, as individuals, also try to do the same, and we often look for "bargains" or the "best deal." For example, suppose we need to purchase several pizzas and have only $75 to spend. How can we determine the maximum number of slices that we can purchase if large pizzas with 12 slices sell for $12 and medium pizzas with 8 slices sell for $9. We'll answer this question in Example 1.

Why **This is Important** Problem-solving skills can help you find solutions to problems you may encounter in everyday life.

Solving mathematical puzzles and real-life mathematical problems can be enjoyable. You should work as many exercises in this section as possible. By doing so, you will sample a variety of problem-solving techniques.

You can approach any problem by using a general procedure developed by George Polya. Before learning Polya's problem-solving procedure, let's consider an example that illustrates the procedure.

Example 1 *Saving Money When Purchasing Pizza*

Karen Morris plans to purchase pizza for a party she is hosting. Pizza Corner sells medium pizzas (14" diameter) for $9 and large pizzas (17" diameter) for $12. A medium pizza has 8 slices and a large pizza has 12 slices. Only entire pizzas are sold. Assume the pizza slices are all about the same size.

a) Determine the maximum number of slices of pizza that Karen can purchase for $75 or less.

b) If the maximum number of slices determined in part (a) is purchased in the most economical way, how much will the pizzas cost?

Solution

a) The first thing to do is read the problem carefully. Read it at least twice. Be sure you understand the facts given and what you are being asked to find. Next, make a list of the given facts and determine which facts are relevant to answering the question or questions asked.

GIVEN INFORMATION

Party host: Karen Morris

Pizza shop: Pizza Corner

A medium pizza costs $9.

A medium pizza has a 14" diameter.

A medium pizza contains 8 slices.

A large pizza costs $12.

A large pizza has a 17" diameter.

A large pizza contains 12 slices.

Only entire pizzas can be purchased.

We need to determine the maximum number of slices Karen can purchase for $75 or less. To determine this number, we need to know the number of slices in each pizza and the cost of each pizza. We also need to know that only entire pizzas can be purchased.

RELEVANT INFORMATION

A medium pizza costs $9.

A medium pizza contains 8 slices.

A large pizza costs $12.

A large pizza contains 12 slices.

Only entire pizzas can be purchased.

The next step is to determine the answer to the question. That is, we need to determine the maximum number of slices that can be purchased for $75 or less.

We now need a plan for solving the problem. One method is to set up a table or chart to compare costs of different combinations of pizzas. Start by using the maximum number of large pizzas that can be purchased. Then reduce the number of large pizzas and add more medium pizzas. In each case, we need to keep the cost at $75 or less.

Because one large pizza costs $12, we can determine the number of large pizzas that can be purchased by dividing 75 by 12. Because the quotient is 6.25 and only entire pizzas can be purchased, only 6 large pizzas can be purchased. Six large pizzas would cost $12 \times 6 = \$72$. Because medium pizzas cost $9, there would not be enough money left to purchase any medium pizzas. Since large pizzas have 12 slices, 6 large pizzas provide $12 \times 6 = 72$ slices. Thus, for $75 or less, one option is 6 large pizzas, which gives 72 slices. This option is illustrated in the first row of the table below. Also given in the table is the cost of this option, which is $72. We complete the other rows of the table in a similar manner.

Large Pizzas and Medium Pizzas	Number of Slices	Cost
6 large and 0 medium	$(6 \times 12) + (0 \times 8) = 72$	$72
5 large and 1 medium	$(5 \times 12) + (1 \times 8) = 68$	$69
4 large and 3 medium	$(4 \times 12) + (3 \times 8) = 72$	$75
3 large and 4 medium	$(3 \times 12) + (4 \times 8) = 68$	$72
2 large and 5 medium	$(2 \times 12) + (5 \times 8) = 64$	$69
1 large and 7 medium	$(1 \times 12) + (7 \times 8) = 68$	$75
0 large and 8 medium	$(0 \times 12) + (8 \times 8) = 64$	$72

The question asks us to find the maximum number of slices of pizza that can be purchased for $75 or less. From the second column of the table, we see that the answer is 72 slices of pizza. This result can be obtained in two different ways: either 6 large pizzas and 0 medium pizzas or 4 large pizzas and 3 medium pizzas.

b) When comparing the two possibilities for purchasing the 72 slices of pizza discussed in part (a), we see that the most economical way to purchase the slices is to purchase 6 large pizzas and 0 medium pizzas. The cost is $72. ∎

Following is a general procedure for problem solving as given by George Polya. Note that Example 1 demonstrates many of these guidelines.

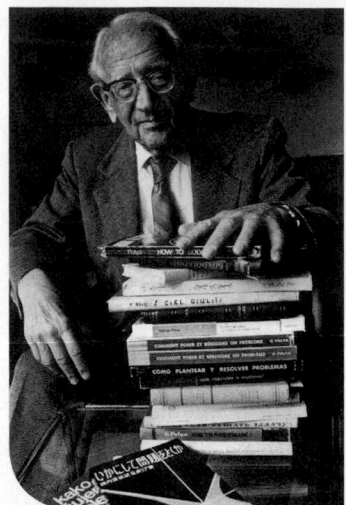

PROCEDURE

GUIDELINES FOR PROBLEM SOLVING

1. *Understand the problem.*
   - Read the problem *carefully* at least twice. In the first reading, get a general overview of the problem. In the second reading, determine (a) exactly what you are being asked to find and (b) what information the problem provides.
   - Try to make a sketch to illustrate the problem. Label the information given.
   - Make a list of the given facts that are pertinent to the problem.
   - Determine if the information you are given is sufficient to solve the problem.
2. *Devise a plan to solve the problem.*
   - Have you seen the problem or a similar problem before? Are the procedures you used to solve the similar problem applicable to the new problem?
   - Can you express the problem in terms of an algebraic equation? (We explain how to write algebraic equations in Chapter 6.)
   - Look for patterns or relationships in the problem that may help in solving it.
   - Can you express the problem more simply?
   - Can you substitute smaller or simpler numbers to make the problem more understandable?
   - Will listing the information in a table help in solving the problem?
   - Can you make an educated guess at the solution? Sometimes if you know an approximate solution, you can work backward and eventually determine the correct procedure to solve the problem.
3. *Carry out the plan.*
   - Use the plan you devised in Step 2 to solve the problem.
4. *Check the results.*
   - Ask yourself, "Does the answer make sense?" and "Is the answer reasonable?" If the answer is not reasonable, recheck your method for solving the problem and your calculations.
   - Can you check the solution using the original statement?
   - Is there an alternative method to arrive at the same conclusion?
   - Can the results of this problem be used to solve other problems?

The following examples show how to apply the guidelines for problem solving.

▲ *San Antonio, Texas*

┌ **Example 2** *Shuttle Revenue*

Airport Express shuttle service provides service from San Antonio International Airport to downtown hotels, approximately 10 miles away. One particular shuttle makes 16 round trips per day, carrying 5 passengers per trip. The fare each way is $18. What are the receipts from one day's operation for this particular shuttle?

Solution   We need to find the total receipts from one day's operation. Let's make a list of all the information given and mark with an asterisk (*) the information that is pertinent to solving the problem.

   Distance from airport to downtown hotels ≈ 10 miles
   * Number of round trips per day = 16
   * Number of passengers per trip = 5
   * Fare each way = $18

All the information is needed to solve the problem except the distance between the airport and the downtown hotels. To determine the total receipts for the day, we need to know the number of round trips per day, the number of passengers per trip, and the round trip cost per passenger. The product of these three numbers will yield the total daily receipts. For a round trip, the cost per passenger is $18 × 2 = $36.

   Thus the total receipts for one day's operation = 16 × 5 × $36 = $2880. ∎

In Example 2, we could have used 32 one-way trips at a fare of $18 per person to obtain the answer. Why?

Example 3   *Retirement*

It is never too early to start planning for retirement. U.S. Census Bureau data indicate that at age 65 the average woman will live another 20 years and the average man will live another 17.2 years. The data also indicate that about 33% of the average person's retirement income will come from Social Security.

    When discussing retirement planning, many investment firms and financial planners use the graph in Fig. 1.1,* which shows how long a typical retiree's assets (or "nest egg") will last based on the percentage of the assets withdrawn each year.

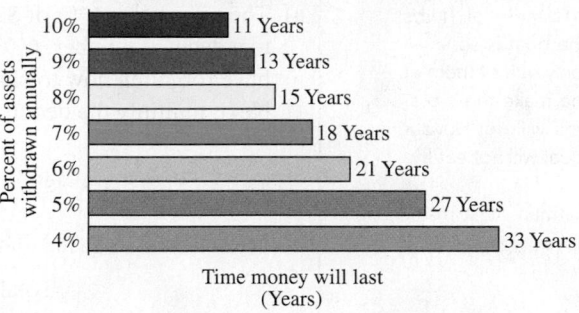

Figure 1.1

a) If a typical retiree has retirement assets of $500,000, how much can he or she withdraw annually if he or she wishes the assets to last 21 years?

b) How much should a retiree have in assets if he or she wishes to withdraw $25,000 annually and wishes his or her assets to last 18 years?

Solution

a) Quite a bit of information is provided in the example. We will first need to determine what information is needed to answer the question. To answer the question, we only need to use the information provided in the graph. From the graph, we can see that for assets to last 21 years, about 6% of the assets can be withdrawn annually. The amount that can be withdrawn annually is found as follows.

$$\text{Amount} = 6\% \text{ of assets}$$
$$\text{Amount} = 0.06\,(500{,}000) = 30{,}000$$

Thus, about $30,000 can be withdrawn annually.

b) Again, to solve this part of the example, we only need the information provided in the graph. From the graph, we can determine that if a retiree wishes for his or her assets to last 18 years, then 7% of the assets can be withdrawn annually. We need to determine the total assets such that 7% of the total assets is $25,000.

$$7\% \text{ of assets} = \$25{,}000 \quad \text{or} \quad 0.07 \times \text{assets} = \$25{,}000$$

Because 0.07 is multiplied by the assets to obtain $25,000, we can determine the assets by dividing the $25,000 by 0.07 as follows.

$$\text{Assets} = \frac{25{,}000}{0.07} = 357{,}142.86$$

Therefore, if the retiree has assets of about $357,142.86, he or she will be able to withdraw $25,000 annually and the assets will last 18 years.   ■

---

*The information in this graph is based on past performance of the stock market, with 50% invested in large company stocks and 50% invested in intermediate-term bonds. Past performance is not indicative of future results.

Example 4 *Determining a Tip*

The cost of Freddie Rojo's meal before tax is $28.00.

a) If a $6\frac{1}{2}\%$ sales tax is added to his bill, determine the total cost of the meal including tax.

b) If Freddie wants to leave a 10% tip on the *pretax* cost of the meal, how much should he leave?

c) If he wants to leave a 15% tip on the *pretax* cost of the meal, how much should he leave?

Solution

a) The sales tax is $6\frac{1}{2}\%$ of $28.00. To determine the sales tax, first change the $6\frac{1}{2}\%$ to a decimal number. $6\frac{1}{2}\%$ when written as a decimal number is 0.065 (if you have forgotten how to change a percent to a decimal number, read Section 11.1). Next, multiply the decimal number, 0.065, by the amount, $28.00.

$$\text{Sales tax} = 6\tfrac{1}{2}\% \text{ of } 28.00$$
$$= 0.065(28.00) = 1.82$$

The sales tax is $1.82. The total bill is the cost of the meal + the sales tax.

$$\text{Total bill} = \text{cost of meal} + \text{sales tax}$$
$$= 28.00 + 1.82 = 29.82$$

Thus, the bill, including sales tax, is $29.82.

b) To find 10% of any number, we can multiply the number by 0.10.

$$10\% \text{ of pretax cost} = 0.10(28.00)$$
$$= 2.80$$

A simple way to find 10% of any number is to simply move the decimal point in the number one place to the left. Moving the decimal point in $28.00 one place to the left gives $2.80, the same answer we obtained by our calculations.

c) To find 15% of $28.00, multiply as follows.

$$15\% \text{ of } 28.00 = 0.15(28.00) = 4.20$$

Thus, 15% of $28.00 is $4.20. A second method to find a 15% tip is to find 10% of the cost, as in part (b), then add to it half that amount. Following this procedure, we get

$$\$2.80 + \frac{\$2.80}{2} = \$2.80 + \$1.40 = \$4.20$$

In most cases, tips are rounded. If the service is excellent, some people leave a 20% tip. Can you give two methods to determine a 20% tip on $28.00? Determine the 20% tip now. ∎

Example 5 *A Recipe for 6*

The chart at the top of page 25 shows the amount of each ingredient recommended to make 2, 4, and 8 servings of Potato Buds. Determine the amount of each ingredient necessary to make 6 servings of Potato Buds by using the following procedures.

a) Multiply the amount for 2 servings by 3.*

b) Add the amounts for 2 servings to the amounts for 4 servings.

c) Find the average of the amounts for 4 servings and for 8 servings.

---

*Addition, subtraction, multiplication, and division of fractions are discussed in detail in Section 5.3.

d) Subtract the amounts for 2 servings from the amounts for 8 servings.

e) Compare the answers for parts (a) through (d). Are they the same? If not, explain why not.

f) Which is the correct procedure for obtaining 6 servings?

Servings	2	4	8
Water	$\frac{2}{3}$ cup	$1\frac{1}{3}$ cups	$2\frac{2}{3}$ cups
Milk	2 tbsp	$\frac{1}{3}$ cup	$\frac{2}{3}$ cup
Butter or margarine	1 tbsp	2 tbsp	4 tbsp
Salt*	$\frac{1}{4}$ tsp	$\frac{1}{2}$ tsp	1 tsp
Potato Buds	$\frac{2}{3}$ cup	$1\frac{1}{3}$ cups	$2\frac{2}{3}$ cups

*Less salt can be used if desired.

Solution

a) We multiply the amounts for 2 servings by 3.

Water: $3\left(\frac{2}{3}\right) = 2$ cups

Milk: $3(2) = 6$ tablespoons (tbsp)

Butter or margarine: $3(1) = 3$ tbsp

Salt: $3\left(\frac{1}{4}\right) = \frac{3}{4}$ teaspoon (tsp)

Potato Buds: $3\left(\frac{2}{3}\right) = 2$ cups

b) We find the amount of each ingredient by adding the amount for 2 and 4 servings.

Water: $\frac{2}{3}$ cup $+ 1\frac{1}{3}$ cups $= 2$ cups

Milk: 2 tbsp $+ \frac{1}{3}$ cup

To add these two amounts, we must convert one of them so that both ingredients have the same units. By looking in a cookbook or a book of conversion factors, we see that 16 tbsp $= 1$ cup. The milk in part (a) was given in tablespoons, so we convert $\frac{1}{3}$ cup to tablespoons to compare answers. One-third cup equals $\frac{1}{3}(16) = \frac{16}{3}$ or $5\frac{1}{3}$ tbsp. Therefore,

Milk: 2 tbsp $+ 5\frac{1}{3}$ tbsp $= 7\frac{1}{3}$ tbsp

Let's continue with the rest of the ingredients:

Butter: 1 tbsp $+ 2$ tbsp $= 3$ tbsp

Salt: $\frac{1}{4}$ tsp $+ \frac{1}{2}$ tsp $= \frac{3}{4}$ tsp

Potato Buds: $\frac{2}{3}$ cup $+ 1\frac{1}{3}$ cups $= 2$ cups

c) We compute the amounts of the ingredients by finding the average of the amounts for 4 and 8 servings. We do so by adding the amounts for each ingredient and dividing the sum by 2.

Water: $\dfrac{1\frac{1}{3} \text{ cups} + 2\frac{2}{3} \text{ cups}}{2} = \dfrac{4 \text{ cups}}{2} = 2$ cups

Milk: $\dfrac{\frac{1}{3} \text{ cup} + \frac{2}{3} \text{ cup}}{2} = \dfrac{1 \text{ cup}}{2} = \frac{1}{2}$ cup (or 8 tbsp)

Butter: $\dfrac{2 \text{ tbsp} + 4 \text{ tbsp}}{2} = \dfrac{6 \text{ tbsp}}{2} = 3$ tbsp

Salt: $\dfrac{\frac{1}{2} \text{ tsp} + 1 \text{ tsp}}{2} = \dfrac{\frac{3}{2} \text{ tsp}}{2} = \frac{3}{4}$ tsp

$$\text{Potato Buds: } \frac{1\frac{1}{3}\text{ cups} + 2\frac{2}{3}\text{ cups}}{2} = \frac{4\text{ cups}}{2} = 2\text{ cups}$$

d) We obtain the amounts of ingredients by subtracting the amounts for 2 servings from the amounts for 8 servings.

Water: $2\frac{2}{3}$ cups $-\frac{2}{3}$ cup $= 2$ cups

$$\begin{aligned}\text{Milk: } \tfrac{2}{3}\text{ cup} - 2\text{ tbsp} &= \tfrac{2}{3}(16)\text{ tbsp} - 2\text{ tbsp}\\ &= \tfrac{32}{3}\text{ tbsp} - \tfrac{6}{3}\text{ tbsp}\\ &= \tfrac{26}{3}\text{ tbsp, or } 8\tfrac{2}{3}\text{ tbsp}\end{aligned}$$

Butter: 4 tbsp $-$ 1 tbsp $=$ 3 tbsp

Salt: 1 tsp $-\frac{1}{4}$ tsp $=\frac{3}{4}$ tsp

Potato Buds: $2\frac{2}{3}$ cups $-\frac{2}{3}$ cup $= 2$ cups

e) Comparing the answers in parts (a) through (d), we find that the amounts of all ingredients, except milk, are the same. For milk, we get the following results.

Part (a): Milk $= 6$ tbsp   Part (c): Milk $= 8$ tbsp

Part (b): Milk $= 7\frac{1}{3}$ tbsp   Part (d): Milk $= 8\frac{2}{3}$ tbsp

Why are all these answers different? After rechecking, we find that all our calculations are correct, so we must look deeper. Note that milk is the only ingredient that has different units for 2 servings and 4 servings. Let's check the relationship between 2 tbsp and $\frac{1}{3}$ cup. In going from 2 servings to 4 servings, we would expect that $\frac{1}{3}$ cup should be twice 2 tbsp. We know that 1 cup $= 16$ tbsp, so

$$\tfrac{1}{3}\text{ cup} = \tfrac{1}{3}(16) = \tfrac{16}{3} = 5\tfrac{1}{3}\text{ tbsp}$$

Therefore, instead of the 4 tbsp of milk we expected for 4 servings, we get $5\frac{1}{3}$ tbsp. This change causes all our calculations for milk to be different.

f) Which is the correct answer? Because all our calculations for milk are correct, there is no single correct answer. All our answers are correct. Using $8\frac{2}{3}$ tbsp instead of 6 tbsp might make the Potato Buds a little thinner. When we cook, we generally do not add the *exact* amount recommended. We rely on experience to alter the recommended amounts according to individual taste.   ∎

Many real-life problems, such as the one in Example 6, can be solved by using proportions. A proportion is a statement of equality between two ratios (or fractions.)*

Example 6   *Spraying Weed Killer*

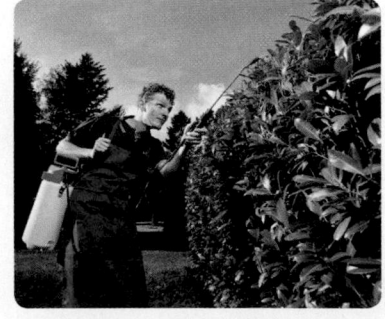

The instructions on the Ortho Weed-B-Gon lawn weed killer indicate that to cover 1000 square feet (ft²) of lawn, 20 teaspoons (tsp) of the weed killer should be mixed in 5 gallons (gal) of water. Ron Haines wishes to spray his lawn with the weed killer using his pressurized sprayer.

a) How much weed killer should be mixed with 8 gal of water to get a solution of the proper strength?

b) How much weed killer is needed to cover an area of 2820 ft² of lawn?

> Solution

a) Use the information that 20 teaspoons of weed killer is to be mixed with 5 gal of water.

---

*Proportions are discussed in greater detail in Section 6.2.

RECREATIONAL MATH

East Meets West: Magic Squares

A Chinese myth says that in about 2200 B.C., a divine tortoise emerged from the Yellow River. On his back was a special diagram of numbers from which all mathematics was derived. The Chinese called this diagram Lo Shu. The Lo Shu diagram is the first known magic square.

Arab traders brought the Chinese magic square to Europe during the Middle Ages, when the plague was killing millions of people. Magic squares were considered strong talismans against evil, and possession of a magic square was thought to ensure health and wealth. For more magic square problems, see Exercises 53–55 on page 33.

Given ratio $\begin{cases} \dfrac{20 \text{ tsp}}{5 \text{ gal water}} = \dfrac{? \text{ tsp}}{8 \text{ gal}} \end{cases}$ ← Item to be found
← Other information given

Notice in the proportion that teaspoons and gallons are placed in the same relative positions. Often, the unknown quantity is replaced with an x. The proportion may be written as follows and solved using cross-multiplication.

$$\frac{20}{5} = \frac{x}{8}$$

$$20(8) = 5x \qquad \text{Cross multiplication}$$

$$160 = 5x$$

$$\frac{160}{5} = \frac{\cancel{5}x}{\cancel{8}} \qquad \text{Divide both sides of the equation by 5 to solve for } x.$$

$$32 = x$$

Thus, Ron must mix 32 tsp [or $10\frac{2}{3}$ tablespoons (tbsp) or $\frac{2}{3}$ cup] of the weed killer with 8 gal of water. This answer seems reasonable because we would expect to get an answer greater than 20 tsp.

b) To answer this question, we use the same procedure discussed in part (a). This time, we will use the information that 1000 ft^2 requires 20 tsp of weed killer. The areas may be placed either on the top or the bottom of the fraction, as long as they are placed in the same relative position.

Given ratio $\begin{cases} \dfrac{1000 \text{ sq ft}}{20 \text{ tsp}} = \dfrac{2820 \text{ sq ft}}{? \text{ tsp}} \end{cases}$ ← Other information given
← Item to be found

Now replace the question mark with an x and solve the proportion.

$$\frac{1000}{20} = \frac{2820}{x}$$

$$1000(x) = 20(2820) \qquad \text{Cross multiplication}$$

$$1000x = 56,400$$

$$\frac{\cancel{1000}x}{\cancel{1000}} = \frac{56,400}{1000} \qquad \text{Divide both sides of the equation by 1000 to solve for } x.$$

$$x = 56.4$$

Thus, about 56.4 tsp are needed. This answer is reasonable because we would expect the answer to be more than twice the 20 tsp required for 1000 ft^2. ∎

Most of the problems solved so far have been practical ones. Many people, however, enjoy solving brainteasers. One example of such a puzzle follows.

Example 7 *Magic Squares*

A magic square is a square array of numbers such that the numbers in all rows, columns, and diagonals have the same sum. Use the digits 1, 2, 3, 4, 5, 6, 7, 8, and 9 to construct a magic square.

Solution The first step is to create a figure with nine cells, as in Fig.1.2(a) on page 28. We must place the nine numbers in the cells so that the same sum is obtained in each row, column, and diagonal. Common sense tells us that 7, 8, and 9 cannot be in the same row, column, or diagonal. We need some small and large numbers in the same row, column, and diagonal. To see a relationship, we list the numbers in order:

$$1, 2, 3, 4, \boxed{5}, 6, 7, 8, \boxed{9}$$

Note that the middle number is 5 and the smallest and largest numbers are 1 and 9, respectively. The sum of 1, 5, and 9 is 15. If the sum of 2 and 8 is added to 5, the sum is 15. Likewise 3, 5, 7, and 4, 5, 6 have sums of 15. We see that in each group of three numbers the sum is 15 and 5 is a member of the group.

(a)   (b)   (c)   (d)

Figure 1.2

Because 5 is the middle number in the list of numbers, place 5 in the center square. Place 9 and 1 to the left and right of 5, as in Fig. 1.2(a). Now we place the 2 and the 8. The 8 cannot be placed next to 9 because $8 + 9 = 17$, which is greater than 15. Place the smaller number 2 next to the larger number 9. We elected to place the 2 in the lower left-hand cell and the 8 in the upper right-hand cell, as in Fig. 1.2(b). The sum of 8 and 1 is 9. To arrive at a sum of 15, we place 6 in the lower right-hand cell, as in Fig. 1.2(c). The sum of 9 and 2 is 11. To arrive at a sum of 15, we place 4 in the upper left-hand cell as in Fig. 1.2(c). Now the diagonals 2, 5, 8, and 4, 5, 6 have sums of 15. The numbers that remain to be placed in the empty cells are 3 and 7. Using arithmetic, we can see that 3 goes in the top middle cell and 7 goes in the bottom middle cell, as in Fig. 1.2(d). A check shows that the sum in all the rows, columns, and diagonals is 15. ∎

The solution to Example 7 is not unique. Other arrangements of the nine numbers in the cells will produce a magic square. Also, other techniques of arriving at a solution for a magic square may be used. In fact, the process described will not work if the number of squares is even, for example, 16 instead of 9. Magic squares are not limited to the operation of addition or to the set of counting numbers.

SECTION 1.3   *Exercises*

Practice the Skills/Problem Solving

1. ***Reading a Map*** The scale on a map is 1 inch = 12 miles. How long a distance is a route on the map if it measures 5.75 in.? 69 mi

2. ***Blueprints*** Tony Schmidt, an architect, is designing a new enclosure for the elephants at a zoo. The scale of his plan is 1 in. = 2.5 yd. He draws a 20.1-in. line on the blueprint to represent the northern boundary of the enclosure. What actual distance does this boundary line represent? 50.25 yd

3. ***Height of a Tree*** At a given time of day, the ratio of the height of an object to the length of its shadow is the same for all objects. If a 3-ft stick in the ground casts a shadow of 1.2 ft, find the height of a tree that casts a shadow that is 19.36 ft. 48.4 ft

4. ***Grass Seed*** A bag of Turf Builder Sun and Shade Mix grass seed covers an area of 4000 ft². How many bags are needed to cover an area of 35,000 ft²? 8.75 bags

5. ***College Tuition Cost*** According to the College Board, the average tuition at a public four-year college increased by 6.4% from 2009 to 2010. The average tuition at a public four-year college in 2009 was $7605. Determine the average tuition at a public four-year college in 2010. Round your answer to the nearest dollar. $8092

6. ***Hotel Room Rate*** The average price of a hotel room in Las Vegas decreased by 30% from 2008 to 2009. The average price of a hotel room in Las Vegas in 2008 was $117. Determine the average price of a hotel room in Las Vegas in 2009. $81.90

7. ***How Americans Spend Their Money*** The circle graph at the top of page 29 shows the percent of Americans' net monthly income spent on housing, entertainment/miscellaneous, transportation, food, insurance/retirement, and healthcare. Patricia Peck has a net monthly income of $1750. Assuming this graph applies to Patricia's spending,

   a) how much more money per month does Patricia spend on entertainment/miscellaneous than on food? $117.25

   b) how much more money per month does Patricia spend on housing than on transportation? $295.75

**How Americans Spend
Their Money**

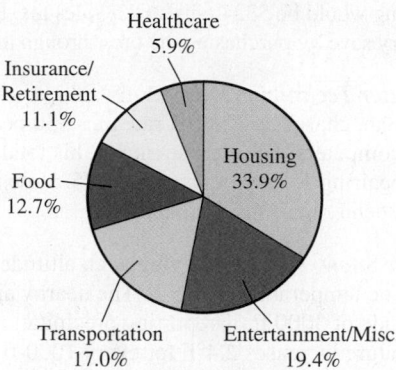

Source: U.S. Bureau of Labor Statistics

8. *Experience Level of U.S Teachers* The circle graph below shows the percent of U.S. teachers with 0–3, 4–10, 11–20, and more than 21 years of teaching experience. In 2009, there were 6.2 million elementary and secondary teachers in the United States.

a) How many more teachers had 11–20 years of teaching experience than 0–3 years? 558,000

b) How many more teachers had 4–10 years of teaching experience than 11–20 years? 496,000

**Years of Experience
of U.S. Teachers**

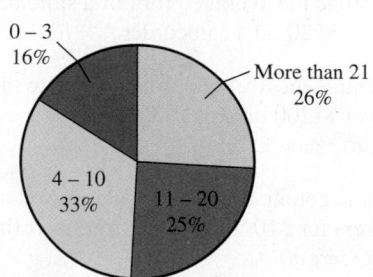

Source: Scholastic

9. *Housing Market* The following tables show where the average U.S. house prices have increased the most and decreased the most during 2004–2009. The tables also show the percent change from 2008–2009 for those areas.

Where House Prices Have Increased the Most		
	%Change 2004–2009	%Change 2008–2009
Wenatchee, WA	66.86	−2.25
Coeur-d'Alene, ID	61.40	−1.92
Virginia Beach, VA	55.24	−1.25
Spokane, WA	55.14	−1.46
Honolulu, HI	54.46	−1.06
Flagstaff, AZ	53.26	−1.85
Bellingham, WA	52.39	−1.04

Where House Prices Have Decreased the Most		
	% Change 2004–2009	% Change 2008–2009
Merced, CA	−29.13	8.33
Stockton, CA	−21.78	3.21
Detroit, MI	−19.80	2.90
Modesto, CA	−18.83	3.30
Vallejo, CA	−16.64	−0.23

Source: Federal Housing Finance Agency

a) If a house in Honolulu, HI, cost $200,000 in 2004, how much did a similar house cost in 2009? $308,920

b) If a house in Detroit, MI, cost $180,000 in 2008, how much did a similar house cost in 2009? $185,220

c) From 2008 to 2009, how much more did a $200,000 house in Flagstaff, AZ, decrease in price than a $200,000 house in Bellingham, WA? $1620

10. *Subway Cost* Chandler Heisinger buys a monthly MetroCard, which entitles him to unlimited subway travel in New York City, for $81 per month. Without the Metrocard, each subway ride costs $2.00. How many rides per month would Chandler have to take so that the cost of the rides with the MetroCard is less than the cost of the rides without the MetroCard? 41 rides

11. *Buying a Computer* Emily Putnam wants to purchase a computer that sells for $1250. She can either pay the total amount at the time of purchase or she can agree to pay the store $120 down and $80 a month for 15 months. How much money can she save by paying the total amount at the time of purchase? $70

12. *Flu Shots* The price of a flu shot at Maxim Health Systems increased by 20% from 2006 to 2009. In 2006, Maxim Health Systems charged $25 for a flu shot. If Maxim Health sold flu shots to 2 million people in 2006 and to 2 million people in 2009, how much more money did they earn from selling flu shots in 2009 than in 2006? $10,000,000

13. *Buying a House* The Browns want to purchase a house that costs $140,000. They plan to take out a $100,000 mortgage on the house and put $40,000 as a down payment. The bank informs them that with a 15-year mortgage their monthly payment would be $777.83 and with a 30-year mortgage their monthly payment would be $521.65. Determine the amount they would save on the cost of the house if they selected the 15-year mortgage rather than the 30-year mortgage. $47,784.60

14. *Getting an 80 Average* On four exams, Wallace Memmer's grades were 79, 93, 91, and 68. What grade must he obtain on his fifth exam to have an 80 average? 69

15. *Playing a Lottery* In one state lottery game, you must select four-digits (digits may be repeated). If your number matches exactly the four-digits selected by the lottery commission, you win.

   a) How many different numbers may be chosen? 10,000

   b) If you purchase one lottery ticket, what is your chance of winning? 1 in 10,000

16. *Energy Value and Energy Consumption* The table gives the approximate energy values of some foods, in kilojoules (kJ), and the energy requirements of some activities.

   a) How soon would you use up the energy from a fried egg by swimming? 9.2 min

   b) How soon would you use up the energy from a hamburger by walking? 62 min

   c) How soon would you use up the energy from a piece of strawberry shortcake by cycling? 40 min

   d) How soon would you use up the energy from a hamburger and a chocolate milkshake by running? 47 min

Food	Energy Value (kJ)	Activity	Energy Consumption (kJ/min)
Chocolate milkshake	2200	Walking	25
Fried egg	460	Cycling	35
Hamburger	1550	Swimming	50
Strawberry shortcake	1400	Running	80
Glass of skim milk	350		

17. *Gas Mileage* Wendy Weisner fills her gas tank completely and makes a note that the odometer reads 38,451.4 miles. The next time she put gas in her car, filling the tank took 12.6 gal and the odometer read 38,687.0 miles. Determine the number of miles per gallon that Wendy's car got on this tank of gas. ≈ 18.7 mpg

18. *Saving for a Stereo* Fernando Diez works 40 hours per week and makes $8.50 per hour.

   a) How much money can he expect to earn in 1 year (52 weeks)? $17,680

   b) If he saves all the money he earns, how long will he have to work to save for a stereo receiver that costs $1275? 3.75 weeks

19. *Mail-Order Purchase* Mary Liotta purchased 4 tires by mail order. She paid $52.80 per tire plus $5.60 per tire for shipping and handling. There is no sales tax on this purchase because the tires were purchased out of state. She also had to pay

$8.56, including tax, per tire for mounting and balancing. At a local tire store, her total for the 4 tires with mounting and balancing would be $324 plus an 8% sales tax. How much did Mary save by purchasing the tires through the mail? $82.08

20. *Computer Technician* Dave Maliwauki, a computer technician, charges a $25 flat rate plus $30 per hour to repair computers. During one month, his total income from repairing 15 computers was $885. How many hours did he spend repairing computers? 17 hours

21. *Rain or Snow* A plane is flying at an altitude of 15,000 ft, where the temperature is −6°F. The nearby airport, at an altitude of 3000 ft, is reporting precipitation. If the temperature increases 2.4°F for every 1000-ft decrease in altitude, will the precipitation at the airport be rain or snow? Assume that rain changes to snow at 32°F. Snow

22. *Profit Margins* The following chart shows retail stores' average percent profit margin on certain items.

Product Category	Average Profit Margin (%)
Video equipment	12
Audio components	14
Stereo speakers	20–25
Extended warranties	50–60

Source: *Consumer Reports*

   a) Determine the average profit of a store that has the list price of $620 on a camcorder. $74.40

   b) Determine the average profit of a store that has a list price of $1200 on a pair of speakers (use a 22% profit margin). $264

   c) If you negotiate and get the salesperson to sell the speakers for $1000, find the store's profit (use a 22% profit margin). $64

23. *Income Taxes* The federal income tax rate schedule for a joint return in 2010 is illustrated in the table. If Steve and Maureen Tomlin paid $13,365 in federal taxes, find the family's adjusted gross income. $84,010

Adjusted Gross Income	Taxes
$0–$16,750	10% of income
$16,750–$68,000	$1675 + 15% of amount over $16,750
$68,000–$137,300	$9362.50 + 25% of amount over $68,000
$137,300–$209,250	$26,687.50 + 28% of amount over $137,300
$209,250–$373,650	$46,833.50 + 33% of amount over $209,250
$373,650 and above	$101,085.50 + 35% of amount over $373,650

24. Leaking Faucet A faucet is leaking at a rate of one drop of water per second. Assume that the volume of one drop of water is 0.1 cubic centimeter (0.1 cm³).

a) Determine the volume of water in cubic centimeters lost in 1 year. 3,153,600 cm³

b) How many days would it take to fill a rectangular basin 30 cm by 20 cm by 20 cm? ≈ 1.4 days

25. Wasted Water A faucet leaks 1 oz of water per minute.

a) How many gallons of water are wasted in a year? (A gallon contains 128 oz.) 4106.25 gal

b) If water costs $11.20 per 1000 gal, how much additional money is being spent on the water bill? $45.99

26. Airport Parking The chart shows parking rates at John F. Kennedy (JFK) Airport in New York, New York, as of August 1, 2011.

JFK Airport Parking Rates			
Short-term Rates			
First half hour	$\frac{1}{2}$ hour–1 hour	Each Additional Half Hour After the First Hour	Daily Maximum
$3	$6	$3	$33

Long-term Rates Daily	Additional Day 0–8 Hours
$18	$6

a) Jeff Grace is going out of town for 5 full days. How much will he save by parking in the long-term lot rather than the short-term lot? $75

b) What is the cost of parking in the short-term lot for 4 hours? $24

c) If Jeff plans to park at the airport for 5 hours, is it cheaper to park in short-term or long-term parking? How much is the difference? Long term by $12

27. Tire Pressure When a car's tire pressure is 30 pounds per square inch (psi), it averages 20.8 mpg of gasoline. If the tire pressure is increased to 35 psi, the car averages 21.6 mpg of gasoline.

a) If Mr. Levy drives an average of 20,000 mi per year, how many gallons of gasoline will he save in a year by increasing his tire pressure from 30 to 35 psi? ≈ 35.61 gal

b) If gasoline costs $3.00 per gallon, how much will he save in a year? $106.83

c) If we assume that there are about 140 million cars in the United States and that these changes are typical of each car, how many gallons of gasoline would be saved if all drivers increased their cars' tire pressure ? ≈ 4,985,400,000 gal

28. Toys and Games The table illustrates the 10 countries that spent the most money, per person, on toys and games in 2008. The table also shows the total amount of money spent on toys and games for each country.

Country	Amount Spent per person ($)	Total Amount Spent (in millions $)
United Kingdom	184.90	11,237.53
Australia	177.89	3633.20
United States	151.40	45,592.59
France	147.30	9385.96
Netherlands	130.70	2165.70
Sweden	120.60	1089.02
Belgium	113.70	1181.34
Canada	105.80	3532.66
Spain	93.40	3778.03
Italy	85.70	4983.46

Source: Euromonitor International

a) By looking at the data provided, is it possible to determine the population of each country? If so, explain how to do so. Divide the total amount spent by the amount spent per person.

b) Using the procedure you gave in part (a), determine the population of the United States. 301.14 million

c) Using the procedure you gave in part (a), determine the population of the United Kingdom. 60.78 million

29. Adjusting for Inflation Assume that the rate of inflation is 6% per year for the next 2 years. What will the price of a dishwasher be 2 years from now if the dishwasher costs $799 today? $897.76

30. Investing You place $1000 in a mutual fund. The first year, the value of the fund increases by 10%. The second year, the value of the fund decreases by 10%. Determine the value of the fund at the end of the second year. Is it greater than, less than, or equal to your initial investment? $990, less than initial investment

31. X-rays With a certain medical insurance policy, the customer must first pay an annual $100 deductible, and then the policy covers 80% of the cost of x-rays. The first insurance claims for a specific year submitted by Yungchen Cheng are for two x-rays. The first x-ray cost $640, and the second x-ray cost $920. How much, in total, will Yungchen need to pay for these x-rays? $392

32. *Buying a Yacht* Four partners decide to share the cost of a yacht equally. By bringing in an additional partner, they can reduce the cost to each of the five partners by $3000. What is the total cost of the yacht? $60,000

33. *Making Cream of Wheat* The following amounts of ingredients are recommended to make various servings of Nabisco Instant Cream of Wheat. *Note:* 16 tbsp = 1 cup.

Ingredient	1 Serving	2 Servings	4 Servings
Mix water or milk	1 cup	2 cups	$3\frac{3}{4}$ cups
With salt (optional)	$\frac{1}{8}$ tsp	$\frac{1}{4}$ tsp	$\frac{1}{2}$ tsp
Add Cream of Wheat	3 tbsp	$\frac{1}{2}$ cup	$\frac{3}{4}$ cups

Determine the amount of each ingredient needed to make 3 servings using the following procedures.

a) Multiply the amounts for 1 serving by 3.
  Water/milk: 3 cups; salt: $\frac{3}{8}$ tsp; Cream of Wheat: 9 tbsp (or $\frac{9}{16}$ cup)
b) Find the average of the amounts for 2 and 4 servings.
  Water/milk: $2\frac{7}{8}$ cups; salt: $\frac{3}{8}$ tsp; Cream of Wheat: $\frac{5}{8}$ cup (10 tbsp)
c) Subtract the amounts for 1 serving from the amounts for 4 servings.
  Water/milk: $2\frac{3}{4}$ cups; salt: $\frac{3}{8}$ tsp; Cream of Wheat: $\frac{9}{16}$ cup (or 9 tbsp)
d) Compare the answers obtained in parts (a) through (c) and explain any differences. *

34. *Making Rice* Following are the amounts of ingredients recommended to make various servings of Uncle Ben's Original Converted Rice. *Note:* 1 tbsp = 3 tsp.

Ingredient	2 Servings	4 Servings	6 Servings	12 Servings
Rice (cups)	$\frac{1}{2}$	1	$1\frac{1}{2}$	3
Water (cups)	$1\frac{1}{3}$	$2\frac{1}{4}$	$3\frac{1}{3}$	6
Salt (teaspoons)	$\frac{1}{4}$	$\frac{1}{2}$	$\frac{3}{4}$	$1\frac{1}{2}$
Butter	1 tsp	2 tsp	1 tbsp	2 tbsp

Determine the amount of each ingredient needed to make 8 servings using the following procedures.

a) Multiply the amount for 2 servings by 4. *

b) Multiply the amount for 4 servings by 2. *

c) Add the amounts for 2 and 6 servings. *

d) Subtract the amount for 4 servings from the amount for 12 servings. *

e) Compare the answers obtained in parts (a) through (d) and explain any differences. Differences exist in water because the amount for 4 servings is not twice that for 2 servings.

35. *Purchasing DVDs* The manager of the video department at Target plans to purchase a large number of DVDs of the movie *Toy Story* 3. One supplier is selling boxes of 20 DVD movies for $240, and a second supplier is selling boxes of 12 DVD movies for $180. Only complete boxes of DVD movies can be purchased.

a) If the manager can purchase boxes of DVD movies from either or both suppliers, determine the maximum number of DVD movies that can be purchased for $425. Indicate how many boxes of 20 and how many boxes of 12 will be purchased. 1 box of 20 and 1 box of 12

b) How much will the DVD movies cost? $420

36. *Who Will Win?* Steve Kilner and Mark Ernsthausen ran a 100-yard race. Mark won by 5 yards, which means Steve had run only 95 yards when Mark crossed the finish line. They decided to race again, with Mark starting 5 yards behind the starting line. Assuming both runners run the second race at the same pace as the first race, who will win? Mark

37. *One Square Foot* How many square inches, 1 in. by 1 in., fit in an area of 1 square foot, 1 ft by 1 ft? 144 square inches

38. *Cubic Inches* How many cubic inches fit in 1 cubic foot? 1728 cubic inches

39. *Rectangle* If the length and width of a rectangle each double, what happens to the area of the rectangle? The area is 4 times as large.

40. *A Square Partition* A 20 ft by 20 ft carpet is partitioned into 5 ft by 5 ft squares. How many squares will there be? 16

41. *Cube* If the length, width, and height of a cube all double, what happens to the volume of the cube? The volume is 8 times as large.

42. *Pole in a Lake* A pole is in the middle of a small lake. One half of the pole is in the ground. One third of the pole is covered by water. Eleven feet, or one sixth, of the pole are out of water. What is the length of the pole? 66 ft

43. *Buying Candy* How much do 10 pieces of candy cost if 1000 pieces cost $10? 10¢

*See Instructor Answer Appendix

44. *A Balance* On the balance below, where should the one missing block ■ be placed so that the balance would balance on the triangle (the fulcrum). Assume that each block has the same weight. at −1

45. *Ties, Ties, Ties* I have at least three ties. All my ties are red except two. All my ties are blue except two. All my ties are brown except two. How many ties do I have? 3

46. *Palindromes* A *palindrome* is a number (or word) that reads the same forward and backward. The numbers 1991 and 43234 are examples of palindromes. How many palindromes are there between the numbers 2000 and 3000? List them. 10: 2002, 2112, 2222, 2332, 2442, 2552, 2662, 2772, 2882, 2992

47. *Supermarket Display* The figure shows grapefruits in a supermarket display stacked in a *square pyramid* (the base is a square).

  a) How many grapefruits are in the pyramid shown if the base has 4 grapefruits by 4 grapefruits? 30

  b) How many grapefruits would be in a square pyramid if the base has 7 grapefruits by 7 grapefruits? 140

48. *Balancing a Scale* If you have a balance scale and only the four weights 1 gram (g), 3 g, 9 g, and 27 g, explain how you could show that an object had the following weights. (*Hint:* Weights must be added to both sides of the balance scale.)

  a) 5 g*   b) 16 g *

49. *Numbers in Circles* Place the numbers 1 through 6 in the circles below so that the sum along each of the three straight lines is the same. Each number must be used exactly once. (*Note:* There is more than one correct answer.)

50. *Cuts in Cheese* If you make the three complete cuts in the cheese as shown, how many pieces of cheese will you have? Eight pieces

51. *Magic Square* Create a magic square by using the numbers 2, 4, 6, 8, 10, 12, 14, 16, and 18. The sum of the numbers in every column, row, and diagonal must be 30. *

52. *Magic Square* Create a magic square by using the numbers 3, 4, 5, 6, 7, 8, 9, 10, and 11. The sum of the numbers in every column, row, and diagonal must be 21. *

In Exercises 53–55, use the three magic squares illustrated to obtain the answers.

8	1	6
3	5	7
4	9	2

3	2	7
8	4	0
1	6	5

10	9	14
15	11	7
8	13	12

53. *Magic Square* Examine the 3 by 3 magic squares and find the sum of the four corner entries of each magic square. How can you determine the sum by using a key number in the magic square? The sum of the four corners is 4 times the number in the center.

54. *Magic Square* For a 3 by 3 magic square, how can you determine the sum of the numbers in any particular row, column, or diagonal by using a key value in the magic square? Multiply the center number by 3.

55. *Magic Square* For a 3 by 3 magic square, how can you determine the sum of all the numbers in the square by using a key value in the magic square? Multiply the center number by 9.

56. *Stack of Cubes* Identical cubes are stacked in the corner of a room as shown. How many of the cubes are not visible? 20 cubes

57. *Dominos* Consider a domino with six dots as shown. Two ways of connecting the three dots on the left with the three dots on the right are illustrated. Using three lines, in how many ways can the three dots on the left be connected with the three dots on the right? 6 ways

58. *Handshakes All Around* Five salespeople gather for a sales meeting. How many handshakes will each person make if each must shake hands with each of the four others? 4

*See Instructor Answer Appendix

59. *Consecutive Digits* Place the digits 1 through 8 in the eight boxes so that each digit is used exactly once and no two consecutive digits touch horizontally, vertically, or diagonally. *

60. *A Digital Clock* Digital clocks display numerals by lighting all or some of the seven parts of the pattern shown. If each digit 0 through 9 is displayed once, which of the seven parts is used least often? Which part is used most often? *

61. *A Grid* Place five 1's, five 2's, five 3's, five 4's, and five 5's in a 5 × 5 grid so that each digit—that is, 1, 2, 3, 4, 5—appears exactly once in each row and exactly once in each column. *

Challenge Problems/Group Activities

62. *Insurance Policies* Ray Kelley owns two cars (a Ford Mustang and a Ford Focus), a house, and a rental apartment. He has auto insurance for both cars, a homeowner's policy, and a policy for the rental property. The costs of the policies are

    Mustang: $1648 per year
    Focus: $1530 per year
    Homeowner's: $640 per year
    Rental property: $750 per year

Ray is considering taking out a $1 million personal umbrella liability policy. The annual cost of the umbrella policy would be $450. If he has the umbrella policy, he can lower the limits on parts of his auto policies and still have equal or better protection. If Ray purchases the umbrella policy, he can reduce his premium on the Mustang by $90 per year and his premium on the Focus by 12%. If he purchases the umbrella policy and reduces the amount he pays for auto insurance, what is the net amount he is actually paying for the umbrella policy? $176.40

63. *A Sports Puzzle* Peter, Paul, and Mary are three sports professionals. One is a tennis player, one is a golfer, and one is a skier. They live in three adjacent houses on City View Drive. From the following information, determine which is the professional skier. (*Hint:* A table may be helpful.)

    Mary does not play tennis.
    Peter skis and plays tennis, but does not golf.
    The golfer and the skier live next to each other.
    Three years ago, Paul broke his leg skiing and has not tried it since.

Mary lives in the last house.
The golfer and the tennis player share a common backyard swimming pool. Mary is the skier.

64. *Counting Triangles* How many triangles are in the figure?

44

65. *Finding the Area* Rectangle ABCD is made up entirely of squares. The black square has a side of 1 unit. Find the area of rectangle ABCD.

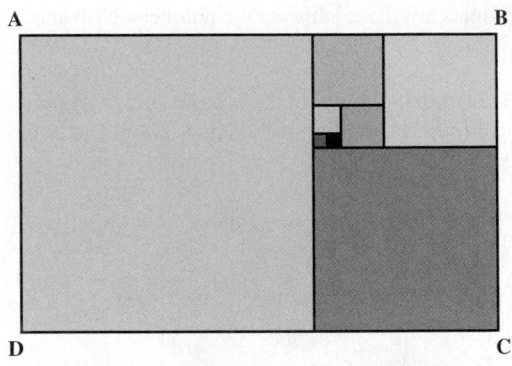

714 square units

66. *Spending Money* Samantha Smith went into a store and spent half her money and then spent $20 more. Samantha then went into a second store and spent half her remaining money and then spent $20 more. After spending money in the second store, Samantha had no money left. How much money did she have when she went into the first store? $120

67. *Boxes of Fruit* There are three boxes on a table, each with a label. Thomas Abernathy knows that one box contains grapes, one box contains cherries, and the third box contains both grapes and cherries. He also knows that the three labels used—grapes, cherries, and grapes and cherries—were mixed up and that none of the boxes received the correct label. He opens just one box and, without looking into the box, takes out one piece of fruit. He looks at the fruit and immediately labels all the boxes correctly. Which box did Thomas open? How did he know how to correctly label the boxes? *

Internet/Research Activities

68. *Puzzles* Many fun and interesting puzzle books and magazines are available. Using this chapter and puzzle books as a guide, construct five of your own puzzles and present them to your instructor.

<table>
<tr><td colspan="2">**CHAPTER 1** *Summary*</td></tr>
</table>

Important Facts and Concepts	**Examples and Discussion**
Section 1.1	
The **natural numbers** or **counting numbers** are 1, 2, 3, 4,....	Examples 1, 2, 4, 5, pages 2–4
A **conjecture** is a prediction based on specific observations.	Example 4, page 3
A **counterexample** is a special case that satisfies all the conditions of a conjecture, but proves the conjecture false.	Discussion page 4
Inductive reasoning is the process of reasoning to a general conclusion through observations of specific cases.	Examples 1 and 2, pages 2–3
Deductive reasoning is the process of reasoning to a specific conclusion from a general statement.	Example 6, pages 4–5
Section 1.2	
Estimation is the process of arriving at an approximate answer to a question.	Examples 1–7, pages 9–13
Section 1.3	
Guidelines for Problem Solving	
1. Understand the problem. 2. Devise a plan to solve the problem. 3. Carry out the plan. 4. Check the results.	Discussion page 22 Examples 1–7, pages 20–28

CHAPTER 1 *Review Exercises*

1.1 †

In Exercises 1–8, use inductive reasoning to predict the next three numbers or figures in the pattern.

1. 7, 12, 17, 22, ... 27, 32, 37

2. 2, 5, 10, 17, ... 26, 37, 50

3. −3, 6, −12, 24, ... −48, 96, −192

4. 5, 7, 10, 14, 19, ... 25, 32, 40

5. 25, 24, 22, 19, 15, ... 10, 4, −3

6. 6, 3, $\frac{3}{2}$, $\frac{3}{4}$, ... $\frac{3}{8}$, $\frac{3}{16}$, $\frac{3}{32}$

7. ◔, ⊟, ◔, ⊟, ... *

8. ▱, ▱, ▱, ▱, ▱, ... *

9. *Pattern* Examine the grid above and to the right for a pattern and then select the answer which completes the pattern. (*Hint:* Think about rotating groups of four squares at a time.)

   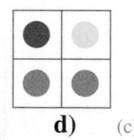

a)   b)   c)   d)   (c)

10. Pick any number and multiply the number by 10. Add 5 to the product. Divide the sum by 5. Subtract 1 from the quotient.

a) What is the relationship between the number you started with and the final number?
   The final number is twice the original number.

b) Arbitrarily select some different numbers and repeat the process. Record the original number and the results.
   The final number is twice the original number.

c) Make a conjecture about the original number and the final number. The final number is twice the original number.

d) Prove, using deductive reasoning, the conjecture you made in part (c). n, $10n$, $10n + 5$, $\frac{10n + 5}{5} = 2n + 1$, $2n + 1 - 1 = 2n$

---

†The number in color indicates the section in which the material is covered.

*See Instructor Answer Appendix

11. Pick any number between 1 and 20. Add 5 to the number. Multiply the sum by 6. Subtract 12 from the product. Divide the difference by 2. Divide the quotient by 3. Subtract the number you started with from the quotient. What is your answer? Try this process with a different number. Make a conjecture as to what your final answer will always be. This process will always result in an answer of 3.

12. *Counterexample* Find a counterexample to the statement "The sum of two squares is an even number." $1^2 + 2^2 = 5$

1.2

In Exercises 13–25, estimate the answer. Your answers may vary from those given in the back of the book, depending on how you round to arrive at the answer, but your answers should be something near the answers given.

13. $210,302 \times 2002$ 420,000,000

14. $215.9 + 128.752 + 3.6 + 861 + 792$ 2000

15. 19% of 1025 200

16. *Distance* Estimate the distance from your wrist to your elbow and estimate the length of your foot. Which do you think is greater? With the help of a friend, measure both lengths to determine which is longer. Answers will vary.

17. *Cost* Estimate the cost of 52 shovels if the cost is $99.97 per shovel. $5000

18. *Sales Tax* Estimate the amount of a 7% sales tax on an Oriental rug that costs $1999. $140

19. *Walking Speed* Estimate your average walking speed in miles per hour if you walked 1.1 mi in 22 min. 3 mph

20. *Groceries* Estimate the total cost of six grocery items that cost $2.49, $0.79, $1.89, $0.10, $2.19, and $6.75. $14.00

21. *A Walking Path* The scale of the map is $\frac{1}{4}$ in. = 0.1 mi. Estimate the distance of the walking path indicated in red. 2 mi

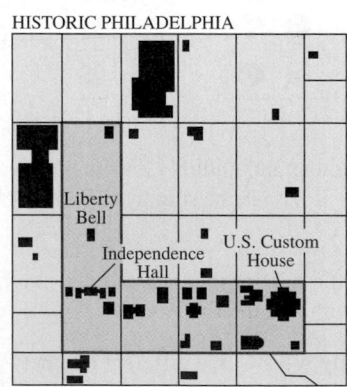

HISTORIC PHILADELPHIA

In Exercises 22 and 23, refer to the following graph, which illustrates the number of registered nurses (RNs) needed (demand) and the number of RNs available (supply) from 2000 to 2010. The graph also illustrates the projected number of RNs needed and the projected number of RNs available from 2011 to 2020.

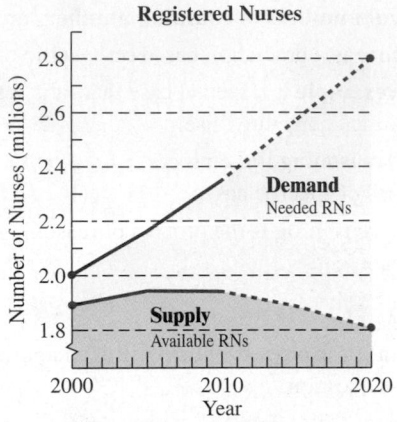

Source: U.S. Bureau of Health Professions

22. Estimate the difference in the number of RNs needed and the number of RNs available in 2010. 0.4 million

23. Estimate the difference in the projected number of RNs needed and the projected number of RNs available in 2020. 1.0 million

24. *Estimating an Area* If each square represents one square unit, estimate the size of the shaded area. 13 square units

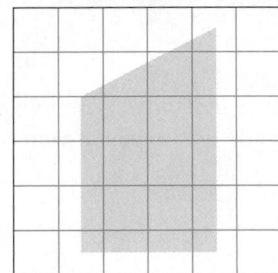

25. *Railroad Car Estimation* The scale of a model railroad is 1 in. = 12.5 ft. Estimate the size of an actual box car if this drawing is the same size as the model box car. Length ≈ 22 ft; height ≈ 8 ft

1.3

Solve the following problems.

26. *Buying a Copy Machine* David Stewart can buy a copier from Staples for $500 that prints, copies, and scans. He can either pay the total amount at the time of purchase, or

he can agree to pay the store $50 down and $40 a month for 12 months. How much money can he save by paying the total amount at the time of purchase? $30

27. *Buying in Quantity* A six-pack of cola costs $2.69. A carton of 4 six-packs costs $9.60. How much will be saved by purchasing the carton rather than 4 individual six-packs? $1.16

28. *Renting a Post Hole Digger* The cost to rent a gas-powered post hole digger from Taylor Rental is $45 for 8 hours, and the cost from Admar Rental is $8 per hour. If Justin Calhoun plans to rent a post hole digger for 6 hours, which is the better deal, and by how much?
Taylor Rental is less expensive by $3

29. *Fishing Charter* Sam Stevens and four other friends want to schedule a 6-hour fishing trip on Lake Ontario with Reel Easy Sport Fishing. The cost for five people is $445. The cost for six people is $510. How much money per person will Sam and each of his friends save if they can find one more friend to go on their fishing trip? Assume that they will split the total cost equally. $4

30. *Applying Fertilizer* Ron Williams needs to apply fertilizer to his lawn on his farm. A 30-pound bag of fertilizer will cover an area of 2500 square feet.

a) How many pounds are needed to cover an area of 24,000 square feet? 288 lb

b) If Ron has only 150 pounds of fertilizer, how many square feet can he fertilize? 12,500 ft²

31. *Auto Insurance* Most insurance companies reduce premiums by 10% until age 25 for people who successfully pass a driver's education course. A particular driver's education course costs $60. Patrick Flanigan, who just turned 18, has auto insurance that costs $1030 per year. By taking the driver's education course, how much would he save in auto insurance, including the cost of the course, from the age of 18 until the age of 25? $661

32. *Pediatric Dosage* If 1.5 milligrams of a medicine is to be given for 10 lb of body weight, how many milligrams should be given to a child who weighs 47 lb? 7.05 mg

33. *Qualifying for a Mortgage* Banks will usually grant an applicant a mortgage if the monthly payments are not greater than 28% of the person's take-home pay. What is the maximum monthly mortgage payment you can make if your gross salary is $5000 a month and your payroll deductions are 30% of your gross salary? $980

34. *Flying West* New York City is on eastern standard time, St. Louis is on central standard time (1 hr earlier than eastern standard time), and Las Vegas is on Pacific standard time (3 hr earlier than eastern standard time). A flight leaves New York City at 9 A.M. eastern standard time, stops for 50 min in St. Louis, and arrives in Las Vegas at 1:35 P.M. Pacific time. How long is the plane actually flying?
6 hr 45 min

35. *Crossing Time Zones* The international date line is an imaginary line of longitude (from the North Pole to the South Pole) on Earth's surface between Japan and Hawaii in the Pacific Ocean. Crossing the line east to west adds a day to the present date. Crossing the line west to east subtracts a day. At 3:00 P.M. on July 25 in Hawaii, what is the time and date in Tokyo, Japan, which is four time zones to the west? July 26, 11:00 A.M.

36. a) If one mile = 5280 feet, what is 1 mile per hour equal to in feet per second? ≈ 1.47 ft/sec

b) What is 55 miles per hour equal to in feet per second? ≈ 80.67 ft/sec

37. *Dot Pattern* If the following pattern is continued, how many dots will be in the hundredth figure?

 201

38. *Magic Square* The following magic square uses each number from 6 to 21 exactly once. Complete the magic square by using the unused numbers from 6 through 21 exactly once. *

21	7		18
10		15	
14	12	11	17
9	19		

39. *Magic Square* Create a magic square by using the numbers 13, 15, 17, 19, 21, 23, 25, 27, and 29. The sum of the numbers in every row, column, and diagonal must be 63. *

40. *Microbes in a Jar* A colony of microbes doubles in number every second. A single microbe is placed in a jar, and in an hour the jar is full. When was the jar half full? 59 min 59 sec

*See Instructor Answer Appendix

41. *Brothers and Sisters* Jim Carraway has four more brothers than sisters. How many more brothers than sisters does his sister Mary have? 6

42. *A Missing Dollar* Three friends check into a single room in a motel and pay $10 apiece. The room costs $25 instead of $30, so a clerk is sent to the room to give $5 back. The friends each take back $1, and the clerk is given $2 for his trouble. Now each of the friends paid $9, a total of $27, and the clerk received $2. What happened to the missing dollar? *

43. *The Average Weight* Four women in a room have an average weight of 130 lb. A fifth woman who weighs 180 lb enters the room. Find the average weight of all five women. 140 lb

44. *Change for a Dollar* Could a person have $1.15 worth of change in his pocket and still not be able to give someone change for a dollar bill? If so, what coins might he have? *

45. *Volume of a Cube* Here is a flat pattern for a cube to be formed by folding. The sides of each square are 6 cm. Find the volume of the cube.

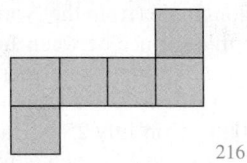

216 cm³

46. *The Heavier Coin* You have 13 coins, which all look alike. Twelve coins weigh exactly the same, but the other one is heavier. You have a pan balance. Tell how to find the heavier coin in just three weighings. *

47. *The Sum of Numbers* Find the sum of the first 500 counting numbers. (*Hint:* Group in pairs.) 125,250

48. *Balancing a Scale* On a balance scale, three green balls balance six blue balls, two yellow balls balance five blue balls, and six blue balls balance four white balls. How many blue balls are needed to balance four green, two yellow, and two white balls? 16 blue

49. *Palindromes* How many three-digit numbers greater than 100 are palindromes? 90

50. *Figures* Describe the fifth figure. *

51. *Patterns* How many orange tiles will be required to build the sixth figure in this pattern? 61

52. *Sum of Numbers* Place the numbers 1 through 12 in the 12 circles so that the sum of the numbers in each of the six rows is 26. Use each number from 1 through 12 exactly once. *

53. *People in a Line* People stand in a line at movies, the grocery store, and many other places.

a) In how many ways can two people stand in a line? 2

b) In how many ways can three people stand in a line? 6

c) In how many ways can four people stand in a line? 24

d) In how many ways can five people stand in a line? 120

e) Using the results from parts (a) through (d), make a conjecture about the number of ways in which *n* people can stand in a line. $n(n-1)(n-2)\ldots 1$, (or n!), where n = the number of people in line

*See Instructor Answer Appendix

CHAPTER 1) *Test*

In Exercises 1 and 2, use inductive reasoning to determine the next three numbers in the pattern.

1. 3, 9, 15, 21, ... 27, 33, 39   **2.** $1, \frac{1}{2}, \frac{1}{4}, \frac{1}{8}, \ldots$ $\frac{1}{16}, \frac{1}{32}, \frac{1}{64}$

3. Pick any number, multiply the number by 5, and add 10 to the number. Divide the sum by 5. Subtract 1 from the quotient.

a) What is the relationship between the number you started with and the final answer?
The result is the original number plus 1

b) Arbitrarily select some different numbers and repeat the process. Record the original number and the results. The result is the original number plus 1.

c) Make a conjecture about the relationship between the original number and the final answer.
The result will always be the original number plus 1.

d) Prove, using deductive reasoning, the conjecture made in part (c). $n, 5n, 5n + 10, \frac{5n + 10}{5} = n + 2,$ $n + 2 - 1 = n + 1$

In Exercises 4 and 5, estimate the answers.

4. $0.21 \times 82,000$ 16,000

5. $\frac{175,000}{0.09}$ 1,700,000

6. *Estimating Area* If each square represents one square unit, estimate the area of the shaded figure.

9 square units

7. *Body Mass Index* The federal government gives a procedure to determine if a child is overweight. To make this decision, first determine the child's body mass index (BMI). Then compare the BMI with one of the two charts, one for boys and one for girls, provided by the government. Below, we give the chart for boys up to age 20. To determine a child's BMI:

1) Divide the child's weight (in pounds) by the child's height (in inches).

2) Divide the results from part 1 by the child's height again.

3) Multiply the result from part 2 by 703.

Richard is a 14-year-old boy who weighs 130 lb and is 63 in. tall.

a) Determine his BMI. ≈ 23.03

b) Does he appear to be at risk for being overweight, or is he overweight? Explain. He is in the at-risk range.

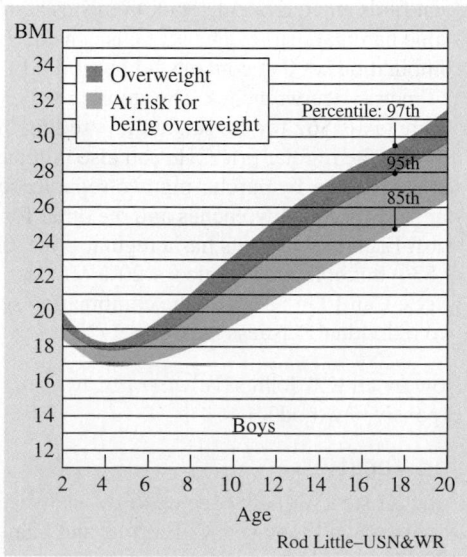

8. *Holding Multiple Jobs* The following graph shows the number of American men and women who held multiple jobs, as of July 2009.

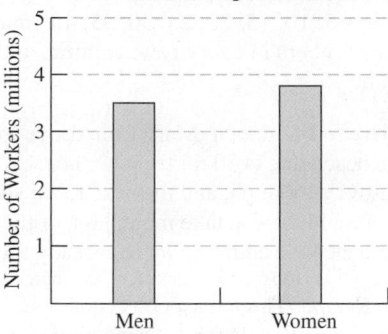

Source: U.S. Bureau of Labor Statistics

a) Estimate the number of American men who held multiple jobs. 3.5 million

b) Estimate the difference between the number of American women and American men who held multiple jobs. 0.3 million

9. *Cell Phone Cost* Verizon Wireless charges $59.99 for its Basic Plan for cell phones, which includes 900 minutes of call time. The company charges $0.40 for each additional minute. If the Smiths' cell phone bill for December was $85.99, how many additional minutes did they use during that month? 65 min

10. *Cans of Soda* At a local store a six-pack of soda costs $2.59 and individual cans cost $0.80. What is the maximum number of cans of soda that can be purchased for $15? 32 cans

11. *Cutting Wood* How much time does it take Carla Knab, a carpenter, to cut a 10-ft length of wood into four equal pieces, if each cut takes $2\frac{1}{2}$ min? $7\frac{1}{2}$ min

12. *Determining Size* In this photo of *Sunflowers*, an 1889 painting by Vincent van Gogh, 1 in. equals 15.8 in. on the actual painting. Find the dimensions of the actual painting. ≈ 39.5 in. by 29.6 in. (The actual dimensions are 100.5 cm by 76.5 cm.)

▲ Sunflowers *by Vincent van Gogh*

13. *Payment Shortfall* Monica Wilson gets $12.75 per hour with time and a half for any time over 40 hours per week. If she works a 50-hr week and gets paid $652.25, by how much was she underpaid? $49.00

14. *Magic Square* Create a magic square by using the numbers 5, 10, 15, 20, 25, 30, 35, 40, and 45. The sum of the numbers in every row, column, and diagonal must be 75. *

15. *A Drive to the Beach* Mary Chin drove from her home to the beach that is 30 mi from her house. The first 15 mi she drove at 60 mph, and the next 15 mi she drove at 30 mph. Would the trip take more, less, or the same time if she traveled the entire 30 mi at a steady 45 mph? Less time if she had driven at 45 mph for the entire trip

16. *Chili Recipe* Three teaspoons equal one tablespoon. A recipe for chili calls for $\frac{1}{2}$ teaspoon of salt for 2 pounds of ground beef. How many tablespoons of salt are needed for 6 pounds of ground beef? $\frac{1}{2}$ tablespoon

17. *Area of a Concrete Walkway* A 10 meter by 12 meter rectangular lawn has a concrete walkway 1 meter wide around the outside of the lawn. What is the area of the walkway? 48 square meters

18. *Jelly Bean Guess* One guess is off by 9, another guess is off by 17, and yet another guess is off by 31. How many jelly beans are in the jar above and to the right? 243 jelly beans

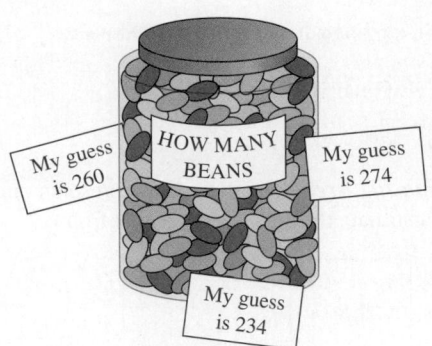

19. *Buying Plants* David Mackin wants to purchase nine herb plants. Countryside Nursery has herbs that are on sale at three for $3.99. David has a coupon for 25% off an unlimited number of herb plants at the original price of $1.75 per plant.

   a) Determine the cost of purchasing nine plants at the sale price. $11.97

   b) Determine the cost of purchasing nine plants if the coupon is used. $11.81

   c) Which is the least expensive way to purchase the nine plants, and by how much? Save 16 cents by using the 25% off coupon.

20. *Arranging Letters* In how many different ways can four letters, A, B, C, D, be arranged? 24

*See Instructor Answer Appendix

GROUP PROJECTS

Holiday Shopping

1. It is December 1 and John needs to begin his holiday shopping. He intends to purchase gifts for three people: his girlfriend, Melissa; his mother, Ruth; and his father, Don. He doesn't want to spend more than a total of $325, including the 7% sales tax.

   a) If John were to spend the $325 equally among the three people, approximate the amount that would be spent on each person.

   b) If John were to spend the $325 equally among the three people, determine the maximum amount, *before tax*, that he could spend on each person and not exceed the maximum of $325, including tax.

   c) John decides to get a new set of wrenches for his father. He sees the specific set he wants on sale at Sears. He calls four Sears stores to see if they have the set of wrenches in stock. They all reply that the set is out of stock. He decides that calling additional Sears stores is useless because he believes that they will also tell him that the set of wrenches is out of stock. What type of reasoning did John use in arriving at his conclusion? Explain.

   d) John finds an equivalent set of wrenches at a True Value hardware store. The set he is considering is a combination set that contains both standard U.S. size and metric size wrenches. The store's regular price before tax is $62 for the set, but it is selling them for 10% off the regular price. He can also purchase the same wrenches by purchasing two separate sets, one for standard U.S. size wrenches and the other for metric sizes. Each of these sets has a regular price, before tax, of $36, but both are on sale for 20% off their regular prices. Can John purchase the combination set or the two individual sets less expensively?

   e) How much will John save, *after tax*, by using the less expensive method?

Going on Vacation

2. Bob and Kristen Williams decide to go on a vacation. They live in San Francisco, California, and plan to drive to New Orleans, Louisiana.

a) Obtain a map that shows routes that they may take from San Francisco to New Orleans. Write directions for them from San Francisco to New Orleans via the shortest distance. Use major highways whenever possible.

b) Use the scale on the map to estimate the one-way distance to New Orleans.

c) If the Williams estimate that they will average 50 mph (including comfort stops), estimate the travel time, in hours, to New Orleans.

d) If the Williams want to travel about 400 miles per day, locate a town in the vicinity of where they will stop each evening.

e) If they begin each segment of the trip each day at 9 A.M., at about what time will they look for a hotel each evening?

f) Use the information provided in parts (a) through (e) to estimate the time of day they will arrive in New Orleans.

g) Estimate the mileage of a typical midsized car and the cost per gallon of a gallon of regular unleaded gasoline. Then estimate the cost of gasoline for the Williams' trip.

h) Estimate the cost of a typical breakfast, a typical lunch, and a typical dinner for two adults, and the cost of a typical motel room. Then estimate the total cost, including meals, gas, and lodging, for the Williams' trip from San Francisco to New Orleans (one way).

Problem Solving

3. Four acrobats who bill themselves as the "Tumbling Tumbleweeds" finish up their act with the amazing "Human Pillar," in which the acrobats form a tower, each one standing on the shoulders of the one below. Each acrobat (Ernie, Jed, Tex, and Zeke Tumbleweed) wears a different distinctive item of western garb (chaps, holster, Stetson hat, or leather vest) in the act. Can you identify the members of the "Human Pillar," from top to bottom, by name and apparel?

a) Jed Tumbleweed is not on top, but he is somewhere above the man in the Stetson.

b) Zeke Tumbleweed does not wear the holster.

c) The man in the vest is not on top.

d) The man in the chaps is somewhere above Tex but somewhere below Zeke.

ORDER	NAME	APPAREL
_____	_____	_____
_____	_____	_____
_____	_____	_____
_____	_____	_____

2

Sets

Why This is Important

A basic human impulse is to sort or classify things. As you will see in this chapter, putting elements into sets helps you order and arrange your world. It allows you to deal with large quantities of information. Set building is a learning tool that helps answer the question, What are the characteristics of this group? For example, when students read a college catalog to determine which courses fulfill their degree requirements, they are looking for courses that are in a particular set. Studying sets is also important because sets underlie other mathematical topics such as logic and abstract algebra.

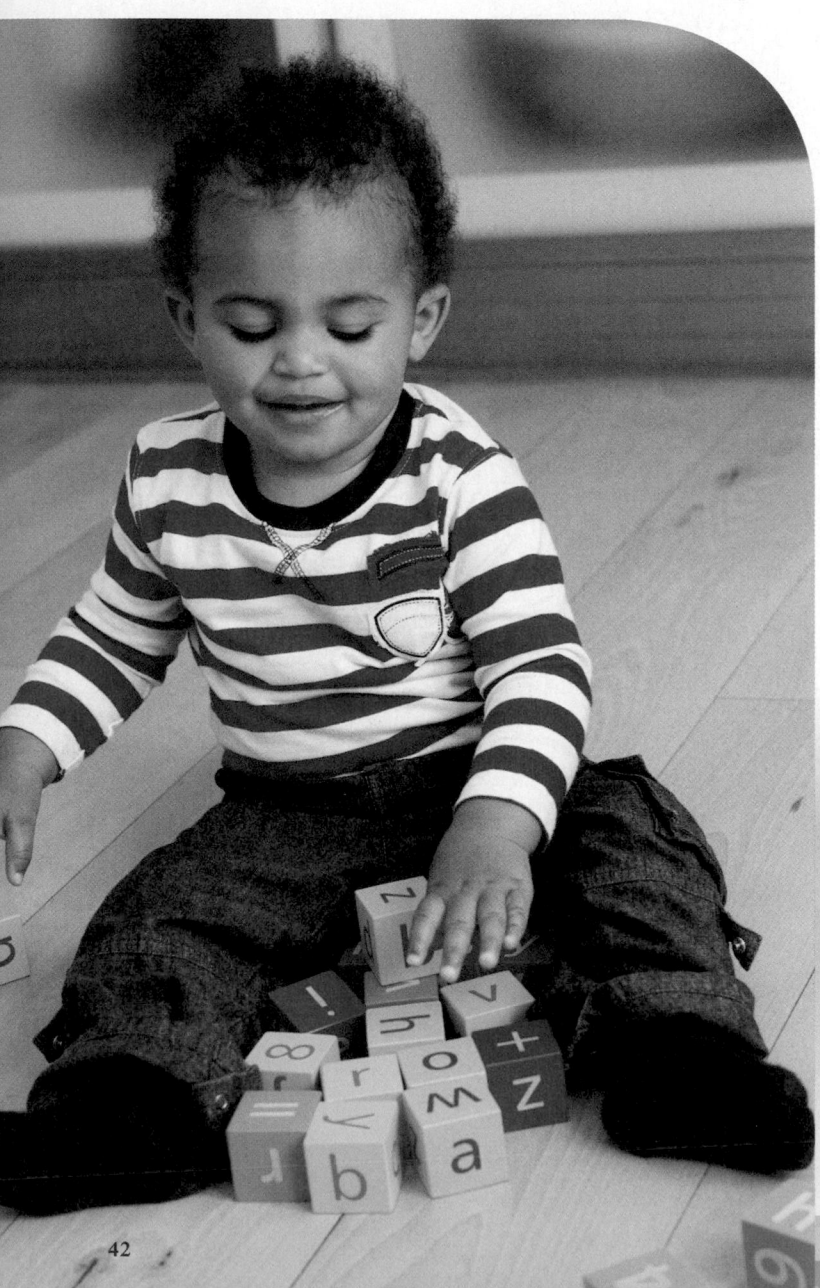

◀ Children learn how to classify sets, such as shapes and colors, at a very early age.

Set Concepts

▲ *Many different restaurant categories include McDonald's*

Can you think of a few different categories or groups to which the restaurant McDonald's belongs? One way you could categorize McDonald's is as a fast food restaurant. Another way is as a restaurant selling hamburgers. A third way is as a restaurant selling breakfast. In this section, we will discuss ways to sort or classify objects. We will also discuss different methods that can be used to indicate collections of objects.

Why *This is Important* Set classifications are important in a range of applications from placing students in courses to classifying stars in the universe.

We encounter sets in many different ways every day of our lives. A *set* is a collection of objects, which are called *elements* or *members* of the set. For example, the United States is a collection, or set, of 50 states plus the District of Columbia. The 50 individual states plus the District of Columbia are the members or elements of the set that is called the United States.

A set is *well defined* if its contents can be clearly determined. The set of U.S. presidents is a well-defined set because its contents, the presidents, can be named. The set of the three best movies is not a well-defined set because the word *best* is interpreted differently by different people. In this text, we use only well-defined sets.

Three methods are commonly used to indicate a set: (1) description, (2) roster form, and (3) set-builder notation.

The method of indicating a set by *description* is illustrated in Example 1.

Example 1 *Description of Sets*

Write a description of the set containing the elements Monday, Tuesday, Wednesday, Thursday, Friday, Saturday, Sunday.

Solution The set is the days of the week. ∎

Listing the elements of a set inside a pair of *braces*, { }, is called *roster form*. The braces are an essential part of the notation because they identify the contents as a set. For example, $\{1, 2, 3\}$ is notation for the set whose elements are 1, 2, and 3, but (1, 2, 3) and [1, 2, 3] are not sets because parentheses and brackets do not indicate a set. For a set written in roster form, commas separate the elements of the set. The order in which the elements are listed is not important.

Sets are generally named with capital letters. For example, the name commonly selected for the set of *natural numbers* or *counting numbers* is *N*.

Definition: Natural Numbers
$$N = \{1, 2, 3, 4, 5, \dots\}$$

The three dots after the 5, called an *ellipsis,* indicate that the elements in the set continue in the same manner. An ellipsis followed by a last element indicates that the elements continue in the same manner up to and including the last element. This notation is illustrated in Example 2(b).

Profile in Mathematics

Georg Cantor

Georg Cantor (1845–1918), born in St. Petersburg, Russia, is recognized as the founder of set theory. Cantor's creative work in mathematics was nearly lost when his father insisted that he become an engineer rather than a mathematician. His two major books on set theory, *Foundations of General Theory of Aggregates* and *Contributions to the Founding of the Theory of Transfinite Numbers*, were published in 1883 and 1895, respectively. See the Profile in Mathematics on page 85 for more information on Cantor and Leopold Kronecker.

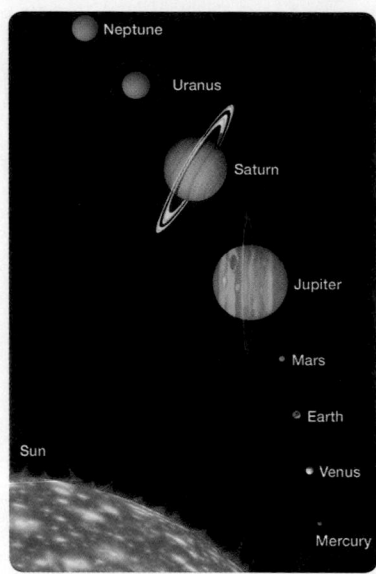

▲ *The planets of Earth's solar system.*

Example 2 *Roster Form of Sets*

Express the following in roster form.

a) Set A is the set of natural numbers less than 6.

b) Set B is the set of natural numbers less than or equal to 80.

c) Set P is the set of planets in Earth's solar system.

Solution

a) The natural numbers less than 6 are 1, 2, 3, 4, and 5. Thus, set A in roster form is
$A = \{1, 2, 3, 4, 5\}$.

b) $B = \{1, 2, 3, 4, \ldots, 80\}$. The 80 after the ellipsis indicates that the elements continue in the same manner up to and including the number 80.

c) $P = \{$Mercury, Venus, Earth, Mars, Jupiter, Saturn, Uranus, Neptune$\}$*   ∎

Example 3 *The Word* Inclusive

Express the following in roster form.

a) The set of natural numbers between 7 and 12.

b) The set of natural numbers between 7 and 12, inclusive.

Solution

a) $A = \{8, 9, 10, 11\}$

b) $B = \{7, 8, 9, 10, 11, 12\}$. Note that the word *inclusive* indicates that the values of 7 and 12 are included in the set.   ∎

The symbol $\in$, read, "is an element of," is used to indicate membership in a set. In Example 3, because 8 is an element of set A, we write $8 \in A$. This may also be written $8 \in \{8, 9, 10, 11\}$. We may also write $6 \notin A$, meaning that 6 is not an element of set A.

Set-builder notation (sometimes called *set-generator notation*) may be used to symbolize a set. Set-builder notation is frequently used in algebra. The following example illustrates its form.

D	$=$	$\{$	x	$\mid$	Condition(s) $\}$
↑	↑	↑	↑	↑	↑
Set D	is	the set of	all elements x	such that	the condition(s) x must meet in order to be a member of the set.

Consider $E = \{x \mid x \in N \text{ and } x > 10\}$. The statement is read: "Set E is the set of all the elements x such that x is a natural number and x is greater than 10." The conditions that x must meet to be a member of the set are $x \in N$, which means that x must be a natural number, and $x > 10$, which means that x must be greater than 10. The numbers that meet both conditions are the set of natural numbers greater than 10. Set E in roster form is

$$E = \{11, 12, 13, 14, \ldots\}$$

Example 4 *Using Set-Builder Notation*

a) Write set $B = \{1, 2, 3, 4, 5\}$ in set-builder notation.

b) Write, in words, how you would read set B in set-builder notation.

---

*In August 2006, Pluto was reclassified as a dwarf planet.

Solution

a) Because set B consists of the natural numbers less than 6, we write

$$B = \{x \mid x \in N \text{ and } x < 6\}$$

Another acceptable answer is $B = \{x \mid x \in N \text{ and } x \leq 5\}$.

b) Set B is the set of all elements x such that x is a natural number and x is less than 6.

Example 5 *Roster Form to Set-Builder Notation*

a) Write set $C = \{$North America, South America, Europe, Asia, Australia, Africa, Antarctica$\}$ in set-builder notation.

b) Write in words how you would read set C in set-builder notation.

Solution

a) $C = \{x \mid x \text{ is a continent}\}$.

b) Set C is the set of all elements x such that x is a continent.

Example 6 *Set-Builder Notation to Roster Form*

Write set $A = \{x \mid x \in N \text{ and } 2 \leq x < 8\}$ in roster form.

Solution $A = \{2, 3, 4, 5, 6, 7\}$

Example 7 *Oldest Colleges in the United States*

The table shows the 10 oldest colleges in the United States. Let set C be the set of colleges that are located in Virginia that are among the 10 oldest colleges in the United States. Write set C in roster form.

▲ *Harvard University*

Ten Oldest Colleges in the United States	State	Year Chartered
Harvard University	Massachusetts	1636
College of William and Mary	Virginia	1692
Yale University	Connecticut	1701
University of Pennsylvania	Pennsylvania	1740
Moravian College	Pennsylvania	1742
Princeton University	New Jersey	1746
Washington and Lee University	Virginia	1749
Columbia University	New York	1754
Brown University	Rhode Island	1764
Rutgers	New Jersey	1766

Source: National Center for Education Statistics

Solution By examining the table, we find that two colleges located in Virginia appear in the table. They are College of William and Mary and Washington and Lee University. Thus, set $C = \{$College of William and Mary, Washington and Lee University$\}$.

A set is said to be *finite* if it either contains no elements or the number of elements in the set is a natural number. The set $B = \{2, 4, 6, 8, 10\}$ is a finite set because the number of elements in the set is 5, and 5 is a natural number. A set that is not finite is said to be *infinite*. The set of counting numbers is one example of an infinite set. Infinite sets are discussed in more detail in Section 2.6.

Another important concept is equality of sets.

Definition: Equal Sets
Set A is **equal** to set B, symbolized by $A = B$, if and only if set A and set B contain exactly the same elements.

For example, if set $A = \{1, 2, 3\}$ and set $B = \{3, 1, 2\}$, then $A = B$ because they contain exactly the same elements. The order of the elements in the set is not important. If two sets are equal, both must contain the same number of elements. The number of elements in a set is called its *cardinal number*.

Definition: Cardinal Number
The **cardinal number** of set A, symbolized by $n(A)$, is the number of elements in set A.

Both set $A = \{1, 2, 3\}$ and set $B = \{\text{England, Brazil, Japan}\}$ have a cardinal number of 3; that is, $n(A) = 3$, and $n(B) = 3$. We can say that set A and set B both have a cardinality of 3.

Two sets are said to be *equivalent* if they contain the same number of elements.

Definition: Equivalent Sets
Set A is **equivalent** to set B if and only if $n(A) = n(B)$.

Any sets that are equal must also be equivalent. Not all sets that are equivalent are equal, however. The sets $D = \{\text{a, b, c}\}$ and $E = \{\text{apple, orange, pear}\}$ are equivalent because both have the same cardinal number, 3. Because the elements differ, however, the sets are not equal.

Two sets that are equivalent or have the same cardinality can be placed in *one-to-one correspondence*. Set A and set B can be placed in one-to-one correspondence if every element of set A can be matched with exactly one element of set B and every element of set B can be matched with exactly one element of set A. For example, there is a one-to-one correspondence between the student names on a class list and the student identification numbers because we can match each student with a student identification number.

Consider set S, states, and set C, state capitals.

$$S = \{\text{North Carolina, Georgia, South Carolina, Florida}\}$$

$$C = \{\text{Columbia, Raleigh, Tallahassee, Atlanta}\}$$

Two different one-to-one correspondences for sets S and C follow.

$$S = \{\text{North Carolina, Georgia, South Carolina, Florida}\}$$

$$C = \{\text{Columbia, Raleigh, Tallahassee, Atlanta}\}$$

$$S = \{\text{North Carolina, Georgia, South Carolina, Florida}\}$$

$$C = \{\text{Columbia, Raleigh, Tallahassee, Atlanta}\}$$

Other one-to-one correspondences between sets S and C are possible. Do you know which capital goes with which state?

Null or Empty Set

Some sets do not contain any elements, such as the set of zebras that live in your house.

> **Definition:** **Empty Set**
> The set that contains no elements is called the **empty set** or **null set** and is symbolized by $\{\ \}$ or $\varnothing$.

Note that $\{\varnothing\}$ is not the empty set. This set contains the element $\varnothing$ and has a cardinality of 1. The set $\{0\}$ is also not the empty set because it contains the element 0. It also has a cardinality of 1.

Example 8 *Natural Number Solutions*

Indicate the set of natural numbers that satisfies the equation $x + 2 = 0$.

Solution The values that satisfy the equation are those natural numbers that make the equation a true statement. Only the number -2 satisfies this equation. Because -2 is not a natural number, the solution set of this equation is $\{\ \}$ or $\varnothing$. ∎

Universal Set

Another important set is a *universal set*.

> **Definition:** **Universal Set**
> A **universal set**, symbolized by U, is a set that contains all the elements for any specific discussion.

When a universal set is given, only the elements in the universal set may be considered when working the problem. If, for example, the universal set for a particular problem is defined as $U = \{1, 2, 3, 4, \ldots, 10\}$, then only the natural numbers 1 through 10 may be used in that problem.

SECTION 2.1 *Exercises*

Warm Up Exercises

In Exercises 1–12, fill in the blank with an appropriate word, phrase, or symbol(s).

1. A collection of objects is called a(n) _____. Set

2. Three dots placed in a set to show that the set continues in the same manner is called a(n) _____. Ellipsis

3. The three ways a set can be written are _____ , _____ , and _____ .
   Description, Roster form, Set-builder notation

4. A set that contains no elements or the number of elements in the set is a natural number is called a(n)_____ set. Finite

5. A a set that is not finite is called a(n) _____ . set.
   Infinite

6. Two sets that contain the same elements are called _____ sets. Equal

7. Two sets that contain the same number of elements are called _____ sets. Equivalent

8. The number of elements in a set is called the _____ number. Cardinal

9. The set that contains no elements is called the _____ set. Empty or null

10. The two ways to indicate an empty set are _____ and _____ . $\{\ \}$, $\varnothing$

11. A set that contains all the elements for any specific discussion is called a(n) _____ set. Universal

12. Two sets that have the same cardinal number can be placed in a(n) _____ correspondence. One-to-one

Practice the Skills

In Exercises 13–18, determine whether each set is well defined or not well defined.

13. The set of the best colleges Not well defined

14. The set of the most interesting courses at your school
Not well defined

15. The set of states that have a common border with Kansas
Well defined

16. The set of the four states in the United States having the largest population on January 1, 2010 Well defined

17. The set of astronauts who walked on the moon Well defined

▲ *Eugene A. Cernan on the moon*

18. The set of the most interesting teachers at your school
Not well defined

In Exercises 19–24, determine whether each set is finite or infinite.

19. $\{1, 3, 5, 7, \dots\}$ Infinite

20. The set of multiples of 4 between 0 and 50 Finite

21. The set of odd numbers greater than 25 Infinite

22. The set of fractions between 1 and 2 Infinite

23. The set of odd numbers greater than 15 Infinite

24. The set of apple trees in Gro-More Farms Orchards Finite

In Exercises 25–34, express each set in roster form. You may need to use the Internet or some other reference source.

25. The set of states in the United States whose names begin with the letter M {Maine, Maryland, Massachusetts, Michigan, Minnesota, Mississippi, Missouri, Montana}

26. The set of countries in Europe whose names begin with S
{San Marino, Scotland, Serbia, Slovakia, Slovenia, Spain, Sweden, Switzerland}

27. The set of natural numbers between 10 and 178
{11, 12, 13, 14, …, 177}

28. $C = \{x \mid x + 6 = 10\}$ $C = \{4\}$

29. $B = \{x \mid x \in N \text{ and } x \text{ is even}\}$ $B = \{2, 4, 6, 8, \dots\}$

30. The set of states west of the Mississippi River that have a common border with the state of Florida { } or ∅

31. The set of football players over the age of 70 who are still playing in the National Football League { } or ∅

32. The set of states in the United States that have a common border with the state of Washington {Idaho, Oregon}

33. $E = \{x \mid x \in N \text{ and } 14 \leq x < 85\}$
$E = \{14, 15, 16, 17, \dots, 84\}$

34. The set of states in the United States that are not in the contiguous 48 states {Alaska, Hawaii}

In Exercises 35–38, use the following table, which shows the attendance, in millions, at the 10 most visited museums in the world in 2008. Let the 10 museums in the list represent the universal set.

Museum	Attendance (in millions)	Location
1. Louvre Museum	8.50	Paris, France
2. British Museum	5.93	London, UK
3. National Gallery of Art	4.96	Washington, DC
4. Tate Modern	4.95	London, UK
5. Metropolitan Museum of Art	4.82	New York, NY
6. Vatican Museums	4.44	Vatican City
7. National Gallery	4.38	London, UK
8. Musee d'Orsay	3.03	Paris, France
9. Musee d'Art Moderne Prado	2.98	Paris, France
10. Museum of Modern Art	2.90	New York, NY

Source: The *Art Newspaper*

Use the list to determine each set in roster form.

35. The set of museums in which the attendance was more than 4.5 million *

36. The set of museums in which the attendance was less than 3 million *

37. The set of museums in which the attendance was between 2 million and 4 million *

38. The set of museums in which the attendance was between 3.5 million and 5.5 million *

In Exercises 39–42, use the graph on page 49, which shows iPod sales, in millions, for the years 2003–2008.

Use the graph to determine each set in roster form.

39. The set of years in which iPod sales were more than 52 million {2007, 2008}

*See Instructor Answer Appendix

40. The set of years in which iPod sales were less than 8 million {2003}

41. The set of years in which iPod sales were between 8 million and 60 million {2004, 2005, 2006, 2007}

42. The set of years in which iPod sales were more than 65 million { } or ∅

iPod Sales

In Exercises 43–50, express each set in set-builder notation.

43. $B = \{7, 8, 9, 10, 11, 12, 13, 14\}$ $B = \{x \mid x \in N \text{ and } 6 < x < 15\}$
or $B = \{x \mid x \in N \text{ and } 7 \le x \le 14\}$

44. $A = \{1, 2, 3, 4, 5, 6, 7, 8, 9\}$ $A = \{x \mid x \in N \text{ and } x < 10\}$ or
$A = \{x \mid x \in N \text{ and } x \le 9\}$

45. $C = \{3, 6, 9, 12, \dots\}$ $C = \{x \mid x \in N \text{ and } x \text{ is a multiple of } 3\}$

46. $D = \{5, 10, 15, 20, \dots\}$
$D = \{x \mid x \in N \text{ and } x \text{ is a multiple of } 5\}$

47. E is the set of odd natural numbers. $E = \{x \mid x \in N \text{ and } x \text{ is odd}\}$

48. A is the set of national holidays in the United States in July.
$A = \{x \mid x \text{ is Independence Day}\}$

49. C is the set of months that contain less than 30 days.
$C = \{x \mid x \text{ is February}\}$

50. $F = \{15, 16, 17, \dots, 100\}$ $F = \{x \mid x \in N \text{ and } 15 \le x \le 100\}$
or $F = \{x \mid x \in N \text{ and } 14 < x < 101\}$

In Exercises 51–58, write a description of each set.

51. $A = \{1, 2, 3, 4, 5, 6, 7\}$
Set A is the set of natural numbers less than or equal to 7.

52. $D = \{3, 6, 9, 12, 15, 18, \dots\}$
Set D is the set of natural numbers that are multiples of 3.

53. $V = \{a, e, i, o, u\}$
Set V is the set of vowels in the English alphabet.

54. $S = \{$Bashful, Doc, Dopey, Grumpy, Happy, Sleepy, Sneezy$\}$ Set S is the set of the seven dwarfs in *Snow White and the Seven Dwarfs.*

▲ *Snow White and the Seven Dwarfs*

55. $T = \{$oak, maple, elm, pine, $\dots\}$
Set T is the set of species of trees.

56. $E = \{x \mid x \in N \text{ and } 4 \le x < 11\}$
Set E is the set of natural numbers greater than or equal to 4 and less than 11.

57. $S = \{$spring, summer, fall, winter$\}$
Set S is the set of seasons.

58. $B = \{$John Lennon, Ringo Starr, Paul McCartney, George Harrison$\}$ Set B is the set of members of the Beatles.

▲ *The Beatles*

In Exercises 59–62, use the following list, which shows the 10 countries with the most cellular subscribers, in millions, as of 2008. Let the 10 countries in the list represent the universal set.

Country	Number of Subscribers
1. China	649.70
2. India	376.12
3. United States	260.00
4. Russia	172.00
5. Brazil	151.90
6. Indonesia	115.60
7. Japan	102.98
8. Germany	101.50
9. Pakistan	91.40
10. United Kingdom	70.00

Source: CIA

Use the list to determine each set in roster form.

59. $\{x \mid x$ is a country with at least 250 million cellular subscribers$\}$ {China, India, United States}

60. $\{x \mid x$ is a country with fewer than 100 million cellular subscribers$\}$ {Pakistan, United Kingdom}

61. $\{x \mid x$ is a country with between 100 million and 200 million cellular subscribers$\}$ {Russia, Brazil, Indonesia, Japan, Germany}

62. $\{x \mid x$ is a country with between 250 million and 500 million cellular subscribers$\}$ {India, United States}

In Exercises 63–66, use the following graph, which shows the cost of a 30-second commercial during the Super Bowl from 1996 to 2011. Let the 16 years represent the universal set.

Use the graph to represent each set in roster form.

63. The set of years in which the cost of a Super Bowl commercial was more than $2.5 million
{2008, 2009, 2010, 2011}

64. The set of years in which the cost of a Super Bowl commercial was less than $2.0 million
{1996, 1997, 1998, 1999}

65. The set of years in which the cost of a Super Bowl commercial was between $2.0 million and $2.5 million
{2000, 2001, 2002, 2003, 2004, 2005, 2007}

66. The set of years in which the cost of a Super Bowl commercial was more than $2.5 million and less then $3 million
{2008, 2010}

Cost of a 30-Second Commercial During the Super Bowl

Source: www.industry.bnet.com

In Exercises 67–74, state whether each statement is true or false. If false, give the reason.

67. $\{e\} \in \{a, e, i, o, u\}$ False; {e} is a set, and not an element of the set.

68. $b \in \{a, b, c, d, e, f\}$ True

69. $h \in \{a, b, c, d, e, f\}$ False; h is not an element of the set.

70. Mickey Mouse $\in$ {characters created by Walt Disney} True

71. $3 \notin \{x \,|\, x \in N \text{ and } x \text{ is odd}\}$ False; 3 is an element of the set.

72. Amazon $\in$ {rivers in the United States}
False; the Amazon is a river in South America, not the United States.

73. *Titanic* $\in$ {top 10 motion pictures with the greatest revenues} True

74. $2 \in \{x \,|\, x \text{ is an odd natural number}\}$
False; 2 is an even natural number.

In Exercises 75–78, for the sets $A = \{2, 4, 6, 8\}$, $B = \{1, 3, 7, 9, 13, 21\}$, $C = \{\ \}$, and $D = \{\#, \&, \%, \square, *\}$.

75. Determine $n(A)$. 4

76. Determine $n(B)$. 6

77. Determine $n(C)$. 0

78. Determine $n(D)$. 5

In Exercises 79–84, determine whether the pairs of sets are equal, equivalent, both, or neither.

79. $A = \{$algebra, geometry, trigonometry$\}$,
$B = \{$geometry, trigonometry, algebra$\}$ Both

80. $A = \{7, 9, 10\}$, $B = \{a, b, c\}$ Equivalent

81. $A = \{$grapes, apples, oranges$\}$,
$B = \{$grapes, peaches, apples, oranges$\}$ Neither

82. A is the set of Siamese cats.
B is the set of cats. Neither

83. A is the set of letters in the word *bank*.
B is the set of letters in the word *post*. Equivalent

84. A is the set of states.
B is the set of state capitals. Equivalent

Problem Solving

85. Set-builder notation is often more versatile and efficient than listing a set in roster form. This versatility is illustrated with the following two sets.

$$A = \{x \,|\, x \in N \text{ and } x > 2\}$$
$$B = \{x \,|\, x > 2\}$$

a) Write a description of set A and set B. Set A is the set of natural numbers greater than 2. Set B is the set of all numbers greater than 2.

b) Explain the difference between set A and set B.
(*Hint:* Is $4\frac{1}{2} \in A$? Is $4\frac{1}{2} \in B$?) Set A contains only natural numbers. Set B contains other types of numbers, including fractions and decimal numbers.

c) Write set A in roster form. $A = \{3, 4, 5, 6, \dots\}$

d) Can set B be written in roster form? Explain your answer. No; because there are an infinite number of elements between any two elements in set B, we cannot write set B in roster form.

86. Consider sets A and B below
$$A = \{x \,|\, 2 < x \leq 5 \text{ and } x \in N\}$$
and
$$B = \{x \,|\, 2 < x \leq 5\}$$

a) Write a description of set A and set B. *

b) Explain the difference between set A and set B.
Set B contains fractions and decimal numbers, set A does not.

c) Write set A in roster form. $A = \{3, 4, 5\}$

d) Can set B be written in roster form? Explain your answer. No; because there are an infinite number of elements between any two elements in set B, we cannot write set B in roster form.

*A cardinal number answers the question "How many?" An **ordinal number** describes the relative position that an element occupies. For example, Molly's desk is the third desk from the aisle.*

*See Instructor Answer Appendix

In Exercises 87–90, determine whether the number used is a cardinal number or an ordinal number.

87. J. K. Rowling has written 7 Harry Potter books.   Cardinal

▲ *J. K. Rowling*

88. Study the chart on page 25 in the book.   Ordinal

89. Lincoln was the sixteenth president of the United States.   Ordinal.

90. Emily paid $35 for her new blouse.   Cardinal

91. Describe three sets of which you are a member.
Answers will vary.

92. Describe three sets that have no members. *

93. Write a short paragraph explaining why the universal set and the empty set are necessary in the study of sets.
Answers will vary.

Challenge Problem/Group Activity

94. a) In a given exercise, a universal set is not specified, but we know that actor Orlando Bloom is a member of the universal set. Describe five different possible universal sets of which Orlando Bloom is a member. *

b) Write a description of one set that includes all the universal sets in part (a).   The set of all the people in the world

Internet/Research Activity

95. Georg Cantor is recognized as the founder and a leader in the development of set theory. Do research and write a paper on his life and his contributions to set theory and to the field of mathematics. References include history of mathematics books, encyclopedias, and the Internet.

*See Instructor Answer Appendix

SECTION 2.2 Subsets

▲ *The set of intercollegiate sports includes basketball.*

Consider the following sets. Set $A = \{$ baseball, basketball, hockey $\}$. Set $B = \{$ baseball, football, basketball, hockey, softball $\}$. Note that each element of set A is also an element of set B. In this section, we will discuss how to illustrate the relationship between two sets, A and B, when each element of set A is also an element of set B.

Why *This is Important*   The relationship between sets is important throughout life. For example, to gain a promotion at work, you may need to fulfill different sets of criteria.

In our complex world, we often break larger sets into smaller, more manageable sets, called *subsets*. For example, consider the set of people in your class. Suppose we categorize the set of people in your class according to the first letter of their last name (the A's, B's, C's, etc.). When we do so, each of these sets may be considered a subset of the original set. Each of these subsets can be separated further. For example, the set of people whose last name begins with the letter A can be categorized as either male or female or by their age. Each of these collections of people is also a subset. A given set may have many different subsets.

Definition: Subset
Set A is a **subset** of set B, symbolized by $A \subseteq B$, if and only if all the elements of set A are also elements of set B.

The symbol $A \subseteq B$ indicates that "set A is a subset of set B." The symbol $\not\subseteq$ is used to indicate "is not a subset." Thus, $A \not\subseteq B$ indicates that set A is not a subset of set B. *To show that set A is not a subset of set B, we must find at least one element of set A that is not an element of set B.*

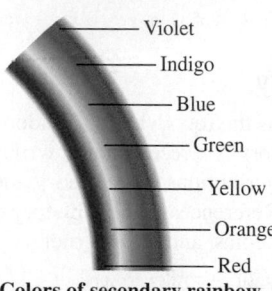
Example 1   A Subset?

Determine whether set A is a subset of set B.

a) $A = \{\text{rain, snow, sleet}\}$
   $B = \{\text{rain, snow, sleet, hail}\}$

b) $A = \{q, r, s, t\}$
   $B = \{q, r\}$

c) $A = \{x \mid x \text{ is a yellow fruit}\}$
   $B = \{x \mid x \text{ is a red fruit}\}$

d) $A = \{\text{vanilla, chocolate, rocky road}\}$
   $B = \{\text{chocolate, vanilla, rocky road}\}$

Solution

a) All the elements of set A are contained in set B, so $A \subseteq B$.

b) The elements s and t are in set A but not in set B, so $A \not\subseteq B$ (A is not a subset of B). In this example, however, all the elements of set B are contained in set A; therefore, $B \subseteq A$.

c) There are fruits, such as bananas, that are in set A that are not in set B, so $A \not\subseteq B$.

d) All the elements of set A are contained in set B, so $A \subseteq B$. Note also that $B \subseteq A$. In fact, set $A =$ set B. ∎

Proper Subsets

Definition: Proper Subset

Set A is a **proper subset** of set B, symbolized by $A \subset B$, if and only if all the elements of set A are elements of set B and set $A \neq$ set B (that is, set B must contain at least one element not in set A).

Consider the sets $A = \{\text{red, blue, yellow}\}$ and $B = \{\text{red, orange, yellow, green, blue, violet}\}$. Set A is a *subset* of set B, $A \subseteq B$, because every element of set A is also an element of set B. Set A is also a *proper subset* of set B, $A \subset B$, because set A and set B are not equal. Now consider $C = \{\text{car, bus, train}\}$ and $D = \{\text{train, car, bus}\}$. Set C is a subset of set D, $C \subseteq D$, because every element of set C is also an element of set D. Set C, however, is not a proper subset of set D, $C \not\subset D$, because set C and set D are equal sets.

Example 2   A Proper Subset?

Determine whether set A is a proper subset of set B.

a) $A = \{\text{jazz, pop, hip hop}\}$
   $B = \{\text{classical, jazz, pop, rap, hip hop}\}$

b) $A = \{a, b, c, d\}$ $B = \{a, c, b, d\}$

Solution

a) All the elements of set A are contained in set B, and sets A and B are not equal; thus, $A \subset B$.

b) Set $A =$ set B, so $A \not\subset B$. (However, $A \subseteq B$.) ∎

Every set is a subset of itself, but no set is a proper subset of itself. For all sets A, $A \subseteq A$, but $A \not\subset A$. For example, if $A = \{1, 2, 3\}$, then $A \subseteq A$ because every element of set A is contained in set A, but $A \not\subset A$ because set $A =$ set A.

MATHEMATICS TODAY

The Ladder of Life

In biology, the science of classifying all living things is called *taxonomy*. More than 2000 years ago, Aristotle formalized animal classification with his "ladder of life": higher animals, lower animals, higher plants, lower plants. Today, living organisms are classified into six kingdoms (or sets) called animalia, plantae, archaea, eubacteria, fungi, and protista. Even more general groupings of living things are made according to shared characteristics. The groupings, from most general to most specific, are kingdom, phylum, class, order, family, genus, and species. For example, a zebra, *Equus burchelli*, is a member of the genus *Equus*, as is the horse, *Equus caballus*. Both the zebra and the horse are members of the universal set called the kingdom of animals and the same family, Equidae; they are members of different species (*E. burchelli* and *E. caballus*), however.

Why **This is Important** Scientists use sets to classify and catorgize animals, plants, and all forms of life.

Let $A = \{\ \}$ and $B = \{1, 2, 3, 4\}$. Is $A \subseteq B$? To show $A \nsubseteq B$, you must find at least one element of set A that is not an element of set B. Because this cannot be done, $A \subseteq B$ must be true. Using the same reasoning, we can show that *the empty set is a subset of every set, including itself.*

Example 3 *Element or Subset?*

Determine whether the following are true or false.

a) $3 \in \{3, 4, 5\}$

b) $\{3\} \in \{3, 4, 5\}$

c) $\{3\} \in \{\{3\}, \{4\}, \{5\}\}$

d) $\{3\} \subseteq \{3, 4, 5\}$

e) $3 \subseteq \{3, 4, 5\}$

f) $\{\ \} \subseteq \{3, 4, 5\}$

Solution

a) $3 \in \{3, 4, 5\}$ is a true statement because 3 is an element of the set $\{3, 4, 5\}$.

b) $\{3\} \in \{3, 4, 5\}$ is a false statement because $\{3\}$ is a set, and the set $\{3\}$ is not an element of the set $\{3, 4, 5\}$.

c) $\{3\} \in \{\{3\}, \{4\}, \{5\}\}$ is a true statement because $\{3\}$ is an element in the set. The elements of the set $\{\{3\}, \{4\}, \{5\}\}$ are themselves sets.

d) $\{3\} \subseteq \{3, 4, 5\}$ is a true statement because every element of the first set is an element of the second set.

e) $3 \subseteq \{3, 4, 5\}$ is a false statement because the 3 is not in braces, so it is not a set and thus cannot be a subset. The 3 is an element of the set as indicated in part (a).

f) $\{\ \} \subseteq \{3, 4, 5\}$ is a true statement because the empty set is a subset of every set. ■

Number of Subsets

How many distinct subsets can be made from a given set? The empty set has no elements and has exactly one subset, the empty set. A set with one element has two subsets. A set with two elements has four subsets. A set with three elements has eight subsets. This information is illustrated in Table 2.1.

Table 2.1 Number of Subsets

Set	Subsets	Number of Subsets
$\{\ \}$	$\{\ \}$	$1 = 2^0$
$\{a\}$	$\{a\}$	
	$\{\ \}$	$2 = 2^1$
$\{a, b\}$	$\{a, b\}$	
	$\{a\}, \{b\}$	
	$\{\ \}$	$4 = 2 \times 2 = 2^2$
$\{a, b, c\}$	$\{a, b, c\}$	
	$\{a, b\}, \{a, c\}, \{b, c\}$	
	$\{a\}, \{b\}, \{c\}$	
	$\{\ \}$	$8 = 2 \times 2 \times 2 = 2^3$

By continuing this table with larger and larger sets, we can develop a general expression for finding the number of distinct subsets that can be made from any given set.

Number of Distinct Subsets

The **number of distinct subsets** of a finite set A is 2^n, where n is the number of elements in set A.

Every set is a subset of itself, but no set is a proper subset of itself. Thus, the number of proper subsets will always be one less than the number of subsets that can be made from any given set. We summarize this concept in the following expression.

Number of Distinct Proper Subsets

The **number of distinct proper subsets** of a finite set A is $2^n - 1$, where n is the number of elements in set A.

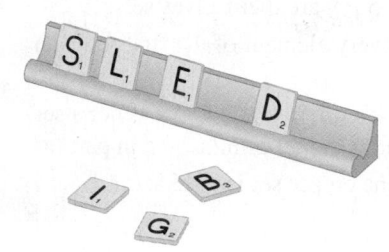

Example 4   *Distinct Subsets*

a) Determine the number of distinct subsets for the set $\{S, L, E, D\}$.

b) List all the distinct subsets for the set $\{S, L, E, D\}$.

c) How many of the distinct subsets are proper subsets?

Solution

a) Since the number of elements in the set is 4, the number of distinct subsets is
$2^4 = 2 \times 2 \times 2 \times 2 = 16$.

b)
$\{S, L, E, D\}$ $\{S, L, E\}$ $\{S, L\}$ $\{S\}$ $\{\ \}$
$\{S, L, D\}$ $\{S, E\}$ $\{L\}$
$\{S, E, D\}$ $\{S, D\}$ $\{E\}$
$\{L, E, D\}$ $\{L, E\}$ $\{D\}$
$\{L, D\}$
$\{E, D\}$

c) There are 15 proper subsets. Every subset except $\{S, L, E, D\}$ is a proper subset. ∎

Example 5   *Car Options*

Brigette Martineau is ordering a new car. She can order some, all, or none of the following options: power windows, MP3 player port, leather interior, alarm system, sun roof, and navigation system. How many different variations of the set of options are possible?

Solution
Brigette can order the car with no options, any one option, any two options, any three options, and so on, up to six options. One technique used in problem solving is to consider similar problems that you have solved previously. If you think about this problem, you will realize that it is the same as asking how many distinct subsets can be made from a set with six elements. The number of different variations of the set of options is the same as the number of possible subsets of a set that has six elements. There are 2^6, or 64, possible subsets of a set with six elements. Thus, there are 64 possible variations of the set of options for the car. ∎

Exercises

Warm Up Exercises

In Exercises 1–4, fill in the blank with an appropriate word, phrase, or symbol(s).

1. If all the elements of set *A* are also elements of set *B*, then set *A* is a(n) _____ of set *B*. Subset

2. If all the elements of set *A* are also elements of set *B*, and set *A* ≠ set *B*, then set *A* is a (n) _____ subset of set *B*. Proper

3. The expression for determining the number of distinct subsets for a set with *n* distinct elements is _____ . 2^n

4. The expression for determining the number of distinct proper subsets for a set with *n* distinct elements is _____ . $2^n - 1$

Practice the Skills

In Exercises 5–26, answer true or false. If false, give the reason.

5. { book } ⊆ { magazine, newspaper, book } True

6. { Italy} ⊆ { Italy, Spain, France, Switzerland, Austria } True

7. { McIntosh, Red Delicious } ⊆ { Empire, Gala, Cortland, Red Delicious } False; McIntosh is not in the second set.

8. { pepper, salt } ⊆ { salt, butter, mayonnaise } False; pepper is not in the second set.

9. { motorboat, kayak } ⊂ { kayak, fishing boat, motorboat, sailboat } True

10. { polar bear, tiger, lion } ⊂ { tiger, lion, polar bear, penguin } True

11. { 4, 2, 7 } ⊂ { 4, 7, 2 } False; no set is a proper subset of itself.

12. { c, a, r, t } ⊂ { t, r, a, c } False; no set is a proper subset of itself.

13. Xbox 360 ∈ { PSIII, Wii, Xbox 360 } True

14. LaGuardia ∈ { JFK, LaGuardia, Newark } True

15. { swimming } ∈ { sailing, water skiing, swimming } False; {swimming} is a set not an element.

16. { } ∈ {1, 3, 5, 7} False; { } is a set, not an element.

17. 5 ∉ { 2, 4, 6 } True

18. { } ⊆ { table, chair, sofa } True

19. { red } ⊂ { red, blue, green } True

20. { 3, 5, 9 } ⊄ { 3, 9, 5 } True

21. { } = { ∅ } False; the set { ∅ } contains the element ∅.

22. ∅ = { } True

23. { 0 } = ∅ False; the set { 0 } contains the element 0.

24. { } ⊆ { } True

25. 0 = { } False; 0 is a number and { } is a set.

26. { 1 } ∈ { { 1 }, { 2 }, { 3 } } True

In Exercises 27–34, determine whether A = B, A ⊆ B, B ⊆ A, A ⊂ B, B ⊂ A, or if none of these applies. (There may be more than one answer.)

27. A = { penny, nickel, dime, quarter }
    B = { penny, quarter } B ⊆ A, B ⊂ A

28. A = { x | x ∈ N and x < 6 }
    B = { x | x ∈ N and 1 ≤ x ≤ 5 } A = B, A ⊆ B, B ⊆ A

29. Set *A* is the set of states that border the Atlantic Ocean. Set *B* is the set of states east of the Mississippi River. A ⊆ B, A ⊂ B

30. A = { 1, 3, 5, 7, 9 }
    B = { 3, 9, 5, 7, 6 } None

31. A = { x | x is a brand of soft drink }
    B = { A & W, Coca-Cola, Dr Pepper, Mountain Dew } B ⊆ A, B ⊂ A

32. A = { x | x is a sport that uses a ball }
    B = { basketball, soccer, tennis } B ⊆ A, B ⊂ A

33. Set *A* is the set of natural numbers between 2 and 7. Set *B* is the set of natural numbers greater than 2 and less than 7. A = B, A ⊆ B, B ⊆ A

34. Set *A* is the set of all cars manufactured by General Motors. Set *B* is the set of sports cars manufactured by General Motors. B ⊆ A, B ⊂ A

In Exercises 35–38, list all the subsets of the sets given.

35. D = ∅ { }

36. A = { ○ } { }, { ○ }

37. B = { cow, horse } { }, { cow }, { horse }, { cow, horse }

38. $C = \{$ steak, pork, chicken $\}$ { }, {steak}, {pork}, {chicken}, {steak, pork}, {steak, chicken}, {pork, chicken}, {steak, pork, chicken}

Problem Solving

39. For set $A = \{a, b, c, d\}$,

   a) list all the subsets of set A.*

   b) state which of the subsets in part (a) are not proper subsets of set A. $\{a, b, c, d\}$

40. A set contains nine elements.

   a) How many subsets does it have? 2^9, or 512, subsets

   b) How many proper subsets does it have? 511 proper subsets

In Exercises 41–52, If the statement is true for all sets A and B, write "true." If it is not true for all sets A and B, write "false." Assume that $A \neq \varnothing, U \neq \varnothing,$ and $A \subset U$.

41. If $A \subseteq B$, then $A \subset B$.
False

42. If $A \subset B$, then $A \subseteq B$.
True

43. $A \subseteq A$ True

44. $A \subset A$ False

45. $\varnothing \subset A$ True

46. $\varnothing \subseteq A$ True

47. $A \subseteq U$ True

48. $\varnothing \subset \varnothing$ False

49. $\varnothing \subset U$ True

50. $U \subseteq \varnothing$ False

51. $\varnothing \subseteq \varnothing$ True

52. $U \subset \varnothing$ False

53. *Ordering a Pizza* Jasmine Sullivan is ordering a pizza at Domino's Pizza. She can add any of the following toppings: olives, pepperoni, sausage, onions, green peppers, mushrooms, anchovies, and ham. How many different variations of the pizza and toppings can be made? 2^8 or 256

54. *Building a House* The Jacobsens are planning to build a house in a new development. They can either build the base model offered by the builder or add any of the following options: deck, hot tub, security system, hardwood flooring. How many different variations of the house are possible? 2^4 or 16

55. *Salad Toppings* Donald Wheeler is ordering a salad at a Ruby Tuesday restaurant. He can purchase a salad consisting of just lettuce, or he can add any of the following items: cucumber, onion, tomato, carrot, green pepper, olive, mushroom. How many different variations of a salad are possible? 2^7 or 128

56. *Telephone Features* A customer with Verizon can order telephone service with some, all, or none of the following features: call waiting, call forwarding, caller identification, three-way calling, voice mail, fax line. How many different variations of the set of features are possible? 2^6 or 64

57. If $E \subseteq F$ and $F \subseteq E$, what other relationship exists between E and F? $E = F$

58. How can you determine whether the set of boys is equivalent to the set of girls at a roller-skating rink? If there is a one-to-one correspondence between boys and girls, then the sets are equivalent.

59. For the set $D = \{a, b, c\}$

   a) is a an element of set D?   Yes

   b) is c a subset of set D?   No

   c) is $\{a, b\}$ a subset of set D?   Yes

Challenge Problem/Group Activity

60. *Hospital Expansion* A hospital has four members on the board of directors: Arnold, Benitez, Cathy, and Dominique.

   a) When the members vote on whether to add a wing to the hospital, how many different ways can they vote (abstentions are not allowed)? For example, Arnold—yes, Benitez—no, Cathy—no, and Dominique—yes is one of the many possibilities. 16

   b) Make a listing of all the possible outcomes of the vote. For example, the vote described in part (a) could be represented as (YNNY). *

   c) How many of the outcomes given in part (b) would result in a majority supporting the addition of a wing to the hospital? That is, how many of the outcomes have three or more Y's? 5 out of 16

Recreational Mathematics

61. How many elements must a set have if the number of proper subsets of the set is $\frac{1}{2}$ of the total number of subsets of the set? 1

62. If $A \subset B$ and $B \subset C$, must $A \subset C$?   Yes

63. If $A \subset B$ and $B \subseteq C$, must $A \subset C$?   Yes

64. If $A \subseteq B$ and $B \subseteq C$, must $A \subset C$?   No

Internet/Research Activity

65. On page 53, we discussed the ladder of life. Do research and indicate all the different classifications in the Linnaean system, from most general to the most specific, in which a koala belongs.

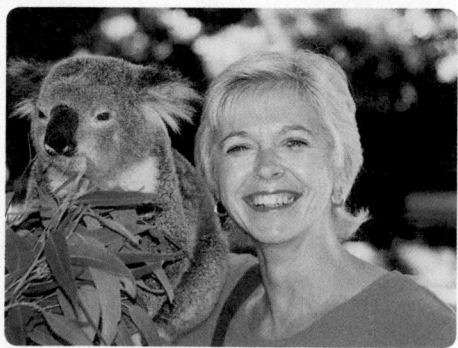

SECTION 2.3 Venn Diagrams and Set Operations

Suppose you go to a store to purchase a new laptop and tell a computer sales-person that you wish to purchase a laptop with a 14-inch display *and* 4 GB of memory. The salesperson was a bit distracted and thought you said you wanted to purchase a laptop with a 14-inch display *or* 4 GB of memory. Which laptops are in the set of laptops with a 14-inch display *and* 4 GB of memory? Which laptops are in the set of laptops with a 14-inch display *or* 4 GB of memory? These two questions are quite different. The first involves laptops joined by the word *and*. The second involves laptops joined by the word *or*. In this section, you will learn how to illustrate these and other set relationships.

▲ *Some Laptops have A 14-inch display, some laptops have 4 GB of memory, and some laptops have a 14-inch display and 4 GB of memory.*

Why *This is Important* Words such as *and* and *or* have important meaning in a variety of everyday applications, such as ordering from a menu or understanding the meaning of a legal document.

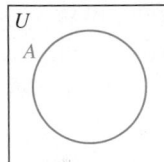

Figure 2.1

A useful technique for illustrating set relationships is the Venn diagram, named for English mathematician John Venn (1834–1923). Venn invented the diagrams and used them to illustrate ideas in his text on symbolic logic, published in 1881.

In a Venn diagram, a rectangle usually represents the universal set, *U*. The items inside the rectangle may be divided into subsets of the universal set. The subsets are usually represented by circles. In Fig. 2.1, the circle labeled *A* represents set *A*, which is a subset of the universal set.

Two sets may be represented in a Venn diagram in any of four different ways, as shown in Fig. 2.2. Two sets *A* and *B* are *disjoint* when they have no elements in common. Two disjoint sets *A* and *B* are illustrated in Fig. 2.2(a). If set *A* is a proper subset of set *B*, $A \subset B$, the two sets may be illustrated as in Fig. 2.2(b). If set *A* contains exactly the same elements as set *B*, that is, $A = B$, the two sets may be illustrated as in Fig. 2.2(c). Two sets *A* and *B* with some elements in common are shown in Fig. 2.2(d), which is regarded as the most general form of a Venn diagram.

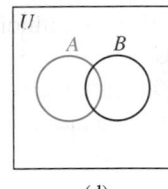

(a)   (b)

(c)   (d)

Figure 2.2

If we label the regions of the diagram in Fig. 2.2(d) using I, II, III, and IV, we can illustrate the four possible cases with this one diagram, Fig. 2.3.

CASE 1: DISJOINT SETS When sets *A* and *B* are disjoint, they have no elements in common. Therefore, region II of Fig. 2.3 is empty.

CASE 2: SUBSETS When $A \subseteq B$, every element of set *A* is also an element of set *B*. Thus, there can be no elements in region I of Fig. 2.3. If $B \subseteq A$, however, then region III of Fig. 2.3 is empty.

CASE 3: EQUAL SETS When set $A = $ set *B*, all the elements of set *A* are elements of set *B* and all the elements of set *B* are elements of set *A*. Thus, regions I and III of Fig. 2.3 are empty.

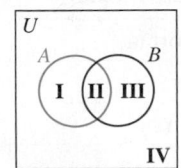

Figure 2.3

CASE 4: OVERLAPPING SETS When sets *A* and *B* have elements in common, those elements are in region II of Fig. 2.3. The elements that belong to set *A* but not to set *B* are in region I. The elements that belong to set *B* but not to set *A* are in region III.

In each of the four cases, any element belonging to the universal set but not belonging to set *A* or set *B* is placed in region IV.

Next we introduce set operations. Venn diagrams will be helpful in understanding set operations. The basic operations of arithmetic are $+$, $-$, $\times$, and $\div$. When we see these symbols, we know what procedure to follow to determine the answer. Some of the operations in set theory are $'$, $\cap$, $\cup$, $-$, and $\times$. They represent complement, intersection, union, difference, and Cartesian product, respectively.

Complement

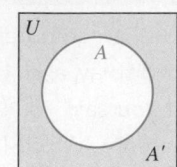

Figure 2.4

Definition: Complement

The **complement** of set A, symbolized by A', is the set of all the elements in the universal set that are not in set A.

In Fig. 2.4, the shaded region outside set A within the universal set represents the complement of set A, or A'.

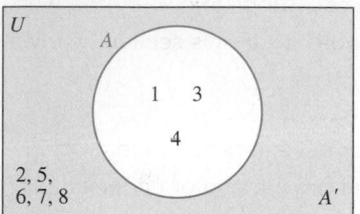

Figure 2.5

┌ **Example 1** *A Set and Its Complement*

Given

$$U = \{1, 2, 3, 4, 5, 6, 7, 8\} \text{ and } A = \{1, 3, 4\}$$

find A' and illustrate the relationship among sets U, A, and A' in a Venn diagram.

Solution The elements in U that are not in set A are 2, 5, 6, 7, 8. Thus, $A' = \{2, 5, 6, 7, 8\}$. The Venn diagram is illustrated in Fig. 2.5. ■

Intersection

The word *intersection* brings to mind the area common to two crossing streets. The red car in the figure is in the intersection of the two streets. The set operation intersection is defined as follows.

Definition: Intersection

The **intersection** of sets A and B, symbolized by $A \cap B$, is the set containing all the elements that are common to both set A and set B.

The shaded region, region II, in Fig. 2.6 represents the intersection of sets A and B.

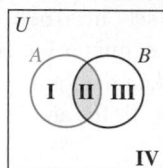

Figure 2.6

┌ **Example 2** *Sets with Overlapping Regions*

Let the universal set, U, represent the 50 states in the United States. Let set A represent the set of states with a population of more than 10 million people as of 2009. Let set B represent the set of states that have at least one city with a population of more than 1 million people, as of 2009 (see the table). Draw a Venn diagram illustrating the relationship between set A and set B.

States with a Population of More Than 10 Million People	States with at Least One City with a Population of More Than 1 Million People
California	California
Texas	Texas
New York	New York
Florida	Illinois
Illinois	Pennsylvania
Pennsylvania	Arizona
Ohio	

Source: Bureau of the U.S. Census

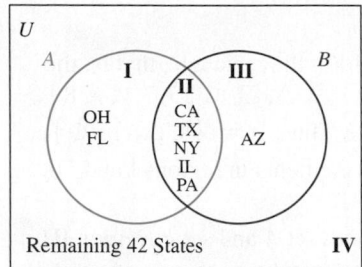

Figure 2.7

Solution First determine the intersection of sets A and B. The states common to both sets are California, Texas, New York, Illinois, and Pennsylvania. Therefore,

$$A \cap B = \{\text{California, Texas, New York, Illinois, Pennsylvania}\}$$

Place these elements in region II of Fig. 2.7. Complete region I by determining the elements in set A that have not been placed in region II. Therefore, Ohio and Florida are placed in region I. Complete region III by determining the elements in set B that have not been placed in region II. Thus, Arizona is placed in region III. Finally, place those elements in U that are not in either set within the rectangle but are outside both circles. This group includes the remaining 42 states, which are placed in region IV. ■

Example 3 *The Intersection of Sets*

Given

$$U = \{1, 2, 3, 4, 5, 6, 7, 8, 9, 10\}$$
$$A = \{1, 2, 3, 8\}$$
$$B = \{1, 3, 6, 7, 8\}$$
$$C = \{\ \}$$

find

a) $A \cap B$.   b) $A \cap C$.   c) $A' \cap B$.   d) $(A \cap B)'$.

Solution

a) $A \cap B = \{1, 2, 3, 8\} \cap \{1, 3, 6, 7, 8\} = \{1, 3, 8\}$. The elements common to both set A and set B are 1, 3, and 8.

b) $A \cap C = \{1, 2, 3, 8\} \cap \{\ \} = \{\ \}$. There are no elements common to both set A and set C.

c) To determine $A' \cap B$, we must first determine A'.
$$A' = \{4, 5, 6, 7, 9, 10\}$$
$$A' \cap B = \{4, 5, 6, 7, 9, 10\} \cap \{1, 3, 6, 7, 8\}$$
$$= \{6, 7\}$$

d) To find $(A \cap B)'$, first determine $A \cap B$.
$$A \cap B = \{1, 3, 8\} \text{ from part (a)}$$
$$(A \cap B)' = \{1, 3, 8\}' = \{2, 4, 5, 6, 7, 9, 10\}$$
■

Union

The word *union* means to unite or join together, as in marriage, and that is exactly what is done when we perform the operation of union.

> **Definition: Union**
> The **union** of set A and set B, symbolized by $A \cup B$, is the set containing all the elements that are members of set A or of set B (or of both sets).

The three shaded regions of Fig. 2.8, regions I, II, and III, together represent the union of sets A and B. If an element is common to both sets, it is listed only once in the union of the sets.

(Figure 2.8: Venn diagram with regions I, II, III shaded, IV unshaded, labeled $A \cup B$)

Figure 2.8

Example 4 *Determining Sets from a Venn Diagram*

Use the Venn diagram in Fig. 2.9 to determine the following sets.

a) U b) A c) B' d) $A \cap B$

e) $A \cup B$ f) $(A \cup B)'$ g) $n(A \cup B)$

Figure 2.9

Solution

a) The universal set consists of all the elements within the rectangle, that is, the elements in regions I, II, III, and IV. Thus, $U = \{9, \triangle, \square, \bigcirc, 3, 7, ?, \#, 8\}$.

b) Set A consists of the elements in regions I and II. Thus, $A = \{9, \triangle, \square, \bigcirc\}$.

c) B' consists of the elements outside set B, or the elements in regions I and IV. Thus, $B' = \{9, \triangle, \#, 8\}$.

d) $A \cap B$ consists of the elements that belong to both set A and set B (region II). Thus, $A \cap B = \{\square, \bigcirc\}$.

e) $A \cup B$ consists of the elements that belong to set A or set B (regions I, II, or III). Thus, $A \cup B = \{9, \triangle, \square, \bigcirc, 3, 7, ?\}$.

f) $(A \cup B)'$ consists of the elements in U that are not in $A \cup B$. Thus, $(A \cup B)' = \{\#, 8\}$.

g) $n(A \cup B)$ represents the *number of elements* in the union of sets A and B. Thus, $n(A \cup B) = 7$, as there are seven elements in the union of sets A and B. ■

Example 5 *The Union of Sets*

Given

$$U = \{1, 2, 3, 4, 5, 6, 7, 8, 9, 10\}$$
$$A = \{1, 2, 4, 6\}$$
$$B = \{1, 3, 6, 7, 9\}$$
$$C = \{\ \}$$

determine each of the following.

a) $A \cup B$ b) $A \cup C$ c) $A' \cup B$ d) $(A \cup B)'$

Solution

a) $A \cup B = \{1, 2, 4, 6\} \cup \{1, 3, 6, 7, 9\} = \{1, 2, 3, 4, 6, 7, 9\}$

b) $A \cup C = \{1, 2, 4, 6\} \cup \{\ \} = \{1, 2, 4, 6\}$. Note that $A \cup C = A$.

c) To determine $A' \cup B$, we must determine A'.

$$A' = \{3, 5, 7, 8, 9, 10\}$$
$$A' \cup B = \{3, 5, 7, 8, 9, 10\} \cup \{1, 3, 6, 7, 9\}$$
$$= \{1, 3, 5, 6, 7, 8, 9, 10\}$$

d) Determine $(A \cup B)'$ by first determining $A \cup B$, and then find the complement of $A \cup B$.

$$A \cup B = \{1, 2, 3, 4, 6, 7, 9\} \text{ from part (a)}$$
$$(A \cup B)' = \{1, 2, 3, 4, 6, 7, 9\}' = \{5, 8, 10\}$$

■

Example 6 *Union and Intersection*

Given

$$U = \{a, b, c, d, e, f, g\}$$
$$A = \{a, b, e, g\}$$
$$B = \{a, c, d, e\}$$
$$C = \{b, e, f\}$$

determine each of the following.

a) $(A \cup B) \cap (A \cup C)$ b) $(A \cup B) \cap C'$ c) $A' \cap B'$

Solution

a) $(A \cup B) \cap (A \cup C) = \{a, b, c, d, e, g\} \cap \{a, b, e, f, g\}$
$$= \{a, b, e, g\}$$

b) $(A \cup B) \cap C' = \{a, b, c, d, e, g\} \cap \{a, c, d, g\}$
$$= \{a, c, d, g\}$$

c) $A' \cap B' = \{c, d, f\} \cap \{b, f, g\}$
$$= \{f\}$$

■

The Meaning of *and* and *or*

The words *and* and *or* are very important in many areas of mathematics. We use these words in several chapters in this book, including Ch.12, Probability. The word *and* is generally interpreted to mean *intersection*, whereas *or* is generally interpreted to mean *union*. Suppose $A = \{1, 2, 3, 5, 6, 8\}$ and $B = \{1, 3, 4, 7, 9, 10\}$. The elements that belong to set A *and* set B are 1 and 3. These are the elements in the intersection of the sets. The elements that belong to set A *or* set B are 1, 2, 3, 4, 5, 6, 7, 8, 9, and 10. These are the elements in the union of the sets.

The Relationship Between $n(A \cup B)$, $n(A)$, $n(B)$, and $n(A \cap B)$

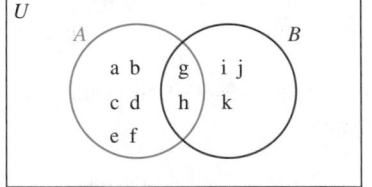

Figure 2.10

Having looked at unions and intersections, we can now determine a relationship between $n(A \cup B)$, $n(A)$, $n(B)$, and $n(A \cap B)$. Suppose set A has eight elements, set B has five elements, and $A \cap B$ has two elements. How many elements are in $A \cup B$? Let's make up some arbitrary sets that meet the criteria specified and draw a Venn diagram. If we let set $A = \{a, b, c, d, e, f, g, h\}$, then set B must contain five elements, two of which are also in set A. Let set $B = \{g, h, i, j, k\}$. We construct a Venn diagram by filling in the intersection first, as shown in Fig. 2.10. The number of elements in $A \cup B$ is 11. The elements g and h are in both sets, and if we add $n(A) + n(B)$, we are counting these elements twice.

To find the number of elements in the union of sets A and B, we can add the number of elements in sets A and B and then subtract the number of elements common to both sets.

The Number of Elements in $A \cup B$
For any finite sets A and B,
$$n(A \cup B) = n(A) + n(B) - n(A \cap B)$$

┌─ **Example 7** *How Many Visitors Speak Spanish or French?*

The results of a survey of visitors at the Grand Canyon showed that 25 speak Spanish, 14 speak French, and 4 speak both Spanish and French. How many speak Spanish or French?

Solution If we let set A be the set of visitors who speak Spanish and let set B be the set of visitors who speak French, then we need to determine $n(A \cup B)$. We can use the above formula to find $n(A \cup B)$.

$$n(A \cup B) = n(A) + n(B) - n(A \cap B)$$
$$n(A \cup B) = 25 + 14 - 4$$
$$= 35$$

Thus, 35 of the visitors surveyed speak either Spanish or French.

■

┌─ Example **8** *The Number of Elements in Set A*

Of the homes listed for sale with RE/MAX, 39 have either a three-car garage or a fireplace, 31 have a fireplace, and 18 have both a three-car garage and a fireplace. How many of these homes have a three-car garage?

Solution If we let set A be the set of homes with a three-car garage and set B be the set of homes with a fireplace, we need to determine $n(A)$. We are given the number of homes with either a three-car garage or a fireplace, which is $n(A \cup B)$. We are also given the number of homes with a fireplace, $n(B)$, and the number of homes that have both a three-car garage and a fireplace, $n(A \cap B)$. We can use the formula $n(A \cup B) = n(A) + n(B) - n(A \cap B)$ to solve for $n(A)$.

$$n(A \cup B) = n(A) + n(B) - n(A \cap B)$$
$$39 = n(A) + 31 - 18$$
$$39 = n(A) + 13$$
$$39 - 13 = n(A) + 13 - 13$$
$$26 = n(A)$$

Thus, the number of homes listed for sale that have a three-car garage is 26. ■

Two other set operations are the difference of two sets and the Cartesian product. We will first discuss the difference of two sets.

Difference of Two Sets

Definition: Difference of Two Sets
The **difference of two sets** A and B, symbolized $A - B$, is the set of elements that belong to set A but not to set B.

Using set-builder notation, the difference of two sets A and B is indicated by $A - B = \{x \mid x \in A \text{ and } x \notin B\}$. The shaded region, region I, in Fig. 2.11 represents the difference of two sets A and B, or $A - B$.

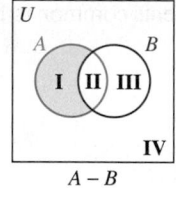

$A - B$

Figure 2.11

┌─ Example **9** *The Difference of Two Sets*

Given

$$U = \{a, b, c, d, e, f, g, h, i, j, k\}$$
$$A = \{b, d, e, f, g, h\}$$
$$B = \{a, b, d, h, i\}$$
$$C = \{b, e, g\}$$

determine

a) $A - B$ b) $A - C$ c) $A' - B$ d) $A - C'$

Solution

a) $A - B$ is the set of elements that are in set A but not set B. The elements that are in set A but not set B are e, f, and g. Therefore, $A - B = \{e, f, g\}$.

b) $A - C$ is the set of elements that are in set A but not set C. The elements that are in set A but not set C are d, f, and h. Therefore, $A - C = \{d, f, h\}$.

c) To determine $A' - B$, we must first determine A'.

$$A' = \{a, c, i, j, k\}$$

$A' - B$ is the set of elements that are in set A' but not set B. The elements that are in set A' but not set B are c, j, and k. Therefore, $A' - B = \{c, j, k\}$.

d) To determine $A - C'$, we must first determine C'.

$$C' = \{a, c, d, f, h, i, j, k\}$$

$A - C'$ is the set of elements that are in set A but not set C'. The elements that are in set A but not set C' are b, e, and g. Therefore, $A - C' = \{b, e, g\}$.   ■

Next we discuss the Cartesian product.

Cartesian Product

> ### Definition: Cartesian Product
> The **Cartesian product** of set A and set B, symbolized by $A \times B$ and read "A cross B," is the set of all possible *ordered pairs* of the form (a, b), where $a \in A$ and $b \in B$.

To determine the ordered pairs in a Cartesian product, select the first element of set A and form an ordered pair with each element of set B. Then select the second element of set A and form an ordered pair with each element of set B. Continue in this manner until you have used each element of set A.

Example 10 *The Cartesian Product of Two Sets*

Given $A = \{$orange, banana, apple$\}$ and $B = \{1, 2\}$, determine the following.

a) $A \times B$ b) $B \times A$ c) $A \times A$ d) $B \times B$

Solution

a) $A \times B = \{$(orange, 1), (orange, 2) (banana, 1), (banana, 2), (apple, 1), (apple, 2)$\}$

b) $B \times A = \{$(1, orange), (1, banana), (1, apple), (2, orange), (2, banana), (2, apple)$\}$

c) $A \times A = \{$(orange, orange), (orange, banana), (orange, apple), (banana, orange), (banana, banana), (banana, apple), (apple, orange), (apple, banana), (apple, apple)$\}$

d) $B \times B = \{(1, 1), (1, 2), (2, 1), (2, 2)\}$ ■

We can see from Example 10 that, in general, $A \times B \neq B \times A$. The ordered pairs in $A \times B$ are not the same as the ordered pairs in $B \times A$ because (orange, 1) $\neq$ (1, orange).

In general, if a set A has m elements and a set B has n elements, then the number of ordered pairs in $A \times B$ will be $m \times n$. In Example 10, set A contains 3 elements and set B contains 2 elements. Notice that $A \times B$ contains 3×2 or 6 ordered pairs.

SECTION 2.3 *Exercises*

Warm Up Exercises

In exercises 1–8, fill in the blank with an appropriate word, phrase, or symbol(s).

1. The set of all the elements in the universal set that are not in set A is called the _____ of set A. Complement

2. The set containing all the elements that are members of set A or of set B or of both sets is called the _____ of set A and set B. Union

3. The set containing all the elements that are common to both set A and set B is called the _____ of set A and set B. Intersection

4. The set of elements that belong to set A, but not to set B, is called the _____ of two sets A and B. Difference

5. The set of all possible ordered pairs of the form (a, b), where $a \in A$ and $b \in B$, is called the _____ product of set A and set B. Cartesian

6. If set A has m elements and set B has n elements, the Cartesian product $A \times B$ has _____ elements. $m \times n$

7. Two sets with no elements in common are called _____ sets. Disjoint

8. In a Venn diagram with two overlapping sets there are _____ regions. Four

Practice the Skills

In Exercises 9–13, use Fig. 2.2 as a guide to draw a Venn diagram that illustrates the situation described.

9. Set A and set B are disjoint sets. *

10. $A \subset B$ *

11. $B \subset A$ *

12. $A = B$ *

13. Set A and set B are overlapping sets. *

14. Which set operation is the word *or* generally interpreted to mean? *Or* is generally interpreted to mean *union*.

15. Which set operation is the word *and* generally interpreted to mean? *And* is generally interpreted to mean *intersection*.

16. Give the relationship between $n(A \cup B), n(A), n(B)$, and $n(A \cap B)$. $n(A \cup B) = n(A) + n(B) - n(A \cap B)$

Problem Solving

17. *Cellular Telephones* For the sets $U, A,$ and $B,$ construct a Venn diagram and place the elements in the proper regions. *

$U = \{$iPhone, Blackberry, LG, DROID, Samsung, Nokia, Motorola, Sony$\}$

$A = \{$iPhone, Blackberry, LG, Motorola, DROID$\}$

$B = \{$LG, DROID, Nokia, Motorola$\}$

18. *National Parks* For the sets U, A, and B, construct a Venn diagram and place the elements in the proper regions. *

$U = \{$Badlands, Death Valley, Glacier, Grand Teton, Mammoth Cave, Mount Rainier, North Cascades, Shenandoah, Yellowstone, Yosemite$\}$

$A = \{$Badlands, Glacier, Grand Teton, Mount Rainier, Yellowstone$\}$

$B = \{$Death Valley, Glacier, Mammoth Cave, Mount Rainier, Yosemite$\}$

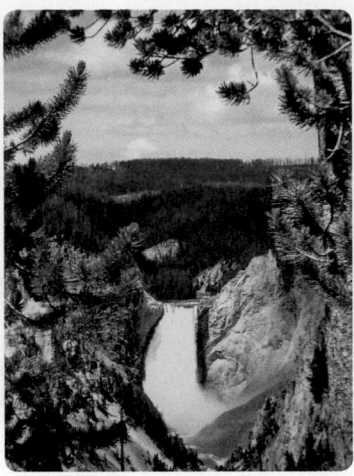

▲ *Yellowstone National Park*

19. *Occupations* The following table shows the fastest-growing occupations for college graduates, based on employment in 2008 and the estimated employment in 2016. Let the occupations in the table represent the universal set. *

Fastest-Growing Occupations for College Graduates, 2008–2016		
	Employment (in thousands of jobs)	
Occupation	**2008**	**2016**
Biomedical engineers (BE)	16	28
Network systems analysts (NSA)	292	448
Financial examiners (FE)	27	38
Medical scientists (MS)	109	154
Physicians assistants (PA)	75	104
Biochemists (B)	23	32
Athletic trainers (AT)	16	22
Dental hygienists (DH)	174	237
Veterinary technicians (VT)	80	108
Computer software engineers (CSE)	515	690

Source: U.S. Bureau of Labor Statistics

Let $A =$ the set of fastest-growing occupations for college graduates whose 2008 employment was at least 80,000.

Let $B =$ the set of fastest-growing occupations for college graduates whose estimated employment in 2016 is at least 200,000.

Using the abbreviations listed in the table for each occupation, construct a Venn diagram illustrating the sets.

*See Instructor Answer Appendix

20. *Racing Standings* The following table shows the 2009 NASCAR Sprint Cup Series Final Standings, with the 10 drivers having the highest point total and the number of races won. Let the drivers in the table represent the universal set.*

2009 NASCAR Sprint Cup Series Final Standings		
Driver	Points	Wins
Jimmie Johnson	6652	7
Mark Martin	6511	5
Jeff Gordon	6473	1
Kurt Busch	6446	2
Denny Hamlin	6335	4
Tony Stewart	6309	4
Greg Biffle	6292	0
Juan Montoya	6252	0
Ryan Newman	6175	0
Kasey Kahne	6128	2

Source: NASCAR

Let A = the set of drivers with more than 6400 points

Let B = the set of drivers with more than 1 win

Construct a Venn diagram illustrating the sets. Use the driver's initials in the Venn diagram.

21. Let U represent the set of animals in U.S. zoos. Let A represent the set of animals in the San Diego zoo. Describe A'.
The set of animals in U.S. zoos that are not in the San Diego Zoo

▲ *San Diego Zoo*

22. Let U represent the set of U.S. colleges and universities. Let A represent the set of U.S. colleges and universities in the state of Mississippi. Describe A'. The set of U.S. colleges and universities that are not in the state of Mississippi

In Exercises 23–28,

U is the set of farms in the United States.

A is the set of farms that produce corn.

B is the set of farms that produce tomatoes.

Describe each of the following sets in words.

23. A' The set of farms in the United States that do not produce corn

24. B' The set of farms in the United States that do not produce tomatoes

25. $A \cup B$ The set of farms in the United States that produce corn or produce tomatoes

26. $A \cap B$ The set of farms in the United States that produce corn and produce tomatoes

27. $A \cap B'$ The set of farms in the United States that produce corn and do not produce tomatoes

28. $A \cup B'$ The set of farms in the United States that produce corn or do not produce tomatoes

In Exercises 29–34,

U is the set of furniture stores.

A is the set of furniture stores that sell mattresses.

B is the set of furniture stores that sell outdoor furniture.

C is the set of furniture stores that sell leather furniture.

Describe the following sets.

29. $A \cup C$ The set of furniture stores that sell mattresses or leather furniture

30. $A \cap B$ The set of furniture stores that sell mattresses and outdoor furniture

31. $B' \cap C$ The set of furniture stores that do not sell outdoor furniture and sell leather furniture

32. $A \cap B \cap C$ The set of furniture stores that sell mattresses, outdoor furniture, and leather furniture

33. $A \cup B \cup C$ The set of furniture stores that sell mattresses or outdoor furniture or leather furniture

34. $A' \cup C'$ The set of furniture stores that do not sell mattresses or do not sell leather furniture

In Exercises 35–42, use the Venn diagram in Fig. 2.12 to list the set of elements in roster form.

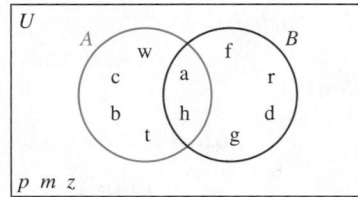

Figure 2.12

35. A {b, c, t, w, a, h}   **36.** B {a, d, f, g, h, r}

37. $A \cap B$ {a, h}   **38.** U
{c, w, b, t, a, h, d, f, g, r, p, m, z}

*See Instructor Answer Appendix

39. $A \cup B$
{c, w, b, t, a, h, f, r, d, g}

40. $(A \cup B)'$ {p, m, z}

41. $A' \cap B'$ {p, m, z}

42. $(A \cap B)'$
{c, w, b, t, d, f, g, r, p, m, z}

In Exercises 43–50, use the Venn diagram in Fig. 2.13 to list the set of elements in roster form.

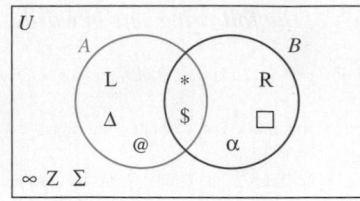

Figure 2.13

43. A {L, Δ, @, $, *}

44. B {*, $, R, □, α}

45. U
{L, Δ, @, *, $, R, □, α, ∞, Σ, Z}

46. $A \cap B$ {*, $}

47. $A' \cup B$
{R, □, α, *, $, ∞, Z, Σ}

48. $A \cup B'$
{L, Δ, @, *, $, ∞, Σ, Z}

49. $A' \cap B$ {R, □, α}

50. $(A \cup B)'$ {∞, Σ, Z}

In Exercises 51–60, let

$$U = \{1, 2, 3, 4, 5, 6, 7, 8\}$$
$$A = \{1, 2, 4, 5, 7\}$$
$$B = \{2, 3, 5, 6\}$$

Determine the following.

51. $A \cup B$ {1, 2, 3, 4, 5, 6, 7}

52. $A \cap B$ {2, 5}

53. B' {1, 4, 7, 8}

54. $A \cup B'$ {1, 2, 4, 5, 7, 8}

55. $(A \cup B)'$ {8}

56. $A' \cap B'$ {8}

57. $(A \cup B)' \cap B$ { }

58. $(A \cup B) \cap (A \cup B)'$ { }

59. $(B \cup A)' \cap (B' \cup A')$ {8}

60. $A' \cup (A \cap B)$ {2, 3, 5, 6, 8}

In Exercises 61–70, let

$$U = \{a, b, c, d, e, f, g, h, i, j, k\}$$
$$A = \{a, c, d, f, g, i\}$$
$$B = \{b, c, d, f, g\}$$
$$C = \{a, b, f, i, j\}$$

Determine the following.

61. B' {a, e, h, i, j, k}

62. $B \cup C$ {a, b, c, d, f, g, i, j}

63. $A \cap C$ {a, f, i}

64. $A' \cup B'$ {a, b, e, h, i, j, k}

65. $(A \cap C)'$
{b, c, d, e, g, h, j, k}

66. $(A \cap B) \cup C$
{a, b, c, d, f, g, i, j}

67. $A \cup (C \cap B)'$
{a, c, d, e, f, g, h, i, j, k}

68. $A \cup (C' \cup B')$
{a, c, d, e, f, g, h, i, j, k}

69. $(A' \cup C) \cup (A \cap B)$
{a, b, c, d, e, f, g, h, i, j, k}, or U

70. $(C \cap B) \cap (A' \cap B)$ {b}

In Exercises 71–78, let

$$U = \{1, 2, 3, 4, 5, 6, 7, 8, 9, 10\}$$
$$A = \{1, 2, 4, 6, 9\}$$
$$B = \{1, 3, 4, 5, 8\}$$
$$C = \{4, 5, 9\}$$

Determine the following.

71. $A - B$ {2, 6, 9}

72. $A - C$ {1, 2, 6}

73. $A - B'$ {1, 4}

74. $A' - C$ {3, 7, 8, 10}

75. $(A - B)'$ {1, 3, 4, 5, 7, 8, 10}

76. $(A - B)' - C$
{1, 3, 7, 8, 10}

77. $C - A'$ {4, 9}

78. $(C - A)' - B$ {2, 6, 7, 9, 10}

In Exercises 79–84, let

$$A = \{a, b, c\}$$
$$B = \{1, 2\}$$

79. Determine $A \times B$. {(a, 1), (a, 2), (b, 1), (b, 2), (c, 1), (c, 2)}

80. Determine $B \times A$. {(1, a), (1, b), (1, c), (2, a), (2, b), (2, c)}

81. Does $A \times B = B \times A$?
No. The ordered pairs are not the same. For example, (a, 1) ≠ (1, a).

82. Determine $n(A \times B)$. 6

83. Determine $n(B \times A)$. 6

84. Does $n(A \times B) = n(B \times A)$? Yes

Problem Solving

In Exercises 85–98, let

$$U = \{x \,|\, x \in N \text{ and } x < 10\}$$
$$A = \{x \,|\, x \in N \text{ and } x \text{ is odd and } x < 10\}$$
$$B = \{x \,|\, x \in N \text{ and } x \text{ is even and } x < 10\}$$
$$C = \{x \,|\, x \in N \text{ and } x < 6\}$$

Determine the following.

85. $A \cap B$ { }

86. $A \cup B$
{1, 2, 3, 4, 5, 6, 7, 8, 9}, or U

87. $A' \cup B$ {2, 4, 6, 8}, or B

88. $(B \cup C)'$ {7, 9}

89. $A \cap C'$ {7, 9}

90. $A \cap B'$ {1, 3, 5, 7, 9}, or A

91. $(B \cap C)'$
{1, 3, 5, 6, 7, 8, 9}

92. $(A \cup C) \cap B$ {2, 4}

93. $(C' \cup A) \cap B$ {6, 8}

94. $(C \cap B) \cup A$
{1, 2, 3, 4, 5, 7, 9}

95. $(A \cap B)' \cup C$
{1, 2, 3, 4, 5, 6, 7, 8, 9}, or U

96. $(A' \cup C) \cap B$ {2, 4, 6, 8}, or B

97. $(A' \cup B') \cap C$ {1, 2, 3, 4, 5}, or C

98. $(A' \cap C) \cup (A \cap B)$ {2, 4}

99. When will a set and its complement be disjoint? Explain and give an example. A set and its complement will always be disjoint. For example, if $U = \{1, 2, 3\}$ and $A = \{1, 2\}$, then $A' = \{3\}$, and $A \cap A' = \{ \}$.

100. When will $n(A \cap B) = 0$? Explain and give an example. $n(A \cap B) = 0$ when A and B are disjoint sets. $A = \{1, 3\}, B = \{2, 4\}, n(A \cap B) = 0$

101. *Pet Ownership* The results of a survey of customers at PetSmart showed that 27 owned dogs, 38 owned cats, and 16 owned both dogs and cats. How many people owned either a dog or a cat? 49

102. *Student Council and Intramurals* At Madison High School, 46 students participated in student council or intramurals, 30 participated in student council, and 4 participated in student council and intramurals. How many students participated in intramurals? 20

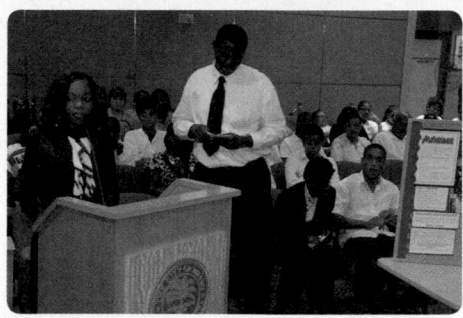

103. Consider the formula

$$n(A \cup B) = n(A) + n(B) - n(A \cap B)$$

a) Show that this relation holds for $A = \{a, b, c, d\}$ and $B = \{b, d, e, f, g, h\}$. $8 = 4 + 6 - 2$

b) Make up your own sets A and B, each consisting of at least six elements. Using these sets, show that the relation holds. Answers will vary.

c) Use a Venn diagram and explain why the relation holds for any two sets A and B. Answers will vary.

104. The Venn diagram in Fig. 2.14 shows a technique of labeling the regions to indicate membership of elements in a particular region. Define each of the four regions with a set statement. (*Hint: $A \cap B'$* defines region I.)

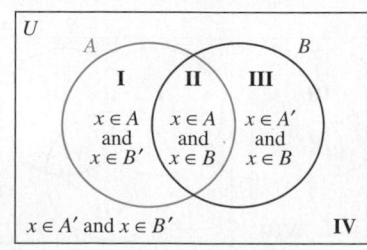

Figure 2.14

In Exercises 105–114, let $U = \{0, 1, 2, 3, 4, 5, ... \}$, $A = \{1, 2, 3, 4, ... \}$, $B = \{4, 8, 12, 16, ... \}$, and $C = \{2, 4, 6, 8, ... \}$. Determine the following.

105. $A \cup B$ $\{1, 2, 3, 4, ...\}$, or A

106. $A \cap B$ $\{4, 8, 12, 16, ...\}$, or B

107. $B \cup C$ $\{2, 4, 6, 8, ...\}$, or C

108. $B \cap C$ $\{4, 8, 12, 16, ...\}$, or B

109. $A \cap C$ $\{2, 4, 6, 8, ...\}$, or C

110. $A' \cap C$ $\{\}$

111. $B' \cap C$ $\{2, 6, 10, 14, 18, ...\}$

112. $(B \cup C)' \cup C$ $\{0, 1, 2, 3, 4, ...\}$, or U

113. $(A \cap C) \cap B'$ $\{2, 6, 10, 14, 18, ...\}$

114. $U' \cap (A \cup B)$ $\{\}$

Challenge Problems/Group Activities

In Exercises 115–122, determine whether the answer is $\varnothing$, A, or U. (Assume $A \neq \varnothing, A \neq U$.)

115. $A \cap A'$ $\{\}$

116. $A \cup A'$ U

117. $A \cup \varnothing$ A

118. $A \cap \varnothing$ $\varnothing$

119. $A' \cup U$ U

120. $A \cap U$ A

121. $A \cup U$ U

122. $A \cap A$ A

In Exercises 123–128, determine the relationship between set A and set B if

123. $A \cap B = B.$ $B \subseteq A$

124. $A \cup B = B.$ $A \subseteq B$

125. $A \cap B = \varnothing.$ A and B are disjoint sets.

126. $A \cup B = A.$ $B \subseteq A$

127. $A \cap B = A.$ $A \subseteq B$

128. $A \cup B = \varnothing.$
Both A and B must be $\{\}$, and therefore they are equal sets.

SECTION 2.4

Venn Diagrams with Three Sets and Verification of Equality of Sets

▲ *Venn diagrams can be used to answer questions regarding the number of people participating in an intramural activity at a college.*

Suppose a college offers intramurals in basketball, flag football, and softball. Is there a way the director of intramurals can determine which students participate in all three activities or which students participate in exactly two of these activities? The answer is yes by using a *Venn Diagram*. A Venn diagram that can be used to convey important information quickly and efficiently.

Why *This is Important* Classifying sets using diagrams often helps us understand the relationship among various sets.

In Section 2.3, we learned how to use Venn diagrams to illustrate two sets. Venn diagrams can also be used to illustrate three sets.

For three sets, *A*, *B*, and *C*, the diagram is drawn so the three sets overlap (Fig. 2.15), creating eight regions. The diagrams in Fig. 2.16 emphasize selected regions of three intersecting sets. *When constructing Venn diagrams with three sets, we generally start with region V and work outward,* as explained in the procedure given on page 69.

Figure 2.15

Figure 2.16

> **PROCEDURE**   **GENERAL PROCEDURE FOR CONSTRUCTING VENN DIAGRAMS WITH THREE SETS, *A*, *B*, AND *C***
>
> 1. Determine the elements to be placed in region V by finding the elements that are common to all three sets, $A \cap B \cap C$.
>
> 2. Determine the elements to be placed in region II. Find the elements in $A \cap B$. The elements in this set belong in regions II and V. Place the elements in the set $A \cap B$ that are not listed in region V in region II. The elements in regions IV and VI are found in a similar manner.
>
> 3. Determine the elements to be placed in region I by determining the elements in set *A* that are not in regions II, IV, and V. The elements in regions III and VII are found in a similar manner.
>
> 4. Determine the elements to be placed in region VIII by finding the elements in the universal set that are not in regions I through VII.

Example 1 illustrates the general procedure.

Example 1   *Constructing a Venn Diagram for Three Sets*

Construct a Venn diagram illustrating the following sets.

$$U = \{1, 2, 3, 4, 5, 6, 7, 8, 9, 10, 11, 12, 13, 14, 15\}$$
$$A = \{1, 4, 8, 9, 10, 12\}$$
$$B = \{2, 4, 5, 9, 10, 13\}$$
$$C = \{1, 3, 4, 8, 9, 11\}$$

Solution   First find the intersection of all three sets. Because the elements 4 and 9 are in all three sets, $A \cap B \cap C = \{4, 9\}$. The elements 4 and 9 are placed in region V in Fig.2.17. Next complete region II by determining the intersection of sets *A* and *B*.

$$A \cap B = \{4, 9, 10\}$$

$A \cap B$ consists of regions II and V. The elements 4 and 9 have already been placed in region V, so 10 must be placed in region II.

Now determine what numbers go in region IV.

$$A \cap C = \{1, 4, 8, 9\}$$

Since 4 and 9 have already been placed in region V, place the 1 and 8 in region IV. Now determine the numbers to go in region VI.

$$B \cap C = \{4, 9\}$$

Since both the 4 and 9 have been placed in region V, there are no numbers to be placed in region VI. Now complete set *A*. The only element of set *A* that has not previously been placed in regions II, IV, or V is 12. Therefore, place the element 12 in region I. The element 12 that is placed in region I is only in set *A* and not in set *B* or set *C*. Using set *B*, complete region III using the same general procedure used to determine the numbers in region I. Using set *C*, complete region VII by using the same procedure used to complete regions I and III. To determine the elements in region VIII, find the elements in *U* that have not been placed in regions I–VII. The elements 6, 7, 14, and 15 have not been placed in regions I–VII, so place them in region VIII. ∎

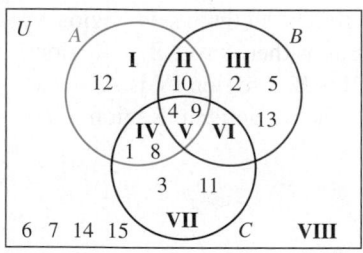

Figure 2.17

Venn diagrams can be used to illustrate and analyze many everyday problems. One example follows.

Example **2** *Blood Types*

Human blood is classified (typed) according to the presence or absence of the specific antigens A, B, and Rh in the red blood cells. Antigens are highly specified proteins and carbohydrates that will trigger the production of antibodies in the blood to fight infection. Blood containing the Rh antigen is labeled positive, +, while blood lacking the Rh antigen is labeled negative, −. Blood lacking both A and B antigens is called type O. Sketch a Venn diagram with three sets A, B, and Rh and place each type of blood listed in the proper region. A person has only one type of blood.

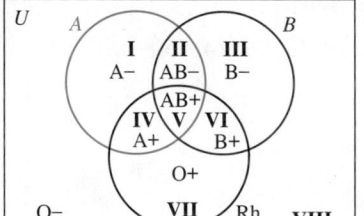

Figure 2.18

Solution

As illustrated in Chapter 1, the first thing to do is to read the question carefully and make sure you understand what is given and what you are asked to find. There are three antigens A, B, and Rh. Therefore, begin by naming the three circles in a Venn diagram with the three antigens; see Fig. 2.18.

Any blood containing the Rh antigen is positive, and any blood not containing the Rh antigen is negative. Therefore, all blood in the Rh circle is positive, and all blood outside the Rh circle is negative. The intersection of all three sets, region V, is AB+. Region II contains only antigens A and B and is therefore AB−. Region I is A− because it contains only antigen A. Region III is B−, region IV is A+, and region VI is B+. Region VII is O+, containing only the Rh antigen. Region VIII, which lacks all three antigens, is O−.   ■

Verification of Equality of Sets

In this chapter, for clarity we may refer to operations on sets, such as $A \cup B'$ or $A \cap B \cap C$, as *statements involving sets* or simply as *statements*. Now we discuss how to determine if two statements involving sets are equal.

Consider the question: Is $A' \cup B = A' \cap B$ *for all sets A and B*? For the specific sets $U = \{1, 2, 3, 4, 5\}$, $A = \{1, 3\}$, and $B = \{2, 4, 5\}$, is $A' \cup B = A' \cap B$? To answer the question, we do the following.

Find $A' \cup B$	Find $A' \cap B$
$A' = \{2, 4, 5\}$	$A' = \{2, 4, 5\}$
$B = \{2, 4, 5\}$	$B = \{2, 4, 5\}$
$A' \cup B = \{2, 4, 5\}$	$A' \cap B = \{2, 4, 5\}$

For these sets, $A' \cup B = A' \cap B$, because both set statements are equal to $\{2, 4, 5\}$. At this point you may believe that $A' \cup B = A' \cap B$ for all sets A and B.

If we select the sets $U = \{1, 2, 3, 4, 5\}$, $A = \{1, 3, 5\}$, and $B = \{2, 3\}$, we see that $A' \cup B = \{2, 3, 4\}$ and $A' \cap B = \{2\}$. For this case, $A' \cup B \neq A' \cap B$.

Thus, we have proved that $A' \cup B \neq A' \cap B$ for all sets A and B by using a *counterexample*. A counterexample, as explained in Chapter 1, is an example that shows a statement is not true.

In Chapter 1, we explained that proofs involve the use of *deductive reasoning*. Recall that deductive reasoning begins with a general statement and works to a specific conclusion. To verify, or determine whether set statements are equal for any two sets selected, we use deductive reasoning with Venn diagrams. Venn diagrams are used because they can illustrate general cases. To determine if statements that contain sets, such as $(A \cup B)'$ and $A' \cap B'$, are equal for all sets A and B, we use the regions of Venn diagrams. If both statements represent the same regions of the Venn diagram, then the statements are equal for all sets A and B. See Example 3.

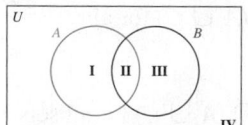

Figure 2.19

Example 3 *Equality of Sets*

Determine whether $(A \cup B)' = A' \cap B'$ for all sets A and B.

Solution Draw a Venn diagram with two sets A and B, as in Fig. 2.19. Label the regions as indicated.

Find $(A \cup B)'$

Set	Corresponding Regions
A	I, II
B	II, III
$A \cup B$	I, II, III
$(A \cup B)'$	IV

Find $A' \cap B'$

Set	Corresponding Regions
A'	III, IV
B'	I, IV
$A' \cap B'$	IV

Both statements are represented by the same region, IV, of the Venn diagram. Thus, $(A \cup B)' = A' \cap B'$ for all sets A and B. ∎

In Example 3, when we proved that $(A \cup B)' = A' \cap B'$, we started with two general sets and worked to the specific conclusion that both statements represented the same regions of the Venn diagram. We showed that $(A \cup B)' = A' \cap B'$ *for all sets A and B*. No matter what sets we choose for A and B, this statement will be true. For example, let $U = \{1, 2, 3, 4, 5, 6, 7, 8, 9, 10\}$, $A = \{3, 4, 6, 10\}$, and $B = \{1, 2, 4, 5, 6, 8\}$.

$$(A \cup B)' = A' \cap B'$$
$$\{1, 2, 3, 4, 5, 6, 8, 10\}' = \{3, 4, 6, 10\}' \cap \{1, 2, 4, 5, 6, 8\}'$$
$$\{7, 9\} = \{1, 2, 5, 7, 8, 9\} \cap \{3, 7, 9, 10\}$$
$$\{7, 9\} = \{7, 9\}$$

We can also use Venn diagrams to prove statements involving three sets.

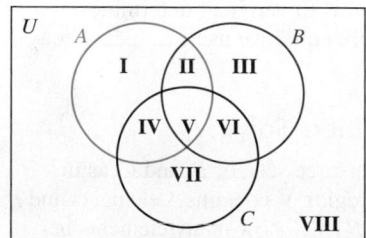

Figure 2.20

Example 4 *Equality of Sets*

Determine whether $A \cup (B \cap C) = (A \cup B) \cap (A \cup C)$ for all sets, A, B, and C.

Solution Because the statements include three sets, A, B, and C, three circles must be used. The Venn diagram illustrating the eight regions is shown in Fig. 2.20.

First we will find the regions that correspond to $A \cup (B \cap C)$, and then we will find the regions that correspond to $(A \cup B) \cap (A \cup C)$. If both answers are the same, the statements are equal.

MATHEMATICS TODAY

Using Venn Diagrams

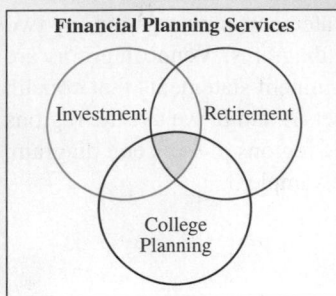

Financial Planning Services

A financial planning company uses the Venn diagram above to illustrate the financial planning services it offers. From the diagram, we can see that this company offers advice in an "intersection" of the areas investment, retirement, and college planning, the intersection of all three sets.

We categorize items on a daily basis. Children are taught how to categorize items at an early age when they learn how to classify items according to color, shape, and size. Biologists categorize items when they classify organisms according to shared characteristics.

Why **This is Important** A Venn diagram is a very useful tool to help order and arrange items and to picture the relationship between sets.

Find $A \cup (B \cap C)$

Set	Corresponding Regions
A	I, II, IV, V
$B \cap C$	V, VI
$A \cup (B \cap C)$	I, II, IV, V, VI

Find $(A \cup B) \cap (A \cup C)$

Set	Corresponding Regions
$A \cup B$	I, II, III, IV, V, VI
$A \cup C$	I, II, IV, V, VI, VII
$(A \cup B) \cap (A \cup C)$	I, II, IV, V, VI

The regions that correspond to $A \cup (B \cap C)$ are I, II, IV, V, and VI, and the regions that correspond to $(A \cup B) \cap (A \cup C)$ are also I, II, IV, V, and VI. The results show that both statements are represented by the same regions, namely, I, II, IV, V, and VI, and therefore $A \cup (B \cap C) = (A \cup B) \cap (A \cup C)$ for all sets A, B, and C. ∎

In Example 4, we proved that $A \cup (B \cap C) = (A \cup B) \cap (A \cup C)$ for all sets A, B, and C. Show that this statement is true for the specific sets $U = \{1, 2, 3, 4, 5, 6, 7, 8, 9, 10\}$, $A = \{1, 2, 3, 7\}$, $B = \{2, 3, 4, 5, 7, 9\}$, and $C = \{1, 4, 7, 8, 10\}$.

De Morgan's Laws

In set theory, logic, and other branches of mathematics, a pair of related theorems known as De Morgan's laws make it possible to transform statements and formulas into alternative and often more convenient forms. In set theory, *De Morgan's laws* are symbolized as follows.

De Morgan's Laws

1. $(A \cap B)' = A' \cup B'$
2. $(A \cup B)' = A' \cap B'$

Law 2 was verified in Example 3. We suggest that you verify law 1 at this time. The laws were expressed verbally by William of Ockham in the fourteenth century. In the nineteenth century, Augustus De Morgan expressed them mathematically. De Morgan's laws will be discussed more thoroughly in Chapter 3, Logic.

SECTION 2.4   *Exercises*

Warm Up Exercises

In Exercises 1–4, fill in the blank with an appropriate word, phrase, or symbol(s).

1. The number of regions created when constructing a Venn diagram with three overlapping sets is _____ . 8

2. a) When constructing a Venn diagram with three overlapping sets, region _____ is generally completed first. V

   b) When constructing a Venn diagram with three overlapping sets, after completing region V, the next regions generally completed are II, IV, and _____ . VI

3. Complete DeMorgan's laws:

   a) $(A \cup B)' = $ _____ $A' \cap B'$

   b) $(A \cap B)' = $ _____ $A' \cup B'$

4. When using Venn diagrams to verify or determine whether set statements are equal we use _____ reasoning. Deductive

Practice the Skills/Problem Solving

5. A Venn diagram contains three sets, A, B, and C, as in Fig. 2.15 on page 68. If region V contains 4 elements and there are 12 elements in $B \cap C$, how many elements belong in region VI? Explain. 8

6. A Venn diagram contains three sets, A, B, and C, as in Fig. 2.15 on page 68. If region V contains 4 elements and there are 9 elements in $A \cap B$, how many elements belong in region II? Explain. 5

7. a) For $U = \{1, 2, 3, 4, 5\}$, $A = \{1, 4, 5\}$, and $B = \{1, 4, 5\}$, does $A \cup B = A \cap B$? Yes

b) By observing the answer to part (a), can we conclude that $A \cup B = A \cap B$ for all sets A and B? Explain. No, one specific case cannot be used as proof.

c) Using a Venn diagram, determine if $A \cup B = A \cap B$ for all sets A and B. No, not equal

8. Construct a Venn diagram illustrating the following sets. *
$$U = \{a, b, c, d, e, f, g, h, i, j\}$$
$$A = \{c, d, e, g, h, i\}$$
$$B = \{a, c, d, g\}$$
$$C = \{c, f, i, j\}$$

9. Construct a Venn diagram illustrating the following sets. *
$U = \{$*Cinderella, Pinocchio, Ratatouille, Fantasia, Dumbo, Bambi, Pocahontas, Hercules, Mulan, Tarzan, Cars*$\}$

$A = \{$*Bambi, Hercules, Pocahontas, Tarzan*$\}$

$B = \{$*Ratatouille, Bambi, Mulan, Hercules*$\}$

$C = \{$*Pocahontas, Cinderella, Bambi, Ratatouille, Fantasia*$\}$

▲ *Bambi*

10. Construct a Venn diagram illustrating the following sets. *
$U = \{$microwave oven, freezer, dishwasher, refrigerator, washer, dryer, toaster, blender, food processor, iron$\}$

$A = \{$toaster, blender, iron, dishwasher, washer, dryer$\}$

$B = \{$dishwasher, iron, freezer$\}$

$C = \{$washer, dryer, iron, freezer, microwave oven$\}$

11. Construct a Venn diagram illustrating the following sets. *
$U = \{$American Eagle, Best Buy, Wal-Mart, Kmart, Target, Sears, JCPenney, Costco, Kohl's, Gap, Gap Kids, Foot Locker, Old Navy, Macy's$\}$

$A = \{$American Eagle, Wal-Mart, Target, JCPenney, Old Navy$\}$

$B = \{$Best Buy, Target, Costco, Old Navy, Macy's$\}$

$C = \{$Target, Sears, Kohl's, Gap, JCPenney$\}$

12. Construct a Venn diagram illustrating the following sets. *
$U = \{$Louis Armstrong, Glenn Miller, Stan Kenton, Charlie Parker, Duke Ellington, Benny Goodman, Count Basie, John Coltrane, Dizzy Gillespie, Miles Davis, Thelonius Monk$\}$

$A = \{$Stan Kenton, Count Basie, Dizzy Gillespie, Duke Ellington, Thelonius Monk$\}$

$B = \{$Louis Armstrong, Glenn Miller, Count Basie, Duke Ellington, Miles Davis$\}$

$C = \{$Count Basie, Miles Davis, Stan Kenton, Charlie Parker, Duke Ellington$\}$

13. *Olympic Medals* Consider the following table, which shows countries that won at least 25 medals in the 2008 Summer Olympics. Let the countries in the table represent the universal set.

Country	Gold Medals	Silver Medals	Bronze Medals	Total Medals
United States	36	38	36	110
China	51	21	28	100
Russia	23	21	28	72
Great Britain	19	13	15	47
Australia	14	15	17	46
Germany	16	10	15	41
France	7	16	17	40
South Korea	13	10	8	31
Italy	8	10	10	28
Ukraine	7	5	15	27
Japan	9	6	10	25

Source: United States Olympic Committee.

Let A = set of countries that won at least 30 gold medals.
Let B = set of countries that won at least 15 silver medals.
Let C = set of countries that won at least 10 bronze medals.

Construct a Venn diagram that illustrates the sets A, B, and C. *

14. *Popular TV Shows* Construct a Venn diagram illustrating the following sets. *

$U = \{$*American Idol (AI), CSI, Dancing with the Stars (DWS), Family Guy (FG), Gossip Girl (GG), Monday Night Football (MNF), NCIS, Sunday Night Football (SNF), Survivor (S)*$\}$.

$A = \{$*AI, CSI, DWS, SNF, NCIS*$\}$

$B = \{$*AI, DWS, SNF, NCIS, MNF*$\}$

$C = \{$*AI, CSI, SNF, NClS, MNF, S*$\}$

Rankings of Fruit-Producing Countries For Exercises 15–20, use the following table, which shows the top 10 countries for production of apples, oranges, and nuts, The universal set is the set of countries listed in the world.

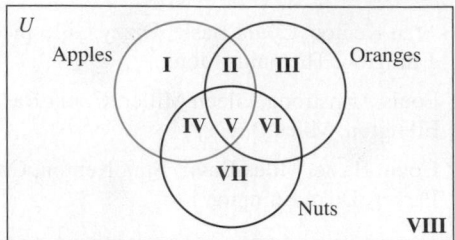

Figure 2.21

Ranking of Fruit-Producing countries		
Apples	**Oranges**	**Nuts**
1. China	1. Brazil	1. United States
2. United States	2. United States	2. Indonesia
3. Iran	3. Mexico	3. Mexico
4. Turkey	4. India	4. Ethiopia
5. Russia	5. China	5. China
6. Italy	6. Spain	6. Australia
7. India	7. Indonesia	7. Guatemala
8. France	8. Iran	8. Portugal
9. Chile	9. Italy	9. Thailand
10. Argentina	10. Egypt	10. Philippines

Source: Food and Agriculture of the United Nations

Indicate in which region, I–VIII in Fig. 2.21, each of the following countries belongs.

15. Italy II

16. United States V

17. Canada VIII

18. Portugal VII

19. Spain III

20. Mexico VI

Figures In Exercises 21–32, indicate in Fig. 2.22 the region in which each of the figures would be placed.

Figure 2.22

21. ● VI   **22.** ⬡ VIII   **23.** ▲ III

24. ⬤ IV   **25.** ⬢ III   **26.** ▮ I

27. ● V   **28.** ▫ III   **29.** ▲ II

30. ▢ VIII   **31.** ⬤ VII **32.** ○ VI

Senate Bills During a session of the U.S. Senate, three bills were voted on. The votes of six senators are shown below the figure. Determine in which region of Fig. 2.23 each senator would be placed. The set labeled Bill 1 represents the set of senators who voted yes on Bill 1, and so on.

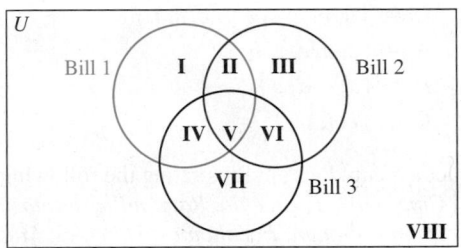

Figure 2.23

SENATOR	BILL 1	BILL 2	BILL 3
33. Hutchinson	yes	no	no I
34. Kerry	no	no	yes VII
35. McCain	no	no	no VIII
36. Mikulski	yes	yes	yes V
37. Rand	no	yes	yes VI
38. Reid	no	yes	no III

In Exercises 39–52, use the Venn diagram in Fig. 2.24 to list the sets in roster form.

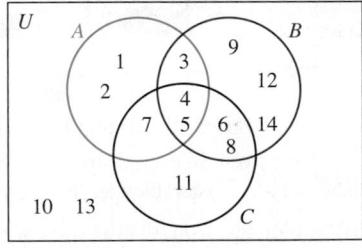

Figure 2.24

39. A $\{1, 2, 3, 4, 5, 7\}$

40. U $\{1, 2, 3, 4, 5, 6, 7, 8, 9, 10, 11, 12, 13, 14\}$

41. B $\{3, 4, 5, 6, 8, 9, 12, 14\}$

42. C $\{4, 5, 6, 7, 8, 11\}$

43. $A \cap B$ $\{3, 4, 5\}$

44. $A \cap C$ $\{4, 5, 7\}$

45. $(B \cap C)'$ $\{1, 2, 3, 7, 9, 10, 11, 12, 13, 14\}$

46. $A \cap B \cap C$ $\{4, 5\}$

47. $A \cup B$ $\{1, 2, 3, 4, 5, 6, 7, 8, 9, 12, 14\}$

48. $B \cup C$ $\{3, 4, 5, 6, 7, 8, 9, 11, 12, 14\}$

49. $(A \cup C)'$ $\{9, 10, 12, 13, 14\}$

50. $A \cap (B \cup C)$ $\{3, 4, 5, 7\}$

51. A' $\{6, 8, 9, 10, 11, 12, 13, 14\}$

52. $(A \cup B \cup C)'$ $\{10, 13\}$

In Exercises 53–60, use Venn diagrams to determine whether the following statements are equal for all sets A and B.

53. $(A \cap B)'$, $A' \cup B'$ Yes

54. $(A \cap B)'$, $A' \cup B$ No

55. $A' \cup B'$, $A \cap B$ No

56. $(A \cup B)'$, $(A \cap B)'$ No

57. $A' \cup B'$, $(A \cup B)'$ No

58. $A' \cap B'$, $A \cup B'$ No

59. $(A' \cap B)'$, $A \cup B'$ Yes

60. $A' \cap B'$, $(A' \cap B')'$ No

In Exercises 61–70, use Venn diagrams to determine whether the following statements are equal for all sets A, B, and C.

61. $A \cap (B \cup C)$, $(A \cap B) \cup C$ No

62. $A \cup (B \cap C)$, $(B \cap C) \cup A$ Yes

63. $A \cap (B \cup C)$, $(B \cup C) \cap A$ Yes

64. $A \cup (B \cap C)'$, $A' \cap (B' \cup C)$ No

65. $A \cap (B \cup C)$, $(A \cap B) \cup (A \cap C)$ Yes

66. $A \cup (B \cap C)$, $(A \cup B) \cap (A \cup C)$ Yes

67. $A \cup (B \cup C)'$, $A \cup (B' \cap C')$ Yes

68. $(A \cup B) \cap (B \cup C)$, $B \cup (A \cap C)$ Yes

69. $(A \cup B)' \cap C$, $(A' \cup C') \cap (B' \cup C)$ No

70. $(C \cap B)' \cup (A \cap B)'$, $A \cap (B \cap C)$ No

In Exercises 71–74, use set statements to write a description of the shaded area. Use union, intersection and complement as necessary. More than one answer may be possible.

71.

$(A \cup B)'$

72.

$(A \cap B)'$

73.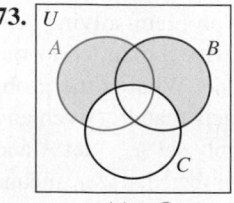

$(A \cup B) \cap C'$

74.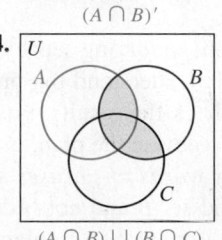

$(A \cap B) \cup (B \cap C)$

75. Let
$$U = \{1, 2, 3, 4, 5, 6, 7, 8, 9, 10\}$$
$$A = \{1, 2, 3, 4\}$$
$$B = \{3, 6, 7\}$$
$$C = \{6, 7, 9\}$$

a) Show that $(A \cup B) \cap C = (A \cap C) \cup (B \cap C)$ for these sets. Both equal $\{6, 7\}$.

b) Make up your own sets A, B, and C. Verify that $(A \cup B) \cap C = (A \cap C) \cup (B \cap C)$ for your sets A, B, and C. Answers will vary.

c) Use Venn diagrams to verify that $(A \cup B) \cap C = (A \cap C) \cup (B \cap C)$ for all sets A, B, and C.
Both are represented by the regions IV, V, VI.

76. Let
$$U = \{a, b, c, d, e, f, g, h, i\}$$
$$A = \{a, c, d, e, f\}$$
$$B = \{c, d\}$$
$$C = \{a, b, c, d, e\}$$

a) Determine whether $(A \cup C)' \cap B = (A \cap C)' \cap B$ for these sets. Yes

b) Make up your own sets, A, B, and C. Determine whether $(A \cup C)' \cap B = (A \cap C)' \cap B$ for your sets. Answer will vary.

c) Determine whether $(A \cup C)' \cap B = (A \cap C)' \cap B$ for all sets A, B, and C. No

77. *Blood Types* A hematology text gives the following information on percentages of the different types of blood worldwide.

Type	Positive Blood, %	Negative Blood, %
A	37	6
O	32	6.5
B	11	2
AB	5	0.5

Construct a Venn diagram similar to the one in Example 2 and place the correct percentage in each of the eight regions. *

78. Define each of the eight regions in Fig. 2.25 using sets A, B, and C and a set operation. (*Hint:* $A \cap B' \cap C'$ defines region I.)

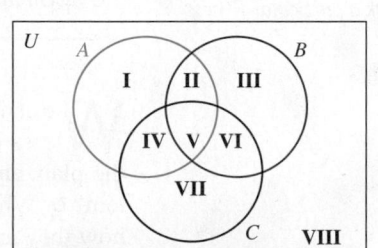

I $A \cap B' \cap C'$
II $A \cap B \cap C'$
III $A' \cap B \cap C'$
IV $A \cap B' \cap C$
V $A \cap B \cap C$
VI $A' \cap B \cap C$
VII $A' \cap B' \cap C$
VIII $A' \cap B' \cap C'$

Figure 2.25

*See Instructor Answer Appendix

79. *Categorizing Contracts* J & C Mechanical Contractors wants to classify its projects. The contractors categorize set A as construction projects, set B as plumbing projects, and set C as projects with a budget greater than $300,000.

a) Draw a Venn diagram that can be used to categorize the company projects according to the listed criteria. *

b) Determine the region of the diagram that contains construction projects and plumbing projects with a budget greater than $300,000. Describe the region using sets A, B, and C with set operations. Use union, intersection, and complement as necessary. V; $A \cap B \cap C$

c) Determine the region of the diagram that contains plumbing projects with a budget greater than $300,000 that are not construction projects. Describe the region using sets A, B and C with set operations. Use union, intersection, and complement as necessary. VI; $A' \cap B \cap C$

d) Determine the region of the diagram that contains construction projects and nonplumbing projects whose budget is less than or equal to $300,000. Describe the region using sets A, B, and C with set operations. Use union, intersection, and complement as necessary. I; $A \cap B' \cap C'$

Challenge Problem/Group Activity

80. We were able to determine the number of elements in the union of two sets with the formula

$$n(A \cup B) = n(A) + n(B) - n(A \cap B).$$

Can you determine a formula for finding the number of elements in the union of three sets? In other words, write a formula to determine $n(A \cup B \cup C)$. [*Hint*: The formula

will contain each of the following: $n(A)$, $n(B)$, $n(C)$, $n(A \cap B \cap C')$, $n(A \cap B' \cap C)$, $n(A' \cap B \cap C)$, and $2n(A \cap B \cap C)$.*

Recreational Mathematics

81. a) Construct a Venn diagram illustrating four sets, A, B, C, and D. (*Hint*: Four circles cannot be used, and you should end up with 16 *distinct* regions.) Have fun! *

b) Label each region with a set statement (see Exercise 78). Check all 16 regions to make sure that *each is distinct*. *

Internet/Research Activity

82. The two Venn diagrams below illustrate what happens when colors are added or subtracted. Do research in an art text, an encyclopedia, the Internet, or another source and write a report explaining the creation of the colors in the Venn diagrams, using such terms as union of colors and subtraction (or difference) of colors.

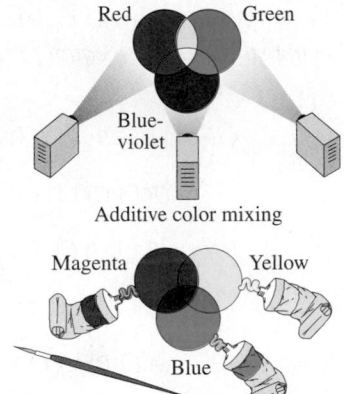

Additive color mixing

Subtractive color mixing

*See Instructor Answer Appendix

Applications of Sets

▲ *We can use a Venn diagram to determine how many members of a health club took a particular fitness class.*

The members of a health club were surveyed about taking fitness classes at the club. Suppose the results of the survey show how many members took a yoga class, how many members took a spinning class, and how many members took a class in yoga and a class in spinning. How can the manager of the club use this information to determine how many members took only a yoga class? In this section, we will learn how to use Venn diagrams to answer this type of question.

Why **This is Important** As you read through this section, you will see many real-life applications of set theory.

We can solve practical problems involving sets by using the problem-solving process discussed in Chapter 1: Understand the problem, devise a plan, carry out the plan, and then examine and check the results. First determine: What is the problem? or What am I looking for? To devise the plan, list all the facts that are given and how they are related. *Look for key words or phrases* such as "only set A," "set A and set B," "set A or set B," "set A and set B and not set C." Remember that *and* means intersection, *or* means union, and *not* means complement. The problems we solve in this section contain two or three sets of elements, which can be represented in a Venn diagram. Our plan will generally include drawing a Venn diagram, labeling the diagram, and filling in the regions of the diagram.

Whenever possible, follow the procedure in Section 2.4 for completing the Venn diagram and then answer the questions. *Remember: When drawing Venn diagrams, we generally start with the intersection of the sets and work outward.*

Example 1 *Yogurt Taste Test*

A yogurt company wishes to introduce a new yogurt flavor. The company is considering two flavors: raspberry cheesecake (R) and orange creme (O). In a survey of 250 people it was found that

180 people liked raspberry cheesecake.

139 people liked orange creme.

82 people liked both flavors.

Of those surveyed, how many people

a) did not like either raspberry cheesecake or orange creme?

b) liked raspberry cheesecake, but not orange creme?

c) liked orange creme, but not raspberry cheesecake?

d) liked either raspberry cheesecake or orange creme?

Solution The problem provides the following information.

The number of people surveyed is 250: $n(U) = 250$.

The number of people surveyed who liked raspberry cheesecake is 180: $n(R) = 180$.

The number of people surveyed who liked orange creme is 139: $n(O) = 139$.

The number of people surveyed who liked both raspberry cheesecake and orange creme is 82: $n(R \cap O) = 82$.

We illustrate this information on the Venn diagram shown in Fig. 2.26. We already know that $R \cap O$ corresponds to region II. Because $n(R \cap O) = 82$, we write 82 in region II. Set R consists of regions I and II. We know that set R, the number of people who liked raspberry cheesecake, contains 180 people. Therefore, region I contains $180 - 82 = 98$ people. We write the number 98 in region I. Set O consists of regions II and III. Because $n(O) = 139$, the total in these two regions must be 139. Region II contains 82, leaving $139 - 82$, or 57, for region III. We write 57 in region III.

The total number of people surveyed who liked raspberry cheesecake or orange creme is found by adding the numbers in regions I, II, and III. Therefore $n(R \cup O) = 98 + 82 + 57 = 237$. The number in region IV is the difference between $n(U)$ and $n(R \cup O)$. There are $250 - 237$, or 13, members in region IV.

a) The people surveyed who did not like either raspberry cheesecake or orange creme are those people in the universal set who are not contained in set R or set O. The 13 people in region IV did not like raspberry cheesecake or orange creme.

b) The 98 people in region I are those people surveyed who liked raspberry cheesecake, but not orange creme.

c) The 57 people in region III are those people surveyed who liked orange creme, but not raspberry cheesecake.

d) The people in regions I, II, or III are those people surveyed who liked either raspberry cheesecake or orange creme. Thus, $98 + 82 + 57$, or 237, people surveyed liked either raspberry cheesecake or orange creme. Notice that the 82 people in region II who like both flavors are included in those people surveyed who liked either raspberry cheesecake or orange creme. ∎

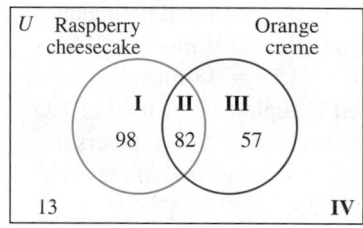

Figure 2.26

Similar problems involving three sets can be solved, as illustrated in Example 2.

┌ **Example 2** *Software Purchases*

CompUSA has recorded recent sales for three types of computer software: games, educational software, and utility programs. The following information regarding software purchases was obtained from a survey of 893 customers.

> 545 purchased games.
>
> 497 purchased educational software.
>
> 290 purchased utility programs.
>
> 297 purchased games and educational software.
>
> 196 purchased educational software and utility programs.
>
> 205 purchased games and utility programs.
>
> 157 purchased all three types of software.

Use a Venn diagram to answer the following questions. How many customers purchased

a) none of these types of software?

b) only games?

c) at least one of these types of software?

d) exactly two of these types of software?

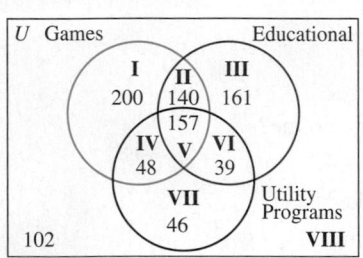

Figure 2.27

Solution   Begin by constructing a Venn diagram with three overlapping circles. One circle represents games, another educational software, and the third utilities. See Fig 2.27. Label the eight regions.

  Whenever possible, work from the center of the diagram outward. First fill in region V. Since 157 customers purchased all three types of software, we place 157 in region V. Next determine the number to be placed in region II. Regions II and V together represent the customers who purchased both games and educational software. Since 297 customers purchased both of these types of software, the sum of the numbers in these regions must be 297. Since 157 have already been placed in region V, $297 - 157 = 140$ must be placed in region II. Now we determine the number to be placed in region IV. Since 205 customers purchased both games and utility programs, the sum of the numbers in regions IV and V must be 205. Since 157 have already been placed in region V, $205 - 157 = 48$ must be placed in region IV. Now determine the number to be placed in region VI. A total of 196 customers purchased educational software and utility programs. The numbers in regions V and VI must total 196. Since 157 have already been placed in region V, the number to be placed in region VI is $196 - 157 = 39$.

  Now that we have determined the numbers for regions V, II, IV, and VI, we can determine the numbers to be placed in regions I, III, and VII. We are given that 545 customers purchased games. The sum of the numbers in regions I, II, IV, and V must be 545. To determine the number to be placed in region I, subtract the amounts in regions II, IV, and V from 545. There must be $545 - 140 - 48 - 157 = 200$ in region I. Determine the numbers to be placed in regions III and VII in a similar manner.

$$\text{Region III} = 497 - 140 - 157 - 39 = 161$$
$$\text{Region VII} = 290 - 48 - 157 - 39 = 46$$

  Now that we have determined the numbers in regions I through VII, we can determine the number to be placed in region VIII. Adding the numbers in regions I through VII yields a sum of 791. The difference between the total number of customers surveyed, 893, and the sum of the numbers in regions I through VII must be placed in region VIII.

$$\text{Region VIII} = 893 - 791 = 102$$

  Now that we have completed the Venn diagram, we can answer the questions.

a) One hundred two customers did not purchase any of these types of software. These customers are indicated in region VIII.

b) Region I represents those customers who purchased only games. Thus, 200 customers purchased only games.

c) The words *at least one* mean "one or more." All those in regions I through VII purchased at least one of the types of software. The sum of the numbers in regions I through VII is 791, so 791 customers purchased at least one of the types of software.

d) The customers in regions II, IV, and VI purchased exactly two of the types of software. Summing the numbers in these regions $140 + 48 + 39$ we find that 227 customers purchased exactly two of these types of software. Notice that we did not include the customers in region V. Those customers purchased all three types of software. ∎

The procedure to work problems like those given in Example 2 is generally the same. Start by completing region V. Next complete regions II, IV, and VI. Then complete regions I, III, and VII. Finally, complete region VIII. When you are constructing Venn diagrams, be sure to check your work carefully.

Example 3 *Travel Packages*

Liberty Travel surveyed 125 potential customers. The following information was obtained.

> 68 wished to travel to Hawaii.
>
> 53 wished to travel to Las Vegas.
>
> 47 wished to travel to Disney World.
>
> 34 wished to travel to Hawaii and Las Vegas.
>
> 26 wished to travel to Las Vegas and Disney World.
>
> 23 wished to travel to Hawaii and Disney World.
>
> 18 wished to travel to all three destinations.

Use a Venn diagram to answer the following questions. How many of those surveyed

a) did not wish to travel to any of these destinations?

b) wished to travel only to Hawaii?

c) wished to travel to Disney World *and* Las Vegas, but not to Hawaii?

d) wished to travel to Disney World *or* Las Vegas, but not to Hawaii?

e) wished to travel to exactly one of these destinations?

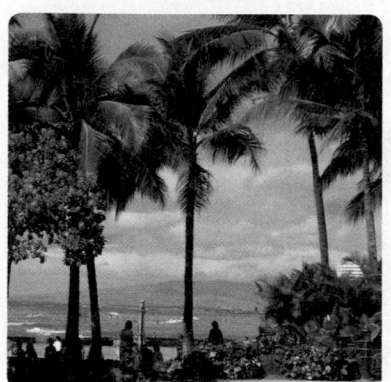

▲ *Hawaii*

Solution The Venn diagram is constructed using the procedures we outlined in Example 2. The diagram is illustrated in Fig. 2.28. We suggest you construct the diagram by yourself now and check your diagram with Fig. 2.28.

a) Twenty-two potential customers did not wish to travel to any of these destinations (see region VIII).

b) Twenty-nine potential customers wished to travel only to Hawaii (see region I).

c) Those potential customers in region VI wished to travel to Disney World *and* Las Vegas, but not to Hawaii. Therefore, eight customers satisfied the criteria.

d) The word *or* in this type of problem means one or the other or both. All the potential customers in regions II, III, IV, V, VI, and VII wished to travel to Disney World or Las Vegas. Those in regions II, IV, and V also wished to travel to Hawaii. The potential customers that wished to travel to Disney World or Las Vegas, but not to Hawaii, are found by adding the numbers in regions III, VI, and VII. There are $16 + 8 + 11 = 35$ potential customers who satisfy the criteria.

e) Those potential customers in regions I, III, and VII wished to travel to exactly one of the destinations. Therefore, $29 + 16 + 11 = 56$ customers wished to travel to exactly one of these destinations. ∎

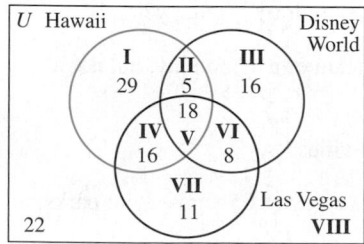

Figure 2.28

Practice The Skills/Problem Solving

In Exercises 1–15, draw a Venn diagram to obtain the answers. *

1. *Market Purchases* During the fall festival at Wambach's Farmer's market, 200 customers made the following purchases.

> 109 purchased pumpkins.
>
> 98 purchased pies.
>
> 61 purchased both pumpkins and pies.

Of those surveyed,

a) how many purchased only pumpkins? 48

b) how many purchased only pies? 37

c) how many did not purchase either of these items? 54

2. *Landscape Purchases* Agway Lawn and Garden collected the following information regarding purchases from 130 of its customers.

> 74 purchased shrubs.
>
> 70 purchased trees.
>
> 41 purchased both shrubs and trees.

Of those surveyed,

a) how many purchased only shrubs? 33

b) how many purchased only trees? 29

c) how many did not purchase either of these items? 27

3. *Real Estate* The Maiellos are moving to Wilmington, Delaware. Their real estate agent located 83 houses listed for sale, in the Wilmington area, in their price range. Of these houses listed for sale,

> 47 had a family room.
>
> 42 had a deck.
>
> 30 had a family room and a deck.

How many had

a) a family room but not a deck? 17

b) a deck but not a family room? 12

c) either a family room or a deck? 59

4. *Racing* Fleet Foot Racing interviewed 150 long-distance runners to determine the type of races in which they participated. The following information was determined.

> 102 participated in a marathon.
>
> 93 participated in a triathlon.
>
> 55 participated in both a marathon and a triathlon.

How many

a) participated in only a marathon? 47

b) participated in only a triathlon? 38

c) participated in either a marathon or a triathlon? 140

d) had not participated in either a marathon or a triathlon? 10

5. *Cultural Activities* Thirty-three U.S. cities were researched to determine whether they had a professional sports team, a symphony, or a children's museum. The following information was determined.

> 16 had a professional sports team.
>
> 17 had a symphony.
>
> 15 had a children's museum.
>
> 11 had a professional sports team and a symphony.
>
> 7 had a professional sports team and a children's museum.
>
> 9 had a symphony and children's museum.
>
> 5 had all three activities.

How many of the cities surveyed had

a) only a professional sports team? 3

b) a professional sports team and a symphony, but not a children's museum? 6

c) a professional sports team or a symphony? 22

d) a professional sports team or a symphony, but not a children's museum? 11

e) exactly two of the activities? 12

6. *Amusement Parks* In a survey of 85 amusement parks, it was found that

> 24 had a hotel on site.
>
> 55 had water slides.
>
> 38 had a wave pool.
>
> 13 had a hotel on site and water slides.
>
> 10 had a hotel on site and a wave pool.
>
> 19 had water slides and a wave pool.
>
> 7 had all three features.

How many of the amusement parks surveyed had

a) only water slides? 30

b) exactly one of these features? 54

c) at least one of these features? 82

d) exactly two of these features? 21

e) none of these features? 3

7. **Book Purchases** A survey of 85 customers was taken at Barnes & Noble regarding the types of books purchased. The survey found that

    44 purchased mysteries.

    33 purchased science fiction.

    29 purchased romance novels.

    13 purchased mysteries and science fiction.

    5 purchased science fiction and romance novels.

    11 purchased mysteries and romance novels.

    2 purchased all three types of books.

How many of the customers surveyed purchased

a) only mysteries? 22

b) mysteries and science fiction, but not romance novels? 11

c) mysteries or science fiction? 64

d) mysteries or science fiction, but not romance novels? 50

e) exactly two types? 23

8. **Movies** A survey of 350 customers was taken at Regal Cinemas in Austin, Texas, regarding the type of movies customers liked. The following information was determined.

    196 liked dramas.

    153 liked comedies.

    88 liked science fiction.

    59 liked dramas and comedies.

    37 liked dramas and science fiction.

    32 liked comedies and science fiction.

    21 liked all three types of movies.

Of the customers surveyed, how many liked

a) none of these types of movies? 20

b) only dramas? 121

c) exactly one of these types of movies? 244

d) exactly two of these types of movies? 65

e) dramas or comedies? 290

9. **Jobs at a Restaurant** Panera Bread compiled the following information regarding 30 of its employees. The following was determined.

    8 cooked food.

    9 washed dishes.

    18 operated the cash register.

    4 cooked food and washed dishes.

    5 washed dishes and operated the cash register.

    3 cooked food and operated the cash register.

    2 did all three jobs.

How many of the employees

a) only cooked food ? 3

b) only operated the cash register? 12

c) washed dishes and operated the cash register but did not cook food? 3

d) washed dishes or operated the cash register but did not cook food? 17

e) did at least two of these jobs? 8

10. **Electronic Devices** In a survey of college students, it was found that

    356 owned an iPod.

    293 owned a laptop.

    285 owned a gaming system.

    193 owned an iPod and a laptop.

    200 owned an iPod and a gaming system.

    139 owned a laptop and a gaming system.

    68 owned an iPod, a laptop, and a gaming system.

    26 owned none of these devices.

a) How many college students were surveyed? 496

Of the college students surveyed, how many owned

b) an iPod and a gaming system, but not a laptop? 132

c) a laptop, but neither an iPod nor a gaming system? 29

d) exactly two of these devices? 328

e) at least one of these devices? 470

11. **Homeowners' Insurance Policies** A committee of the Florida legislature decided to analyze 350 homeowners' insurance policies to determine if the consumers' homes

were covered for damage due to sinkholes, mold, and floods. The following results were determined.

170 homes were covered for damage due to sinkholes.

172 homes were covered for damage due to mold.

234 homes were covered for damage due to floods.

105 homes were covered for damage due to sinkholes and mold.

115 homes were covered for damage due to mold and floods.

109 homes were covered for damage due to sinkholes and floods.

78 homes were covered for damage due to all three conditions.

How many of the homes

a) were covered for damage due to mold but were not covered for damage due to sinkholes? 67

b) were covered for damage due to sinkholes or mold? 237

c) were covered for damage due to mold and floods but were not covered for damage due to sinkholes? 37

d) were not covered for damage due to any of the three conditions? 25

12. *Appetizers Survey* Da Tulio's Restaurant hired Dennis Goldstein to determine what kind of appetizers customers liked. He surveyed 100 people, with the following results: 78 liked shrimp cocktail, 56 liked mozzarella sticks, and 35 liked both shrimp cocktail and mozzarella sticks. Every person interviewed liked one or the other or both kinds of appetizers. Does this result seem correct? Explain your answer. No; only 99 of 100 interviewed are accounted for.

13. *Discovering an Error* An immigration agent sampled cars going from the United States into Canada. In his report, he indicated that of the 85 cars sampled,

35 cars were driven by women.

53 cars were driven by U.S. citizens.

43 cars had two or more passengers.

27 cars were driven by women who are U.S. citizens.

25 cars were driven by women and had two or more passengers.

20 cars were driven by U.S. citizens and had two or more passengers.

15 cars were driven by women who are U.S. citizens and had two or more passengers.

After his supervisor reads the report, she explains to the agent that he made a mistake. Explain how his supervisor knew that the agent's report contained an error. In a Venn diagram, regions II, IV, and V contain a total of 37 cars driven by women. This total is greater than the 35 cars driven by the women, as given in the exercise.

Challenge Problems/Group Activities

14. *Parks* A survey of 300 parks showed the following.

15 had only camping.

20 had only hiking trails.

35 had only picnicking.

185 had camping.

140 had camping and hiking trails.

125 had camping and picnicking.

210 had hiking trails.

Determine the number of parks that

a) had at least one of these features. 290

b) had all three features. 95

c) did not have any of these features. 10

d) had exactly two of these features. 125

15. *Surveying Farmers* A survey of 500 farmers in a midwestern state showed the following.

125 grew only wheat.

110 grew only corn.

90 grew only oats.

200 grew wheat.

60 grew wheat and corn.

50 grew wheat and oats.

180 grew corn.

Determine the number of farmers who

a) grew at least one of the three. 410

b) grew all three. 35

c) did not grow any of the three. 90

d) grew exactly two of the three. 50

16. *Family Reunion* When the Montesano family members discussed where their annual reunion should take place, they found that of all the family members,

  8 would not go to a park.

  7 would not go to a beach.

  11 would not go to the family cottage.

  3 would go to neither a park nor a beach.

  4 would go to neither a beach nor the family cottage.

  6 would go to neither a park nor the family cottage.

  2 would not go to a park or a beach or to the family cottage.

  1 would go to all three places.

What is the total number of family members? 16

Recreational Mathematics

17. *Number of Elements* A universal set U consists of 12 elements. If sets A, B, and C are proper subsets of U and $n(U) = 12$, $n(A \cap B) = n(A \cap C) = n(B \cap C) = 6$, $n(A \cap B \cap C) = 4$, and $n(A \cup B \cup C) = 10$, determine

a) $n(A \cup B)$ 10

b) $n(A' \cup C)$ 10

c) $n(A \cap B)'$ 6

Infinite Sets

▲ *Georg Cantor, founder of set theory*

Which set is larger, the set of integers or the set of even integers? One might argue that because the set of even integers is a subset of the set of integers, the set of integers must be larger than the set of even integers. Yet both sets are infinite sets, so how can we determine which set is larger? This question puzzled mathematicians for centuries until 1874, when Georg Cantor developed a method of determining the cardinal number of an infinite set. In this section, we will discuss infinite sets and how to determine the number of elements in an infinite set.

Why This is Important The concept of infinity and which sets contain more elements has led to the expansion and understanding of many mathematical and scientific concepts.

On page 45, we state that a finite set is a set in which the number of elements is zero or the number of elements can be expressed as a natural number. On page 46, we define a one-to-one correspondence. To determine the number of elements in a finite set, we can place the set in a one-to-one correspondence with a subset of the set of counting numbers. For example, the set $A = \{\#, ?, \$\}$ can be placed in one-to-one correspondence with set $B = \{1, 2, 3\}$, a subset of the set of counting numbers.

$$A = \{\#, ?, \$\}$$
$$\downarrow \ \downarrow \ \downarrow$$
$$B = \{1, 2, 3\}$$

Because the cardinal number of set B is 3, the cardinal number of set A is also 3. Any two sets, such as set A and set B, that can be placed in a one-to-one correspondence must have the same number of elements (therefore the same cardinality) and must be equivalent sets. Note that $n(A)$ and $n(B)$ both equal 3.

German mathematician Georg Cantor (1845–1918), known as the father of set theory, thought about sets that were not bounded. He called an unbounded set an *infinite set* and provided the following definition.

> **Definition: Infinite Set**
> An **infinite set** is a set that can be placed in a one-to-one correspondence with a proper subset of itself.

In Example 1, we use Cantor's definition of an infinite set to show that the set of counting numbers is infinite.

Example 1 *The Set of Natural Numbers*

Show that $N = \{1, 2, 3, 4, 5, \ldots, n, \ldots\}$ is an infinite set.

Solution To show that the set N is infinite, we establish a one-to-one correspondence between the counting numbers and a proper subset of itself. By removing the first element from the set of counting numbers, we get the set $\{2, 3, 4, 5, 6, \ldots\}$, which is a proper subset of the set of counting numbers. Now we establish the one-to-one correspondence.

$$\text{Counting numbers} = \{1, 2, 3, 4, 5, \ldots, \quad n, \ldots\}$$
$$\downarrow \downarrow \downarrow \downarrow \downarrow \qquad \downarrow$$
$$\text{Proper subset} \quad = \{2, 3, 4, 5, 6, \ldots, n + 1, \ldots\}$$

Note that for any number, n, in the set of counting numbers, its corresponding number in the proper subset is one greater, or $n + 1$. We have now shown the desired one-to-one correspondence, and thus the set of counting numbers is infinite. ∎

Note in Example 1 that we showed the pairing of the general terms $n \rightarrow (n + 1)$. Showing a one-to-one correspondence of infinite sets requires showing the pairing of the general terms in the two infinite sets.

In the set of counting numbers, n represents the general term. For any other set of numbers, the general term will be different. The general term in any set should be written in terms of n such that when 1 is substituted for n in the general term, we get the first number in the set; when 2 is substituted for n in the general term, we get the second number in the set; when 6 is substituted for n in the general term, we get the sixth number in the set; and so on.

Consider the set $\{4, 9, 14, 19, \ldots\}$. Suppose we want to write the general term for this set (or sequence) of numbers. What would the general term be? The numbers differ by 5, so the general term will be of the form $5n$ plus or minus some number. Substituting 1 for n yields $5(1)$, or 5. Because the first number in the set is 4, we need to subtract 1 from the 5. Thus, the general term is $5n - 1$. Note that when $n = 1$, the value is $5(1) - 1$ or 4; when $n = 2$, the value is $5(2) - 1$ or 9; when $n = 3$, the value is $5(3) - 1$ or 14; and so on. Therefore, we write the set of numbers with the general term as

$$\{4, 9, 14, 19, \ldots, 5n - 1, \ldots\}$$

Now that you are aware of how to determine the general term of a set of numbers, we can do some more problems involving sets.

Example 2 *The Set of Even Numbers*

Show that the set of even counting numbers $\{2, 4, 6, 8, \ldots, 2n, \ldots\}$ is an infinite set.

Solution   First create a proper subset of the set of even counting numbers by removing the first number from the set. Then establish a one-to-one correspondence.

$$\text{Even counting numbers:} \quad \{2, 4, 6, 8, \ldots, \quad 2n, \ldots\}$$
$$\downarrow \downarrow \downarrow \downarrow \qquad\qquad \downarrow$$
$$\text{Proper subset:} \qquad\qquad \{4, 6, 8, 10, \ldots, 2n + 2, \ldots\}$$

A one-to-one correspondence exists between the two sets, so the set of even counting numbers is infinite.   ■

Example 3   *The Set of Multiples of Five*

Show that the set $\{5, 10, 15, 20, \ldots, 5n, \ldots\}$ is an infinite set.

Solution

$$\text{Given set:} \qquad\quad \{5, 10, 15, 20, 25, \ldots, \quad 5n, \ldots\}$$
$$\downarrow \downarrow \downarrow \downarrow \downarrow \qquad\quad \downarrow$$
$$\text{Proper subset:} \quad \{10, 15, 20, 25, 30, \ldots, 5n + 5, \ldots\}$$

Therefore, the given set is an infinite set.   ■

Countable Sets

In his work with infinite sets, Cantor developed ideas on how to determine the cardinal number of an infinite set. He called the cardinal number of infinite sets "transfinite cardinal numbers" or "transfinite powers." He defined a set as *countable* if it is finite or if it can be placed in a one-to-one correspondence with the set of counting numbers. All infinite sets that can be placed in a one-to-one correspondence with the set of counting numbers have cardinal number *aleph-null*, symbolized $\aleph_0$ (the first Hebrew letter, aleph, with a zero subscript, read "null").

Example 4   *The Cardinal Number of the Set of Even Numbers*

Show that the set of even counting numbers has cardinal number $\aleph_0$.

Solution   In Example 2, we showed that the set of even counting numbers is infinite by setting up a one-to-one correspondence between the set and a proper subset of itself.

Now we will show that it is countable and has cardinality $\aleph_0$ by setting up a one-to-one correspondence between the set of counting numbers and the set of even counting numbers.

$$\text{Counting numbers:} \qquad N = \{1, 2, 3, 4, \ldots, n, \ldots\}$$
$$\downarrow \downarrow \downarrow \downarrow \quad\; \downarrow$$
$$\text{Even counting numbers:} \quad E = \{2, 4, 6, 8, \ldots, 2n, \ldots\}$$

For each number n in the set of counting numbers, its corresponding number is $2n$. Since we found a one-to-one correspondence between the set of counting numbers and the set of even counting numbers, the set of even counting numbers is countable. Thus, the cardinal number of the set of even counting numbers is $\aleph_0$; that is, $n(E) = \aleph_0$. As we mentioned earlier, the set of even counting numbers is an infinite set, since it can be placed in a one-to-one correspondence with a proper subset of itself. Therefore, the set of even counting numbers is both infinite and countable.   ■

Definition: Cardinal Number of Infinite Sets

Any set that can be placed in a one-to-one correspondence with the set of counting numbers has **cardinal number** (or cardinality) $\aleph_0$ and is infinite and is countable.

┌───
Example 5   *The Cardinal Number of the Set of Odd Numbers*

Show that the set of odd counting numbers has cardinality $\aleph_0$.

Solution   To show that the set of odd counting numbers has cardinality $\aleph_0$, we need to show a one-to-one correspondence between the set of counting numbers and the set of odd counting numbers.

Counting numbers: $N = \{1, 2, 3, 4, 5, \dots,\quad n\ ,\dots\}$
$$\downarrow \downarrow \downarrow \downarrow\qquad\qquad \downarrow$$
Odd counting numbers: $O = \{1, 3, 5, 7, 9, \dots, 2n - 1, \dots\}$

Since there is a one-to-one correspondence, the odd counting numbers have cardinality $\aleph_0$; that is, $n(O) = \aleph_0$.   ∎
└───

We have shown that both the odd and the even counting numbers have cardinality $\aleph_0$. Merging the odd counting numbers with the even counting numbers gives the set of counting numbers, and we may reason that

$$\aleph_0 + \aleph_0 = \aleph_0$$

This result may seem strange, but it is true. What could such a statement mean? Well, consider a hotel with infinitely many rooms. If all the rooms are occupied, the hotel is, of course, full. If more guests appear, wanting accommodations, will they be turned away? The answer is *no,* for if the room clerk were to reassign each guest to a new room with a room number twice that of the present room, all the odd-numbered rooms would become unoccupied and there would be space for infinitely many more guests!

Cantor showed that there are different orders of infinity. Sets that are countable and have cardinal number $\aleph_0$ are the lowest order of infinity. Cantor showed that the set of integers and the set of rational numbers (fractions of the form p/q, where $q \neq 0$) are infinite sets with cardinality $\aleph_0$. He also showed that the set of real numbers (discussed in Chapter 5) could not be placed in a one-to-one correspondence with the set of counting numbers and that they have a higher order of infinity.

▲ *. . . where there's always room for one more. . .*

Exercises

Warm Up Exercises

In exercises 1–2, fill in the blank with an appropriate word, phrase, or symbol(s).

1. A set that can be placed in a one-to-one correspondence with a proper subset of itself is called a(n) _____ set. Infinite

2. A set that is finite or can be placed in a one-to-one correspondence with the set of counting numbers is called a(n)_____ set. Countable

Practice the Skills

In Exercises 3–12, show that the set is infinite by placing it in a one-to-one correspondence with a proper subset of itself. Be sure to show the pairing of the general terms in the sets.

3. $\{3, 4, 5, 6, 7, \dots\}$ *

4. $\{30, 31, 32, 33, 34, \dots\}$ *

5. $\{3, 5, 7, 9, 11, \dots\}$ *

6. $\{20, 22, 24, 26, 28, \dots\}$ *

7. $\{5, 9, 13, 17, 21, \dots\}$ *

8. $\{6, 11, 16, 21, 26, \dots\}$ *

9. $\left\{\frac{1}{2}, \frac{1}{4}, \frac{1}{6}, \frac{1}{8}, \frac{1}{10}, \dots\right\}$ *

10. $\left\{1, \frac{1}{2}, \frac{1}{3}, \frac{1}{4}, \frac{1}{5}, \dots\right\}$ *

11. $\left\{\frac{4}{11}, \frac{5}{11}, \frac{6}{11}, \frac{7}{11}, \frac{8}{11}, \dots\right\}$ *

12. $\left\{\frac{6}{13}, \frac{7}{13}, \frac{8}{13}, \frac{9}{13}, \frac{10}{13}, \dots\right\}$ *

*See Instructor Answer Appendix

In Exercises 13–22, show that the set has cardinal number $\aleph_0$ by establishing a one-to-one correspondence between the set of counting numbers and the given set. Be sure to show the pairing of the general terms in the sets.

13. $\{3, 6, 9, 12, 15, \ldots\}$ *   **14.** $\{40, 41, 42, 43, 44, \ldots\}$ *

15. $\{4, 6, 8, 10, 12, \ldots\}$ *   **16.** $\{0, 2, 4, 6, 8, \ldots\}$ *

17. $\{2, 5, 8, 11, 14, \ldots\}$ *   **18.** $\{7, 11, 15, 19, 23, \ldots\}$ *

19. $\{\frac{1}{3}, \frac{1}{6}, \frac{1}{9}, \frac{1}{12}, \frac{1}{15}, \ldots\}$ *   **20.** $\{\frac{1}{2}, \frac{1}{4}, \frac{1}{6}, \frac{1}{8}, \ldots\}$ *

21. $\{\frac{1}{3}, \frac{1}{4}, \frac{1}{5}, \frac{1}{6}, \frac{1}{7}, \ldots\}$ *   **22.** $\{\frac{1}{2}, \frac{2}{3}, \frac{3}{4}, \frac{4}{5}, \frac{5}{6}, \ldots\}$ *

Challenge Problems/Group Activities

In Exercises 23–26, show that the set has cardinality $\aleph_0$ by establishing a one-to-one correspondence between the set of counting numbers and the given set.

23. $\{1, 4, 9, 16, 25, \ldots\}$ *   **24.** $\{2, 4, 8, 16, 32, \ldots\}$ *

25. $\{3, 9, 27, 81, 243, \ldots\}$ *   **26.** $\{\frac{1}{3}, \frac{1}{6}, \frac{1}{12}, \frac{1}{24}, \frac{1}{48}, \ldots\}$ *

Recreational Mathematics

In Exercises 27–31, insert the symbol $<$, $>$, or $=$ in the shaded area to make a true statement.

27. $\aleph_0$ ___ $\aleph_0 + \aleph_0 =$ **28.** $2\aleph_0$ ___ $\aleph_0 + \aleph_0 =$

29. $2\aleph_0$ ___ $\aleph_0 =$ **30.** $\aleph_0 + 5$ ___ $\aleph_0 + 3 =$

31. $n(N)$ ___ $\aleph_0 =$

32. There are a number of paradoxes (a statement that appears to be true and false at the same time) associated with infinite sets and the concept of infinity. One of these, called *Zeno's Paradox,* is named after the mathematician Zeno, born about 496 B.C. in Italy. According to Zeno's paradox, suppose Achelles starts out 1 meter behind a tortoise. Also, suppose Achelles walks 10 times as fast as the tortoise crawls. When Achelles reaches the point where the tortoise started, the tortoise is 1/10 of a meter ahead of Achelles; when Achelles reaches the point where the tortoise was 1/10 of a meter ahead, the tortoise is now 1/100 of a meter ahead; and so on. According to Zeno's Paradox, Achelles gets closer and closer to the tortoise but never catches up to the tortoise.

a) Do you believe the reasoning process is sound? If not, explain why not. Answers will vary.

b) In actuality, if this situation were real, would Achelles ever pass the tortoise? No

Internet/Research Activities

33. Do research to explain how Cantor proved that the set of rational numbers has cardinal number $\aleph_0$.

34. Do research to explain how it can be shown that the real numbers do not have cardinal number $\aleph_0$.

*See Instructor Answer Appendix

CHAPTER 2 *Summary*

Important Facts and Concepts	Examples and Discussion
Section 2.1	
Methods Used to Indicate a Set	
Description	Example 1, page 43
Roster Form	Examples 2–3, 5–7 pages 44, 45
Set-Builder Notation	Examples 4–6, pages 44–45

Symbol	Meaning	
$\in$	is an element of	Examples 4–6, pages 44–45
$\notin$	is not an element of	
$n(A)$	number of elements in set A	
$\varnothing$ or $\{\ \}$	the empty set	
U	the universal set	

Section 2.2

Symbol	Meaning	
$\subseteq$	is a subset of	Examples 1 and 3, pages 52–53
$\nsubseteq$	is not a subset of	
$\subset$	is a proper subset of	
$\not\subset$	is not a proper subset of	

Number of distinct subsets of a finite set with n elements is 2^n.   Examples 4 and 5, pages 54

Section 2.3

Symbol	Meaning	
′	complement	Examples 1, 3–6, pages 57, 58–61
$\cap$	intersection	Examples 2, 3, 6, pages 58–61
$\cup$	union	Examples 4–6, pages 57–61
−	difference of two sets	Example 9, page 62
$\times$	cartesian product	Example 10, page 63

And is generally interpreted to mean *intersection*.   Examples 7 and 8, pages 61–62

Or is generally interpreted to mean *union*.   Examples 7 and 8, pages 61–62

For any sets A and B,   Examples 7 and 8, pages 61–62
$n(A \cup B) = n(A) + n(B) - n(A \cap B)$

Section 2.4

De Morgan's Laws

$$(A \cap B)' = A' \cup B'$$ Example 3, page 71
$$(A \cup B)' = A' \cap B'$$

Section 2.6

An **infinite set** is a set that can be placed in a one-to-one   Examples 1–5, pages 84–86, Discussion
correspondence with a proper subset of itself.   pages 83–84

$\aleph_0$ aleph-null   Examples 4–5, pages 85–86

Countable sets   Examples 4–5, pages 85–86

CHAPTER 2   *Review Exercises*

2.1, 2.2, 2.3, 2.4, 2.6

In Exercises 1–14, state whether each statement is true or false. If false, give a reason.

1. The set of cities located in the state of Indiana is a well-defined set. True

2. The set of the three best movies is a well-defined set.
   False; the word *best* makes the statement not well defined.
3. maple $\in$ { oak, elm, maple, sycamore } True

4. $\{\ \} \subset \varnothing$ False; no set is a proper subset of itself.

5. $\{3, 6, 9, 12, \dots\}$ and $\{2, 4, 6, 8, \dots\}$ are disjoint sets. False; the elements 6, 12, 18, 24, ... are members of both sets.

6. $\{a, b, c, 1, 2\}$ is an example of a set in roster form. True

7. { purple, green, yellow } = { green, pink, yellow }
   False; both sets do not contain exactly the same elements.
8. { apple, orange, banana, pear } is equivalent to { tomato, corn, spinach, radish }. True

9. If $A = \{a, e, i, o, u\}$, then $n(A) = 5$. True

10. $A = \{1, 3, 5, 7, \dots\}$ is a countable set. True

11. $A = \{1, 4, 7, 10, \dots, 31\}$ is a finite set. True

12. $\{2, 5, 7\} \subseteq \{2, 5, 7, 10\}$. True

13. $\{x \mid x \in N \text{ and } 3 < x \leq 9\}$ is a set in set-builder notation. True

14. $\{x \mid x \in N \text{ and } 2 < x \leq 12\} \subseteq \{1, 2, 3, 4, 5, \dots, 20\}$
    True

In Exercises 15–18, express each set in roster form.

15. Set *A* is the set of odd natural numbers between
5 and 16. $A = \{7, 9, 11, 13, 15\}$

16. Set *B* is the set of states that border Kansas.
{Colorado, Nebraska, Missouri, Oklahoma}

17. $C = \{x \mid x \in N \text{ and } x < 162\}$ $C = \{1, 2, 3, 4, \dots, 161\}$

18. $D = \{x \mid x \in N \text{ and } 8 < x \leq 80\}$ $D = \{9, 10, 11, 12, \dots, 80\}$

In Exercises 19–22, express each set in set-builder notation.

19. Set *A* is the set of natural numbers between 50 and 150.
$A = \{x \mid x \in N \text{ and } 50 < x < 150\}$
20. Set *B* is the set of natural numbers greater than 42.
$B = \{x \mid x \in N \text{ and } x > 42\}$
21. Set *C* is the set of natural numbers less than 7.
$C = \{x \mid x \in N \text{ and } x < 7\}$
22. Set *D* is the set of natural numbers between 27 and 51,
inclusive. $D = \{x \mid x \in N \text{ and } 27 \leq x \leq 51\}$

In Exercises 23–26, express each set with a written description.

23. $A = \{x \mid x$ is a capital letter of the English alphabet from
E through M inclusive $\}$ *A is the set of capital letters in
the English alphabet from E through M, inclusive.*
24. $B = \{$ penny, nickel, dime, quarter, half-dollar $\}$
B is the set of U.S. coins with a value of less than a dollar.
25. $C = \{a, b, c\}$ *C is the set of the first three lowercase letters in the
English alphabet.*
26. $D = \{x \mid 3 \leq x < 9\}$
D is the set of numbers greater than or equal to 3 and less than 9

In Exercises 27–36, let

$$U = \{1, 2, 3, 4, \dots, 10\}$$
$$A = \{1, 3, 5, 7\}$$
$$B = \{3, 7, 9, 10\}$$
$$C = \{1, 7, 10\}$$

Determine the following.

27. $A \cap B$ $\{3, 7\}$

28. $A \cup B'$ $\{1, 2, 3, 4, 5, 6, 7, 8\}$

29. $A' \cap B$ $\{9, 10\}$

30. $(A \cup B)' \cup C$ $\{1, 2, 4, 6, 7, 8, 10\}$

31. $A - B$ $\{1, 5\}$

32. $A - C'$ $\{1, 7\}$

33. $A \times C$ $\{(1, 1), (1, 7), (1, 10), (3, 1), (3, 7), (3, 10), (5, 1), (5, 7),$
$(5, 10), (7, 1), (7, 7), (7, 10)\}$
34. $B \times A$ $\{(3, 1), (3, 3), (3, 5), (3, 7), (7, 1), (7, 3), (7, 5), (7, 7), (9, 1),$
$(9, 3), (9, 5), (9, 7), (10, 1), (10, 3), (10, 5), (10, 7)\}$
35. The number of subsets of set *B* 16

36. The number of proper subsets of set *A* 15

37. For the following sets, construct a Venn diagram and place
the elements in the proper region. *

$U = \{$ lion, tiger, leopard, cheetah, puma, lynx, panther,
jaguar $\}$

$A = \{$ tiger, puma, lynx $\}$

$B = \{$ lion, tiger, jaguar, panther $\}$

$C = \{$ tiger, lynx, cheetah, panther $\}$

In Exercises 38–43, use Fig. 2.29 to determine the sets.

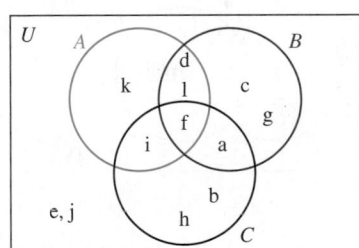

Figure 2.29

38. $A \cup B$ $\{a, c, d, f, g, i, k, l\}$ **39.** $A \cap B'$ $\{i, k\}$

40. $A \cup B \cup C$ $\{a, b, c, d, f, g, h, i, k, l\}$

41. $A \cap B \cap C$ $\{f\}$ **42.** $(A \cup B) \cap C$ $\{a, f, i\}$

43. $(A \cap B) \cup C$ $\{a, b, d, f, h, i, l\}$

*Construct a Venn diagram to determine whether the
following statements are true for all sets A, B, and C.*

44. $(A' \cup B')' = A \cap B$ True

45. $(A \cup B') \cup (A \cup C') = A \cup (B \cap C)'$ True

In Exercises 46–51, use the following table, which shows the amount of sugar, in grams (g) and caffeine, in milligrams (mg), in an 8-oz serving of selected beverages. Let the beverages listed represent the universal set.

Beverage	Sugar (grams, g)	Caffeine (milligrams, mg)
Mountain Dew	31	37
Coca-Cola	27	23
Pepsi	27	25
Sprite	26	0
Brewed coffee	0	108
Brewed tea	0	47
Orange juice	24	0
Grape juice	40	0
Gatorade	14	0
Red Bull	26	76
Vitamin Water	13	17
Water	0	0

Source: International Food Information Council

Let A be the set of beverages that contain at least 20 g of sugar.

Let B be the set of beverages that contain at least 20 mg of caffeine.

Indicate in Fig 2.30 in which region, I–IV, each of the following beverages belongs.

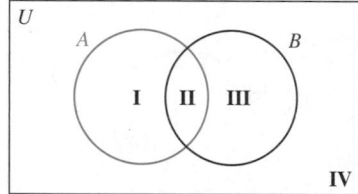

Figure 2.30

46. Pepsi II   **47.** Brewed coffee III

48. Orange juice I   **49.** Vitamin Water IV

50. Gatorade IV   **51.** Mountain Dew II

52. Red Bull II

2.5

53. *Pizza Survey* A pizza chain was willing to pay $1 to each person interviewed about his or her likes and dislikes of types of pizza crust. Of the people interviewed, 200 liked thin crust, 270 liked thick crust, 70 liked both, and 50 did not like pizza at all. What was the total cost of the survey? $450

54. *Shopping Preferences* Visitors to a shopping mall in Atlanta, Georgia, were surveyed to determine their preference for shopping in wholesale warehouse stores. The following information was determined.

58 shopped in BJ's Wholesale Club.

49 shopped in Sam's Club.

45 shopped in Costco.

15 shopped in BJ's Wholesale Club and Sam's Club.

16 shopped in BJ's Wholesale Club and Costco.

12 shopped in Sam's Club and Costco.

5 shopped in all three stores.

17 did not shop in any of the three stores.

Construct a Venn diagram and then determine how many people*

a) completed the survey. 131

b) shopped only in BJ's Wholesale Club. 32

c) shopped in BJ's Wholesale Club and Sam's Club, but not Costco. 10

d) shopped in BJ's Wholesale Club or Costco, but not Sam's Club. 65

55. *TV Choices TV Guide* surveyed 510 subscribers asking which of the following three crime investigation shows they watched on a regular basis: *CSI:Crime Scene Investigation, CSI:Miami,* and *CSI:NY.* The results of the 510 questionnaires that were returned showed that

175 watched *CSI:NY.*

227 watched *CSI:Miami.*

285 watched *CSI:Crime Scene Investigation.*

100 watched *CSI:NY* and *CSI:Miami.*

96 watched *CSI:NY* and *CSI:Crime Scene Investigation.*

87 watched *CSI:Miami* and *CSI:Crime Scene Investigation.*

59 watched all three shows.

Construct a Venn diagram and determine how many people

a) watched only *CSI:NY.* 38

b) watched exactly one of these shows. 298

c) watched *CSI:Miami* and *CSI:Crime Scene Investigation,* but not *CSI:NY.* 28

d) watched *CSI:NY* or *CSI:Crime Scene Investigation,* but not *CSI:Miami.* 236

e) watched exactly two of these shows. 106

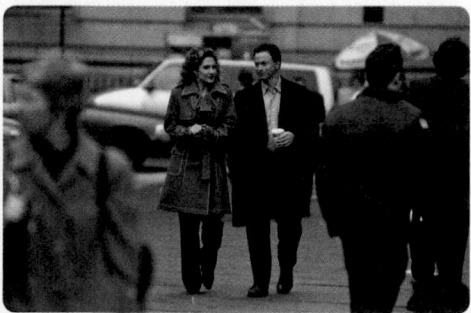

▲ *Actors from CSI:NY*

2.6

In Exercises 56 and 57, show that the sets are infinite by placing each set in a one-to-one correspondence with a proper subset of itself.

56. $\{2, 4, 6, 8, 10, \dots\}$ *

57. $\{3, 5, 7, 9, 11, \dots\}$ *

In Exercises 58 and 59, show that each set has cardinal number $\aleph_0$ by setting up a one-to-one correspondence between the set of counting numbers and the given set.

58. $\{5, 8, 11, 14, 17, \dots\}$ *

59. $\{4, 9, 14, 19, 24, \dots\}$ *

*See Instructor Answer Appendix

CHAPTER 2) *Test*

In Exercises 1–8, state whether each is true or false. If the statement is false, explain why.

1. $\{2, y, \triangle, \$\}$ is equivalent to $\{p, \#, 4, \square\}$. True

2. $\{3, 5, 9, h\} = \{9, 5, 3, j\}$
False; the sets do not contain exactly the same elements.

3. $\{\text{star, moon, sun}\} \subset \{\text{star, moon, sun, planet}\}$ True

4. $\{7\} \subseteq \{x \mid x \in N \text{ and } x < 7\}$
False; the second set has no subset that contains the element 7.

5. $\{p, q, r, s\}$ has 15 subsets.
False; the set has 2^4, or 16 subsets.

6. If $A \cap B = \{\ \}$, then A and B are disjoint sets. True

7. For any set A, $A \cup A' = \{\ \}$.
False; for any set A, $A \cup A' = U$, not $\{\ \}$.

8. For any set A, $A \cap U = A$. True

In Exercises 9 and 10, use set

$$A = \{x \mid x \in N \text{ and } x < 10\}$$

9. Write set A in roster form. $A = \{1, 2, 3, 4, 5, 6, 7, 8, 9\}$

10. Write a description of set A.
Set A is the set of natural numbers less than 10.

In Exercises 11–16, use the following information.

$$U = \{3, 5, 7, 9, 11, 13, 15\}$$
$$A = \{3, 5, 7, 9\}$$
$$B = \{7, 9, 11, 13\}$$
$$C = \{3, 11, 15\}$$

Determine the following.

11. $A \cap B$ $\{7, 9\}$

12. $A \cup C'$ $\{3, 5, 7, 9, 13\}$

13. $A \cap (B \cap C')$ $\{7, 9\}$

14. $n(A \cap B')$ 2

15. $A - B$ $\{3, 5\}$

16. $A \times C$ *

17. Using the sets provided for Exercises 11–16, draw a Venn diagram illustrating the relationship among the sets. *

18. Use a Venn diagram to determine whether

$$A \cap (B \cup C') = (A \cap B) \cup (A \cap C')$$

for all sets A, B, and C. Show your work. Equal

19. *Water Activities* A survey of 155 residents of Lake Placid were asked what kind of water activities they participated in on a daily basis during the summer months. The following information was determined.

107 swam.

90 sailed.

76 water skied.

57 swam and sailed.

54 swam and water skied.

52 sailed and water skied.

35 swam, sailed, and water skied.

Construct a Venn diagram and then determine the number of residents who participated in

a) exactly one of these activities. 52

b) none of these activities. 10

c) at least two of these activities. 93

d) swimming and sailing, but not water skiing. 22

e) swimming or sailing, but not water skiing. 69

f) only water skiing. 5

20. Show that the following set is infinite by setting up a one-to-one correspondence between the set and a proper subset of itself. *

$$\{7, 8, 9, 10, \dots\}$$

*See Instructor Answer Appendix

GROUP PROJECTS

Selecting a Family Pet

1. The Wilcox family is considering buying a dog. They have established several criteria for the family dog: It must be one of the breeds listed in the table, must not shed, must be less than 16 in. tall, and must be good with children.

   a) Using the information in the table,* construct a Venn diagram in which the universal set is the dogs listed. Indicate the set of dogs to be placed in each region of the Venn diagram.

   b) From the Venn diagram constructed in part (a), determine which dogs will meet the criteria set by the Wilcox family. Explain.

Breed	Sheds	Less than 16 in.	Good with children
Airedale	no	no	no
Basset hound	yes	yes	yes
Beagle	yes	yes	yes
Border terrier	no	yes	yes
Cairn terrier	no	yes	no
Cocker spaniel	yes	yes	yes
Collie	yes	no	yes
Dachshund	yes	yes	no
Poodle, miniature	no	yes	no
Schnauzer, miniature	no	yes	no
Scottish terrier	no	yes	no
Wirehaired fox terrier	no	yes	no

Classification of the Domestic Cat

2. Read the Mathematics Today feature on page 53. Do research and indicate the name of the following groupings to which the domestic cat belongs.

   a) Kingdom

   b) Phylum

   c) Class

   d) Order

   e) Family

   f) Genus

   g) Species

Who Lives Where

3. On Diplomat Row, an area of Washington, DC, there are five houses. Each owner is a different nationality, each has a different pct, each has a different favorite food, each has a different favorite drink, and each house is painted a different color.

   > The green house is directly to the right of the ivory house.
   > The Senegalese has the red house.
   > The dog belongs to the Spaniard.
   > The Afghanistani drinks tea.
   > The person who eats cheese lives next door to the fox.
   > The Japanese eats fish.
   > Milk is drunk in the middle house.
   > Apples are eaten in the house next to the horse.
   > Ale is drunk in the green house.
   > The Norwegian lives in the first house.
   > The peach eater drinks whiskey.
   > Apples are eaten in the yellow house.
   > The banana eater owns a snail.
   > The Norwegian lives next door to the blue house.

   For each house find

   a) the color.

   b) the nationality of the occupant.

   c) the owner's favorite food.

   d) the owner's favorite drink.

   e) the owner's pet.

   f) Finally, the crucial question is: Does the zebra's owner drink vodka or ale?

---

*The information is a collection of the opinions of an animal psychologist, Dr. Daniel Tortora, and a group of veterinarians.

3

Logic

What You Will Learn

- Statements, quantifiers, and compound statements
- Statements involving the words *not, and, or, if . . . then . . .,* and *if and only if*
- Truth tables for negations, conjunctions, disjunctions, conditional statements, and biconditional statements
- Self-contradictions, tautologies, and implications
- Equivalent statements, De Morgan's laws, and variations of conditional statements
- Symbolic arguments and standard forms of arguments
- Euler diagrams and syllogistic arguments
- Using logic to analyze switching circuits

Why This is Important

The study of logic enables us to communicate effectively, make more convincing arguments, and develop patterns of reasoning for decision making. Logic is also used in the programming of modern electronic devices such as cell phones and digital cameras.

◀ *Logic is used in the programming of cell phones and digital cameras.*

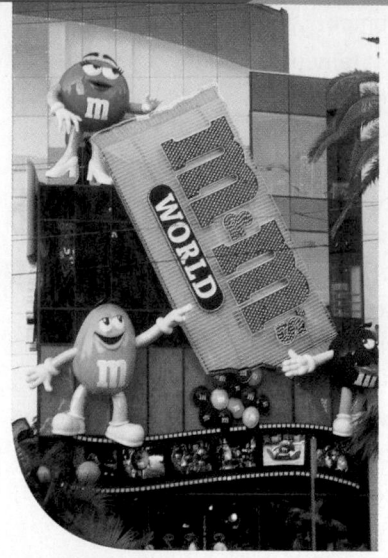

▲ *"Melts in your mouth, not in your hands." Logic symbols can be used to help us analyze statements made by advertisers.*

Advertisements often rely on spoken or written statements that are used to favorably portray the advertised product and form a convincing argument that will persuade us to purchase the product. Some familiar advertising statements are: *Don't leave home without it; It takes a licking and keeps on ticking; Sometimes you feel like a nut, sometimes you don't; When it rains it pours*; and *Melts in your mouth, not in your hands*. In this section, we will learn how to represent statements using logic symbols that may help us better understand the nature of the statement. We will use these symbols throughout the chapter to analyze more complicated statements.

Why *This is Important* Statements appear in everyday life—for example, in legal documents, product instructions, and game rules in addition to advertising.

History

The ancient Greeks were the first people to systematically analyze the way humans think and arrive at conclusions. Aristotle (384–322 B.C.) organized the study of logic for the first time in a work called *Organon*. As a result of his work, Aristotle is called the father of logic. The logic from this period, called *Aristotelian logic*, has been taught and studied for more than 2000 years.

Since Aristotle's time, the study of logic has been continued by other great philosophers and mathematicians. Gottfried Wilhelm Leibniz (1646–1716) had a deep conviction that all mathematical and scientific concepts could be derived from logic. As a result, he became the first serious student of *symbolic logic*. One difference between symbolic logic and Aristotelian logic is that in symbolic logic, as its name implies, symbols (usually letters) represent written statements. A self-educated English mathematician, George Boole (1815–1864), is considered to be the founder of symbolic logic because of his impressive work in this area. Among Boole's publications are *The Mathematical Analysis of Logic* (1847) and *An Investigation of the Law of Thought* (1854). Mathematician Charles Dodgson, better known as Lewis Carroll, incorporated many interesting ideas from logic into his books *Alice's Adventures in Wonderland* and *Through the Looking Glass* and his other children's stories.

Logic has been studied through the ages to exercise the mind's ability to reason. Understanding logic will enable you to think clearly, communicate effectively, make more convincing arguments, and develop patterns of reasoning that will help you in making decisions. It will also help you to detect the fallacies in the reasoning or arguments of others such as advertisers and politicians. Studying logic has other practical applications, such as helping you to understand wills, contracts, and other legal documents.

The study of logic is also good preparation for other areas of mathematics. If you preview Chapter 12, on probability, you will see formulas for the probability of *A* or *B* and the probability of *A* and *B*, symbolized as *P(A or B)* and *P(A and B)*, respectively. Special meanings of common words such as *or* and *and* apply to all areas of mathematics. The meaning of these and other special words is discussed in this chapter.

Logic and the English Language

In reading, writing, and speaking, we use many words such as *and, or,* and *if . . . then . . .* to connect thoughts. In logic we call these words *connectives*. How are these words interpreted in daily communication? A judge announces to a convicted offender, "I hereby sentence you to five months of community service *and* a fine of $100." In this case, we normally interpret the word *and* to indicate that *both* events will take place. That is, the person must perform community service and must also pay a fine.

Now suppose a judge states, "I sentence you to six months in prison *or* 10 months of community service." In this case, we interpret the connective *or* as meaning the convicted person must either spend the time in jail or perform community service, but not both. The word *or* in this case is the *exclusive or*. When the exclusive *or* is used, one or the other of the events can take place, but *not both*.

In a restaurant, a waiter asks, "May I interest you in a cup of soup or a sandwich?" This question offers three possibilities: You may order soup, you may order a sandwich, or you may order both soup and a sandwich. The *or* in this case is the *inclusive or*. When the inclusive *or* is used, one or the other, *or both* events can take place. *In this chapter, when we use the word* or *in a logic statement, it will mean the inclusive* or *unless stated otherwise.*

If–then statements are often used to relate two ideas, as in the bank policy statement "If the average daily balance is greater than $500, then there will be no service charge." If–then statements are also used to emphasize a point or add humor, as in the statement "If the Cubs win, then I will be a monkey's uncle."

Now let's look at logic from a mathematical point of view.

Statements and Logical Connectives

A sentence that can be judged either true or false is called a *statement*. Labeling a statement true or false is called *assigning a truth value* to the statement. Here are some examples of statements.

1. The Brooklyn Bridge goes over San Francisco Bay.
2. Disney World is in Idaho.
3. The Mississippi River is the longest river in the United States.

In each case, we can say that the sentence is either true or false. Statement 1 is false because the Brooklyn Bridge does not go over San Francisco Bay. Statement 2 is false because Disney World is in Florida. By looking at a map or reading an almanac, we can determine that the Mississippi River is the longest river in the United States; therefore, statement 3 is true.

The three sentences discussed above are examples of *simple statements* because they convey one idea. Sentences combining two or more ideas that can be assigned a truth value are called *compound statements*. Compound statements are discussed shortly.

Quantifiers

Sometimes it is necessary to change a statement to its opposite meaning. To do so, we use the *negation* of a statement. For example, the negation of the statement "Emily is at home" is "Emily is not at home." The negation of a true statement is always a false statement, and the negation of a false statement is always a true statement. We must use special caution when negating statements containing the words *all*, *none* (or *no*), and *some*. These words are referred to as *quantifiers*.

Consider the statement "All lakes contain fresh water." We know this statement is false because the Great Salt Lake in Utah contains salt water. Its negation must therefore be true. We may be tempted to write its negation as "No lake contains fresh water," but this statement is also false because Lake Superior contains fresh water. Therefore, "No lakes contain fresh water" is not the negation of "All lakes contain fresh water." The correct negation of "All lakes contain fresh water" is "Not all lakes contain fresh water" or "At least one lake does not contain fresh water" or "Some lakes do not contain fresh water." These statements all imply that at least one lake does not contain fresh water, which is a true statement.

▲ *The Brooklyn Bridge in New York City*

George Boole, Augustus De Morgan, and other mathematicians of the nineteenth century were anxious to make logic an abstract science that would operate like algebra but be applicable to all fields. One of the problems logicians faced was that verbal language could be ambiguous and could easily lead to confusion and contradiction. Comedians Bud Abbott and Lou Costello had fun with the ambiguity of language in their skit about the baseball players: "Who's on first, What's on second, I Don't Know is on third—Yeah, but who's on first?"

Now consider the statement "No birds can swim." This statement is false because at least one bird, the penguin, can swim. Therefore, the negation of this statement must be true. We may be tempted to write the negation as "All birds can swim," but because this statement is also false it cannot be the negation. The correct negation of the statement is "Some birds can swim" or "At least one bird can swim," each of which is a true statement.

Now let's consider statements involving the quantifier *some,* as in "Some students have a driver's license." This statement is true, meaning that at least one student has a driver's license. The negation of this statement must therefore be false. The negation is "No student has a driver's license," which is a false statement.

Consider the statement "Some students do not ride motorcycles." This statement is true because it means "At least one student does not ride a motorcycle." The negation of this statement must therefore be false. The negation is "All students ride motorcycles," which is a false statement.

The negation of quantified statements is summarized as follows:

Form of statement	Form of negation
All are.	Some are not.
None are.	Some are.
Some are.	None are.
Some are not.	All are.

The following diagram might help you to remember the statements and their negations:

All are.   None are.
Some are.   Some are not.

The quantifiers diagonally opposite each other are the negations of each other.

Example 1 *Write Negations*

Write the negation of each statement.

a) Some telephones can take photographs.

b) All houses have two stories.

Solution

a) Since *some* means "at least one," the statement "Some telephones can take photographs" is the same as "At least one telephone can take photographs." Because it is a true statement, its negation must be false. The negation is "No telephones can take photographs," which is a false statement.

b) The statement "All houses have two stories" is a false statement, since some houses have one story, some have three stories, and some may have more than three stories. Its negation must therefore be true. The negation may be written as "Some houses do not have two stories" or "Not all houses have two stories" or "At least one house does not have two stories." Each of these statements is true. ■

Compound Statements

Statements consisting of two or more simple statements are called **compound statements**. The connectives often used to join two simple statements are

and,   or,   if, … then …,   if and only if

In addition, we consider a simple statement that has been negated to be a compound statement. The word *not* is generally used to negate a statement.

To reduce the amount of writing in logic, it is common to represent each simple statement with a lowercase letter. For example, suppose we are discussing the simple statement "Leland is a farmer." Instead of writing "Leland is a farmer" over and over again, we can let p represent the statement "Leland is a farmer." Thereafter we can simply refer to the statement with the letter p. It is customary to use the letters p, q, r, and s to represent simple statements, but other letters may be used instead. Let's now look at the connectives used to make compound statements.

Not Statements

The negation is symbolized by $\sim$ and read "not." For example, the negation of the statement "Steve is a college student" is "Steve is not a college student." If p represents the simple statement "Steve is a college student," then $\sim p$ represents the compound statement "Steve is not a college student." For any statement p, $\sim(\sim p) = p$. For example, the negation of the statement "Steve is not a college student" is "Steve is a college student."

Consider the statement "Inga is not at home." This statement contains the word *not*, which indicates that it is a negation. To write this statement symbolically, we let p represent "Inga *is* at home." Then $\sim p$ would be "Inga is not at home." *We will use this convention of letting letters such as p, q, or r represent statements that are not negated. We will represent negated statements with the negation symbol,$\sim$.*

And Statements

The *conjunction* is symbolized by $\wedge$ and read "and." The $\wedge$ looks like an A (for And) with the bar missing. Let p and q represent the simple statements.

p: You will perform 5 months of community service.

q: You will pay a \$100 fine.

Then the following is the conjunction written in symbolic form.

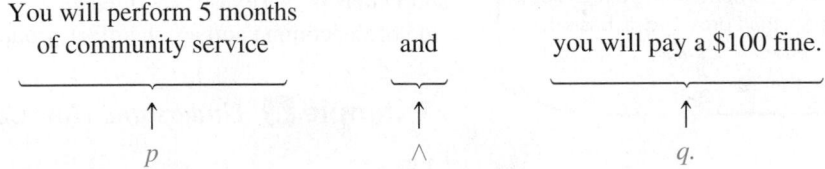

The conjunction is generally expressed as *and*. Other words sometimes used to express a conjunction are *but, however,* and *nevertheless.*

Example 2 *Write a Conjunction*

Write the following conjunction in symbolic form.

Green Day is not on tour, but Green Day is recording a new CD.

Solution Let t and r represent the simple statements.

t: Green Day is on tour.

r: Green Day is recording a new CD.

In symbolic form, the compound statement is $\sim t \wedge r$. ∎

In Example 2, the compound statement is "Green Day is not on tour, but Green Day is recording a new CD." This statement could also be represented as "Green Day is not on tour, but *they* are recording a new CD." In this problem, it should be clear the word *they* means *Green Day*. Therefore, the statement "Green Day is not on tour, but they are recording a new CD" would also be symbolized as $\sim t \wedge r$.

Or Statements

The *disjunction* is symbolized by ∨ and read "or." The *or* we use in this book (except where indicated in the exercise sets) is the *inclusive or* described on page 95.

Example 3 *Write a Disjunction*

Let

  p: Maria will go to the circus.
  q: Maria will go to the zoo.

Write the following statements in symbolic form.

a) Maria will go to the circus or Maria will go to the zoo.

b) Maria will go to the zoo or Maria will not go to the circus.

c) Maria will not go to the circus or Maria will not go to the zoo.

Solution

a) $p \lor q$ b) $q \lor \sim p$ c) $\sim p \lor \sim q$ ∎

Because *or* represents the *inclusive or,* the statement "Maria will go to the circus or Maria will go to the zoo" in Example 3(a) may mean that Maria will go to the circus, or that Maria will go to the zoo, or that Maria will go to both the circus *and* the zoo. The statement in Example 3(a) could also be written as "Maria will go to the circus or the zoo."

When a compound statement contains more than one connective, a comma can be used to indicate which simple statements are to be grouped together. When we write the compound statement symbolically, *the simple statements on the same side of the comma are to be grouped together within parentheses.*

For example, "Pink is a singer (*p*) or Jennifer Aniston is an actress (*j*), and Dallas is in Texas (*d*)" is written $(p \lor j) \land d$. Note that the *p* and *j* are both on the same side of the comma in the written statement. They are therefore grouped together within parentheses. The statement "Pink is a singer, or Jennifer Aniston is an actress and Dallas is in Texas" is written $p \lor (j \land d)$. In this case, *j* and *d* are on the same side of the comma and are therefore grouped together within parentheses.

Example 4 *Understand How Commas Are Used to Group Statements*

Let

  p: Dinner includes soup.
  q: Dinner includes salad.
  r: Dinner includes the vegetable of the day.

Write the following statements in symbolic form.

a) Dinner includes soup, and salad or the vegetable of the day.

b) Dinner includes soup and salad, or the vegetable of the day.

Solution

a) The comma tells us to group the statement "Dinner includes salad" with the statement "Dinner includes the vegetable of the day." Note that both statements are on the same side of the comma. The statement in symbolic form is $p \land (q \lor r)$.

   In mathematics, we always evaluate the information within the parentheses first. Since the conjunction, ∧, is outside the parentheses and is evaluated *last,* this statement is considered a *conjunction.*

b) The comma tells us to group the statement "Dinner includes soup" with the statement "Dinner includes salad." Note that both statements are on the same side of the comma. The statement in symbolic form is $(p \wedge q) \vee r$. Since the disjunction, $\vee$, is outside the parentheses and is evaluated *last,* this statement is considered a *disjunction.* ∎

The information provided in Example 4 is summarized below.

Statement	Symbolic representation	Type of statement
Dinner includes soup, and salad or the vegetable of the day.	$p \wedge (q \vee r)$	conjunction
Dinner includes soup and salad, or the vegetable of the day.	$(p \wedge q) \vee r$	disjunction

A negation symbol has the effect of negating only the statement that directly follows it. To negate a compound statement, we must use parentheses. When a negation symbol is placed in front of a statement in parentheses, it negates the entire statement in parentheses. The negation symbol in this case is read, "It is not true that … " or "It is false that … "

Example 5   *Change Symbolic Statements into Words*

Let

    p: The house is for sale.

    q: We can afford to buy the house.

Write the following symbolic statements in words.

a) $p \wedge \sim q$ b) $\sim p \vee \sim q$ c) $\sim (p \wedge q)$

Solution

a) The house is for sale and we cannot afford to buy the house.

b) The house is not for sale or we cannot afford to buy the house.

c) It is false that the house is for sale and we can afford to buy the house. ∎

Recall that the word *but* may also be used in a conjunction. Therefore, Example 5(a) could also be written "The house is for sale, *but* we cannot afford to buy the house." Part (b) of Example 5 is a disjunction, since it can be written $(\sim p) \vee (\sim q)$. Part (c), which is $\sim (p \wedge q)$, is a negation since the negation symbol negates the entire statement within parentheses. The similarity of these two statements is discussed in Section 3.4.

Occasionally, we come across a *neither–nor* statement, such as "John is neither handsome nor rich." This statement means that John is not handsome *and* John is not rich. If p represents "John is handsome" and q represents "John is rich," this statement is symbolized by $\sim p \wedge \sim q$.

If–Then Statements

The *conditional* is symbolized by $\rightarrow$ and is read "if–then." The statement $p \rightarrow q$ is read "If p, then q."[*] The conditional statement consists of two parts: the part that precedes the arrow is the *antecedent,* and the part that follows the arrow is the *consequent.*[†] In the conditional statement $p \rightarrow q$, the p is the antecedent and the q is the consequent.

---

[*]Some books indicate that $p \rightarrow q$ may also be read "p implies q." Many higher-level mathematics books, however, indicate that $p \rightarrow q$ may be read "p implies q" only under certain conditions. Implications are discussed in Section 3.3.

[†]Some books refer to the antecedent as the hypothesis or premise and the consequent as the conclusion.

In the conditional statement $\sim(p \lor q) \rightarrow (p \land q)$, the antecedent is $\sim(p \lor q)$ and the consequent is $(p \land q)$. An example of a conditional statement is "If you drink your milk, then you will grow up to be healthy." A conditional symbol may be placed between any two statements even if the statements are not related.

Sometimes the word *then* in a conditional statement is not explicitly stated. For example, the statement "If you get an A, I will buy you a car" is a conditional statement because it actually means "If you get an A, then I will buy you a car."

▲ *Zoe* by Beth Anderson

Example 6   *Write Conditional Statements*

Let

p: The portrait is a pastel.

q: The portrait is by Beth Anderson.

Write the following statements symbolically.

a) If the portrait is a pastel, then the portrait is by Beth Anderson.

b) If the portrait is by Beth Anderson, then the portrait is not a pastel.

c) It is false that if the portrait is by Beth Anderson then the portrait is a pastel.

Solution

a) $p \rightarrow q$ b) $q \rightarrow \sim p$ c) $\sim(q \rightarrow p)$ ∎

Example 7   *Use Commas When Writing a Symbolic Statement in Words*

Let

p: Jorge is enrolled in calculus.

q: Jorge's major is criminal justice.

r: Jorge's major is engineering.

Write the following symbolic statements in words and indicate whether the statement is a negation, conjunction, disjunction, or conditional.

a) $(q \rightarrow \sim p) \lor r$ b) $q \rightarrow (\sim p \lor r)$

Solution   The parentheses indicate where to place the commas in the sentences.

a) "If Jorge's major is criminal justice then Jorge is not enrolled in calculus, or Jorge's major is engineering." This statement is a disjunction because $\lor$ is outside the parentheses.

b) "If Jorge's major is criminal justice, then Jorge is not enrolled in calculus or Jorge's major is engineering." This statement is a conditional because $\rightarrow$ is outside the parentheses. ∎

If and Only if Statements

The *biconditional* is symbolized by $\leftrightarrow$ and is read "if and only if." The phrase *if and only if* is sometimes abbreviated as "iff." The statement $p \leftrightarrow q$ is read "p if and only if q."

Example 8   *Write Statements Using the Biconditional*

Let

p: Alex plays goalie on the lacrosse team.

q: The Titans win the Champion's Cup.

Write the following symbolic statements in words.

a) $p \leftrightarrow q$ c) $q \leftrightarrow \sim p$ b) $\sim(p \leftrightarrow \sim q)$

Solution

a) Alex plays goalie on the lacrosse team if and only if the Titans win the Champion's Cup.

b) The Titans win the Champion's Cup if and only if Alex does not play goalie on the lacrosse team.

c) It is false that Alex plays goalie on the lacrosse team if and only if the Titans do not win the Champion's Cup.   ■

You will learn later that $p \leftrightarrow q$ means the same as $(p \rightarrow q) \wedge (q \rightarrow p)$. Therefore, the statement "I will go to college if and only if I can pay the tuition" has the same logical meaning as "If I go to college then I can pay the tuition, and if I can pay the tuition then I will go to college."

A summary of the connectives discussed in this section is given in Table 3.1.

Table 3.1 Logical Connectives

Formal Name	Symbol	Read	Symbolic Form
Negation	~	"Not"	$\sim p$
Conjunction	∧	"And"	$p \wedge q$
Disjunction	∨	"Or"	$p \vee q$
Conditional	→	"If-then"	$p \rightarrow q$
Biconditional	↔	"If and only if"	$p \leftrightarrow q$

SECTION 3.1   *Exercises*

Warm Up Exercises

In exercises 1–8, fill in the blanks with an appropriate word, phrase, or symbol(s).

1. A sentence that can be judged either true or false is called a _____. Statement

2. A statement that conveys only one idea is called a _____ statement. Simple

3. A statement that consists of two or more simple statements is called a _____ statement. Compound

4. Words such as *all, none* (or *no*), and *some* are examples of _____. Quantifiers

5. a) The negation is symbolized by ~ and is read "_____." Not

    b) The conjunction is symbolized by ∧ and is read "_____." And

    c) The disjunction is symbolized by ∨ and is read "_____." Or

d) The conditional is symbolized by → and is read "_____." If–then

e) The biconditional is symbolized by ↔ and is read "_____." If and only if

6. The negation of the statement *Some cars are hybrids* is: _____ cars are hybrids. No

7. The negation of the statement *All golf courses are green* is: _____ golf courses are not green. Some

8. The negation of the statement *Some drivers are not safe* is: _____ drivers are safe. All

Practice the Skills/Problem Solving

In Exercises 9–18, indicate whether the statement is a simple statement or a compound statement. If it is a compound statement, indicate whether it is a negation, conjunction, disjunction, conditional, or biconditional by using both the word and its appropriate symbol (for example, "a negation," ~).

9. John Waters is scuba diving. Simple statement

10. If you have a cold, then you should eat some chicken soup. Compound; conditional, →

11. Time will go backwards if and only if you travel faster than the speed of light. Compound; biconditional, ↔

12. Louis Armstrong did not play the drums. Compound; negation, ~

13. Bobby Glewen joined the Army and he got married. Compound; conjunction, ∧

14. The book was neither a novel nor an autobiography. Compound; conjunction, ∧

15. If Cathy Smith walks 4 miles today, then she will be sore tomorrow. Compound; conditional, →

16. Inhibor Melendez will be admitted to law school if and only if he earns his bachelor's degree. Compound; biconditional, ↔

17. It is false that Jeffery Hilt is a high school teacher and a grade school teacher. Compound; negation, ~

18. The hurricane did $400,000 worth of damage to DeSoto County. Simple statement

In Exercises 19–28, write the negation of the statement.

19. All butterflies are insects. Some butterflies are not insects.

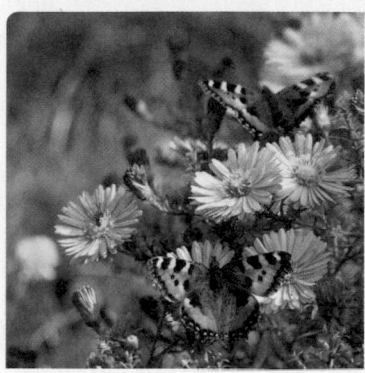

20. All houses are wired using parallel circuits. Some houses are not wired using parallel circuits.

21. Some turtles do not have claws. All turtles have claws.

22. No teachers made the roster. Some teachers made the roster.

23. No bicycles have three wheels. Some bicycles have three wheels.

24. All horses have manes. Some horses do not have manes.

25. Some pedestrians are in the crosswalk. No pedestrians are in the crosswalk.

26. Some dogs with long hair do not get cold. All dogs with long hair get cold.

27. No Holsteins are Guernseys. Some Holsteins are Guernseys.

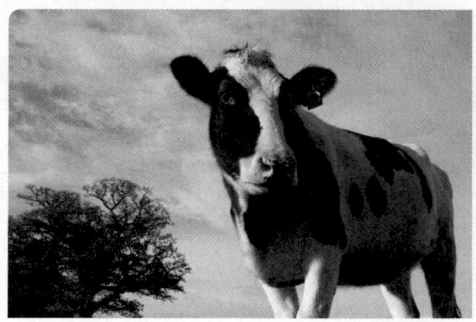

28. Some vitamins contain sugar. No vitamins contain sugar.

In Exercises 29–34, write the statement in symbolic form.

Let

   p: A panther has a long tail.

   q: A bobcat can purr.

29. A panther does not have a long tail. $\sim p$

30. A panther has a long tail and a bobcat can purr. $p \wedge q$

31. A bobcat cannot purr or a panther does not have a long tail. $\sim q \vee \sim p$

32. A bobcat cannot purr if and only if a panther does not have a long tail. $\sim q \leftrightarrow \sim p$

33. If a panther does not have a long tail, then a bobcat cannot purr. $\sim p \rightarrow \sim q$

34. A bobcat cannot purr, but a panther has a long tail. $\sim q \wedge p$

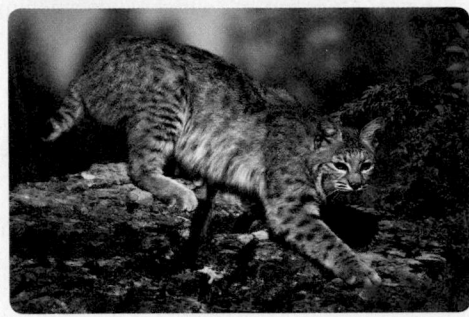

In Exercises 35–40, write the statement in symbolic form.

Let

p: The chili is spicy.

q: The sour cream is cold.

35. The chili is not spicy, but the sour cream is cold. $\sim p \wedge q$

36. Neither is the chili spicy nor is the sour cream cold. $\sim p \wedge \sim q$

37. The sour cream is not cold if and only if the chili is spicy. $\sim q \leftrightarrow p$

38. If the chili is spicy, then the sour cream is not cold. $p \rightarrow \sim q$

39. It is false that the chili is spicy or the sour cream is cold. $\sim (p \vee q)$

40. It is false that if the sour cream is not cold then the chili is spicy. $\sim (\sim q \rightarrow p)$

In Exercises 41–50, write the compound statement in words.

Let

p: Joe has an iPad.

q: Brie has a MacBook.

41. $\sim q$ *

42. $\sim p$ *

43. $p \wedge q$ *

44. $q \vee p$ *

45. $\sim p \rightarrow q$ *

46. $\sim p \leftrightarrow \sim q$ *

47. $\sim p \vee \sim q$ *

48. $\sim (q \vee p)$ *

49. $\sim (p \wedge q)$ *

50. $\sim p \wedge \sim q$ *

In Exercises 51–60, write the statements in symbolic form.

Let

p: The temperature is 90°.

q: The air conditioner is working.

r: The apartment is hot.

51. The temperature is 90° and the air conditioner is not working, and the apartment is hot. $(p \wedge \sim q) \wedge r$

52. The temperature is not 90° and the air conditioner is working, but the apartment is hot. $(\sim p \wedge q) \wedge r$

53. The temperature is 90° and the air conditioner is working, or the apartment is hot. $(p \wedge q) \vee r$

54. If the apartment is hot and the air conditioner is working, then the temperature is 90°. $(r \wedge q) \rightarrow p$

55. If the temperature is 90°, then the air conditioner is working or the apartment is not hot. $p \rightarrow (q \vee \sim r)$

56. The temperature is not 90° if and only if the air conditioner is not working, or the apartment is not hot. $(\sim p \leftrightarrow \sim q) \vee \sim r$

57. The apartment is hot if and only if the air conditioner is working, and the temperature is 90°. $(r \leftrightarrow q) \wedge p$

58. It is false that if the apartment is hot then the air conditioner is not working. $\sim (r \rightarrow \sim q)$

59. If the air conditioner is working, then the temperature is 90° if and only if the apartment is hot. $q \rightarrow (p \leftrightarrow r)$

60. The apartment is hot or the air conditioner is not working, if and only if the temperature is 90°. $(r \vee \sim q) \leftrightarrow p$

In Exercises 61–70, write each symbolic statement in words.

Let

p: The water is 70°.

q: The sun is shining.

r: We go swimming.

61. $(p \vee q) \wedge \sim r$ *

62. $(p \wedge q) \vee r$ *

63. $\sim p \wedge (q \vee r)$ *

64. $(q \rightarrow p) \vee r$ *

65. $\sim r \rightarrow (q \wedge p)$ *

66. $(q \wedge r) \rightarrow p$ *

67. $(q \rightarrow r) \wedge p$ *

68. $\sim p \rightarrow (q \vee r)$ *

69. $(q \leftrightarrow p) \wedge r$ *

70. $q \rightarrow (p \leftrightarrow r)$ *

Dinner Menu In Exercises 71–74 on page 104, use the following information to arrive at your answers. Many restaurant dinner menus include statements such as the following. All dinners are served with a choice of: Soup or Salad, and Potatoes or Pasta, and Carrots or Peas. Which of the following selections are permissible? If a selection is not permissible, explain why. See the discussion of the exclusive or on page 95.

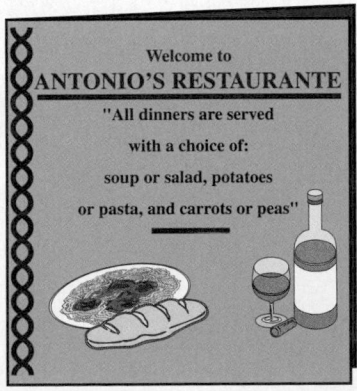

71. Soup, salad, and peas   Not permissible; you cannot have both soup and salad. The *or* used on menus is the *exclusive or*.

72. Salad, pasta, and carrots   Permissible

73. Soup, potatoes, pasta, and peas *

74. Soup, pasta, and potatoes *

In Exercises 75–83, (a) select letters to represent the simple statements and write each statement symbolically by using parentheses and (b) indicate whether the statement is a negation, conjunction, disjunction, conditional, or biconditional.

75. I bought the watch in Tijuana and I did not pay $100.
   a) $w \wedge \sim p$ b) Conjunction

76. If the conference is in Las Vegas, then we can see Blue Man Group or we can play poker.   a) $c \rightarrow (s \vee p)$ b) Conditional

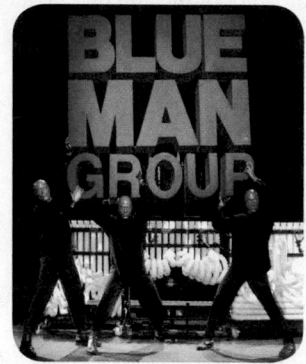

▲ *Blue Man Group*

77. It is false that if your speed is below the speed limit then you will not get pulled over.   a) $\sim(b \rightarrow \sim p)$ b) Negation

78. If dinner is ready then we can eat, or we cannot go to the restaurant.   a) $(d \rightarrow e) \vee \sim r$ b) Disjunction

79. If the food has fiber or the food has vitamins, then you will be healthy.   a) $(f \vee v) \rightarrow h$ b) Conditional

80. If Corliss is teaching then Faye is in the math lab, if and only if it is not a weekend.   a) $(c \rightarrow f) \leftrightarrow \sim w$ b) Biconditional

81. You may take this course, if and only if you did not fail the previous course or you passed the placement test.
   a) $c \leftrightarrow (\sim f \vee p)$ b) Biconditional

82. If the car has gas and the battery is charged, then the car will start.   a) $(g \wedge b) \rightarrow s$ b) Conditional

83. The classroom is empty if and only if it is the weekend, or it is 7 A.M.   a) $(c \leftrightarrow w) \vee s$ b) Disjunction

Challenge Problems/Group Activities

84. *An Ancient Question*   If Zeus could do anything, could he build a wall that he could not jump over? Explain your answer.   Answers will vary.

85. a) Make up three simple statements and label them p, q, and r. Then write compound statements to represent $(p \vee q) \wedge r$ and $p \vee (q \wedge r)$.   Answers will vary.

b) Do you think that the statements for $(p \vee q) \wedge r$ and $p \vee (q \wedge r)$ mean the same thing? Explain.
Answers will vary.

Recreational Mathematics

86. *Sudoku*   Refer to the *Recreational Mathematics* on page 96. Complete the following Sudoku puzzle. *

	8			3				
9			6	1				4
5	1	9				8	6	3
	6					4	8	
5								1
2	4					5		
4	3	5			8	1	9	
2			5	1			7	
			2			6		

Internet/Research Activities

87. *Legal Documents*   Obtain a legal document such as a will or rental agreement and copy one page of the document. Circle every connective used. Then list the number of times each connective appeared. Be sure to include conditional statements from which the word *then* was omitted from the sentence. Give the page and your listing to your instructor.

88. Write a report on the life and accomplishments of George Boole, who was an important contributor to the development of logic. In your report, indicate how his work eventually led to the development of the computer. References include encyclopedias, history of mathematics books, and the Internet.

Truth Tables for Negation, Conjunction, and Disjunction

▲ *Under what conditions is the statement Subway sells the most sandwiches or Taco Bell sells the most burritos true?*

Consider the following statement: Subway sells the most sandwiches or Taco Bell sells the most burritos. Under what conditions can the statement be considered true? Under what conditions can the statement be considered false? In this section, we will introduce a tool used to help us analyze such statements.

Why *This is Important* Understanding when logical statements are true is essential to many different applications in everyday life.

A *truth table* is a device used to determine when a compound statement is true or false. Five basic truth tables are used in constructing other truth tables. Three are discussed in this section (Tables 3.2, 3.4, and 3.7), and two are discussed in the next section. Section 3.5 uses truth tables in determining whether a logical argument is valid or invalid.

Negation

The first truth table is for *negation*. If p is a true statement, then the negation of p, "not p," is a false statement. If p is a false statement, then "not p" is a true statement. For example, if the statement "The shirt is blue" is true, then the statement "The shirt is not blue" is false. These relationships are summarized in Table 3.2. For a simple statement, there are exactly two true–false cases, as shown.

If a compound statement consists of two simple statements p and q, there are four possible cases, as illustrated in Table 3.3. Consider the statement "The test is today and the test covers Chapter 5." The simple statement "The test is today" has two possible truth values, true or false. The simple statement "The test covers Chapter 5" also has two truth values, true or false. Thus, for these two simple statements there are four distinct possible true–false arrangements. Whenever we construct a truth table for a compound statement that consists of two simple statements, we begin by listing the four true–false cases shown in Table 3.3.

Conjunction

To illustrate the conjunction, consider the following situation. You have recently purchased a new house. To decorate it, you ordered a new carpet and new furniture from the same store. You explain to the salesperson that the carpet must be delivered before the furniture. He promises that the carpet will be delivered on Thursday and that the furniture will be delivered on Friday.

To help determine whether the salesperson kept his promise, we assign letters to each simple statement. Let p be "The carpet will be delivered on Thursday" and q be "The furniture will be delivered on Friday." The salesperson's statement written in symbolic form is $p \wedge q$. There are four possible true–false situations to be considered (Table 3.4).

CASE 1: p is true and q is true. The carpet is delivered on Thursday and the furniture is delivered on Friday. The salesperson has kept his promise and the compound statement is true. Thus, we put a T in the $p \wedge q$ column.

CASE 2: p is true and q is false. The carpet is delivered on Thursday but the furniture is not delivered on Friday. Since the furniture was not delivered as promised, the compound statement is false. Thus, we put an F in the $p \wedge q$ column.

Table 3.2 Negation

	p	$\sim p$
Case 1	T	F
Case 2	F	T

Table 3.3

	p	q
Case 1	T	T
Case 2	T	F
Case 3	F	T
Case 4	F	F

Table 3.4 Conjunction

	p	q	$p \wedge q$
Case 1	T	T	T
Case 2	T	F	F
Case 3	F	T	F
Case 4	F	F	F

CASE 3: p is false and q is true. The carpet is not delivered on Thursday but the furniture is delivered on Friday. Since the carpet was not delivered on Thursday as promised, the compound statement is false. Thus, we put an F in the $p \wedge q$ column.

CASE 4: p is false and q is false. The carpet is not delivered on Thursday and the furniture is not delivered on Friday. Since the carpet and furniture were not delivered as promised, the compound statement is false. Thus, we put an F in the $p \wedge q$ column.

Examining the four cases, we see that in only one case did the salesperson keep his promise: in case 1. Therefore, case 1 (T, T) is true. In cases 2, 3, and 4, the salesperson did not keep his promise and the compound statement is false. The results are summarized in Table 3.4, the truth table for the conjunction.

The **conjunction** $p \wedge q$ is true only when both p and q are true.

Disjunction

Consider the job description in the margin that describes several job requirements. Who qualifies for the job? To help analyze the statement, translate it into symbolic form. Let p be "A requirement for the job is a two-year college degree in civil technology" and q be "A requirement for the job is five years of related experience." The statement in symbolic form is $p \vee q$. For the two simple statements, there are four distinct cases (see Table 3.5).

CASE 1: p is true and q is true. A candidate has a two-year college degree in civil technology and five years of related experience. The candidate has both requirements and qualifies for the job. Consider qualifying for the job as a true statement and not qualifying as a false statement. Since the candidate qualifies for the job, we put a T in the $p \vee q$ column.

CASE 2: p is true and q is false. A candidate has a two-year college degree in civil technology but does not have five years of related experience. The candidate still qualifies for the job with the two-year college degree. Thus, we put a T in the $p \vee q$ column.

CASE 3: p is false and q is true. The candidate does not have a two-year college degree in civil technology but does have five years of related experience. The candidate still qualifies for the job with the five years of related experience. Thus, we put a T in the $p \vee q$ column.

CASE 4: p is false and q is false. The candidate does not have a two-year college degree in civil technology and does not have five years of related experience. The candidate does not meet either of the two requirements and therefore does not qualify for the job. Thus, we put an F in the $p \vee q$ column.

In examining the four cases, we see that there is only one case in which the candidate does not qualify for the job: case 4. As this example indicates, an *or* statement will be true in every case, except when both simple statements are false. The results are summarized in Table 3.5, the truth table for the disjunction.

The **disjunction** $p \vee q$ is true when either p is true, q is true, or both p and q are true.

The disjunction $p \vee q$ is false only when p and q are both false.

Constructing Truth Tables

We will now construct additional truth tables for statements involving the negation, conjunction, and disjunction. We summarize these compound statements on page 107.

Civil Technician

Municipal program for redevelopment seeks on-site technician. **The applicant must have a two-year college degree in civil technology or five years of related experience.** Interested candidates please call 555-1234.

Table 3.5 Disjunction

p	q	$p \vee q$
T	T	T
T	F	T
F	T	T
F	F	F

Negation, Conjunction, and Disjunction

- **Negation** $\sim p$ is read "not p." If p is true, then $\sim p$ is false; if p is false, then $\sim p$ is true. In other words, $\sim p$ will always have the *opposite* truth value of p.
- **Conjunction** $p \wedge q$ is read *"p and q."* $p \wedge q$ is true only when both p and q are true.
- **Disjunction** $p \vee q$ is read *"p or q."* $p \vee q$ is true when either p is true, q is true, or both p and q are true. In other words, $p \vee q$ is false only when both p and q are false.

We will discuss two methods for constructing truth tables. Although the two methods produce tables that will look different, the answer columns will be the same regardless of which method you use.

Example 1 *Construct a Truth Table*

Construct a truth table for $p \wedge \sim q$.

Solution Because there are two statements, p and q, construct a truth table with four cases; see Table 3.6(a). Then write the truth values under the p in the compound statement and label this column 1, as in Table 3.6(b). Copy these truth values directly from the p column on the left. Write the corresponding truth values under the q in the compound statement and call this column 2, as in Table 3.6(c). Copy the truth values for column 2 directly from the q column on the left. Now find the truth values of $\sim q$ by negating the truth values in column 2 and call this column 3, as in

Table 3.6

(a)

	p	q	$p \wedge \sim q$
Case 1	T	T	
Case 2	T	F	
Case 3	F	T	
Case 4	F	F	

(b)

p	q	p	$\wedge$	$\sim q$
T	T	T		
T	F	T		
F	T	F		
F	F	F		
		1		

(c)

p	q	p	$\wedge$	$\sim$	q
T	T	T			T
T	F	T			F
F	T	F			T
F	F	F			F
		1			2

(d)

p	q	p	$\wedge$	$\sim$	q
T	T	T		F	T
T	F	T		T	F
F	T	F		F	T
F	F	F		T	F
		1		3	2

(e)

p	q	p	$\wedge$	$\sim$	q
T	T	T	F	F	T
T	F	T	T	T	F
F	T	F	F	F	T
F	F	F	F	T	F
		1	4	3	2

Table 3.6(d). Use the conjunction table, Table 3.4, and the entries in the columns labeled 1 and 3 to complete the column labeled 4, as in Table 3.6(e). The results in column 4 are obtained as follows:

Row 1: T $\wedge$ F is F.   Row 2: T $\wedge$ T is T.
Row 3: F $\wedge$ F is F.   Row 4: F $\wedge$ T is F.

The answer is always the last column completed. The columns labeled 1, 2, and 3 are only aids in arriving at the answer labeled column 4. ∎

The statement $p \wedge \sim q$ in Example 1 actually means $p \wedge (\sim q)$. In the future, instead of listing a column for q and a separate column for its negation, we will make one column for $\sim q$, which will have the opposite values of those in the q column on the left. Similarly, when we evaluate $\sim p$, we will use the opposite values of those in the p column on the left. This procedure is illustrated in Example 2.

In Example 1, we spoke about *cases* and also *columns*. Consider Table 3.6(e) on page 107. This table has four cases indicated by the four different rows of the two left-hand (unnumbered) columns. The four *cases* are TT, TF, FT, and FF. In every truth table with two letters, we list the four cases (the first two columns) first. Then we complete the remaining columns in the truth table. In Table 3.6(e), after completing the two left-hand columns, we complete the remaining columns in the order indicated by the numbers below the columns. We will continue to place numbers below the columns to show the order in which the columns are completed.

In discussion of the truth table in Example 2, and all following truth tables, if we say column 1, it means the column labeled 1. Column 2 will mean the column labeled 2, and so on.

Example 2 *Construct and Interpret a Truth Table*

a) Construct a truth table for the following statement: Jo is not an artist and Jo is not a musician.

b) Under which conditions will the compound statement be true?

c) Suppose "Jo is an artist" is a false statement and "Jo is a musician" is a true statement. Is the compound statement given in part (a) true or false?

Solution

a) First write the simple statements in symbolic form by using simple nonnegated statements.

Let

p: Jo is an artist.
q: Jo is a musician.

Therefore, the compound statement may be written $\sim p \wedge \sim q$. Now construct a truth table with four cases, as shown in Table 3.7.

Fill in the column labeled 1 by negating the truth values under p on the far left. Fill in the column labeled 2 by negating the values under q in the second column from the left. Fill in the column labeled 3 by using the columns labeled 1 and 2 and the definition of conjunction.

In the first row, to determine the entry for column 3, we use false for $\sim p$ and false for $\sim q$. Since false $\wedge$ false is false (see case 4 of Table 3.4 on page 105), we place an F in column 3, row 1. In the second row, we use false for $\sim p$ and true for $\sim q$. Since false $\wedge$ true is false (see case 3 of Table 3.4), we place an F in column 3, row 2. In the third row, we use true for $\sim p$ and false for $\sim q$. Since true $\wedge$ false is false (see case 2 of Table 3.4), we place an F in column 3, row 3. In the fourth row, we use true for $\sim p$ and true for $\sim q$. Since true $\wedge$ true is true (see case 1 of Table 3.4), we place a T in column 3, row 4.

b) The compound statement in part (a) will be true only in case 4 (circled in blue) when both simple statements, p and q, are false, that is, when Jo is not an artist and Jo is not a musician.

c) We are told that p, "Jo is an artist," is a false statement and that q, "Jo is a musician," is a true statement. From the truth table (Table 3.7), we can determine that when p is false and q is true, the compound statement, case 3 (circled in red), is false. ∎

TIMELY TIP

When constructing truth tables it is very important to keep your entries in neat columns and rows. If you are using lined paper, put only one row of the table on each line. If you are not using lined paper, using a straightedge may help you correctly enter the information into the truth table's rows and columns.

Table 3.7

p	q	$\sim p$	$\wedge$	$\sim q$
T	T	F	F	F
T	F	F	F	T
F	T	T	Ⓕ	F
F	F	T	Ⓣ	T
		1	3	2

Table 3.8

p	q	$\sim$	$(\sim q$	$\vee$	$p)$
T	T	F	F	T	T
T	F	F	T	T	T
F	T	T	F	F	F
F	F	F	T	T	F
		4	1	3	2

Example 3 *Truth Table with a Negation*

Construct a truth table for $\sim(\sim q \vee p)$.

Solution First construct the standard truth table listing the four cases. Then work within parentheses. The order to be followed is indicated by the numbers below the columns (see Table 3.8). Under $\sim q$, column 1, write the negation of the q column. Then, in column 2, copy the values from the p column. Next, complete the *or* column, column 3, using columns 1 and 2 and the truth table for the disjunction (see Table 3.5 on page 106). The *or* column is false only when both statements are false, as in case 3. Finally, negate the values in the *or* column, column 3, and place these negated values in column 4. By examining the truth table you can see that the compound statement $\sim(\sim q \vee p)$ is true only in case 3, that is, when p is false and q is true. ∎

PROCEDURE CONSTRUCTING TRUTH TABLES

1. Study the compound statement and determine whether it is a negation, conjunction, disjunction, conditional, or biconditional statement, as was done in Section 3.1. The answer to the truth table will appear under $\sim$ if the statement is a negation, under $\wedge$ if the statement is a conjunction, under $\vee$ if the statement is a disjunction, under $\rightarrow$ if the statement is a conditional, and under $\leftrightarrow$ if the statement is a biconditional.

2. Complete the columns under the simple statements, p, q, r, and their negations, $\sim p$, $\sim q$, $\sim r$, within parentheses, if present. If there are nested parentheses (one pair of parentheses within another pair), work with the innermost pair first.

3. Complete the column under the connective within the parentheses, if present. You will use the truth values of the connective in determining the final answer in step 5.

4. Complete the column under any remaining statements and their negations.

5. Complete the column under any remaining connectives. Recall that the answer will appear under the column determined in step 1. If the statement is a conjunction, disjunction, conditional, or biconditional, you will obtain the truth values for the connective by using the last column completed on the left side and on the right side of the connective. If the statement is a negation, you will obtain the truth values by negating the truth values of the last column completed within the grouping symbols on the right side of the negation. Be sure to circle or highlight your answer column or number the columns in the order they were completed.

Table 3.9

p	q	$(\sim p$	$\vee$	$q)$	$\wedge$	$\sim p$
T	T	F	T	T	F	F
T	F	F	F	F	F	F
F	T	T	T	T	T	T
F	F	T	T	F	T	T
		1	3	2	5	4

Example 4 *Use the General Procedure to Construct a Truth Table*

Construct a truth table for the statement $(\sim p \vee q) \wedge \sim p$.

Solution We will follow the general procedure outlined in the box. This statement is a conjunction, so the answer will be under the conjunction symbol. Complete columns under $\sim p$ and q within the parentheses and call these columns 1 and 2, respectively (see Table 3.9). Complete the column under the disjunction, $\vee$, using the truth values in columns 1 and 2, and call this column 3. Next complete the column under $\sim p$, and call this column 4. The answer, column 5, is determined from the definition of the conjunction and the truth values in column 3, the last column completed on the left side of the conjunction, and column 4. ∎

So far, all the truth tables we have constructed have contained at most two simple statements. Now we will explain how to construct a truth table that consists of three simple statements, such as $(p \wedge q) \wedge r$. When a compound statement consists of three simple statements, there are eight different true–false possibilities,

Table 3.10

	p	*q*	*r*
Case 1	T	T	T
Case 2	T	T	F
Case 3	T	F	T
Case 4	T	F	F
Case 5	F	T	T
Case 6	F	T	F
Case 7	F	F	T
Case 8	F	F	F

as illustrated in Table 3.10. To begin such a truth table, write four Ts and four Fs in the column under *p*. Under the second statement, *q*, pairs of Ts alternate with pairs of Fs. Under the third statement, *r*, T alternates with F. This technique is not the only way of listing the cases, but it ensures that each case is unique and that no cases are omitted.

Example 5   *Construct a Truth Table with Eight Cases*

a) Construct a truth table for the statement "Santana is home and he is not at his desk, or he is sleeping."

b) Suppose that "Santana is home" is a false statement, that "Santana is at his desk" is a true statement, and that "Santana is sleeping" is a true statement. Is the compound statement in part (a) true or false?

Solution

a) First we will translate the statement into symbolic form.

Let

p: Santana is home.

q: Santana is at his desk.

r: Santana is sleeping.

In symbolic form, the statement is $(p \land \sim q) \lor r$.

Since the statement is composed of three simple statements, there are eight cases. Begin by listing the eight cases in the three left-hand columns; see Table 3.11. By examining the statement, you can see that it is a disjunction. Therefore, the answer will be in the $\lor$ column. Fill out the truth table by working in parentheses first. Place values under p, column 1, and $\sim q$, column 2. Then find the conjunctions of columns 1 and 2 to obtain column 3. Place the values of r in column 4. To obtain the answer, column 5, use columns 3 and 4 and the information for the disjunction contained in Table 3.5 on page 106.

Table 3.11

p	*q*	*r*	(*p*	∧	~*q*)	∨	*r*
T	T	T	T	F	F	T	T
T	T	F	T	F	F	F	F
T	F	T	T	T	T	T	T
T	F	F	T	T	T	T	F
F	T	T	F	F	F	(T)	T
F	T	F	F	F	F	F	F
F	F	T	F	F	T	T	T
F	F	F	F	F	T	F	F
			1	3	2	5	4

b) We are given the following:

p: Santana is home—false.

q: Santana is at his desk—true.

r: Santana is sleeping—true.

We need to find the truth value of the following case: false, true, true. In case 5 of the truth table, p, q, and r are F, T, and T, respectively. Therefore, under these conditions, the original compound statement is true (as circled in the table).   ∎

We have learned that a truth table with one simple statement has two cases, a truth table with two simple statements has four cases, and a truth table with three simple statements has eight cases. In general, *the number of distinct cases in a truth table with n distinct simple statements is 2^n.* The compound statement $(p \vee q) \vee (r \wedge \sim s)$ has four simple statements, p, q, r, s. Thus, a truth table for this compound statement would have 2^4, or 16, distinct cases.

When we construct a truth table, we determine the truth values of a compound statement for every possible case. If we want to find the truth value of the compound statement for any specific case when we know the truth values of the simple statements, we do not have to develop the entire table. For example, to determine the truth value for the statement

$$2 + 3 = 5 \quad \text{and} \quad 1 + 1 = 3$$

we let p be $2 + 3 = 5$ and q be $1 + 1 = 3$. Now we can write the compound statement as $p \wedge q$. We know that p is a true statement and q is a false statement. Thus, we can substitute T for p and F for q and evaluate the statement:

$$p \wedge q$$
$$T \wedge F$$
$$F$$

Therefore, the compound statement $2 + 3 = 5$ and $1 + 1 = 3$ is a false statement.

Alternate Method for Constructing Truth Tables

We now present an alternate method for constructing truth tables. We will use the alternate method to construct truth tables for the same statements we analyzed in Examples 1, 2, and 3.

Example 6 *Use the Alternate Method to Construct a Truth Table*

Construct a truth table for $p \wedge \sim q$.

Solution We begin by constructing the first two columns of a truth table with four cases, as shown in Table 3.12 (a). We will add additional columns to Table 3.12(a) to develop our answer column. Since we wish to find the truth table for the compound statement $p \wedge \sim q$, we need to be able to compare the truth values for p with the truth values for $\sim q$. Table 3.12(a) already has a column showing the truth values for p. We next add a column showing the truth values for $\sim q$, as shown in Table 3.12(b). Recall that the values of $\sim q$ are the opposite of those for q.

Finally, we add the answer column for the compound statement $p \wedge \sim q$, as shown as shown in Table 3.12(c). To determine the truth values for the $p \wedge \sim q$ column, use the p column and the $\sim q$ column, and the conjunction table, Table 3.4,

Table 3.12

(a)

	p	q
Case 1	T	T
Case 2	T	F
Case 3	F	T
Case 4	F	F

(b)

p	q	$\sim q$
T	T	F
T	F	T
F	T	F
F	F	T

(c)

p	q	$\sim q$	$p \wedge \sim q$
T	T	F	F
T	F	T	T
F	T	F	F
F	F	T	F

↑　　　　↑　　　　↑
Use these columns to determine the answer column

on page 105. Note that the answer column of Table 3.12(c) is the same as the answer column of Table 3.6(e) on page 107. ∎

Example 7 *Use the Alternate Method to Construct a Truth Table*

Construct a truth table for $\sim p \wedge \sim q$.

Solution Begin by constructing a truth table with four cases, as shown in Table 3.13(a). Since we wish to find the truth table for the compound statement $\sim p \wedge \sim q$, we will add a column for $\sim p$ and a column for $\sim q$, as shown in Table 3.13(b).

Table 3.13

(a)

p	q
T	T
T	F
F	T
F	F

(b)

p	q	~p	~q
T	T	F	F
T	F	F	T
F	T	T	F
F	F	T	T

(c)

p	q	~p	~q	~p ∧ ~q
T	T	F	F	F
T	F	F	T	F
F	T	T	F	F
F	F	T	T	T

↑   ↑   ↑
Use these columns to determine the answer column

Finally, we add our answer column for the compound statement $\sim p \wedge \sim q$. To determine the truth values for the $\sim p \wedge \sim q$ column, use the $\sim p$ column and the $\sim q$ column, and the conjunction table, Table 3.4, on page 105. Note that the answer column of Table 3.13(c) is the same as the answer column of Table 3.7 on page 108. ∎

Example 8 *Use the Alternate Method to Construct a Truth Table*

Construct a truth table for $\sim(\sim q \vee p)$.

Solution Begin by constructing a truth table with four cases, as shown in Table 3.14(a). To complete the truth table, we will work within parentheses first. Thus, we next add a column for $\sim q$, as shown in Table 3.14(b). We then will construct a column for the expression within parentheses $\sim q \vee p$ by using the $\sim q$ column and the p column, and the disjunction table, Table 3.5, on page 106.

Table 3.14

(a)

p	q
T	T
T	F
F	T
F	F

(b)

p	q	~q
T	T	F
T	F	T
F	T	F
F	F	T

(c)

p	q	~q	~q ∨ p
T	T	F	T
T	F	T	T
F	T	F	F
T	F	T	T

↑   ↑   ↑
Use these columns to determine the ~q ∨ p column

Table 3.15

p	q	~q	~q ∨ p	~(~q ∨ p)
T	T	F	T	F
T	F	T	T	F
F	T	F	F	T
F	F	T	T	F

↑   ↑
Take the opposite of this column to get the answer column

Finally, we add the answer column for the compound statement, $\sim(\sim q \vee p)$, as shown in Table 3.15. To determine the truth values for the $\sim(\sim q \vee p)$ column, take the opposite values of those shown in the $\sim q \vee p$ column. Note that the answer column of Table 3.15 is the same as the answer column of Table 3.8 on page 109. ∎

We have demonstrated two methods for constructing truth tables. Unless your instructor indicates otherwise, you may use either method. Although both methods will always lead to the correct answer, the alternate method gets more cumbersome and takes up more space as we construct truth tables with more statements. *In the remainder of this chapter, we will demonstrate the construction of truth tables using only the first method.*

Determine Truth Values Without Constructing a Truth Table

In the remaining examples in this section, we will determine the truth values of compound statements without constructing a truth table.

Example 9 *Determine the Truth Value of a Compound Statement*

Determine the truth value for each simple statement. Then, using these truth values, determine the truth value of the compound statement.

a) 15 is less than or equal to 9.

b) George Washington was the first U.S. president or Abraham Lincoln was the second U.S. president, but there has not been a U.S. president born in Antarctica.

Solution

a) Let

$$p: \quad \text{15 is less than 9.}$$
$$q: \quad \text{15 is equal to 9.}$$

The statement "15 is less than or equal to 9" means that 15 is less than 9 or 15 is equal to 9. The compound statement can be expressed as $p \vee q$. We know that both p and q are false statements, since 15 is greater than 9, so we substitute F for p and F for q and evaluate the statement:

$$p \vee q$$
$$\text{F} \vee \text{F}$$
$$\text{F}$$

Therefore, the compound statement "15 is less than or equal to 9" is a false statement.

b) Let

$$p: \quad \text{George Washington was the first U.S. president.}$$
$$q: \quad \text{Abraham Lincoln was the second U.S. president.}$$
$$r: \quad \text{There has been a U.S. president who was born in Antarctica.}$$

The compound statement can be written in symbolic form as $(p \vee q) \wedge \sim r$. Recall that *but* is used to express a conjunction. We know that p is a true statement and that q is a false statement. We also know that r is a false statement since all U.S. presidents must be born in the United States. Thus, since r is a false statement, the negation, $\sim r$, is a true statement. So we will substitute T for p, F for q, and T for $\sim r$ and then evaluate the statement:

$$(p \vee q) \wedge \sim r$$
$$(\text{T} \vee \text{F}) \wedge \text{T}$$
$$\text{T} \wedge \text{T}$$
$$\text{T}$$

Therefore, the original compound statement is a true statement.   ∎

Example 10 *Pet Ownership in the United States*

The number of pets owned in the United States in 2009 is shown in Figure 3.1. Use this graph to determine the truth value of the following statement: There are more dogs owned than cats and there are fewer reptiles owned than birds, or the most numerous pets owned are not fish.

Pets Owned in the United States (millions)

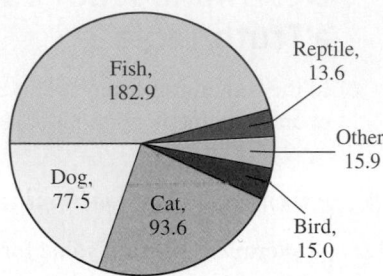

Source: American Pet Products Manufacturing Association

Figure 3.1

Solution Let

p: There are more dogs owned than cats.
q: There are fewer reptiles owned than birds.
r: The most numerous pets owned are fish.

The given compound statement can be written in symbolic form as $(p \land q) \lor \sim r$. From Fig. 3.1, we see that statement p is false: There are actually more cats owned than dogs. We also see that statement q is true: There are fewer reptiles owned than birds. We also see that statement r is true: The most numerous pets owned are fish. Since r is true, its negation, $\sim r$, is false. Therefore, we substitute F for p, T for q, and F for $\sim r$, which gives

$$(p \land q) \lor \sim r$$
$$(F \land T) \lor F$$
$$F \lor F$$
$$F$$

Thus, the original compound statement is a false statement.   ■

SECTION 3.2   *Exercises*

Warm Up Exercises

In Exercises 1–4, fill in the blanks with an appropriate word, phrase, or symbol(s).

1. The negation $\sim p$ will always have the _____ truth value of p. Opposite

2. The conjunction $p \land q$ is true only when both p and q are _____. True

3. The disjunction $p \lor q$ is false only when both p and q are _____. False

4. A truth table for a compound statement with

a) one distinct simple statement will have _____ cases. Two

b) two distinct simple statements will have _____ cases. Four

c) three distinct simple statements will have _____ cases. Eight

Practice the Skills/Problem Solving

In Exercises 5–18, construct a truth table for the statement.

5. $p \wedge \sim p$ F
              F

6. $p \vee \sim p$ T
              T

7. $q \vee \sim p$ *

8. $p \wedge \sim q$ *

9. $\sim p \vee \sim q$ *

10. $\sim (p \vee \sim q)$ *

11. $\sim (p \wedge \sim q)$ *

12. $\sim (\sim p \wedge \sim q)$ *

13. $\sim q \vee (p \wedge r)$ *

14. $(p \vee \sim q) \wedge r$ *

15. $r \vee (p \wedge \sim q)$ *

16. $(r \wedge q) \wedge \sim p$ *

17. $(r \vee \sim p) \wedge \sim q$ *

18. $\sim p \wedge (q \vee r)$ *

In Exercises 19–26, write the statement in symbolic form and construct a truth table.

19. Train recorded *Hey, Soul Sister* and The Black Eyed Peas recorded *Where Is the Love?* *

▲ *The Black Eyed Peas*

20. We can eat at McDonald's, but we cannot eat breakfast. *

21. I have worked all week, but I have not been paid. *

22. It is false that Robert A. Farinelli is the president or that Pauline Chow is the treasurer. *

23. It is false that Jasper Adams is a tutor and Mark Russo is a secretary. *

24. Mike made pizza and Dennis made a chef salad, but Gil burned the lemon squares. *

25. The copier is out of toner, or the lens is dirty or the corona wires are broken. *

26. I am hungry, and I want to eat a healthy lunch and I want to eat in a hurry. *

In Exercises 27–36, determine the truth value of the statement if

    a) p is true, q is false, and r is true.

    b) p is false, q is true, and r is true.

27. $(p \vee q) \wedge \sim r$ a) False   b) False

28. $p \vee (q \wedge \sim r)$ a) True   b) False

29. $(\sim p \wedge \sim q) \vee \sim r$ a) False   b) False

30. $\sim p \wedge (\sim q \vee \sim r)$ a) False   b) False

31. $(p \vee \sim q) \wedge \sim (p \wedge \sim r)$ a) True   b) False

32. $(p \wedge \sim q) \vee r$ a) True   b) True

33. $(\sim r \wedge p) \vee q$ a) False   b) True

34. $\sim q \vee (r \wedge p)$ a) True   b) False

35. $(\sim p \vee \sim q) \vee (\sim r \vee q)$ a) True   b) True

36. $(\sim r \wedge \sim q) \wedge (\sim r \vee \sim p)$ a) False   b) False

In Exercises 37–44, determine the truth value for each simple statement. Then use these truth values to determine the truth value of the compound statement. (You may have to use a reference source such as the Internet or an encyclopedia.)

37. $8 + 7 = 20 - 5$ and $63 \div 7 = 3 \cdot 3$ True

38. $0 < -3$ or $5 \geq 10$ False

39. Florida is in Canada or Texas borders Mexico. True

40. Washington, DC is west of the Mississippi River and Virginia is an island in the Pacific Ocean. False

41. Quentin Tarantino is a movie director and Zac Efron is an actor, but Scarlett Johansson is not an actress. False

▲ *Scarlett Johansson*

42. Quebec is in Texas or Toronto is in California, and Cedar Rapids is in Iowa. False

43. Iraq is in Africa or Iran is in South America, and Syria is in the Middle East. False

*See Instructor Answer Appendix

44. Holstein is a breed of cattle and collie is a breed of dogs, or beagle is not a breed of cats. True

Number of Movies Produced In Exercises 45–48, use the table to determine the truth value of each simple statement. Then determine the value of the compound statement.

Countries with the Highest Number of Feature Films Produced in 2008	
Country	**Number of Films**
India	1325
United States	520
Japan	418
China	406
France	240

Source: Screen Digest Magazine

45. India produced more feature films than the United States and China produced more feature films than Japan. False

46. India produced more than twice as many feature films as the United States and India produced more feature films than Japan, China, and France combined. True

47. The United States produced more feature films than Japan, but Japan produced more feature films than China. True

48. The United States produced more than twice as many feature films as France or Japan produced more feature films than India. True

Sleep Time In Exercises 49–52, use the graph, which shows the number of hours Americans sleep, to determine the truth value of each simple statement. Then determine the truth value of the compound statement.

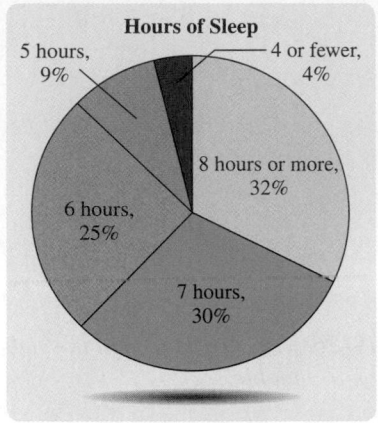

Hours of Sleep
- 5 hours, 9%
- 4 or fewer, 4%
- 8 hours or more, 32%
- 6 hours, 25%
- 7 hours, 30%

49. It is false that 30% of Americans get 6 hours of sleep each night and 9% get 5 hours of sleep each night. True

50. Twenty-five percent of Americans get 6 hours of sleep each night, and 30% get 7 hours of sleep each night or 9% do not get 5 hours of sleep each night. True

51. Thirteen percent of Americans get 5 or fewer hours of sleep each night or 32% get 6 or more hours of sleep each night, and 30% get 8 or more hours of sleep each night. False

52. Over one-half of all Americans get 7 or fewer hours of sleep each night, and over one-quarter get 6 or fewer hours of sleep each night. True

In Exercises 53–56, let

    p: Tanisha owns a convertible.

    q: Joan owns a Volvo.

Translate each statement into symbols. Then construct a truth table for each compound statement and indicate under what conditions the compound statement is true.

53. Tanisha owns a convertible and Joan does not own a Volvo. *

54. Tanisha does not own a convertible, but Joan owns a Volvo. *

55. Tanisha owns a convertible or Joan does not own a Volvo. *

56. Tanisha does not own a convertible or Joan does not own a Volvo. *

In Exercises 57–60 on page 117, let

    p: The house is owned by an engineer.

    q: The heat is solar generated.

    r: The car is run by electric power.

*See Instructor Answer Appendix

Translate each statement into symbols. Then construct a truth table for each and indicate under what conditions the compound statement is true.

57. The car is run by electric power or the heat is solar generated, but the house is owned by an engineer. *

58. The house is owned by an engineer and the heat is solar generated, or the car is run by electric power. *

59. The heat is solar generated, or the house is owned by an engineer and the car is not run by electric power. *

60. The house is not owned by an engineer, and the car is not run by electric power and the heat is solar generated. *

Obtaining a Loan In Exercises 61 and 62, read the requirements and each applicant's qualifications for obtaining a loan.

   a) Identify which of the applicants would qualify for the loan.

   b) For the applicants who do not qualify for the loan, explain why.

61. To qualify for a loan of $40,000, an applicant must have a gross income of $28,000 if single, $46,000 combined income if married, and assets of at least $6,000. *

   Mrs. Rusinek, married with three children, earns $42,000. Mr. Rusinek does not have an income. The Rusineks have assets of $42,000.

   Mr. Duncan is not married, works in sales, and earns $31,000. He has assets of $9000.

   Mrs. Tuttle and her husband have total assets of $43,000. One earns $35,000, and the other earns $23,500.

62. To qualify for a loan of $45,000, an applicant must have a gross income of $30,000 if single, $50,000 combined income if married, and assets of at least $10,000. *

   Mr. Argento, married with two children, earns $37,000. Mrs. Argento earns $15,000 at a part-time job. The Argentos have assets of $25,000.

   Ms. McVey, single, has assets of $19,000. She works in a store and earns $25,000.

   Mr. Siewert earns $24,000 and Ms. Fox, his wife, earns $28,000. Their assets total $8000.

63. *Airline Special Fares* An airline advertisement states, "To get the special fare you must purchase your tickets between January 1 and February 15 and fly round trip between March 1 and April 1. You must depart on a Monday, Tuesday, or Wednesday, and return on a Tuesday, Wednesday, or Thursday, and stay over at least one Saturday."

   a) Determine which of the following individuals will qualify for the special fare.
      Wing Park qualifies; the other four do not.

   b) If the person does not qualify for the special fare, explain why. *

      Wing Park plans to purchase his ticket on January 15, depart on Monday, March 3, and return on Tuesday, March 18.

Gina Vela plans to purchase her ticket on February 1, depart on Wednesday, March 12, and return on Thursday, April 3.

Kara Shavo plans to purchase her ticket on February 14, depart on Tuesday, March 4, and return on Monday, March 19.

Christos Supernaw plans to purchase his ticket on January 4, depart on Monday, March 10, and return on Thursday, March 13.

Alex Chang plans to purchase his ticket on January 1, depart on Monday, March 3, and return on Monday, March 10.

▲ *See Exercise 63*

Problem Solving/Group Activities

In Exercises 64 and 65, construct a truth table for the symbolic statement.

64. $\sim[(\sim(p \lor q)) \lor (q \land r)]$ *

65. $[(q \land \sim r) \land (\sim p \lor \sim q)] \lor (p \lor \sim r)$ *

66. On page 111, we indicated that a compound statement consisting of n simple statements had 2^n distinct true–false cases.

   a) How many distinct true–false cases does a truth table containing simple statements p, q, r, and s have? 16

   b) List all possible true–false cases for a truth table containing the simple statements p, q, r, and s. *

   c) Use the list in part (b) to construct a truth table for $(q \land p) \lor (\sim r \land s)$. *

   d) Construct a truth table for $(\sim r \land \sim s) \land (\sim p \lor q)$. *

67. Must $(p \land \sim q) \lor r$ and $(q \land \sim r) \lor p$ have the same number of trues in their answer columns? Explain. Yes

Internet/Research Activities

68. Do research and write a report on each of the following.

   a) The relationship between *negation* in logic and *complement* in set theory.

   b) The relationship between *conjunction* in logic and *intersection* in set theory.

   c) The relationship between *disjunction* in logic and *union* in set theory.

            *See Instructor Answer Appendix

Truth Tables for the Conditional and Biconditional

Suppose I said to you, "If you get an A, then I will buy you a car." As we discussed in Section 3.1, this statement is called a *conditional* statement. In this section, we will discuss under what conditions a conditional statement is true and under what conditions a conditional statement is false.

Why *This is Important* Understanding when conditional statements are true is essential to understanding logic and real-life documents such as wills, trusts, and contracts.

▲ *Under what conditions is the statement* If you get an A, then I will buy you a car *true?*

Table 3.16 Conditional

p	q	$p \rightarrow q$
T	T	T
T	F	F
F	T	T
F	F	T

Conditional

In Section 3.1, we mentioned that the statement preceding the conditional symbol is called the *antecedent* and that the statement following the conditional symbol is called the *consequent*. For example, consider $(p \lor q) \rightarrow [\sim(q \land r)]$. In this statement, $(p \lor q)$ is the antecedent and $[\sim(q \land r)]$ is the consequent.

To develop a truth table for the conditional statement, consider the statement "If you get an A, then I will buy you a car." Assume this statement is true except when I have actually broken my promise to you.

Let
  p: You get an A.
  q: I buy you a car.

Translated into symbolic form, the statement becomes $p \rightarrow q$. Let's examine the four cases shown in Table 3.16.

CASE 1: (T, T) You get an A, and I buy a car for you. I have met my commitment, and the statement is true.

CASE 2: (T, F) You get an A, and I do not buy a car for you. I have broken my promise, and the statement is false.

What happens if you don't get an A? If you don't get an A, I no longer have a commitment to you, and therefore I cannot break my promise.

CASE 3: (F, T) You do not get an A, and I buy you a car. I have not broken my promise, and therefore the statement is true.

CASE 4: (F, F) You do not get an A, and I don't buy you a car. I have not broken my promise, and therefore the statement is true.

The conditional statement is false when the antecedent is true and the consequent is false. In every other case the conditional statement is true.

The **conditional statement** $p \rightarrow q$ is true in every case except when p is a true statement and q is a false statement.

Example 1 *A Truth Table with a Conditional*

Construct a truth table for the statement $\sim p \rightarrow \sim q$.

Solution Because this statement is a conditional, the answer will lie under the $\rightarrow$. Fill out the truth table by placing the appropriate truth values under $\sim p$, column 1,

Table 3.17

p	q	$\sim p$	$\rightarrow$	$\sim q$
T	T	F	T	F
T	F	F	T	T
F	T	T	F	F
F	F	T	T	T
		1	3	2

Table 3.18

p	q	r	p	$\rightarrow$	$(\sim q$	$\wedge$	$r)$
T	T	T	T	F	F	F	T
T	T	F	T	F	F	F	F
T	F	T	T	T	T	T	T
T	F	F	T	F	T	F	F
F	T	T	F	T	F	F	T
F	T	F	F	T	F	F	F
F	F	T	F	T	T	T	T
F	F	F	F	T	T	F	F
			4	5	1	3	2

and under $\sim q$, column 2 (see Table 3.17). Then, using the information given in the truth table for the conditional (Table 3.16 on page 118) and the truth values in columns 1 and 2, determine the solution, column 3. In row 1, the antecedent, $\sim p$, is false and the consequent, $\sim q$, is also false. Row 1 is F $\rightarrow$ F, which according to row 4 of Table 3.16, is T. Likewise, row 2 of Table 3.17 is F $\rightarrow$ T, which is T. Row 3 is T $\rightarrow$ F, which is F. Row 4 is T $\rightarrow$ T, which is T. ∎

Example 2 *A Conditional Truth Table with Three Simple Statements*

Construct a truth table for the statement $p \rightarrow (\sim q \wedge r)$.

Solution Because this statement is a conditional, the answer will lie under the $\rightarrow$. Work within the parentheses first. Place the truth values under $\sim q$, column 1, and r, column 2 (Table 3.18). Then take the conjunction of columns 1 and 2 to obtain column 3. Next, place the truth values under p in column 4. To determine the answer, column 5, use columns 3 and 4 and the information of the conditional statement given in Table 3.16. Column 4 represents the truth values of the antecedent, and column 3 represents the truth values of the consequent. Remember that the conditional is false only when the antecedent is true and the consequent is false, as in cases (rows) 1, 2, and 4 of column 5. ∎

Example 3 *Examining an Advertisement*

An advertisement for Perky Morning coffee makes the following claim: "If you drink Perky Morning coffee, then you will not be sluggish and you will have a great day." Translate the statement into symbolic form and construct a truth table.

Solution Let

p: You drink Perky Morning coffee.
q: You will be sluggish.
r: You will have a great day.

In symbolic form, the claim is

$$p \rightarrow (\sim q \wedge r)$$

This symbolic statement is identical to the statement in Table 3.18, and the truth tables are the same. Column 3 represents the truth values of $(\sim q \wedge r)$, which corresponds to the statement "You will not be sluggish and you will have a great day." Note that column 3 is true in cases (rows) 3 and 7. In case 3, since p is true, you drank Perky Morning coffee. In case 7, however, since p is false, you did not drink Perky Morning coffee. From this information we can conclude that it is possible for you to not be sluggish and for you to have a great day without drinking Perky Morning coffee. ∎

A truth table cannot by itself determine whether a compound statement is true or false. However, a truth table does allow us to examine all possible cases for compound statements.

Biconditional

The *biconditional statement* $p \leftrightarrow q$ means that $p \rightarrow q$ and $q \rightarrow p$, or, symbolically, $(p \rightarrow q) \wedge (q \rightarrow p)$. To determine the truth table for $p \leftrightarrow q$, we will construct the truth table for $(p \rightarrow q) \wedge (q \rightarrow p)$ (Table 3.19 on page 120). Table 3.20 on page 120 shows the truth values for the biconditional statement.

Table 3.19

p	q	$(p$	$\rightarrow$	$q)$	$\land$	$(q$	$\rightarrow$	$p)$
T	T	T	T	T	T	T	T	T
T	F	T	F	F	F	F	T	T
F	T	F	T	T	F	T	F	F
F	F	F	T	F	T	F	T	F
		1	3	2	7	4	6	5

Table 3.20 Biconditional

p	q	$p \leftrightarrow q$
T	T	T
T	F	F
F	T	F
F	F	T

From Table 3.20 we see that the biconditional statement is true when the antecedent and the consequent have the same truth value and false when the antecedent and consequent have different truth values.

> The **biconditional statement** $p \leftrightarrow q$ is true only when p and q have the same truth value, that is, when both are true or both are false.

Example 4 *A Truth Table Using a Biconditional*

Construct a truth table for the statement $\sim p \leftrightarrow (\sim q \rightarrow r)$.

Solution Since there are three letters, there must be eight cases. The parentheses indicate that the answer must be under the biconditional, as shown in Table 3.21. Use columns 1 and 4 to obtain the answer in column 5. When columns 1 and 4 have the same truth values, place a T in column 5. When columns 1 and 4 have different truth values, place an F in column 5.

Table 3.21

p	q	r	$\sim p$	$\leftrightarrow$	$(\sim q$	$\rightarrow$	$r)$
T	T	T	F	F	F	T	T
T	T	F	F	F	F	T	F
T	F	T	F	F	T	T	T
T	F	F	F	T	T	F	F
F	T	T	T	T	F	T	T
F	T	F	T	T	F	T	F
F	F	T	T	T	T	T	T
F	F	F	T	F	T	F	F
			1	5	2	4	3

In Section 3.2, we showed that finding the truth value of a compound statement for a specific case does not require constructing an entire truth table. Examples 5 and 6 illustrate this technique for the conditional and the biconditional.

Example 5 *Determine the Truth Value of a Compound Statement*

Determine the truth value of the statement $(\sim p \leftrightarrow q) \rightarrow (\sim q \leftrightarrow r)$ when p is false, q is true, and r is false.

Solution Substitute the truth value for each simple statement:

$$(\sim p \leftrightarrow q) \to (\sim q \leftrightarrow r)$$
$$(T \leftrightarrow T) \;\to\; (F \leftrightarrow F)$$
$$T \qquad \to \qquad T$$
$$T$$

For this specific case, the statement is true.　■

Example 6 *Determine the Truth Value of a Compound Statement*

Determine the truth value for each simple statement. Then use the truth values to determine the truth value of the compound statement.

a) If 15 is an even number, then 29 is an even number.

b) Vanderbilt University is in Tennessee and Wake Forest University is in Alaska, if and only if Syracuse University is in Alabama.

Solution

a) Let

$$p\text{:}\quad \text{15 is an even number.}$$
$$q\text{:}\quad \text{29 is an even number.}$$

Then the statement "If 15 is an even number, then 29 is an even number" can be written $p \to q$. Since 15 is not an even number, p is a false statement. Also, since 29 is not an even number, q is a false statement. We substitute F for p and F for q and evaluate the statement:

$$p \to q$$
$$F \to F$$
$$T$$

Therefore, "If 15 is an even number, then 29 is an even number" is a true statement.

b) Let

$$p\text{:}\quad \text{Vanderbilt University is in Tennessee.}$$
$$q\text{:}\quad \text{Wake Forest University is in Alaska.}$$
$$r\text{:}\quad \text{Syracuse University is in Alabama.}$$

The original compound statement can be written $(p \wedge q) \leftrightarrow r$. By checking the Internet or other references we can find that Vanderbilt University is in Tennessee, Wake Forest University is in North Carolina, and Syracuse University is in New York. Therefore, p is a true statement, but q and r are false statements. We will substitute T for p, F for q, and F for r and evaluate the compound statement:

$$(p \wedge q) \leftrightarrow r$$
$$(T \wedge F) \leftrightarrow F$$
$$F \qquad \leftrightarrow F$$
$$T$$

Therefore, the original compound statement is true.　■

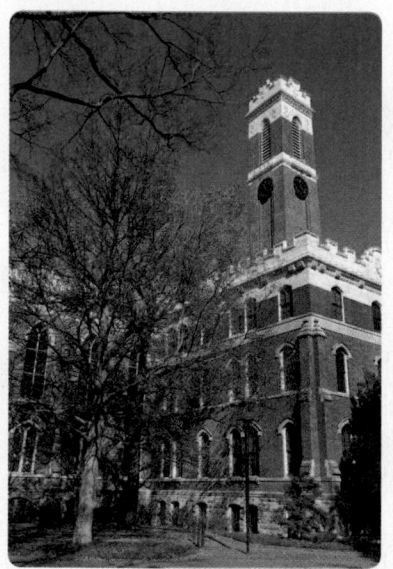

▲ *Vanderbilt University*

Example 7 *Using Real Data in Compound Statements*

The graph in Fig. 3.2 on page 122 represents the student population by age group in 2009 for the State College of Florida (SCF). Use this graph to determine the truth value of the following compound statements.

Satisfiability Problems

Suppose you are hosting a dinner party for seven people: Yasumasa, Marie, Albert, Stephen, Leonhard, Karl, and Emmy. You need to develop a seating plan around your circular dining room table that would satisfy all your guests. Albert and Emmy are great friends and must sit together. Yasumasa and Karl haven't spoken to each other in years and cannot sit by each other. Leonhard must sit by Marie or by Albert, but he cannot sit by Karl. Stephen insists he sit by Albert. Can you come up with a plan that would satisfy all your guests? Now imagine the difficulty of such a problem as the list of guests, and their demands, grows.

Problems such as this are known as *satisfiability* problems. The symbolic logic you are studying in this chapter allows computer scientists to represent these problems with symbols and solve the problems using computers. Even with the fastest computers, some satisfiability problems take an enormous amount of time to solve.

One solution to the problem posed above is shown upside down below. Exercises 79 and 80 on page 127 have other satisfiability problems.

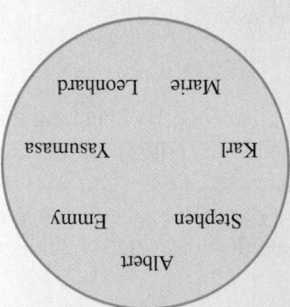

State College of Florida Population by Age Group

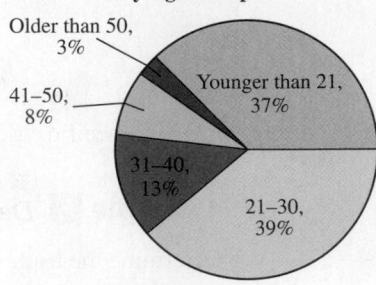

Older than 50, 3%

41–50, 8%

Younger than 21, 37%

31–40, 13%

21–30, 39%

Source: www.scf.edu

Figure 3.2

a) If 37% of the SCF population is younger than 21 or 26% of the SCF population is age 21–30, then 13% of the SCF population is age 31–40.

b) 3% of the SCF population is older than 50 and 8% of the SCF population is age 41–50, if and only if 19% of the SCF population is age 21–30.

Solution

a) Let

p: 37% of the SCF population is younger than 21.
q: 26% of the SCF population is age 21–30.
r: 13% of the SCF population is age 31–40.

Then the original statement can be written $(p \lor q) \rightarrow r$. We can see from Fig. 3.2 that both p and r are true statements and that q is a false statement. Substitute T for p, F for q, and T for r and evaluate the statement:

$$(p \lor q) \rightarrow r$$
$$(T \lor F) \rightarrow T$$
$$T \quad \rightarrow T$$
$$T$$

Therefore, "If 37% of the SCF population is younger than 21 or 26% of the SCF population is age 21–30, then 13% of the SCF population is age 31–40" is a true statement.

b) Let

p: 3% of the SCF population is older than 50.
q: 8% of the SCF population is age 41–50.
r: 19% of the SCF population is age 21–30.

Then the original statement can be written $(p \land q) \leftrightarrow r$. We can see from Fig. 3.2 that p and q are both true statements and r is a false statement. Substitute T for p, T for q, and F for r and evaluate the statement:

$$(p \land q) \leftrightarrow r$$
$$(T \land T) \leftrightarrow F$$
$$T \quad \leftrightarrow F$$
$$F$$

Therefore, the original statement, "3% of the SCF population is older than 50 and 8% of the SCF population is age 41–50, if and only if 19% of the SCF population is age 21–30," is a false statement.

Self-Contradictions, Tautologies, and Implications

Two special situations can occur in the truth table of a compound statement: The statement may always be false, or the statement may always be true. We give such statements special names.

> **Definition: Self-contradiction**
>
> A **self-contradiction** is a compound statement that is always false.

When every truth value in the answer column of the truth table is false, then the statement is a self-contradiction.

Table 3.22

p	q	$(p \leftrightarrow q)$	$\wedge$	$(p$	$\leftrightarrow$	$\sim q)$
T	T	T	F	T	F	F
T	F	F	F	T	T	T
F	T	F	F	F	T	F
F	F	T	F	F	F	T
		1	5	2	4	3

Example 8 *All Falses, a Self-Contradiction*

Construct a truth table for the statement $(p \leftrightarrow q) \wedge (p \leftrightarrow \sim q)$.

Solution See Table 3.22. In this example, the truth values are false in each case of column 5. This statement is an example of a self-contradiction or a *logically false statement*. ■

> **Definition: Tautology**
>
> A **tautology** is a compound statement that is always true.

When every truth value in the answer column of the truth table is true, the statement is a tautology.

Example 9 *All Trues, a Tautology*

Construct a truth table for the statement $(p \wedge q) \rightarrow (p \vee r)$.

Solution The answer is given in column 3 of Table 3.23. The truth values are true in every case. Thus, the statement is an example of a tautology or a *logically true statement*.

Table 3.23

p	q	r	$(p \wedge q)$	$\rightarrow$	$(p \vee r)$
T	T	T	T	T	T
T	T	F	T	T	T
T	F	T	F	T	T
T	F	F	F	T	T
F	T	T	F	T	T
F	T	F	F	T	F
F	F	T	F	T	T
F	F	F	F	T	F
			1	3	2

The conditional statement $(p \wedge q) \rightarrow (p \vee r)$ is a tautology. Conditional statements that are tautologies are called *implications*. In Example 9, we can say that $p \wedge q$ implies $p \vee r$.

▲ *"Heads I win, tails you lose." Do you think that this statement is a tautology, self-contradiction, or neither? See Exercise 77 on page 126.*

Definition: Implication

An **implication** is a conditional statement that is a tautology.

In any implication the antecedent of the conditional statement implies the consequent. In other words, if the antecedent is true, then the consequent must also be true. That is, the consequent will be true whenever the antecedent is true.

Table 3.24

p	q	$[(p \land q)$	$\land$	$p]$	$\rightarrow$	q
T	T	T	T	T	T	T
T	F	F	F	T	T	F
F	T	F	F	F	T	T
F	F	F	F	F	T	F
		1	3	2	5	4

Example 10 *An Implication?*

Determine whether the conditional statement $[(p \land q) \land p] \rightarrow q$ is an implication.

Solution If the conditional statement is a tautology, the conditional statement is an implication. Because the conditional statement is a tautology (see Table 3.24), the conditional statement is an implication. The antecedent $[(p \land q) \land p]$ implies the consequent q. Note that the antecedent is true only in case 1 and that the consequent is also true in case 1. ∎

SECTION 3.3 *Exercises*

Warm Up Exercises

In Exercises 1–6, fill in the blanks with an appropriate word, phrase, or symbol(s).

1. The conditional statement $p \rightarrow q$ is _____ only when p is true and q is false. False

2. In the conditional statement $p \rightarrow q$,

   a) The lower-case letter p represents the _____.
   Antecedent

   b) The lower-case letter q represents the _____.
   Consequent

3. The biconditional statement $p \leftrightarrow q$ is _____ only when p and q have the same truth value. True

4. A compound statement that is always true is known as a _____. Tautology

5. A compound statement that is always false is known as a _____. Self-contradiction

6. A conditional statement that is a tautology is known as an _____. Implication

Practice the Skills

In Exercises 7–16, construct a truth table for the statement.

7. $\sim p \rightarrow q$ *

8. $\sim p \rightarrow \sim q$ *

9. $\sim(p \rightarrow \sim q)$ *

10. $\sim(\sim p \leftrightarrow q)$ *

11. $\sim q \leftrightarrow p$ *

12. $(p \leftrightarrow q) \rightarrow p$ *

13. $p \leftrightarrow (q \lor p)$ *

14. $(\sim q \land p) \rightarrow \sim q$ *

15. $q \rightarrow (p \rightarrow \sim q)$ *

16. $(p \lor q) \leftrightarrow (p \land q)$ *

In Exercises 17–24, construct a truth table for the statement.

17. $\sim p \rightarrow (q \land r)$ *

18. $q \lor (p \rightarrow \sim r)$ *

19. $(q \lor \sim r) \leftrightarrow \sim p$ *

20. $(p \land r) \rightarrow (q \lor r)$ *

21. $(\sim r \lor \sim q) \rightarrow p$ *

22. $[r \land (q \lor \sim p)] \leftrightarrow \sim p$ *

23. $(p \rightarrow q) \leftrightarrow (\sim q \rightarrow \sim r)$ *

24. $(\sim p \leftrightarrow \sim q) \rightarrow (\sim q \leftrightarrow r)$ *

*See Instructor Answer Appendix

In Exercises 25–30, write the statement in symbolic form. Then construct a truth table for the symbolic statement.

25. If it is raining, then the baseball game is canceled and we can eat dinner together. *

26. We advance in the tournament if and only if Max plays, or Pondo does not show up. *

27. The election was fair if and only if the polling station stayed open until 8 P.M., or we will request a recount. *

28. If the dam holds then we can go fishing, if and only if the pole is not broken. *

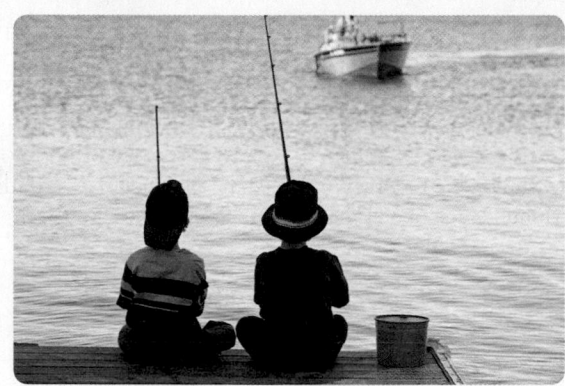

29. If Mary Andrews does not send me an e-mail then we can call her, or we can write to Mom. *

30. It is false that if Eileen Jones went to lunch, then she cannot take a message and we will have to go home. *

In Exercises 31–36, determine whether the statement is a tautology, self-contradiction, or neither.

31. $\sim p \rightarrow p$ Neither

32. $(\sim p \vee q) \leftrightarrow \sim q$ Neither

33. $\sim p \wedge (q \leftrightarrow \sim q)$ Self-contradiction

34. $(p \wedge \sim q) \rightarrow q$ Neither

35. $(\sim q \rightarrow p) \vee \sim q$ Tautology

36. $[(p \rightarrow q) \vee r] \leftrightarrow [(p \wedge q) \rightarrow r]$ Neither

In Exercises 37–42, determine whether the statement is an implication.

37. $\sim p \rightarrow p$ Not an implication

38. $p \rightarrow (p \vee q)$ Implication

39. $\sim p \rightarrow \sim (p \wedge q)$ Implication

40. $(p \vee q) \rightarrow (p \vee \sim r)$ Not an implication

41. $[(p \rightarrow q) \wedge (q \rightarrow p)] \rightarrow (p \leftrightarrow q)$ Implication

42. $[(p \vee q) \wedge r] \rightarrow (p \vee q)$ Implication

In Exercises 43–52, if p is true, q is false, and r is true, find the truth value of the statement.

43. $p \rightarrow (q \rightarrow r)$ True

44. $(p \wedge \sim q) \rightarrow \sim r$ False

45. $(p \wedge q) \leftrightarrow (q \vee r)$ False

46. $r \rightarrow (\sim p \leftrightarrow \sim q)$ False

47. $(\sim p \wedge \sim q) \vee \sim r$ False

48. $\sim [p \rightarrow (q \wedge r)]$ True

49. $(\sim p \leftrightarrow r) \vee (\sim q \leftrightarrow r)$ True

50. $(r \rightarrow \sim p) \wedge (q \rightarrow \sim r)$ False

51. $\sim [(p \vee q) \leftrightarrow (p \rightarrow \sim r)]$ True

52. $[(\sim r \rightarrow \sim q) \vee (p \wedge \sim r)] \rightarrow q$ False

Problem Solving

In Exercises 53–60, determine the truth value for each simple statement. Then, using the truth values, determine the truth value of the compound statement.

53. If $\sqrt{25} = 5$, then $\sqrt{49} = 7$. True

54. If $5 < 1$, then $7 > 10$. True

55. If a cat has whiskers or a fish can swim, then a dog lays eggs. False

56. If Dallas is in Texas and St. Louis is in Missouri, then Detroit is in California. False

57. Apple makes computers, if and only if Nike makes sports shoes or Rolex makes watches. True

58. Spike Lee is a movie director, or if Halle Berry is a school teacher then George Clooney is a circus clown. True

59. Mother's Day is in May and Father's Day is in December, if and only if Thanksgiving is in April. True

60. Honda makes automobiles or Honda makes motorcycles, if and only if Toyota makes cereal. False

In Exercises 61–64, use the information provided about the moons for the planets Jupiter and Saturn to determine the truth values of the simple statements. Then determine the truth value of the compound statement.

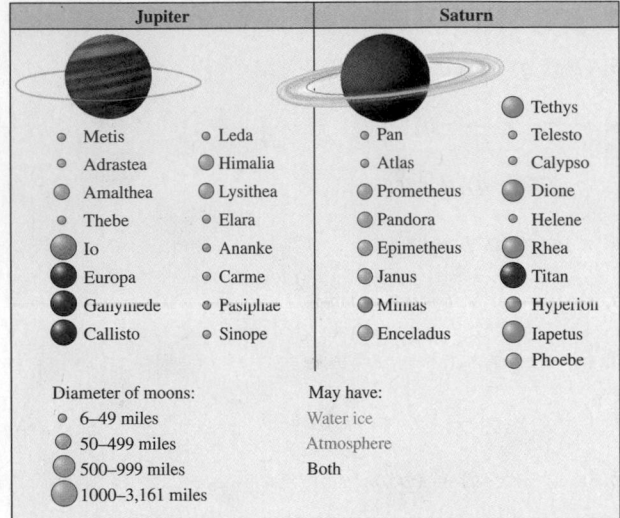

Source: Data from *Time* Magazine

61. ***Jupiter's Moons*** Io has a diameter of 1000–3161 miles or Thebe may have water, and Io may have atmosphere. True

62. ***Moons of Saturn*** Titan may have water and Titan may have atmosphere, if and only if Janus may have water. False

63. ***Moon Comparisons*** Phoebe has a larger diameter than Rhea if and only if Callisto may have water ice, and Calypso has a diameter of 6–49 miles. False

64. ***Moon Comparisons*** If Jupiter has 16 moons or Saturn does not have 18 moons, then Saturn has 7 moons that may have water ice. True

College Credits *In Exercises 65 and 66, use the graph to determine the truth value of each simple statement. Then determine the truth value of the compound statement.*

The following graph shows the number of credits in various categories needed by Jose Silva to earn his Associate in Arts degree from Keiser University.

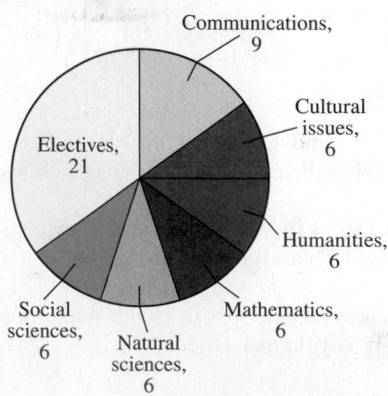

Credits Needed for an A.A. Degree

65. The number of communications credits needed is more than the number of mathematics credits needed and the number of cultural issues credits needed is equal to the number of humanities credits needed, if and only if the number of social sciences credits needed is more than the number of natural sciences credits needed. False

66. If the number of elective credits needed is 21 or the number of communications credits needed is 15, then the number of humanities credits needed is equal to the number of mathematics credits needed. True

In Exercises 67–72, suppose both of the following statements are false.

  p: Muhundan spoke at the teachers' conference.

  q: Muhundan received the outstanding teacher award.

Find the truth values of each compound statement.

67. If Muhundan received the outstanding teacher award, then Muhundan spoke at the teachers' conference. True

68. If Muhundan spoke at the teachers' conference, then Muhundan did not receive the outstanding teacher award. True

69. If Muhundan did not receive the outstanding teacher award, then Muhundan spoke at the teachers' conference. False

70. Muhundan did not receive the outstanding teacher award if and only if Muhundan spoke at the teachers' conference. False

71. Muhundan received the outstanding teacher award if and only if Muhundan spoke at the teachers' conference. True

72. If Muhundan did not receive the outstanding teacher award, then Muhundan did not speak at the teachers' conference. True

73. ***A New Computer*** Your parents make the following statement to your sister, "If you get straight A's this semester, then we will buy you a new computer." At the end of the semester your parents buy your sister a new computer. Can you conclude that your sister got straight A's? Explain. *

74. ***Job Interview*** Consider the statement "If your interview goes well, then you will be offered the job." If you are interviewed and then offered the job, can you conclude that your interview went well? Explain. *

Challenge Problems/Group Activities

In Exercises 75 and 76, construct truth tables for the symbolic statement.

75. $[p \lor (q \rightarrow \sim r)] \leftrightarrow (p \land \sim q)$ *

76. $[(r \rightarrow \sim q) \rightarrow \sim p] \lor (q \leftrightarrow \sim r)$ *

77. Is the statement "Heads I win, tails you lose" a tautology, a self-contradiction, or neither? Explain your answer. *

*See Instructor Answer Appendix

78. Construct a truth table for

a) $(p \lor q) \to (r \land s)$. T F F F T F F F T F F F T T T T

b) $(q \to \sim p) \lor (r \leftrightarrow s)$. T F F T T T T T T T T T T T T T

Recreational Mathematics

79. *Satisfiability Problem* Refer to the Recreational Mathematics box on page 122 and then solve the following satisfiability problem. Allen, Booker, Chris, and Dennis all were born in the same year—one in January, one in February, one in March, and one in April. Chris was born before Dennis. Dennis was born two months after Booker. Booker was born after Allen, but before Chris. Find out who was born in each month. *

80. *Cat Puzzle* Solve the following puzzle. The Joneses have four cats. The parents are Tiger and Boots, and the kittens are Sam and Sue. Each cat insists on eating out of its own bowl. To complicate matters, each cat will eat only its own brand of cat food. The colors of the bowls are red, yellow, green, and blue. The different types of cat food are Whiskas, Friskies, Nine Lives, and Meow Mix. Tiger will eat Meow Mix if and only if it is in a yellow bowl. If Boots is to eat her food, then it must be in a yellow bowl.

Mrs. Jones knows that the label on the can containing Sam's food is the same color as his bowl. Boots eats Whiskas. Meow Mix and Nine Lives are packaged in a brown paper bag. The color of Sue's bowl is green if and only if she eats Meow Mix. The label on the Friskies can is red. Match each cat with its food and the bowl of the correct color. *

81. *The Youngest Triplet* The Barr triplets have an annoying habit: Whenever a question is asked of the three of them, two tell the truth and the third lies. When I asked them which of them was born last, they replied as follows.

> *Mary:* Katie was born last.
> *Katie:* I am the youngest.
> *Annie:* Mary is the youngest.

Which of the Barr triplets was born last?

Katie was born last. Katie and Mary are saying the same thing.

Internet/Research Activity

82. Select an advertisement from the Internet, a newspaper, or a magazine that makes or implies a conditional statement. Analyze the advertisement to determine whether the consequent necessarily follows from the antecedent. Explain your answer. (See Example 3.)

*See Instructor Answer Appendix

SECTION 3.4 Equivalent Statements

▲ *Which statement is equivalent to If it is sunny, then we go to the beach?*

Suppose your friend makes the following statements:

> If it is sunny, then we go to the beach.
>
> If we go to the beach, then it is sunny.
>
> If it is not sunny, then we do not go to the beach.
>
> If we do not go to the beach, then it is not sunny.

Are these statements all saying the same thing, or does each one say something completely different from the others? In this section, we will study how we can answer this question by using logic symbols and truth tables. We also will learn to identify variations of conditional statements.

Why *This is Important* Understanding when two statements are equivalent is important to understanding advertisers' claims, political statements, and legal documents.

Equivalent statements are an important concept in the study of logic.

Definition: Equivalent

Two statements are **equivalent**, symbolized ⇔,* if both statements have exactly the same truth values in the answer columns of the truth tables.

Sometimes the words *logically equivalent* are used in place of the word *equivalent*.

---

*The symbol ≡ is also used to indicate equivalent statements.

To determine whether two statements are equivalent, construct a truth table for each statement and compare the answer columns of the truth tables. If the answer columns are identical, the statements are equivalent. If the answer columns are not identical, the statements are not equivalent.

Example 1 *Equivalent Statements*

Determine whether the following two statements are equivalent.

$$p \wedge (q \vee r)$$
$$(p \wedge q) \vee (p \wedge r)$$

Solution Construct a truth table for each statement (see Table 3.25).

Table 3.25

p	*q*	*r*	*p*	$\wedge$	*(q ∨ r)*	*(p ∧ q)*	$\vee$	*(p ∧ r)*
T	T	T	T	T	T	T	T	T
T	T	F	T	T	T	T	T	F
T	F	T	T	T	T	F	T	T
T	F	F	T	F	F	F	F	F
F	T	T	F	F	T	F	F	F
F	T	F	F	F	T	F	F	F
F	F	T	F	F	T	F	F	F
F	F	F	F	F	F	F	F	F
			1	3	2	1	3	2

Because the truth tables have the same answer (column 3 for both tables), the statements are equivalent. Therefore, we can write

$$p \wedge (q \vee r) \Leftrightarrow (p \wedge q) \vee (p \wedge r)$$

Example 2 *Are the Following Equivalent Statements?*

Determine whether the following statements are equivalent.

a) If your homework is finished and you have washed the dishes, then you can watch television.

b) If your homework is not finished or you have not washed the dishes, then you cannot watch television.

Solution First write each statement in symbolic form, then construct a truth table for each statement. If the answer columns of both truth tables are identical, then the statements are equivalent. If the answer columns are not identical, then the statements are not equivalent.

Let

p: Your homework is finished.
q: You have washed the dishes.
r: You can watch television.

In symbolic form, the statements are

a) $(p \wedge q) \to r$.   b) $(\sim p \vee \sim q) \to \sim r$.

The truth tables for these statements are given in Tables 3.26 and 3.27, respectively. The answers in the columns labeled 5 are not identical, so the statements are not equivalent.

Table 3.26

p	*q*	*r*	*(p*	$\wedge$	*q)*	$\to$	*r*
T	T	T	T	T	T	T	T
T	T	F	T	T	T	F	F
T	F	T	T	F	F	T	T
T	F	F	T	F	F	T	F
F	T	T	F	F	T	T	T
F	T	F	F	F	T	T	F
F	F	T	F	F	F	T	T
F	F	F	F	F	F	T	F
			1	3	2	5	4

Table 3.27

p	*q*	*r*	*(~p*	$\vee$	*~q)*	$\to$	*~r*
T	T	T	F	F	F	T	F
T	T	F	F	F	F	T	T
T	F	T	F	T	T	F	F
T	F	F	F	T	T	T	T
F	T	T	T	T	F	F	F
F	T	F	T	T	F	T	T
F	F	T	T	T	T	F	F
F	F	F	T	T	T	T	T
			1	3	2	5	4

┌─ **Example 3** *Which Statements Are Logically Equivalent?*

Determine which statement is logically equivalent to "It is not true that the tire is both out of balance and flat."

a) If the tire is not flat, then the tire is not out of balance.

b) The tire is not out of balance or the tire is not flat.

c) The tire is not flat and the tire is not out of balance.

d) If the tire is not out of balance, then the tire is not flat.

Solution To determine whether any of the choices are equivalent to the given statement, first write the given statement and the choices in symbolic form. Then construct truth tables and compare the answer columns of the truth tables.

Let

$$p: \quad \text{The tire is out of balance.}$$
$$q: \quad \text{The tire is flat.}$$

The given statement may be written "It is not true that the tire is out of balance and the tire is flat." The statement is expressed in symbolic form as $\sim (p \land q)$. Using p and q as indicated, choices (a) through (d) may be expressed symbolically as

a) $\sim q \to \sim p$.   b) $\sim p \lor \sim q$.   c) $\sim q \land \sim p$.   d) $\sim p \to \sim q$.

Now construct a truth table for the given statement (Table 3.28) and for each statement (a) through (d), given in Table 3.29 (a) through (d). By examining the truth tables, we see that the given statement, $\sim (p \land q)$, is logically equivalent to choice (b), $\sim p \lor \sim q$. Therefore, the correct answer is "The tire is not out of balance or the tire is not flat." This statement is logically equivalent to the statement "It is not true that the tire is both out of balance and flat."

Table 3.28

p	q	$\sim$	$(p$	$\land$	$q)$
T	T	F	T	T	T
T	F	T	T	F	F
F	T	T	F	F	T
F	F	T	F	F	F
		4	1	3	2

Table 3.29

		(a)			(b)			(c)			(d)		
p	q	$\sim q$	$\to$	$\sim p$	$\sim p$	$\lor$	$\sim q$	$\sim q$	$\land$	$\sim p$	$\sim p$	$\to$	$\sim q$
T	T	F	T	F	F	F	F	F	F	F	F	T	F
T	F	T	F	F	F	T	T	T	F	F	F	T	T
F	T	F	T	T	T	T	F	F	F	T	T	F	F
F	F	T	T	T	T	T	T	T	T	T	T	T	T

De Morgan's Laws

Example 3 showed that a statement of the form $\sim (p \land q)$ is equivalent to a statement of the form $\sim p \lor \sim q$. Thus, we may write $\sim (p \land q) \Leftrightarrow \sim p \lor \sim q$. This equivalent statement is one of two special laws called De Morgan's laws. The laws, named after Augustus De Morgan, an English mathematician, were first introduced in Section 2.4, where they applied to sets.

De Morgan's Laws

1. $\sim (p \land q) \Leftrightarrow \sim p \lor \sim q$
2. $\sim (p \lor q) \Leftrightarrow \sim p \land \sim q$

You can demonstrate that De Morgan's second law is true by constructing and comparing truth tables for $\sim(p \lor q)$ and $\sim p \land \sim q$. Do so now.

When using De Morgan's laws, if it becomes necessary to negate an already negated statement, use the fact that $\sim(\sim p)$ is equivalent to p. For example, the negation of the statement "Today is not Monday" is "Today is Monday."

Example 4 *Use De Morgan's Laws*

Select the statement that is logically equivalent to "I do not have investments, but I do not have debts."

a) I do not have investments or I do not have debts.

b) It is false that I have investments and I have debts.

c) It is false that I have investments or I have debts.

d) I have investments or I have debts.

Solution To determine which statement is equivalent, write each statement in symbolic form.

Let

$$p: \quad \text{I have investments.}$$
$$q: \quad \text{I have debts.}$$

The statement "I do not have investments, but I do not have debts" written symbolically is $\sim p \land \sim q$. Recall that the word *but* means the same thing as *and*. Now, write parts (a) through (d) symbolically.

a) $\sim p \lor \sim q$ b) $\sim(p \land q)$ c) $\sim(p \lor q)$ d) $p \lor q$

De Morgan's law shows that $\sim p \land \sim q$ is equivalent to $\sim(p \lor q)$. Therefore, the answer is (c): "It is false that I have investments or I have debts." ∎

Example 5 *Using De Morgan's Laws to Write an Equivalent Statement*

Write a statement that is logically equivalent to "It is not true that tomatoes are poisonous or eating peppers cures the common cold."

Solution Let

$$p: \quad \text{Tomatoes are poisonous.}$$
$$q: \quad \text{Eating peppers cures the common cold.}$$

The given statement is of the form $\sim(p \lor q)$. Using the second of De Morgan's laws, we see that an equivalent statement in symbols is $\sim p \land \sim q$. Therefore, an equivalent statement in words is "Tomatoes are not poisonous and eating peppers does not cure the common cold." ∎

Consider $\sim(p \land q) \Leftrightarrow \sim p \lor \sim q$, one of De Morgan's laws. To go from $\sim(p \land q)$ to $\sim p \lor \sim q$, we negate both the p and the q within parentheses; change the conjunction, $\land$, to a disjunction, $\lor$; and remove the negation symbol preceding the left parentheses and the parentheses themselves. We can use a similar procedure to obtain equivalent statements. For example,

$$\sim(\sim p \land q) \Leftrightarrow p \lor \sim q$$
$$\sim(p \land \sim q) \Leftrightarrow \sim p \lor q$$

We can use a similar procedure to obtain equivalent statements when a disjunction is within parentheses. Note that

$$\sim(\sim p \lor q) \Leftrightarrow p \land \sim q$$
$$\sim(p \lor \sim q) \Leftrightarrow \sim p \land q$$

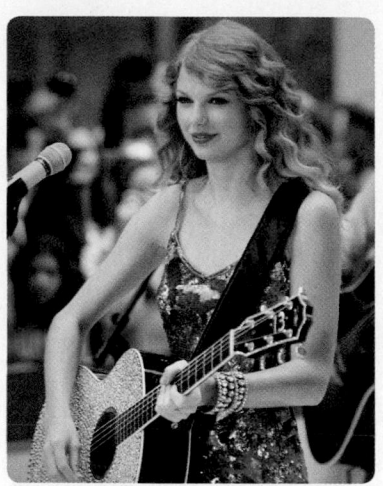

▲ *Taylor Swift*

Profile In Mathematics

Augustus De Morgan

Augustus De Morgan (1806–1871), the son of a member of the East India Company, was born in India and educated at Trinity College, Cambridge (UK). One of the great reformers of logic in the nineteenth century, De Morgan made his greatest contribution to the subject by realizing that logic as it had come down from Aristotle was narrow in scope and could be applied to a wider range of arguments. His work laid the foundation for modern, symbolic logic.

┌ Example **6** *Using De Morgan's Laws to Write an Equivalent Statement*

Use De Morgan's laws to write a statement logically equivalent to "Taylor Swift did not win an Academy of Country Music award, but she had a top-selling record."

Solution Let

  p: Taylor Swift won an Academy of Country Music award.
  q: Taylor Swift had a top-selling record.

The statement written symbolically is $\sim p \wedge q$. Earlier we showed that

$$\sim p \wedge q \Leftrightarrow \sim(p \vee \sim q)$$

Therefore, the statement "It is false that Taylor Swift won an Academy of Country Music award or Taylor Swift did not have a top-selling record" is logically equivalent to the given statement. ∎

There are strong similarities between the topics of sets and logic. We can see them by examining De Morgan's laws for sets and logic.

De Morgan's laws: set theory	De Morgan's laws: logic
$(A \cap B)' = A' \cup B'$	$\sim(p \wedge q) \Leftrightarrow \sim p \vee \sim q$
$(A \cup B)' = A' \cap B'$	$\sim(p \vee q) \Leftrightarrow \sim p \wedge \sim q$

The complement in set theory, $'$, is similar to the negation, $\sim$, in logic. The intersection, $\cap$, is similar to the conjunction, $\wedge$; and the union, $\cup$, is similar to the disjunction, $\vee$. If we were to interchange the set symbols with the logic symbols, De Morgan's laws would remain, but in a different form.

  Both $'$ and $\sim$ can be interpreted as *not*.

  Both $\cap$ and $\wedge$ can be interpreted as *and*.

  Both $\cup$ and $\vee$ can be interpreted as *or*.

For example, the set statement $A' \cup B$ can be written as a statement in logic as $\sim a \vee b$.

Statements containing connectives other than *and* and *or* may have equivalent statements. To illustrate this point, construct truth tables for $p \rightarrow q$ and for $\sim p \vee q$. The truth tables will have the same answer columns and therefore the statements are equivalent. We summarize this as follows.

> **The Conditional Statement Written As a Disjunction**
> $$p \rightarrow q \Leftrightarrow \sim p \vee q$$

With these equivalent statements, we can write a conditional statement as a disjunction or a disjunction as a conditional statement. For example, the statement "If the game is polo, then you ride a horse" can be equivalently stated as "The game is not polo or you ride a horse."

To change a conditional statement to a disjunction, negate the antecedent, change the conditional symbol to a disjunction symbol, and keep the consequent the same. To change a disjunction statement to a conditional statement, negate the first statement, change the disjunction symbol to a conditional symbol, and keep the second statement the same.

┌ Example **7** *Rewriting a Disjunction as a Conditional Statement*

Write a conditional statement that is logically equivalent to "The Oregon Ducks will win or the Oregon State Beavers will lose." Assume that the negation of winning is losing.

Solution   Let

p: The Oregon Ducks will win.
q: The Oregon State Beavers will win.

The original statement may be written symbolically as $p \vee \sim q$. To write an equivalent conditional statement, negate the first statement, p, change the disjunction symbol to a conditional symbol, and keep the second statement the same. Symbolically, the equivalent statement is $\sim p \rightarrow \sim q$. The equivalent statement in words is "If the Oregon Ducks lose, then the Oregon State Beavers will lose." ∎

Negation of the Conditional Statement

Now we will discuss how to negate a conditional statement. To negate a conditional statement we use the fact that $p \rightarrow q \Leftrightarrow \sim p \vee q$ and De Morgan's laws. Examples 8 and 9 show the process.

Example 8 *The Negation of a Conditional Statement*

Determine a statement equivalent to $\sim (p \rightarrow q)$.

Solution   Begin with $p \rightarrow q \Leftrightarrow \sim p \vee q$, negate both statements, and use De Morgan's laws.

$$p \rightarrow q \Leftrightarrow \sim p \vee q$$
$$\sim (p \rightarrow q) \Leftrightarrow \sim (\sim p \vee q) \qquad \text{Negate both statements.}$$
$$\Leftrightarrow p \wedge \sim q \qquad \text{De Morgan's laws}$$

Therefore, $\sim (p \rightarrow q)$ is equivalent to $p \wedge \sim q$. ∎

We summarize the result of Example 8 as follows.

> **The Negation of the Conditional Statement Written As a Conjunction**
>
> $$\sim (p \rightarrow q) \Leftrightarrow p \wedge \sim q$$

Example 9 *Write an Equivalent Statement*

Write a statement that is equivalent to "It is false that if you hang the picture then it will be crooked."

Solution   Let

p: You hang the picture.
q: The picture will be crooked.

The given statement can be represented symbolically as $\sim (p \rightarrow q)$. We illustrated in Example 8 that $\sim (p \rightarrow q)$ is equivalent to $p \wedge \sim q$. Therefore, an equivalent statement is "You hang the picture and the picture will not be crooked." ∎

Using the fact that $\sim (p \rightarrow q) \Leftrightarrow p \wedge \sim q$, can you determine what $\sim (p \rightarrow \sim q)$ is equivalent to as a conjunction? If you answered $p \wedge q$ you answered correctly.

Variations of the Conditional Statement

We know that $p \rightarrow q$ is equivalent to $\sim p \vee q$. Are any other statements equivalent to $p \rightarrow q$? Yes, there are many. Now let's look at the variations of the conditional statement to determine whether any are equivalent to the conditional statement. *The variations of the conditional statement are made by switching and/or negating the antecedent and the consequent of a conditional statement.* The variations of the conditional statement are the *converse* of the conditional, the *inverse* of the conditional, and the *contrapositive* of the conditional.

Listed here are the variations of the conditional with their symbolic form and the words we say to read each one.

Variations of the Conditional Statement

Name	Symbolic form	Read
Conditional	$p \rightarrow q$	"If p, then q"
Converse of the conditional	$q \rightarrow p$	"If q, then p"
Inverse of the conditional	$\sim p \rightarrow \sim q$	"If not p, then not q"
Contrapositive of the conditional	$\sim q \rightarrow \sim p$	"If not q, then not p"

TIMELY TIP

The contrapositive statement is always equivalent to the original conditional statement.

To write the converse of the conditional statement, switch the order of the antecedent and the consequent. To write the inverse, negate both the antecedent and the consequent. To write the contrapositive, switch the order of the antecedent and the consequent and then negate both of them.

Are any of the variations of the conditional statement equivalent? To determine the answer, we can construct a truth table for each variation, as shown in Table 3.30. It reveals that *the conditional statement is equivalent to the contrapositive statement and that the converse statement is equivalent to the inverse statement.*

Table 3.30

p	q	Conditional $p \rightarrow q$	Contrapositive $\sim q \rightarrow \sim p$	Converse $q \rightarrow p$	Inverse $\sim p \rightarrow \sim q$
T	T	T	T	T	T
T	F	F	F	T	T
F	T	T	T	F	F
F	F	T	T	T	T

Example 10 *The Converse, Inverse, and Contrapositive*

For the conditional statement "If the song contains sitar music, then the song was written by George Harrison," write the

a) converse. b) inverse. c) contrapositive.

Solution

a) Let

p: The song contains sitar music.

q: The song was written by George Harrison.

The conditional statement is of the form $p \rightarrow q$, so the converse must be of the form $q \rightarrow p$. Therefore, the converse is "If the song was written by George Harrison, then the song contains sitar music."

▲ *A sitar.*

b) The inverse is of the form $\sim p \rightarrow \sim q$. Therefore, the inverse is "If the song does not contain sitar music, then the song was not written by George Harrison."

c) The contrapositive is of the form $\sim q \rightarrow \sim p$. Therefore, the contrapositive is "If the song was not written by George Harrison, then the song does not contain sitar music." ∎

Example 11 *Determine the Truth Values*

Let

p: The number is divisible by 10.

q: The number is divisible by 5.

Write the following statements and determine which are true.

a) The conditional statement, $p \rightarrow q$

b) The converse of $p \rightarrow q$

c) The inverse of $p \rightarrow q$

d) The contrapositive of $p \rightarrow q$

Solution

a) The conditional statement in symbols is $p \rightarrow q$. Therefore, in words the conditional statement is *If the number is divisible by 10, then the number is divisible by 5*. This statement is true. A number divisible by 10 must also be divisible by 5, since 5 is a divisor of 10.

b) The converse of the conditional statement in symbols is $q \rightarrow p$. Therefore, in words the converse is *If the number is divisible by 5, then the number is divisible by 10*. This statement is false. For example, 15 is divisible by 5, but 15 is not divisible by 10.

c) The inverse of the conditional statement in symbols is $\sim p \rightarrow \sim q$. Therefore, in words the inverse is *If the number is not divisible by 10, then the number is not divisible by 5*. This statement is false. For example, 25 is not divisible by 10, but 25 is divisible by 5.

d) The contrapositive of the conditional statement in symbols is $\sim q \rightarrow \sim p$. Therefore, in words the contrapositive is *If the number is not divisible by 5, then the number is not divisible by 10*. This statement is true. Any number that is not divisible by 5 cannot be divisible by 10, since 5 is a divisor of 10. ∎

Because the contrapositive statement is always equivalent to the original conditional statement, in Example 11 d) we should have expected the answer to be a true statement because the original conditional statement was also a true statement.

Example 12 *Use the Contrapositive*

Use the contrapositive to write a statement logically equivalent to "If you don't eat your meat, then you can't have any pudding."

Solution   Let

p: You do eat your meat.

q: You can have any pudding.

The given statement written symbolically is

$$\sim p \rightarrow \sim q$$

RECREATIONAL MATH

Kakuro

Like Sudoku (see the *Recreational Mathematics* box on Sudoku on page 97), Kakuro is a puzzle that requires logic. The puzzle resembles a crossword puzzle but uses numbers for clues instead of words. The aim of the game is to fill all the blank squares in the grid with only the digits 1–9 so that the numbers you enter add up to the corresponding clues. For example, in the puzzle shown below, the 17 near the upper left corner of the puzzle is a clue that indicates that the two numbers that you place in the two squares to the right of the 17 must add up to equal 17. The 9 near the upper left corner of the puzzle is a clue that indicates that the two numbers that you place in the two squares below the 9 must add up to equal 9.

In addition, you may not repeat any digits in any given "word" or string of numbers.

For more information and more puzzles, see www.kakuro.com. The solution to the above puzzle can be found in the answer section in the back of this book. For an additional puzzle, see Exercise 83 on page 140.

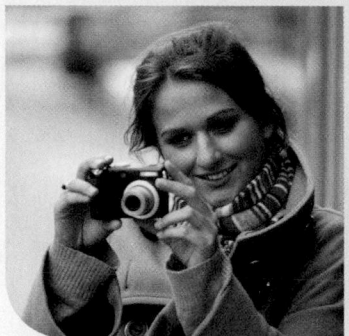
The contrapositive of the statement is

$$q \rightarrow p$$

Therefore, an equivalent statement is "If you can have any pudding, then you do eat your meat."   ∎

The contrapositive of the conditional is very important in mathematics. Consider the statement "If a^2 is not a whole number, then a is not a whole number." Is this statement true? You may find this question difficult to answer. Writing the statement's contrapositive may enable you to answer the question. The contrapositive is "If a is a whole number, then a^2 is a whole number." Since the contrapositive is a true statement, the original statement must also be true.

Example 13 *Which Are Equivalent?*

Determine which, if any, of the following statements are equivalent. You may use De Morgan's laws, the fact that $p \rightarrow q \Leftrightarrow \sim p \vee q$, information from the variations of the conditional, or truth tables.

a) If you leave by 9 A.M., then you will get to your destination on time.

b) You do not leave by 9 A.M. or you will get to your destination on time.

c) It is false that you will get to your destination on time or you did not leave by 9 A.M.

d) If you do not get to your destination on time, then you did not leave by 9 A.M.

Solution Let

> $p:$ You leave by 9 A.M.
> $q:$ You will get to your destination on time.

In symbolic form, the four statements are

a) $p \rightarrow q.$ b) $\sim p \vee q.$ c) $\sim(q \vee \sim p).$ d) $\sim q \rightarrow \sim p.$

Which of these statements are equivalent? Earlier in this section, you learned that $p \rightarrow q$ is equivalent to $\sim p \vee q$. Therefore, statements (a) and (b) are equivalent. Statement (d) is the contrapositive of statement (a). Therefore, statement (d) is also equivalent to statement (a) and statement (b). Statements (a), (b), and (d) all have the same truth table (Table 3.31).

Table 3.31

p	q	(a) $p \rightarrow q$	(b) $\sim p \vee q$	(d) $\sim q \rightarrow \sim p$
T	T	T	T	T
T	F	F	F	F
F	T	T	T	T
F	F	T	T	T

Now let's look at statement (c). To determine whether $\sim(q \vee \sim p)$ is equivalent to the other statements, we will construct its truth table (Table 3.32) and compare the answer column with the answer columns in Table 3.31.

Table 3.32

p	q	$\sim$	(c) $(q$	$\vee$	$\sim p)$
T	T	F	T	T	F
T	F	T	F	F	F
F	T	F	T	T	T
F	F	F	F	T	T
		4	1	3	2

> None of the three answer columns of the truth table in Table 3.31 is the same as the answer column of the truth table in Table 3.32. Therefore $\sim(q \vee \sim p)$ is not equivalent to any of the other statements. Therefore, only statements (a), (b), and (d) are equivalent to each other. ∎

SECTION 3.4 *Exercises*

Warm Up Exercises

In Exercises 1–8, fill in the blanks with an appropriate word, phrase, or symbol(s).

1. Statements that have exactly the same truth values in the answer columns of their truth tables are called _____ statements. Equivalent

2. DeMorgan's laws state that

   a) $\sim(p \wedge q)$ is equivalent to _____, and $\sim p \vee \sim q$

   b) $\sim(p \vee q)$ is equivalent to _____. $\sim p \wedge \sim q$

3. The conditional statement $p \to q$ is equivalent to the following disjunction statement: _____. $\sim p \vee q$

4. The negation of the conditional statement $\sim(p \to q)$ is equivalent to the following conjunction statement: _____. $p \wedge \sim q$

5. Given the conditional statement $p \to q$, the converse of the conditional statement in symbolic form is _____. $q \to p$

6. Given the conditional statement $p \to q$, the inverse of the conditional statement in symbolic form is _____. $\sim p \to \sim q$

7. Given the conditional statement $p \to q$, the contrapositive of the conditional statement in symbolic form is _____. $\sim q \to \sim p$

8. Of the converse, inverse, and contrapositive, only the contrapositive of the conditional statement is _____ to the conditional statement. Equivalent

Practice the Skills

In Exercises 9–18, use De Morgan's laws to determine whether the two statements are equivalent.

9. $\sim(p \wedge q), \sim p \wedge \sim q$ Not equivalent

10. $\sim(p \wedge q), \sim p \vee \sim q$ Equivalent

11. $\sim(p \vee q), \sim p \wedge \sim q$ Equivalent

12. $\sim(p \vee q), \sim p \vee \sim q$ Not equivalent

13. $\sim(\sim p \wedge q), p \wedge \sim q$ Not equivalent

14. $\sim(\sim p \wedge q), p \vee \sim q$ Equivalent

15. $(\sim p \vee \sim q) \to r, \sim(p \wedge q) \to r$ Equivalent

16. $q \to \sim(p \wedge \sim r), q \to \sim p \vee r$ Equivalent

17. $\sim(p \to \sim q), p \wedge q$ Equivalent

18. $\sim(\sim p \to q), \sim p \wedge \sim q$ Equivalent

In Exercises 19–30, use a truth table to determine whether the two statements are equivalent.

19. $p \to q, \sim p \vee q$ Equivalent

20. $\sim(p \to q), p \wedge \sim q$ Equivalent

21. $\sim q \to \sim p, p \to q$ Equivalent

22. $q \to p, \sim p \to \sim q$ Equivalent

23. $(p \vee q) \vee r, p \vee (q \vee r)$ Equivalent

24. $p \vee (q \wedge r), \sim p \to (q \wedge r)$ Equivalent

25. $p \wedge (q \vee r), (p \wedge q) \vee r$ Not equivalent

26. $\sim(q \to p) \vee r, (p \vee q) \wedge \sim r$ Not equivalent

27. $(p \to q) \wedge (q \to p), (p \leftrightarrow q)$ Equivalent

28. $[\sim(p \to q)] \wedge [\sim(q \to p)], \sim(p \leftrightarrow q)$ Not equivalent

Problem Solving

In Exercises 29–34, use De Morgan's laws to write an equivalent statement for the sentence.

29. It is false that Oregon borders the Atlantic Ocean and Delaware borders the Pacific Ocean. Oregon does not border the Atlantic Ocean or Delaware does not border the Pacific Ocean.

30. It is false that Greg Dietrich selects formulas or Moana Karsteter applies concepts. Greg Dietrich does not select formulas and Moana Karsteter does not apply concepts.

31. The dog was neither a bulldog nor was the dog a boxer. It is false that the dog was a bulldog or the dog was a boxer.

32. The pot roast is hot, but it is not well done. It is false that the pot roast is not hot or it is well done.

33. If Ashley Tabai takes the new job, then she will not move or she will buy a new house in town. If Ashley Tabai takes the new job, then it is false that she will move and she will not buy a new house in town.

34. If Phil Murphy buys us dinner, then we will not go to the top of the CN Tower but we will be able to walk to the Red Bistro Restaurant. *

In Exercises 35–40, use the fact that $p \rightarrow q$ is equivalent to $\sim p \vee q$ to write an equivalent form of the given statement.

35. If Janette Campbell buys a new car, then she sells her old car. Janette Campbell does not buy a new car or she sells her old car.

36. Byron Dyce did not walk to the meeting or we started late. If Byron Dyce walked to the meeting then we started late.

37. Bob the Tomato visited the nursing home or he did not visit the Cub Scout meeting. If Bob the Tomato did not visit the nursing home then he did not visit the Cub Scout meeting.

38. If Joanne Ernst goes to the Lightning game, then she will not go to the Rays game. Joanne Ernst does not go to the Lightning game or she will not go to the Rays game.

39. Chase is not hiding or the pitcher is broken. If Chase is hiding, then the pitcher is broken.

40. If Weezer is not on the radio, then Tim Ollendick is working. Weezer is on the radio or Tim Ollendick is working.

In Exercises 41–48, use the fact that $\sim (p \rightarrow q)$ is equivalent to $p \wedge \sim q$ to write the statement in an equivalent form.

41. It is false that if we go to Chicago, then we will go to Navy Pier. We go to Chicago and we do not go to Navy Pier.

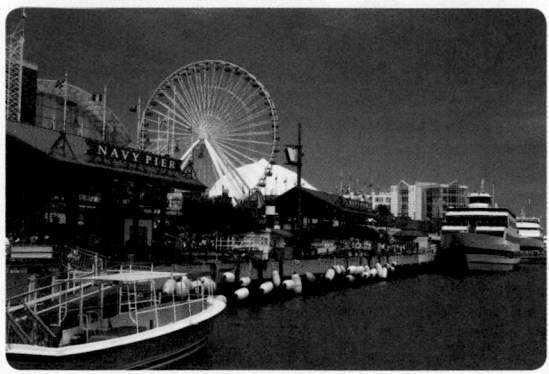

▲ *Navy Pier in Chicago*

42. It is false that if General Electric makes the telephone, then the telephone is made in the United States. General Electric makes the telephone and the telephone is not made in the United States.

43. I am cold and the heater is not working. It is false that if I am cold then the heater is working.

44. The Badgers beat the Nittany Lions and the Bucks beat the 76ers. It is false that if the Badgers beat the Nittany Lions then the Bucks did not beat the 76ers.

45. It is not true that if Amazon has a sale then we will buy $100 worth of books. Amazon has a sale and we will not buy $100 worth of books.

46. Thompson is sick today but Allen didn't go to school. It is false that if Thompson is sick today then Allen went to school.

47. John Deere will hire new workers and the city of Dubuque will retrain the workers. It is false that if John Deere will hire new workers then the city of Dubuque will not retrain the workers.

48. My cell phone is not a Blackberry but my cell phone has a keyboard. It is false that if my cell phone is not a Blackberry then my cell phone does not have a keyboard.

In Exercises 49–54, write the converse, inverse, and contrapositive of the statement. (For Exercise 54, use De Morgan's laws.)

49. If Nanette Berry teaches macramé, then she needs extra yarn. *

50. If the water is running, then Linus is getting a drink. *

51. If I go to Mexico, then I buy silver jewelry. *

52. If Bob Dylan records a new CD, then he will go on tour. *

53. If that annoying paper clip shows up on my computer screen, then I will scream. *

54. If the sun is shining, then we will go down to the marina and we will take out the sailboat. *

In Exercises 55–60, write the contrapositive of the statement. Use the contrapositive to determine whether the conditional statement is true or false.

55. If a natural number is divisible by 14, then the natural number is divisible by 7. If a natural number is not divisible by 7, then the natural number is not divisible by 14. True.

56. If the quadrilateral is a parallelogram, then the opposite sides are parallel. If the opposite sides are not parallel, then the quadrilateral is not a parallelogram. True.

57. If a natural number is divisible by 3, then the natural number is divisible by 6. If a natural number is not divisible by 6, then the natural number is not divisible by 3. False.

58. If $1/n$ is not a natural number, then n is not a natural number. If n is a natural number, then $\frac{1}{n}$ is a natural number. False.

59. If two lines do not intersect in at least one point, then the two lines are parallel. If two lines are not parallel, then the two lines intersect in at least one point. True.

60. If $\frac{m \cdot a}{m \cdot b} \neq \frac{a}{b}$, then m is not a counting number. If m is a counting number, then $\frac{m \cdot a}{m \cdot b} = \frac{a}{b}$. True.

In Exercises 61–74, determine which, if any, of the three statements are equivalent (see Example 13).

61. a) If the ball lands in foul territory, then the runner returns to the base.

b) If the runner returns to the base, then the ball lands in foul territory.

c) The runner does not return to the base or the ball lands in foul territory. b) and c) are equivalent.

*See Instructor Answer Appendix

62. a) If Fido is our dog's name, then Rex is not our dog's name.

b) It is false that Fido is our dog's name and Rex is not our dog's name.

c) Fido is not our dog's name or Rex is our dog's name.
b) and *c)* are equivalent.

63. a) The office is not cool and the copier is jammed.

b) If the office is not cool, then the copier is not jammed.

c) It is false that the office is cool or the copier is not jammed. *a)* and *c)* are equivalent.

64. a) The test is not written or the review sheet is not ready.

b) If the test is written, then the review sheet is ready.

c) It is false that the review sheet is ready and the test is not written. None are equivalent.

65. a) Today is not Sunday or the library is open.

b) If today is Sunday, then the library is not open.

c) If the library is open, then today is not Sunday.
b) and *c)* are equivalent.

66. a) If you are fishing at 1 P.M., then you are driving a car at 1 P.M.

b) You are not fishing at 1 P.M. or you are driving a car at 1 P.M.

c) It is false that you are fishing at 1 P.M. and you are not driving a car at 1 P.M. a), b), and c) are equivalent.

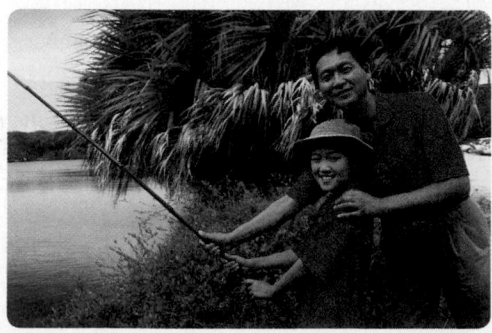

67. a) The grass grows and the trees are blooming.

b) If the trees are blooming, then the grass does not grow.

c) The trees are not blooming or the grass does not grow.
b) and c) are equivalent.

68. a) Johnny Patrick is chosen as department chair if and only if he is the only candidate.

b) If Johnny Patrick is chosen as department chair then he is the only candidate, and if Johnny Patrick is the only candidate then he is chosen as department chair.

c) Johnny Patrick is not chosen as department chair and he is not the only candidate. a) and b) are equivalent.

69. a) If the corn bag goes in the hole, then you are awarded three points.

b) It is false that the corn bag goes in the hole and you are awarded three points.

c) The corn bag does not go in the hole and you are not awarded three points. None are equivalent.

70. a) Fitz and the Tantrums will not go on tour if and only if James King does not play the saxophone.

b) It is false that Fitz and the Tantrums will go on tour if and only if James King does not play the saxophone.

c) If Fitz and the Tantrums go on tour, then James King plays saxophone. a) and b) are equivalent.

71. a) If the pay is good and today is Monday, then I will take the job.

b) If I do not take the job, then it is false that the pay is good or today is Monday.

c) The pay is good and today is Monday, or I will take the job.
None are equivalent.

72. a) If you are 18 years old and a citizen of the United States, then you can vote in the presidential election.

b) You can vote in the presidential election, if and only if you are a citizen of the United States and you are 18 years old.

c) You cannot vote in the presidential election, or you are 18 years old and you are not a citizen of the United States. None are equivalent.

73. a) The package was sent by Federal Express, or the package was not sent by United Parcel Service but the package arrived on time.

b) The package arrived on time, if and only if it was sent by Federal Express or it was not sent by United Parcel Service.

c) If the package was not sent by Federal Express, then the package was not sent by United Parcel Service but the package arrived on time. a) and c) are equivalent.

74. a) The mortgage rate went down, if and only if Tim purchased the house and the down payment was 10%.

b) The down payment was 10%, and if Tim purchased the house then the mortgage rate went down.

c) If Tim purchased the house, then the mortgage rate went down and the down payment was not 10%. None are equivalent.

Concept/Writing Exercises

75. If p and q represent two simple statements, and if $p \rightarrow q$ is a false statement, what must be the truth value of the converse, $q \rightarrow p$? Explain. *

76. If p and q represent two simple statements, and if $p \rightarrow q$ is a false statement, what must be the truth value of the inverse, $\sim p \rightarrow \sim q$? Explain. *

77. If p and q represent two simple statements, and if $p \rightarrow q$ is a false statement, what must be the truth value of the contrapositive, $\sim q \rightarrow \sim p$? Explain. False. A conditional statement and its contrapositive always have the same truth values.

78. If p and q represent two simple statements, and if $p \rightarrow q$ is a true statement, what must be the truth value of the contrapositive, $\sim q \rightarrow \sim p$? Explain. True. A conditional statement and its contrapositive always have the same truth values.

Challenge Problems/Group Activities

79. We learned that $p \rightarrow q \Leftrightarrow \sim p \lor q$. Determine a conjunction that is equivalent to $p \rightarrow q$. (*Hint:* There are many answers.) Answers will vary.

80. Determine whether $\sim[\sim(p \lor \sim q)] \Leftrightarrow p \lor \sim q$. Explain the method(s) you used to determine your answer. They are equivalent since $\sim(\sim p) \Leftrightarrow p$.

81. In an appliance or device that uses fuzzy logic, a change in one condition causes a change in a second condition. For example, in a camera, if the brightness increases, the lens aperture automatically decreases to get the proper exposure. Name at least 10 appliances or devices that make use of fuzzy logic and explain how fuzzy logic is used in each appliance or device. See the *Mathematics Today* box on page 135. Answers will vary.

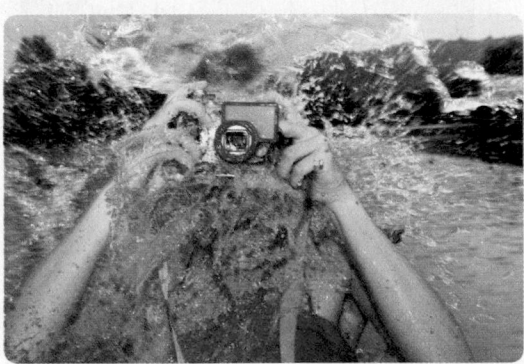

82. In symbolic logic, a statement is either true or false (consider true to have a value of 1 and false a value of 0). In fuzzy logic, nothing is true or false, but everything is a matter of degree. For example, consider the statement "The sun is shining." In fuzzy logic, this statement may have a value between 0 and 1 and may be constantly changing. For example, if the sun is partially blocked by clouds, the value of this statement may be 0.25. In fuzzy logic, the values of connective statements are found as follows for statements p and q.

Not p has a truth value of $1 - p$.

$p \land q$ has a truth value equal to the lesser of p and q.

$p \lor q$ has a truth value equal to the greater of p and q.

$p \rightarrow q$ has a truth value equal to the lesser of 1 and $1 - p + q$.

$p \leftrightarrow q$ has a truth value equal to $1 - |p - q|$, that is, 1 minus the absolute value* of p minus q.

Suppose the statement "p: The sun is shining" has a truth value of 0.25 and the statement "q: Mary is getting a tan" has a truth value of 0.20. Find the truth value of

a) $\sim p$ 0.75

b) $\sim q$ 0.80

c) $p \land q$ 0.20

d) $p \lor q$ 0.25

e) $p \rightarrow q$ 0.95

f) $p \leftrightarrow q$ 0.95

---

*Absolute values are discussed in Section 13.8.

*See Instructor Answer Appendix

Recreational Exercises

83. *Kakuro*   Refer to the *Recreational Mathematics* box on page 134. Complete the following Kakuro puzzle. *

Internet/Research Activities

84. Do research and write a report on fuzzy logic.

85. Read one of Lewis Carroll's books and write a report on how he used logic in the book. Give at least five specific examples.

86. Do research and write a report on the life and achievements of Augustus De Morgan. Indicate in your report his contributions to sets and logic.

*See Instructor Answer Appendix

SECTION 3.5   Symbolic Arguments

Consider the following statements.

> If Carrie Underwood sings the national anthem, then The Who will play at halftime.

> Carrie Underwood sings the national anthem.

If you accept these two statements as true, then what logical conclusion could you draw? Do you agree that you can logically conclude that The Who will play at halftime? In this section, we will use our knowledge of logic to study the structure of such statements to draw logical conclusions.

▲ *The Who plays during halftime of Super Bowl XLIV.*

Why **This is Important**   Drawing logical conclusions from a given set of statements is an important application of logic. Also, we use logic daily in decision making after considering all the facts we know to be true.

Previously in this chapter, we used symbolic logic to determine the truth value of a compound statement. We now extend those basic ideas to determine whether we can draw logical conclusions from a set of given statements. Consider once again the two statements.

> If Carrie Underwood sings the national anthem, then The Who will play at halftime.

> Carrie Underwood sings the national anthem.

These statements in the following form constitute what we will call a *symbolic argument*.

Premise 1:	If Carrie Underwood sings the national anthem, then The Who will play at halftime.
Premise 2:	Carrie Underwood sings the national anthem
Conclusion:	The Who will play at halftime.

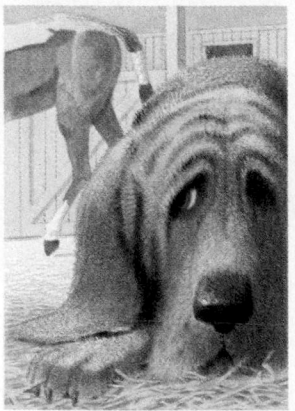
A *symbolic argument* consists of a set of *premises* and a *conclusion*. It is called a symbolic argument because we generally write it in symbolic form to determine its validity.

> ### Definition: Valid and Invalid Arguments
> An **argument is valid** when its conclusion necessarily follows from a given set of premises.
> An **argument is invalid** or a **fallacy** when the conclusion does not necessarily follow from the given set of premises.

An argument that is not valid is invalid. The argument just presented is an example of a valid argument, as the conclusion necessarily follows from the premises. Now we will discuss a procedure to determine whether an argument is valid or invalid. We begin by writing the argument in symbolic form. To write the argument in symbolic form, we let p and q be

p: Carrie Underwood sings the national anthem.

q: The Who will play at halftime.

Symbolically, the argument is written

Premise 1: $p \rightarrow q$
Premise 2: p
Conclusion $\therefore q$ (The three-dot-triangle is read "therefore.")

Write the argument in the following form.

If   [*premise 1*   **and**   *premise 2*]   **then**   *conclusion*
     $[(p \rightarrow q)$ $\wedge$ $p]$ $\rightarrow$ q

Then construct a truth table for the statement $[(p \rightarrow q) \wedge p] \rightarrow q$ (Table 3.33). *If the truth table answer column is true in every case, then the statement is a tautology, and the argument is valid. If the truth table is not a tautology, then the argument is invalid.* Since the statement is a tautology (see column 5), the conclusion necessarily follows from the premises and the argument is valid.

Table 3.33

p	q	$[(p \rightarrow q)$	$\wedge$	$p]$	$\rightarrow$	q
T	T	T	T	T	T	T
T	F	F	F	T	T	F
F	T	T	F	F	T	T
F	F	T	F	F	T	F
		1	3	2	5	4

Once we have demonstrated that an argument in a particular form is valid, all arguments with exactly the same form will also be valid. In fact, many of these forms have been assigned names. The argument form just discussed,

$$p \rightarrow q$$
$$p$$
$$\therefore q$$

is called the *law of detachment*, or *modus ponens*.

▲ *Alaska*

Example 1 *Determining Validity Without a Truth Table*

Determine whether the following argument is valid or invalid.

> If Canada is north of the United States, then Alaska is in Mexico.
> Canada is north of the United States.
>
> ∴ Alaska is in Mexico.

Solution Translate the argument into symbolic form.

Let

> c: Canada is north of the United States.
> a: Alaska is in Mexico.

In symbolic form, the argument is

$$c \rightarrow a$$
$$\underline{c \qquad\quad}$$
$$\therefore a$$

This argument is also the law of detachment. Therefore, it is a valid argument. ■

Note that the argument in Example 1 is valid even though the conclusion, "Alaska is in Mexico," is a false statement. It is also possible to have an invalid argument in which the conclusion is a true statement. *When an argument is valid, the conclusion necessarily follows from the premises. It is not necessary for the premises or the conclusion to be true statements in an argument.*

> **PROCEDURE**   **TO DETERMINE WHETHER AN ARGUMENT IS VALID**
>
> 1. Write the argument in symbolic form.
> 2. Compare the form of the argument with forms that are known to be valid or invalid. If there are no known forms to compare it with, or you do not remember the forms, go to step 3.
> 3. If the argument contains two premises, write a conditional statement of the form
>
> $$[(\text{premise 1}) \wedge (\text{premise 2})] \rightarrow \text{conclusion}$$
>
> 4. Construct a truth table for the statement in step 3.
> 5. If the answer column of the truth table has all trues, the statement is a tautology, and the argument is valid. If the answer column does not have all trues, the argument is invalid.

Examples 1 through 4 contain two premises. When an argument contains more than two premises, step 3 of the procedure will change slightly, as will be explained shortly.

Example 2 *Determining the Validity of an Argument With a Truth Table*

Determine whether the following argument is valid or invalid.

> If you watch *Good Morning America*, then you see Robin Roberts.
> You did not see Robin Roberts.
>
> ∴ You did not watch *Good Morning America*.

▲ *Robin Roberts*

Solution We first write the argument in symbolic form.

Let

p: You watch *Good Morning America*.

q: You see Robin Roberts.

In symbolic form, the argument is

$$p \rightarrow q$$
$$\sim q$$
$$\overline{\therefore \ \sim p}$$

As we have not tested an argument in this form, we will construct a truth table to determine whether the argument is valid or invalid. We write the argument in the form $[(p \rightarrow q) \land \sim q] \rightarrow \sim p$, and construct a truth table (Table 3.34). Since the answer, column 5, has all T's, the argument is valid.

Table 3.34

p	q	$[(p \rightarrow q)$	$\land$	$\sim q]$	$\rightarrow$	$\sim p$
T	T	T	F	F	T	F
T	F	F	F	T	T	F
F	T	T	F	F	T	T
F	F	T	T	T	T	T
		1	3	2	5	4

The argument form in Example 2 is an example of the *law of contraposition*, or *modus tollens*.

Example 3 *Another Symbolic Argument*

Determine whether the following argument is valid or invalid.

The grass is green or the grass is full of weeds.
The grass is not green.

$\therefore$ The grass is full of weeds.

Solution Let

p: The grass is green.

q: The grass is full of weeds.

In symbolic form, the argument is

$$p \lor q$$
$$\sim p$$
$$\overline{\therefore \ q}$$

As this form is not one of those we are familiar with, we will construct a truth table. We write the argument in the form $[(p \lor q) \land \sim p] \rightarrow q$. Next we construct a truth table, as shown in Table 3.35 on page 144. The answer to the truth table, column 5, is true in *every case*. Therefore, the statement is a tautology, and the argument is valid.

MATHEMATICS TODAY

Freedom of Speech or Misleading Advertising?

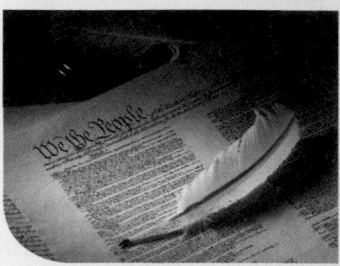

The first amendment to the United States Constitution guarantees that Americans have the freedom of speech. There are, however, limits to what we may say or write. For example, companies are limited in what they can say or write to advertise their products. The Federal Trade Commission (FTC) states that "ads must be truthful and not misleading; that advertisers must have evidence to back up their assertions; and that ads cannot be unfair." Although most advertisements are truthful and fair, some enter into a "gray area" of truthfulness. Some of these breaches of fairness may be found in logical fallacies either made directly or implicitly by the context of the ad's wording or artwork. The FTC has the responsibility to take action against companies they believe are violating their policies. For more information regarding actions taken by the FTC against fraudulent advertisers, go to www.ftc.gov.

Why **This is Important** As a consumer you need to be able to determine if a conclusion made by a company necessarily follows from the information given, or if the company is providing you with a misleading conclusion.

Table 3.35

p	q	$[(p \lor q)$	$\land$	$\sim p]$	$\rightarrow$	q
T	T	T	F	F	T	T
T	F	T	F	F	T	F
F	T	T	T	T	T	T
F	F	F	F	T	T	F
		1	3	2	5	4

The argument form in Example 3 is an example of a *disjunctive syllogism*. Other standard forms of arguments are given in the following chart.

Standard Forms of Arguments

Valid Arguments	*Law of Detachment*	*Law of Contraposition*	*Law of Syllogism*	*Disjunctive Syllogism*
	$p \rightarrow q$	$p \rightarrow q$	$p \rightarrow q$	$p \lor q$
	p	$\sim q$	$q \rightarrow r$	$\sim p$
	$\therefore q$	$\therefore \sim p$	$\therefore p \rightarrow r$	$\therefore q$

Invalid Arguments	*Fallacy of the Converse*	*Fallacy of the Inverse*		
	$p \rightarrow q$	$p \rightarrow q$		
	q	$\sim p$		
	$\therefore p$	$\therefore \sim q$		

As we saw in Example 1, it is not always necessary to construct a truth table to determine whether or not an argument is valid. The next two examples will show how we can identify an argument as one of the standard arguments given in the chart above.

Example 4   *Identifying a Standard Argument*

Determine whether the following argument is valid or invalid.

> If you are on Facebook, then you see my pictures.
> If you see my pictures, then you know I have a dog.
> _____
> ∴ If you are on Facebook, then you know I have a dog.

Solution   Let

> p: You are on Facebook.
> q: You see my pictures.
> r: You know I have a dog.

In symbolic form, the argument is

$$p \rightarrow q$$
$$q \rightarrow r$$
$$\therefore p \rightarrow r$$

The argument is in the form of the law of syllogism. Therefore, the argument is valid, and there is no need to construct a truth table.

Example 5 *Identifying Common Fallacies in Arguments*

Determine whether the following arguments are valid or invalid.

a)

> If it is snowing, then we put salt on the driveway.
> We put salt on the driveway.
> _____
> ∴ It is snowing.

b)

> If it is snowing, then we put salt on the driveway.
> It is not snowing.
> _____
> ∴ We do not put salt on the driveway.

Solution

a) Let

p: It is snowing.

q: We put salt on the driveway.

In symbolic form, the argument is

$$p \rightarrow q$$
$$q$$
$$\overline{\therefore p}$$

This argument is in the form of the fallacy of the converse. Therefore, the argument is a fallacy, or invalid.

b) Using the same symbols defined in the solution to part (a), in symbolic form, the argument is

$$p \rightarrow q$$
$$\sim p$$
$$\overline{\therefore \sim q}$$

This argument is in the form of the fallacy of the inverse. Therefore, the argument is a fallacy, or invalid. ∎

Now we consider an argument that has more than two premises. When an argument contains more than two premises, the statement we test, using a truth table, is formed by taking the conjunction of all the premises as the antecedent of a conditional statement and the conclusion as the consequent of the conditional statement. One example is an argument of the form

$$p_1$$
$$p_2$$
$$p_3$$
$$\overline{\therefore c}$$

We evaluate the truth table for $[p_1 \wedge p_2 \wedge p_3] \rightarrow c$. When we evaluate $[p_1 \wedge p_2 \wedge p_3]$, it makes no difference whether we evaluate $[(p_1 \wedge p_2) \wedge p_3]$ or $[p_1 \wedge (p_2 \wedge p_3)]$ because both give the same answer. In Example 6, we evaluate $[p_1 \wedge p_2 \wedge p_3]$ from left to right; that is, $[(p_1 \wedge p_2) \wedge p_3]$.

TIMELY TIP

If you are not sure whether an argument with two premises is one of the standard forms or if you do not remember the standard forms, you can always determine whether a given argument is valid or invalid by using a truth table. To do so, follow the boxed procedure on page 142.

In Example 5(b), if you did not recognize that this argument was of the same form as the fallacy of the inverse you could construct the truth table for the conditional statement

$$[(p \rightarrow q) \wedge \sim p] \rightarrow \sim q$$

The true–false values under the conditional column, →, would be T, T, F, T. Since the statement is not a tautology, the argument is invalid.

Example **6** *An Argument with Three Premises*

Use a truth table to determine whether the following argument is valid or invalid.

If my cell phone company is Verizon, then I can call you free of charge.
I can call you free of charge or I can send you a text message.
I can send you a text message or my cell phone company is Verizon.

∴ My cell phone company is Verizon.

Solution This argument contains three simple statements.

Let

p: My cell phone company is Verizon.
q: I can call you free of charge.
r: I can send you a text message.

In symbolic form, the argument is

$$p \rightarrow q$$
$$q \lor r$$
$$r \lor p$$
$$\overline{}$$
$$\therefore p$$

Write the argument in the form

$$[(p \rightarrow q) \land (q \lor r) \land (r \lor p)] \rightarrow p.$$

Now construct the truth table (Table 3.36). The answer, column 7, is not true in every case. Thus, the argument is a fallacy, or invalid.

Table 3.36

p	q	r	$[(p \rightarrow q)$	$\land$	$(q \lor r)$	$\land$	$(r \lor p)]$	$\rightarrow$	p
T	T	T	T	T	T	T	T	T	T
T	T	F	T	T	T	T	T	T	T
T	F	T	F	F	T	F	T	T	T
T	F	F	F	F	F	F	T	T	T
F	T	T	T	T	T	T	T	F	F
F	T	F	T	T	T	F	F	T	F
F	F	T	T	T	T	T	T	F	F
F	F	F	T	F	F	F	F	T	F
			1	3	2	5	4	7	6

Let's now investigate how we can arrive at a valid conclusion from a given set of premises.

Example **7** *Determine a Logical Conclusion*

Determine a logical conclusion that follows from the given statements. "If the price of gas is below $4.00 per gallon, then we will drive to the Offspring concert. We will not drive to the Offspring concert. Therefore ... "

Solution If you recognize a specific form of an argument, you can use your knowledge of that form to draw a logical conclusion.

Let

p:	The price of gas is below \$4.00 per gallon.
q:	We will drive to the Offspring concert.

The argument is of the following form.

$$p \rightarrow q$$
$$\frac{\sim q}{\therefore \; ?}$$

If the question mark is replaced with a $\sim p$, this argument is of the form of the law of contraposition. Thus, a logical conclusion is "Therefore, the price of gas is not below \$4.00 per gallon." ∎

SECTION 3.5   *Exercises*

Warm Up Exercises

In Exercises 1–6, fill in the blanks with an appropriate word, phrase, or symbol(s).

1. When the conclusion of an argument necessarily follows from the given set of premises it is a(n) _____ argument. Valid

2. When the conclusion of an argument does not necessarily follow from the given set of premises it is a(n) _____ argument. Invalid

3. An argument that is invalid is also known as a(n) _____. Fallacy

4. To determine the validity of an argument with two premises, construct a truth table for a conditional statement of the form [(premise 1) ∧ (premise 2)] → _____. Conclusion

5. If the conditional statement referred to in Exercise 4 is a tautology, then the argument is a(n) _____ argument. Valid

6. If the conditional statement referred to in Exercise 4 is not a tautology, then the argument is a(n) _____ argument. Invalid

For Exercises 7–12, identify the standard form of the argument.

7. $p \rightarrow q$ Fallacy of the _____. Inverse
   $\dfrac{\sim p}{\therefore \sim q}$

8. $p \rightarrow q$ Law of _____. Detachment
   $\dfrac{p}{\therefore q}$

9. $p \; \vee \; q$ Disjunctive _____. Syllogism
   $\dfrac{\sim p}{\therefore q}$

10. $p \rightarrow q$ Fallacy of the _____. Converse
    $\dfrac{q}{\therefore p}$

11. $p \rightarrow q$ Law of _____. Syllogism
    $\dfrac{q \rightarrow r}{\therefore p \rightarrow r}$

12. $p \rightarrow q$ Law of _____. Contraposition
    $\dfrac{\sim q}{\therefore \sim p}$

Practice the Skills

In Exercises 13–32, determine whether the argument is valid or invalid. You may compare the argument to a standard form, given on page 144, or use a truth table.

13. $a \rightarrow b$ Invalid
    $\dfrac{\sim a}{\therefore \sim b}$

14. $c \vee d$ Valid
    $\dfrac{\sim c}{\therefore d}$

15. $e \rightarrow f$ Valid
    $\dfrac{e}{\therefore f}$

16. $g \rightarrow h$ Valid
    $\dfrac{h \rightarrow i}{\therefore g \rightarrow i}$

17. $j \vee k$ Valid
    $\dfrac{\sim k}{\therefore j}$

18. $l \rightarrow m$ Valid
    $\dfrac{\sim m}{\therefore \sim l}$

19. $n \rightarrow o$ Invalid
    $\dfrac{o}{\therefore n}$

20. $r \rightarrow s$ Valid
    $\dfrac{r}{\therefore s}$

21. $t \rightarrow u$ Invalid
$\dfrac{\sim t}{\therefore \sim u}$

22. $v \rightarrow w$ Invalid
$\dfrac{w}{\therefore v}$

23. $x \rightarrow y$ Valid
$y \rightarrow z$
$\overline{\therefore \ x \rightarrow z}$

24. $x \rightarrow y$ Invalid
$\sim x$
$\overline{\therefore \ \sim y}$

25. $p \leftrightarrow q$ Valid
$q \wedge r$
$\overline{\therefore \ p \vee r}$

26. $p \leftrightarrow q$ Valid
$q \rightarrow r$
$\overline{\therefore \ \sim r \rightarrow \sim p}$

27. $r \leftrightarrow p$ Invalid
$\sim p \wedge q$
$\overline{\therefore \ p \wedge r}$

28. $p \vee q$ Invalid
$r \wedge p$
$\overline{\therefore \ q}$

29. $p \rightarrow q$ Invalid
$q \vee r$
$r \vee p$
$\overline{\therefore \ p}$

30. $p \rightarrow q$ Valid
$q \rightarrow r$
$r \rightarrow p$
$\overline{\therefore \ q \rightarrow p}$

31. $p \rightarrow q$ Valid
$r \rightarrow \sim p$
$p \vee r$
$\overline{\therefore \ q \vee \sim p}$

32. $p \leftrightarrow q$ Valid
$p \vee r$
$q \rightarrow r$
$\overline{\therefore \ q \vee r}$

Problem Solving

In Exercises 33–48, (a) translate the argument into symbolic form and (b) determine if the argument is valid or invalid. You may compare the argument to a standard form or use a truth table.

33. If the lighthouse works, then the boat can stay out late.

The boat cannot stay out late.

$\therefore$ The lighthouse does not work. *

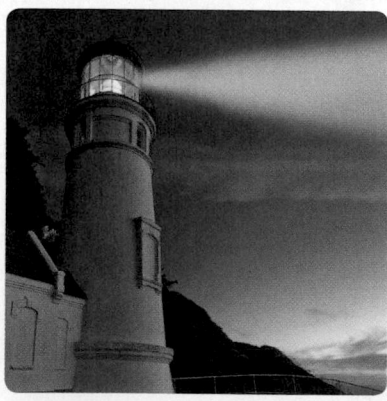

34. If the car is a Road Runner, then the car is fast.

The car is fast.

$\therefore$ The car is a Road Runner. *

35. If the baby is a boy, then we will name him Alexander Martin.

The baby is a boy.

$\therefore$ We will name him Alexander Martin. *

36. If I can get my child to preschool by 8:45 A.M., then I can take the 9:00 A.M. class.

If I can take the 9:00 A.M. class, then I can be done by 2:00 P.M.

$\therefore$ If I can get my child to preschool by 8:45 A.M., then I can be done by 2:00 P.M. *

37. If the guitar is a Les Paul model, then the guitar is made by Gibson.

The guitar is not made by Gibson.

$\therefore$ The guitar is not a Les Paul model. *

38. We will go for a bike ride or we will go shopping.

We will not go shopping.

$\therefore$ We will go for a bike ride. *

39. If we planted the garden by the first Friday in April, then we will have potatoes by the Fourth of July.

We will have potatoes by the Fourth of July.

$\therefore$ We planted the garden by the first Friday in April. *

40. If you pass general chemistry, then you can take organic chemistry.

You pass general chemistry.

$\therefore$ You can take organic chemistry. *

41. Erica Kane will marry Samuel Woods or Erica Kane will marry David Hayward.

Erica Kane will not marry Samuel Woods.

$\therefore$ Erica Kane will marry David Hayward. *

42. If Nicholas Thompson teaches this course, then I will get a passing grade.

I did not get a passing grade.

$\therefore$ Nicholas Thompson did not teach this course. *

43. If it is cold, then graduation will be held indoors.

If graduation is held indoors, then the fireworks will be postponed.

$\therefore$ If it is cold, then the fireworks will be postponed. *

44. If the canteen is full, then we can go for a walk.
We can go for a walk and we will not get thirsty.

∴ If we go for a walk, then the canteen is not full. *

45. Marie works at the post office and Jim works for Target.
If Jim works for Target, then Tommy gets an internship.

∴ If Tommy gets an internship, then Marie works at the post office. *

46. Vitamin C helps your immune system or niacin helps reduce cholesterol.
If niacin helps reduce cholesterol, then vitamin E enhances your skin.

∴ Vitamin C helps your immune system and vitamin E enhances your skin. *

47. It is snowing and I am going skiing.
If I am going skiing, then I will wear a coat.

∴ If it is snowing, then I will wear a coat. *

48. The garden has vegetables or the garden has flowers.
If the garden does not have flowers, then the garden has vegetables.

∴ The garden has flowers or the garden has vegetables. *

In Exercises 49–58, translate the argument into symbolic form. Then determine whether the argument is valid or invalid.

49. If you read *The Order of the Phoenix* then you can understand *The Half-Blood Prince*. You cannot understand *The Half-Blood Prince*. Therefore, you did not read *The Order of the Phoenix*. *

50. The printer has a clogged nozzle or the printer does not have toner. The printer has toner. Therefore, the printer has a clogged nozzle. *

51. Max is playing Game Boy with the sound off or Max is wearing headphones. Max is not playing Game Boy with the sound off. Therefore, Max is wearing headphones. *

52. If the cat is in the room, then the mice are hiding. The mice are not hiding. Therefore, the cat is not in the room. *

53. The test was easy and I received a good grade. The test was not easy or I did not receive a good grade. Therefore, the test was not easy. *

54. If Bonnie passes the bar exam, then she will practice law. Bonnie will not practice law. Therefore, Bonnie did not pass the bar exam. *

55. The baby is crying but the baby is not hungry. If the baby is hungry then the baby is crying. Therefore, the baby is hungry. *

56. If the car is new, then the car has air conditioning. The car is not new and the car has air conditioning. Therefore, the car is not new. *

57. If you liked *This Is Spinal Tap* then you liked *Best in Show*. If you liked *Best in Show* then you did not like *A Mighty Wind*. Therefore, if you liked *This Is Spinal Tap* then you liked *A Mighty Wind*. *

58. The engineering courses are difficult and the chemistry labs are long. If the chemistry labs are long, then the art tests are easy. Therefore, the engineering courses are difficult and the art tests are not easy. *

In Exercises 59–64, using the standard forms of arguments and other information you have learned, supply what you believe is a logical conclusion to the argument. Verify that the argument is valid for the conclusion you supplied.

59. If you throw more than 60 pitches, then you must rest for three days. You throw more than 60 pitches.
Therefore, ... Therefore, you must rest for three days.

60. If the temperature hits 100°, then we will go swimming. We did not go swimming.
Therefore, ... Therefore, the temperature did not hit 100°.

61. I am stressed out or I have the flu.
I do not have the flu.
Therefore, ... Therefore, I am stressed out.

62. If I can get Nick to his piano lesson by 3:30 P.M., then I can do my shopping.
If I can do my shopping, then we do not need to order pizza again.
Therefore, ... Therefore, if I can get Nick to his piano lesson by 3:30 P.M., then we do not need to order pizza again.

63. If you close the deal, then you will get a commission. You did not get a commission.
Therefore, ... Therefore, you did not close the deal.

64. If Katherine is at her ballet lesson, then Allyson will take a nap.
Katherine is at her ballet lesson.
Therefore, ...   Therefore, Allyson will take a nap.

Concept/Writing Exercises

65. Is it possible for an argument to be invalid if its conclusion is true? Explain your answer. *

66. Is it possible for an argument to be valid if its conclusion is false? Explain your answer. *

67. Is it possible for an argument to be invalid if the premises are all true? Explain your answer. *

68. Is it possible for an argument to be valid if the premises are all false? Explain your answer. *

Challenge Problems/Group Activities

69. Determine whether the argument is valid or invalid.

If Lynn wins the contest or strikes oil, then she will be rich.

If Lynn is rich, then she will stop working.

∴ If Lynn does not stop working, then she did not win the contest. Valid

70. Is it possible for an argument to be invalid if the conjunction of the premises is false in every case of the truth table? Explain your answer. *

Recreational Mathematics

71. René Descartes was a seventeenth-century French mathematician and philosopher. One of his most memorable statements is, "I think, therefore, I am." This statement is the basis for the following joke.

Descartes walks into an inn. The innkeeper asks Descartes if he would like something to drink. Descartes replies, "I think not," and promptly vanishes into thin air!

This joke can be summarized in the following argument: If I think, then I am. I think not. Therefore, I am not.

a) Represent this argument symbolically.
$$\begin{array}{c} p \to q \\ \sim p \\ \hline \therefore \sim q \end{array}$$

b) Is it a valid argument? No

c) Explain your answer using either a standard form of argument or using a truth table.
This argument is the fallacy of the inverse.

Internet/Research Activities

72. Show how logic is used in advertising. Discuss several advertisements and show how logic is used to persuade the reader.

73. Find examples of valid (or invalid) arguments in printed matter such as newspaper or magazine articles. Explain why the arguments are valid (or invalid).

*See Instructor Answer Appendix

SECTION 3.6   Euler Diagrams and Syllogistic Arguments

▲ Ben Stiller

While trying to select a movie to watch, you think, "All Ben Stiller movies are comedies. Ben Stiller is in the movie *The Hardy Men*. Therefore, *The Hardy Men* is a comedy." This type of argument will be discussed in this section.

Why **This is Important**   Understanding arguments is an important part of the study of logic, and it is useful in making real-life decisions.

In Section 3.5, we showed how to determine the validity of *symbolic arguments* using truth tables and comparing the arguments to standard forms. This section presents another form of argument called a *syllogistic argument*, better known by the shorter name *syllogism*. The validity of a syllogistic argument is determined by using Euler (pronounced "oiler") diagrams, as is explained shortly.

Syllogistic logic, a deductive process of arriving at a conclusion, was developed by Aristotle in about 350 B.C. Aristotle considered the relationships among the four types of statements that follow.

All _____ are _____.
No _____ are _____.
Some _____ are _____.
Some _____ are not _____.

Examples of these statements are as follows: *All doctors are tall. No doctors are tall. Some doctors are tall. Some doctors are not tall.* Since Aristotle's time, other types of statements have been added to the study of syllogistic logic, two of which are

_____ is a _____.
_____ is not a _____.

Examples of these statements are as follows: *Maria is a doctor. Maria is not a doctor.*

The difference between a symbolic argument and a syllogistic argument can be seen in the following chart. Symbolic arguments use the connectives *and, or, not, if–then,* and *if and only if.* Syllogistic arguments use the quantifiers *all, some,* and *none,* which were discussed in Section 3.1.

Symbolic Arguments Versus Syllogistic Arguments

	Words or phrases used	*Method of determining validity*
Symbolic argument	and, or, not, if–then, if and only if	Truth tables or by comparison with standard forms of arguments
Syllogistic argument	all are, some are, none are, some are not	Euler diagrams

As with symbolic logic, the premises and the conclusion together form an argument. An example of a syllogistic argument is

> All German shepherds are dogs.
> All dogs bark.
> ――――――――――――――
> ∴ All German shepherds bark.

This is an example of a valid argument. Recall from Section 3.5 that an argument is *valid* when its conclusion necessarily follows from a given set of premises. Recall that an argument in which the conclusion does not necessarily follow from the given premises is said to be an *invalid argument* or a *fallacy.*

Before we give another example of a syllogism, let's review the Venn diagrams discussed in Section 2.3 in relationship with Aristotle's four statements.

All *A*s are *B*s	No *A*s are *B*s	Some *A*s are *B*s	Some *A*s are not *B*s
			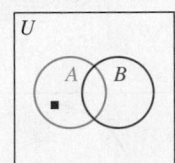
If an element is in set *A*, then it is in set *B*.	If an element is in set *A*, then it is not in set *B*.	There is at least one element that is in both set *A* and set *B*.	There is at least one element that is in set *A* that is not in set *B*.

One method used to determine whether an argument is valid or is a fallacy is by means of an *Euler diagram*, named after Leonhard Euler, who used circles to represent sets in syllogistic arguments. The technique of using Euler diagrams is illustrated in Example 1.

Example 1 *Using an Euler Diagram*

Determine whether the following syllogism is valid or invalid.

> All keys are made of brass.
> All things made of brass are valuable.
> _____
> ∴ All keys are valuable.

Solution To determine whether this syllogism is valid or not valid, we will construct an Euler diagram. We begin with the first premise, "All keys are made of brass." As shown in Fig. 3.3, the inner blue circle labeled *K* represents the set of all keys and the outer red circle labeled *B* represents the set of all brass objects. The first premise requires that the inner blue circle must be entirely contained within the outer red circle. Next, we will represent the second premise, "All things made of brass are valuable." As shown in Fig. 3.4, the outermost black circle labeled *V* represents the set of all valuable objects. The second premise dictates that the red circle, representing the set of brass objects, must be entirely contained within the black circle, representing the set of valuable objects. Now, examine the completed Euler diagram in Fig. 3.4. Note that the premises force the set of keys to be within the set of valuable objects. Therefore, the argument is valid since the conclusion, "All keys are valuable," necessarily follows from the set of premises.   ∎

Figure 3.3

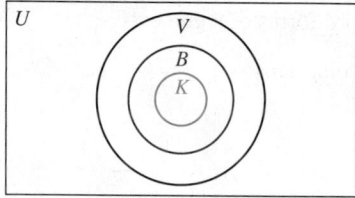

Figure 3.4

The syllogism in Example 1 is valid even though the conclusion, "All keys are valuable," is not a true statement. Similarly, a syllogism can be invalid, or a fallacy, even if the conclusion is a true statement.

When we determine the validity of an argument, we are determining whether the conclusion necessarily follows from the premises. When we say that an argument is valid, we are saying that if all the premises are true statements, then the conclusion must also be a true statement.

The form of the argument determines its validity, not the particular statements. For example, consider the syllogism

> All Earth people have two heads.
> All people with two heads can fly.
> _____
> ∴ All Earth people can fly.

The form of this argument is the same as that of the previous valid argument in Example 1. Therefore, this argument is also valid.

Example 2 *Analyzing a Syllogism*

Determine whether the following syllogism is valid or invalid.

> All patriots are Americans.
> Betsy is a patriot.
> _____
> ∴ Betsy is an American.

Solution The statement "All patriots are Americans" is illustrated in Fig. 3.5. Note that the *P* circle must be completely inside the *A* circle. The second premise, "Betsy is a patriot," tells us that Betsy must be placed in the inner circle labeled *P* (Fig. 3.6). The Euler diagram illustrates, that by placing Betsy inside the *P* circle, Betsy must also be inside the *A* circle. Therefore, the conclusion "Betsy is an American" necessarily follows from the premises and the argument is valid.   ∎

Figure 3.5

Figure 3.6

In both Example 1 and Example 2, we had no choice as to where the second premise was to be placed in the Euler diagram. In Example 1, the set of brass objects had to be placed inside the set of valuable objects. In Example 2, Betsy had to be placed inside the set of patriots. Often when determining the truth value of a syllogism, a premise can be placed in more than one area in the diagram. *We always try to draw the Euler diagram so that the conclusion **does not necessarily** follow from the premises. If that can be done, then the conclusion **does not necessarily** follow from the premises and the argument is invalid.* If we cannot show that the argument is invalid, only then do we accept the argument as valid. We illustrate this process in Example 3.

Example 3 *Ballerinas and Athletes*

Determine whether the following syllogism is valid or is invalid.

> All ballerinas are athletic.
> Keyshawn is athletic.
> ―――――――――
> ∴ Keyshawn is a ballerina.

Solution The premise "All ballerinas are athletic" is illustrated in Fig. 3.7(a). The next premise, "Keyshawn is athletic," tells us that Keyshawn must be placed in the set of athletic people. Two diagrams in which both premises are satisfied are shown in Fig. 3.7(b) and (c). By examining Fig. 3.7(b), however, we see that Keyshawn is not a ballerina. Therefore, the conclusion "Keyshawn is a ballerina" does not necessarily follow from the set of premises. Thus, the argument is invalid, or a fallacy.

  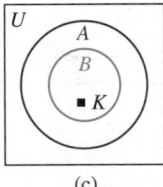

(a) (b) (c)

Figure 3.7

Example 4 *Parrots and Chickens*

Determine whether the following syllogism is valid or invalid.

> No parrots eat chicken.
> Fletch does not eat chicken.
> ―――――――――
> ∴ Fletch is a parrot.

Solution The first premise tells us that parrots and things that eat chicken are disjoint sets—that is, sets that do not intersect. The diagram in Fig. 3.8 satisfies the two given premises and also shows that Fletch is not a parrot. Therefore, the argument is invalid, or is a fallacy.

Figure 3.8

TIMELY TIP

Note that in Example 4 if we placed Fletch in circle *P*, the argument would appear to be valid. Remember that *whenever testing the validity of an argument, always try to show that the argument is invalid.* If there is any way of showing that the conclusion does not necessarily follow from the premises, then the argument is invalid.

Example 5 *A Syllogism Involving the Word Some*

Determine whether the following syllogism is valid or invalid.

> All *A*s are *B*s.
> Some *B*s are *C*s.
> ―――――――――
> ∴ Some *A*s are *C*s.

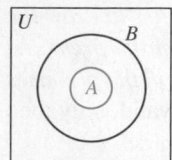

Figure 3.9

Solution The premise "All *A*s are *B*s" is illustrated in Fig. 3.9. The premise "Some *B*s are *C*s" means that there is at least one *B* that is a *C*. We can illustrate this set of premises in four ways, as illustrated in Fig. 3.10.

(a)

(b)

(c)

(d)

Figure 3.10

In all four illustrations, we see that (1) all *A*s are *B*s and (2) some *B*s are *C*s. The conclusion is "Some *A*s are *C*s." Since at least one of the illustrations, Fig. 3.10(a), shows that the conclusion does not necessarily follow from the given premises, the argument is invalid. ∎

Example 6 *Fish and Cows*

Determine whether the following syllogism is valid or invalid.

> No fish are mammals.
> All cows are mammals.
> ――――――――――――――
> ∴ No fish are cows.

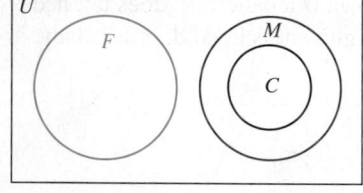

Figure 3.11

Solution The first premise tells us that fish and mammals are disjoint sets, as shown in Fig. 3.11. The second premise tells us that the set of cows is a subset of the set of mammals. Therefore, the circle representing the set of cows must go within the circle representing the set of mammals.

Note that the set of fish and the set of cows cannot be made to intersect without violating a premise. Thus, the conclusion "No fish are cows" necessarily follows from the premises and the argument is valid. Note that we did not say that this conclusion is true, only that the argument is valid. ∎

SECTION 3.6 *Exercises*

Warm Up Exercises

In Exercises 1–6, fill in the blanks with an appropriate word, phrase, or symbol(s).

1. The validity of a syllogistic argument can be determined using a(n) _____ diagram. Euler

2. If an Euler diagram can only be drawn in a way in which the conclusion necessarily follows from the premises, the syllogistic argument is a(n) _____ argument. Valid

3. If an Euler diagram can be drawn in a way in which the conclusion does not necessarily follow from the premises, the syllogistic argument is a(n) _____ argument. Invalid

4. The following Euler diagram can represent the statement _____ As are Bs. All

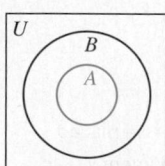

5. The following Euler diagram can represent the statement _____ As are Bs. No

6. The following Euler diagram can represent the statement _____ As are Bs. Some

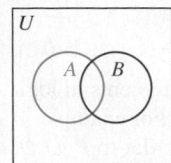

Practice the Skills/Problem Solving

In Exercises 7–28, use an Euler diagram to determine whether the syllogism is valid or invalid.

7. All gingerbread men can sing.

Gingy is a gingerbread man.

∴ Gingy can sing. Valid

8. All cats have whiskers.

All things with whiskers are dogs.

∴ All cats are dogs. Valid

9. No PCs are Macs.

All Dells are PCs.

∴ No Dells are Macs. Valid

10. All dolphins are mammals.

All mammals are vertebrates.

∴ All dolphins are vertebrates. Valid

11. All fishermen wear boots.

Percy wears boots.

∴ Percy is a fisherman. Invalid

12. All golfers have rain gear.

John Pearse has rain gear.

∴ John Pearse is a golfer. Invalid

13. No horses buck.

Palominos are horses.

∴ Palominos do not buck. Valid

14. No jockeys weigh more than 200 pounds.

Deb Otto is not a jockey.

∴ Deb Otto weighs more than 200 pounds. Invalid

15. Some mushrooms are poisonous.

A morel is a mushroom.

∴ A morel is poisonous. Invalid

16. Some skunks are tame.

Pepé is a skunk.

∴ Pepé is not tame. Invalid

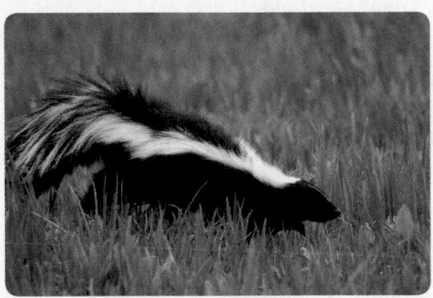

17. Some stamps are collectors' items.

Some collectors' items are valuable.

∴ Some stamps are valuable. Invalid

18. Some professional golfers give golf lessons.

All people who belong to the PGA are professional golfers.

∴ All people who belong to the PGA give golf lessons. Invalid

19. No lawn weeds are flowers.

Sedge is not a flower.

∴ Sedge is a lawn weed. Invalid

20. Some caterpillars are furry.

All furry things are mammals.

∴ Some caterpillars are mammals. Valid

21. Some flowers love sunlight.

All things that love sunlight love water.

∴ Some flowers love water. Valid

22. Some CD players are MP3 players.

All iPods are MP3 players.

∴ Some CD players are iPods. Invalid

23. No scarecrows are tin men.

No tin men are lions.

∴ No scarecrows are lions. Invalid

24. All pilots can fly.

All astronauts can fly.

∴ Some pilots are astronauts. Invalid

25. Some dogs wear glasses.

Fido wears glasses.

∴ Fido is a dog. Invalid

26. All rainy days are cloudy.

Today it is cloudy.

∴ Today is a rainy day. Invalid

27. All sweet things taste good.

All things that taste good are fattening.

All things that are fattening put on pounds.

∴ All sweet things put on pounds. Valid

28. All books have red covers.

All books that have red covers contain 200 pages.

Some books that contain 200 pages are novels.

∴ All books that contain 200 pages are novels. Invalid

Concept/Writing Exercises

29. Can an argument be valid if the conclusion is a false statement? Explain your answer. Yes, if the conclusion necessarily follows from the premises, the argument is valid.

30. Can an argument be invalid if the conclusion is a true statement? Explain. Yes, if the conclusion does not follow from the set of premises, the argument is invalid, even if the conclusion is a true statement.

Challenge Problem/Group Activity

31. *Sets and Logic* Statements in logic can be translated into set statements: For example, $p \wedge q$ is similar to $P \cap Q$; $p \vee q$ is similar to $P \cup Q$; and $p \rightarrow q$ is equivalent to $\sim p \vee q$, which is similar to $P' \cup Q$. Euler diagrams can also be used to show that arguments similar to those discussed in Section 3.5 are valid or invalid. Use Euler diagrams to show that the following symbolic argument is invalid.

$$p \rightarrow q$$
$$p \vee q$$
$$\overline{\therefore \sim p}$$

Internet/Research Activity

32. Leonhard Euler is considered one of the greatest mathematicians of all time. Do research and write a report on Euler's life. Include information on his contributions to sets and to logic. Also indicate other areas of mathematics in which he made important contributions. References include encyclopedias, history of mathematics books, and the Internet.

SECTION 3.7   Switching Circuits

▲ *What must be true for a lamp to produce light?*

Suppose you are sitting at your desk and want to turn on a lamp so you can read a book. If a wall switch controls the power to the outlet that the lamp is plugged into and the lamp has an on/off switch, what conditions must be true for the lamp's bulb to light? The wiring in our homes can be explained and described using logic.

Why *This is Important* Analyzing electrical circuits is one of the most important applications of logic.

Using Symbolic Statements to Represent Circuits

A common application of logic is switching circuits. To understand the basic concepts of switching circuits, let us examine a few simple circuits that are common in most homes. The typical lamp has a cord, which is plugged into a wall outlet. Somewhere between the bulb in the lamp and the outlet is a switch to turn the lamp on and off. A switch is often referred to as being on or off. When the switch is in the *on* position, the current flows through the switch and the bulb lights up. When the switch is in the *on* position, we can say that the switch is *closed* and that current will flow through the switch. When the switch is in the *off* position, the current does not flow through the switch and the bulb does not light. When the switch is in the *off* position, we can say that the switch is *open*, and the current does not flow through the switch. The basic configuration of a switch is shown in Fig. 3.12.

Figure 3.12

Table 3.37

Switch	Lightbulb
T	on (switch closed)
F	off (switch open)

Figure 3.13

Figure 3.14

Table 3.38

p	q	Light	$p \land q$
T	T	on (T)	T
T	F	off (F)	F
F	T	off (F)	F
F	F	off (F)	F

Figure 3.15

Table 3.39

p	q	Light	$p \lor q$
T	T	on (T)	T
T	F	on (T)	T
F	T	on (T)	T
F	F	off (F)	F

Electric circuits can be expressed as logical statements. We represent switches as letters, using T to represent a closed switch (or current flow) and F to represent an open switch (or no current flow). This relationship is indicated in Table 3.37.

Occasionally, we have a wall switch connected to a wall outlet and a lamp plugged into the wall outlet (Fig. 3.13). We then say that the wall switch and the switch on the lamp are in *series*, meaning that for the bulb in the lamp to light, both switches must be on at the same time (Fig. 3.14). On the other hand, the bulb will not light if either switch is off or if both switches are off. In either of these conditions, the electricity will not flow through the circuit. In a *series circuit*, the current can take only one path. If any switch in the path is open, the current cannot flow.

To illustrate this situation symbolically, let p represent the wall switch and q the lamp switch. The letter T will be used to represent both a closed switch and the bulb lighting. The letter F will represent an open switch and the bulb not lighting. Thus, we have four possible cases.

CASE 1: Both switches are closed; that is, p is T and q is T. The light is on, T.

CASE 2: Switch p is closed and switch q is open; that is, p is T and q is F. The light is off, F.

CASE 3: Switch p is open and switch q is closed; that is, p is F and q is T. The light is off, F.

CASE 4: Both switches are open; that is, p is F and q is F. The light is off, F.

Table 3.38 summarizes the results. The on–off results are the same as the truth table for the conjunction p ∧ q if we think of "on" as true and "off" as false.

Series Circuits
Switches in **series** will always be represented with a conjunction, ∧.

Another type of electric circuit used in the home is the *parallel circuit*, in which there are two or more paths that the current can take. If the current can pass through either path or both (see Fig. 3.15), the light will go on. The letter T will be used to represent both a closed switch and the bulb lighting. The letter F will represent an open switch and the bulb not lighting. Thus, we have four possible cases.

CASE 1: Both switches are closed; that is, p is T and q is T. The light is on, T.

CASE 2: Switch p is closed and switch q is open; that is, p is T and q is F. The light is on, T.

CASE 3: Switch p is open and switch q is closed; that is, p is F and q is T. The light is on, T.

CASE 4: Both switches are open; that is, p is F and q is F. The light is off, F.

Table 3.39 summarizes the results. The on–off results are the same as the $p \lor q$ truth table if we think of "on" as true and "off" as false.

Parallel Circuits
Switches in **parallel** will always be represented with a disjunction, ∨.

Sometimes it is necessary to have two or more switches in the same circuit that will both be open at the same time and both be closed at the same time. In such circuits, we will use the same letter to represent both switches. For example, in the circuit shown in Fig. 3.16, there are two switches labeled p. Therefore, both of these switches must be open at the same time and both must be closed at the same time. One of the p switches cannot be open at the same time the other p switch is closed.

We can now combine some of these basic concepts to analyze more circuits.

Figure 3.16

Example **1** *Representing a Switching Circuit with Symbolic Statements*

a) Write a symbolic statement that represents the circuit shown in Fig. 3.16.

b) Construct a truth table to determine when the light will be on.

Solution

a) In Fig. 3.16, there is a blue switch p on the left, and to the right there is a branch containing a red switch p and a switch q. The current must flow through the blue switch p into the branch on its right. Therefore, the blue switch p is in series with the branch containing the red switch p and switch q. After the current flows through the blue switch p it reaches the branch on its right. At this point, the current has the option of flowing into the red switch p, switch q, or both of these switches. Therefore, the branch containing the red switch p and switch q is a parallel branch. We say these two switches are in parallel. The entire circuit in symbolic form is $p \land (p \lor q)$. Note that the parentheses are very important. Without parentheses, the symbolic statement could be interpreted as $(p \land p) \lor q$. The diagram for $(p \land p) \lor q$ is illustrated in Fig. 3.17. We shall see later in this section that the circuits in Fig. 3.16 and Fig. 3.17 are not the same.

Figure 3.17

Table 3.40

p	q	p	$\land$	$(p \lor q)$
T	T	T	T	T
T	F	T	T	T
F	T	F	F	T
F	F	F	F	F
		1	3	2

b) The truth table for the statement (Table 3.40) indicates that the light will be on only in the cases in which p is true or when switch p is closed. ∎

Example **2** *Representing a Switching Circuit with Symbolic Statements*

a) Write a symbolic statement that represents the circuit in Fig. 3.18.

b) Construct a truth table to determine when the light will be on.

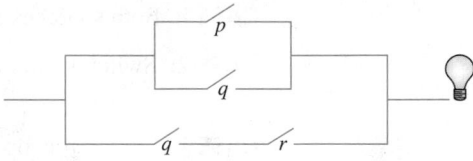

Figure 3.18

Solution

a) The upper branch of the circuit contains two switches, p and q, in parallel. We can represent that branch with the statement $p \lor q$. The lower branch of the circuit has two switches, q and r, in series. We can represent that branch with the statement $q \land r$. The upper branch is in parallel with the lower branch. Putting the two branches together, we get the statement $(p \lor q) \lor (q \land r)$.

b) The truth table for the statement (Table 3.41 on page 159) shows that cases 7 and 8 are false. Thus, the light will be off in these two cases and on in all the other cases. In examining the truth values, we see that the statement is false only in the cases in which both p and q are false, or when both switches p and q are open. By examining the diagram or truth table, we can see that the current will flow if switch p is closed or switch q is closed.

Table 3.41

p	q	r	$(p \vee q)$	$\vee$	$(q \wedge r)$
T	T	T	T	T	T
T	T	F	T	T	F
T	F	T	T	T	F
T	F	F	T	T	F
F	T	T	T	T	T
F	T	F	T	T	F
F	F	T	F	F	F
F	F	F	F	F	F
			1	3	2

Drawing Switching Circuits that Represent Symbolic Statements

We will next study how to draw a switching circuit that represents a given symbolic statement. Suppose we are given the statement $(p \wedge q) \vee r$ and are asked to construct a circuit corresponding to it. Remember that $\wedge$ indicates a series branch and $\vee$ indicates a parallel branch. Working first within parentheses, we see that switches p and q are in series. This series branch is in parallel with switch r, as indicated in Fig. 3.19.

Occasionally, it is necessary to have two switches in the same circuit such that when one switch is open, the other switch is closed; and when one switch is closed, the other switch is open. Therefore, the two switches will never both be open together and never be closed together. This situation can be represented by using p for one of the switches and $\overline{p}$ for the other switch. The switch labeled $\overline{p}$ corresponds to $\sim p$ in a logic statement. For example, in a series circuit, $p \wedge \sim p$ would be represented by Fig. 3.20. In this case, the light would never go on; the switches would counteract each other. When switch p is closed, switch $\overline{p}$ is open; and when p is open, $\overline{p}$ is closed.

Figure 3.19

Figure 3.20

Figure 3.21

Figure 3.22

Example 3 *Representing a Symbolic Statement as a Switching Circuit*

Draw a switching circuit that represents $[(p \wedge \sim q) \vee (r \vee q)] \wedge s$.

Solution In the statement, p and $\sim q$ have $\wedge$ between them, so switches p and $\overline{q}$ are in series, as represented in Fig. 3.21. Also in the statement, r and q have $\vee$ between them, so switches r and q are in parallel, as represented in Fig. 3.22.

Because $(p \wedge \sim q)$ and $(r \vee q)$ are connected with $\vee$, the two branches are in parallel with each other. The parallel branches are represented in Fig. 3.23. Finally, s in the statement is connected to the rest of the statement with $\wedge$. Therefore, switch s is in series with the entire rest of the circuit, as illustrated in Fig. 3.24.

Figure 3.23   Figure 3.24

Equivalent Circuits

Sometimes two circuits that look very different will actually have the exact same conditions under which the light will be on. If we were to analyze the truth tables for the corresponding symbolic statements for such circuits, we would find that they have identical answer columns. In other words, the corresponding symbolic statements are equivalent.

> ### Definition: Equivalent Circuits
> **Equivalent circuits** are two circuits that have equivalent corresponding symbolic statements.

To determine whether two circuits are equivalent, we will analyze the answer columns of the truth tables of their corresponding symbolic statements. If the answer columns from their corresponding symbolic statements are identical, then the circuits are equivalent.

Example 4 *Are the Circuits Equivalent?*

Determine whether the two circuits are equivalent.

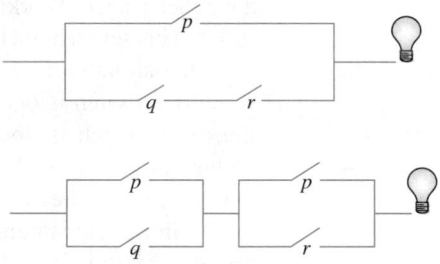

Solution The symbolic statement that represents the first circuit is $p \vee (q \wedge r)$. The symbolic statement that represents the second circuit is $(p \vee q) \wedge (p \vee r)$. The truth tables for these statements are shown in Table 3.42.

Table 3.42

p	q	r	p	$\vee$	$(q \wedge r)$	$(p \vee q)$	$\wedge$	$(p \vee r)$
T	T	T	T	T	T	T	T	T
T	T	F	T	T	F	T	T	T
T	F	T	T	T	F	T	T	T
T	F	F	T	T	F	T	T	T
F	T	T	F	T	T	T	T	T
F	T	F	F	F	F	T	F	F
F	F	T	F	F	F	F	F	T
F	F	F	F	F	F	F	F	F

Note that the answer columns for the two statements are identical. Therefore, $p \vee (q \wedge r)$ is equivalent to $(p \vee q) \wedge (p \vee r)$ and the two circuits are equivalent. ■

SECTION 3.7

Exercises

Warm Up Exercises

In Exercises 1–4, fill in the blanks with an appropriate word, phrase, or symbol(s).

1. A conjunction, ∧, is used to represent switches in a(n) _____ circuit. Series

2. A disjunction, ∨, is used to represent switches in a(n) _____ circuit. Parallel

3. When a switch labeled as p is open, a switch labeled as $\overline{p}$ is _____. Closed

4. Two circuits are equivalent if they have equivalent _____ statements. Symbolic

Practice the Skills/Problem Solving

In Exercises 5–12, (a) write a symbolic statement that represents the circuit and (b) construct a truth table to determine when the lightbulb will be on. That is, determine which switches must be open and which switches must be closed for the lightbulb to be on.

5.

6.

7.

8.

9.

10.

11.

12.

In Exercises 13–20, draw a switching circuit that represents the symbolic statement.

13. $p \land q$ *

14. $p \lor (q \land r)$ *

15. $(p \lor q) \land r$ *

16. $\sim p \land (q \lor r)$ *

17. $(p \lor q) \land (r \lor s)$ *

18. $(p \land q) \lor (r \land s)$ *

19. $[(p \lor q) \lor (r \land q)] \land (\sim p)$ *

20. $[(p \lor q) \land r] \lor (\sim p \land q)$ *

In Exercises 21–26, represent each circuit with a symbolic statement. Then use a truth table to determine if the circuits are equivalent.

21.

$p \lor \sim q$; $\overline{p} \land q$; not equivalent

22.

$p \land (q \lor r)$; $(p \land q) \lor (p \land r)$; equivalent

23.

$[(p \land q) \lor r] \land p$; $(q \lor r) \land p$; equivalent

24.

$(p \lor r) \land (q \lor r)$; $(p \land q) \lor r$; equivalent

25.

$(p \lor \sim p) \land q \land r$; $p \land q \land r$; not equivalent

26.

$[(p \land q) \lor (r \land \sim q)] \lor (r \land \sim p)$; $(p \lor r) \land (q \lor r)$; equivalent

*See Instructor Answer Appendix

Concept/Writing Exercises

27. Explain why the lightbulb will never go on in the following circuit. *

28. Explain why the lightbulb will always be on in the following circuit.*

Challenge Problems/Group Activities

29. Design a circuit that can be represented by

  a) $p \rightarrow q$ *   **b)** $\sim(p \rightarrow q)$ *

  (*Hint*: See Section 3.4.)

30. Design two circuits that each involve switches labeled p, q, r, and s that appear to be different but are actually equivalent circuits. Answers will vary.

Internet/Research Activities

31. Digital computers use gates that work like switches to perform calculations. (See *Did You Know?* box on page 160.) Information is fed into the gates and information leaves the gates, according to the type of gate. The three basic gates used in computers are the NOT gate, the AND gate, and or OR gate. Do research on the three types of gates.

  a) Explain how each gate works.

  b) Explain the relationship between each gate and the corresponding logic connectives *not*, *and*, and *or*.

  c) Illustrate how two or more gates can be combined to form a more complex gate.
  *See Instructor Answer Appendix

CHAPTER 3   *Summary*

Important Facts and Concepts

Examples

Section 3.1
Quantifiers

Example 1, page 96

Form of Statement	Form of Negation
All are.	Some are not.
None are.	Some are.
Some are.	None are.
Some are not.	All are.

Summary of Connectives

Examples 2–8, pages 97–101

Formal Name	Symbol	Read	Symbolic Form
Negation	$\sim$	not	$\sim p$
Conjunction	$\wedge$	and	$p \wedge q$
Disjunction	$\vee$	or	$p \vee q$
Conditional	$\rightarrow$	if–then	$p \rightarrow q$
Biconditional	$\leftrightarrow$	if and only if	$p \leftrightarrow q$

Section 3.2 & Section 3.3
Basic Truth Tables

Examples 1–10, pages 107–114
Examples 1–10, pages 118–124

Negation				Conjunction	Disjunction	Conditional	Biconditional
p	$\sim p$	p	q	$p \wedge q$	$p \vee q$	$p \rightarrow q$	$p \leftrightarrow q$
T	F	T	T	T	T	T	T
F	T	T	F	F	T	F	F
		F	T	F	T	T	F
		F	F	F	F	T	T

Section 3.4
De Morgan's Laws

Examples 4–6, pages 130–131

$$\sim(p \wedge q) \Leftrightarrow \sim p \vee \sim q$$
$$\sim(p \vee q) \Leftrightarrow \sim p \wedge \sim q$$

Section 3.4

Other Equivalent Forms

$$p \rightarrow q \Leftrightarrow \sim p \ \lor \ q$$
$$\sim(p \rightarrow q) \Leftrightarrow p \ \land \ \sim q$$
$$p \leftrightarrow q \Leftrightarrow [(p \rightarrow q) \ \land \ (q \rightarrow p)]$$

Examples 7–9, pages 131–132

Variations of the Conditional Statement

Examples 10–12, pages 133–135

Name	Symbolic Form	Read
Conditional	$p \rightarrow q$	If p, then q.
Converse of the conditional	$q \rightarrow p$	If q, then p.
Inverse of the conditional	$\sim p \rightarrow \sim q$	If not p, then not q.
Contrapositive of the conditional	$\sim q \rightarrow \sim p$	If not q, then not p.

Section 3.5

Standard Forms of Valid Arguments

Examples 1–4, pages 142–144

Law of Detachment	Law of Contraposition	Law of Syllogism	Disjunctive Syllogism
$p \rightarrow q$	$p \rightarrow q$	$p \rightarrow q$	$p \ \lor \ q$
p	$\sim q$	$q \rightarrow r$	$\sim p$
$\therefore q$	$\therefore \sim p$	$\therefore p \rightarrow r$	$\therefore q$

Standard Forms of Invalid Arguments

Example 5, page 145

Fallacy of the Converse	Fallacy of the Inverse
$p \rightarrow q$	$p \rightarrow q$
q	$\sim p$
$\therefore p$	$\therefore \sim q$

Section 3.5 & Section 3.6

Symbolic Argument vs. Syllogistic Argument

Examples 1–5, pages 142–145
Examples 1–6, pages 152–154

	Words or Phrases Used	Method of Determining Validity
Symbolic argument	and, or, not, if–then, if and only if	Truth tables or by comparison with standard forms of arguments
Syllogistic argument	all are, some are, none are, some are not	Euler diagrams

Section 3.7

Switching Circuits as Symbolic Statements

Examples 1–4, pages 158–160

Switches in series will always be represented with a conjunction, $\land$.

Switches in parallel will always be represented with a disjunction, $\lor$.

CHAPTER 3   *Review Exercises*

3.1

In Exercises 1–4, write the negation of the statement.

1. All Scions are Toyotas. Some Scions are not Toyotas.

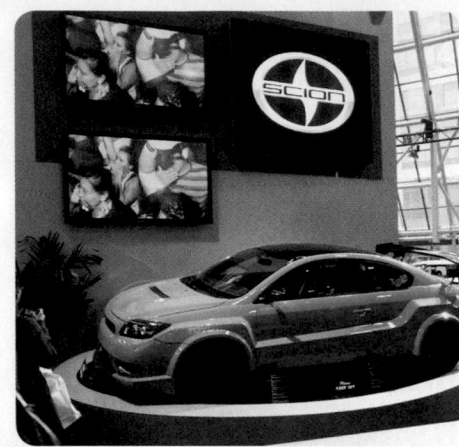

2. No pets are allowed in this park.
Some pets are allowed in this park.

3. Some women are presidents. No women are presidents.

4. Some pine trees are not green. All pine trees are green.

In Exercises 5–10, write each compound statement in words.

> *p*:   The coffee is Maxwell House.
> *q*:   The coffee is hot.
> *r*:   The coffee is strong.

5. $p \lor q$ *

6. $\sim q \land r$ *

7. $q \rightarrow (r \land \sim p)$ *

8. $p \leftrightarrow \sim r$ *

9. $\sim p \leftrightarrow (r \land \sim q)$ *

10. $(p \lor \sim q) \land \sim r$ *

3.2

In Exercises 11–16, use the statements for p, q, and r as in Exercises 5–10 to write the statement in symbolic form.

11. The coffee is Maxwell House or the coffee is strong. $p \lor r$

12. If the coffee is strong, then the coffee is not Maxwell House. $r \rightarrow \sim p$

13. If the coffee is strong then the coffee is hot, or the coffee is not Maxwell House. $(r \rightarrow q) \lor \sim p$

14. The coffee is hot if and only if the coffee is Maxwell House, and the coffee is not strong. $(q \leftrightarrow p) \land \sim r$

15. The coffee is strong and the coffee is hot, or the coffee is not Maxwell House. $(r \land q) \lor \sim p$

16. It is false that the coffee is strong and the coffee is hot. $\sim (r \land q)$

In Exercises 17–22, construct a truth table for the statement.

17. $(p \lor q) \land \sim p$ *

18. $q \leftrightarrow (p \lor \sim q)$ *

19. $(p \lor q) \leftrightarrow (p \lor r)$ *

20. $p \land (\sim q \lor r)$ *

21. $p \rightarrow (q \land \sim r)$ *

22. $(p \land q) \rightarrow \sim r$ *

3.2, 3.3

In Exercises 23–26, determine the truth value of the statement. You may need to use a reference such as the Internet or an encyclopedia.

23. If ESPN is a sports network then CNN is a news network, if and only if Nickelodeon is a cooking network. False

24. President's Day is in February, or Memorial Day is in May and Labor Day is in December. True

25. If Oregon borders the Pacific Ocean or California borders the Atlantic Ocean, then Minnesota is south of Texas. False

26. $15 - 7 = 22$ or $4 + 9 = 13$, and $9 - 8 = 1$. True

3.3

In Exercises 27–30, determine the truth value of the statement when p is T, q is F, and r is F.

27. $(\sim p \rightarrow q) \land \sim (q \lor r)$ True

28. $(p \leftrightarrow q) \rightarrow (\sim p \lor r)$ True

29. $\sim r \leftrightarrow [(p \lor q) \leftrightarrow \sim p]$ False

30. $\sim [(q \land r) \rightarrow (\sim p \lor r)]$ False

*See Instructor Answer Appendix

3.4

In Exercises 31–34, determine whether the pairs of statements are equivalent. You may use De Morgan's laws, the fact that $(p \to q) \Leftrightarrow (\sim p \lor q)$, the fact that $\sim(p \to q) \Leftrightarrow (p \land \sim q)$, truth tables, or equivalent forms of the conditional statement.

31. $\sim(p \land \sim q)$, $\sim p \land q$ Not equivalent

32. $p \lor q$, $\sim p \to q$ Equivalent

33. $\sim p \lor (q \land r)$, $(\sim p \lor q) \land (\sim p \lor r)$ Equivalent

34. $(\sim q \to p) \land p$, $\sim(\sim p \leftrightarrow q) \lor p$ Not equivalent

In Exercises 35–39, use De Morgan's laws, the fact that $(p \to q) \Leftrightarrow (\sim p \lor q)$, or the fact that $\sim(p \to q) \Leftrightarrow (p \land \sim q)$, to write an equivalent statement for the given statement.

35. Lady Gaga sang "Poker Face" and Jay-Z did not sing "Beamer, Benz, or Bentley." It is false that if Lady Gaga sang "Poker Face", then Jay-Z sang "Beamer, Benz, or Bentley".

36. Lynn Swann played for the Steelers or Jack Tatum played for the Raiders. If Lynn Swann did not play for the Steelers, then Jack Tatum played for the Raiders.

37. It is not true that Altec Lansing only produces speakers or Harman Kardon only produces stereo receivers. Altec Lansing does not produce only speakers and Harman Kardon does not produce only stereo receivers.

38. Travis Tritt did not win an Academy Award and Randy Jackson does not do commercials for Milk Bone Dog Biscuits. It is false that Travis Tritt won an Academy Award or Randy Jackson does commercials for Milk Bone Dog Biscuits.

39. If the temperature is not above 32°, then we will go ice fishing at O'Leary's Lake. The temperature is above 32° or we will go ice fishing at O'Leary's Lake.

In Exercises 40–44, write the (a) converse, (b) inverse, and (c) contrapositive for the given statement.

40. If you listen to Jim Rome, then you know Jay Stu. *

41. If we take the table to *Antiques Roadshow*, then we will learn the table's value. *

42. If you do not advertise, then you do not sell more doughnuts.*

43. If the desk is made by Winner's Only and the desk is in the Rose catalog, then we will not buy a desk at Miller's Furniture. *

44. If you get straight A's on your report card, then I will let you attend the prom. *

In Exercises 45–48, determine which, if any, of the three statements are equivalent.

45. a) If you swim every day, then you lose five pounds.

   b) You do not swim every day or you lose five pounds.

   c) It is false that you swim every day and you do not lose five pounds. a), b), and c) are equivalent.

46. a) The screwdriver is on the workbench if and only if the screwdriver is not on the counter.

   b) If the screwdriver is not on the counter, then the screwdriver is not on the workbench.

   c) It is false that the screwdriver is on the counter and the screwdriver is not on the workbench. None are equivalent.

47. a) If $2 + 3 = 6$, then $3 + 1 = 5$.

   b) $2 + 3 = 6$ if and only if $3 + 1 \neq 5$.

   c) If $3 + 1 \neq 5$, then $2 + 3 \neq 6$. a) and c) are equivalent.

48. a) If the sale is on Tuesday and I have money, then I will go to the sale.

   b) If I go to the sale, then the sale is on Tuesday and I have money.

   c) I go to the sale, or the sale is on Tuesday and I have money. None are equivalent.

*See Instructor Answer Appendix

3.5

In Exercises 49–52, determine whether the argument is valid or invalid. You may compare the argument to a standard form or use a truth table.

49. $p \rightarrow q$ Invalid
$$\frac{q}{\therefore p}$$

50. $p \wedge q$ Valid
$$\frac{q \rightarrow r}{\therefore p \rightarrow r}$$

51. If Jose Macias is the manager, then Kevin Geis is the coach.

If Kevin Geis is the coach, then Tim Weisman is the umpire.

∴ If Jose Macias is the manager, then Tim Weisman is the umpire. Valid

52. If the astronaut visits the space station, then the astronaut uses the space shuttle. The astronaut uses the space shuttle or the astronaut uses the Soyuz spacecraft. Therefore, the astronaut does not use the Soyuz spacecraft. Invalid

▲ *The International Space Station*

3.6

In Exercises 53–56, use an Euler diagram to determine whether the argument is valid or invalid.

53. All registered nurses went to college.

Some bookkeepers went to college.

∴ Some bookkeepers are registered nurses. Invalid

54. All hackysack players are students.

Joel Knutson is a hackysack player.

∴ Joel Knutson is a student. Valid

55. No Beatles are Rolling Stones.

Some Rolling Stones are Small Faces.

∴ No Beatles are Small Faces. Invalid

56. All bears are furry.

Teddy is furry.

∴ Teddy is a bear. Invalid

3.7

57. a) Write the corresponding symbolic statement of the circuit shown. $p \wedge [(q \wedge r) \vee \sim p]$

b) Construct a truth table to determine when the lightbulb will be on. The lightbulb will be on when p, q, and r are all closed.

58. Construct a diagram of a circuit that corresponds to the symbolic statement $(p \vee q) \vee (p \wedge q)$. *

59. Determine whether the circuits shown are equivalent.
Equivalent

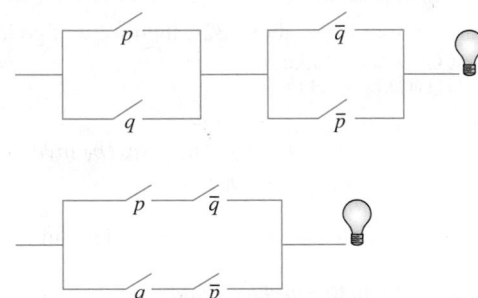

CHAPTER 3) *Test*

In Exercise 1–3, write the statement in symbolic form

> p: Phobos is a moon of Mars.
> q: Callisto is a moon of Jupiter.
> r: Rosalind is a moon of Uranus.

▲ *Callisto, a moon of Jupiter*

1. Phobos is a moon of Mars and Rosalind is a moon of Uranus, or Callisto is not a moon of Jupiter. $(p \wedge r) \vee \sim q$

2. If Rosalind is a moon of Uranus then Callisto is a moon of Jupiter, or Phobos is not a moon of Mars. $(r \rightarrow q) \vee \sim p$

3. It is false that Rosalind is a moon of Uranus if and only if Callisto is not a moon of Jupiter. $\sim(r \leftrightarrow \sim q)$

In Exercises 4 and 5, use p, q, and r as above to write each symbolic statement in words.

4. $(\sim p \wedge r) \leftrightarrow \sim q$ *

5. $(p \vee \sim q) \rightarrow r$ *

In Exercises 6 and 7, construct a truth table for the given statement.

6. $[\sim(p \rightarrow r)] \wedge q$ *

7. $(q \leftrightarrow \sim r) \vee p$ *

In Exercises 8 and 9, find the truth value of the statement.

8. $2 + 6 = 8$ or $7 - 12 = 5$. True

9. Harrison Ford is an actor or Gerald Ford was a president, if and only if the Mississippi is a river. True

In Exercises 10 and 11, given that p is true, q is false, and r is true, determine the truth value of the statement.

10. $(r \vee q) \leftrightarrow (p \wedge \sim q)$ True

11. $[\sim(r \rightarrow \sim p)] \wedge (q \rightarrow p)$ True

12. Determine whether the pair of statements are equivalent. Equivalent

$$\sim p \vee q, \quad \sim(p \wedge \sim q)$$

In Exercises 13 and 14, determine which, if any, of the three statements are equivalent.

13. a) If the bird is red, then it is a cardinal.

   b) The bird is not red or it is a cardinal.

   c) If the bird is not red, then it is not a cardinal.
   a) and b) are equivalent.

14. a) It is not true that the test is today or the concert is tonight.

   b) The test is not today and the concert is not tonight.

   c) If the test is not today, then the concert is not tonight.
   a) and b) are equivalent.

15. *Translate the following argument into symbolic form. Determine whether the argument is valid or invalid by comparing the argument to a recognized form or by using a truth table.*

   If the soccer team wins the game, then Sue played fullback. If Sue played fullback, then the team is in second place. Therefore, if the soccer team wins the game, then the team is in second place. *

16. *Use an Euler diagram to determine whether the syllogism is valid or is a fallacy.*

   All living things contain carbon.
   Roger contains carbon.
   _____
   ∴ Therefore, Roger is a living thing. Invalid

In Exercises 17 and 18, write the negation of the statement.

17. All highways are roads. Some highways are not roads.

18. Nick played football and Max played baseball.
   Nick did not play football or Max did not play baseball.

19. Write the converse, inverse, and contrapositive of the conditional statement "If the garbage truck comes, then today is Saturday." *

20. Construct a diagram of a circuit that corresponds to $(p \wedge q) \vee (\sim p \vee \sim q)$ *

*See Instructor Answer Appendix

GROUP PROJECTS

Computer Gates

1. Gates in computers work on the same principles as switching circuits. The three basic types of gate are the NOT gate, the AND gate, and the OR gate. Each is illustrated along with a table that indicates current flow entering and exiting the gate. If current flows into a NOT gate, then no current exits, and vice versa. Current exits an AND gate only when both inputs have a current flow. Current exits an OR gate if current flows through either, or both, inputs. In the table, a 1 represents a current flow and a 0 indicates no current flow. For example, in the AND gate, if there is a current flow in input A (I_a has a value of 1) and no current flow in input B (I_b has a value of 0), there is no current flow in the output (O has a value of 0); see row 2 of the AND Gate table.

NOT gate

Input ——▷o—— Output

NOT gate

I	O
1	0
0	1

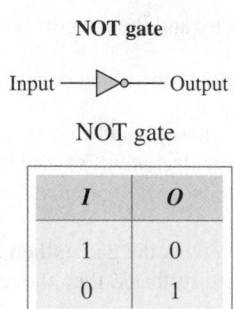

AND gate   **OR gate**

Input A ——⊐D—— Output   Input A ——⊃D—— Output
Input B ——   Input B ——

AND gate   OR gate

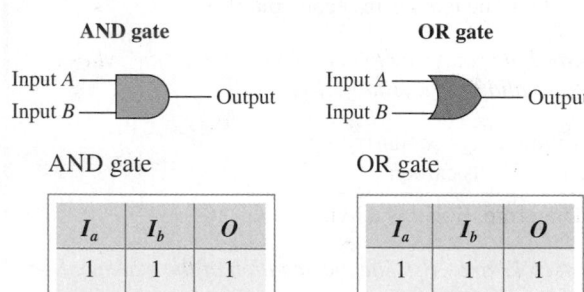

I_a	I_b	O
1	1	1
1	0	0
0	1	0
0	0	0

I_a	I_b	O
1	1	1
1	0	1
0	1	1
0	0	0

a) If 1 is considered true and 0 is considered false, explain how these tables are similar to the *not, and,* and *or* truth tables.

For the inputs indicated in the following figures determine whether the output is 1 or 0.

b) I_a —1— ⊃D— ▷o— Output
I_b —0—

c) I_a —1— ⊐D— Output
I_b —0— ▷o—

d) I_a —1— •— ▷— ⊐D ⊃D— Output
I_b —1— •— ▷—

e) What values for I_a and I_b will give an output of 1 in the figure in part (d)? Explain how you determined your answer.

f) Construct a truth table using 1's and 0's for the following gate. Your truth table should have columns I_a, I_b, and O and should indicate the four possible cases for the inputs and each corresponding output.

I_a ——▷o—— ⊃D—— Output
I_b ——

Logic Game

2. a) Shown is a photograph of a logic game at the Ontario Science Centre. There are 12 balls on top of the game board, numbered from left to right, with ball 1 on the extreme left and ball 12 on the extreme right. On the platform in front of the players are 12 buttons. Button 1 corresponds to ball 1, button 2 corresponds to ball 2, and so on. When 6 buttons are pushed, the 6 respective balls are released. When 1 or 2 balls reach an *and* gate or an *or* gate, a single ball may or may not pass through the gate. The object of the game is to select a proper combination of 6 buttons that will allow 1 ball to reach the bottom. Using your knowledge of *and* and *or*, select a combination of 6 buttons that will result in a win. (There is more than one answer.) Explain how you determined your answer.

b) Construct a game similar to this one where 15 balls are at the top and 8 balls must be selected to allow 1 ball to reach the bottom.

c) Indicate all solutions to the game you constructed in part (c).

4

Systems of Numeration

What You Will Learn

- Additive, multiplicative, and ciphered systems of numeration
- Place-value systems of numeration
- Egyptian, Hindu–Arabic, Roman, Chinese, Ionic Greek, Babylonian, and Mayan numerals
- Converting base 10 numerals to numerals in other bases
- Converting numerals in other bases to base 10 numerals
- Performing addition, subtraction, multiplication, and division in other bases
- Other computational methods such as duplation and mediation, the lattice method, and Napier's rods

Why This is Important

The number system most of the world uses today, called the Hindu–Arabic system, is only one way to communicate numerically. In this chapter, we will study other systems of numeration. We will also study how to perform basic arithmetic in other bases and with methods other than those most of us were taught when we were children.

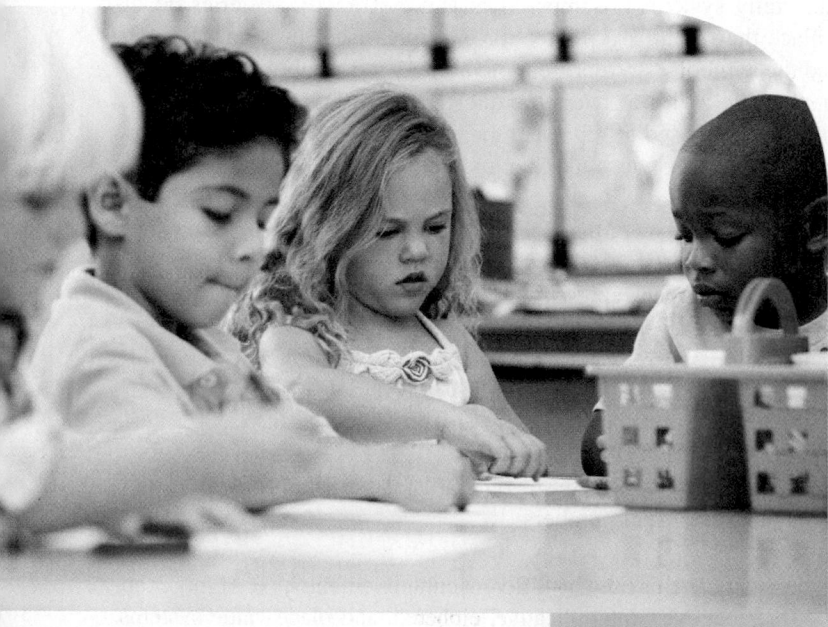

◄ There are many ways that we can communicate numerically.

We are all familiar with the numerals we grew up with: 1, 2, 3, and so forth. Now think of another set of numerals. You may have thought of Roman numerals: I, II, III, and so forth. Some common modern-day uses of Roman numerals include clock and watch numbers, the copyright year on movie and television credits, outlines, and page numbers at the beginning of books. Perhaps an even more famous use of Roman numerals is their use in the logo for the Super Bowl each year. In this section, we will study several sets of numerals besides our familiar 1, 2, 3, ….

Why **This is Important**   By studying other numerals, we can gain a better understanding of the underlying concepts used in many applications of mathematics.

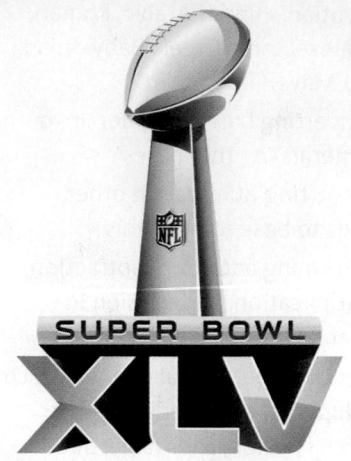

▲ *Roman numerals are used each year in The Super Bowl Logo.*

Just as the first attempts to write were made long after the development of speech, the first representation of numbers by symbols came long after people had learned to count. A tally system using physical objects, such as scratch marks in the soil or on a stone, notches on a stick, pebbles, or knots on a vine, was probably the earliest method of recording numbers.

In primitive societies, such a tally system adequately served the limited need for recording livestock, agriculture, or whatever was counted. As civilization developed, however, more efficient and accurate methods of calculating and keeping records were needed. Because tally systems are impractical and inefficient, societies developed symbols to replace them. The Egyptians, for example, used the symbol ∩, and the Babylonians used the symbol ❮ to represent the number we symbolize by 10.

A *number* is a quantity, and it answers the question "How many?" A *numeral* is a symbol such as ∩, ❮, or 10 used to represent the number. We think a number but write a numeral. The distinction between number and numeral will be made here only if it is helpful to the discussion.

In language, relatively few letters of the alphabet are used to construct a large number of words. Similarly, in arithmetic, a small variety of numerals can be used to represent all numbers. In general, when representing a number, we use as few numerals as possible. One of the greatest accomplishments of humankind has been the development of systems of numeration, whereby all numbers are "created" from a few symbols. Without such systems, mathematics would not have developed to its present level.

> **Definition:** **System of Numeration**
> A **system of numeration** consists of a set of numerals and a scheme or rule for combining the numerals to represent numbers.

Four types of numeration systems used by different cultures are the topic of this chapter. They are additive (or repetitive), multiplicative, ciphered, and place-value systems. You do not need to memorize all the symbols, but you should understand the principles behind each system. By the end of this chapter, we hope that you better understand the system we use, the *Hindu–Arabic system*, and its relationship to other types of systems.

Additive Systems

An additive system is one in which the number represented by a particular set of numerals is simply the sum of the values of the numerals. The additive system of numeration is one of the oldest and most primitive types of numeration systems. One of the first additive systems, the Egyptian hieroglyphic system, dates back to about 3000 B.C. The Egyptians used symbols for the powers of 10: 10^0 or 1, 10^1 or 10, 10^2 or $10 \cdot 10$, 10^3 or $10 \cdot 10 \cdot 10$, and so on. Table 4.1 lists the Egyptian hieroglyphic numerals with the equivalent Hindu–Arabic numerals.

To write the number 600 in Egyptian hieroglyphics, we write the numeral for 100 six times: ૧૧૧૧૧૧.

Table 4.1 Egyptian Hieroglyphics

Hindu–Arabic Numerals	Egyptian Numerals	Description
1	I	Staff (vertical stroke)
10	∩	Heel bone (arch)
100	૧	Scroll (coiled rope)
1000	₰	Lotus flower
10,000	⌐	Pointing finger
100,000	⋈	Tadpole (or whale)
1,000,000	⚡	Astonished person

Example 1 *From Egyptian to Hindu–Arabic Numerals*

Write the following numeral as a Hindu–Arabic numeral.

$$\text{ഡ൧൧൧∩IIII}$$

Solution

$$10,000 + 10,000 + 10,000 + 100 + 100 + 100 + 10 + 1 + 1 + 1 + 1$$
$$= 30,314 \qquad ■$$

Example 2 *From Hindu–Arabic to Egyptian Numerals*

Write 43,628 as an Egyptian numeral.

Solution

$$43,628 = 40,000 + 3000 + 600 + 20 + 8$$

$$\text{⌐⌐⌐⌐₰₰₰૧૧૧૧૧૧∩∩IIIIIIII} \qquad ■$$

In the Egyptian hieroglyphic system, the order of the symbols is not important. For example, ⋈II / ૧૧∩ and II૧૧⋈∩ both represent 100,212.

Users of additive systems easily accomplished addition and subtraction by combining or removing symbols. Multiplication and division were more difficult; they were performed by a process called *duplation and mediation* (see Section 4.5). The Egyptians had no symbol for zero, but they did have an understanding of fractions. The symbol ⌣ was used to take the reciprocal of a number; thus, ⌣III meant $\frac{1}{3}$ and ⌣∩I was $\frac{1}{11}$. Writing large numbers in the Egyptian hieroglyphic system takes longer than in other systems because so many symbols have to be listed. For example, 45 symbols are needed to represent 99,999.

The Roman numeration system, a second example of an additive system, was developed later than the Egyptian system. Roman numerals (Table 4.2 on page 172) were used in most European countries until the eighteenth century. They are still commonly seen on buildings, on clocks, and in books. Roman numerals are selected letters of the Roman alphabet.

Table 4.2 Roman Numerals

Roman numerals	I	V	X	L	C	D	M
Hindu–Arabic numerals	1	5	10	50	100	500	1000

The Roman system has two advantages over the Egyptian system. The first is that it uses the subtraction principle as well as the addition principle. Starting from the left, we add each numeral unless its value is smaller than the value of the numeral to its right. In that case, we subtract its value from the value of the numeral to its right. Only the numbers 1, 10, 100, 1000, … can be subtracted, and they can only be subtracted from the next two higher numbers. For example, C (100) can be subtracted only from D (500) or M (1000). The symbol DC represents 500 + 100, or 600, and CD represents 500 − 100, or 400. Similarly, MC represents 1000 + 100, or 1100, and CM represents 1000 − 100, or 900.

Example 3 *From Roman Numerals to Hindu–Arabic Numerals*

Write MCCLXXXI as a Hindu–Arabic numeral.

Solution Since each numeral is larger than the one on its right, no subtraction is necessary.

$$MCCLXXXI = 1000 + 100 + 100 + 50 + 10 + 10 + 10 + 1$$
$$= 1281$$

Example 4 *From Roman Numerals to Hindu–Arabic Numerals*

Write CMLXIV as a Hindu–Arabic numeral.

Solution As you read the numerals from left to right, you will note that C (100) has a smaller value than M (1000) and that C is to the left of M. Therefore, CM represents 1000 − 100, or 900. Also note that I (1) has a smaller value than V (5) and that I is to the left of V. Therefore, IV represents 5 − 1, or 4. The rest of the numerals can be added from left to right.

$$CMLXIV = (1000 − 100) + 50 + 10 + (5 − 1) = 964$$

Example 5 *Writing a Roman Numeral*

Write 439 as a Roman numeral.

Solution

$$439 = 400 + 30 + 9$$

To represent 400, we will subtract 100 (C) from 500 (D). We will place C to the left of D to indicate the subtraction (500 – 100). Likewise, to represent 9, we will subtract 1 (I) from 10 (X). We will place I to the left of X to indicate the subtraction (10 – 1). To represent 30 we will simply write X three times. Therefore,

$$439 = 400 + 30 + 9 = (500 − 100) + 10 + 10 + 10 + (10 − 1)$$
$$= CDXXXIX$$

In the Roman numeration system, a symbol is not repeated more than three consecutive times. For example, the number 646 would be written DCXLVI instead of DCXXXXVI.

The second advantage of the Roman numeration system over the Egyptian numeration system is that it makes use of the multiplication principle for numerals greater than 1000. A bar above a symbol or group of symbols indicates that the symbol or symbols are to be multiplied by 1000. Thus, $\overline{V} = 5 \times 1000 = 5000$, $\overline{X} = 10 \times 1000 = 10,000$, and $\overline{CD} = 400 \times 1000 = 400,000$. Other examples are $\overline{VI} = 6 \times 1000 = 6000$, $\overline{XIX} = 19 \times 1000 = 19,000$, and $\overline{XCIV} = 94 \times 1000 = 94,000$. This practice greatly reduces the number of symbols needed to write large numbers.

Example 6 *Writing a Large Roman Numeral*

Write 12,345 as a Roman numeral.

Solution

$$12,345 = (12 \times 1000) + 300 + 40 + 5$$
$$= [(10 + 1 + 1) \times 1000] + (100 + 100 + 100) + (50 - 10) + 5$$
$$= \overline{XII}CCCXLV$$

Multiplicative Systems

Multiplicative numeration systems are more similar to our Hindu–Arabic system than are additive systems. In a multiplicative system, 642 might be written (6) (100) (4) (10) (2) or

$$6$$
$$100$$
$$4$$
$$10$$
$$2$$

Note that no addition signs are needed in the representation. From this illustration, try to formulate a rule explaining how multiplicative systems work.

The principal example of a multiplicative system is the traditional Chinese system. The numerals used in this system are given in Table 4.3.

Table 4.3 Traditional Chinese Numerals

Traditional Chinese numerals	零	一	二	三	四	五	六	七	八	九	十	百	千
Hindu–Arabic numerals	0	1	2	3	4	5	6	7	8	9	10	100	1000

Chinese numerals are always written vertically. The numeral on top will be from 1 to 9 inclusive. This numeral is to be multiplied by the power of 10 below it. Thus, 20 is written

$$\left.\begin{array}{c}二\\十\end{array}\right\} 2 \times 10 = 20$$

and 400 is written

$$\left.\begin{array}{c}四\\百\end{array}\right\} 4 \times 100 = 400$$

Example 7   *A Traditional Chinese Numeral*

Write 538 as a Chinese numeral.

Solution

$$538 = \begin{cases} 500 = & \begin{cases} 5 \\ 100 \end{cases} \\ 30 = & \begin{cases} 3 \\ 10 \end{cases} \\ 8 = & \quad 8 \end{cases}$$

Note that in Example 7 the units digit, the 8, is not multiplied by a power of the base.

When writing Chinese numerals, there are some special cases that need to be considered. When writing a numeral between 11 and 19 it is not necessary to include the 1 before the 10. Thus, 18 would be written 十 rather than ─十. Another special case involves the use of zero.

When more than one consecutive zero occurs (except at the end of a numeral) you need to write a zero, but only once for two or more consecutive zeros. Zeros are not included at the end of numerals. The top two illustrations that follow show how zeros are used within a numeral, and the bottom two show that zeros are not used at the end of a numeral.

$$406 = \begin{cases} 4 \times 100 = 400 \\ 0 \times 10 = \quad 0 \\ 6 \qquad = \quad 6 \end{cases} \qquad 4006 = \begin{cases} 4 \times 1000 = 4000 \\ 0 \times 100 = 0 \\ 0 \times 10 = 0 \\ 6 = 6 \end{cases}$$

$$460 = \begin{cases} 4 \times 100 = 400 \\ 6 \times 10 = \quad 60 \end{cases} \qquad 4600 = \begin{cases} 4 \times 1000 = 4000 \\ 6 \times 100 = 600 \end{cases}$$

Example 8   *Traditional Chinese Numerals*

Write the following as traditional Chinese numerals.
a) 7080   b) 7008

Solution In part (a), there is one zero between the 7 and the 8. In part (b), there are two zeros between the 7 and the 8. As just mentioned, the symbol for zero is used only once in each of these numerals.

$$\text{a) } 7080 = \begin{cases} 7 \times 1000 \\ 0 \times 100 \\ 8 \times 10 \end{cases} \qquad 7008 = \begin{cases} 7 \times 1000 \\ 0 \times 100, \\ 0 \times 10 \\ 8 \end{cases}$$

> **TIMELY TIP**
>
> Notice the difference between our Hindu–Arabic numeration system, which is a positional numeration system, and the Chinese system, which is a multiplicative numeration system. Below we show how to write 5678 as a Chinese numeral if the Chinese system was a positional value system similar to ours.
>
> | Multiplicative | Positional Value |
> |:---:|:---:|
> | 五 5 | 五 5 |
> | 千 1000 | 六 6 |
> | 六 6 | 七 7 |
> | 百 100 | 八 8 |
> | 七 7 | |
> | 十 10 | |
> | 八 8 | |
>
> Note that the multiples of base 10 are removed when writing positional value numerals. We will discuss positional value systems in more detail shortly.

Ciphered Systems

A ciphered numeration system is one in which there are numerals for numbers up to and including the base and for multiples of the base. The numbers represented by a particular set of numerals is the sum of the values of the numerals.

Ciphered numeration systems require the memorization of many different symbols but have the advantage that numbers can be written in a compact form. The ciphered numeration system that we discuss is the Ionic Greek system (Table 4.4). The Ionic Greek system was developed in about 3000 B.C., and it used letters of the Greek alphabet for numerals. Other ciphered systems include the Hebrew, Coptic, Hindu, Brahmin, Syrian, Egyptian Hieratic, and early Arabic systems.

Table 4.4 Ionic Greek Numerals

1	α	alpha	60	ξ	xi
2	β	beta	70	o	omicron
3	γ	gamma	80	π	pi
4	δ	delta	90	φ^*	koppa
5	ϵ	epsilon	100	ρ	rho
6	f^*	digamma	200	σ	sigma
7	ζ	zeta	300	τ	tau
8	η	eta	400	υ	upsilon
9	θ	theta	500	ϕ	phi
10	ι	iota	600	χ	chi
20	κ	kappa	700	ψ	psi
30	λ	lambda	800	ω	omega
40	μ	mu	900	$ℤ^*$	sampi
50	ν	nu			

*Ancient Greek letters not used in the classic or modern Greek language.

The classic Greek alphabet contains only 24 letters; however, 27 symbols were needed. Thus, the Greeks used three obsolete Greek letters—f, ϙ, and ℤ—that are not part of the classic Greek alphabet. To distinguish words from numerals, the Greeks would place a mark similar to our apostrophe to the right and above each letter that was used as a numeral. In this text, we will not use this mark because we will not be using Greek words and numerals together.

We can write 45 as 40 + 5. When 45 is written as a Greek numeral, the plus sign is omitted:

$$45 = \mu\epsilon$$

Similarly, 768 written as a Greek numeral is $\psi\xi\eta$.

When the Greek letter iota, ι, is placed to the left and above a numeral, it represents the numeral multiplied by 1000. For example,

$${}^\iota\theta = 9 \times 1000 = 9000$$

$${}^\iota\zeta = 7 \times 1000 = 7000$$

Example 9   *The Ionic Greek System: A Ciphered System*

Write $\omega\lambda\theta$ as a Hindu–Arabic numeral.

Solution $\omega = 800$, $\lambda = 30$, and $\theta = 9$. The sum is 839. ∎

Example 10   *Writing an Ionic Greek Numeral*

Write 1654 as an Ionic Greek numeral.

Solution

$$
\begin{aligned}
1654 &= 1000 + 600 + 50 + 4 \\
&= (1 \times 1000) + 600 + 50 + 4 \\
&= {}^\iota\alpha \qquad\quad \chi \quad\; \nu \quad\; \delta \\
&= {}^\iota\alpha\,\chi\,\nu\,\delta
\end{aligned}
$$

∎

SECTION 4.1   *Exercises*

Warm Up Exercises

In Exercises 1–8, fill in the blanks with an appropriate word, phrase, or symbol(s).

1. A number is a quantity, and it answers the question "_____?" How many

2. A symbol used to represent a number is called a _____. Numeral

3. The system of numeration that we presently use is the _____ system. Hindu–Arabic

4. The Egyptian hieroglyphic system and the Roman numeration system are examples of _____ numeration systems. Additive

5. As you read a Roman numeral from left to right, if a smaller number comes before a larger number, you should _____ the smaller number from the larger number. Subtract

6. A bar above a Roman numeral means to multiply that numeral by _____. 1000

7. The Chinese numeration system is an example of a _____ numeration system. Multiplicative

8. The Ionic Greek numeration system is an example of a _____ numeration system. Ciphered

Practice the Skills

In Exercises 9–14, write the Egyptian numeral as a Hindu–Arabic numeral.

9. ꝯꝯ∩∩∩IIII 234

10. 𓍢ꝯꝯꝯII 1302

11. 𓍢𓍢ꝯꝯꝯꝯ∩∩III 2423

12. 𓆼𓆼𓆼𓍢ꝯꝯ∩ 41,210

13. 𓂭𓆼𓆼𓍢𓍢𓍢𓍢ꝯꝯ∩IIII 334,214

14. ✹✹✹𓂭𓂭ꝯꝯ∩∩∩∩I 3,300,431

In Exercises 15–20, write the numeral as an Egyptian numeral.

15. 42 ∩∩∩∩II

16. 153 9∩∩∩∩∩IIII

17. 2045 ⌇⌇∩∩∩∩IIIII

18. 1812 ⌇999999999∩II

19. 173,845 *

20. 3,235,614 *

In Exercises 21–32, write the Roman numeral as a Hindu–Arabic numeral.

21. XVI 16

22. XIV 14

23. CXCIV 194

24. CDLXXXVIII 488

25. MMDCXLII 2642

26. MCMLXIV 1964

27. MMCMXLVI 2946

28. MDCCXLVI 1746

29. $\overline{\text{X}}$MMDCLXVI 12,666

30. $\overline{\text{L}}$MCMXLIV 51,944

31. $\overline{\text{IX}}$CDLXIV 9464

32. $\overline{\text{V}}$MCCCXXXIII 6333

In Exercises 33–44, write the numeral as a Roman numeral.

33. 24 XXIV

34. 99 XCIX

35. 555 DLV

36. 744 DCCXLIV

37. 1914 MCMXIV

38. 4285 $\overline{\text{IV}}$CCLXXXV

39. 4793 $\overline{\text{IV}}$DCCXCIII

40. 6274 $\overline{\text{VI}}$CCLXXIV

41. 9999 $\overline{\text{IX}}$CMXCIX

42. 14,315 $\overline{\text{XIV}}$CCCXV

43. 20,644 $\overline{\text{XX}}$DCXLIV

44. 99,999 $\overline{\text{XCIX}}$CMXCIX

In Exercises 45–52, write the Chinese numeral as a Hindu–Arabic numeral.

45. 七十四 74

46. 六十二 62

47. 四千零八十一 4081

48. 三千零二十九 3029

49. 八千五百五十 8550

50. 三千四百八十七 3487

51. 四千零三 4003

52. 五千六百零二 5602

In Exercises 53–60, write the numeral as a traditional Chinese numeral.

53. 53 *

54. 178 *

55. 378 *

56. 2001 *

57. 4260 *

58. 6905 *

59. 7056 *

60. 3009 *

In Exercises 61–66, write the numeral as a Hindu–Arabic numeral.

61. $\pi\alpha$ 81

62. $\psi o\beta$ 772

63. $\sigma o \theta$ 279

64. ⅀ ϵ 905

65. $'\beta\,\omega\,\pi\,\gamma$ 2883

66. $'\zeta\,\upsilon\,\xi\,\zeta$ 7467

In Exercises 67–72, write the numeral as an Ionic Greek numeral.

67. 33 $\lambda\gamma$

68. 245 $\sigma\mu\epsilon$

69. 726 $\psi\kappa\digamma$

70. 2008 $'\beta\eta$

71. 5005 $'\epsilon\epsilon$

72. 9999 $'\theta\vartheta\varsigma\theta$

In Exercises 73–76, write the numeral as numerals in the indicated systems of numeration.

73. ⌇∩∩I in Hindu–Arabic, Roman, traditional Chinese, and Greek *

74. MCMXXXVI in Hindu–Arabic, Egyptian, Greek, and traditional Chinese *

75. 五百二十七 in Hindu–Arabic, Egyptian, Roman, and Greek *

76. $\nu\kappa\beta$ in Hindu–Arabic, Egyptian, Roman, and traditional Chinese *

Concept/Writing Exercises

77. What is the difference between a number and a numeral? A number is a quantity, and it answers the question "How many?" A numeral is a symbol used to represent the number.

78. What is a system of numeration? A system of numeration consists of a set of numerals and a scheme or rule for combining the numerals to represent numbers.

*See Instructor Answer Appendix

Challenge Problems/Group Activities

79. Write the Roman numeral for 999,999. C̄M̄X̄C̄ĪX̄CMXCIX

80. Make up your own additive system of numeration and indicate the symbols and rules used to represent numbers. Using your system of numeration, write

a) your age. Answers will vary.

b) the year you were born. Answers will vary.

c) the current year. Answers will vary.

Recreational Mathematics

81. Without using any type of writing instrument, what can you do to make the following incorrect statement a correct statement? Turn the book upside down.

$$XI + I = X$$

82. Words and numerals that read the same both backward and forward are called *palindromes*. Some examples are the words CIVIC and RACECAR, and the numerals 121 and 32523. Using Roman numerals, list the last year that was a palindrome. MM

83. Which year in the past 2000 years required the most Roman numerals to write? Write out the year in Roman numerals. 1888, MDCCCLXXXVIII

Internet/Research Activities

84. *Egypt, China, and Greece* In this section, we discussed the numeration systems of Egypt, China, and Greece. Choose one of these countries and write a paper that does the following.

a) State the current numerals used in your chosen country.

b) Explain how that country's current system of numeration works. If more than one system is used, discuss the system used most commonly.

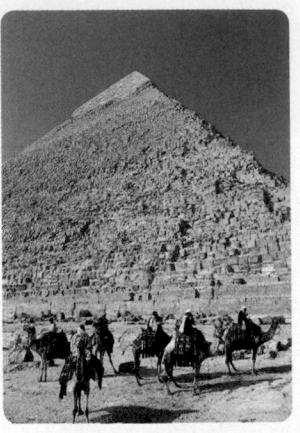

▲ Great Pyramid of Khufu in Giza, Egypt

Place-Value or Positional-Value Numeration Systems

▲ *Place value is used in many games on The Price is Right.*

Have you ever watched the television game show *The Price is Right*? Chances are that you have seen one of the many games that require contestants to place digits in the correct order to guess the price of a car, appliance, or other fabulous prize. Such games require the contestant to have an understanding of the concept of *place value* that is used in our modern number system. In this section, we will study two other number systems that also rely on place value.

Why **This is Important** By studying other place-value numeration systems, we will gain a better understanding of our own numeration system.

Eighteenth-century mathematician Pierre Simon, Marquis de Laplace, speaking of the positional principle, said: "The idea is so simple that this very simplicity is the reason for our not being sufficiently aware of how much attention it deserves."

Today the most common type of numeration system is the place-value system. The Hindu–Arabic numeration system, used in the United States and many other countries, is an example of a place-value system. In a *place-value system*, which is also called a *positional-value system*, the value of the symbol depends on its position in the representation of the number. For example, the 2 in 20 represents 2 tens, and the 2 in 200 represents 2 hundreds. A true positional-value system requires a *base* and a set of symbols, including a symbol for zero and one for each counting number less than the base. Although any number can be written in any base, the most common positional system is the base 10 system which is called the *decimal number system.*

The Hindus in India are credited with the invention of zero and the other symbols used in our system. The Arabs, who traded regularly with the Hindus, also adopted the system, thus the name Hindu–Arabic. Not until the middle of the fifteenth century, however, did the Hindu–Arabic numerals take the form we know today.

The Hindu–Arabic numerals and the positional system of numeration revolutionized mathematics by making addition, subtraction, multiplication, and division much easier to learn and very practical to use. Merchants and traders no longer had to depend on the counting board or abacus. The first group of mathematicians who computed with the Hindu–Arabic system, rather than with pebbles or beads on a wire, were known as the "algorists."

In the Hindu–Arabic system, the symbols 0, 1, 2, 3, 4, 5, 6, 7, 8, and 9 are called *digits*. The base 10 system was developed from counting on fingers, and the word *digit* comes from the Latin word for fingers.

The positional values in the Hindu–Arabic system are

$$\ldots, (10)^5, (10)^4, (10)^3, (10)^2, 10, 1$$

To evaluate a numeral in the Hindu–Arabic system, we multiply the first digit on the right by 1. We multiply the second digit from the right by the base, 10. We multiply the third digit from the right by the base squared, 10^2 or 100. We multiply the fourth digit from the right by the base cubed, 10^3 or 1000, and so on. In general, we multiply the digit n places from the right by 10^{n-1}. Therefore, we multiply the digit eight places from the right by 10^7. Using the place-value rule, we can write a number in *expanded form*. In expanded form, 1234 is written

$$1234 = (1 \times 10^3) + (2 \times 10^2) + (3 \times 10) + (4 \times 1)$$

or

$$(1 \times 1000) + (2 \times 100) + (3 \times 10) + 4$$

Babylonian Numerals

The oldest known numeration system that resembled a place-value system was developed by the Babylonians in about 2500 B.C. Their system resembled a place-value system with a base of 60, a sexagesimal system. It was not a true place-value system because it lacked a symbol for zero. The lack of a symbol for zero led to a great deal of ambiguity and confusion. Table 4.5 gives the Babylonian numerals.

The positional values in the Babylonian system are

$$\ldots, (60)^3, (60)^2, 60, 1$$

In a Babylonian numeral, a gap is left between the characters to distinguish between the various place values. From right to left, the sum of the first group of numerals is multiplied by 1. The sum of the second group is multiplied by 60. The sum of the third group is multiplied by $(60)^2$, and so on.

Table 4.5 Babylonian Numerals

Babylonian numerals	❚	◀
Hindu–Arabic numerals	1	10

Example 1 *The Babylonian System: A Positional-Value System*

Write ◀◀❚   ◀◀◀❚ as a Hindu-Arabic numeral.

Solution

$$\underbrace{◀◀❚}_{60's} \qquad \underbrace{◀◀◀❚}_{units}$$

$$\underbrace{10 + 10 + 1}_{60's} \qquad \underbrace{10 + 10 + 10 + 1}_{units}$$

$$(21 \times 60) + (31 \times 1)$$
$$1260 + 31 = 1291$$

The Babylonians used the symbol ⟨ symbol ⟩ to indicate subtraction. The numeral ⟨ symbol ⟩ represents $10 - 2$, or 8. The numeral ⟨ symbol ⟩ represents $40 - 3$, or 37 in base 10 or decimal notation.

Example 2 *From Babylonian to Hindu–Arabic Numerals*

Write ⟨ symbol ⟩ ⟨ symbol ⟩ ⟨ symbol ⟩ as a Hindu–Arabic numeral.

Solution The place value of these three groups of numerals from left to right is

$$(60)^2, \quad 60, \quad 1$$
or
$$3600, \quad 60, \quad 1$$

The numeral in the group on the right has a value of $20 - 2$, or 18. The numeral in the center group has a value of $10 + 1$, or 11. The numeral on the left represents $1 + 1$, or 2. Multiplying each group by its positional value gives

$$(2 \times 60^2) + (11 \times 60) + (18 \times 1)$$
$$= (2 \times 3600) + (11 \times 60) + (18 \times 1)$$
$$= 7200 + 660 + 18$$
$$= 7878$$

To explain the procedure used to convert from a Hindu–Arabic numeral to a Babylonian numeral, we will consider a length of time. How can we change 9820 seconds into hours, minutes, and seconds? Since there are 3600 seconds in an hour (60 seconds to a minute and 60 minutes to an hour), we can find the number of hours in 9820 seconds by dividing 9820 by 60^2, or 3600.

$$
\begin{array}{r}
2 \quad \leftarrow \text{Hours} \\
3600\overline{)9820} \\
7200 \\
\hline
2620 \quad \leftarrow \text{Remaining seconds}
\end{array}
$$

Now we can determine the number of minutes by dividing the remaining seconds by 60, the number of seconds in a minute.

$$
\begin{array}{r}
43 \quad \leftarrow \text{Minutes} \\
60\overline{)2620} \\
2400 \\
\hline
220 \\
180 \\
\hline
40 \quad \leftarrow \text{Remaining seconds}
\end{array}
$$

Since the remaining number of seconds, 40, is less than the number of seconds in a minute, our task is complete.

$$9820 \text{ sec} = 2 \text{ hr}, 43 \text{ min}, 40 \text{ sec}$$

The same procedure is used to convert a decimal (base 10) numeral to a Babylonian numeral or any numeral in a different base.

Example 3 *From Hindu–Arabic to Babylonian Numerals*

Write 2519 as a Babylonian numeral.

Solution The Babylonian numeration system has positional values of

$$\ldots, 60^3, 60^2, 60, 1$$

which can be expressed as

$$\ldots, 216000, 3600, 60, 1$$

The largest positional value less than or equal to 2519 is 60. To determine how many groups of 60 are in 2519, divide 2519 by 60.

$$
\begin{array}{r}
41 \quad \leftarrow \text{Groups of 60} \\
60\overline{)2519} \\
240 \\
\hline
119 \\
60 \\
\hline
59 \quad \leftarrow \text{Units remaining}
\end{array}
$$

Thus, $2519 \div 60 = 41$ with remainder 59. There are 41 groups of 60 and 59 units remaining. Because the remainder, 59, is less than the base, 60, no further division is necessary. The remainder represents the number of units when the numeral is written in expanded form. Therefore, $2519 = (41 \times 60) + (59 \times 1)$. When written as a Babylonian numeral, 2519 is

$$\text{《《《《Ⅰ} \quad \text{《《《《《《《₸Ⅰ} \quad \blacksquare$$

Example 4 *Using Division to Determine a Babylonian Numeral*

Write 6270 as a Babylonian numeral.

Solution Divide 6270 by the largest positional value less than or equal to 6270. That value is 3600.

$$6270 \div 3600 = 1 \text{ with remainder } 2670$$

There is one group of 3600 in 6270. Next divide the remainder 2670 by 60 to determine the number of groups of 60 in 2670.

$$2670 \div 60 = 44 \text{ with remainder } 30$$

There are 44 groups of 60 and 30 units remaining.

$$6270 = (1 \times 60^2) + (44 \times 60) + (30 \times 1)$$

Thus, 6270 written as a Babylonian numeral is

$$\text{Ⅰ} \quad \text{《《《《ⅠⅠⅠⅠ} \quad \text{《《《} \quad \blacksquare$$

Example 5 *A Babylonian Numeral with a Blank Space*

Write 7223 as a Babylonian numeral.

Solution As we did in the last example, we begin by dividing 7223 by 3600.

$$7223 \div 3600 = 2 \text{ with remainder } 23$$

Therefore, there are two groups of 3600 in 7223. The next positional value in the Babylonian numeration system is 60. However, the remainder from the above division, 23, is less than 60. So there are zero groups of 60 in 7223 and 23 units remaining. Therefore, we can write 7223 as follows:

$$7223 = (2 \times 60^2) + (0 \times 60) + (23 \times 1)$$

Recall that the Babylonian numeration system does not contain a symbol for 0. Therefore, we will need to leave a larger blank space when writing the numeral. This larger blank space will indicate that there are no 60s present in 7223.

$$7223 = \left(\underline{2 \times 60^2}\right) + (0 + 60) + (\underline{23 \times 1})$$

The larger blank space here represents 0 groups of 60.

Mayan Numerals

Another place-value system is the Mayan numeration system. The Mayans, who lived on the Yucatan Peninsula in present-day Mexico, developed a sophisticated numeration system based on their religious and agricultural calendar. The numerals in this system are written vertically rather than horizontally, with the units position on the bottom. In the Mayan system, the numeral in the bottom row is to be multiplied by 1. The numeral in the second row from the bottom is to be multiplied by 20. The numeral in the third row is to be multiplied by 18×20, or 360. You probably expected the numeral in the third row to be multiplied by 20^2 rather than 18×20. It is believed that the Mayans used 18×20 so that their numeration system would conform to their calendar of 360 days. The positional values above 18×20 are 18×20^2, 18×20^3, and so on.

Positional Values in the Mayan System

$\dots 18 \times (20)^3,$	$18 \times (20)^2,$	$18 \times 20,$	$20,$	1
or $\dots 144{,}000,$	$7200,$	$360,$	$20,$	1

The digits 0, 1, 2, 3, $\dots$, 19 of the Mayan system are formed by a simple grouping of dots and lines, as shown in Table 4.6.

Table 4.6 Mayan Numerals

0	1	2	3	4	5	6	7	8	9
10	11	12	13	14	15	16	17	18	19

Example 6 *The Mayan System: A Positional-Value System*

Write as a Hindu–Arabic numeral.

Solution In the Mayan numeration system, the first three positional values are

$$18 \times 20$$
$$20$$
$$1$$

$$= 11 \times (18 \times 20) = 3960$$
$$= 3 \times 20 \qquad = 60$$
$$= 16 \times 1 \qquad = \underline{16}$$
$$4036$$

Example 7 *From Mayan to Hindu–Arabic Numerals*

Write ⋮ as a Hindu–Arabic numeral.

Solution

$$
\begin{aligned}
\bullet\bullet &= 2 \times [18 \times (20)^2] &&= 14{,}400\\
\bullet\bullet\bullet &= 8 \times (18 \times 20) &&= 2880\\
\overset{\bullet}{=} &= 11 \times 20 &&= 220\\
\bullet\bullet\bullet\bullet &= 4 \times 1 &&= \underline{4}\\
& && \quad 17{,}504
\end{aligned}
$$

Example 8 *From Hindu–Arabic to Mayan Numerals*

Write 4025 as a Mayan numeral.

Solution To convert from a Hindu–Arabic to a Mayan numeral, we use a procedure similar to the one used to convert to a Babylonian numeral. The Mayan positional values are ..., 7200, 360, 20, 1. The greatest positional value less than or equal to 4025 is 360. Divide 4025 by 360.

$$4025 \div 360 = 11 \text{ with remainder } 65$$

There are 11 groups of 360 in 4025. Next, divide the remainder, 65, by 20.

$$65 \div 20 = 3 \text{ with remainder } 5$$

There are 3 groups of 20 with five units remaining.

$$4025 = (11 \times 360) + (3 \times 20) + (5 \times 1)$$

4025 written as a Mayan numeral is

$$
\left.\begin{array}{r}
11 \times 360\\
3 \times 20\\
5 \times 1
\end{array}\right\} =
$$

TIMELY TIP

Notice that changing a numeral from the Babylonian or Mayan numeration system *to the Hindu–Arabic* (or decimal or base 10) system involves *multiplication*. Changing a numeral from *the Hindu–Arabic system* to the Babylonian or Mayan numeration system involves *division*.

SECTION 4.2 *Exercises*

Warm Up Exercises

In Exercises 1–12, fill in the blanks with an appropriate word, phrase, or symbol(s).

1. Another name for a place-value system is a(n) _____ value system. Positional

2. In the numeral 234, the 2 represents 2 _____. Hundreds

3. In the numeral 234, the 3 represents 3 _____. Tens

4. In the numeral 234, the 4 represents 4 _____. Units

5. The most common positional system is the decimal number system which uses a base of _____. 10

6. The base 10 system was developed from counting on _____. Fingers

7. When we write 789 as $(7 \times 10^2) + (8 \times 10) + (9 \times 1)$ the number is written in _____ form. Expanded

8. The Babylonian system is not considered a true place-value system because it lacked a symbol for _____. Zero

9. The base used in the Babylonian system is _____. 60

10. In the Babylonian numeration system,

   a) the symbol ❚ represents the numeral _____. 1

   b) the symbol ❬ represents the numeral _____. 10

   c) the symbol ❚ indicates _____. Subtraction

11. It is believed that the Mayans used 18×20 instead of 20^2 so that their numeration system would conform to their _____, which had 360 days. Calendar

12. In the Mayan numeration system,

   a) the symbol ⬯ represents the numeral _____. 0

   b) the symbol • represents the numeral _____. 1

   c) the symbol —— represents the numeral _____. 5

Practice the Skills

In Exercises 13–24, write the Hindu–Arabic numeral in expanded form.

13. 58 $(5 \times 10) + (8 \times 1)$ **14.** 93 $(9 \times 10) + (3 \times 1)$

15. 712   **16.** 562
   $(7 \times 100) + (1 \times 10) + (2 \times 1)$ $(5 \times 100) + (6 \times 10) + (2 \times 1)$

17. 897   **18.** 3769 *
   $(8 \times 100) + (9 \times 10) + (7 \times 1)$

19. 4387   **20.** 23,468 *
   $(4 \times 1000) + (3 \times 100) + (8 \times 10) + (7 \times 1)$

21. 16,402 *   **22.** 125,678 *

23. 346,861 *   **24.** 3,765,934 *

In Exercises 25–30, write the Babylonian numeral as a Hindu–Arabic numeral.

25. ❬❬❬❬❚❚ 32

26. ❬❬❚❚ 19

27. ❬❚❚❚ ❚❚❚❚ 784

28. ❬❚ ❬❬❚❚❚❚ 677

29. ❚ ❬❬❬❚ ❬❚❚❚ 4868

30. ❬ ❚❚ 3602

In Exercises 31–36, write the numeral as a Babylonian numeral.

31. 41 *   **32.** 129 *

33. 471 *   **34.** 512 *

35. 3605 *   **36.** 12,435 *

In Exercises 37–42, write the Mayan numeral as a Hindu–Arabic numeral.

37. ••• 73
     •••

38. == 207
     ••

39. ••• 4682
     ⬯
     ••

40. •• 2707
     ••••
     ••

41. •• 4000
     ••
     ⬯

42. •• 930
     ==
     ==

In Exercises 43–48, write the numeral as a Mayan numeral.

43. 18 *   **44.** 257 *

45. 297 *   **46.** 406 *

47. 2163 *   **48.** 17,708 *

In Exercises 49 and 50, write the numeral in the indicated systems of numeration.

49. —— in Hindu–Arabic and Babylonian *
     ••
     ••••

50. ❬❬❬❚❚❚ in Hindu–Arabic and Mayan *

In Exercises 51 and 52, suppose a place-value numeration system has base ⬡, with digits represented by the symbols △, ◌, ☐, and ⊙. Write each expression in expanded form.

51. △ ☐ ◌ *   **52.** ⊙ △ ◌ *

Concept/Writing Exercises

53. Describe two ways that the Mayan place-value system differs from the Hindu–Arabic place-value system. The Mayan system has a different base and the numerals are written vertically.

54. a) The Babylonian system did not have a symbol for zero. Why did this lead to some confusion? *

   b) Write 133 and 7980 as Babylonian numerals. *

Challenge Problems/Group Activities

55. a) Write the Mayan numeral for 999,999. *

   b) Write the Babylonian numeral for 999,999. *

*See Instructor Answer Appendix

In Exercises 56–59, first convert each numeral to a Hindu–Arabic numeral and then perform the indicated operation. Finally, convert the answer back to a numeral in the original numeration system.

56. ⅋⅋ ‹‹ ⅋⅋⅋ + ‹‹⅋⅋⅋ *   57. ⅋⅋⅋ ‹‹‹⅋⅋⅋ − ‹‹‹⅋⅋ *

58. *   59. ... *

60. *Your Own System* Create your own place-value system. Write 2013 in your system. Answers will vary.

Internet/Research Activities

61. Investigate and write a report on the development of the Hindu–Arabic system of numeration. Start with the earliest records of this system in India.

62. The Arabic numeration system currently in use is a base 10 positional-value system, which uses different symbols than the Hindu–Arabic numeration system. Write the symbols used in the Arabic system of numeration and their equivalent symbols in the Hindu–Arabic numeration system. Write 54, 607, and 2000 in Arabic numerals.

*See Instructor Answer Appendix

SECTION 4.3   Other Bases

▲ *Electronic devices have computer chips that use numeral bases other than base 10.*

Have you done any of the following today: sent a text message, spent time on Facebook, browsed the Internet, checked your email, listened to your iPod, talked on your cell phone, or gotten directions from a GPS device? These activities all involve using a device with a computer chip that operates with numerals other than our familiar base 10 (decimal) numerals. In this section, we will study base 2 (binary), base 8 (octal), and base 16 (hexadecimal) numerals, all of which are used in most modern computers and electronic devices.

Why *This is Important* In addition to learning about the mathematics used in electronic devices, studying other bases helps us better understand how our own decimal system works.

The positional values in the Hindu-Arabic numeration system are

$$\ldots, (10)^4, (10)^3, (10)^2, 10, 1$$

The positional values in the Babylonian numeration system are

$$\ldots, (60)^4, (60)^3, (60)^2, 60, 1$$

Thus, 10 and 60 are called the *bases* of the Hindu-Arabic and Babylonian systems, respectively.

Any counting number greater than 1 may be used as a base for a positional-value numeration system. If a positional-value system has a base b, then its positional values will be

$$\ldots, b^4, b^3, b^2, b, 1$$

The positional values in a base 8 system are

$$\ldots, 8^4, 8^3, 8^2, 8, 1$$

and the positional values in a base 2 system are

$$\ldots, 2^4, 2^3, 2^2, 2, 1$$

As we indicated in Section 4.2, the Mayan numeration system is based on the number 20. It is not, however, a true base 20 positional-value system. Why not?

The reason for the almost universal acceptance of base 10 numeration systems is that most human beings have 10 fingers. Even so, there are still some positional-value numeration systems that use bases other than 10. Some societies are still using a base 2 numeration system. They include some groups of people in Australia, New Guinea, Africa, and South America. Bases 3 and 4 are also used in some areas of South America. Base 5 systems were used by some primitive tribes in Bolivia, but the tribes are now extinct. The pure base 6 system occurs only sparsely in Northwest Africa. Base 6 also occurs in other systems in combination with base 12, the *duodecimal* system.

Our society still contains remnants of other base systems from other cultures. For example, there are 12 inches in a foot and 12 months in a year. Base 12 is also evident in the dozen, the 24-hour day, and the gross (12×12). Remains of base 60 are found in measurements of time (60 seconds to 1 minute, 60 minutes to 1 hour) and angles (60 seconds to 1 minute, 60 minutes to 1 degree).

Computers and many other electronic devices make use of three numeration systems: the *binary* (base 2), the *octal* (base 8), and the *hexadecimal* (base 16) numeration systems. One familiar example of the binary numeration system is the bar codes found on most items purchased in stores today. Computers can use the binary numeration system because the binary number system consists of only the digits 0 and 1. These digits can be represented with electronic switches that are either off (0) or on (1). All data that we enter into a computer can be converted into a series of single binary digits. Each binary digit is known as a *bit*. The octal numeration system is used when eight bits of data are grouped together to form a *byte*. In the American Standard Code for Information Interchange (ASCII) code, the byte 01000001 represents the character A, and 01100001 represents the character a. Other characters along with their decimal, binary, octal, and hexadecimal representation can be found at the web site www.asciitable.com. The hexadecimal numeration system is used to create computer languages. Two such examples of computer languages that rely on the hexadecimal system are HTML and CSS, both of which are used heavily in creating Internet web pages. Computers can easily convert between binary (base 2), octal (base 8), and hexadecimal (base 16) numbers.

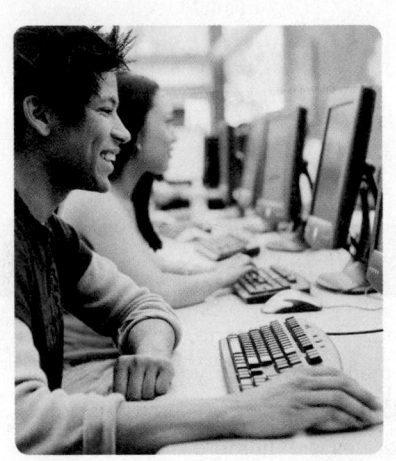

▲ *Computers make use of the binary, octal, and hexadecimal number systems.*

Bases Less Than 10

A place-value system with base b must have b distinct symbols, one for zero and one for each numeral less than the base. A base 6 system must have symbols for 0, 1, 2, 3, 4, and 5. All numerals in base 6 are constructed from these 6 symbols. A base 8 system must have symbols for 0, 1, 2, 3, 4, 5, 6, and 7. All numerals in base 8 are constructed from these 8 symbols, and so on.

A numeral in a base other than base 10 will be indicated by a subscript to the right of the numeral. Thus, 123_5 represents a base 5 numeral. The numeral 123_6 represents a base 6 numeral. The value of 123_5 is not the same as the value of 123_{10}, and the value of 123_6 is not the same as the value of 123_{10}. A base 10 numeral may be written without a subscript. For example, 123 means 123_{10} and 456 means 456_{10}. For clarity in certain problems, we will use the subscript 10 to indicate a numeral in base 10.

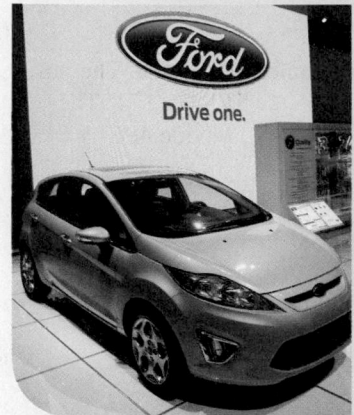
The symbols that represent the base itself, in any base b, are 10_b. For example, in base 5, the symbols 10_5 represent the number five. Note that $10_5 = 1 \times 5 + 0 \times 1 = 5 + 0 = 5_{10}$, or the number five in base 10. The symbols 10_5 mean one group of 5 and no units. In base 6, the symbols 10_6 represent the number six. The symbols 10_6 represent one group of 6 and no units, and so on.

To change a numeral in a base other than 10 to a base 10 numeral, we follow the same procedure we used in Section 4.2 to change the Babylonian and Mayan numerals to base 10 numerals. Multiply each digit by its respective positional value. Then find the sum of the products.

Example 1 Converting from Base 5 to Base 10

Convert 243_5 to base 10.

Solution In base 5, the positional values are $\ldots, 5^3, 5^2, 5, 1$. In expanded form,

$$243_5 = (2 \times 5^2) + (4 \times 5) + (3 \times 1)$$
$$= (2 \times 25) + (4 \times 5) + (3 \times 1)$$
$$= 50 + 20 + 3$$
$$= 73$$

In Example 1, the units digit in 243_5 is 3. Notice that 3_5 has the same value as 3_{10}, since both are equal to 3 units. That is, $3_5 = 3_{10}$. If n is a digit less than the base b, and the base b is less than or equal to 10, then $n_b = n_{10}$.

Example 2 Converting from Base 8 to Base 10

Convert 7054_8 to base 10.

Solution In base 8, the positional values are $\ldots, 8^3, 8^2, 8, 1$. In expanded form,

$$7054_8 = (7 \times 8^3) + (0 \times 8^2) + (5 \times 8) + (4 \times 1)$$
$$= (7 \times 512) + (0 \times 64) + (5 \times 8) + (4 \times 1)$$
$$= 3584 + 0 + 40 + 4$$
$$= 3628$$

Example 3 Converting from Base 2 to Base 10

Convert 110010_2 to base 10.

Solution

$$110010_2 = (1 \times 2^5) + (1 \times 2^4) + (0 \times 2^3) + (0 \times 2^2) + (1 \times 2) + (0 \times 1)$$
$$= (1 \times 32) + (1 \times 16) + (0 \times 8) + (0 \times 4) + (1 \times 2) + (0 \times 1)$$
$$= 32 + 16 + 0 + 0 + 2 + 0$$
$$= 50$$

To change a base 10 numeral to a different base, we will use a procedure similar to the one we used to convert base 10 numerals to Babylonian and Mayan numerals, as was explained in Section 4.2. Divide the base 10 numeral by the highest power of the new base that is less than or equal to the given base 10 numeral. Record this quotient. Then divide the remainder by the next smaller power of the new base and record this quotient. Repeat this procedure until the remainder is less than the new base. The answer is the set of quotients listed from left to right, with the remainder on the far right. This procedure is illustrated in Examples 4 and 5.

Example 4 *Converting from Base 10 to Base 8*

Convert 486 to base 8.

Solution We are converting a numeral in base 10 to a numeral in base 8. The positional values in the base 8 system are $\ldots, 8^3, 8^2, 8, 1$, or $\ldots, 512, 64, 8, 1$. The highest power of 8 that is less than or equal to 486 is 8^2, or 64. Divide 486 by 64.

First digit in answer

$$486 \div 64 = 7 \text{ with remainder } 38$$

Therefore, there are seven groups of 8^2 in 486. Next divide the remainder, 38, by 8.

Second digit in answer

$$38 \div 8 = 4 \text{ with remainder } 6$$

Third digit in answer

There are four groups of 8 in 38 and 6 units remaining. Since the remainder, 6, is less than the base, 8, no further division is required.

$$= (7 \times 64) + (4 \times 8) + (6 \times 1)$$
$$= (7 \times 8^2) + (4 \times 8) + (6 \times 1)$$
$$= 746_8$$

Notice that we placed the subscript 8 to the right of 746 to show that it is a base 8 numeral.

Example 5 *Converting from Base 10 to Base 3*

Convert 273 to base 3.

Solution The place values in the base 3 system are $\ldots, 3^6, 3^5, 3^4, 3^3, 3^2, 3, 1$, or $\ldots, 729, 243, 81, 27, 9, 3, 1$. The highest power of the base that is less than or equal to 273 is 3^5, or 243. Successive divisions by the powers of the base give the following result.

$$273 \div 243 = 1 \text{ with remainder } 30$$
$$30 \div 81 = 0 \text{ with remainder } 30$$
$$30 \div 27 = 1 \text{ with remainder } 3$$
$$3 \div 9 = 0 \text{ with remainder } 3$$
$$3 \div 3 = 1 \text{ with remainder } 0$$

The remainder, 0, is less than the base, 3, so no further division is necessary. To obtain the answer, list the quotients from top to bottom followed by the remainder in the last division.

We can represent 273 as one group of 243, no groups of 81, one group of 27, no groups of 9, one group of 3, and no units.

$$273 = (1 \times 243) + (0 \times 81) + (1 \times 27) + (0 \times 9) + (1 \times 3) + (0 \times 1)$$
$$= (1 \times 3^5) + (0 \times 3^4) + (1 \times 3^3) + (0 \times 3^2) + (1 \times 3) + (0 \times 1)$$
$$= 101010_3$$

Bases Greater Than 10

Recall that a place-value system with base b must have symbols for the digits from 0 up to one less than the base. For example, base 6 uses the digits 0, 1, 2, 3, 4, and 5; and base 8 uses the digits 0, 1, 2, 3, 4, 5, 6, and 7. What happens if the base is larger than ten? We will need single digit symbols to represent the numbers ten, eleven, twelve, . . . up to one less than the base. *In this textbook, whenever a base larger than ten is used we will use the capital letter A to represent ten, the capital letter B to represent eleven, the capital letter C to represent twelve, and so on.* For example, for base 12, known as the *duodecimal system*, we use the symbols 0, 1, 2, 3, 4, 5, 6, 7, 8, 9, A, and B, where A represents ten and B represents eleven. For base 16, known as the hexadecimal system, we use the symbols 0, 1, 2, 3, 4, 5, 6, 7, 8, 9, A, B, C, D, E, and F.

Example 6 *Converting to and from Base 12*

a) Convert $39BA_{12}$ to base 10.
b) Convert 6893 to base 12.

Solution

a) In base 12, the positional values are $\ldots 12^3, 12^2, 12, 1$ or $\ldots 1728, 144, 12, 1$. Since B has the value of eleven and A has the value of ten, we perform the following calculation.

$$39BA_{12} = (3 \times 12^3) + (9 \times 12^2) + (11 \times 12) + (10 \times 1)$$
$$= (3 \times 1728) + (9 \times 144) + 132 + 10$$
$$= 5184 + 1296 + 132 + 10 = 6622$$

b) The highest power of base 12 that is less than or equal to 6893 is 12^3, or 1728. To convert 6893 to base 12, we will use a process similar to the one we used in Examples 4 and 5. Remember that in base 12 we represent ten with the numeral A and eleven with the numeral B.

$$6893 \div 1728 = 3 \text{ with remainder } 1709$$
$$1709 \div 144 = B \text{ with remainder } 125 \quad \text{Note that B has a value of eleven}$$
$$125 \div 12 = A \text{ with remainder } 5 \quad \text{Note that A has a value of ten}$$

The remainder, 5, is less than the base, 12, so no further division is necessary. Thus, the answer is $3BA5_{12}$. To check this answer, perform the calculation $(3 \times 12^3) + (11 \times 12^2) + (10 \times 12) + (5 \times 1)$ to verify that you obtain 6893 in base 10. ∎

Example 7 *Converting to and from Base 16*

a) Convert $7DE_{16}$ to base 10.   b) Convert 6713 to base 16.

Solution

a) In a base 16 system, the positional values are $\ldots, 16^3, 16^2, 16, 1$ or $\ldots$ 4096, 256, 16, 1. Since D has a value of thirteen and E has a value of fourteen, we perform the following calculation.

$$7DE_{16} = (7 \times 16^2) + (D \times 16) + (E \times 1)$$
$$= (7 \times 256) + (13 \times 16) + (14 \times 1)$$
$$= 1792 + 208 + 14$$
$$= 2014$$

b) The highest power of base 16 less than or equal to 6713 is 16^3, or 4096. If we obtain a quotient greater than nine but less than sixteen, we will use the corresponding letter A through F.

$$6713 \div 4096 = 1 \text{ with remainder } 2617$$
$$2617 \div 256 = A \text{ with remainder } 57 \quad \text{Note that A has a value of ten}$$
$$57 \div 16 = 3 \text{ with remainder } 9$$

Thus, $6713 = 1A39_{16}$.

TIMELY TIP

It is important to remember the following items presented in this section
- If a numeral is shown without a base, we assume the numeral is a base 10 numeral.
- When converting a base 10 numeral to a different base, your answer should never contain a digit greater than or equal to that different base.
- When changing a numeral given in a base other than 10 to a numeral in base 10, use multiplication.
- When changing a base 10 numeral to a numeral in a different base, use division.

SECTION 4.3   *Exercises*

Warm Up Exercises

In Exercises 1–4, fill in the blanks with an appropriate word, phrase, or symbol(s).

1. In the numeral 623_8, the 8 is called the _____. Base

2. In the numeral 623_8, the 6 represents $6 \times$ _____. 8^2

3. In the numeral 623_8, the 2 represents $2 \times$ _____. 8

4. Computers and other electronic devices make use of the following numeration systems:

   a) base 2, also called _____ . Binary

   b) base 8, also called _____. Octal

   c) base 16, also called _____. Hexadecimal

Practice the Skills

In Exercises 5–22, convert the given numeral to a numeral in base 10.

5. 1_2 1
6. 10_2 2
7. 13_5 8
8. 31_5 16
9. 241_8 161
10. 765_8 501
11. 309_{12} 441
12. 1005_{12} 1733
13. 573_{16} 1395
14. 423_{16} 1059
15. 110101_2 53
16. 1110111_2 119
17. 7654_8 4012
18. 5032_8 2586
19. $A91_{12}$ 1549
20. $B52_{12}$ 1646
21. $C679_{16}$ 50,809
22. $D20E_{16}$ 53,774

In Exercises 23–36, convert each of the following to a numeral in the base indicated.

23. 9 to base 2 1001_2
24. 14 to base 2 1110_2
25. 23 to base 3 212_3
26. 73 to base 3 2201_3
27. 53 to base 4 311_4
28. 591 to base 4 21033_4
29. 102 to base 5 402_5
30. 549 to base 7 1413_7
31. 1098 to base 8 2112_8
32. 2921 to base 8 5551_8
33. 9004 to base 12 5264_{12}
34. 13,312 to base 12 7854_{12}
35. 9455 to base 16 $24EF_{16}$
36. 39,885 to base 16 $9BCD_{16}$

In Exercises 37–44, convert 2013 to a numeral in the base indicated.

37. 3 2202120_3
38. 4 133131_4
39. 5 31023_5
40. 6 13153_6
41. 7 5604_7
42. 9 2676_9
43. 15 $8E3_{15}$
44. 17 $6G7_{17}$

Problem Solving

In Exercises 45–48, on page 191 assume the numerals given are in a base 5 numeration system. Assume the numerals in this system and their equivalent Hindu–Arabic numerals are

$\bigcirc = 0$ $\ominus = 1$ $\oplus = 2$ $\ominus = 3$ $\oplus = 4$

Write the Hindu–Arabic numerals equivalent to each of the following.

45. ①⊖$_5$ 23

46. ①⊖$_5$ 13

47. ⊖○⊖$_5$ 78

48. ①①⊖$_5$ 73

In Exercises 49–52, write the Hindu–Arabic numerals in the numeration system discussed in Exercises 45–48.

49. 19 *

50. 23 *

51. 74 *

52. 85 *

In Exercises 53–56, suppose colors as indicated below represent numerals in a base 4 numeration system.

● = 0 ● = 1 ● = 2 ● = 3

Write the Hindu–Arabic numerals equivalent to each of the following.

53. $_4$ 14

54. $_4$ 7

55. $_4$ 36

56. ●●●$_4$ 57

In Exercises 57–60, write the Hindu–Arabic numerals in the base 4 numeration system discussed in Exercises 53–56. You will need to use the colors indicated above to write the answer.

57. 10 *

58. 15 *

59. 60 *

60. 56 *

61. *Another Conversion Method* There is an alternative method for changing a base 10 numeral to a different base. This method will be used to convert 328 to base 5. Dividing 328 by 5 gives a quotient of 65 and a remainder of 3. Write the quotient below the dividend and the remainder on the right, as shown.

$$5\,|\,\underline{328} \qquad \text{remainder}$$
$$\quad 65 \qquad\qquad 3$$

Continue this process of division by 5.

			remainder	
5	328			(In the last division, since the
5	65	3	↑	dividend, 2, is smaller than the
5	13	0		divisor, 5, the quotient is 0 and
5	2	3	Answer	the remainder is 2.)
	0	2		

Note that the division continues until the quotient is zero. The answer is read from the bottom number to the top number in the remainder column. Thus, $328 = 2303_5$.

a) Convert 683 to base 5 by this method. 10213_5

b) Convert 763 to base 8 by this method. 1373_8

Concept/Writing Exercises

62. a) What is 0_4 equal to in base 10? 0

   b) What is 1_4 equal to in base 10? 1

   c) What is 2_4 equal to in base 10? 2

   d) What is 3_4 equal to in base 10? 3

   e) In general, if n is a digit less than the base b, and the base b is less than or equal to 10, then describe what n_b is equal to in base 10. n

63. a) What is 10_2 equal to in base 10? 2

   b) What is 10_8 equal to in base 10? 8

   c) What is 10_{16} equal to in base 10? 16

   d) What is 10_{32} equal to in base 10? 32

   e) In general, for any base b, what is 10_b equal to in base 10? b

64. a) What is 11_2 equal to in base 10? 3

   b) What is 11_8 equal to in base 10? 9

   c) What is 11_{16} equal to in base 10? 17

   d) What is 11_{32} equal to in base 10? 33

   e) In general, for any base b, what is 11_b equal to in base 10? $b + 1$

Challenge Problems/Group Activities

65. Find b if $111_b = 43$. $b = 6$

66. Find d if $ddd_5 = 124$. $d = 4$

67. a) Use the numerals 0, 1, and 2 to write the first 20 numbers in the base 3 numeration system. *

   b) What is the next numeral after 222_3? 1000_3

68. *Computer Code* The ASCII code used by most computers uses the last seven positions of an eight-bit byte to represent all the characters on a standard keyboard. How many different orderings of 0's and 1's (or how many different characters) can be made by using the last seven positions of an eight-bit byte? $2^7 = 128$

69. a) *Your Own Numeration System* Make up your own base 20 positional-value numeration system. Indicate the 20 numerals you will use to represent the 20 numbers less than the base. Answers will vary.

   b) Write 523 and 5293 in your base 20 numeration system. Answers will vary.

* See Instructor Answer Appendix

Recreational Mathematics

70. *The Price Is Right* Refer to the *Recreational Mathematics* on page 187. Determine the correct order in which to place the digits 1, 2, 5, 7, and 9 to match the price of the 2011 Chevrolet Cruze LTZ.

▲ *Place the digits 1, 2, 5, 7, and 9 in the correct order to match the price of the car.*

$ ____ ____, ____ ____ ____ $ 21,975

71. Suppose a base 4 place-value system has its digits represented by colors as follows:

● = 0   ● = 1   ● = 2   ●

a) Determine the value of ● ● ● ● ●$_4$ in base 10. 876

b) Write 177 in the base 4 system using only the four colors given in the exercise. *

Internet/Research Activities

72. Investigate and write a report on the use of the duodecimal (base 12) system of numeration. You may wish to contact the Dozenal Society (see the *Did You Know?* on page 189) for more information.

73. We mentioned at the beginning of this section that some societies still use a base 2 and base 3 numeration system. These societies are in Australia, New Guinea, Africa, and South America. Write a report on these societies, covering the symbols they use and how they combine these symbols to represent numbers in their numeration system.

*See Instructor Answer Appendix

SECTION 4.4   Computation in Other Bases

▲ *Students do arithmetic by "carrying" and "borrowing."*

You may recall learning how to add, subtract, multiply, and divide when you were in grade school. You may recall "carrying" when adding and "borrowing" when subtracting. For example, when performing 75 + 18, you would add 5 and 8 to get 13. You would write down the 3 and "carry the 1." When performing 43 − 19 you would "borrow from the 4" so you could perform 13 − 9 to get 4. In this section, we will use similar procedures when working with numerals that have bases other than base 10.

Why *This is Important* By working in other bases, we will gain a better understanding of our own base 10 place-value system.

Addition

When computers perform calculations, they do so in base 2, the binary system. In this section, we will explain how to perform calculations in base 2 and other bases.

In a base 2 system, the only digits are 0 and 1, and the place values are

$$\ldots,\ 2^4, 2^3, 2^2, 2, 1$$
$$\text{or}\quad \ldots, 16,\ \ 8,\ \ 4,\ \ 2, 1$$

Suppose we want to add $1_2 + 1_2$. The subscript 2 indicates that we are adding in base 2. Remember that the answer to $1_2 + 1_2$ must be written using only the digits 0 and 1. The sum of $1_2 + 1_2$ is 10_2, which represents 1 group of two and 0 units in base 2. Recall that 10_2 means $(1 \times 2) + (0 \times 1)$.

If we wanted to find the sum of $10_2 + 1_2$, we would add the digits in the right-hand, or units, column. Since $0_2 + 1_2 = 1_2$, the sum of $10_2 + 1_2 = 11_2$.

Table 4.7 Base 2 Addition Table

+	0	1
0	0	1
1	1	10

We are going to work additional examples and exercises in base 2, so rather than performing individual calculations in every problem, we can construct and use an addition table, Table 4.7, for base 2 (just as we used an addition table in base 10 when we first learned to add in base 10).

Example 1 *Adding in Base 2*

Add $\quad 1101_2$
$\quad\quad\underline{+\ 111_2}$

Solution Begin by adding the digits in the right-hand, or units, column. From previous discussion, and as can be seen in Table 4.7, $1_2 + 1_2 = 10_2$. Place the 0 under the units column and carry the 1 to the 2's column, the second column from the right.

$$
\begin{array}{cccc}
2^3 & 2^2 & 2 & 1 \quad \text{Place value of columns}\\
\downarrow & \downarrow & \downarrow & \downarrow \\
1 & 1 & {}^1 0 & 1 \\
+ & & 1 & 1 \quad 1 \\
\hline
& & & 0_2
\end{array}
$$

Now add the three digits in the 2's column, $1_2 + 0_2 + 1_2$. Treat it as $(1_2 + 0_2) + 1_2$. Therefore, add $1_2 + 0_2$ to get 1_2, then add $1_2 + 1_2$ to get 10_2. Place the 0 under the 2's column and carry the 1 to the 2^2 column (the third column from the right).

$$
\begin{array}{ccc}
1 & {}^1 1 & {}^1 0 \quad 1 \\
+ & 1 & 1 \quad 1 \\
\hline
& 0 & 0_2
\end{array}
$$

Now add the three 1's in the 2^2 column to get $(1_2 + 1_2) + 1_2 = 10_2 + 1_2 = 11_2$. Place the 1 under the 2^2 column and carry the 1 to the 2^3 column (the fourth column from the right).

$$
\begin{array}{cccc}
{}^1 1 & {}^1 1 & {}^1 0 & 1 \\
+ & & 1 & 1 \quad 1 \\
\hline
& 1 & 0 & 0_2
\end{array}
$$

Now add the two 1's in the 2^3 column, $1_2 + 1_2 = 10_2$. Place the 10 as follows.

$$
\begin{array}{ccccc}
& {}^1 1 & {}^1 1 & {}^1 0 & 1 \\
+ & & & 1 & 1 \quad 1 \\
\hline
1 & 0 & 1 & 0 & 0_2
\end{array}
$$

Therefore, the sum is 10100_2. ∎

Let's now look at addition in a base 5 system. In base 5, the only digits are 0, 1, 2, 3, and 4, and the positional values are

$$\ldots,\quad 5^4,\ 5^3,\ 5^2, 5, 1$$
or $\quad \ldots, 625, 125,\ 25, 5, 1$

What is the sum of $4_5 + 3_5$? We can consider this to mean $(1 + 1 + 1 + 1) + (1 + 1 + 1)$. We can regroup the seven 1's into one group of five and two units as $(1 + 1 + 1 + 1 + 1) + (1 + 1)$. Thus, the sum of $4_5 + 3_5 = 12_5$ (circled in

MATHEMATICS TODAY

Speaking to Machines

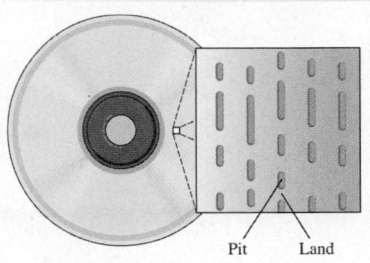

Pit Land

Besides our familiar base 10 numeration system, one of the most significant numeration systems is the binary, or base 2, numeration system. Computers use binary to process information and "talk" to one another. When a computer receives a command or data, each character must first be converted into a binary numeral for the computer to understand and use it. The binary system is also used to record audio and video on Blu-ray discs (BDs), digital video discs (DVDs), and compact discs (CDs). Sound and images are stored in a binary system of pits and "lands" (nonpits). To play the disc, a laser beam tracks along the spiral and recognizes a pit as a 0 and a land as a 1. The binary sequence of 0s and 1s is then converted back into sound and images.

Why *This is Important* The recording of information on discs is just one of the many examples of how other numeration systems are used in technology.

Table 4.8 Base 5 Addition Table

+	0	1	2	3	4
0	0	1	2	3	4
1	1	2	3	4	10
2	2	3	4	10	11
3	3	4	10	11	12
4	4	10	11	(12)	13

Table 4.8). Recall that 12_5 means $(1 \times 5) + (2 \times 1)$. We can use this same procedure in obtaining the remaining values in the base 5 addition table.

Example 2 *Use the Base 5 Addition Table*

Add $\quad 34_5$
$\quad\quad + 23_5$

Solution First determine from Table 4.8 that $4_5 + 3_5$ is 12_5. Record the 2 and carry the 1 to the 5's column.

$$\begin{array}{r} {}^1 3 \ 4_5 \\ + 2 \ 3_5 \\ \hline 2_5 \end{array}$$

Add the numbers in the second column, $(1_5 + 3_5) + 2_5 = 4_5 + 2_5 = 11_5$. Record the 11.

$$\begin{array}{r} {}^1 3 \ 4_5 \\ + \ \ 2 \ 3_5 \\ \hline 1 \ 1 \ 2_5 \end{array}$$

The sum is 112_5. ∎

Example 3 *Add in Base 5*

Add $\quad 2314_5$
$\quad\quad + 3101_5$

Solution

$$\begin{array}{r} 2 \ 3 \ {}^1 1 \ 4_5 \\ + \ 3 \ 1 \ 0 \ 1_5 \\ \hline 1 \ 0 \ 4 \ 2 \ 0_5 \end{array}$$

The sum is 10420_5. ∎

You can develop an addition table for any base and use it to add in that base. As you get more comfortable with addition in other bases, however, you may prefer to add in other bases by using mental arithmetic. To do so, convert the sum from the given base to base 10 and then convert the base 10 numeral back into the given base. You must clearly understand how to convert from base 10 to the given base, as discussed in Section 4.3. For example, to add $7_9 + 8_9$, add $7 + 8$ in base 10 to get 15_{10} and then mentally convert 15_{10} to 16_9 using the procedure given earlier. Remember, 16_9 when converted to base 10 becomes $(1 \times 9) + (6 \times 1)$, or 15. Addition using this procedure is illustrated in Examples 4 and 5.

Example 4 *Adding in Base 10; Converting to Base 3*

Add $\quad 1022_3$
$\quad\quad + 2121_3$

Solution To solve this problem, make the necessary conversions by using mental arithmetic. $2 + 1 = 3_{10} = 10_3$. Record the 0 and carry the 1.

$$\begin{array}{r} 1 \ 0 \ {}^1 2 \ 2_3 \\ + 2 \ 1 \ 2 \ 1_3 \\ \hline 0_3 \end{array}$$

$1 + 2 + 2 = 5_{10} = 12_3$. Record the 2 and carry the 1.

$$\begin{array}{r} 1 \ {}^1 0 \ {}^1 2 \ 2_3 \\ + 2 \ 1 \ 2 \ 1_3 \\ \hline 2 \ 0_3 \end{array}$$

$1 + 0 + 1 = 2_{10} = 2_3$. Record the 2.

$$\begin{array}{r} 1 \;{}^{1}0 \;{}^{1}2 \; 2_3 \\ + \,2 \; 1 \; 2 \; 1_3 \\ \hline 2 \; \; 2 \; \; 0_3 \end{array}$$

$1 + 2 = 3_{10} = 10_3$. Record the 10.

$$\begin{array}{r} 1022_3 \\ + \; 2121_3 \\ \hline 10220_3 \end{array}$$

The sum is 10220_3. ∎

Subtraction

Subtraction can also be performed in bases other than base 10. Always remember that when you "borrow," you borrow the amount of the base given in the subtraction problem. For example, if subtracting in base 5, when you borrow, you borrow 5. If subtracting in base 12, when you borrow, you borrow 12.

Example 5 *Subtracting in Base 5*

Subtract
$$\begin{array}{r} 3032_5 \\ -1004_5 \end{array}$$

Solution We will perform the subtraction in base 10 and convert the results to base 5. Since 4 is greater than 2, we must borrow one group of 5 from the preceding column. This action gives a sum of $5 + 2$, or 7, in base 10. Now we subtract 4 from 7; the difference is 3. We complete the problem in the usual manner. The 3 in the second column becomes a 2, $2 - 0 = 2$. In the third column, $0 - 0 = 0$. Finally, in the fourth column, $3 - 1 = 2$.

$$\begin{array}{r} 3032_5 \\ -1004_5 \\ \hline 2023_5 \end{array}$$
∎

In the next example, we will subtract base 12 numerals. Recall from Section 4.3 that we use the capital letter A to represent the number ten and the capital letter B to represent the number eleven in base 12.

Example 6 *Subtracting in Base 12*

Subtract
$$\begin{array}{r} 9 \; 1 \; B_{12} \\ -2 \; A \; 2_{12} \end{array}$$

Solution Recall that B represents eleven. Therefore, in the units column we have $11 - 2 = 9$. Next, recall that A represents ten. Therefore, in the next column we must subtract 10 from 1. Since 10 is greater than *1*, borrowing is necessary. We must borrow one group of 12 from the preceding column. We then have a sum of $12 + 1$, or 13. We can now subtract 10 from 13 and the difference is 3. The 9 in the third column becomes 8, and $8 - 2 = 6$.

$$\begin{array}{r} 9 \; 1 \; B_{12} \\ -2 \; A \; 2_{12} \\ \hline 6 \; 3 \; 9_{12} \end{array}$$
∎

Multiplication

Multiplication can also be performed in bases other than base 10. Doing so is helped by forming a multiplication table for the base desired. Suppose we want to determine the product of $4_5 \times 3_5$. In base 10, 4×3 means there are four groups of three units. Similarly, in a base 5 system, $4_5 \times 3_5$ means there are four groups of three units, or

$$(1 + 1 + 1) + (1 + 1 + 1) + (1 + 1 + 1) + (1 + 1 + 1)$$

Regrouping the 12 units above into groups of five gives

$$(1 + 1 + 1 + 1 + 1) + (1 + 1 + 1 + 1 + 1) + (1 + 1)$$

or two groups of five, and two units. Thus, $4_5 \times 3_5 = 22_5$.

We can construct other values in the base 5 multiplication table in the same way. You may, however, find it easier to multiply the values in the base 10 system and then change the product to base 5 by using the procedure discussed in Section 4.3. Multiplying 4×3 in base 10 gives 12, and converting 12 from base 10 to base 5 gives 22_5.

The product of $4_5 \times 3_5$ is circled in Table 4.9, the base 5 multiplication table. The other values in the table may be found by either method discussed.

Table 4.9 Base 5 Multiplication Table

×	0	1	2	3	4
0	0	0	0	0	0
1	0	1	2	3	4
2	0	2	4	11	13
3	0	3	11	14	22
4	0	4	13	(22)	31

Example 7 *Using the Base 5 Multiplication Table*

Multiply 13_5
             $\underline{\times\ 3_5}$

Solution Use the base 5 multiplication table to find the products. When the product consists of two digits, record the right digit and carry the left digit. Multiplying gives $3_5 \times 3_5 = 14_5$. Record the 4 and carry the 1.

$$\begin{array}{r} {}^{1}13_5 \\ \underline{\times\ 3_5} \\ 4 \end{array}$$

$(3_5 \times 1_5) + 1_5 = 4_5$. Record the 4.

$$\begin{array}{r} {}^{1}13_5 \\ \underline{\times\ 3_5} \\ 44_5 \end{array}$$

The product is 44_5.   ◼

Constructing a multiplication table is often tedious, especially when the base is large. To multiply in a given base without the use of a table, multiply in base 10 and convert the products to the appropriate base before recording them. This procedure is illustrated in Example 8.

Example 8 *Multiplying in Base 7*

Multiply 43_7
            $\underline{\times\ 25_7}$

Solution $5 \times 3 = 15_{10} = (2 \times 7) + (1 \times 1) = 21_7$. Record the 1 and carry the 2.

$$\begin{array}{r} {}^{2}43_7 \\ \underline{\times\ 25_7} \\ 1 \end{array}$$

$(5 \times 4) + 2 = 20 + 2 = 22_{10} = (3 \times 7) + (1 \times 1) = 31_7$. Record the 31.

$$\begin{array}{r} {}^2 43_7 \\ \times\ 25_7 \\ \hline 311 \end{array}$$

$2 \times 3 = 6_{10} = 6_7$. Record the 6.

$$\begin{array}{r} {}^2 43_7 \\ \times\ 25_7 \\ \hline 311 \\ 6 \end{array}$$

$2 \times 4 = 8_{10} = (1 \times 7) + (1 \times 1) = 11_7$. Record the 11. Now add in base 7 to determine the answer. Remember, in base 7, there are no digits greater than 6.

$$\begin{array}{r} {}^2 43_7 \\ \times\ 25_7 \\ \hline 311 \\ 116 \\ \hline 1501_7 \end{array}$$

Division

Division is performed in much the same manner as long division in base 10. A detailed example of a division in base 5 is illustrated in Example 9. The same procedure is used for division in any other base.

Example 9 Dividing in Base 5

Divide $2_5 \overline{)143_5}$.

Solution Using the multiplication table for base 5, Table 4.9 on page 196, we list the multiples of the divisor, 2.

$$\begin{aligned} 2_5 \times 1_5 &= 2_5 \\ 2_5 \times 2_5 &= 4_5 \\ 2_5 \times 3_5 &= 11_5 \\ 2_5 \times 4_5 &= 13_5 \end{aligned}$$

Since $2_5 \times 4_5 = 13_5$, which is the largest product less than 14_5, 2_5 divides into 14_5 four times.

$$\begin{array}{r} 4 \\ 2_5 \overline{)143_5} \\ 13 \\ \hline 1 \end{array}$$

Subtract 13_5 from 14_5. The difference is 1_5. Record the 1. Now bring down the 3 as when dividing in base 10.

$$\begin{array}{r} 4 \\ 2_5 \overline{)143_5} \\ 13 \\ \hline 13 \end{array}$$

We see that $2_5 \times 4_5 = 13_5$. Use this information to complete the problem.

$$\begin{array}{r} 44_5 \\ 2_5 \overline{)143_5} \\ 13 \\ \hline 13 \\ 13 \\ \hline 0 \end{array}$$

Therefore, $143_5 \div 2_5 = 44_5$ with remainder 0_5.

A division problem can be checked by multiplication. If the division was performed correctly, (quotient $\times$ divisor) + remainder = dividend. We can check Example 9 as follows.

$$(44_5 \times 2_5) + 0_5 = 143_5$$

$$\begin{array}{r} 44_5 \\ \times\ \ 2_5 \\ \hline 143_5 \end{array} \quad \text{Check}$$

Example 10 *Dividing in Base 8*

Divide $6_8)\overline{4071_8}$.

Solution   The multiples of 6 in base 8 are

$$6_8 \times 1_8 - 6_8 \quad 6_8 \times 2_8 = 14_8 \quad 6_8 \times 3_8 = 22_8 \quad 6_8 \times 4_8 = 30_8$$
$$6_8 \times 5_8 = 36_8 \quad 6_8 \times 6_8 = 44_8 \quad 6_8 \times 7_8 = 52_8$$

$$\begin{array}{r} 536_8 \\ 6_8)\overline{4071_8} \\ 36 \\ \hline 27 \\ 22 \\ \hline 51 \\ 44 \\ \hline 5 \end{array}$$

Thus, the quotient is 536_8, with remainder 5_8.

Be careful when subtracting! In the above division problem, we had to borrow when subtracting 6 from 0 and when subtracting 4 from 1. Remember that we borrow 10_8, which is the same as 8 in base 10.

CHECK: Does $(536_8 \times 6_8) + 5_8 = 4071_8$?

$$\begin{array}{r} 536_8 \\ \times\ \ \ 6_8 \\ \hline 4064_8 + 5_8 = 4071_8 \quad \text{True} \end{array}$$

■

SECTION 4.4   *Exercises*

Warm Up Exercises

In Exercises 1–6, fill in the blanks with an appropriate word, phrase, or symbol(s).

1. In base 5, $3_5 + 4_5 =$ _____ . 12_5

2. In base 16, we use the letter A to represent the number _____ . 10

3. In base 5 subtraction, when we borrow, we must borrow one group of _____ from the preceding column. 5

4. The positional values in a base 2 (binary) numeration system are $\ldots 2^4,$ _____ $, 2^2, 2, 1.$ 2^3

5. In base 5, $3_5 \times 4_5 =$ _____ . 22_5

6. The positional values in a base 8 (octal) numeration system are $\ldots 8^4,$ _____ $, 8^2, 8, 1.$ 8^3

Practice the Skills

In Exercises 7–18, add in the indicated base.

7. $\begin{array}{r} 33_5 \\ +41_5 \end{array}$ 124_5

8. $\begin{array}{r} 23_4 \\ +\ 12_4 \end{array}$ 101_4

9. $\begin{array}{r} 110_2 \\ +\ 111_2 \end{array}$ 1101_2

10. $\begin{array}{r} 253_6 \\ +\ 514_6 \end{array}$ 1211_6

11. 799_{12} $9B5_{12}$
$+ 218_{12}$

12. 222_3 1021_3
$+ 22_3$

13. 1112_3 2200_3
$+ 1011_3$

14. 470_{12} $7B7_{12}$
$+ 347_{12}$

15. 14631_7 24001_7
$+ 6040_7$

16. 1341_8 1702_8
$+ 341_8$

17. 1110_2 10100_2
$+ 110_2$

18. $43A_{16}$ $8D0_{16}$
$+ 496_{16}$

In Exercises 19–30, subtract in the indicated base.

19. 32_5 3_5
-24_5

20. 353_6 105_6
-244_6

21. 338_9 54_9
-274_9

22. $A3B3_{12}$ $81BB_{12}$
$- 21B4_{12}$

23. 1101_2 110_2
$- 111_2$

24. 1221_3 1012_3
$- 202_3$

25. 1001_2 11_2
$- 110_2$

26. 2173_8 317_8
-1654_8

27. 4223_7 3616_7
$- 304_7$

28. 4232_5 1341_5
-2341_5

29. 2100_3 1011_3
-1012_3

30. $4E7_{16}$ $35E_{16}$
-189_{16}

In Exercises 31–42, multiply in the indicated base.

31. 42_5 134_5
$\times 2_5$

32. 32_4 222_4
$\times 3_4$

33. 212_3 1201_3
$\times 2_3$

34. 37_8 1017_8
$\times 21_8$

35. 512_6 21020_6
$\times 23_6$

36. 124_{12} 720_{12}
$\times 6_{12}$

37. $B12_{12}$ 77676_{12}
$\times 83_{12}$

38. $6A3_{12}$ $13BB0_{12}$
$\times 24_{12}$

39. 111_2 100011_2
$\times 101_2$

40. 584_9 15457_9
$\times 24_9$

41. 316_7 6031_7
$\times 16_7$

42. $7A9_{12}$ 9266_{12}
$\times 12_{12}$

In Exercises 43–54, divide in the indicated base.

43. $1_2 \overline{)110_2}$ 110_2

44. $2_8 \overline{)730_8}$ 354_8

45. $3_7 \overline{)506_7}$ 146_7 R2_7

46. $4_5 \overline{)302_5}$ 34_5 R1_5

47. $2_4 \overline{)312_4}$ 123_4

48. $6_{12} \overline{)431_{12}}$ 86_{12} R1_{12}

49. $2_4 \overline{)213_4}$ 103_4 R1_4

50. $5_6 \overline{)214_6}$ 24_6 R2_6

51. $3_5 \overline{)224_5}$ 41_5 R1_5

52. $4_6 \overline{)210_6}$ 31_6 R2_6

53. $6_7 \overline{)404_7}$ 45_7 R2_7

54. $3_7 \overline{)2101_7}$ 500_7 R1_7

Problem Solving

In Exercises 55–58, the numerals in a base 5 numeration system are as illustrated with their equivalent Hindu–Arabic numerals.

$\bigcirc = 0$ $\ominus = 1$ $\ovoid = 2$ $\ominus = 3$ $\oslash = 4$

Add the following base 5 numerals.

55. *

56. *

57. *

58. *

In Exercises 59–66, assume the numerals given are in a base 4 numeration system. In this system, suppose colors are used as numerals, as indicated below.

● $=0$, ● $=1$, ● $=2$, ● $=3$,

Add the following base 4 numerals. Your answers will contain a variety of the colors indicated.

59. *

60. *

61. *

62. *

Subtract the following in base 4. Your answer will contain a variety of the colors indicated.

63. *

64. *

65. *

66. *

Challenge Problems/Group Activities

In Exercises 67–68, perform the indicated operation.

67. FAB_{16} $3EAC_{16}$
$\times 4_{16}$

68. $D_{16} \overline{)FACE_{16}}$ $134A_{16}$ RC_{16}

*See Instructor Answer Appendix

69. Consider the multiplication

$$462_8$$
$$\times\ 35_8$$

a) Multiply the numerals in base 8. 21252_8

b) Convert 462_8 and 35_8 to base 10. 306 and 29

c) Multiply the base 10 numerals determined in part (b). 8874

d) Convert the answer obtained in base 8 in part (a) to base 10. 8874

e) Are the answers obtained in parts (c) and (d) the same? Why or why not? Yes

70. Determine b, by trial and error, if $1304_b = 204$. 5

71. In a base 4 system, each of the four numerals is represented by one of the following colors: *

Determine the value of each color if the following addition is true in base 4.

Internet/Research Activities

72. Write a report on how computers use the binary (base 2), octal (base 8), and hexadecimal (base 16) numeration systems.

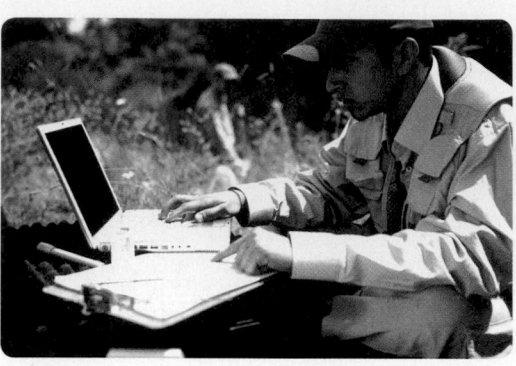

73. One method used by computers to perform subtraction is the "end around carry method." Do research and write a report explaining, with specific examples, how a computer performs subtraction by using the end around carry method.

*See Instructor Answer Appendix

Early Computational Methods

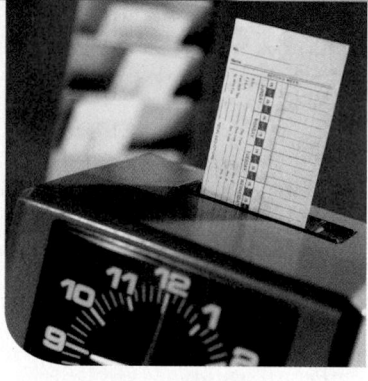

▲ *Multiplication can be used to calculate the amount of your paycheck.*

Suppose that last week you worked at your job for 27 hours at a rate of $8 per hour. How much money did you make? You may find the answer by multiplying 27×8 "by hand."

$$^5 27$$
$$\times\ \ 8$$
$$\overline{216}$$

Although most of us would use this method, it is not the only method for multiplying two numbers together. Early civilizations used various other methods. In this section, we will study three other methods of multiplication.

Why *This is Important* Studying other methods of multiplication can help us better understand how the traditional multiplication algorithm works.

Duplation and Mediation

The first method of multiplication we will study is *duplation and mediation*. This method, also known as *Russian peasant multiplication*, is still used in parts of Russia today. Duplation refers to doubling one number, and mediation refers to halving one number. The duplation and mediation method is similar to a method used by the ancient Egyptians as described on the Rhind Papyrus. Example 1 illustrates this method of multiplication.

Example 1   *Using Duplation and Mediation*

Multiply 19 × 17 using duplation and mediation.

Solution   Write 19 and 17 with a dash between the two numbers. Divide the number on the left, 19, by 2, drop the remainder, and place the quotient, 9, under the 19. Double the number on the right, 17, to obtain 34, and place it under the 17. You will then have the following number pairs.

$$19 - 17$$
$$9 - 34$$

Continue this process, dividing the number in the left-hand column by 2, disregarding the remainder, and doubling the number in the right-hand column, as shown below. When a 1 appears in the left-hand column, stop.

$$19 - 17$$
$$9 - 34$$
$$4 - 68$$
$$2 - 136$$
$$1 - 272$$

Next, cross out all the even numbers in the left-hand column and the corresponding numbers in the right-hand column.

$$19 - 17$$
$$9 - 34$$
$$4 - 68$$
$$2 - 136$$
$$1 - 272$$

Now add the remaining numbers in the right-hand column to obtain
$17 + 34 + 272 = 323$. The number obtained, 323, is the product of 19 and 17. Thus $19 \times 17 = 323$.   ∎

Lattice Multiplication

Another method of multiplication is *lattice multiplication*. This method's name comes from the use of a grid, or lattice, when multiplying two numbers. It is also known as the *gelosia* method. The lattice method was brought to Europe in the 1200s by Fibonacci, who likely learned it from the Egyptians, Arabs, or Hindus (see the *Profile in Mathematics* on page 278).

Example 2   *Using Lattice Multiplication*

Multiply 312 × 75 using lattice multiplication.

Solution   To multiply 312 × 75 using lattice multiplication, first construct a rectangle consisting of three columns (one for each digit of 312) and two rows (one for each digit of 75).

Place the digits 3, 1, 2 above the boxes and the digits 7, 5 on the right of the boxes, as shown in Fig. 4.1 on page 202. Then place a diagonal in each box.

Complete each box by multiplying the number on top of the box by the number to the right of the box (Fig. 4.2). Place the units digit of the product below the diagonal and the tens digit of the product above the diagonal.

Figure 4.1

Figure 4.2

Figure 4.3

Add the numbers along the diagonals, as shown with the blue shaded arrows in Fig. 4.3, starting with the bottom right diagonal. If the sum in a diagonal is 10 or greater, record the units digit below the rectangle and carry the tens digit to the next diagonal to the left.

For example, when adding 4, 1, and 5 (along the second blue diagonal from the right), the sum is 10. Record the 0 below the rectangle and carry the 1 to the next blue diagonal. The sum of $1 + 1 + 7 + 0 + 5$ is 14. Record the 4 and carry the 1 to the next blue diagonal. The sum of the numbers in the next blue diagonal is $1 + 0 + 1 + 1$ or 3.

The answer is read down the left-hand column and along the bottom, as shown by the purple arrow in Fig. 4.3. Therefore, $312 \times 75 = 23,400$. ■

Napier's Rods

The third method used to multiply numbers was developed from the lattice method by John Napier in the early 1600s and is known as *Napier's rods* or *Napier's bones*. This method is similar to that used in modern computers. Napier developed a system of separate rods (which were often made out of bones) numbered 0 through 9 and an additional rod for an index, numbered vertically 1 through 9 (Fig. 4.4). Each rod is divided into 10 blocks. Each block below the first block contains a multiple of the number in the first block, with a diagonal separating the digits. The units digits are placed to the right of the diagonals and the tens digits to the left. Example 3 explains how Napier's rods are used to multiply numbers.

INDEX	0	1	2	3	4	5	6	7	8	9
1	0/0	0/1	0/2	0/3	0/4	0/5	0/6	0/7	0/8	0/9
2	0/0	0/2	0/4	0/6	0/8	1/0	1/2	1/4	1/6	1/8
3	0/0	0/3	0/6	0/9	1/2	1/5	1/8	2/1	2/4	2/7
4	0/0	0/4	0/8	1/2	1/6	2/0	2/4	2/8	3/2	3/6
5	0/0	0/5	1/0	1/5	2/0	2/5	3/0	3/5	4/0	4/5
6	0/0	0/6	1/2	1/8	2/4	3/0	3/6	4/2	4/8	5/4
7	0/0	0/7	1/4	2/1	2/8	3/5	4/2	4/9	5/6	6/3
8	0/0	0/8	1/6	2/4	3/2	4/0	4/8	5/6	6/4	7/2
9	0/0	0/9	1/8	2/7	3/6	4/5	5/4	6/3	7/2	8/1

Figure 4.4

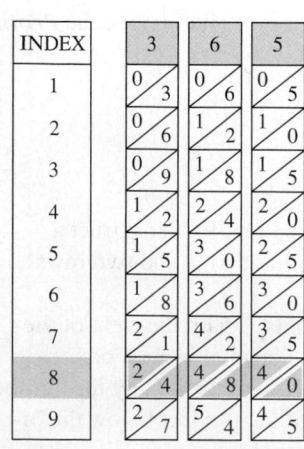

Figure 4.5

Example 3 *Using Napier's Rods*

Multiply 8×365, using Napier's rods.

Solution To multiply 8×365, line up the rods 3, 6, and 5 to the right of the index 8, as shown in Fig. 4.5. Below the 3, 6, and 5 place the blocks that contain the products of 8×3, 8×6, and 8×5, respectively. To obtain the answer, add along the diagonals as in the lattice method.

Thus, $8 \times 365 = 2920$.

Example 4 illustrates the procedure to follow to multiply numbers containing more than one digit, using Napier's rods.

Example 4 Using Napier's Rods to Multiply Two- and Three-Digit Numbers

Multiply 48×365, using Napier's rods.

Solution $48 \times 365 = (40 + 8) \times 365$

Write $(40 + 8) \times 365 = (40 \times 365) + (8 \times 365)$. To find 40×365, determine 4×365 and multiply the product by 10. To evaluate 4×365, set up Napier's rods for 3, 6, and 5 with index 4, and then evaluate along the diagonals, as indicated.

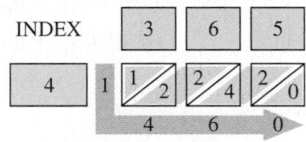

Therefore, $4 \times 365 = 1460$. Then $40 \times 365 = 1460 \times 10 = 14,600$.

$$48 \times 365 = (40 \times 365) + (8 \times 365)$$
$$= 14,600 + 2920$$
$$= 17,520$$

$8 \times 365 = 2920$
from Example 3

SECTION 4.5 Exercises

Warm Up Exercises

In Exercises 1–4, fill in the blanks with an appropriate word, phrase, or symbol(s).

1. When determining the product 24×19, using duplation and mediation,

　　a) the 24 is _____ by 2, and Divided

　　b) the 19 is _____. Doubled

2. When using duplation and mediation, when you divide the number on the left by two you disregard the _____. Remainder

3. When determining the product 438×23, using lattice multiplication, first construct a rectangle consisting of _____ columns and _____ rows. Three, two

4. When using lattice multiplication, after using multiplication to complete the boxes in the rectangle, add the numbers along the _____. Diagonals

Practice the Skills

In Exercises 5–12, multiply using duplation and mediation.

5. 11×28 308

6. 26×18 468

7. 39×17 663

8. 138×41 5658

9. 35×236 8260

10. 96×53 5088

11. 93 × 93 8649

12. 49 × 124 6076

In Exercises 13–20, use lattice multiplication to determine the product.

13. 3 × 251 753

14. 5 × 372 1860

15. 7 × 596 4172

16. 9 × 509 4581

17. 75 × 12 900

18. 47 × 259 12,173

19. 314 × 652 204,728

20. 634 × 832 527,488

In Exercises 21–28, multiply using Napier's rods.

21. 2 × 56 112

22. 4 × 73 292

23. 5 × 82 410

24. 6 × 171 1026

25. 5 × 125 625

26. 75 × 125 9375

27. 9 × 6742 60,678

28. 7 × 3456 24,192

Problem Solving

In Exercises 29 and 30, we show lattice multiplications. (a) Determine the numbers being multiplied. (b) Determine the product.

29.

a) 253 × 46
b) 11,638

30.

a) 475 × 263
b) 124,925

In Exercises 31 and 32, we solve a multiplication problem using Napier's rods. (a) Determine the numbers being multiplied. Each empty box contains a single digit. (b) Determine the product.

31.

a) 4 × 382
b) 1528

32.

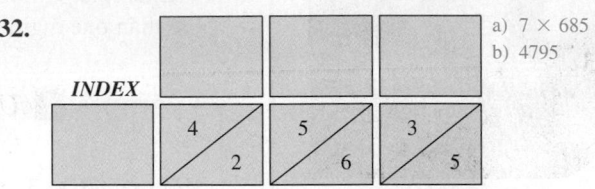

a) 7 × 685
b) 4795

Challenge Problems/Group Activities

In Exercises 33 and 34, use the method of duplation and mediation to perform the multiplication. See Section 4.1 for Egyptian and Roman numerals. Write the answer in the numeration system in which the exercise is given.

33. (∩|||) • (∩∩||) *

34. (XXVI) · (LXVII) MDCCXLII

In Exercises 35 and 36, (a) use lattice multiplication to perform the multiplication. (Hint: Be sure not to list any number greater than or equal to the base within the box.) Write the answer in the base in which the exercise is given. (b) Multiply the numbers as explained in Section 4.4. If you do not obtain the results obtained in part (a), explain why.

35. 21_3 × 21_3 1211_3

36. 24_5 × 234_5 123331_5

Internet/Research Activities

37. In addition to Napier's rods, John Napier is credited with making other important contributions to mathematics. Write a report on John Napier and his contributions to mathematics.

38. Write a paper explaining why the duplation and mediation method works.

*See Instructor Answer Appendix

CHAPTER 4) *Summary*

Important Facts and Concepts	Examples/Discussion
Section 4.1	
Additive Numeration Systems	
Egyptian Hieroglyphics (see Table 4.1, page 171)	Discussion page 171, Examples 1–2, page 171
Roman Numerals (see Table 4.2, page 172)	Discussion pages 171–172, Examples 3–6, pages 172–173
Multiplicative Numeration Systems	
Traditional Chinese Numerals (see Table 4.3, page 173)	Discussion page 173, Examples 7–8, page 174
Ciphered Numeration Systems	
Ionic Greek Numerals (see Table 4.4, page 175)	Discussion pages 175–176, Examples 9–10, page 176
Section 4.2	
Place-Value Numeration Systems	
Babylonian Numerals (see Table 4.5, page 179)	Discussion page 179, Examples 1–5, pages 179–182
Mayan Numerals (see Table 4.6, page 182)	Discussion page 182, Examples 6–8, pages 182–183
Section 4.3	
Positional Values in Base b	
$\ldots b^4, b^3, b^2, b, 1$	Discussion pages 185–186, Examples 1–7, pages 187–190
Section 4.4	
Computation in Other Bases	
Addition and Subtraction	Examples 1–6, pages 193–195
Multiplication and Division	Examples 7–10, pages 196–198
Section 4.5	
Early Computation Methods	
Duplation and Mediation	Example 1, page 201
Lattice Multiplication	Example 2, page 201
Napier's Rods	Examples 3–4, pages 202–203

CHAPTER 4) *Review Exercises*

4.1, 4.2

In Exercises 1–4, write the Egyptian numeral as a Hindu–Arabic numeral.

1. � $_{321}$

2. $_{42,053}$

3. $_{200,421}$

4. $_{1,214,330}$

In Exercises 5–8, write the Hindu–Arabic numeral as an Egyptian numeral.

5. 4302 *

6. 10,200 *

7. 124,321 *

8. 1,003,042 *

*See Instructor Answer Appendix

In Exercises 9–12, write the Roman numeral as a Hindu–Arabic numeral.

9. XXIV 24   **10.** CXLII 142

11. MMCDXXXVII 2437   **12.** $\overline{\text{V}}$DCCLIX 5759

In Exercises 13–16, write the Hindu-Arabic numeral as a Roman numeral.

13. 29 XXIX   **14.** 547 DXLVII

15. 1964 MCMLXIV   **16.** 6491 $\overline{\text{VI}}$CDXCI

In Exercises 17–20, write the Chinese numeral as a Hindu–Arabic numeral.

17. 三十二 32   **18.** 四十五 45   **19.** 二百六十七 267   **20.** 三千四百二十九 3429

In Exercises 21–24, write the Hindu–Arabic numeral as a Chinese numeral.

21. 23 *   **22.** 54 *

23. 492 *   **24.** 2652 *

In Exercises 25–28, write the Ionic Greek numeral as a Hindu–Arabic numeral.

25. $\mu\beta$ 42   **26.** $\psi\pi\theta$ 789

27. $\chi\epsilon$ 605   **28.** $'\gamma\tau\lambda\delta$ 3334

In Exercises 29–32, write the Hindu–Arabic numeral as an Ionic Greek numeral.

29. 78 $o\eta$ **30.** 521 $\phi\kappa\alpha$

31. 867 $\omega\xi\zeta$ **32.** 4219 $'\delta\sigma\iota\theta$

In Exercises 33–36, write the Babylonian numeral as a Hindu–Arabic numeral.

33. 123   **34.** 189

35. 3673   **36.** 7388

In Exercises 37–40, write the Hindu–Arabic numeral as a Babylonian numeral.

37. 181 *   **38.** 3679 *

39. 7280 *   **40.** 36,184 *

In Exercises 41–44, write the Mayan numeral as a Hindu–Arabic numeral.

41. 63   **42.** 721

43. 1367   **44.** 15,923

In Exercises 45–48, write the Hindu–Arabic numeral as a Mayan numeral.

45. 69 *   **46.** 812 *

47. 1571 *   **48.** 17,913 *

4.3

In Exercises 49–54, convert the numeral to a Hindu–Arabic numeral.

49. 47_8 39   **50.** 101_2 5

51. 130_4 28   **52.** 3425_7 1244

53. $A94_{12}$ 1552   **54.** 20220_3 186

In Exercises 55–60, convert 463 to a numeral in the base indicated.

55. base 2 111001111_2 **56.** base 3 122011_3

57. base 4 13033_4 **58.** base 8 717_8

59. base 12 327_{12} **60.** base 16 $1CF_{16}$

4.4

In Exercises 61–66, add in the base indicated.

61. $\begin{array}{r} 52_7 \\ + 55_7 \end{array}$ 140_7 **62.** $\begin{array}{r} 10110_2 \\ + 11001_2 \end{array}$ 101111_2

63. $\begin{array}{r} 9B_{12} \\ + 87_{12} \end{array}$ 166_{12} **64.** $\begin{array}{r} 2B9_{16} \\ + 456_{16} \end{array}$ $70F_{16}$

65. $\begin{array}{r} 3024_5 \\ + 4023_5 \end{array}$ 12102_5 **66.** $\begin{array}{r} 3407_8 \\ + 7014_8 \end{array}$ 12423_8

In Exercises 67–72, subtract in the base indicated.

67. $\begin{array}{r} 4032_7 \\ - 321_7 \end{array}$ 3411_7 **68.** $\begin{array}{r} 1001_2 \\ - 101_2 \end{array}$ 100_2

69. $\begin{array}{r} A7B_{12} \\ - 95_{12} \end{array}$ $9A6_{12}$ **70.** $\begin{array}{r} 4321_5 \\ - 442_5 \end{array}$ 3324_5

71. $\begin{array}{r} 1713_8 \\ -1243_8 \end{array}$ 450_8 **72.** $\begin{array}{r} F64_{16} \\ -2A3_{16} \end{array}$ $CC1_{16}$

*See Instructor Answer Appendix

In Exercises 73–78, multiply in the base indicated.

73. 1011_2 110111_2
$\times\ 101_2$

74. 221_3 21102_3
$\times\ 22_3$

75. 34_5 1314_5
$\times\ 21_5$

76. 476_8 13632_8
$\times\ 23_8$

77. 126_{12} 5656_{12}
$\times\ 47_{12}$

78. $1A3_{16}$ $1D76_{16}$
$\times\ 12_{16}$

In Exercises 79–84, divide in the base indicated.

79. $2_3\overline{)120_3}$ $21_3\,R1_3$

80. $2_4\overline{)320_4}$ 130_4

81. $3_5\overline{)130_5}$ $23_5\,R1_5$

82. $4_6\overline{)3020_6}$ 433_6

83. $3_6\overline{)2034_6}$ $411_6\,R1_6$

84. $6_8\overline{)5072_8}$ $664_8\,R2_8$

4.5

85. Multiply 142×24, using the duplation and mediation method. 3408

86. Multiply 142×24, using lattice multiplication. 3408

87. Multiply 142×24, using Napier's rods. 3408

CHAPTER 4 Test

In Exercises 1–6, convert the numeral to a Hindu–Arabic numeral.

1. MMCDLXXXIV 2484

2. ⟨⟨⟨ᛏ ⟨ᛏᛏᛏᛏᛏ 1275

3. 八千零九十 8090

4. 969

5. ⟨∢𝕄ʃʃⲯ⌒⌒⌒∩II 122,142

6. ʹβψμϵ 2745

In Exercises 7–11, convert the base 10 numeral to a numeral in the numeration system indicated.

7. 2124 to Egyptian *

8. 2476 to Ionic Greek *

9. 1434 to Mayan *

10. 1596 to Babylonian *

11. 3706 to Roman MMMDCCVI

In Exercises 12–13, convert the given numeral to a numeral in base 10.

12. 403_5 103

13. $3A7_{12}$ 559

In Exercises 14–15, convert the following numerals to a numeral in the base indicated.

14. 36 to base 2 100100_2

15. 2938 to base 16 $B7A_{16}$

In Exercises 16–18, perform the indicated operations.

16. 1101_2
$+\ 1011_2$ 11000_2

17. 45_6
$\times\ 23_6$ 2003_6

18. $3_5\overline{)1210_5}$ 220_5

19. Multiply 35×28, using duplation and mediation. 980

20. Multiply 43×196, using lattice multiplication. 8428

* See Instructor Answer Appendix

GROUP PROJECTS

U.S. Postal Service Bar Codes

Wherever we look nowadays, we see bar codes. We find them on items we buy at grocery stores and department stores and on many pieces of mail we receive. There are various types of bar codes, but each can be considered a type of numeration system. Although bar codes may vary in design, most are made up of a series of long and short bars. (New bar codes now being developed use a variety of shapes.) In this group project, we explain how postal bar codes are used.

The U.S. Postal Service introduced a bar coding system for zip codes in 1976. The system became known as Postnet (*post*al *n*umeric *e*ncoding *t*echnique), and it has been refined over the years. Our basic zip code consists of five digits. The post office would like us to use the basic zip code followed

by a hyphen and four additional digits. The post office refers to this nine-digit zip code as "zip + 4."

The Postnet bar code uses a series of long and short bars. A bar code may contain either 52 or 62 bars. The code designates the location to which the letter is being sent. The following bar code, with 52 bars, is for an address in Pittsburgh, Pennsylvania.

15250-7406 (Pittsburgh, PA)

In bar codes, each short bar represents 0 and each long bar represents 1. Each code starts and ends with a long bar that is *not* used in determining the zip + 4. If the code contains 52 bars, the code represents the zip + 4 and an extra digit referred to as a check digit. If the code contains 62 bars, it contains the zip + 4, the last two digits of the address number, and a check digit. If the code contains 52 bars, the sum of the zip + 4 and the check digit must equal a number that is divisible by 10. If the code contains 62 bars, the sum of the zip + 4, the last two digits of the address number, and the check digit must equal a number that is divisible by 10. The check digit is added to make each sum divisible by 10.

In a postal bar code, each of the digits 0 through 9 is represented by a series of five digits containing zeros and ones:

11000 (0) 00011 (1) 00101 (2) 00110 (3) 01001 (4)

01010 (5) 01100 (6) 10001 (7) 10010 (8) 10100 (9)

Consider the postal code from Pittsburgh given earlier. If you disregard the bar on the left, the next five bars are ▮▮||. Since each small bar represents a 0 and each large bar represents a 1, these five bars can be represented as 00011. From the chart, we see that this represents the number 1. The first five bars (after the bar on the far left has been excluded) tell the region of the country in which the address is located on the map shown below. Notice that Pennsylvania is located, along with New York and Delaware, in the region marked 1 on the map.

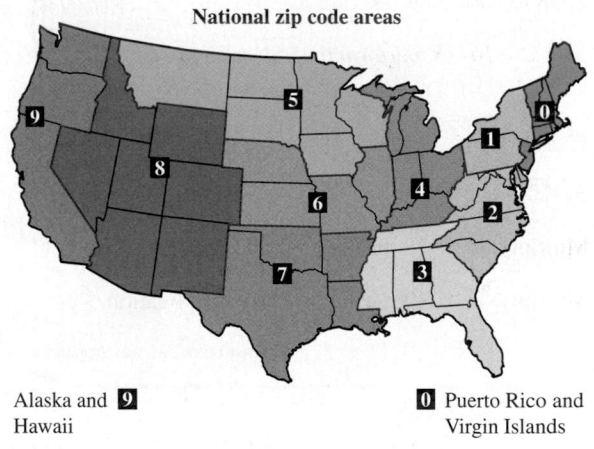

National zip code areas

Alaska and **9**   **0** Puerto Rico and
Hawaii   Virgin Islands

The second five lines in the bar code, ▮|▮|▮, represent 01010 and have a value of 5. The other digits in the zip + 4 are determined in a similar manner. This code has 52 bars. The 45 bars, after the first bar, give the zip + 4. If you add the digits in the zip + 4, you get $1 + 5 + 2 + 5 + 0 + 7 + 4 + 0 + 6 = 30$. Since 30 is divisible by 10, the five bars to the left of the bar on the very right should be 0. Note that ▮▮||| is represented as 11000 and has a value of 0. If, for example, the sum of the nine digits in the zip + 4 were 36, then the last five digits would need to represent the number 4, to make the sum of the digits divisible by 10. The five bars to the left of the last bar on the right are always used as a check.

Now let's work some problems.

a) For the Postnet code

▮|▮▮▮||▮▮|▮|▮||▮▮||▮▮▮|▮|▮|▮|▮|▮||▮|▮|▮▮▮▮||▮

determine the zip + 4 and the check digit. Then check by adding the zip + 4 and the check digit. Is the sum divisible by 10?

b) For each of the following Postnet codes, determine the zip + 4, the last two numbers of the address number (if applicable), and the check digit.

i.) |▮|▮||▮▮||▮|▮|▮|▮|▮▮||▮|▮||▮|▮▮||▮||▮||▮|▮|

ii.) |▮▮||▮|▮|▮|▮||▮▮|▮||▮▮||▮|▮|▮|▮▮||▮|▮|▮||▮▮||▮|▮||▮▮|▮|

c) Construct the Postnet code of long and short bars for each of the numbers. The numbers represent the zip + 4 and the last two digits of the address number. Do not forget the check digit.

i) 32226-8600-34

ii) 20794-1063-50

d) Construct the 52-bar Postnet code for your college's zip + 4. Don't forget to include the check digit.

5

Number Theory and the Real Number System

Why This is Important

Every time we use a computer, make a telephone call, or watch television we use a device that relies on numbers to operate. In addition to playing many roles in our everyday lives, numbers are also used to describe the natural world, communicate information, and model problems facing scientists and researchers. In this chapter, we will see how number theory, the study of numbers and their properties, makes all these roles possible.

Number theory has many applications that help scientists and researchers solve problems in many areas including communications, biology medicine, computers, and other modern technical devices.

◄ Number theory helps scientists and researchers model problems.

Number Theory

▲ *There are many ways to display 48 pieces of chocolate.*

Suppose you decide to start your own chocolate candy company. You would like to sell boxes containing 48 pieces of candy. You must decide how to arrange the pieces within the box. You could have six rows with eight pieces in each row, or four rows with twelve pieces in each row, or three layers with four rows each with four pieces in each row. Each of these possibilities involves writing the number 48 as the product of two or more smaller numbers. In this section, we will discuss many other similar problems related to the writing of numbers as the product of smaller numbers.

Why *This is Important* Writing numbers as the product of smaller numbers has many applications to the branch of mathematics we know as number theory.

This chapter introduces *number theory*, the study of numbers and their properties. The numbers we use to count are called the *counting numbers* or *natural numbers*. Because we begin counting with the number 1, the set of natural numbers begins with 1. The set of natural numbers is frequently denoted by N:

$$N = \{1, 2, 3, 4, 5, \dots\}$$

Any natural number can be expressed as a product of two or more natural numbers. For example, $8 = 2 \times 4$, $16 = 4 \times 4$, and $19 = 1 \times 19$. The natural numbers that are multiplied together are called *factors* of the product. For example,

$$2 \times 4 = 8$$

Factors

A natural number may have many factors. For example, what pairs of numbers have a product of 18?

$$1 \cdot 18 = 18$$
$$2 \cdot 9 = 18$$
$$3 \cdot 6 = 18$$

The numbers 1, 2, 3, 6, 9, and 18 are all factors of 18. Each of these numbers divides 18 without a remainder.

If a and b are natural numbers, we say that a is a *divisor* of b or a *divides b*, symbolized $a \mid b$ if the quotient of b divided by a has a remainder of 0. If a divides b, then b is *divisible* by a. For example, 4 divides 12, symbolized $4 \mid 12$, since the quotient of 12 divided by 4 has a remainder of 0. Note that 12 is divisible by 4. The notation $7 \nmid 12$ means that 7 does not divide 12. Note that every factor of a natural number is also a divisor of the natural number. *Caution:* Do not confuse the symbols $a \mid b$ and a / b; $a \mid b$ means "a divides b" and a / b means "a divided by b" ($a \div b$). The symbols a / b and $a \div b$ indicate that the operation of division is to be performed, and b may or may not be a divisor of a.

Prime and Composite Numbers

Every natural number greater than 1 can be classified as either a prime number or a composite number.

Profile In Mathematics

Eratosthenes of Cyrene

Eratosthenes of Cyrene (275–195 B.C.) was born in northern Africa near the present-day city of Shahhat, Libya. Eratosthenes is best known for being the first to estimate accurately the diameter of Earth. He is also credited for developing a method of finding prime numbers known as the **sieve of Eratosthenes**. Although he is most known for his work in mathematics, Eratosthenes also was influential in the fields of history, geography, and astronomy. In addition, Eratosthenes served for many years as the director of the famous library in Alexandria, Egypt. Although Eratosthenes was a highly regarded scholar throughout the ancient world, only fragments of his writing remain today. Eratosthenes was near 80 years old when, after going blind, he died from voluntary starvation.

Definition: Prime Number

A **prime number** is a natural number greater than 1 that has exactly two factors (or divisors), itself and 1.

The number 5 is a prime number because it is divisible only by the factors 1 and 5. The first eight prime numbers are 2, 3, 5, 7, 11, 13, 17, and 19. The number 2 is the only even prime number. All other even numbers have at least three divisors: 1, 2, and the number itself.

Definition: Composite Number

A **composite number** is a natural number that is divisible by a number other than itself and 1.

Any natural number greater than 1 that is not prime is composite. The first eight composite numbers are 4, 6, 8, 9, 10, 12, 14, and 15.

The number 1 is neither prime nor composite; it is called a *unit*. The number 38 has at least three divisors, 1, 2, and 38, and hence is a composite number. In contrast, the number 23 is a prime number since its only divisors are 1 and 23.

More than 2000 years ago, the ancient Greeks developed a technique for determining which numbers are prime numbers and which are not. This technique is known as the *sieve of Eratosthenes*, for the Greek mathematician Eratosthenes of Cyrene, who first used it.

To find the prime numbers less than or equal to any natural number, say, 50, using this method, list the first 50 counting numbers (Fig. 5.1). Cross out 1 since it is not a prime number. Circle 2, the first prime number. Then cross out all the multiples of 2: 4, 6, 8, ..., 50. Circle the next prime number, 3. Cross out all multiples of 3 that are not already crossed out. Continue this process of crossing out multiples of prime numbers until you reach the prime number p, such that $p \cdot p$, or p^2, is greater than the last number listed, in this case 50. Therefore, we next circle 5 and cross out its multiples. Then circle 7 and cross out its multiples. The next prime number is 11, and $11 \cdot 11$, or 121, is greater than 50, so you are done. At this point, circle all the remaining numbers to obtain the prime numbers less than or equal to 50. The prime numbers less than or equal to 50 are 2, 3, 5, 7, 11, 13, 17, 19, 23, 29, 31, 37, 41, 43, and 47.

$$
\begin{array}{cccccccccc}
\cancel{1} & ② & ③ & \cancel{4} & ⑤ & \cancel{6} & ⑦ & \cancel{8} & \cancel{9} & \cancel{10} \\
⑪ & \cancel{12} & ⑬ & \cancel{14} & \cancel{15} & \cancel{16} & ⑰ & \cancel{18} & ⑲ & \cancel{20} \\
\cancel{21} & \cancel{22} & ㉓ & \cancel{24} & \cancel{25} & \cancel{26} & \cancel{27} & \cancel{28} & ㉙ & \cancel{30} \\
㉛ & \cancel{32} & \cancel{33} & \cancel{34} & \cancel{35} & \cancel{36} & ㊲ & \cancel{38} & \cancel{39} & \cancel{40} \\
㊶ & \cancel{42} & ㊸ & \cancel{44} & \cancel{45} & \cancel{46} & ㊿ & \cancel{48} & \cancel{49} & \cancel{50}
\end{array}
$$

Figure 5.1

Now we turn our attention to composite numbers and their factors. The rules of divisibility given in the chart on page 212 are helpful in finding divisors (or factors) of composite numbers.

The test for divisibility by 6 is a particular case of the general statement that the product of two prime divisors of a number is a divisor of the number. Thus, for example, if both 3 and 7 divide a number, then 21 will also divide the number.

Rules of Divisibility

Divisible by	Test	Example
2	The number is even.	924 is divisible by 2 since 924 is even.
3	The sum of the digits of the number is divisible by 3.	924 is divisible by 3 since the sum of the digits, 9 + 2 + 4 = 15, and 15 is divisible by 3.
4	The number formed by the last two digits of the number is divisible by 4.	924 is divisible by 4 since the number formed by the last two digits, 24, is divisible by 4.
5	The number ends in 0 or 5.	265 is divisible by 5 since the number ends in 5.
6	The number is divisible by both 2 and 3.	924 is divisible by 6 since it is divisible by both 2 and 3.
8	The number formed by the last three digits of the number is divisible by 8.	5824 is divisible by 8 since the number formed by the last three digits, 824, is divisible by 8.
9	The sum of the digits of the number is divisible by 9.	837 is divisible by 9 since the sum of the digits, 18, is divisible by 9.
10	The number ends in 0.	290 is divisible by 10 since the number ends in 0.

Note that the chart does not list rules for the divisibility for the number 7. The rule for 7 is given in Exercise 92 on page 220. You may find after using the rule that the easiest way to check divisibility by 7 is simply to perform the division.

Example 1 *Using the Divisibility Rules*

Determine whether 384,540 is divisible by

a) 2   b) 3   c) 4   d) 5   e) 6   f) 8   g) 9   h) 10

Solution

a) 2: since 384,540 is even, it is divisible by 2.

b) 3: the sum of the digits of 384,540 is 3 + 8 + 4 + 5 + 4 + 0 = 24. Since 24 is divisible by 3, the number 384,540 is divisible by 3.

c) 4: the number formed by the last two digits is 40. Since 40 is divisible by 4, the number 384,540 is divisible by 4.

d) 5: since 384,540 has 0 as the last digit, the number 384,540 is divisible by 5.

e) 6: since 384,540 is divisible by both 2 and 3, the number 384,540 is divisible by 6.

f) 8: the number formed by the last three digits is 540. Since 540 is not divisible by 8, the number 384,540 is not divisible by 8.

g) 9: the sum of the digits of 384,540 is 24. Since 24 is not divisible by 9, the number 384,540 is not divisible by 9.

h) 10: since 384,540 has 0 as the last digit, the number 384,540 is divisible by 10. ∎

Every composite number can be expressed as a product of prime numbers. The process of breaking a given composite number down into a product of prime numbers is called *prime factorization*. The prime factorization of 18 is 3 × 3 × 2. No other natural number listed as a product of primes will have the same prime factorization as 18. The *fundamental theorem of arithmetic* states this concept formally. (A *theorem* is a statement or proposition that can be proven true.)

The Fundamental Theorem of Arithmetic
Every composite number can be expressed as a *unique* product of prime numbers.

In writing the prime factorization of a number, the order of the factors is immaterial. For example, we may write the prime factors of 18 as $3 \times 3 \times 2$ or $2 \times 3 \times 3$ or $3 \times 2 \times 3$.

A number of techniques can be used to find the prime factorization of a number. Two methods are illustrated.

Method 1: Branching

To find the prime factorization of a number, select any two numbers whose product is the number to be factored. If the factors are not prime numbers, continue factoring each composite number until all factors are prime.

Example 2 *Prime Factorization by Branching*

Write 1500 as a product of primes.

Solution Select any two numbers whose product is 1500. Among the many choices, two possibilities are $15 \cdot 100$ and $30 \cdot 50$. First consider $15 \cdot 00$. Since neither 15 nor 100 is a prime number, find any two numbers whose product is 15 and any two numbers whose product is 100. Continue branching as shown in Fig. 5.2 until the numbers in the last row are all prime numbers. To determine the answer, write the product of all the prime factors. The branching diagram is sometimes called a *factor tree*.

Figure 5.2

Figure 5.3

We see that the numbers in the last row of factors in Fig. 5.2 are all prime numbers. Thus, the prime factorization of 1500 is $3 \cdot 5 \cdot 2 \cdot 5 \cdot 2 \cdot 5 = 2 \cdot 2 \cdot 3 \cdot 5 \cdot 5 \cdot 5 = 2^2 \cdot 3 \cdot 5^3$. Note from Fig. 5.3 that choosing 30 and 50 as the first pair of factors also leads to the same prime factorization of $2^2 \cdot 3 \cdot 5^3$. ∎

Method 2: Division

To obtain the prime factorization of a number by this method, divide the given number by the smallest prime number by which it is divisible. Place the quotient under the given number. Then divide the quotient by the smallest prime number by which it is divisible and again record the quotient. Repeat this process until the quotient is a prime number. The prime factorization is the product of all the prime divisors and the prime (or last) quotient. This procedure is illustrated in Example 3.

Profile In Mathematics

Srinivasa Ramanujan

One of the most interesting mathematicians of modern times is Srinivasa Ramanujan (1887–1920). Born to an impoverished middle-class family in India, he virtually taught himself higher mathematics. He went to England to study with the number theorist G. H. Hardy. Hardy tells the story of a taxicab ride he took to visit Ramanujan. The cab had the license plate number 1729, and he challenged the young Indian to find anything interesting in that. Without hesitating, Ramanujan pointed out that it was the smallest positive integer that could be represented in two different ways as the sum of two cubes: $1^3 + 12^3$ and $9^3 + 10^3$.

Example 3 Prime Factorization by Division

Write 1500 as a product of prime numbers.

Solution   Because 1500 is an even number, the smallest prime number that divides it is 2. Divide 1500 by 2. Place the quotient, 750, below the 1500. Continue to divide each quotient by the smallest prime number that divides it.

2	1500
2	750
3	375
5	125
5	25
	5

The final quotient, 5, is a prime number, so we stop. The prime factorization is determined by multiplying all divisors on the left side and the final prime number quotient as shown by the shaded arrow. Thus, the prime factorization of 1500 is

$$2 \cdot 2 \cdot 3 \cdot 5 \cdot 5 \cdot 5 = 2^2 \cdot 3 \cdot 5^3.$$

Note that despite the different methods used in Examples 2 and 3, the answer is the same.

Greatest Common Divisor

The discussion in Section 5.3 of how to reduce fractions makes use of the greatest common divisor (GCD). We will now discuss how to determine the GCD of a set of numbers. One technique of finding the GCD is to use prime factorization.

Definition: Greatest Common Divisor

The **greatest common divisor (GCD)** of a set of natural numbers is the largest natural number that divides (without remainder) every number in that set.

What is the GCD of 12 and 18? One way to determine the GCD is to list the divisors (or factors) of 12 and 18:

Divisors of 12   {**1, 2, 3**, 4, **6**, 12}

Divisors of 18   {**1, 2, 3, 6**, 9, 18}

The common divisors are 1, 2, 3, and 6. Therefore, the greatest common divisor is 6.

If the numbers are large, this method of finding the GCD is not practical. The GCD can be found more efficiently by using prime factorization.

PROCEDURE   TO DETERMINE THE GREATEST COMMON DIVISOR OF TWO OR MORE NUMBERS

1. Determine the prime factorization of each number.
2. List each prime factor with the *smallest* exponent that appears in each of the prime factorizations.
3. Determine the product of the factors found in Step 2.

Example 4 illustrates this procedure.

Example 4 *Using Prime Factorization to Determine the GCD*

Determine the GCD of 54 and 90.

Solution The branching method of finding the prime factors of 54 and 90 is illustrated in Fig. 5.4.

a) The prime factorization of 54 is $2 \cdot 3^3$, and the prime factorization of 90 is $2 \cdot 3^2 \cdot 5$.

b) The prime factors with the smallest exponents that appear in each of the factorizations of 54 and 90 are 2 and 3^2. Note that because 5 is not in the prime factorization of 54, it is not included when determining the GCD.

c) The product of the factors found in Step 2 is $2 \cdot 3^2 = 2 \cdot 9 = 18$. The GCD of 54 and 90 is 18. Eighteen is the largest natural number that divides both 54 and 90. ■

Figure 5.4

Example 5 *Determining the GCD*

Determine the GCD of 315 and 450.

Solution

a) The prime factorization of 315 is $3^2 \cdot 5 \cdot 7$, and the prime factorization of 450 is $2 \cdot 3^2 \cdot 5^2$. You should verify these answers using either the branching method or the division method.

b) The prime factors with the smallest exponents that appear in each of the factorizations of 315 and 450 are 3^2 and 5.

c) The product of the factors found in Step 2 is $3^2 \cdot 5 = 9 \cdot 5 = 45$. The greatest common divisor of 315 and 450 is 45. It is the largest natural number that will evenly divide both 315 and 450. ■

Least Common Multiple

To perform addition and subtraction of fractions (Section 5.3), we use the least common multiple (LCM). We will now discuss how to determine the LCM of a set of numbers.

> **Definition: Least Common Multiple**
> The **least common multiple (LCM)** of a set of natural numbers is the smallest natural number that is divisible (without remainder) by each element of the set.

What is the least common multiple of 12 and 18? One way to determine the LCM is to list the multiples of each number:

Multiples of 12 $\{12, 24, \mathbf{36}, 48, 60, \mathbf{72}, 84, 96, \mathbf{108}, 120, 132, \mathbf{144}, \dots \}$

Multiples of 18 $\{18, \mathbf{36}, 54, \mathbf{72}, 90, \mathbf{108}, 126, \mathbf{144}, 162, \dots \}$

Some common multiples of 12 and 18 are 36, 72, 108, and 144. The least common multiple, 36, is the smallest number that is divisible by both 12 and 18. Usually, the most efficient method of finding the LCM is to use prime factorization.

> **PROCEDURE   TO DETERMINE THE LEAST COMMON MULTIPLE OF TWO OR MORE NUMBERS**
>
> 1. Determine the prime factorization of each number.
> 2. List each prime factor with the *greatest* exponent that appears in any of the prime factorizations.
> 3. Determine the product of the factors found in Step 2.

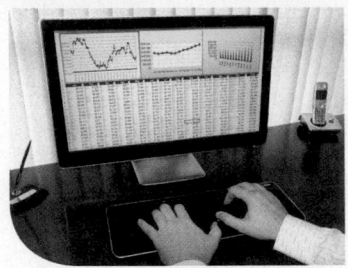
Example 6 illustrates this procedure.

Example 6 *Using Prime Factorization to Determine the LCM*

Determine the LCM of 54 and 90.

Solution

a) Determine the prime factors of each number. In Example 4, we determined that

$$54 = 2 \cdot 3^3 \quad \text{and} \quad 90 = 2 \cdot 3^2 \cdot 5$$

b) List each prime factor with the greatest exponent that appears in either of the prime factorizations: $2, 3^3, 5$.

c) Determine the product of the factors found in Step 2:

$$2 \cdot 3^3 \cdot 5 = 2 \cdot 27 \cdot 5 = 270$$

Thus, 270 is the LCM of 54 and 90. It is the smallest natural number that is divisible by both 54 and 90. ∎

Example 7 *Determining the LCM*

Determine the LCM of 315 and 450.

Solution

a) Determine the prime factorization of each number. In Example 5, we determined that

$$315 = 3^2 \cdot 5 \cdot 7 \quad \text{and} \quad 450 = 2 \cdot 3^2 \cdot 5^2$$

b) List each prime factor with the greatest exponent that appears in either of the prime factorizations: $2, 3^2, 5^2, 7$.

c) Determine the product of the factors from Step (b)

$$2 \cdot 3^2 \cdot 5^2 \cdot 7 = 2 \cdot 9 \cdot 25 \cdot 7 = 3150$$

Thus, 3150 is the least common multiple of 315 and 450. It is the smallest natural number that is evenly divisible by both 315 and 450. ∎

The Search For Larger Prime Numbers

More than 2000 years ago, the Greek mathematician Euclid proved that there is no largest prime number. Mathematicians, however, continue to strive to find larger and larger prime numbers.

Marin Mersenne (1588–1648), a seventeenth-century monk, found that numbers of the form $2^n - 1$ are often prime numbers when n is a prime number. For example,

$$2^2 - 1 = 4 - 1 = 3 \qquad 2^3 - 1 = 8 - 1 = 7$$
$$2^5 - 1 = 32 - 1 = 31 \qquad 2^7 - 1 = 128 - 1 = 127$$

Numbers of the form $2^n - 1$ that are prime are referred to as *Mersenne primes*. The first 10 Mersenne primes occur when $n = 2, 3, 5, 7, 13, 17, 19, 31, 61, 89$.

GIMPS

The Great Internet Mersenne Prime Search (GIMPS) was started by George Woltman in 1996 to coordinate the computing efforts of thousands of people interested in finding new Mersenne prime numbers. Anyone with a computer and Internet access can join the project. GIMPS uses idle time on the participants' computers to search for prime numbers. As of this writing, the largest prime number discovered so far was found by Edson Smith, a computer resource manager at UCLA, in conjunction with GIMPS on August 23, 2008. The number, $2^{43,112,609} - 1$, was the forty-fifth known Mersenne prime number and the eleventh found by GIMPS participants. Since then, two smaller Mersenne prime numbers have also been found using GIMPS.

Why *This is Important* Finding larger and larger prime numbers is a major part of the history of mathematics that continues to this day.

The first time the expression $2^n - 1$ does not generate a prime number, for prime number n, is when n is 11. The number $2^{11} - 1$ is a composite number (see Exercise 90 on page 220).

Scientists frequently use Mersenne primes in their search for larger and larger primes. The largest prime number found to date was discovered on August 23, 2008, by Edson Smith, a computer resource manager at UCLA. Smith and his team worked in conjunction with the Great Internet Mersenne Prime Search (GIMPS; see *Mathematics Today*, at left) to use the university's computers during down time to conduct the search. The number is the Mersenne prime $2^{43,112,609} - 1$. This record prime number is the forty-fifth known Mersenne prime (two more, smaller, Mersenne primes have been found since). When written out, it is 12,978,189 digits long. When written using a standard 12-point font, the number is more than 17 miles long!

More About Prime Numbers

Another mathematician who studied prime numbers was Pierre de Fermat (1601–1665). A lawyer by profession, Fermat became interested in mathematics as a hobby. He became one of the finest mathematicians of the seventeenth century. Fermat conjectured that each number of the form $2^{2^n} + 1$, now referred to as a *Fermat number*, was prime for each natural number n. Recall that a *conjecture* is a supposition that has not been proved or disproved. In 1732, Leonhard Euler proved that for $n = 5$, $2^{32} + 1$ was a composite number, thus disproving Fermat's conjecture.

Since Euler's time, mathematicians have been able to evaluate only the sixth, seventh, eighth, ninth, tenth, and eleventh Fermat numbers to determine whether they are prime or composite. Each of these numbers has been shown to be composite. The eleventh Fermat number was factored by Richard Brent and François Morain in 1988. The sheer magnitude of the numbers involved makes it difficult to test these numbers, even with supercomputers.

In 1742, Christian Goldbach conjectured in a letter to Euler that every even number greater than or equal to 4 can be represented as the sum of two (not necessarily distinct) prime numbers (for example, $4 = 2 + 2$, $6 = 3 + 3$, $8 = 3 + 5$, $10 = 5 + 5$, $12 = 5 + 7$). This conjecture became known as *Goldbach's conjecture*, and it remains unproven to this day. The *twin prime conjecture* is another famous long-standing conjecture. *Twin primes* are primes of the form p and $p + 2$ (for example, 3 and 5, 5 and 7, 11 and 13). This conjecture states that there are an infinite number of pairs of twin primes. At the time of this writing, the largest known twin primes are of the form $65,516,468,355 \cdot 2^{333,333} \pm 1$, which was found by a collaborative effort of two research groups, *Twin Prime Search* and *PrimeGrid*, on August 6, 2009.

SECTION 5.1

Exercises

Warm Up Exercises

In Exercises 1–12, fill in the blanks with an appropriate word, phrase, or symbol(s).

1. The study of numbers and their properties is known as number _____. Theory

2. If a is a factor of b, then $b \div a$ is a(n) _____. Integer

3. If a is divisible by b, then $a \div b$ has a remainder of _____. Zero

4. A natural number greater than 1 that has exactly two factors, itself and 1, is known as a(n) _____ number. Prime

5. A natural number that is divisible by a number other than itself and 1 is known as a(n) _____ number. Composite

6. The largest natural number that divides (without remainder) each number in a set of numbers is known as the greatest common _____ of the set of numbers. Divisor

7. The smallest natural number that is divisible (without remainder) by each number in a set of numbers is known as the least common _____ of the set of numbers. Multiple

8. Prime numbers of the form $2^n - 1$, where n is a prime number, are known as _____ prime numbers. Mersenne

9. A supposition or hypothesis that has not been proved or disproved is known as a(n) _____. Conjecture

10. Goldbach's conjecture states that every even number greater than or equal to 4 can be written as the sum of two (not necessarily) distinct _____ numbers. Prime

11. Numbers of the form $2^{2^n} + 1$, where n is a natural number, are known as _____ numbers. Fermat

12. Prime numbers of the form p and $p + 2$, where p is a prime number, are known as _____ prime numbers. Twin

Practice The Skills

13. Use the sieve of Eratosthenes to find the prime numbers up to 100.*

14. Use the sieve of Eratosthenes to find the prime numbers up to 150.*

In Exercises 15–26, determine whether the statement is true or false. Modify each false statement to make it a true statement.

15. 5 is a factor of 15. True

16. $24 \mid 3$ False; $3 \mid 24$.

17. 7 is a multiple of 28. False; 28 is a multiple of 7.

18. 6 is a divisor of 18. True

19. 8 is divisible by 56. False; 56 is divisible by 8.

20. 15 is a factor of 45. True

21. If a number is not divisible by 5, then it is not divisible by 10. True

22. If a number is not divisible by 10, then it is not divisible by 5. False; a number may be divisible by 5 if it is not divisible by 10.

23. If a number is divisible by 3, then every digit of the number is divisible by 3. False; if a number is divisible by 3, then the sum of the digits of the number is divisible by 3.

24. If every digit of a number is divisible by 3, then the number itself is divisible by 3. True

25. If a number is divisible by 2 and 3, then the number is divisible by 6. True

26. If a number is divisible by 3 and 5, then the number is divisible by 15. True

In Exercises 27–32, determine whether the number is divisible by each of the following numbers: 2, 3, 4, 5, 6, 8, 9, and 10.

27. 5390 5390 is divisible by 2, 5, and 10.

28. 30,870 30,870 is divisible by 2, 3, 5, 6, 9, and 10.

29. 72,216 72,216 is divisible by 2, 3, 4, 6, 8, and 9.

30. 170,820 170,820 is divisible by 2, 3, 4, 5, 6, 9, and 10.

31. 1,882,320 1,882,320 is divisible by 2, 3, 4, 5, 6, 8, and 10.

32. 3,941,221 3,941,221 is divisible by none of the numbers.

33. Determine a number that is divisible by 2, 3, 4, 5, and 6.
60 (other answers are possible)

34. Determine a number that is divisible by 3, 4, 5, 9, and 10.
180 (other answers are possible)

In Exercises 35–46, find the prime factorization of the number.

35. 36 $36 = 2^2 \cdot 3^2$

36. 52 $52 = 2^2 \cdot 13$

37. 140 $140 = 2^2 \cdot 5 \cdot 7$

38. 315 $315 = 3^2 \cdot 5 \cdot 7$

39. 332 $332 = 2^2 \cdot 83$

40. 399 $399 = 3 \cdot 7 \cdot 19$

41. 513 $513 = 3^3 \cdot 19$

42. 663 $663 = 3 \cdot 13 \cdot 17$

43. 1336 $1336 = 2^3 \cdot 167$

44. 1313 $1313 = 13 \cdot 101$

45. 2001 $2001 = 3 \cdot 23 \cdot 29$

46. 3190 $3190 = 2 \cdot 5 \cdot 11 \cdot 29$

In Exercises 47–56, find (a) the greatest common divisor (GCD) and (b) the least common multiple (LCM).

47. 6 and 14 a) 2 b) 42

48. 18 and 21 a) 3 b) 126

49. 15 and 25 a) 5 b) 75

50. 32 and 224 a) 32 b) 224

51. 40 and 900 a) 20 b) 1800

52. 120 and 240 a) 120 b) 240

53. 96 and 212 a) 4 b) 5088

54. 240 and 285 a) 15 b) 4560

55. 24, 48, and 128 a) 8 b) 384

56. 18, 78, and 198 a) 6 b) 2574

Problem Solving

57. *Relatively Prime* Two numbers with a greatest common divisor of 1 are said to be *relatively prime*. For example, the numbers 9 and 14 are relatively prime, since their GCD is 1. Determine whether the following pairs of numbers are relatively prime. Write yes or no as your answer.

a) 8, 9 Yes **b)** 21, 30 No **c)** 39, 52 No **d)** 177, 178 Yes

58. The primes 2 and 3 are consecutive natural numbers. Is there another pair of consecutive natural numbers both of which are prime? Explain.*

*See Instructor Answer Appendix

59. Find the next two sets of twin primes that follow the set 11, 13. 17, 19, and 29, 31

60. Find the first five Mersenne prime numbers. 3, 7, 31, 127, and 8191 (note: 2047 is not prime since 23 · 89 = 2047)

61. Find the first three Fermat numbers and determine whether they are prime or composite. 5, 17, and 257 are all prime.

62. Show that Goldbach's conjecture is true for the even numbers 4 through 20.*

63. *Lawn Maintenance* Brenda Sax cuts her grass every six days and trims her shrubs every 16 days. If Brenda cut her grass and trimmed her shrubs on June 1, how many days will it be before she cuts her grass and trims her shrubs on the same day again? 48 days

64. *U.S. Senate Committees* The U.S. Senate consists of 100 members. Senate committees are to be formed so that each of the committees contains the same number of senators and each senator is a member of exactly one committee. The committees are to have more than 2 members but fewer than 50 members. There are various ways that these committees can be formed.

   a) What size committees are possible? 4, 5, 10, 20, 25

   b) How many committees are there for each size?
      25, 20, 10, 5, and 4, respectively

65. *Setting Up Chairs* Jerrett Dumouchel is setting up chairs for his school band concert. He needs to put 120 chairs on the gymnasium floor in rows of equal size, and there must be at least 2 chairs in each row. List the number of rows and the number of chairs in each row that are possible.*

66. *Barbie and Ken* Mary Lois King collects Barbie dolls and Ken dolls. She has 390 Barbie dolls and 468 Ken dolls. Mary Lois wishes to display the dolls in groups so that the same number of dolls are in each group and that each doll belongs to one group. If each group is to consist only of Barbie dolls or only of Ken dolls, what is the largest number of dolls Mary Lois can have in each group? 78 dolls

67. *Toy Car Collection* Martha Goshaw collects Matchbox® and HotWheels® toy cars. She has 70 red cars and 175 blue cars. She wants to line up her cars in groups so that each group has the same number of cars and each group contains only red cars or only blue cars. What is the largest number of cars she can have in a group? 35 cars

68. *Stacking Trading Cards* Desmond Freeman collects trading cards. He has 432 baseball cards and 360 football cards. He wants to make stacks of cards on a table so that each stack contains the same number of cards and each card belongs to one stack. If the baseball and football cards must not be mixed in the stacks, what is the largest number of cards that he can have in a stack? 72 cards

69. *Tree Rows* Elizabeth Dwyer is the manager at Queen Palm Nursery and is in charge of displaying potted trees in rows. Elizabeth has 150 citrus trees and 180 palm trees. She wants to make rows of trees so that each row has the same number of trees and each tree is in a row. If the citrus trees and the palm trees must not be mixed in the rows, what is the largest number of trees that she can have in a row? 30 trees

70. *Car Maintenance* For many sport utility vehicles, it is recommended that the oil be changed every 3500 miles and that the tires be rotated every 6000 miles. If Carmella Gonzalez just had the oil changed and tires rotated on her SUV during the same visit to her mechanic, how many miles will she drive before she has the oil changed and tires rotated again during the same visit? 42,000 miles

71. *Work Schedules* Sara Pappas and Harry Kinnan both work the 3:00 P.M. to 11:00 P.M. shift. Sara has every fifth night off and Harry has every sixth night off. If they both have tonight off, how many days will pass before they have the same night off again? 30 days

72. *Prime Numbers* Consider the first eight prime numbers greater than 3. The numbers are 5, 7, 11, 13, 17, 19, 23, and 29.

   a) Determine which of these prime numbers differs by 1 from a multiple of the number 6. 5, 7, 11, 13, 17, 19, 23, and 29

   b) Use inductive reasoning and the results obtained in part (a) to make a conjecture regarding prime numbers.
      Every prime number greater than 3 differs by 1 from a multiple of 6.

   c) Select a few more prime numbers and determine whether your conjecture appears to be correct.
      This conjecture should appear to be correct.

73. State a procedure that defines a divisibility test for 15.
A number is divisible by 15 if both 3 and 5 divide the number.

*See Instructor Answer Appendix

74. State a procedure that defines a divisibility test for 22.
A number is divisible by 22 if both 2 and 11 divide the number.

Euclidean Algorithm *Another method that can be used to find the greatest common divisor is known as the Euclidean algorithm. We illustrate this procedure by finding the GCD of 60 and 220.*

First divide 220 by 60 as shown below. Disregard the quotient 3 and then divide 60 by the remainder 40. Continue this process of dividing the divisors by the remainders until you obtain a remainder of 0. The divisor in the last division, in which the remainder is 0, is the GCD.

$$
\begin{array}{ccc}
3 & 1 & 2 \\
60)\overline{220} & 40)\overline{60} & 20)\overline{40} \\
\underline{180} & \underline{40} & \underline{40} \\
40 & 20 & 0
\end{array}
$$

Since 40/20 had a remainder of 0, the GCD is 20.

In Exercises 75–80, use the Euclidean algorithm to find the GCD.

75. 15, 40 5   **76.** 12, 28 4

77. 35, 105 35   **78.** 78, 104 26

79. 150, 180 30   **80.** 210, 560 70

Perfect Numbers *A number whose proper factors (factors other than the number itself) add up to the number is called a perfect number. For example, 6 is a perfect number because its proper factors are 1, 2, and 3, and 1 + 2 + 3 = 6. Determine which, if any, of the following numbers are perfect.*

81. 28 Yes

82. 32 No

83. 56 No

84. 496 Yes

Challenge Problems/Group Activities

85. **Number of Factors** The following procedure can be used to determine the *number of factors* (or *divisors*) of a composite number. Write the number in prime factorization form. Examine the exponents on the prime numbers in the prime factorization. Add 1 to each exponent and then find the product of these numbers. This product gives the number of positive divisors of the composite number. For example, the prime factorization of 75 is $3 \cdot 5^2$. The exponents on the prime factors are 1 and 2. Therefore, 75 has $(1 + 1) \cdot (2 + 1) = 2 \cdot 3$ or 6 factors (the factors are 1, 3, 5, 15, 25, and 75).

   a) Use this procedure to determine the number of divisors of 60. 12

   b) To check your answer, list all the divisors of 60. You should obtain the same number of divisors found in part (a). 1, 2, 3, 4, 5, 6, 10, 12, 15, 20, 30, 60

86. Recall that if a number is divisible by both 2 and 3, then the number is divisible by 6. If a number is divisible by

both 2 and 4, is the number necessarily divisible by 8? Explain your answer. *

87. The product of any three consecutive natural numbers is divisible by 6. Explain why. *

88. A number in which each digit except 0 appears exactly three times is divisible by 3. For example, 888,444,555 and 714,714,714 are both divisible by 3. Explain why this outcome must be true. The sum of the digits of such numbers is divisible by 3; therefore, the number itself is divisible by 3.

89. Use the fact that if $a|b$ and $a|c$, then $a|(b + c)$ to determine whether 54,036 is divisible by 18. (*Hint:* Write 54,036 as 54,000 + 36.) Yes

90. Show that the $2^n - 1$ is a (Mersenne) prime for $n = 2, 3, 5$, and 7 but composite for $n = 11$.
3, 7, 31, and 127 are all prime, but 2047 is divisible by 23 and 89.

91. Goldbach also conjectured in his letter to Euler that *every* integer greater than 5 is the sum of three prime numbers. For example, $6 = 2 + 2 + 2$ and $7 = 2 + 2 + 3$. Show that this conjecture is true for integers 8 through 20.*

92. **Divisibility by Seven** The following describes a procedure to determine whether a number is divisible by 7. We will demonstrate the procedure with the number 203.

   i) Remove the units digit from the number, double the units digit, and subtract it from the remaining number. For 203, we will remove the 3, double it to get 6, and then subtract $20 - 6$ to get 14.

   ii) If this new number is divisible by 7, then so is the original number. In our case, since 14 is divisible by 7, then 203 is also divisible by 7.

   iii) If you are not sure if the new number obtained in Step ii is divisible by 7, you can repeat the process described in the first step.

Use the procedure described above to determine whether the following numbers are divisible by 7.

a) 329 Yes

b) 553 Yes

c) 583 No

d) 4823 Yes

Research Activities

93. Conduct an Internet search on the GIMPS project. (See *Mathematics Today* on page 217.) Write a report describing the history and development of the project. Include a current update of the project's findings.

94. Do research and explain what *deficient numbers* and *abundant numbers* are. Give an example of each type of number. References include history of mathematics books, encyclopedias, and the Internet.

*See Instructor Answer Appendix

SECTION 5.2   The Integers

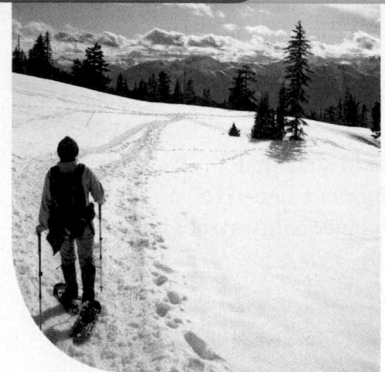

▲ *Fahrenheit temperatures can be positive, negative, or zero.*

Answer the question, What is the temperature, to the nearest degree Fahrenheit, outside right now? Depending on where you are and what time of year it is, you may have answered with a positive number, a negative number, or zero. These numbers are examples of the group of numbers called the *integers* that we will study in this section. We will also study the operations of addition, subtraction, multiplication, and division using the integers.

Why *This is Important*   We all use integers daily. An understanding of the integers and their properties is important to successfully complete our everyday tasks.

In Sections 1.1 and 5.1, we defined the natural or counting numbers:

$$N = \{1, 2, 3, 4, \dots\}$$

Another important set of numbers, the *whole numbers*, help to answer the question, How many?

$$\text{Whole numbers} = \{0, 1, 2, 3, 4, \dots\}$$

Note that the set of whole numbers contains the number 0 but that the set of counting numbers does not. If a farmer were asked how many chickens were in a coop, the answer would be a whole number. If the farmer had no chickens, he or she would answer zero. Although we use the number 0 daily and take it for granted, the number 0 as we know it was not used and accepted until the sixteenth century.

If the temperature is 12°F and drops 20°, the resulting temperature is −8°F. This type of problem shows the need for negative numbers. The set of *integers* consists of the negative integers, 0, and the positive integers.

$$\text{Integers} = \{\underbrace{\dots, -4, -3, -2, -1,}_{\text{Negative integers}} 0, \underbrace{1, 2, 3, \dots}_{\text{Positive integers}}\}$$

The term *positive integers* is yet another name for the natural numbers or counting numbers.

An understanding of addition, subtraction, multiplication, and division of the integers is essential in understanding algebra (Chapter 6). To aid in our explanation of addition and subtraction of integers, we introduce the real number line (Fig. 5.5). To construct the real number line, arbitrarily select a point for zero to serve as the starting point. Place the positive integers to the right of 0, equally spaced from one another. Place the negative integers to the left of 0, using the same spacing. The real number line contains the integers and all the other real numbers that are not integers. Some examples of real numbers that are not integers are indicated in Fig. 5.5, namely, $-\frac{5}{2}, \frac{1}{2}, \sqrt{2},$ and π. We discuss real numbers that are not integers in the next two sections.

Figure 5.5

The arrows at the ends of the real number line indicate that the line continues indefinitely in both directions. Note that for any natural number, n, on the number line, the *opposite of* that number, $-n$, is also on the number line. This real number line was drawn horizontally, but it could just as well have been drawn vertically. In fact, in the next chapter, we show that the axes of a graph are the union of two number lines, one horizontal and the other vertical.

The number line can be used to determine the greater (or lesser) of two integers. Two *inequality symbols* that we will use in this chapter are $>$ and $<$. The symbol $>$ is read "is greater than," and the symbol $<$ is read "is less than." Expressions that contain an inequality symbol are called *inequalities*. On the number line, the numbers increase from left to right. The number 3 is greater than 2, written $3 > 2$. Observe that 3 is to the right of 2. Similarly, we can see that $0 > -1$ by observing that 0 is to the right of -1 on the number line.

Instead of stating that 3 is greater than 2, we could state that 2 is less than 3, written $2 < 3$. Note that 2 is to the left of 3 on the number line. We can also see that $-1 < 0$ by observing that -1 is to the left of 0. The inequality symbol always points to the smaller of the two numbers when the inequality is true.

Example 1 *Writing an Inequality*

Insert either $>$ or $<$ in the shaded area between the paired numbers to make the statement correct.

a) $-7 \blacksquare 8$ b) $-7 \blacksquare -8$ c) $-7 \blacksquare 0$ d) $-7 \blacksquare -4$

Solution

a) $-7 < 8$ since -7 is to the left of 8 on the number line.

b) $-7 > -8$ since -7 is to the right of -8 on the number line.

c) $-7 < 0$ since -7 is to the left of 0 on the number line.

d) $-7 < -4$ since -7 is to the left of -4 on the number line.   ∎

Addition of Integers

Addition of integers can be represented geometrically using a number line. To do so, begin at 0 on the number line. Represent the first addend (the first number to be added) by an arrow starting at 0. Draw the arrow to the right if the addend is positive. If the addend is negative, draw the arrow to the left. From the tip of the first arrow, draw a second arrow to represent the second addend. Draw the second arrow to the right or left, as just explained. The sum of the two integers is found at the tip of the second arrow.

Example 2 *Adding Integers*

Evaluate the following using the number line.

a) $3 + (-5)$ b) $-1 + (-4)$ c) $-6 + 4$ d) $3 + (-3)$

Solution

a)

Thus, $3 + (-5) = -2$.

b)

Thus, $-1 + (-4) = -5$.

c)

Thus, $-6 + 4 = -2$.

d)

Thus, $3 + (-3) = 0$.   ∎

In Example 2(d), the number -3 is said to be the additive inverse of 3 and 3 is the additive inverse of -3 because their sum is 0. In general, the *additive inverse* of the number n is $-n$ since $n + (-n) = 0$. Inverses are discussed more formally in Chapter 10.

Subtraction of Integers

Any subtraction problem can be rewritten as an addition problem. To do so, we use the following rule of subtraction.

> ### Subtraction
> $$a - b = a + (-b)$$

The rule for subtraction indicates that to subtract b from a, *add* the additive inverse of b to a. For example,

$$3 - 5 = 3 + (-5)$$

Subtraction   Addition   Additive inverse of 5

Now we can determine the value of $3 + (-5)$.

Thus, $3 - 5 = 3 + (-5) = -2$.

Example 3   Subtracting Integers

Evaluate $-4 - (-3)$ using the number line.

Solution   We are subtracting -3 from -4. The additive inverse of -3 is 3; therefore, we add 3 to -4. We now add $-4 + 3$ on the number line to obtain the answer -1.

Thus, $-4 - (-3) = -4 + 3 = -1$.   ∎

In Example 3, we found that $-4 - (-3) = -4 + 3$. In general, $a - (-b) = a + b$. As you get more proficient in working with integers, you should be able to answer questions involving them without drawing a number line.

Example 4   Subtracting: Adding the Inverse

Evaluate.

a) $-7 - 3$ b) $-7 - (-3)$ c) $7 - (-3)$ d) $7 - 3$

Solution

a) $-7 - 3 = -7 + (-3) = -10$ b) $-7 - (-3) = -7 + 3 = -4$
c) $7 - (-3) = 7 + 3 = 10$ d) $7 - 3 = 7 + (-3) = 4$ ▪

Example 5 *Elevation Difference*

The highest point on Earth is Mount Everest, in the Himalayas, at a height of 29,035 ft above sea level. The lowest point on Earth is the Mariana Trench, in the Pacific Ocean, at a depth of 36,198 ft below sea level ($-36,198$ ft). Find the vertical height difference between Mount Everest and the Mariana Trench.

Solution We obtain the vertical difference by subtracting the lower elevation from the higher elevation.

$$29,035 - (-36,198) = 29,035 + 36,198 = 65,233$$

The vertical difference is 65,233 ft.   ▪

Multiplication of Integers

The multiplication property of zero is important in our discussion of multiplication of integers. It indicates that the product of 0 and any number is 0.

Multiplication Property of Zero
$$a \cdot 0 = 0 \cdot a = 0$$

We will develop the rules for multiplication of integers using number patterns. The four possible cases are

1. positive integer $\times$ positive integer,

2. positive integer $\times$ negative integer,

3. negative integer $\times$ positive integer, and

4. negative integer $\times$ negative integer.

CASE 1: *POSITIVE INTEGER $\times$ POSITIVE INTEGER* The product of two positive integers can be defined as repeated addition of a positive integer. Thus, $3 \cdot 2$ means $2 + 2 + 2$. This sum will always be positive. Thus, *a positive integer times a positive integer is a positive integer.*

CASE 2: *POSITIVE INTEGER $\times$ NEGATIVE INTEGER* Consider the following patterns:

$$3(3) = 9$$
$$3(2) = 6$$
$$3(1) = 3$$

Note that each time the second factor is reduced by 1, the product is reduced by 3. Continuing the process gives

$$3(0) = 0$$

What comes next?

$$3(-1) = -3$$
$$3(-2) = -6$$

The pattern indicates that *a positive integer times a negative integer is a negative integer.*

We can confirm this result by using the number line. The expression $3(-2)$ means $(-2) + (-2) + (-2)$. Adding $(-2) + (-2) + (-2)$ on the number line, we obtain a sum of -6.

CASE 3: NEGATIVE INTEGER × POSITIVE INTEGER A procedure similar to that used in case 2 will indicate that *a negative integer times a positive integer is a negative integer*.

CASE 4: NEGATIVE INTEGER × NEGATIVE INTEGER We have illustrated that a positive integer times a negative integer is a negative integer. We make use of this fact in the following pattern:

$$4(-4) = -16$$
$$3(-4) = -12$$
$$2(-4) = -8$$
$$1(-4) = -4$$

In this pattern, each time the first term is decreased by 1, the product is increased by 4. Continuing this process gives

$$0(-4) = 0$$
$$(-1)(-4) = 4$$
$$(-2)(-4) = 8$$

This pattern illustrates that *a negative integer times a negative integer is a positive integer*.

The examples were restricted to integers. The rules for multiplication, however, can be used for any numbers. We summarize them as follows.

Rules for Multiplication

1. The product of two numbers with *like signs* (positive × positive or negative × negative) is a *positive number*.
2. The product of two numbers with *unlike signs* (positive × negative or negative × positive) is a *negative number*.

Example 6 *Multiplying Integers*

Evaluate.

a) $5 \cdot 6$ b) $5 \cdot (-6)$ c) $(-5) \cdot 6$ d) $(-5) \cdot (-6)$

Solution

a) $5 \cdot 6 = 30$ b) $5 \cdot (-6) = -30$
c) $(-5) \cdot 6 = -30$ d) $(-5) \cdot (-6) = 30$ ∎

Division of Integers

You may already realize that a relationship exists between multiplication and division.

$$6 \div 2 = 3 \quad \text{means that} \quad 3 \cdot 2 = 6$$
$$\frac{20}{10} = 2 \quad \text{means that} \quad 2 \cdot 10 = 20$$

These examples demonstrate that division is the reverse process of multiplication.

Division

For any a, b, and c where $b \neq 0$, $\dfrac{a}{b} = c$ means that $c \cdot b = a$.

We discuss the four possible cases for division of integers, which are similar to those for multiplication.

CASE 1: *POSITIVE INTEGER ÷ POSITIVE INTEGER* *A positive integer divided by a positive integer is positive.*

$$\frac{6}{2} = 3 \quad \text{since} \quad 3(2) = 6$$

CASE 2: *POSITIVE INTEGER ÷ NEGATIVE INTEGER* *A positive integer divided by a negative integer is negative.*

$$\frac{6}{-2} = -3 \quad \text{since} \quad (-3)(-2) = 6$$

CASE 3: *NEGATIVE INTEGER ÷ POSITIVE INTEGER* *A negative integer divided by a positive integer is negative.*

$$\frac{-6}{2} = -3 \quad \text{since} \quad (-3)(2) = -6$$

CASE 4: *NEGATIVE INTEGER ÷ NEGATIVE INTEGER* *A negative integer divided by a negative integer is positive.*

$$\frac{-6}{-2} = 3 \quad \text{since} \quad 3(-2) = -6$$

The examples were restricted to integers. The rules for division, however, can be used for any numbers. You should realize that division of integers does not always result in an integer. The rules for division are summarized as follows.

Rules for Division
1. The quotient of two numbers with *like signs* (positive ÷ positive or negative ÷ negative) is a *positive number.*
2. The quotient of two numbers with *unlike signs* (positive ÷ negative or negative ÷ positive) is a *negative number.*

Example 7 *Dividing Integers*

Evaluate.

a) $\dfrac{63}{9}$ b) $\dfrac{-63}{9}$ c) $\dfrac{63}{-9}$ d) $\dfrac{-63}{-9}$

Solution

a) $\dfrac{63}{9} = 7$ b) $\dfrac{-63}{9} = -7$ c) $\dfrac{63}{-9} = -7$ d) $\dfrac{-63}{-9} = 7$ ∎

In the definition of division, we stated that the denominator could not be 0. Why not? Suppose we are trying to find the quotient $\frac{5}{0}$. Let's say that this quotient is equal to some number x. Then we would have $\frac{5}{0} = x$. If true, it would mean that $5 = x \cdot 0$. The right side of the equation is $x \cdot 0$, which is equal to 0 for any real value of x. That leads us to conclude that $5 = 0$, which is false. Thus, there is no number that can replace x that makes the equation $\frac{5}{0} = x$ true. Therefore, in mathematics, division by 0 is not allowed and we say that a quotient of any number divided by zero is *undefined*.

SECTION 5.2 Exercises

Warm Up Exercises

In Exercises 1–4, fill in the blanks with an appropriate word, phrase, or symbol(s).

1. The set of numbers $\{0,1,2,3,4,...\}$ is known as the _____ numbers. Whole

2. The rule for subtraction indicates that to subtract b from a, _____ the additive inverse of b to a. Add

3. a) The product of two numbers with *like* signs is a _____ number. Positive

   b) The product of two numbers with *unlike* signs is a _____ number. Negative

4. a) The quotient of two numbers with *unlike* signs is a _____ number. Negative

   b) The quotient of two numbers with *like* signs is a _____ number. Positive

In Exercises 5–6, insert either $>$ or $<$ in the shaded area between the paired numbers to make the statement correct.

5. a) $-3 \ \blacksquare \ 2$ $<$ b) $-3 \ \blacksquare \ -2$ $<$

   c) $-3 \ \blacksquare \ 0$ $<$ d) $-3 \ \blacksquare \ -4$ $>$

6. a) $-5 \ \blacksquare \ -8$ $>$ b) $-5 \ \blacksquare \ 8$ $<$

   c) $-5 \ \blacksquare \ -1$ $<$ d) $-5 \ \blacksquare \ 0$ $<$

Practice the Skills

In Exercises 7–16, evaluate the expression.

7. $-3 + 5$ 2   8. $5 + (-8)$ -3

9. $-10 + 3$ -7 10. $-5 + (-5)$ -10

11. $[6 + (-11)] + 0$ -5 12. $(2 + 5) + (-4)$ 3

13. $[(-3) + (-4)] + 9$ 2   14. $[8 + (-3)] + (-2)$ 3

15. $[(-23) + (-9)] + 11$ -21 16. $[5 + (-13)] + 18$ 10

In Exercises 17–26, evaluate the expression.

17. $3 - 5$ -2 18. $-3 - 7$ -10

19. $-6 - 2$ -8 20. $9 - (-4)$ 13

21. $-5 - (-3)$ -2 22. $-4 - 4$ -8

23. $14 - 20$ -6 24. $8 - (-3)$ 11

25. $[5 + (-3)] - 4$ -2 26. $6 - (8 + 6)$ -8

In Exercises 27–36, evaluate the expression.

27. $-7 \cdot 8$ -56

28. $8(-4)$ -32

29. $(-9)(-9)$ 81

30. $-6(13)$ -78

31. $[(-8)(-2)] \cdot 6$ 96

32. $4(-5)(-6)$ 120

33. $(5 \cdot 6)(-2)$ -60

34. $(-9)(-1)(-2)$ -18

35. $[(-3)(-6)] \cdot [(-5)(8)]$ -720

36. $[(-8 \cdot 4) \cdot 5](-2)$ 320

In Exercises 37–46, evaluate the expression.

37. $-16 \div (-2)$ 8   38. $-54 \div 6$ -9

39. $\dfrac{15}{-15}$ -1 40. $\dfrac{-90}{9}$ -10

41. $56/-8$ -7 42. $-75/15$ -5

43. $-210/14$ -15 44. $186/-6$ -31

45. $144 \div (-3)$ -48 46. $(-900) \div (-4)$ 225

In Exercises 47–56, determine whether the statement is true or false. Modify each false statement to make it a true statement.

47. Every whole number is an integer. True

48. Every integer is a whole number.
    False; every integer is not a whole number.

49. The difference of any two negative integers is a negative integer. False; the difference of two negative integers may be a positive integer, a negative integer, or zero.

50. The sum of any two negative integers is a negative integer. True

51. The product of any two positive integers is a positive integer. True

52. The difference of a positive integer and a negative integer is always a negative integer. False; the difference of a positive integer and a negative integer will always be positive. For example, $5 - (-4) = 9$.

53. The quotient of a negative integer and a positive integer is always a negative number. True

54. The quotient of any two negative integers is a negative number.
    False; the quotient of any two negative integers is a positive integer.

55. The sum of a positive integer and a negative integer is always a positive integer. False; the sum of a positive integer and a negative integer may be a positive integer, a negative integer, or zero.

56. The product of a positive integer and a negative integer is always a positive integer. False; the product of a positive integer and a negative integer is always a negative integer.

In Exercises 57–66, evaluate the expression.

57. $(5 + 7) \div 4$ 3

58. $(-15) \div \left[35 \div (-7)\right]$ 3

59. $\left[(-12)(-3)\right] - 3$ 33

60. $\left[7(-4)\right] - 8$ −36

61. $(4 - 8)(3)$ −12

62. $[18 \div (-2)](-3)$ 27

63. $[2 + (-17)] \div 3$ −5

64. $(5 - 9) \div (-4)$ 1

65. $[(-22)(-3)] \div (2 - 13)$ −6

66. $[15(-4)] \div (-6)$ 10

In Exercises 67–70, write the numbers in increasing order from left to right.

67. 0, −3, 3, −6, 6, −9 −9, −6, −3, 0, 3, 6

68. 100, −10, 1, 0, −1, 10 −10, −1, 0, 1, 10, 100

69. −5, −2, −3, −1, −4, −6 −6, −5, −4, −3, −2, −1

70. 106, 33, −47, −108, 72, −76 −108, −76, −47, 33, 72, 106

Problem Solving

71. *Submarine Depth* The *USS Virginia* submarine is at an underwater depth of 600 feet. It then rises 200 feet, dives 400 feet, and finally dives another 300 feet. What is the *USS Virginia's* final depth? 1100 feet under water

▲ *USS Virginia*

72. *Dow Jones Industrial Average* On May 25, 2010, the Dow Jones Industrial Average (DJIA) opened at 10,067

points. During that day it lost 23 points. On May 26 it lost 70 points. On May 27 it gained 285 points. On May 28 it lost 122 points. Determine the DJIA at closing on May 28, 2010. 10,137

73. *Elevation Difference* Mount Whitney, in the Sierra Nevada mountains of California, is the highest point in the contiguous United States. It is 14,495 ft above sea level. Death Valley, in California and Nevada, is the lowest point in the United States, 282 ft below sea level. Find the vertical height difference between Mount Whitney and Death Valley. 14,777 ft

74. *Extreme Temperatures* The hottest temperature ever recorded in the United States was 134°F, which occurred at Greenland Ranch, California, in Death Valley on July 10, 1913. The coldest temperature ever recorded in the United States was −80°F, which occurred at Prospect Creek Camp, Alaska, in the Endicott Mountains on January 23, 1971. Determine the difference between these two temperatures. 214°F

75. *Time Zone Calculations* Part of a World Standard Time Zones chart used by airlines and the United States Navy is shown. The scale along the bottom is just like a number line with the integers −12, −11,…, 11, 12 on it.

a) Find the difference in time between Amsterdam (zone +1) and Los Angeles (zone −8). 9 hours

b) Find the difference in time between Boston (zone −5) and Puerto Vallarta (zone −7). 2 hours

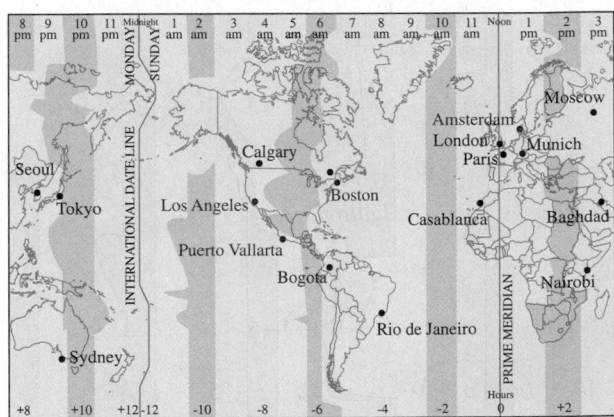

76. *Bus Stops* A city bus currently has 23 people on it. At the next stop, 10 people get off the bus, and 8 people get on the bus. At the next stop, 15 people get off the bus, and 6 people get on the bus. At the next stop, 2 people get off the bus, and 17 people get on. At this point, how many people are on the bus? 27 people

Concept/Writing Exercises

77. Explain why the quotient of a number divided by 0 is undefined. Division by zero is undefined because $\frac{a}{0} = x$ always leads to a false statement.

78. Explain why $\frac{a}{b} = \frac{-a}{-b}$. The quotient of two positive numbers is a positive number, and the quotient of two negative numbers is a positive number.

Challenge Problems/Group Activities

79. Find the quotient:

$$\frac{-1 + 2 - 3 + 4 - 5 + \cdots - 99 + 100}{1 - 2 + 3 - 4 + 5 - \cdots + 99 - 100} \quad -1$$

80. *Pentagonal Numbers* Triangular numbers and square numbers were introduced in the Section 1.1 Exercises. There are also **pentagonal numbers**, which were also studied by the Greeks. Four pentagonal numbers are 1, 5, 12, and 22.

1   5   12   22

a) Determine the next three pentagonal numbers.
  35, 51, and 70
b) Describe a procedure to determine the next five pentagonal numbers without drawing the figures. *

c) Is 72 a pentagonal number? Explain how you determined your answer. Since 70 and 92 are pentagonal numbers, 72 is not a pentagonal number.

81. Place the appropriate plus or minus signs between each digit so that the total will equal 1.
  0 1 2 3 4 5 6 7 8 9 = 1
  0 + 1 − 2 + 3 + 4 − 5 + 6 − 7 − 8 + 9 = 1

Recreational Mathematics

82. *Four 4's* Refer to the *Recreational Mathematics* box on page 225.

a) Use the rules given on page 225 to obtain the following whole numbers: 12, 15, 16, 17, 20. *

b) We will now change our rules to allow the number 44 to count as two of the four 4's. Use the number 44 and two other fours to obtain the whole number 10. *

Internet/Research Activity

83. Do research and write a report on the history of the number 0 in the Hindu–Arabic numeration system.

*See Instructor Answer Appendix

Among the ingredients called for in a recipe for chocolate chip cookies are $2\frac{1}{4}$ cups flour, $\frac{1}{2}$ teaspoon salt, $1\frac{1}{3}$ teaspoons baking soda, $\frac{3}{4}$ cup sugar, and $\frac{3}{4}$ cup brown sugar. How much of each of these ingredients would you need to use if you wish to double the recipe? In this section, we will review the use of fractions such as those in the chocolate chip cookie recipe. We will also learn about the operations of addition, subtraction, multiplication, and division using fractions.

▲ *Rational numbers are frequently used in baking recipes.*

Why **This is Important** Fractions are everywhere in our everyday lives. Kitchen measurements, tool sizes, and many other real-life applications all involve fractions.

We introduced the number line and discussed the integers in Section 5.2. The numbers that fall between the integers on the number line are either rational or irrational numbers. In this section, we discuss the rational numbers, and in Section 5.4, we discuss the irrational numbers.

Any number that can be expressed as a quotient of two integers (denominator not 0) is a rational number.

Definition: Rational Numbers

The set of **rational numbers**, denoted by Q, is the set of all numbers of the form p/q, where p and q are integers and $q \neq 0$.

The following numbers are examples of rational numbers:

$$\frac{1}{3}, \quad \frac{3}{4}, \quad -\frac{7}{8}, \quad 1\frac{2}{3}, \quad 2, \quad 0, \quad \frac{15}{7}$$

The integers 2 and 0 are rational numbers because each can be expressed as the quotient of two integers: $2 = \frac{2}{1}$ and $0 = \frac{0}{1}$. In fact, every integer n is a rational number because it can be written in the form of $\frac{n}{1}$.

Numbers such as $\frac{1}{3}$ and $-\frac{7}{8}$ are also called *fractions*. The number above the fraction line is called the *numerator*, and the number below the fraction line is called the *denominator*.

Reducing Fractions

Sometimes the numerator and denominator in a fraction have a common divisor (or common factor). For example, both the numerator and denominator of the fraction $\frac{6}{10}$ have the common divisor 2. When a numerator and denominator have a common divisor, we can *reduce the fraction to its lowest terms*.

A fraction is said to be in its lowest terms (or reduced) when the numerator and denominator are relatively prime (that is, have no common divisors other than 1). To reduce a fraction to its lowest terms, divide both the numerator and the denominator by the greatest common divisor. Recall that a procedure for finding the greatest common divisor was discussed in Section 5.1.

The fraction $\frac{6}{10}$ is reduced to its lowest terms as follows.

$$\frac{6}{10} = \frac{6 \div 2}{10 \div 2} = \frac{3}{5}$$

Example 1   *Reducing a Fraction to Lowest Terms*

Reduce $\frac{54}{90}$ to its lowest terms.

Solution   On page 215 in Example 4 of Section 5.1, we determined that the GCD of 54 and 90 is 18. Divide the numerator and the denominator by GCD, 18.

$$\frac{54}{90} = \frac{54 \div 18}{90 \div 18} = \frac{3}{5}$$

Since there are no common divisors of 3 and 5 other than 1, the fraction $\frac{3}{5}$ is in its lowest terms.   ∎

Mixed Numbers and Improper Fractions

Consider the number $2\frac{3}{4}$. It is an example of a *mixed number*. It is called a mixed number because it consists of an integer, 2, and a fraction, $\frac{3}{4}$. The mixed number $2\frac{3}{4}$ means $2 + \frac{3}{4}$. The mixed number $-4\frac{1}{4}$ means $-\left(4 + \frac{1}{4}\right)$. Rational numbers greater than 1 or less than -1 that are not integers may be represented as mixed numbers, or as *improper fractions*. An improper fraction is a fraction whose numerator is greater than its denominator. An example of an improper fraction is $\frac{8}{5}$. Figure 5.6 shows both mixed numbers and improper fractions indicated on a number line. In this section, we show how to convert mixed numbers to improper fractions and vice versa.

Figure 5.6

We begin by limiting our discussion to positive mixed numbers and positive improper fractions.

> **PROCEDURE** **CONVERTING A POSITIVE MIXED NUMBER TO AN IMPROPER FRACTION**
>
> 1. Multiply the denominator of the fraction in the mixed number by the integer preceding it.
> 2. Add the product obtained in Step 1 to the numerator of the fraction in the mixed number. This sum is the numerator of the improper fraction we are seeking. The denominator of the improper fraction we are seeking is the same as the denominator of the fraction in the mixed number.

Example 2 *Converting Mixed Numbers to Improper Fractions*

Convert the following mixed numbers to improper fractions.

a) $1\dfrac{3}{4}$ b) $3\dfrac{7}{8}$

Solution

a) $1\dfrac{3}{4} = \dfrac{4 \cdot 1 + 3}{4} = \dfrac{4 + 3}{4} = \dfrac{7}{4}$

b) $3\dfrac{7}{8} = \dfrac{8 \cdot 3 + 7}{8} = \dfrac{24 + 7}{8} = \dfrac{31}{8}$

Notice that both $\frac{7}{4}$ and $\frac{31}{8}$ have numerators that are larger than their denominators; therefore, both numbers are improper fractions. ∎

Now let's discuss converting an improper fraction to a mixed number.

> **PROCEDURE** **CONVERTING A POSITIVE IMPROPER FRACTION TO A MIXED NUMBER**
>
> 1. Divide the numerator by the denominator. Identify the quotient and the remainder.
> 2. The quotient obtained in Step 1 is the integer part of the mixed number. The remainder is the numerator of the fraction in the mixed number. The denominator in the fraction of the mixed number will be the same as the denominator in the original fraction.

Example 3 *From Improper Fraction to Mixed Number*

Convert the following improper fractions to mixed numbers.

a) $\dfrac{8}{5}$ b) $\dfrac{225}{8}$

Solution

a) Divide the numerator, 8, by the denominator, 5.

$$
\begin{array}{r}
1 \quad \leftarrow \text{Quotient} \\
\text{Divisor} \rightarrow \; 5\overline{)8} \quad \leftarrow \text{Dividend} \\
\underline{5} \quad\quad \\
3 \quad \leftarrow \text{Remainder}
\end{array}
$$

Therefore,

$$\frac{8}{5} = 1\frac{3}{5}$$

Quotient ↓

← Remainder
← Divisor

The mixed number is $1\frac{3}{5}$.

b) Divide the numerator, 225, by the denominator, 8.

$$
\begin{array}{r}
28 \\
8)\overline{225} \\
16 \\
\hline
65 \\
64 \\
\hline
1
\end{array}
$$

← Quotient
Divisor → ← Dividend

← Remainder

Therefore,

$$\frac{225}{8} = 28\frac{1}{8}$$

Quotient ↓

← Remainder
← Divisor

The mixed number is $28\frac{1}{8}$. ∎

Up to this point, we have only worked with positive mixed numbers and positive improper fractions. When converting a negative mixed number to an improper fraction, or a negative improper fraction to a mixed number, it is best to ignore the negative sign temporarily. Perform the calculation as described earlier and then reattach the negative sign.

Example 4 *Negative Mixed Numbers and Improper Fractions*

a) Convert $-1\frac{3}{4}$ to an improper fraction.

b) Convert $-\frac{8}{5}$ to a mixed number.

Solution

a) First, ignore the negative sign and examine $1\frac{3}{4}$. We learned in Example 2(a) that $1\frac{3}{4} = \frac{7}{4}$. To convert $-1\frac{3}{4}$ to an improper fraction, we reattach the negative sign. Thus, $-1\frac{3}{4} = -\frac{7}{4}$.

b) We learned in Example 3(a) that $\frac{8}{5} = 1\frac{3}{5}$. Therefore, $-\frac{8}{5} = -1\frac{3}{5}$. ∎

Terminating or Repeating Decimal Numbers

Note the following important property of the rational numbers. *Every rational number when expressed as a decimal number will be either a terminating or a repeating decimal number.*

Examples of terminating decimal numbers are 0.5, 0.75, and 4.65. Examples of repeating decimal numbers are $0.333\ldots$, $0.2323\ldots$, and $8.13456456\ldots$. One way to indicate that a number or group of numbers repeats is to place a bar above the number or group of numbers that repeats. Thus, $0.333\ldots$ may be written $0.\overline{3}$, $0.2323\ldots$ may be written $0.\overline{23}$, and $8.13456456\ldots$ may be written $8.13\overline{456}$.

Example 5 *Terminating Decimal Numbers*

Show that the following rational numbers can be expressed as terminating decimal numbers.

a) $\dfrac{3}{5}$ b) $-\dfrac{13}{20}$ c) $\dfrac{23}{16}$

Solution To express the rational number in decimal form, divide the numerator by the denominator. If you use a calculator or long division, you will obtain the following results.

a) $\dfrac{3}{5} = 0.6$ b) $-\dfrac{13}{20} = -0.65$ c) $\dfrac{23}{16} = 1.4375$ ∎

Example 6 *Repeating Decimal Numbers*

Show that the following rational numbers can be expressed as repeating decimal numbers.

a) $\dfrac{2}{3}$ b) $\dfrac{14}{99}$ c) $1\dfrac{5}{36}$

Solution If you use a calculator or long division, you will see that each fraction results in a repeating decimal number.

a) $2 \div 3 = 0.6666\ldots$ or $0.\overline{6}$

b) $14 \div 99 = 0.141414\ldots$ or $0.\overline{14}$

c) $1\frac{5}{36} = \frac{41}{36} = 1.138888\ldots$ or $1.13\overline{8}$ ∎

Note that in each part of Example 6, the quotient when expressed as a decimal number has no final digit and continues indefinitely. Each number is a repeating decimal number.

When a fraction is converted to a decimal number, the maximum number of digits that can repeat is $n - 1$, where n is the denominator of the fraction. For example, when $\frac{2}{7}$ is converted to a decimal number, the maximum number of digits that can repeat is $7 - 1$, or 6.

Converting Decimal Numbers to Fractions

We can convert a terminating or repeating decimal number into a quotient of integers. The explanation of the procedure will refer to the positional values to the right of the decimal point, as illustrated here:

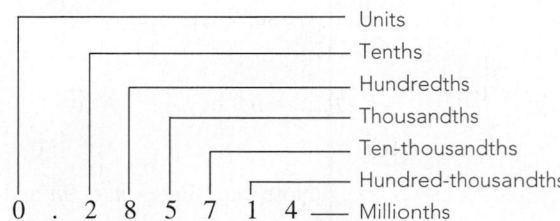

Example 7 demonstrates how to convert from a decimal number to a fraction.

Example 7 *Converting Decimal Numbers to Fractions*

Convert the following terminating decimal numbers to a quotient of integers. If necessary, reduce the quotient to lowest terms.

a) 0.7 b) 0.35 c) 0.016 d) 3.41

Solution When converting a terminating decimal number to a quotient of integers, we observe the last digit to the right of the decimal point. The position of this digit will indicate the denominator of the quotient of integers.

a) $0.7 = \frac{7}{10}$ because the 7 is in the tenths position.

b) $0.35 = \frac{35}{100}$ because the right-most digit, 5, is in the hundredths position. We finish by reducing the fraction to lowest terms:

$$\frac{35}{100} = \frac{35 \div 5}{100 \div 5} = \frac{7}{20}$$

c) $0.016 = \frac{16}{1000}$ because the right-most digit, 6, is in the thousandths position. We finish by reducing the fraction to lowest terms:

$$\frac{16}{1000} = \frac{16 \div 8}{1000 \div 8} = \frac{2}{125}$$

d) We begin by writing 3.41 as the mixed number, $3\frac{41}{100}$ because the right-most digit, 1, is in the hundredths position. To write the mixed number as a ratio of two integers, we follow the procedure shown in Example 2, on page 231:

$$3\frac{41}{100} = \frac{100 \cdot 3 + 41}{100} = \frac{341}{100}$$

The fraction $\frac{341}{100}$ cannot be reduced further. ∎

Converting a repeating decimal number to a quotient of integers is more difficult than converting a terminating decimal number to a quotient of integers. To do so, we must "create" another repeating decimal number with the same repeating digits so that when one repeating decimal number is subtracted from the other repeating decimal number, the difference will be a whole number. To create a number with the same repeating digits, multiply the original repeating decimal number by 10 if one digit repeats, by 100 if two digits repeat, by 1000 if three digits repeat, and so on. Examples 8 through 10 demonstrate this procedure.

Example 8 *Converting a Repeating Decimal Number to a Fraction*

Convert $0.\overline{3}$ to a quotient of integers.

Solution $0.\overline{3} = 0.3\overline{3} = 0.33\overline{3}$, and so on.

Let the original repeating decimal number be n; thus, $n = 0.\overline{3}$. Because one digit repeats, we multiply both sides of the equation by 10, which gives $10n = 3.\overline{3}$. Then we subtract.

$$\begin{array}{r} 10n = 3.\overline{3} \\ - \quad n = 0.\overline{3} \\ \hline 9n = 3.0 \end{array}$$

Note that $10n - n = 9n$ and $3.\overline{3} - 0.\overline{3} = 3.0$.

Next, we solve for n by dividing both sides of the equation by 9.

$$\frac{9n}{9} = \frac{3.0}{9}$$

$$n = \frac{3}{9} = \frac{1}{3}$$

Therefore, $0.\overline{3} = \frac{1}{3}$. Evaluate $1 \div 3$ on a calculator now and see what value you get. ∎

Example 9 *Converting a Repeating Decimal Number to a Fraction*

Convert $0.\overline{35}$ to a quotient of integers.

Solution Let $n = 0.\overline{35}$. Since two digits repeat, multiply both sides of the equation by 100. Thus, $100n = 35.\overline{35}$. Now we subtract n from $100n$.

$$
\begin{array}{r}
100n = 35.\overline{35} \\
- \quad n = 0.\overline{35} \\
\hline
99n = 35
\end{array}
$$

Finally, we divide both sides of the equation by 99.

$$
\frac{99n}{99} = \frac{35}{99}
$$

$$
n = \frac{35}{99}
$$

Therefore, $0.\overline{35} = \frac{35}{99}$. Evaluate $35 \div 99$ on a calculator now and see what value you get. ∎

Example 10 *Converting a Repeating Decimal Number to a Fraction*

Convert $12.14\overline{2}$ to a quotient of integers.

Solution This example is different from the two preceding examples in that the repeating digit, 2, is not directly to the right of the decimal point. When this situation arises, move the decimal point to the right until the repeating terms are directly to its right. For each place the decimal point is moved, the number is multiplied by 10. In this example, the decimal point must be moved two places to the right. Thus, the number must be multiplied by 100.

$$
n = 12.14\overline{2}
$$
$$
100n = 100 \times 12.14\overline{2} = 1214.\overline{2}
$$

Now proceed as in the previous two examples. Since one digit repeats, multiply both sides by 10.

$$
100n = 1214.\overline{2}
$$
$$
10 \times 100n = 10 \times 1214.\overline{2}
$$
$$
1000n = 12142.\overline{2}
$$

Now subtract $100n$ from $1000n$ so that the repeating part will drop out.

$$
\begin{array}{r}
1000n = 12142.\overline{2} \\
- \quad 100n = 1214.\overline{2} \\
\hline
900n = 10928
\end{array}
$$

$$
n = \frac{10{,}928}{900} = \frac{2732}{225}
$$

Therefore, $12.14\overline{2} = \frac{2732}{225}$. Evaluate $2732 \div 225$ on a calculator now and see what value you get. ∎

Multiplication and Division of Fractions

The product of two fractions is found by multiplying the numerators together and multiplying the denominators together.

Multiplication of Fractions

$$\frac{a}{b} \cdot \frac{c}{d} = \frac{a \cdot c}{b \cdot d} = \frac{ac}{bd}, \quad b \neq 0, \quad d \neq 0$$

Example 11 *Multiplying Fractions*

Evaluate.

a) $\dfrac{3}{5} \cdot \dfrac{7}{8}$ b) $\left(\dfrac{-2}{3}\right)\left(\dfrac{-4}{9}\right)$ c) $\left(1\dfrac{7}{8}\right)\left(2\dfrac{1}{4}\right)$

Solution

a) $\dfrac{3}{5} \cdot \dfrac{7}{8} = \dfrac{3 \cdot 7}{5 \cdot 8} = \dfrac{21}{40}$ b) $\left(\dfrac{-2}{3}\right)\left(\dfrac{-4}{9}\right) = \dfrac{(-2)(-4)}{(3)(9)} - \dfrac{8}{27}$

c) $\left(1\dfrac{7}{8}\right)\left(2\dfrac{1}{4}\right) = \dfrac{15}{8} \cdot \dfrac{9}{4} = \dfrac{135}{32} = 4\dfrac{7}{32}$

To divide fractions we make use of the *reciprocal* of a number. The *reciprocal* of any number is 1 divided by that number. The product of a number and its reciprocal must equal 1. Examples of some numbers and their reciprocals follow.

Number		Reciprocal		Product
3	·	$\dfrac{1}{3}$	=	1
$\dfrac{3}{5}$	·	$\dfrac{5}{3}$	=	1
-6	·	$-\dfrac{1}{6}$	=	1

To find the quotient of two fractions, multiply the first fraction by the reciprocal of the second fraction.

Division of Fractions

$$\frac{a}{b} \div \frac{c}{d} = \frac{a}{b} \cdot \frac{d}{c} = \frac{ad}{bc}, \quad b \neq 0, \quad d \neq 0, \quad c \neq 0$$

Example 12 *Dividing Fractions*

Evaluate.

a) $\dfrac{5}{7} \div \dfrac{3}{4}$ b) $\left(-\dfrac{3}{5}\right) \div \dfrac{7}{8}$

Solution

a) $\dfrac{5}{7} \div \dfrac{3}{4} = \dfrac{5}{7} \cdot \dfrac{4}{3} = \dfrac{5 \cdot 4}{7 \cdot 3} = \dfrac{20}{21}$

b) $\left(-\dfrac{3}{5}\right) \div \dfrac{7}{8} = \dfrac{-3}{5} \cdot \dfrac{8}{7} = \dfrac{-3 \cdot 8}{5 \cdot 7} = \dfrac{-24}{35} = -\dfrac{24}{35}$

Addition and Subtraction of Fractions

Before we can add or subtract fractions, the fractions must have a common denominator. A common denominator is another name for a common multiple of the denominators. The *lowest common denominator (LCD)* is the least common multiple of the denominators.

To add or subtract two fractions with a common denominator, we add or subtract their numerators and retain the common denominator.

Addition and Subtraction of Fractions

$$\frac{a}{c} + \frac{b}{c} = \frac{a + b}{c}, \quad c \neq 0; \quad \frac{a}{c} - \frac{b}{c} = \frac{a - b}{c}, \quad c \neq 0$$

Example 13 *Adding and Subtracting Fractions*

Evaluate.

a) $\dfrac{1}{8} + \dfrac{3}{8}$

b) $\dfrac{19}{24} - \dfrac{5}{24}$

Solution

a) $\dfrac{1}{8} + \dfrac{3}{8} = \dfrac{1 + 3}{8} = \dfrac{4}{8} = \dfrac{1}{2}$

b) $\dfrac{19}{24} - \dfrac{5}{24} = \dfrac{19 - 5}{24} = \dfrac{14}{24} = \dfrac{7}{12}$

Note that in Example 13, the denominators of the fractions being added or subtracted were the same; that is, they have a common denominator. *When adding or subtracting two fractions with unlike denominators, first rewrite each fraction with a common denominator. Then add or subtract the fractions.*

Writing fractions with a common denominator is accomplished with the *fundamental law of rational numbers.*

Fundamental Law of Rational Numbers

If a, b, and c are integers, with $b \neq 0$ and $c \neq 0$, then

$$\frac{a}{b} = \frac{a}{b} \cdot \frac{c}{c} = \frac{a \cdot c}{b \cdot c}$$

The terms $\dfrac{a}{b}$ and $\dfrac{a \cdot c}{b \cdot c}$ are called *equivalent fractions*. For example, since $\dfrac{5}{12} = \dfrac{5 \cdot 5}{12 \cdot 5} = \dfrac{25}{60}$, the fractions $\dfrac{5}{12}$ and $\dfrac{25}{60}$ are equivalent fractions. We will see the importance of equivalent fractions in the next two examples.

Example 14 *Subtracting Fractions with Unlike Denominators*

Evaluate $\dfrac{13}{15} - \dfrac{5}{6}$.

Solution Using prime factorization (Section 5.1), we find that the LCM of 15 and 6 is 30. We will therefore express each fraction as an equivalent fraction with a denominator of 30. First, consider $\dfrac{13}{15}$. To obtain a denominator of 30, we must multiply the denominator, 15, by 2. If the denominator is multiplied by 2, the numerator must also be multiplied by 2 to obtain an equivalent fraction. Next, consider $\dfrac{5}{6}$. To obtain a denominator of 30, we must multiply the denominator, 6, by 5. Therefore, we must multiply both numerator and denominator by 5 to obtain an equivalent fraction.

$$\frac{13}{15} - \frac{5}{6} = \left(\frac{13}{15} \cdot \frac{2}{2}\right) - \left(\frac{5}{6} \cdot \frac{5}{5}\right)$$

$$= \frac{26}{30} - \frac{25}{30}$$

$$= \frac{1}{30}$$

Example 15 *Adding Fractions with Unlike Denominators*

Evaluate $\dfrac{1}{54} + \dfrac{1}{90}$.

Solution On page 216, in Example 6 of Section 5.1, we determined that the LCM of 54 and 90 is 270. Rewrite each fraction as an equivalent fraction using the LCM as the common denominator.

$$\frac{1}{54} + \frac{1}{90} = \left(\frac{1}{54} \cdot \frac{5}{5}\right) + \left(\frac{1}{90} \cdot \frac{3}{3}\right)$$

$$= \frac{5}{270} + \frac{3}{270}$$

$$= \frac{8}{270}$$

Now we reduce $\frac{8}{270}$ by dividing both 8 and 270 by 2, their greatest common factor.

$$\frac{8}{270} = \frac{8 \div 2}{270 \div 2} = \frac{4}{135}$$

Example 16 *Rice Preparation*

Following are the instructions given on a box of Minute Rice. Determine the amount of (a) rice and water, (b) salt, and (c) butter or margarine needed to make 3 servings of rice.

Directions
1. Bring water, salt, and butter (or margarine) to a boil.
2. Stir in rice. Cover; remove from heat. Let stand 5 minutes. Fluff with fork.

To Make	Rice & Water (Equal Measures)	Salt	Butter or Margarine (If Desired)
2 servings	$\frac{2}{3}$ cup	$\frac{1}{4}$ tsp	1 tsp
4 servings	$1\frac{1}{3}$ cups	$\frac{1}{2}$ tsp	2 tsp

Solution Since 3 is halfway between 2 and 4, we can find the amount of each ingredient by finding the average of the amount for 2 and 4 servings. To do so, we add the amounts for 2 servings and 4 servings and divide the sum by 2.

a) Rice and water: $\dfrac{\frac{2}{3} + 1\frac{1}{3}}{2} = \dfrac{\frac{2}{3} + \frac{4}{3}}{2} = \dfrac{\frac{6}{3}}{2} = \dfrac{2}{2} = 1$ cup

b) Salt: $\dfrac{\frac{1}{4}+\frac{1}{2}}{2} = \dfrac{\frac{1}{4}+\frac{2}{4}}{2} = \dfrac{\frac{3}{4}}{2} = \dfrac{3}{4}\cdot\dfrac{1}{2} = \dfrac{3}{8}\,\text{tsp}$

c) Butter or margarine: $\dfrac{1+2}{2} = \dfrac{3}{2}$, or $1\frac{1}{2}\,\text{tsp}$ ∎

The solution to Example 16 can be found in other ways. Suggest two other procedures for solving the same problem.

SECTION 5.3

Exercises

Warm Up Exercises

In Exercises 1–12, fill in the blanks with an appropriate word, phrase, or symbol(s).

1. The set of rational numbers is the set of numbers of the form $\dfrac{p}{q}$, where p and q are _____ and $q \neq 0$.
   Integers

2. For the rational number $\dfrac{p}{q}$, p is called the _____.
   Numerator

3. For the rational number $\dfrac{p}{q}$, q is called the _____.
   Denominator

4. Rational numbers such as $2\frac{3}{4}$ and $-1\frac{1}{2}$ are examples of _____ numbers. Mixed

5. Rational numbers such as $\frac{11}{4}$ and $-\frac{3}{2}$ are examples of _____ fractions. Improper

6. The number $\frac{1}{2}$ can be represented as a(n) _____ decimal number. Terminating

7. The number $\frac{1}{3}$ can be represented as a(n) _____ decimal number. Repeating

8. In the decimal number 0.285714, the 2 is in the _____ position. Tenths

9. In the decimal number 0.285714, the 8 is in the _____ position. Hundredths

10. The product of a number and its _____ must equal 1.
    Reciprocal

11. When adding or subtracting two fractions with unlike denominators, first rewrite each fraction with the _____ common denominator. Least

12. The rational numbers $\frac{1}{2}$ and $\frac{5}{10}$ are examples of _____ fractions. Equivalent

Practice the Skills

In Exercises 13–22, reduce each fraction to lowest terms.

13. $\dfrac{3}{6}$ $\frac{1}{2}$

14. $\dfrac{15}{20}$ $\frac{3}{4}$

15. $\dfrac{28}{63}$ $\frac{4}{9}$

16. $\dfrac{36}{56}$ $\frac{9}{14}$

17. $\dfrac{95}{125}$ $\frac{19}{25}$

18. $\dfrac{13}{221}$ $\frac{1}{17}$

19. $\dfrac{112}{176}$ $\frac{7}{11}$

20. $\dfrac{120}{135}$ $\frac{8}{9}$

In Exercises 21–26, convert each mixed number to an improper fraction.

21. $2\dfrac{3}{7}$ $\frac{17}{7}$

22. $3\dfrac{5}{6}$ $\frac{23}{6}$

23. $-1\dfrac{15}{16}$ $-\frac{31}{16}$

24. $-7\dfrac{1}{5}$ $-\frac{36}{5}$

25. $-4\dfrac{15}{16}$ $-\frac{79}{16}$

26. $11\dfrac{9}{16}$ $\frac{185}{16}$

In Exercises 27–30, write the number of inches indicated by the arrows as an improper fraction.

27.
$\frac{9}{8}$

28.
$\frac{9}{4}$

29.
$\frac{15}{8}$

30.
$\frac{3}{2}$

In Exercises 31–36, convert each improper fraction to a mixed number.

31. $\dfrac{8}{3}$ $2\frac{2}{3}$

32. $\dfrac{19}{7}$ $2\frac{5}{7}$

33. $-\dfrac{73}{6}$ $-12\frac{1}{6}$

34. $-\dfrac{157}{12}$ $-13\frac{1}{12}$

35. $-\dfrac{878}{15}$ $-58\frac{8}{15}$

36. $\dfrac{1028}{21}$ $48\frac{20}{21}$

In Exercises 37–44, express each rational number as terminating or repeating decimal number.

37. $\dfrac{3}{10}$ 0.3 **38.** $\dfrac{7}{8}$ 0.875 **39.** $\dfrac{2}{3}$ $0.\overline{6}$ **40.** $\dfrac{1}{6}$ $0.1\overline{6}$

41. $\dfrac{3}{8}$ 0.375 **42.** $\dfrac{23}{7}$ $3.\overline{285714}$ **43.** $\dfrac{13}{6}$ $2.1\overline{6}$ **44.** $\dfrac{115}{15}$ $7.\overline{6}$

In Exercises 45–52, express each terminating decimal number as a quotient of two integers. If possible, reduce the quotient to lowest terms.

45. 0.25 $\frac{25}{100} = \frac{1}{4}$ **46.** 0.13 $\frac{13}{100}$

47. 0.175 $\frac{175}{1000} = \frac{7}{40}$ **48.** 0.375 $\frac{375}{1000} = \frac{3}{8}$

49. 0.2 $\frac{2}{10} = \frac{1}{5}$ **50.** 0.251 $\frac{251}{1000}$

51. 0.0131 $\frac{131}{10,000}$ **52.** 0.2345 $\frac{2345}{10,000} = \frac{469}{2000}$

In Exercises 53–60, express each repeating decimal number as a quotient of two integers. If possible, reduce the quotient to lowest terms.

53. $0.\overline{2}$ $\frac{2}{9}$ **54.** $0.\overline{7}$ $\frac{7}{9}$

55. $0.\overline{9}$ $\frac{1}{1} = 1$ **56.** $0.\overline{23}$ $\frac{23}{99}$

57. $1.\overline{36}$ $\frac{15}{11}$ **58.** $0.\overline{135}$ $\frac{5}{37}$

59. $2.0\overline{5}$ $\frac{37}{18}$ **60.** $2.4\overline{9}$ $\frac{5}{2}$

In Exercises 61–70, perform the indicated operation and reduce your answer to lowest terms.

61. $\dfrac{1}{3} \cdot \dfrac{6}{7}$ $\frac{2}{7}$ **62.** $\dfrac{1}{4} \div \dfrac{5}{8}$ $\frac{2}{5}$

63. $\left(\dfrac{-3}{8}\right)\left(\dfrac{-16}{15}\right)$ $\frac{2}{5}$ **64.** $\left(-\dfrac{3}{5}\right) \div \dfrac{10}{21}$ $-\frac{63}{50}$

65. $\dfrac{7}{8} \div \dfrac{8}{7}$ $\frac{49}{64}$ **66.** $\dfrac{3}{7} \div \dfrac{3}{7}$ 1

67. $\left(\dfrac{3}{5} \cdot \dfrac{4}{7}\right) \div \dfrac{1}{3}$ $\frac{36}{35}$ **68.** $\left(\dfrac{4}{7} \div \dfrac{4}{5}\right) \cdot \dfrac{1}{7}$ $\frac{5}{49}$

69. $\left[\left(-\dfrac{2}{3}\right)\left(\dfrac{5}{8}\right)\right] \div \left(-\dfrac{7}{16}\right)$ $\frac{20}{21}$

70. $\left(\dfrac{7}{15} \cdot \dfrac{5}{8}\right) \div \left(\dfrac{7}{9} \cdot \dfrac{5}{2}\right)$ $\frac{3}{20}$

In Exercises 71–80, perform the indicated operation and reduce your answer to lowest terms.

71. $\dfrac{2}{5} + \dfrac{1}{3}$ $\frac{11}{15}$ **72.** $\dfrac{5}{6} - \dfrac{3}{4}$ $\frac{1}{12}$

73. $\dfrac{2}{11} + \dfrac{5}{22}$ $\frac{9}{22}$ **74.** $\dfrac{5}{12} + \dfrac{7}{36}$ $\frac{11}{18}$

75. $\dfrac{5}{9} - \dfrac{7}{54}$ $\frac{23}{54}$ **76.** $\dfrac{17}{25} - \dfrac{43}{100}$ $\frac{1}{4}$

77. $\dfrac{1}{12} + \dfrac{1}{48} + \dfrac{1}{72}$ $\frac{17}{144}$ **78.** $\dfrac{3}{5} + \dfrac{7}{15} + \dfrac{9}{75}$ $\frac{89}{75}$

79. $\dfrac{1}{30} - \dfrac{3}{40} - \dfrac{7}{50}$ $-\frac{109}{600}$ **80.** $\dfrac{4}{25} - \dfrac{9}{100} - \dfrac{7}{40}$ $-\frac{21}{200}$

Problem Solving

Alternative methods for adding and subtracting two fractions are shown below. These methods may not result in a solution in its lowest terms.

$$\frac{a}{b} + \frac{c}{d} = \frac{ad + bc}{bd} \quad \text{and} \quad \frac{a}{b} - \frac{c}{d} = \frac{ad - bc}{bd}$$

In Exercises 81–86, use the appropriate formula to evaluate the expression.

81. $\dfrac{5}{8} + \dfrac{1}{3}$ $\frac{23}{24}$ **82.** $\dfrac{4}{7} + \dfrac{2}{5}$ $\frac{34}{35}$ **83.** $\dfrac{5}{6} - \dfrac{7}{8}$ $-\frac{1}{24}$

84. $\dfrac{7}{3} - \dfrac{5}{12}$ $\frac{23}{12}$ **85.** $\dfrac{3}{8} + \dfrac{5}{12}$ $\frac{19}{24}$ **86.** $\left(\dfrac{2}{3} + \dfrac{1}{4}\right) - \dfrac{3}{5}$ $\frac{19}{60}$

In Exercises 87–92, evaluate each expression.

87. $\left(\dfrac{1}{3} \cdot \dfrac{6}{7}\right) + \dfrac{1}{4}$ $\frac{15}{28}$ **88.** $\left(\dfrac{1}{6} \div \dfrac{2}{3}\right) - \dfrac{1}{7}$ $\frac{3}{28}$

89. $\left(\dfrac{3}{4} + \dfrac{1}{6}\right) \div \left(2 - \dfrac{7}{6}\right)$ $\frac{11}{10}$ **90.** $\left(\dfrac{1}{3} \cdot \dfrac{3}{7}\right) + \left(\dfrac{3}{5} \cdot \dfrac{10}{11}\right)$ $\frac{53}{77}$

91. $\left(3 - \dfrac{4}{9}\right) \div \left(4 + \dfrac{2}{3}\right)$ $\frac{23}{42}$ **92.** $\left(\dfrac{2}{5} \div \dfrac{4}{9}\right)\left(\dfrac{3}{5} \cdot 6\right)$ $\frac{81}{25}$

In Exercises 93–104, write an expression that will solve the problem and then evaluate the expression.

93. *Height Increase* When David Conway finished his first year of high school, his height was $69\frac{7}{8}$ inches. When he returned to school after the summer, David's height was $71\frac{5}{8}$ inches. How much did David's height increase over the summer? $1\frac{3}{4}$ in.

94. *Thistles* Diane Helbing has four different varieties of thistles invading her pasture. She estimates that of these thistles, $\frac{1}{2}$ are Canada thistles, $\frac{1}{4}$ are bull thistles, $\frac{1}{6}$ are plumeless thistles, and the rest are musk thistles. What fraction of the thistles are musk thistles? $\frac{1}{12}$

95. *Stairway Height* A stairway consists of 14 stairs, each $8\frac{5}{8}$ inches high. What is the vertical height of the stairway? $120\frac{3}{4}$ in.

96. *Alphabet Soup* Margaret Cannata's recipe for alphabet soup calls for (among other items) $\frac{1}{4}$ cup snipped parsley, $\frac{1}{8}$ teaspoon pepper, and $\frac{1}{2}$ cup sliced carrots. Margaret is expecting company and needs to multiply the amounts of the ingredients by $1\frac{1}{2}$ times. Determine the amount of (a) snipped parsley, (b) pepper, and (c) sliced carrots she needs for the soup. a) $\frac{3}{8}$ cup b) $\frac{3}{16}$ tsp c) $\frac{3}{4}$ cup

97. *Sprinkler System* To repair his sprinkler system, Tony Gambino needs a total of $20\frac{5}{16}$ inches of PVC pipe. He has on hand pieces that measure $2\frac{1}{4}$ inches, $3\frac{7}{8}$ inches, and $4\frac{1}{4}$ inches in length. If he can combine these pieces and use them in the repair, how long a piece of PVC pipe will Tony need to purchase to repair his sprinkler system? $9\frac{15}{16}$ in.

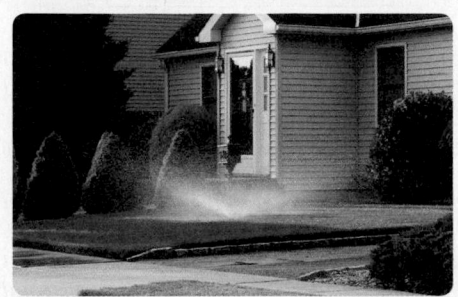

98. *Crop Storage* Todd Schroeder has a silo on his farm in which he can store silage made from his various crops. He currently has a silo that is $\frac{1}{4}$ full of corn silage, $\frac{2}{5}$ full of hay silage, and $\frac{1}{3}$ full of oats silage. What fraction of Todd's silo is currently in use? $\frac{59}{60}$

99. *Department Budget* Jaime Bailey is chair of the humanities department at Santa Fe Community College. Jaime has a budget in which $\frac{1}{2}$ of the money is for photocopying, $\frac{2}{5}$ of the money is for computer-related expenses, and the rest of the money is for student tutors in the foreign languages lab. What fraction of Jaime's budget is for student tutors? $\frac{1}{10}$

100. *Art Supplies* Denise Viale teaches kindergarten and is buying supplies for her class to make papier-mâché piggy banks. Each piggy bank to be made requires $1\frac{1}{4}$ cups of flour. If Denise has 15 students who are going to make piggy banks, how much flour does Denise need to purchase? $18\frac{3}{4}$ cups

101. *Height of a Computer Stand* The instructions for assembling a computer stand include a diagram illustrating its dimensions. Find the total height of the stand. $58\frac{7}{8}$ in.

102. *Width of a Picture* The width of a picture is $24\frac{7}{8}$ in., as shown in the diagram. Find x, the distance from the edge of the frame to the center. $12\frac{7}{16}$ in.

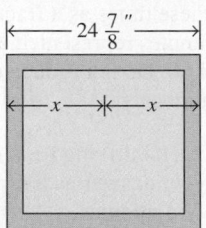

103. *Traveling Interstate 5* While on vacation, Janet Mazerella traveled the full length of Interstate Highway 5 from the U.S.–Canadian border to the U.S.–Mexican border. She recorded the following travel times between cities: Blaine, Washington, to Seattle: 1 hour 49 minutes; Seattle to Portland: 2 hours 48 minutes; Portland to Sacramento: 9 hours 6 minutes; Sacramento to Los Angeles: 6 hours 3 minutes; Los Angeles to San Diego: 2 hours 9 minutes; San Diego to San Ysidro, California: 22 minutes.

a) Write each of these times as a fraction or as a mixed number with minutes represented as a fraction with a denominator of 60. Do not reduce the fractional part of the mixed number. $1\frac{49}{60}, 2\frac{48}{60}, 9\frac{6}{60}, 6\frac{3}{60}, 2\frac{9}{60}, \frac{22}{60}$

b) What is Janet's total driving time from Blaine, Washington, to San Ysidro, California? Give your answer as a mixed number and in terms of hours and minutes. $22\frac{17}{60}$; 22 hours 17 minutes

▲ *Interstate Highway 5*

104. *Traveling Across Texas* While on vacation, Omar Rodriguez traveled the entire length of Interstate Highway 10 in Texas. Omar recorded the following travel times between cities on his trip. Anthony to El Paso: 25 minutes; El Paso to San Antonio: 7 hours

54 minutes; San Antonio to Houston: 3 hours 1 minute; Houston to Beaumont: 1 hour 23 minutes; Beaumont to Orange: 28 minutes.

a) Write each of these times as a fraction or as a mixed number with minutes represented as a fraction with a denominator of 60. Do not reduce the fractional part of the mixed number. $\frac{25}{60}, 7\frac{54}{60}, 3\frac{1}{60}, 1\frac{23}{60}, \frac{28}{60}$

b) What is Omar's total driving time from Anthony to Orange? Give your answer as a mixed number and in terms of hours and minutes. $13\frac{11}{60}$; 13 hours 11 minutes

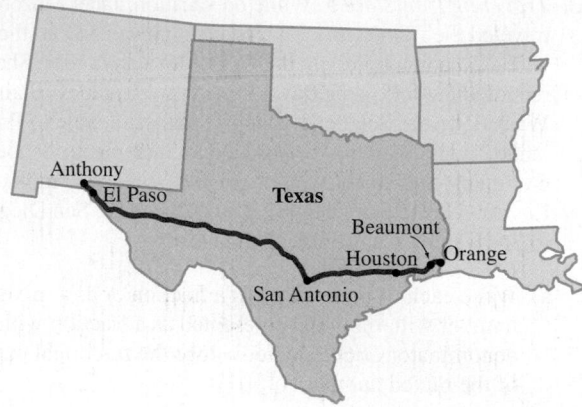

▲ *Interstate Highway 10*

Challenge Problems/Group Activities

105. *Cutting Lumber* If a piece of wood $8\frac{3}{4}$ ft long is to be cut into four equal pieces, find the length of each piece. (Allow $\frac{1}{8}$ in. for each saw cut.) $26\frac{5}{32}$ in.

106. *Dimensions of a Room* A rectangular room measures 8 ft 3 in. by 10 ft 8 in. by 9 ft 2 in. high.

a) Determine the perimeter of the room in feet. Write your answer as a mixed number. $37\frac{5}{6}$ ft

b) Calculate the area of the floor of the room in square feet. 88 ft²

c) Calculate the volume of the room in cubic feet. Use volume = length × width × height. Write your answer as a mixed number. $806\frac{2}{3}$ ft³

107. *Hanging a Picture* The back of a framed picture that is to be hung is shown above on the right. A nail is to be hammered into the wall, and the picture will be hung by the wire on the nail.

a) If the center of the wire is to rest on the nail and a side of the picture is to be 20 in. from the window, how far from the window should the nail be placed? $29\frac{3}{16}$ in.

b) If the top of the frame is to be $26\frac{1}{4}$ in. from the ceiling, how far from the ceiling should the nail be placed? (Assume the wire will not stretch.) 33 in.

c) Repeat part (b) if the wire will stretch $\frac{1}{4}$ in. when the picture is hung. $32\frac{3}{4}$ in.

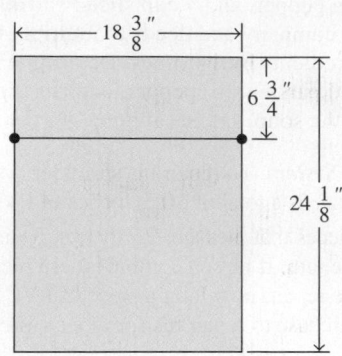

108. *Increasing a Book Size* The dimensions of the cover of a book have been increased from $8\frac{1}{2}$ in. by $9\frac{1}{4}$ in. to $8\frac{1}{2}$ in. by $10\frac{1}{4}$ in. By how many square inches has the surface area increased? Use area = length × width. $8\frac{1}{2}$ in.²

Dense Set of Numbers A set of numbers is said to be a *dense set* if between any two distinct members of the set there exists a third distinct member of the set. The set of integers is not dense since between any two consecutive integers there is not another integer. For example, between 1 and 2 there are no other integers. The set of rational numbers is dense because between any two distinct rational numbers there exists a third distinct rational number. For example, we can find a rational number between 0.243 and 0.244. The number 0.243 can be written as 0.2430, and 0.244 can be written as 0.2440. There are many numbers between these two. Some of them are 0.2431, 0.2435, and 0.243912. In Exercises 109–114, find a rational number between the two numbers in each pair. Many answers are possible.

109. 0.21 and 0.22 0.215

110. 4.005 and 4.05 4.0275

111. −2.176 and −2.175 −2.1755

112. 1.3457 and 1.34571 1.345705

113. 4.872 and 4.873 4.8725

114. −3.7896 and −3.7895 −3.78955

Halfway Between Two Numbers To find a rational number halfway between any two rational numbers given in fraction form, add the two numbers together and divide their sum by 2. In Exercises 115–120, find a rational number halfway between the two fractions in each pair.

115. $\frac{1}{4}$ and $\frac{3}{4}$ $\frac{1}{2}$

116. $\frac{1}{5}$ and $\frac{2}{5}$ $\frac{3}{10}$

117. $\frac{1}{100}$ and $\frac{1}{10}$ $\frac{11}{200}$

118. $\frac{7}{13}$ and $\frac{8}{13}$ $\frac{15}{26}$

119. $\frac{1}{99}$ and $\frac{1}{9}$ $\frac{2}{33}$

120. $\frac{1}{2}$ and $\frac{2}{3}$ $\frac{7}{12}$

121. *Cooking Oatmeal* Following are the instructions given on a box of oatmeal. Determine the amount of water (or milk) and oats needed to make $1\frac{1}{2}$ servings by:

a) Adding the amount of each ingredient needed for 1 serving to the amount needed for 2 servings and dividing by 2. $1\frac{3}{8}$ cup water (or milk) and $\frac{3}{4}$ cup oatmeal

b) Adding the amount of each ingredient needed for 1 serving to half the amount needed for 1 serving.
$1\frac{1}{2}$ cup water (or milk) and $\frac{3}{4}$ cup oatmeal

Directions
1. Boil water or milk and salt (if desired).
2. Stir in oats.
3. Stirring occasionally, cook over medium heat for 5 minutes.

Servings	1	2
Water (or milk)	1 cup	$1\frac{3}{4}$ cup
Oats	$\frac{1}{2}$ cup	1 cup
Salt (optional)	dash	$\frac{1}{8}$ tsp

122. Consider the rational number $0.\overline{9}$.

a) Use the method from Example 8 on page 234 to convert $0.\overline{9}$ to a quotient of integers. 1

b) Find a number halfway between $0.\overline{9}$ and 1 by adding the two numbers and dividing by 2. $0.\overline{9}$

c) Find $\frac{1}{3} + \frac{2}{3}$ by adding the fractions. Now express $\frac{1}{3}$ and $\frac{2}{3}$ as repeating decimals and find the sum using the decimal representation of $\frac{1}{3}$ and $\frac{2}{3}$.
$\frac{1}{3} + \frac{2}{3} = 1, 0.\overline{3} + 0.\overline{6} = 0.\overline{9}$

d) What conclusion can you draw from parts (a), (b), and (c)? $0.\overline{9} = 1$

Recreational Mathematics

123. *Paper Folding* Read the *Recreational Mathematics* box on page 230. Next, take a clean sheet of white paper and fold it in half, fold it in half again, and fold it in half a third time. Now unfold the paper. You should have eight equal regions of the paper.

a) What fraction does each region represent? $\frac{1}{8}$

b) Next, color three of the regions red and one of the regions blue, as shown in the diagram below.

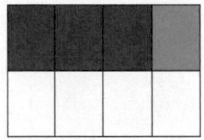

Use the paper to determine the following sum; $\frac{3}{8} + \frac{1}{8}$. Write your answer in reduced form. $\frac{1}{2}$

c) Next, return the paper to its folded state and then fold the paper in half again. Use the blue region of the paper to determine the following product: $\frac{1}{16} \times 2$. $\frac{1}{8}$

d) Use the blue region of the paper to determine the following quotient: $\frac{1}{8} \div 2$. $\frac{1}{16}$

Internet/Research Activity

124. The ancient Greeks are often considered the first true mathematicians. Write a report summarizing the ancient Greeks' contributions to rational numbers. Include in your report what they learned and believed about the rational numbers. References include encyclopedias, history of mathematics books, and Internet Web sites.

SECTION 5.4

The Irrational Numbers and the Real Number System

▲ *The distance from the northwest corner of a football field to the southeast corner is an irrational number.*

A football field is 160 ft wide and 360 ft long. A football player catches the football from a kickoff in the northwest corner of one end zone and runs across the field to the southeast corner of the other end zone, as shown by the dashed line in the diagram.

160 ft

360 ft

How far did the football player run? The answer to this question is an example of an *irrational* number. In this section, we will introduce irrational numbers along with the operations of addition, subtraction, multiplication, and division of irrational numbers. The answer to the above question is $40\sqrt{97}$ feet, or about 394 feet.

> **Why** *This is Important* Irrational numbers play an important role in many areas of mathematics, science, business, and other fields.

$$a^2 + b^2 = c^2$$

Figure 5.7

Pythagoras (ca. 585–500 B.C.), a Greek mathematician, is credited with providing a written proof that in any *right triangle* (a triangle with a 90° angle; see Fig. 5.7), the square of the length of one side (a^2) added to the square of the length of the other side (b^2) equals the square of the length of the hypotenuse (c^2). The formula $a^2 + b^2 = c^2$ is now known as the *Pythagorean theorem*.[*] Pythagoras found that when using the formula, with $a = 1$ and $b = 1$, the value of c was not a rational number.

$$a^2 + b^2 = c^2$$
$$1^2 + 1^2 = c^2$$
$$1 + 1 = c^2$$
$$2 = c^2$$

There is no rational number that when squared will equal 2. This fact prompted a need for a new set of numbers, the irrational numbers.

In Section 5.2, we introduced the real number line. The points on the real number line that are not rational numbers are referred to as irrational numbers. Recall that every rational number is either a terminating or a repeating decimal number. Therefore, irrational numbers, when represented as decimal numbers, will be nonterminating, nonrepeating decimal numbers.

Definition: Irrational Number
An **irrational number** is a real number whose decimal representation is a nonterminating, nonrepeating decimal number.

A nonrepeating decimal number such as 5.12639537… can be used to indicate an irrational number. Notice that no number or set of numbers repeat on a continuous basis, and the three dots at the end of the number indicate that the number continues indefinitely. Nonrepeating number patterns can be used to indicate irrational numbers. For example, 6.1011011101111… and 0.525225222… are both irrational numbers.

The expression $\sqrt{2}$ is read "the square root of 2" or "radical 2." The symbol $\sqrt{}$ is called the *radical sign*, and the number or expression inside the radical sign is called the *radicand*. In $\sqrt{2}$, 2 is the radicand.

The square roots of some numbers are rational, whereas the square roots of other numbers are irrational. The *principal* (or *positive*) *square root* of a number n, written $\sqrt{n}$, is the positive number that, when multiplied by itself, gives n. Whenever we mention the term "square root" in this text, we mean the principal square root. For example,

$$\sqrt{9} = 3 \quad \text{since} \quad 3 \cdot 3 = 9$$
$$\sqrt{36} = 6 \quad \text{since} \quad 6 \cdot 6 = 36$$

Both $\sqrt{9}$ and $\sqrt{36}$ are examples of numbers that are rational numbers because 3 and 6, respectively, are terminating decimal numbers.

We return to the problem faced by Pythagoras: If $c^2 = 2$, then it can be shown that c has a value of $\sqrt{2}$, but what is $\sqrt{2}$ equal to? The $\sqrt{2}$ is an irrational number, and it cannot be expressed as a terminating or repeating decimal number. It can only

---
[*]The Pythagorean theorem is discussed in more detail in Section 9.3.

Pythagoras of Samos founded a philosophical and religious school in southern Italy in the sixth century B.C. The scholars at the school, known as Pythagoreans, produced important works of mathematics, astronomy, and theory of music. Although the Pythagoreans are credited with proving the Pythagorean theorem, it was known to the ancient Babylonians 1000 years earlier. The Pythagoreans were a secret society that formed a model for many secret societies in existence today. One practice was that students were to spend their first three years of study in silence, while their master, Pythagoras, spoke to them from behind a curtain. Among other philosophical beliefs of the Pythagoreans was "that at its deepest level, reality is mathematical in nature."

be approximated by a decimal number: $\sqrt{2}$ is approximately 1.4142136 (to seven decimal places). Later in this section, we will discuss using a calculator to approximate irrational numbers.

Other irrational numbers include $\sqrt{3}$, $\sqrt{5}$, and $\sqrt{37}$. Another important irrational number used to represent the ratio of a circle's circumference to its diameter is pi, symbolized π. Pi is approximately 3.1415927.

We have discussed procedures for performing the arithmetic operations of addition, subtraction, multiplication, and division with rational numbers. We can perform the same operations with the irrational numbers. Before we can proceed, however, we must understand the numbers called perfect squares. Any number that is the square of a natural number is said to be a *perfect square*. Some perfect squares are shown in the following chart.

Natural numbers	1,	2,	3,	4,	5,	6, …
Squares of the natural numbers	1^2,	2^2,	3^2,	4^2,	5^2,	6^2, …
or perfect squares	1,	4,	9,	16,	25,	36, …

The numbers 1, 4, 9, 16, 25, and 36 are some of the perfect square numbers. Can you determine the next two perfect square numbers? How many perfect square numbers are there? The square root of a perfect square number will be a natural number. For example, $\sqrt{1} = 1$, $\sqrt{4} = 2$, $\sqrt{9} = 3$, $\sqrt{16} = 4$, $\sqrt{25} = 5$, and so on.

The number that multiplies a radical is called the radical's *coefficient*. For example, in $3\sqrt{5}$, the 3 is the coefficient of the radical.

Some irrational numbers can be simplified by determining whether there are any perfect square factors in the radicand. If there are, the following rule can be used to simplify the radical.

Product Rule for Radicals

$$\sqrt{a \cdot b} = \sqrt{a} \cdot \sqrt{b}, \quad a \geq 0, \quad b \geq 0$$

To simplify a radical, write the radical as a product of two radicals. One of the radicals should contain the greatest perfect square that is a factor of the radicand in the original expression. Then simplify the radical containing the perfect square factor. For example,

$$\sqrt{18} = \sqrt{9 \cdot 2} = \sqrt{9} \cdot \sqrt{2} = 3 \cdot \sqrt{2} = 3\sqrt{2}$$

and

$$\sqrt{75} = \sqrt{25 \cdot 3} = \sqrt{25} \cdot \sqrt{3} = 5 \cdot \sqrt{3} = 5\sqrt{3}$$

Example 1 *Simplifying Radicals*

Simplify.
a) $\sqrt{18}$ b) $\sqrt{80}$

Solution

a) Since 9 is a perfect square factor of 18, we write

$$\sqrt{18} = \sqrt{9 \cdot 2} = \sqrt{9} \cdot \sqrt{2} = 3 \cdot \sqrt{2} = 3\sqrt{2}$$

Since 2 has no perfect square factors, $\sqrt{2}$ cannot be simplified.

b) Since 16 is a perfect square factor of 80, we write

$$\sqrt{80} = \sqrt{16 \cdot 5} = \sqrt{16} \cdot \sqrt{5} = 4 \cdot \sqrt{5} = 4\sqrt{5}$$

■

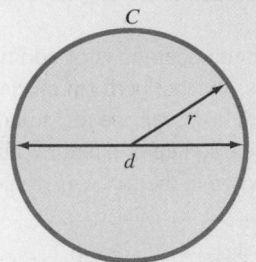
In Example 1(b), you can obtain the correct answer if you start out factoring differently:

$$\sqrt{80} = \sqrt{4 \cdot 20} = \sqrt{4} \cdot \sqrt{20} = 2 \cdot \sqrt{20} = 2\sqrt{20}$$

Note that 20 has 4 as a perfect square factor.

$$2\sqrt{20} = 2\sqrt{4 \cdot 5} = 2 \cdot \sqrt{4} \cdot \sqrt{5} = 2 \cdot 2 \cdot \sqrt{5} = 4\sqrt{5}$$

The second method will eventually give the same answer, but it requires more work. It is best to try to factor out the *largest* perfect square factor from the radicand.

Addition and Subtraction of Irrational Numbers

To add or subtract two or more square roots with the same radicand, add or subtract their coefficients while keeping the common radicand. The answer is the sum or difference of the coefficients multiplied by the common radical.

Example 2 *Adding and Subtracting Radicals with the Same Radicand*

Simplify.
a) $3\sqrt{2} + 7\sqrt{2}$ b) $5\sqrt{7} - 3\sqrt{7} + \sqrt{7}$

Solution

a) $3\sqrt{2} + 7\sqrt{2} = (3 + 7)\sqrt{2} = 10\sqrt{2}$
b) $5\sqrt{7} - 3\sqrt{7} + \sqrt{7} = (5 - 3 + 1)\sqrt{7} = 3\sqrt{7}$

Note that $\sqrt{7} = 1\sqrt{7}$.   ∎

Example 3 *Subtracting Radicals with Different Radicands*

Simplify $5\sqrt{3} - \sqrt{12}$.

Solution   These radicals cannot be subtracted in their present form because they contain different radicands. When that occurs, determine whether one or more of the radicals can be simplified so that they have the same radicand.

$$5\sqrt{3} - \sqrt{12} = 5\sqrt{3} - \sqrt{4 \cdot 3}$$
$$= 5\sqrt{3} - \sqrt{4} \cdot \sqrt{3}$$
$$= 5\sqrt{3} - 2\sqrt{3}$$
$$= (5 - 2)\sqrt{3} = 3\sqrt{3}$$ ∎

Multiplication of Irrational Numbers

When multiplying irrational numbers, we again make use of the product rule for radicals, as introduced on page 245. After the radicands are multiplied, simplify the remaining radical when possible.

Example 4 *Multiplying Radicals*

Simplify.
a) $\sqrt{2} \cdot \sqrt{8}$ b) $\sqrt{5} \cdot \sqrt{11}$ c) $\sqrt{10} \cdot \sqrt{15}$

Solution

a) $\sqrt{2} \cdot \sqrt{8} = \sqrt{2 \cdot 8} = \sqrt{16} = 4$ b) $\sqrt{5} \cdot \sqrt{11} = \sqrt{5 \cdot 11} = \sqrt{55}$
c) $\sqrt{10} \cdot \sqrt{15} = \sqrt{10 \cdot 15} = \sqrt{150} = \sqrt{25 \cdot 6} = \sqrt{25} \cdot \sqrt{6} = 5\sqrt{6}$ ∎

Division of Irrational Numbers

To divide irrational numbers, use the following rule. After performing the division, simplify when possible.

Quotient Rule for Radicals

$$\frac{\sqrt{a}}{\sqrt{b}} = \sqrt{\frac{a}{b}}, \quad a \geq 0, \quad b > 0$$

Example 5 *Dividing Radicals*

Divide.

a) $\dfrac{\sqrt{8}}{\sqrt{2}}$

b) $\dfrac{\sqrt{96}}{\sqrt{2}}$

Solution

a) $\dfrac{\sqrt{8}}{\sqrt{2}} = \sqrt{\dfrac{8}{2}} = \sqrt{4} = 2$

b) $\dfrac{\sqrt{96}}{\sqrt{2}} = \sqrt{\dfrac{96}{2}} = \sqrt{48} = \sqrt{16 \cdot 3} = \sqrt{16} \cdot \sqrt{3} = 4\sqrt{3}$ ∎

Rationalizing the Denominator

A denominator of a fraction is *rationalized* when it contains no radical expressions. To rationalize a denominator that contains only a square root, multiply both the numerator and denominator of the fraction by a number that will result in the radicand in the denominator becoming a perfect square. (This action is the equivalent of multiplying the fraction by 1 because the value of the fraction does not change.) Then simplify the fractions when possible.

Example 6 *Rationalizing the Denominator*

Rationalize the denominator of the following.

a) $\dfrac{5}{\sqrt{2}}$ b) $\dfrac{5}{\sqrt{12}}$ c) $\dfrac{\sqrt{5}}{\sqrt{10}}$

Solution

a) Multiply the numerator and denominator by a number that will make the radicand in the denominator a perfect square.

$$\frac{5}{\sqrt{2}} = \frac{5}{\sqrt{2}} \cdot \frac{\sqrt{2}}{\sqrt{2}} = \frac{5\sqrt{2}}{\sqrt{4}} = \frac{5\sqrt{2}}{2}$$

Note that the 2's in the answer cannot be divided out because one 2 is a radicand and the other is not.

b) $\dfrac{5}{\sqrt{12}} = \dfrac{5}{\sqrt{12}} \cdot \dfrac{\sqrt{3}}{\sqrt{3}} = \dfrac{5\sqrt{3}}{\sqrt{36}} = \dfrac{5\sqrt{3}}{6}$

You could have obtained the same answer to this problem by multiplying both the numerator and denominator by $\sqrt{12}$ and then simplifying. Try to do so now.

c) Write $\dfrac{\sqrt{5}}{\sqrt{10}}$ as $\sqrt{\dfrac{5}{10}}$ and reduce the fraction to obtain $\sqrt{\dfrac{1}{2}}$. By the quotient rule

for radicals, $\sqrt{\dfrac{1}{2}} = \dfrac{\sqrt{1}}{\sqrt{2}}$ or $\dfrac{1}{\sqrt{2}}$. Now rationalize the denominator of $\dfrac{1}{\sqrt{2}}$.

$$\frac{1}{\sqrt{2}} = \frac{1}{\sqrt{2}} \cdot \frac{\sqrt{2}}{\sqrt{2}} = \frac{\sqrt{2}}{2}$$ ∎

Estimating Square Roots Without a Calculator

Consider the irrational number $\sqrt{17}$. The radicand 17 is between the two perfect squares 16 and 25. Since $\sqrt{16} = 4$ and $\sqrt{25} = 5$, we can reason that $\sqrt{17}$ is between 4 and 5. We summarize this discussion as follows.

$$16 < 17 < 25$$
$$\sqrt{16} < \sqrt{17} < \sqrt{25}$$
$$4 < \sqrt{17} < 5$$

Furthermore, since 17 is closer to 16 than it is to 25, we can further estimate that $\sqrt{17}$ is closer to 4 than it is to 5. In other words, $\sqrt{17}$ is between 4 and 4.5.

Example 7 *Estimating Square Roots*

The following diagram is a sketch of a 16-in. ruler marked using $\dfrac{1}{2}$ inches.

```
 1  2  3  4  5  6  7  8  9  10 11 12 13 14 15
|ı|ı|ı|ı|ı|ı|ı|ı|ı|ı|ı|ı|ı|ı|ı|ı|ı|ı|ı|ı|ı|ı|ı|ı|ı|ı|ı|ı|ı|ı|ı|
```

Indicate between which two adjacent ruler marks each of the following irrational numbers will fall.
a) $\sqrt{7}$ b) $\sqrt{89}$

Solution

a) $4 < 7 < 9$
    $\sqrt{4} < \sqrt{7} < \sqrt{9}$
       $2 < \sqrt{7} < 3$

Furthermore, since 7 is closer to 9 than it is to 4, $\sqrt{7}$ is closer to 3 than it is to 2. Thus, $\sqrt{7}$ is between 2.5 and 3.

b) $81 < 89 < 100$
    $\sqrt{81} < \sqrt{89} < \sqrt{100}$
       $9 < \sqrt{89} < 10$

Furthermore, since 89 is closer to 81 than it is to 100, $\sqrt{89}$ is closer to 9 than it is to 10. Thus, $\sqrt{89}$ is between 9 and 9.5. ∎

Approximating Square Roots on a Scientific Calculator

Consider the irrational number the square root of two. We use the symbol $\sqrt{2}$ to represent the *exact value* of this number. Although exact values are important, approximations are also important, especially when working with application problems. We can use a scientific calculator to obtain approximations for square roots. Scientific calculators generally have one of the following square root keys:[*]

$$\boxed{\sqrt{}} \quad \text{or} \quad \boxed{\sqrt{x}}$$

---

[*]If your calculator has the $\sqrt{}$ symbol printed *above* the key instead of on the face of the key, you can access the square root function by first pressing the "2nd" or the "inverse" key.

For simplicity, we will refer to the square root key with the $\boxed{\sqrt{}}$ symbol. To approximate $\sqrt{2}$, perform the following keystrokes:

$$\boxed{2} \quad \boxed{\sqrt{}}$$

or, depending on your model of calculator, you may have to do the following:

$$\boxed{\sqrt{}} \quad \boxed{2} \quad \boxed{\text{ENTER}}$$

The display on your calculator may read 1.414213562. Your calculator may display more or fewer digits. It is important to realize that 1.414213562 is a rational number *approximation* for the irrational number $\sqrt{2}$. The symbol $\approx$ means *is approximately equal to*, and we write

$$\sqrt{2} \approx 1.414213562$$

      ↑   ↑

Exact value (irrational number)   Approximation (rational number)

Example 8 *Approximating Square Roots*

Use a scientific calculator to approximate the following square roots. Round each answer to two decimal places.

a) $\sqrt{7}$ b) $\sqrt{89}$

Solution

a) $\sqrt{7} \approx 2.65$ b) $\sqrt{89} \approx 9.43$

Note that these approximations confirm the estimates that were made in Example 7. ∎

SECTION 5.4   *Exercises*

Warm Up Exercises

In Exercises 1–8, fill in the blanks with an appropriate word, phrase, or symbol(s).

1. A real number whose decimal representation is a nonterminating, nonrepeating decimal number is known as a(n) _____ number. Irrational

2. The symbol $\sqrt{}$ is called the _____ sign. Radical

3. In the expression $5\sqrt{7}$, the 7 is called the _____. Radicand

4. In the expression $5\sqrt{7}$, the 5 is called the radical's _____. Coefficient

5. The principal (or positive) square root of a number n, written $\sqrt{n}$, is the positive number that, when multiplied by _____, gives n. Itself

6. Any number that is the square of a natural number is called a(n) _____ square. Perfect

7. When the denominator of a fraction contains no radical expressions, it is said to be _____. Rationalized

8. Consider the irrational number the square root of two.

  a) We use the symbol $\sqrt{2}$ to represent the _____ value of the number. Exact

  b) The number 1.414213562 is a(n) _____ of the number $\sqrt{2}$. Approximation

Practice the Skills

In Exercises 9–18, determine whether the number is rational or irrational.

9. $\sqrt{9}$ Rational   **10.** $\sqrt{10}$ Irrational

11. $\dfrac{2}{3}$ Rational   **12.** 0.212112111 … Irrational

13. 3.575775777 … Irrational   **14.** π Irrational

15. $\dfrac{22}{7}$ Rational   **16.** 3.14159 Rational

17. 3.14159 … Irrational   **18.** $\dfrac{\sqrt{5}}{\sqrt{5}}$ Rational

In Exercises 19–26, evaluate the expression.

19. $\sqrt{0}$ 0 **20.** $\sqrt{1}$ 1 **21.** $\sqrt{36}$ 6 **22.** $-\sqrt{121}$ −11

23. $-\sqrt{169}$ −13 **24.** $\sqrt{25}$ 5 **25.** $-\sqrt{81}$ −9 **26.** $-\sqrt{36}$ −6

In Exercises 27–36, classify the number as a member of one or more of the following sets: the rational numbers, the integers, the natural numbers, the irrational numbers.

27. 0 Rational number, integer

28. −5 Rational number, integer

29. $\sqrt{9}$ Rational number, integer, natural number

30. $\dfrac{3}{8}$ Rational number

31. 0.040040004 Rational number

32. 2.718 Rational number

33. $-\dfrac{7}{8}$ Rational number

34. 0.123123123 Rational number

35. $0.\overline{123}$ Rational number

36. 0.123112311123... Irrational number

In Exercises 37–44, simplify the radical.

37. $\sqrt{18}$ $3\sqrt{2}$

38. $\sqrt{24}$ $2\sqrt{6}$

39. $\sqrt{45}$ $3\sqrt{5}$

40. $\sqrt{50}$ $5\sqrt{2}$

41. $\sqrt{63}$ $3\sqrt{7}$

42. $\sqrt{75}$ $5\sqrt{3}$

43. $\sqrt{84}$ $2\sqrt{21}$

44. $\sqrt{90}$ $3\sqrt{10}$

In Exercises 45–52, perform the indicated operation.

45. $2\sqrt{3} + 5\sqrt{3}$ $7\sqrt{3}$

46. $5\sqrt{3} - 7\sqrt{3}$ $-2\sqrt{3}$

47. $3\sqrt{20} - 2\sqrt{45}$ 0

48. $2\sqrt{18} - 3\sqrt{50}$ $-9\sqrt{2}$

49. $4\sqrt{12} - 7\sqrt{27}$ $-13\sqrt{3}$

50. $2\sqrt{7} + 5\sqrt{28}$ $12\sqrt{7}$

51. $5\sqrt{3} + 7\sqrt{12} - 3\sqrt{75}$ $4\sqrt{3}$

52. $\sqrt{63} + 13\sqrt{98} - 5\sqrt{112}$ $-17\sqrt{7} + 91\sqrt{2}$

In Exercises 53–60, perform the indicated operation. Simplify the answer when possible.

53. $\sqrt{2}\sqrt{8}$ 4

54. $\sqrt{3}\sqrt{21}$ $3\sqrt{7}$

55. $\sqrt{6}\sqrt{14}$ $2\sqrt{21}$

56. $\sqrt{2}\sqrt{10}$ $2\sqrt{5}$

57. $\dfrac{\sqrt{20}}{\sqrt{5}}$ 2

58. $\dfrac{\sqrt{125}}{\sqrt{5}}$ 5

59. $\dfrac{\sqrt{72}}{\sqrt{8}}$ 3

60. $\dfrac{\sqrt{145}}{\sqrt{5}}$ $\sqrt{29}$

In Exercises 61–68, rationalize the denominator.

61. $\dfrac{1}{\sqrt{2}}$ $\dfrac{\sqrt{2}}{2}$

62. $\dfrac{2}{\sqrt{2}}$ $\sqrt{2}$

63. $\dfrac{\sqrt{7}}{\sqrt{5}}$ $\dfrac{\sqrt{35}}{5}$

64. $\dfrac{\sqrt{2}}{\sqrt{7}}$ $\dfrac{\sqrt{14}}{7}$

65. $\dfrac{\sqrt{20}}{\sqrt{3}}$ $\dfrac{2\sqrt{15}}{3}$

66. $\dfrac{\sqrt{50}}{\sqrt{14}}$ $\dfrac{5\sqrt{7}}{7}$

67. $\dfrac{\sqrt{10}}{\sqrt{6}}$ $\dfrac{\sqrt{15}}{3}$

68. $\dfrac{\sqrt{2}}{\sqrt{27}}$ $\dfrac{\sqrt{6}}{9}$

Problem Solving

Approximating Radicals *The following diagram is a sketch of a 16-in. ruler marked using $\frac{1}{2}$ inches.*

1 2 3 4 5 6 7 8 9 10 11 12 13 14 15

In Exercises 69–74, without using a calculator, indicate between which two adjacent ruler marks each of the following irrational numbers will fall. Support your answer by obtaining an approximation with a calculator.

69. $\sqrt{11}$ Between 3 and 3.5

70. $\sqrt{67}$ Between 8 and 8.5

71. $\sqrt{107}$ in. *

72. $\sqrt{135}$ in. *

73. $\sqrt{170}$ in. *

74. $\sqrt{200}$ in. *

In Exercises 75–80, determine whether the statement is true or false. Rewrite each false statement to make it a true statement. A false statement can be modified in more than one way to be made a true statement.

75. $\sqrt{c}$ is a rational number for any composite number c. *

76. $\sqrt{p}$ is a rational number for any prime number p.
False. $\sqrt{p}$ is an irrational number for any prime number p.

77. The sum of any two rational numbers is always a rational number. True

78. The product of any two rational numbers is always a rational number. True

79. The product of an irrational and a rational number is always an irrational number. *

80. The product of any two irrational numbers is always an irrational number. False. The product of two irrational numbers may be a rational number or an irrational number.

In Exercises 81–84, give an example to show that the stated case can occur.

81. The sum of two irrational numbers may be an irrational number. $3\sqrt{2} + 5\sqrt{2} = 8\sqrt{2}$

82. The sum of two irrational numbers may be a rational number. $\pi + (-\pi) = 0$

83. The product of two irrational numbers may be an irrational number. $\sqrt{2} \cdot \sqrt{3} = \sqrt{6}$

84. The product of two irrational numbers may be a rational number. $\sqrt{2} \cdot \sqrt{8} = \sqrt{16} = 4$

*See Instructor Answer Appendix

85. Height of Boys The median height of boys less than 5 years old can be estimated using the formula $H = 2.9\sqrt{x} + 20.1$, where H is the height in inches and x is the boys' age in months. Estimate the median height of boys who are 30 months old. Round your answer to the nearest tenth of an inch. 36.0 inches

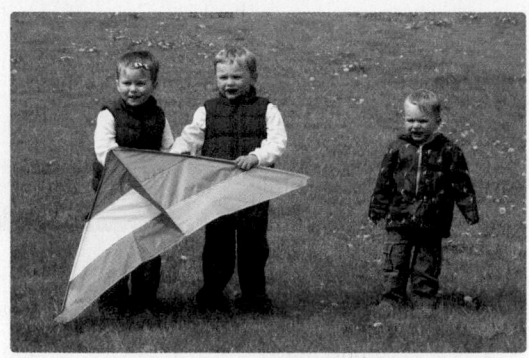

86. A Swinging Pendulum The time T required for a pendulum to swing back and forth may be found by the formula

$$T = 2\pi\sqrt{\frac{l}{g}}$$ $\frac{\pi\sqrt{7}}{7} \approx 1.2$ sec

where l is the length of the pendulum and g is the acceleration of gravity. Determine the time in seconds for the pendulum to swing back and forth if $l = 35$ cm and $g = 980$ cm/sec^2. Round your answer to the nearest tenth of a second.

87. Estimating Speed of a Vehicle The speed that a vehicle was traveling, s, in miles per hour, when the brakes were first applied, can be estimated using the formula

$s = \sqrt{\dfrac{d}{0.04}}$ where d is the length of the vehicle's skid marks, in feet.

a) Estimate the speed of a car that made skid marks 4 ft long. 10 mph

b) Estimate the speed of a car that made skid marks 16 ft long. 20 mph

c) Estimate the speed of a car that made skid marks 64 ft long. 40 mph

d) Estimate the speed of a car that made skid marks 256 ft long. 80 mph

88. Dropping an Object The formula $t = \dfrac{\sqrt{d}}{4}$ can be used to estimate the time, t, in seconds it takes for an object dropped to travel d feet.

a) Estimate the time it takes for an object to drop 100 ft. 2.5 sec

b) Estimate the time it takes for an object to drop 400 ft. 5 sec

c) Estimate the time it takes for an object to drop 900 ft. 7.5 sec

d) Estimate the time it takes for an object to drop 1600 ft. 10 sec

Concept/Writing Exercises

89. Without doing any calculations, determine whether $\sqrt{2} = 1.414$. $\sqrt{2} \neq 1.414$ since $\sqrt{2}$ is irrational and 1.414 is rational.

90. Without doing any calculations, determine whether $\sqrt{17} = 4.123$.
$\sqrt{17} \neq 4.123$ since $\sqrt{17}$ is irrational and 4.123 is rational.

91. The number π is an irrational number. Often the values 3.14 or $\frac{22}{7}$ are used for π. Does π equal either 3.14 or $\frac{22}{7}$?
No. π is irrational; therefore, it cannot equal $\frac{22}{7}$ or 3.14, both of which are rational.

92. Give an example to show that $\sqrt{a + b} \neq \sqrt{a} + \sqrt{b}$.
$\sqrt{9 + 16} \neq 3 + 4, 5 \neq 7$

93. Give an example to show that $\sqrt{a \cdot b} = \sqrt{a} \cdot \sqrt{b}$.
$\sqrt{4 \cdot 9} = \sqrt{4} \cdot \sqrt{9}, \sqrt{36} = 2 \cdot 3, 6 = 6$

94. Give an example to show that for $b \neq 0$, $\sqrt{\dfrac{a}{b}} = \dfrac{\sqrt{a}}{\sqrt{b}}$.
$\sqrt{\dfrac{36}{9}} = \dfrac{\sqrt{36}}{\sqrt{9}}, \sqrt{4} = \dfrac{6}{3}, 2 = 2$

Challenge Problems/Group Activities

95. a) Is $\sqrt{0.04}$ rational or irrational? Explain.
Rational. $\sqrt{0.04} = 0.2$, which is a rational number.
b) Is $\sqrt{0.7}$ rational or irrational? Explain. *

96. One way to find a rational number between two distinct rational numbers is to add the two distinct rational numbers and divide by 2. Do you think that this method will work for finding an irrational number between two distinct irrational numbers? Explain.
No. The sum of two irrational numbers may not be an irrational number.

Recreational Mathematics

97. More Four 4's In the *Recreational Mathematics* box on page 225 and in Exercise 82 on page 229, we introduced some of the basic rules of the game Four 4's. We now expand our operations to include square roots. For example, one way to obtain the whole number 8 is $\sqrt{4} + \sqrt{4} + \sqrt{4} + \sqrt{4} = 2 + 2 + 2 + 2 = 8$. Using at least one square root of 4, $\sqrt{4}$, play Four 4's to obtain the following whole numbers:

a) 11 $(44 \div \sqrt{4}) \div \sqrt{4} = 11$

b) 13 $(44 \div 4) + \sqrt{4} = 13$

c) 14 $4 + 4 + 4 + \sqrt{4} = 14$

d) 18 $\sqrt{4}(4 + 4) + \sqrt{4} = 18$ Other answers are possible.
*See Instructor Answer Appendix

Internet/Research Activities

In Exercises 98 and 99, references include history of mathematics books, encyclopedias, and Internet Web sites.

98. Write a report on the history of the development of the irrational numbers.

99. Write a report on the history of pi. In your report, indicate when the symbol π was first used and list the first 10 digits of π.

▲ *Real number properties are often learned as we learn arithmetic facts.*

Evaluate $10 + 5$ and then evaluate $5 + 10$. Evaluate 10×5 and then evaluate 5×10. Evaluate $10 - 5$ and then evaluate $5 - 10$. Finally, evaluate $10 \div 5$ and then evaluate $5 \div 10$. You will notice that $10 + 5 = 5 + 10$ and that $10 \times 5 = 5 \times 10$. On the other hand, $10 - 5 \neq 5 - 10$ and $10 \div 5 \neq 5 \div 10$. These simple examples demonstrate a certain property that holds for addition and multiplication, but not for subtraction and division. In this section, we will study the set of *real* numbers and their properties.

Why *This is Important* Understanding the properties of real numbers is vital to learning algebra and many other areas of mathematics.

Now that we have discussed both the rational and irrational numbers, we can discuss the real numbers and the properties of the real number system. The union of the rational numbers and the irrational numbers is the *set of real numbers*, symbolized by $\mathbb{R}$.

Figure 5.8 illustrates the relationship among various sets of numbers. It shows that the natural numbers are a subset of the whole numbers, the integers, the rational numbers, and the real numbers. For example, since the number 3 is a natural or counting number, it is also a whole number, an integer, a rational number, and a real number. Since the rational number $\frac{1}{4}$ is outside the set of integers, it is not an integer, a whole number, or a natural number. The number $\frac{1}{4}$ is a real number, however, as is the irrational number $\sqrt{2}$. Note that the real numbers are the union of the rational numbers and the irrational numbers.

Did You Know?

An Important Number

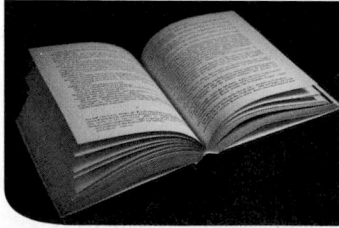

Some years ago, a group of French mathematicians who worked under the collective pseudonym "Monsieur Nicholas Bourbaki" embarked on the development of an encyclopedic description of all mathematics. They devoted 200 pages simply to introduce the innocent-looking concept, the number 1.

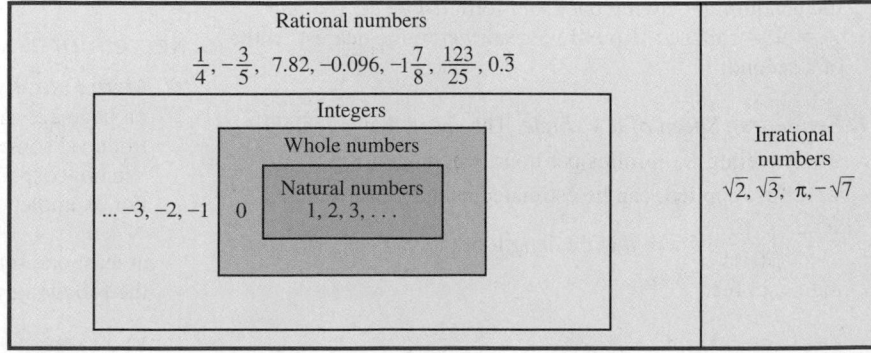

Figure 5.8

The relationship between the various sets of numbers in the real number system can also be illustrated with a tree diagram, as in Fig. 5.9 on page 253.

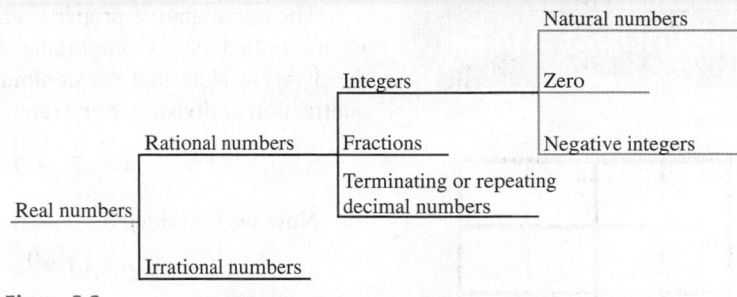

Figure 5.9

Figure 5.9 shows that, for example, the natural numbers are a subset of the integers, the rational numbers, and the real numbers. We can also see, for example, the natural numbers, zero, and the negative integers together form the integers.

Properties of the Real Number System

We are now prepared to consider the properties of the real number system. The first property we will discuss is *closure*.

Definition: Closure

If an operation is performed on any two elements of a set and the result is an element of the set, we say that the set has **closure** or is **closed** under that given operation.

Is the sum of any two natural numbers a natural number? The answer is yes. Thus, we say that the natural numbers are closed under the operation of addition.

Are the natural numbers closed under the operation of subtraction? If we subtract one natural number from another natural number, must the difference always be a natural number? The answer is no. For example, $3 - 5 = -2$, and -2 is not a natural number. Therefore, the natural numbers are not closed under the operation of subtraction.

Example 1 *Closure of Sets*

Determine whether the set of whole numbers is closed under the operations of (a) multiplication and (b) division.

Solution

a) If we multiply any two whole numbers, will the product always be a whole number? You may want to try multiplying several whole numbers. You will see that yes, the product of any two whole numbers is a whole number. Thus, the set of whole numbers is closed under the operation of multiplication.

b) If we divide any two whole numbers, will the quotient always be a whole number? The answer is no. For example $1 \div 2 = \frac{1}{2}$, and $\frac{1}{2}$ is not a whole number. Therefore, the set of whole numbers is not closed under the operation of division. ∎

Next we will discuss three important properties: the commutative property, the associative property, and the distributive property. A knowledge of these properties is essential for the understanding of algebra. We begin with the commutative property.

Commutative Property

Addition	**Multiplication**
$a + b = b + a$	$a \cdot b = b \cdot a$

for any real numbers a and b.

KenKen

8×		4+	
10+		4×	
1			11+
3+			

© 2011 KenKen Puzzle LLC.
www.kenken.com

Like Sudoku and Kakuro (see the *Recreational Mathematics* boxes on page 97 and page 134), KenKen is a puzzle that requires logic. However, KenKen® also requires you to use arithmetic facts. To play KenKen®, fill in the blank squares with the digits 1 through the number of rows or columns contained in the puzzle. For example, the puzzle above has 4 rows and 4 columns; therefore, you fill in the blank squares with the digits 1 through 4. Like Sudoku, you are not allowed to repeat a digit in any row or column. The heavily outlined sets of squares are called cages. The numbers placed in each cage must combine, *in any order*, to produce the given number using the given mathematical operation. For example, the cage in the upper left-hand corner of the puzzle above must contain two digits whose product is 8. The cage in the upper right-hand corner must contain two digits whose sum is 4. Cages with just one box should be filled in with the given number in the top corner. A number can be repeated within a cage as long as it is not in the same row or column. For more information and more puzzles, see www.kenken.com. Complete the above puzzle.

The solution to the above puzzle can be found in the answer section in the back of this book. For an additional puzzle, see Exercise 84 on page 258.

Note: KenKen® is a registered trademark of Nextoy, LLC. Puzzle content © 2011 KenKen Puzzle LLC. All rights reserved.

The commutative property states that the *order* in which two numbers are added or multiplied is not important. For example, $4 + 5 = 5 + 4 = 9$ and $3 \cdot 6 = 6 \cdot 3 = 18$. Note that the commutative property does not hold for the operations of subtraction or division. For example,

$$4 - 7 \neq 7 - 4 \quad \text{and} \quad 9 \div 3 \neq 3 \div 9$$

Now we introduce the associative property.

Associative Property

Addition	Multiplication
$(a + b) + c = a + (b + c)$	$(a \cdot b) \cdot c = a \cdot (b \cdot c)$

for any real numbers a, b, and c.

The associative property states that when adding or multiplying three real numbers, we may place parentheses around any two adjacent numbers. The result is the same regardless of the placement of parentheses. For example,

$$(3 + 4) + 5 = 3 + (4 + 5) \qquad (3 \cdot 4) \cdot 5 = 3 \cdot (4 \cdot 5)$$
$$7 + 5 = 3 + 9 \qquad\qquad 12 \cdot 5 = 3 \cdot 20$$
$$12 = 12 \qquad\qquad\qquad 60 = 60$$

The associative property does not hold for the operations of subtraction or division. For example,

$$(10 - 6) - 2 \neq 10 - (6 - 2) \quad \text{and} \quad (27 \div 9) \div 3 \neq 27 \div (9 \div 3)$$

Note the difference between the commutative property and the associative property. The commutative property involves a change in *order*, whereas the associative property involves a change in *grouping* (or the *association* of numbers that are grouped together).

Another property of the real numbers is the distributive property of multiplication over addition.

Distributive Property of Multiplication Over Addition

$$a \cdot (b + c) = a \cdot b + a \cdot c$$

for any real numbers a, b, and c.

For example, if $a = 3$, $b = 4$, and $c = 5$, then

$$3 \cdot (4 + 5) = (3 \cdot 4) + (3 \cdot 5)$$
$$3 \cdot 9 = 12 + 15$$
$$27 = 27$$

This result indicates that, when using the distributive property, you may either add first and then multiply or multiply first and then add. Note that the distributive property involves two operations, addition and multiplication. Although positive integers were used in the example, any real numbers could have been used.

We frequently use the commutative, associative, and distributive properties without realizing that we are doing so. To add $13 + 4 + 6$, we may add the $4 + 6$ first to get 10. To this sum we then add 13 to get 23. Here we have done the equivalent of placing parentheses around the $4 + 6$. We can do so because of the associative property of addition.

To multiply 102×11 in our heads, we might multiply $100 \times 11 = 1100$ and $2 \times 11 = 22$ and add these two products to get 1122. We are permitted to do so because of the distributive property.

$$102 \times 11 = (100 + 2) \times 11 = (100 \times 11) + (2 \times 11)$$

$$= 1100 + 22 = 1122$$

Example 2 *Identifying Properties of Real Numbers*

Name the property illustrated.

a) $2 + 5 = 5 + 2$
b) $(x + 3) + 5 = x + (3 + 5)$

c) $4 \cdot (3 \cdot y) = (4 \cdot 3) \cdot y$
d) $9(w + 3) = 9 \cdot w + 9 \cdot 3$

e) $5 + (z + 3) = 5 + (3 + z)$
f) $(2p) \cdot 5 = 5 \cdot (2p)$

Solution

a) Commutative property of addition

b) Associative property of addition

c) Associative property of multiplication

d) Distributive property of multiplication over addition

e) The only change between the left and right sides of the equal sign is the order of the z and 3 within the parentheses. The order is changed from $z + 3$ to $3 + z$ using the commutative property of addition.

f) The order of 5 and $(2p)$ is changed by using the commutative property of multiplication. ∎

Example 3 *Simplifying by Using the Distributive Property*

Simplify.

a) $5\left(2 + \sqrt{3}\right)$
b) $\sqrt{7}\left(4 + \sqrt{2}\right)$

Solution

a) $5\left(2 + \sqrt{3}\right) = (5 \cdot 2) + \left(5 \cdot \sqrt{3}\right)$

$$= 10 + 5\sqrt{3}$$

b) $\sqrt{7}\left(4 + \sqrt{2}\right) = \left(\sqrt{7} \cdot 4\right) + \sqrt{7} \cdot \sqrt{2}$

$$= 4\sqrt{7} + \sqrt{14}$$

Note that $\sqrt{7} \cdot 4$ is written $4\sqrt{7}$ ∎

Example 4 *Distributive Property*

Use the distributive property to multiply $2(x + 5)$. Then simplify the result.

Solution $2(x + 5) = 2 \cdot x + 2 \cdot 5$

$$= 2x + 10$$ ∎

Example 5 *Name the Property Used*

Name the property used to go from step to step when simplifying the expression.

a) $3(a + 2) + 5 = (3 \cdot a + 3 \cdot 2) + 5$

$$= (3a + 6) + 5$$

b) $\qquad\qquad = 3a + (6 + 5)$

$$= 3a + 11$$

Solution

a) In this step we rewrote $3(a + 2)$ as $(3 \cdot a + 3 \cdot 2)$, which we then simplified to $(3a + 6)$. This is an example of the *distributive property*.

b) In this step we rewrote $(3a + 6) + 5$ as $3a + (6 + 5)$, which we then simplified to $(3a + 11)$.

This is an example of the *associative property of addition*.   ■

We summarize the properties mentioned in this section as follows, where a, b, and c are any real numbers.

The Properties of Real Numbers

Commutative property of addition	$a + b = b + a$
Commutative property of multiplication	$a \cdot b = b \cdot a$
Associative property of addition	$(a + b) + c = a + (b + c)$
Associative property of multiplication	$(a \cdot b) \cdot c = a \cdot (b \cdot c)$
Distributive property of multiplication over addition	$a \cdot (b + c) = a \cdot b + a \cdot c$

SECTION 5.5   *Exercises*

Warm Up Exercises

In Exercises 1–8, fill in the blanks with an appropriate word, phrase, or symbol(s).

1. The union of the rational numbers and the irrational numbers is the set of _____ numbers. Real

2. The symbol used to represent the set of real numbers is _____. $\mathbb{R}$

3. If an operation is performed on any two elements of a set and the result is still an element of the set, we say that the set is _____ under that given operation. Closed

4. The equation $2 + 3 = 3 + 2$ demonstrates the _____ property of addition. Commutative

5. The equation $4 \cdot 5 = 5 \cdot 4$ demonstrates the _____ property of multiplication. Commutative

6. The equation $(2 + 3) + 4 = 2 + (3 + 4)$ demonstrates the _____ property of addition. Associative

7. The equation $(5 \cdot 6) \cdot 7 = 5 \cdot (6 \cdot 7)$ demonstrates the _____ property of multiplication. Associative

8. The equation $2 \cdot (3 + 4) = 2 \cdot 3 + 2 \cdot 4$ demonstrates the _____ property of multiplication over addition. Distributive

Practice the Skills

In Exercises 9–12, determine whether the natural numbers are closed under the given operation.

9. Addition Yes

10. Division No

11. Subtraction No

12. Multiplication Yes

In Exercises 13–16, determine whether the integers are closed under the given operation.

13. Division No

14. Addition Yes

15. Multiplication Yes

16. Subtraction Yes

In Exercises 17–20, determine whether the rational numbers are closed under the given operation.

17. Addition Yes

18. Subtraction Yes

19. Division No

20. Multiplication Yes

In Exercises 21–24, determine whether the irrational numbers are closed under the given operation.

21. Multiplication No

22. Addition No

23. Subtraction No

24. Division No

In Exercises 25–28, determine whether the real numbers are closed under the given operation.

25. Addition Yes

26. Subtraction Yes

27. Division No

28. Multiplication Yes

29. Does $(5 + x) + 6 = (x + 5) + 6$ illustrate the commutative property or the associative property? Explain your answer.*

30. Does $(x + 5) + 6 = x + (5 + 6)$ illustrate the commutative property or the associative property? Explain your answer.*

31. Give an example to show that the commutative property of addition may be true for the negative integers.
$(-3) + (-4) = (-4) + (-3) = -7$

32. Give an example to show that the commutative property of multiplication may be true for the negative integers.
$(-3)(-4) = (-4)(-3) = 12$

33. Does the commutative property hold for the integers under the operation of subtraction? Give an example to support your answer. No. $4 - 3 \neq 3 - 4$.

34. Does the commutative property hold for the rational numbers under the operation of division? Give an example to support your answer. No. $3 \div 4 \neq 4 \div 3$.

35. Give an example to show that the associative property of addition may be true for the negative integers.
$[(-2) + (-3)] + (-4) = (-2) + [(-3) + (-4)] = -9$

36. Give an example to show that the associative property of multiplication may be true for the negative integers.
$[(-2)(-3)](-4) = (-2)[(-3)(-4)] = -24$

37. Does the associative property hold for the integers under the operation of division? Give an example to support your answer. No. $(16 \div 8) \div 2 \neq 16 \div (8 \div 2)$.

38. Does the associative property hold for the integers under the operation of subtraction? Give an example to support your answer. No. $(10 - 4) - 2 \neq 10 - (4 - 2)$.

39. Does the associative property hold for the real numbers under the operation of division? Give an example to support your answer. No. $(81 \div 9) \div 3 \neq 81 \div (9 \div 3)$.

40. Does $a + (b \cdot c) = (a + b) \cdot (a + c)$? Give an example to support your answer. No. $2 + (3 \cdot 4) \neq (2 + 3) \cdot (2 + 4)$.

In Exercises 41–52, state the name of the property illustrated.

41. $3(y + 5) = 3 \cdot y + 3 \cdot 5$ Distributive property

42. $6 + 7 = 7 + 6$ Commutative property of addition

43. $(7 \cdot 8) \cdot 9 = 7 \cdot (8 \cdot 9)$ Associative property of multiplication

44. $c + d = d + c$ Commutative property of addition

45. $(24 + 7) + 3 = 24 + (7 + 3)$ Associative property of addition

46. $4 \cdot (11 \cdot x) = (4 \cdot 11) \cdot x$ Associative property of multiplication

47. $\sqrt{3} \cdot 7 = 7 \cdot \sqrt{3}$ Commutative property of multiplication

48. $\dfrac{3}{8} + \left(\dfrac{1}{8} + \dfrac{3}{2}\right) = \left(\dfrac{3}{8} + \dfrac{1}{8}\right) + \dfrac{3}{2}$
Associative property of addition

49. $-1(x + 4) = (-1) \cdot x + (-1) \cdot 4$ Distributive property

50. $(r + s) \cdot t = (r \cdot t) + (s \cdot t)$ Distributive property

51. $(r + s) + t = t + (r + s)$ Commutative property of addition

52. $g \cdot (h + i) = (h + i) \cdot g$ Commutative property of multiplication

In Exercises 53–64, use the distributive property to multiply. Then, if possible, simplify the resulting expression.

53. $4(z + 1)$ $4z + 4$

54. $-1(a + b)$ $-a - b$

55. $-\dfrac{3}{4}(x - 12)$ $-\dfrac{3}{4}x + 9$

56. $-x(-y + z)$ $xy - xz$

57. $6\left(\dfrac{x}{2} + \dfrac{2}{3}\right)$ $3x + 4$

58. $24\left(\dfrac{x}{3} - \dfrac{1}{8}\right)$ $8x - 3$

59. $32\left(\dfrac{1}{16}x - \dfrac{1}{32}\right)$ $2x - 1$

60. $15\left(\dfrac{2}{3}x - \dfrac{4}{5}\right)$ $10x - 12$

61. $\sqrt{2}(\sqrt{8} - \sqrt{2})$ 2

62. $-3(2 - \sqrt{3})$ $-6 + 3\sqrt{3}$

63. $5(\sqrt{2} + \sqrt{3})$
$5\sqrt{2} + 5\sqrt{3}$

64. $\sqrt{5}(\sqrt{15} - \sqrt{20})$
$5\sqrt{3} - 10$

In Exercises 65–70, name the property used to go from step to step. You only need to name the properties indicated by an a), b), c), or d). For example, in Exercise 65, you need to supply an answer for part a), and an answer to go from the second step of part a) to part b).

65. a) $4(x + 1) + 6 = (4 \cdot x + 4 \cdot 1) + 6$
$= (4x + 4) + 6$ Distributive property

b) $= 4x + (4 + 6)$
$= 4x + 10$ Associative property of addition

66. a) $2(b + 4) + 1 = (2 \cdot b + 2 \cdot 4) + 1$
$= (2b + 8) + 1$ Distributive property

b) $= 2b + (8 + 1)$
$= 2b + 9$ Associative property of addition

67. a) $7(k + 1) + 2k = (7 \cdot k + 7 \cdot 1) + 2k$
$= (7k + 7) + 2k$ Distributive property

b) $= 7k + (7 + 2k)$
Associative property of addition

c) $= 7k + (2k + 7)$
Commutative property of addition

d) $= (7k + 2k) + 7$
$= 9k + 7$ Associative property of addition

*See Instructor Answer Appendix

68. a) $11(h + 6) + 5h = (11 \cdot h + 11 \cdot 6) + 5h$
$= (11h + 66) + 5h$ Distributive property

b) $= 11h + (66 + 5h)$
Associative property of addition

c) $= 11h + (5h + 66)$
Commutative property of addition

d) $= (11h + 5h) + 66$
$= 16h + 66$
Associative property of addition

69. a) $9 + 2(t + 3) + 7t = 9 + (2 \cdot t + 2 \cdot 3) + 7t$
$= 9 + (2t + 6) + 7t$
Distributive property

b) $= 9 + (6 + 2t) + 7t$
Commutative property of addition

c) $= (9 + 6) + 2t + 7t$
$= 15 + 9t$
Associative property of addition

d) $= 9t + 15$
Commutative property of addition

70. a) $7 + 5(s + 4) + 3s = 7 + (5 \cdot s + 5 \cdot 4) + 3s$
$= 7 + (5s + 20) + 3s$
Distributive property

b) $= 7 + (20 + 5s) + 3s$
Commutative property of addition

c) $= (7 + 20) + 5s + 3s$
$= 27 + 8s$
Associative property of addition

d) $= 8s + 27$
Commutative property of addition

In Exercises 71–74, determine whether the activity can be used to illustrate the commutative property. For the property to hold, the end result must be identical, regardless of the order in which the actions are performed.

71. Feeding your cats and giving your cats water Yes

72. Putting your wallet in your back pocket and putting your keys in your front pocket Yes

73. Washing clothes and drying clothes No

74. Turning on a computer and typing a term paper on the computer No

In Exercises 75–80, determine whether the activity can be used to illustrate the associative property. For the property to hold, doing the first two actions followed by the third

would produce the same end result as doing the second and third actions followed by the first.

75. Putting batteries in your calculator, pressing the ON key, and pressing the 7 key No

76. Filling your car with gas, washing the windshield, and checking the tire pressure Yes

77. Sending a holiday card to your grandmother, sending one to your parents, and sending one to your teacher Yes

78. Mowing the lawn, trimming the bushes, and removing dead limbs from trees Yes

79. Brushing your teeth, washing your face, and combing your hair Yes

80. Cracking an egg, pouring out the egg, and cooking the egg No

Challenge Problems/Group Activities

81. Describe two other activities that can be used to illustrate the commutative property (see Exercises 71–74).
Answers will vary.

82. Describe three other activities that can be used to illustrate the associative property (see Exercises 75–80).
Answers will vary.

83. Does $0 \div a = a \div 0$ (assume $a \neq 0$)? Explain.
No. $0 \div a = 0$ (when $a \neq 0$), but $a \div 0$ is undefined.

Recreational Math

84. *KenKen* Refer to the *Recreational Mathematics* box on page 254. Complete the following KenKen puzzle. *

2	2−	2÷	24×
3−			
	7+		
1−		5+	

85. a) Consider the three words *man eating tiger*. Does (*man eating*) *tiger* mean the same as *man* (*eating tiger*)? No

b) Does (*horse riding*) *monkey* mean the same as *horse* (*riding monkey*)? No

c) Can you find three other nonassociative word triples?
Answers will vary.

Internet/Research Activity

86. A set of numbers that was not discussed in this chapter is the set of *complex numbers*. Write a report on complex numbers. Include their relationship to the real numbers.

*See Instructor Answer Appendix

Rules of Exponents and Scientific Notation

What is the current world population? What is the diameter of an atom? What is the diameter of a galaxy? What is the wavelength of an x-ray? What is the current national federal debt? All these questions have answers that may involve either very large numbers or very small numbers. One way to accurately represent such numbers is with *scientific notation*. In this section, we will study how to use scientific notation when answering questions such as those posed above.

Why *This is Important* Scientific notation is used in many fields of study, including economics, physics, chemistry, and astronomy. Items such as a hard drive's capacity, measured in gigabytes, can also be represented using scientific notation.

▲ *The diameter of an atom may be given in scientific notation.*

An understanding of exponents is important in solving problems in algebra. In the expression 5^2, the 2 is referred to as the *exponent* and the 5 is referred to as the *base*. We read 5^2 as 5 to the second power, or 5 squared, which means

$$5^2 = \underbrace{5 \cdot 5}_{\text{2 factors of 5}}$$

The number 5 to the third power, or 5 cubed, written 5^3, means

$$5^3 = \underbrace{5 \cdot 5 \cdot 5}_{\text{3 factors of 5}}$$

In general, the number b to the nth power, written b^n, means

$$b^n = \underbrace{b \cdot b \cdot b \cdot \cdots \cdot b}_{n \text{ factors of } b}$$

Example 1 *Evaluating the Power of a Number*

Evaluate

a) 5^2 b) $(-3)^2$ c) 3^4 d) 1^{1000} e) 1000^1

Solution

a) $5^2 = 5 \cdot 5 = 25$
b) $(-3)^2 = (-3) \cdot (-3) = 9$
c) $3^4 = 3 \cdot 3 \cdot 3 \cdot 3 = 81$
d) $1^{1000} = 1$
   The number 1 multiplied by itself any number of times equals 1.
e) $1000^1 = 1000$
   Any number with an exponent of 1 equals the number itself. ∎

Did You Know?

A Very Large Number

170,141,183,460,469,231,731,687,303,715,884,105,727 is a very large number. How would you read this number? Take a breath.

170 undecillion, 141 decillion, 183 nonillion, 460 octillion, 469 septillion, 231 sextillion, 731 quintillion, 687 quadrillion, 303 trillion, 715 billion, 884 million, 105 thousand, 727.

Often numbers this large can be represented with an approximation involving scientific notation. This number, however, is a prime number, and its *exact* representation is very important. Mathematicians frequently represent such large numbers by using exponents. Here, another exact, and more efficient, representation of this number is $2^{127} - 1$.

> ## Example 2   *The Importance of Parentheses*
>
> Evaluate.
>
> a) $(-2)^4$ b) -2^4 c) $(-2)^5$ d) -2^5
>
> Solution
>
> a) $(-2)^4 = (-2)(-2)(-2)(-2) = 4(-2)(-2) = -8(-2) = 16$
> b) -2^4 means take the opposite of 2^4 or $-1 \cdot 2^4$.
> $-1 \cdot 2^4 = -1 \cdot 2 \cdot 2 \cdot 2 \cdot 2 = -1 \cdot 16 = -16$
> c) $(-2)^5 = (-2)(-2)(-2)(-2)(-2) = 4(-2)(-2)(-2) = -8(-2)(-2)$
> $= 16(-2) = -32$
> d) $-2^5 = -1 \cdot 2^5 = -1 \cdot 2 \cdot 2 \cdot 2 \cdot 2 \cdot 2 = -1 \cdot 32 = -32$ ∎

From Example 2, we can see that $(-x)^n \neq -x^n$, where n is an even natural number.

Rules of Exponents

Now that we know how to evaluate powers of numbers, we can discuss the rules of exponents. Consider

$$2^2 \cdot 2^3 = \underbrace{2 \cdot 2}_{\text{2 factors}} \cdot \underbrace{2 \cdot 2 \cdot 2}_{\text{3 factors}} = 2^5$$

This example illustrates the product rule for exponents.

> ### Product Rule for Exponents
> $$a^m \cdot a^n = a^{m+n}$$

Therefore, by using the product rule, $2^2 \cdot 2^3 = 2^{2+3} = 2^5$.

> ## Example 3   *Using the Product Rule for Exponents*
>
> Use the product rule to simplify.
>
> a) $3^3 \cdot 3^2$ b) $5 \cdot 5^3$
>
> Solution
>
> a) $3^3 \cdot 3^2 = 3^{3+2} = 3^5 = 243$
> b) $5 \cdot 5^3 = 5^1 \cdot 5^3 = 5^4 = 625$ ∎

Consider

$$\frac{2^5}{2^2} = \frac{2 \cdot 2 \cdot 2 \cdot \cancel{2} \cdot \cancel{2}}{\cancel{2} \cdot \cancel{2}} = 2 \cdot 2 \cdot 2 = 2^3$$

This example illustrates the quotient rule for exponents.

> ### Quotient Rule for Exponents
> $$\frac{a^m}{a^n} = a^{m-n}, \quad a \neq 0$$

Therefore, $\dfrac{2^5}{2^2} = 2^{5-2} = 2^3$.

Example 4 *Using the Quotient Rule for Exponents*

Use the quotient rule to simplify.

a) $\dfrac{3^7}{3^5}$

b) $\dfrac{5^9}{5^5}$

Solution

a) $\dfrac{3^7}{3^5} = 3^{7-5} = 3^2 = 9$

b) $\dfrac{5^9}{5^5} = 5^{9-5} = 5^4 = 625$

■

Consider $2^3 \div 2^3$. The quotient rule gives

$$\frac{2^3}{2^3} = 2^{3-3} = 2^0$$

But $\dfrac{2^3}{2^3} = \dfrac{8}{8} = 1$. Therefore, 2^0 must equal 1. This example illustrates the zero exponent rule.

Zero Exponent Rule

$$a^0 = 1, \quad a \neq 0$$

Note that 0^0 is not defined by the zero exponent rule.

Example 5 *The Zero Power*

Use the zero exponent rule to simplify. Assume $x \neq 0$.

a) 2^0 b) $(-2)^0$ c) -2^0 d) $(5x)^0$ e) $5x^0$

Solution

a) $2^0 = 1$ b) $(-2)^0 = 1$ c) $-2^0 = -1 \cdot 2^0 = -1 \cdot 1 = -1$

d) $(5x)^0 = 1$ e) $5x^0 = 5 \cdot x^0 = 5 \cdot 1 = 5$

■

Consider $2^3 \div 2^5$. The quotient rule yields

$$\frac{2^3}{2^5} = 2^{3-5} = 2^{-2}$$

But $\dfrac{2^3}{2^5} = \dfrac{\cancel{2} \cdot \cancel{2} \cdot \cancel{2}}{\cancel{2} \cdot \cancel{2} \cdot \cancel{2} \cdot 2 \cdot 2} = \dfrac{1}{2^2}$. Since $\dfrac{2^3}{2^5}$ equals both 2^{-2} and $\dfrac{1}{2^2}$, then 2^{-2} must equal $\dfrac{1}{2^2}$. This example illustrates the negative exponent rule.

Negative Exponent Rule

$$a^{-m} = \frac{1}{a^m}, \quad a \neq 0$$

Example 6 *Using the Negative Exponent Rule*

Use the negative exponent rule to simplify.

a) 2^{-3}

b) 5^{-1}

Solution

a) $2^{-3} = \dfrac{1}{2^3} = \dfrac{1}{8}$

b) $5^{-1} = \dfrac{1}{5^1} = \dfrac{1}{5}$

■

Large and Small Numbers

The diameter of a galaxy may be 1×10^5 light-years.

The diameter of an atom may be 1×10^{-10} meter.

Our everyday activities don't require us to deal with quantities much above those in the thousands: $9.95 for lunch, a 100-lap race, a $19,000 car loan, and so on. Yet as modern technology has developed, so has our ability to study all aspects of the universe we live in, from the very large to the very small. Modern technology can be used with the rules of exponents and scientific notation to study everything from the diameter of a galaxy to the diameter of an atom.

Consider $(2^3)^2$.

$$(2^3)^2 = (2^3)(2^3) = 2^{3+3} = 2^6$$

This example illustrates the power rule for exponents.

Power Rule for Exponents

$$(a^m)^n = a^{m \cdot n}$$

Thus, $(2^3)^2 = 2^{3 \cdot 2} = 2^6$.

Example 7 Evaluating a Power Raised to Another Power

Use the power rule to simplify.

a) $(5^4)^3$ b) $(7^2)^5$

Solution

a) $(5^4)^3 = 5^{4 \cdot 3} = 5^{12}$

b) $(7^2)^5 = 7^{2 \cdot 5} = 7^{10}$ ∎

Summary of the Rules of Exponents

$a^m \cdot a^n = a^{m+n}$	Product rule for exponents
$\dfrac{a^m}{a^n} = a^{m-n}, \quad a \neq 0$	Quotient rule for exponents
$a^0 = 1, \quad a \neq 0$	Zero exponent rule
$a^{-m} = \dfrac{1}{a^m}, \quad a \neq 0$	Negative exponent rule
$(a^m)^n = a^{m \cdot n}$	Power rule for exponents

Scientific Notation

Often scientific problems deal with very large and very small numbers. For example, the distance from Earth to the sun is about 93,000,000 miles. The wavelength of a yellow color of light is about 0.0000006 meter. Because working with many zeros is difficult, scientists developed a notation that expresses such numbers with exponents. For example, consider the distance from Earth to the sun, 93,000,000 miles.

$$93,000,000 = 9.3 \times 10,000,000$$
$$= 9.3 \times 10^7$$

The wavelength of a yellow color of light is about 0.0000006 meter.

$$0.0000006 = 6.0 \times 0.0000001$$
$$= 6.0 \times 10^{-7}$$

The numbers 9.3×10^7 and 6.0×10^{-7} are written in a form called *scientific notation*. Each number written in scientific notation is written as a number greater than or equal to 1 and less than 10 multiplied by some power of 10.

Some examples of numbers in scientific notation are

$$3.7 \times 10^3, \quad 2.05 \times 10^{-3}, \quad 5.6 \times 10^8, \quad \text{and} \quad 1.00 \times 10^{-5}$$

Catalan's Conjecture

Eugène Catalan   Preda Mihailescu

Consider all the squares of positive integers:

$1^2 = 1$, $2^2 = 4$, $3^2 = 9$,
$4^2 = 16$,   and so on

Now consider all the cubes of positive integers:

$1^3 = 1$, $2^3 = 8$, $3^3 = 27$,
$4^3 = 64$,   and so on

Next, consider all the fourth powers of positive integers:

$1^4 = 1$, $2^4 = 16$, $3^4 = 81$,
$4^4 = 256$,   and so on

If we were to put *all* powers of the positive integers into one set, the set would begin as follows: {1, 4, 8, 9, 16, 25, 27, 32, 36, 49, 64, ...}. In 1844, Belgian mathematician Eugène Catalan proposed that of all the numbers in this infinite set, only 8 and 9 are consecutive integers. Although this conjecture was easily stated, the formal proof of it eluded mathematicians for more than 150 years. In April 2002, Preda Mihailescu, a Romanian-born mathematician, announced that he had proved Catalan's Conjecture. The study of mathematics involves many conjectures that are often easy to pose, but difficult to prove. For another example of such a conjecture, see the *Mathematics Today* box on page 505 regarding Fermat's Last Theorem.

Eugène Catalan painting: Collections artistiques de l'Université de Liége

The following is a procedure for writing a number in scientific notation.

> **PROCEDURE**   **TO WRITE A NUMBER IN SCIENTIFIC NOTATION**
>
> 1. Move the decimal point in the original number to the right or left until you obtain a number greater than or equal to 1 and less than 10.
>
> 2. Count the number of places you have moved the decimal point to obtain the number in Step 1. If the decimal point was moved to the left, the count is to be considered positive. If the decimal point was moved to the right, the count is to be considered negative.
>
> 3. Multiply the number obtained in Step 1 by 10 raised to the count found in Step 2. (Note that the count determined in Step 2 is the exponent on the base 10.)

Example 8   *Converting from Decimal Notation to Scientific Notation*

Write each number in scientific notation.

a) In 2010, the population of the United States was about 309,500,000.

b) In 2010, the population of China was about 1,348,000,000.

c) In 2010, the population of the world was about 6,828,000,000.

d) The diameter of a hydrogen atom nucleus is about 0.0000000000011 millimeter.

e) The wavelength of an x-ray is about 0.000000000492 meter.

Solution

a) $309{,}500{,}000 = 3.095 \times 10^8$

b) $1{,}348{,}000{,}000 = 1.348 \times 10^9$

c) $6{,}828{,}000{,}000 = 6.828 \times 10^9$

d) $0.0000000000011 = 1.1 \times 10^{-12}$

e) $0.000000000492 = 4.92 \times 10^{-10}$ ■

To convert from a number given in scientific notation to decimal notation, we reverse the procedure.

> **PROCEDURE**   **TO CHANGE A NUMBER IN SCIENTIFIC NOTATION TO DECIMAL NOTATION**
>
> 1. Observe the exponent on the 10.
>
> 2. a) If the exponent is positive, move the decimal point in the number to the right the same number of places as the exponent. Adding zeros to the number might be necessary.
>
>   b) If the exponent is negative, move the decimal point in the number to the left the same number of places as the exponent. Adding zeros might be necessary.

Example 9   *Converting from Scientific Notation to Decimal Notation*

Write each number in decimal notation.

a) The average distance from Mars to the sun is about 1.4×10^8 miles.

b) The half-life of uranium-235 is about 4.5×10^9 years.

c) The average grain size in siltstone is about 1.35×10^{-3} inch.

d) A *millimicron* is a unit of measure used for very small distances. One millimicron is about 3.94×10^{-8} inch.

Solution

a) $1.4 \times 10^8 = 140{,}000{,}000$

b) $4.5 \times 10^9 = 4{,}500{,}000{,}000$

c) $1.35 \times 10^{-3} = 0.00135$

d) $3.94 \times 10^{-8} = 0.0000000394$ ∎

In scientific journals and books, we occasionally see numbers like 10^{15} and 10^{-6}. We interpret these numbers as 1×10^{15} and 1×10^{-6}, respectively, when converting the numbers to decimal form.

Example 10 *Multiplying Numbers in Scientific Notation*

Multiply $(2.1 \times 10^5)(9 \times 10^{-3})$. Write the answer in scientific notation and in decimal notation.

Solution We begin by rewriting the product so that 2.1 and 9 are multiplied together and the powers of 10 are multiplied together.

$$(2.1 \times 10^5)(9 \times 10^{-3}) = (2.1 \times 9)(10^5 \times 10^{-3})$$
$$= 18.9 \times 10^2$$
$$= 1.89 \times 10^3 \quad \text{Scientific notation}$$
$$= 1890 \quad \text{Decimal notation}$$ ∎

Example 11 *Dividing Numbers Using Scientific Notation*

Divide $\dfrac{0.000000000048}{24{,}000{,}000{,}000}$. Write the answer in scientific notation.

Solution First write each number in scientific notation.

$$\frac{0.000000000048}{24{,}000{,}000{,}000} = \frac{4.8 \times 10^{-11}}{2.4 \times 10^{10}} = \left(\frac{4.8}{2.4}\right)\left(\frac{10^{-11}}{10^{10}}\right)$$
$$= 2.0 \times 10^{-11-10}$$
$$= 2.0 \times 10^{-21}$$ ∎

Scientific Notation on the Scientific Calculator

One advantage of using scientific notation when working with very large and very small numbers is the ease with which you can perform operations. Performing these operations is even easier with the use of a scientific calculator. Most scientific calculators have a scientific notation key labeled "Exp," "EXP," or "EE." We will refer to the scientific notation key as $\boxed{\text{EXP}}$. The following keystrokes reading downward can be used to enter the number 4.3×10^6.

Keystroke(s)	Calculator display
4.3	4.3
$\boxed{\text{EXP}}$	4.3^{00}
6	4.3^{06}

Your calculator may have some variations to the display shown here. The display 4.3^{06} means 4.3×10^6. We now will use our calculators to perform some computations using scientific notation.

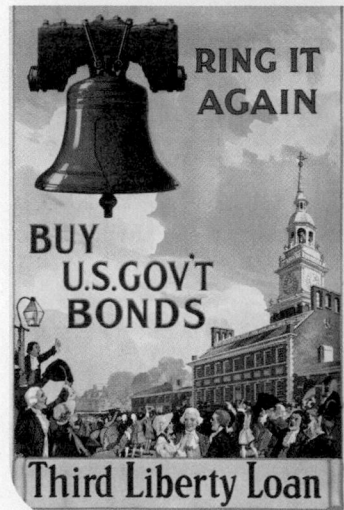
Example 12 *Use Scientific Notation on a Calculator to Find a Product*

Multiply $(4.3 \times 10^6)(2 \times 10^{-4})$ using a scientific calculator. Write the answer in decimal notation.

Solution Our sequence of keystrokes, reading downward, is as follows:

Keystroke(s)	Display	
4.3	4.3	
EXP	4.3^{00}	
6	4.3^{06}	
$\times$	4300000	4.3×10^6 is now entered in the calculator. Most calculators will convert to decimal notation (if the display can show the number)
2	2.	
EXP	$2.^{00}$	
4	$2.^{04}$	Enter the positive form of the exponent
+/−	$2.^{-04}$	Make the exponent negative*
=	860.	Press = to obtain the answer of 860† ∎

Example 13 *Use Scientific Notation on a Calculator to Find a Quotient*

Divide $\dfrac{0.000000000048}{24{,}000{,}000{,}000}$ using a scientific calculator. Write the answer in scientific notation.

Solution We first rewrite the numerator and denominator using scientific notation. See Example 11.

$$\frac{0.000000000048}{24{,}000{,}000{,}000} = \frac{4.8 \times 10^{-11}}{2.4 \times 10^{10}}$$

Next we use a scientific calculator to perform the computation. The keystrokes are as follows:

4.8 EXP 11 +/− ÷ 2.4 EXP 10 =

The display on the calculator is $2.^{-21}$, which means 2.0×10^{-21}.   ∎

Example 14 *U.S. Debt per Person*

On June 18, 2010, the U.S. Department of the Treasury estimated the U.S. federal debt to be about $13.08 trillion. On this same day, the U.S. Bureau of the Census estimated the U.S. population to be about 309.5 million people. Determine the average debt, per person, by dividing the U.S. federal debt by the U.S. population.

---

*Some calculators will require you to enter the negative sign before entering the exponent.
†Some calculators will display the answer in scientific notation. In this case, the display will show $8.6^{\,02}$, which means 8.6×10^2 and equals 860.

> **Solution** We first write the numbers involved using decimal notation. We then convert them to scientific notation.
>
> $$13.08 \text{ trillion} = 13{,}080{,}000{,}000{,}000 = 1.308 \times 10^{13}$$
> $$309.5 \text{ million} = 309{,}500{,}000 = 3.095 \times 10^8$$
>
> Now we divide 1.308×10^{13} by 3.095×10^8, using a scientific calculator. The keystrokes are
>
> $$1.308 \boxed{\text{EXP}} \; 13 \; \boxed{\div} \; 3.095 \boxed{\text{EXP}} \; 8 \; \boxed{=}$$
>
> The display then shows 42261.71244. This number indicates that on June 18, 2010, the U.S. government owed about $42,261.71 per man, woman, and child living in the United States. ∎

SECTION 5.6 · *Exercises*

Warm Up Exercises

In Exercises 1–12, fill in the blanks with an appropriate word, phrase, or symbol(s).

1. In the expression 2^3, the 3 is known as the _____.
   Exponent

2. In the expression 2^3, the 2 is known as the _____. Base

3. The product $x \cdot x \cdot x \cdot x \cdot x$ can also be written as the exponential expression _____. x^5

4. With the product rule for exponents, the expression $x^2 \cdot x^3$ can be simplified to _____. x^5

5. With the quotient rule for exponents, the expression $\dfrac{x^7}{x^4}$ can be simplified to _____. x^3

6. With the zero exponent rule, the expression 7^0 can be simplified to _____. 1

7. With the negative exponent rule, for $x \neq 0$, the expression x^{-5} can be simplified to _____. $\frac{1}{x^5}$

8. With the power rule for exponents, the expression $(x^2)^3$ can be simplified to _____. x^6

9. When written in scientific notation, the number 2013 is _____. 2.013×10^3

10. When written in scientific notation, the number 0.0034 is _____. 3.4×10^{-3}

11. When written in decimal notation, the number 5.73×10^{-5} is _____. 0.0000573

12. When written in decimal notation, the number 1.776×10^3 is _____. 1776

Practice the Skills

In Exercises 13–40, evaluate the expression. Assume $x \neq 0$.

13. a) 3^2 9   b) 2^3 8

14. a) 2^5 32   b) 5^2 25

15. a) $(-5)^2$ 25   b) -5^2 −25

16. a) -3^2 −9   b) $(-3)^2$ 9

17. a) -2^4 −16   b) $(-2)^4$ 16

18. a) $(-3)^4$ 81   b) -3^4 −81

19. a) -4^3 −64   b) $(-4)^3$ −64

20. a) $(-2)^7$ −128   b) -2^7 −128

21. a) $-\left(\dfrac{1}{2}\right)^2$ $-\frac{1}{4}$ b) $\left(-\dfrac{1}{2}\right)^2$ $\frac{1}{4}$

22. a) $-\left(\dfrac{1}{2}\right)^3$ $-\frac{1}{8}$ b) $\left(-\dfrac{1}{2}\right)^3$ $-\frac{1}{8}$

23. a) 100^1 100   b) 1^{100} 1

24. a) 2012^1 2012   b) 1^{2012} 1

25. a) $3^2 \cdot 3^3$ 243   b) $(-3)^2 \cdot (-3)^3$ −243

26. a) $2^3 \cdot 2$ 16   b) $(-2)^3 \cdot (-2)$ 16

27. a) $\dfrac{5^7}{5^5}$ 25   b) $\dfrac{(-5)^7}{(-5)^5}$ 25

28. a) $\dfrac{4^5}{4^2}$ 64   b) $\dfrac{(-4)^5}{(-4)^2}$ −64

29. a) 6^0 1   b) -6^0 −1

30. a) $(-6)^0$ 1 **b)** $-(-6)^0$ −1

31. a) $(6x)^0$ 1 **b)** $6x^0$ 6

32. a) $-6x^0$ −6 **b)** $(-6x)^0$ 1

33. a) 3^{-3} $\frac{1}{27}$ **b)** 7^{-2} $\frac{1}{49}$

34. a) 5^{-1} $\frac{1}{5}$ **b)** 2^{-4} $\frac{1}{16}$

35. a) -9^{-2} $-\frac{1}{81}$ **b)** $(-9)^{-2}$ $\frac{1}{81}$

36. a) -5^{-2} $-\frac{1}{25}$ **b)** $(-5)^{-2}$ $\frac{1}{25}$

37. a) $(2^2)^3$ 64 **b)** $(2^3)^2$ 64

38. a) $\left[\left(\frac{1}{2}\right)^2\right]^3$ $\frac{1}{64}$ **b)** $\left[\left(-\frac{1}{2}\right)^2\right]^3$ $\frac{1}{64}$

39. a) $4^3 \cdot 4^{-2}$ 4 **b)** $2^{-2} \cdot 2^{-2}$ $\frac{1}{16}$

40. a) $(-5)^{-2}(-5)^{-2}$ $\frac{1}{625}$ **b)** $(-1)^{-5}(-1)^{-5}$ 1

In Exercises 41–52, express the number in scientific notation.

41. 415,000 4.15×10^5 **42.** 923,000,000 9.23×10^8

43. 0.00275 2.75×10^{-3} **44.** 0.000034 3.4×10^{-5}

45. 0.56 5.6×10^{-1} **46.** 0.00467 4.67×10^{-3}

47. 19,000 1.9×10^4 **48.** 1,260,000,000 1.26×10^9

49. 0.000186 1.86×10^{-4} **50.** 0.0003 3×10^{-4}

51. 0.00000423 4.23×10^{-6} **52.** 54,000 5.4×10^4

In Exercises 53–62, express the number in decimal notation.

53. 4.2×10^4 42,000 **54.** 3.9×10^5 390,000

55. 1.32×10^{-2} 0.0132 **56.** 4.003×10^7 40,030,000

57. 8.62×10^{-5} 0.0000862 **58.** 2.19×10^{-4} 0.000219

59. 3.12×10^{-1} 0.312 **60.** 4.6×10^1 46

61. 9×10^6 9,000,000 **62.** 7.3×10^4 73,000

In Exercises 63–72, (a) perform the indicated operation without the use of a calculator and express each answer in decimal notation. (b) Confirm your answer from part (a) by using a scientific calculator to perform the operations. If the calculator displays the answer in scientific notation, convert the answer to decimal notation.

63. $(2 \times 10^3)(3.1 \times 10^2)$ 620,000 **64.** $(4.9 \times 10^4)(2 \times 10^3)$ 98,000,000

65. $(5.1 \times 10^1)(3 \times 10^{-4})$ 0.0153 **66.** $(1.6 \times 10^{-2})(4 \times 10^{-3})$ 0.000064

67. $\dfrac{7.5 \times 10^6}{3 \times 10^4}$ 250 **68.** $\dfrac{5.2 \times 10^7}{4 \times 10^9}$ 0.013

69. $\dfrac{8.4 \times 10^{-6}}{4 \times 10^{-3}}$ 0.0021 **70.** $\dfrac{25 \times 10^3}{5 \times 10^{-2}}$ 500,000

71. $\dfrac{4 \times 10^5}{2 \times 10^4}$ 20 **72.** $\dfrac{16 \times 10^3}{8 \times 10^{-3}}$ 2,000,000

In Exercises 73–82, (a) perform the indicated operation without the use of a calculator and express each answer in scientific notation. (b) Confirm your answer from part (a) by using a scientific calculator to perform the operations. If the calculator displays the answer in decimal notation, convert the answer to scientific notation.

73. $(1,000,000)(230,000)$ 2.3×10^{11}

74. $(2,000,000)(0.00025)$ 5×10^2

75. $(0.003)(0.00015)$ 4.5×10^{-7}

76. $(230,000)(3000)$ 6.9×10^8

77. $\dfrac{5,600,000}{80,000}$ 7.0×10^1 **78.** $\dfrac{28,000}{0.004}$ 7.0×10^6

79. $\dfrac{0.00004}{200}$ 2.0×10^{-7} **80.** $\dfrac{0.0012}{0.000006}$ 2.0×10^2

81. $\dfrac{150,000}{0.0005}$ 3.0×10^8 **82.** $\dfrac{24,000}{8,000,000}$ 3.0×10^{-3}

Problem Solving

In Exercises 83–86, list the numbers from smallest to largest.

83. 1.03×10^4; 1.7; 3.6×10^{-3}; 9.8×10^2
3.6×10^{-3}; 1.7; 9.8×10^2; 1.03×10^4

84. 8.5×10^{-5}; 8.2×10^3; 1.3×10^{-1}; 6.2×10^4
8.5×10^{-5}; 1.3×10^{-1}; 8.2×10^3; 6.2×10^4

85. 40,000; 4.1×10^3; 0.00079; 8.3×10^{-5}
8.3×10^{-5}; 0.00079; 4.1×10^3; 40,000

86. 267,000,000; 3.14×10^7; 1,962,000; 4.79×10^6
1,962,000; 4.79×10^6; 3.14×10^7; 267,000,000

In Exercises 87–97, you may use a scientific calculator to perform the necessary operations.

87. *U.S. Debt per Person: 2006 Versus 2010* In Example 14 on page 265, the U.S. government debt was discussed. It was found that the debt in 2010 was about $42,261.71 per person. In 2006, the U.S. government debt was about $8.38 trillion, and the population of the United States was about 299 million.

a) Determine the amount of debt per person in 2006.
$28,026.76

b) How much more per person did the U.S. government owe in 2010 than in 2006? $14,234.95

88. *United Kingdom Debt per Person* In 2010, the United Kingdom's government had a debt of about £923 billion (the pound, symbolized, £, is the United Kingdom's unit of currency). The United Kingdom's population in 2010 was about 62.8 million.

a) Determine the amount of debt per person in 2010 for the United Kingdom. £14,697.45

b) In 2010, £1 was worth about $1.50. Convert the amount found in part (a) to dollars. $22,046.18

89. *U.S. Population* In June 2010, the population of the United States was about 309.5 million people, and the population of the world was about 6.830 billion people. Determine the ratio of the U.S. population to the world's population by dividing the U.S. population by the world's population. Write your answer as a decimal number and round to the nearest thousandth. 0.045

90. *China's Population* In June 2010, the population of China was about 1.319 billion people, and the population of the world was about 6.830 billion people. Determine the ratio of China's population to the world's population by dividing China's population by the world's population. Write your answer as a decimal number and round to the nearest thousandth. 0.193

91. *New York Population Density* In June 2010, the population of the metropolitan New York area was about 17,800,000 people, and the area was about 8683 square kilometers. Determine the metropolitan New York population density by dividing the population by the area. About 2050 people per square kilometer

92. *Mumbai Population Density* In June 2010, the population of the metropolitan Mumbai, India, area was about 14,350,000 people, and the area was about 484 square kilometers. Determine the metropolitan Mumbai population density by dividing the population by the area.
About 29,649 people per square kilometer

93. *Gross Domestic Product* The gross domestic product (GDP) of a country is the total national output of goods and services produced within that country. In 2009, the GDP of the United States was about $14.3 trillion, and the U.S. population was about 308 million people. Determine the U.S. GDP per person by dividing the GDP by the population. Round your answer to the nearest whole dollar. $46,429

94. *China's GDP* In 2009, the GDP (see Exercise 93) of China was about $4.91 trillion, and the population of China was about 1.335 billion people. Determine China's GDP per person by dividing the GDP by the population. Round your answer to the nearest whole dollar. $3678

95. *Traveling to the Moon* The distance from Earth to the moon is approximately 239,000 mi. If a spacecraft travels at a speed of 20,000 mph, how many hours would the spacecraft need to travel from Earth to the moon? Use distance = rate × time. 11.95 hours

▲ *The Moon*

96. *Traveling to Jupiter* The distance from Earth to the planet Jupiter is approximately 4.5×10^8 mi. If a spacecraft traveled at a speed of 25,000 mph, how many hours would the spacecraft need to travel from Earth to Jupiter? Use distance = rate × time. 18,000 hours

97. *Traveling to Proxima Centauri* The star closest in distance to our own sun is Proxima Centauri. The distance from Earth to Proxima Centauri is approximately 2.5×10^{13} miles. If a spacecraft travels at a speed of 20,000 mph, how many hours would the spacecraft need to travel to Proxima Centauri? Use distance = rate × time and write your answer in scientific notation. 1.25×10^9 hours

98. *Computer Speed* As of June 22, 2010, the fastest computer in the world was the Cray Jaguar located at Oak Ridge National Laboratory. This computer is capable of performing about 1.75 quadrillion (1.75×10^{15}) calculations per second. At this rate, how long would it take to perform a task requiring 7.6×10^{65} calculations? Write your answer in scientific notation. 4.343×10^{50} seconds

▲ *The Cray Jaguar computer*

99. *1950 Niagara Treaty* The 1950 Niagara Treaty between the United States and Canada requires that during the tourist season a minimum of 100,000 cubic feet of water per second (ft³/sec) flow over Niagara Falls (another 130,000–160,000 ft³/sec are diverted for power generation). Find the minimum amount of water that will flow over the falls in a 24-hour period during the tourist season. Write your answer in scientific notation. 8.64×10^9 ft³

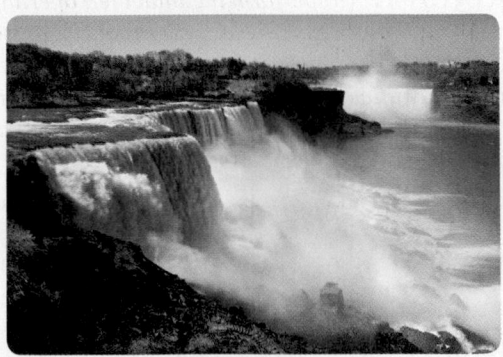

▲ *Niagara Falls*

100. *Bucket Full of Molecules* A drop of water contains about 40 billion molecules. If a bucket has half a million drops of water in it, how many molecules of water are in the bucket? Write your answer in scientific notation. 2.0×10^{16} molecules

101. *Blood Cells in a Cubic Millimeter* If a cubic millimeter of blood contains 5,800,000 red blood cells, how many red blood cells are contained in 50 cubic millimeters of blood? Write your answer in scientific notation. 2.9×10^{8} cells

102. *Radioactive Isotopes* The half-life of a radioactive isotope is the time required for half the quantity of the isotope to decompose. The half-life of uranium-238 is 4.5×10^{9} years, and the half-life of uranium-234 is 2.5×10^{5} years. How many times greater is the half-life of uranium-238 than uranium-234? 18,000 times

103. *Mutual Fund Manager* Lauri Mackey is the fund manager for the Mackey Mutual Fund. This mutual fund has total assets of $1.2 billion. Lauri wants to maintain the investments in this fund according to the following pie chart.

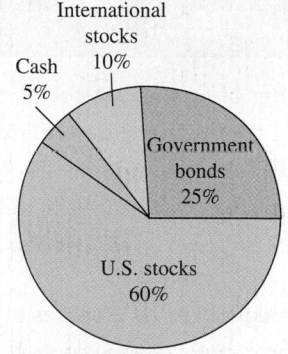

International stocks 10%
Cash 5%
Government bonds 25%
U.S. stocks 60%

a) How much of the $1.2 billion should be invested in U.S. stocks? $720,000,000

b) How much should be invested in government bonds? $300,000,000

c) How much should be invested in international stocks? $120,000,000

d) How much should remain in cash? $60,000,000

104. *Another Mutual Fund Manager* Susan Dratch is the fund manager for the Dratch Mutual Fund. This mutual fund has total assets of $3.4 billion. Susan wants to maintain the investments in this fund according to the following pie chart.

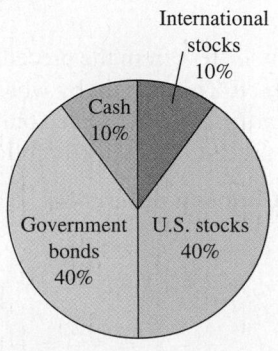

International stocks 10%
Cash 10%
Government bonds 40%
U.S. stocks 40%

a) How much of the $3.4 billion should be invested in U.S. stocks? $1,360,000,000

b) How much should be invested in government bonds? $1,360,000,000

c) How much should be invested in international stocks? $340,000,000

d) How much should remain in cash? $340,000,000

105. *Metric System Comparison* In the metric system, 1 meter = 10^{3} millimeters. How many times greater is a meter than a millimeter? 1000

106. *Milligrams and Kilograms* In the metric system, 1 gram = 10^{3} milligrams and 1 gram = 10^{-3} kilogram. What is the relationship between milligrams and kilograms? 1,000,000 mg = 1 kg

107. *Earth to Sun Comparison* The mass of the sun is approximately 2×10^{30} kilograms, and the mass of Earth is approximately 6×10^{24} kilograms. How many times greater is the mass of the sun than the mass of Earth? Write your answer in decimal notation. 333,333 times

Challenge Problems/Group Activities

108. *Comparing a Million to a Billion* Many people have no idea of the difference in size between a million (1,000,000), a billion (1,000,000,000), and a trillion (1,000,000,000,000).

a) Write a million, a billion, and a trillion in scientific notation. $1 \times 10^{6}, 1 \times 10^{9}, 1 \times 10^{12}$

b) Determine how long it would take to spend one million dollars if you spent $1000 a day. 1000 days (about 2.74 years)

c) Repeat part (b) for one billion dollars. 1,000,000 days (about 2739.73 years)

d) Repeat part (b) for one trillion dollars. 1,000,000,000 days (about 2,739,726.03 years)

e) How many times greater is one billion dollars than one million dollars? 1000 times greater

109. *Speed of Light*

a) Light travels at a speed of 1.86×10^{5} mi/sec. A *light-year* is the distance that light travels in 1 year. Determine the number of miles in a light-year. About 5.87×10^{12} (5.87 trillion) mi

b) Earth is approximately 93,000,000 mi from the sun. How long does it take light from the sun to reach Earth? About 500 sec or 8 min 20 sec

110. *Bacteria in a Culture* The exponential function $E(t) = 2^{10} \cdot 2^{t}$ approximates the number of bacteria in a certain culture after t hours.

a) The initial number of bacteria is determined when $t = 0$. What is the initial number of bacteria? 1024 bacteria

b) How many bacteria are there after $\frac{1}{2}$ hour? ≈ 1448 bacteria

Internet/Research Activities

111. Obtain data from the U.S. Department of the Treasury and from the U.S. Bureau of the Census Internet Web sites to calculate the current U.S. government debt per person. Write a report in which you compare your figure with those obtained in Exercise 87 and Example 14. Include in your report definitions of the following terms: revenues, expenditures, deficit, and surplus.

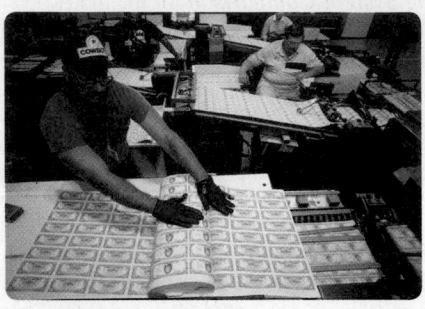

112. *John Allen Paulos* Read the *Profiles in Mathematics* box on page 264. Read one of Paulos's books and write a 500-word report on it.

113. Find an article in a newspaper or magazine that contains scientific notation. Write a paragraph explaining how scientific notation was used. Attach a copy of the article to your report.

SECTION 5.7 Arithmetic and Geometric Sequences

▲ *The modern study of diseases involves the use of mathematics to predict the size of bacteria populations.*

Under optimal laboratory conditions, the number of *Escherichia coli* (*E. coli*) bacteria will double every 17 minutes. If an experiment conducted under optimal conditions begins with 100 bacteria, how many bacteria will be present after 24 hours? Questions such as these are important to the modern study of diseases. In this section, we will study such questions by using lists of numbers known as *sequences*.

Why This is Important Sequences are used throughout many branches of mathematics to model real-life phenomena, such as population growth, disease control, and the inflation rates of currencies.

Now that you can recognize the various sets of real numbers and know how to add, subtract, multiply, and divide real numbers, we can discuss sequences. A *sequence* is a list of numbers that are related to each other by a rule. The numbers that form the sequence are called its *terms*. If your salary increases or decreases by a fixed amount over a period of time, the listing of the amounts, over time, would form an arithmetic sequence. When interest in a savings account is compounded at regular intervals, the listing of the amounts in the account over time will be a geometric sequence.

Arithmetic Sequences

A sequence in which each term after the first term differs from the preceding term by a constant amount is called an *arithmetic sequence*. The amount by which each pair of successive terms differs is called the *common difference*, d. The common difference can be found by subtracting any term from the term that directly follows it.

Examples of arithmetic sequences	Common differences
$1, 5, 9, 13, 17, \ldots$	$d = 5 - 1 = 4$
$-7, -5, -3, -1, 1, \ldots$	$d = -5 - (-7) = -5 + 7 = 2$
$\dfrac{5}{2}, \dfrac{3}{2}, \dfrac{1}{2}, -\dfrac{1}{2}, \ldots$	$d = \dfrac{3}{2} - \dfrac{5}{2} = -\dfrac{2}{2} = -1$

Profile in Mathematics

Carl Friedrich Gauss

Carl Friedrich Gauss (1777–1855), often called the "Prince of Mathematicians," made significant contributions to the fields of algebra, geometry, and number theory. Gauss was only 22 years old when he proved the fundamental theorem of algebra for his doctoral dissertation.

When Gauss was only 10, his mathematics teacher gave him the problem of finding the sum of the first 100 natural numbers, thinking that this task would keep Gauss busy for a while. Gauss recognized a pattern in the sequence of numbers when he considered the sum of the following numbers.

$$1 + 2 + 3 + \cdots + 99 + 100$$
$$100 + 99 + 98 + \cdots + 2 + 1$$
$$101 + 101 + 101 + \cdots + 101 + 101$$

He had the required answer in no time at all. When he added, he had one hundred 101's. Therefore, the sum of the first 100 natural numbers is $\frac{1}{2}(100)(101) = 5050$.

Example 1 *The First Five Terms of an Arithmetic Sequence*

Write the first five terms of the arithmetic sequence with first term 3 and a common difference of 7.

Solution The first term is 3. The second term is $3 + 7$, or 10. The third term is $10 + 7$, or 17. The fourth term is $17 + 7$, or 24. The fifth term is $24 + 7$, or 31. Thus, the first five terms of the arithmetic sequence are 3, 10, 17, 24, 31. ∎

Example 2 *An Arithmetic Sequence with a Negative Difference*

Write the first five terms of the arithmetic sequence with first term 9 and a common difference of -4.

Solution The first five terms of the sequence are

$$9, 5, 1, -3, -7$$ ∎

When discussing a sequence, we often represent the first term as a_1 (read "a sub 1"), the second term as a_2, the fifteenth term as a_{15}, and so on. We use the notation a_n to represent the general or nth term of a sequence. Thus, a sequence may be symbolized as

$$a_1, a_2, a_3, a_4, \ldots, a_n, \ldots$$

For example, in the sequence 2, 5, 8, 11, 14, ..., we have

$$a_1 = 2, a_2 = 5, a_3 = 8, a_4 = 11, a_5 = 14, \ldots.$$

The following formula can be used to determine the nth term of an arithmetic sequence.

General or *n*th Term of an Arithmetic Sequence

For an arithmetic sequence with first term a_1 and common difference d, the general or nth term can be found using the following formula.

$$a_n = a_1 + (n - 1)d$$

Example 3 *Determining the Twelfth Term of an Arithmetic Sequence*

Determine the twelfth term of the arithmetic sequence whose first term is -5 and whose common difference is 3.

Solution To determine the twelfth term, or a_{12}, replace n in the formula with 12, a_1 with -5, and d with 3.

$$a_n = a_1 + (n - 1)d$$
$$a_{12} = -5 + (12 - 1)3$$
$$= -5 + (11)3$$
$$= -5 + 33$$
$$= 28$$

The twelfth term is 28. As a check, we have listed the first 12 terms of the sequence: $-5, -2, 1, 4, 7, 10, 13, 16, 19, 22, 25, 28$. ∎

⌐ Example **4** *Determining an Expression for the nth Term*

Write an expression for the general or *n*th term, a_n, for the sequence 1, 6, 11, 16, ...

Solution   In this sequence, the first term, a_1, is 1 and the common difference, d, is 5. We substitute these values into $a_n = a_1 + (n - 1)d$ to obtain an expression for the *n*th term, a_n.

$$a_n = a_1 + (n - 1)d$$
$$= 1 + (n - 1)5$$
$$= 1 + 5n - 5$$
$$= 5n - 4$$

The expression is $a_n = 5n - 4$. Note that when $n = 1$, the first term is $5(1) - 4 = 1$. When $n = 2$, the second term is $5(2) - 4 = 6$, and so on.   ■

We can use the following formula to find the sum of the first *n* terms in an arithmetic sequence.

Sum of the First *n* Terms in an Arithmetic Sequence

The sum of the first *n* terms of an arithmetic sequence can be found with the following formula where a_1 represents the first term and a_n represents the *n*th term.

$$s_n = \frac{n(a_1 + a_n)}{2}$$

In this formula, s_n represents the sum of the first *n* terms, a_1 is the first term, a_n is the *n*th term, and *n* is the number of terms in the sequence from a_1 to a_n.

⌐ Example **5** *Determining the Sum of an Arithmetic Sequence*

Determine the sum of the first 25 even natural numbers.

Solution   The sequence we are discussing is

$$2, 4, 6, 8, 10, \ldots, 50$$

In this arithmetic sequence the first term is 2, the 25th term is 50, and there are 25 terms; therefore, $a_1 = 2$, $a_{25} = 50$, and $n = 25$. Thus, the sum of the first 25 terms is

$$s_n = \frac{n(a_1 + a_n)}{2}$$
$$s_{25} = \frac{25(2 + 50)}{2}$$
$$= \frac{25(52)}{2}$$
$$= \frac{1300}{2}$$
$$= 650$$

The sum of the first 25 even natural numbers, $2 + 4 + 6 + 8 + \cdots + 50$, is 650.   ■

Geometric Sequences

The next type of sequence we will discuss is the geometric sequence. A *geometric sequence* is one in which the ratio of any term to the term that directly precedes it is a constant. This constant is called the *common ratio*. The common ratio, r, can be found by taking any term except the first and dividing that term by the preceding term.

Examples of geometric sequences	Common ratios
2, 4, 8, 16, 32, ...	$r = 4 \div 2 = 2$; $r = 8 \div 4 = 2$; ...
$-3, 6, -12, 24, -48, ...$	$r = 6 \div (-3) = -2$; $r = (-12) \div 6 = -2$; ...
$\dfrac{2}{3}, \dfrac{2}{9}, \dfrac{2}{27}, \dfrac{2}{81}, ...$	$r = \dfrac{2}{9} \div \dfrac{2}{3} = \left(\dfrac{2}{9}\right)\left(\dfrac{3}{2}\right) = \dfrac{1}{3}$; $r = \dfrac{2}{27} \div \dfrac{2}{9} = \left(\dfrac{2}{27}\right)\left(\dfrac{9}{2}\right) = \dfrac{1}{3}$; ...

To construct a geometric sequence when the first term, a_1, and common ratio, r, are known, multiply the first term by the common ratio to get the second term. Then multiply the second term by the common ratio to get the third term, and so on.

Example 6 *The First Five Terms of a Geometric Sequence*

Write the first five terms of the geometric sequence whose first term, a_1, is 5 and whose common ratio, r, is 2.

Solution The first term is 5. The second term, found by multiplying the first term by 2, is $5 \cdot 2$, or 10. The third term is $10 \cdot 2$, or 20. The fourth term is $20 \cdot 2$, or 40. The fifth term is $40 \cdot 2$, or 80. Thus, the first five terms of the geometric sequence are 5, 10, 20, 40, 80. ∎

The following formula can be used to determine the nth term of a geometric sequence.

General or nth Term of a Geometric Sequence

For a geometric sequence with first term a_1 and common ratio r, the general or nth term can be found using the following formula.

$$a_n = a_1 r^{n-1}$$

Example 7 *Determining the Twelfth Term of a Geometric Sequence*

Determine the twelfth term of the geometric sequence whose first term is -4 and whose common ratio is 2.

Solution In this sequence, $a_1 = -4$, $r = 2$, and $n = 12$. Substituting the values into the formula, we obtain

$$
\begin{aligned}
a_n &= a_1 r^{n-1} \\
a_{12} &= -4 \cdot 2^{12-1} \\
&= -4 \cdot 2^{11} \\
&= -4 \cdot 2048 \\
&= -8192
\end{aligned}
$$

As a check, we have listed the first twelve terms of the sequence:

$-4, -8, -16, -32, -64, -128, -256, -512, -1024, -2048, -4096, -8192$ ∎

Example 8 *Determining an Expression for the nth Term*

Write an expression for the general or nth term, a_n, of the sequence 2, 6, 18, 54, ...

Solution   In this sequence, the first term is 2, so $a_1 = 2$. Note that $\frac{6}{2} = 3$, so $r = 3$. We substitute $a_1 = 2$ and $r = 3$ into $a_n = a_1 r^{n-1}$ to obtain an expression for the nth term, a_n.

$$a_n = a_1 r^{n-1}$$
$$= 2(3)^{n-1}$$

The expression is $a_n = 2(3)^{n-1}$. Note that when $n = 1$, $a_1 = 2(3)^0 = 2(1) = 2$. When $n = 2$, $a_2 = 2(3)^1 = 6$, and so on.   ∎

The following formula can be used to determine the sum of the first n terms of a geometric sequence.

Sum of the First *n* Terms of a Geometric Sequence

The sum of the first n terms of a geometric sequence can be found with the following formula where a_1 represents the first term and r represents the common ratio.

$$s_n = \frac{a_1(1 - r^n)}{1 - r}, \quad r \neq 1$$

Example 9 *Determining the Sum of a Geometric Sequence*

Determine the sum of the first five terms in the geometric sequence whose first term is 4 and whose common ratio is 2.

Solution   In this sequence, $a_1 = 4$, $r = 2$, and $n = 5$. Substituting these values into the formula, we get

$$s_n = \frac{a_1(1 - r^n)}{1 - r}$$
$$s_5 = \frac{4[1 - (2)^5]}{1 - 2}$$
$$= \frac{4(1 - 32)}{-1}$$
$$= \frac{4(-31)}{-1} = \frac{-124}{-1} = 124$$

The sum of the first five terms of the sequence is 124. The first five terms of the sequence are 4, 8, 16, 32, 64. If you add these five numbers, you will obtain the sum 124.   ∎

Example 10 *Pounds and Pounds of Silver*

As a reward for saving his kingdom from a band of thieves, a king offered a knight one of two options. The knight's first option was to be paid 100,000 pounds of silver all at once. The second option was to be paid over the course of a month. On the first day, he would receive one pound of silver. On the second day, he would receive two pounds of silver. On the third day, he would receive four pounds of silver, and so on, each day receiving double the amount given on the previous day. Assuming the month has 30 days, which option would provide the knight with more silver?

Solution   The first option pays the knight 100,000 pounds of silver. The second option pays according to the geometric sequence 1, 2, 4, 8, 16, ... In this sequence,

$a_1 = 1$, $r = 2$, and $n = 30$. The sum of this sequence can be found by substituting these values into the formula to obtain

$$s_n = \frac{a_1(1 - r^n)}{1 - r}$$

$$s_{30} = \frac{1(1 - 2^{30})}{1 - 2}$$

$$= \frac{1 - 1,073,741,824}{-1}$$

$$= \frac{-1,073,741,823}{-1}$$

$$= 1,073,741,823$$

Thus, the knight would get 1,073,741,823 pounds of silver with the second option. Compared with the first option, the second would result in an additional 1,073,641,823 pounds of silver. ∎

SECTION 5.7 *Exercises*

Warm Up Exercises

In Exercises 1–6, fill in the blanks with an appropriate word, phrase, or symbol(s).

1. A list of numbers that are related to each other by a rule is called a(n) _____. Sequence

2. The numbers that form a sequence are called its _____.
Terms

3. A sequence in which each term differs from the preceding term by a constant amount is called a(n) _____ sequence.
Arithmetic

4. The amount by which each pair of successive terms differ in an arithmetic sequence is called the common _____.
Difference

5. A sequence in which the ratio of any term to the term that directly precedes it is a constant is called a(n) _____ sequence. Geometric

6. The constant found by dividing any term in a geometric sequence by the term that directly precedes it is called the common _____. Ratio

Practice the Skills

In Exercises 7–14, write the first five terms of the arithmetic sequence with the first term, a_1, and common difference, d.

7. $a_1 = 3, d = 2$ 3, 5, 7, 9, 11   **8.** $a_1 = 0, d = 3$ 0, 3, 6, 9, 12

9. $a_1 = 25, d = -5$
25, 20, 15, 10, 5

10. $a_1 = -11, d = 5$
−11, −6, −1, 4, 9

11. $a_1 = 5, d = -2$
5, 3, 1, −1, −3

12. $a_1 = -3, d = -4$
−3, −7, −11, −15, −19

13. $a_1 = \frac{3}{4}, d = \frac{1}{4}$ $\frac{3}{4}, 1, \frac{5}{4}, \frac{3}{2}, \frac{7}{4}$

14. $a_1 = \frac{5}{2}, d = -\frac{3}{2}$
$\frac{5}{2}, 1, -\frac{1}{2}, -2, -\frac{7}{2}$

In Exercises 15–22, determine the indicated term for the arithmetic sequence with the first term, a_1, and common difference, d.

15. Determine a_4 when $a_1 = 3, d = 1$. 6

16. Determine a_7 when $a_1 = 12, d = -2$. 0

17. Determine a_{11} when $a_1 = -20, d = 5$. 30

18. Determine a_{12} when $a_1 = 7, d = -3$. −26

19. Determine a_{20} when $a_1 = \frac{4}{5}, d = -1$. $-\frac{91}{5}$

20. Determine a_{14} when $a_1 = \frac{1}{3}, d = \frac{2}{3}$. 9

21. Determine a_{22} when $a_1 = -23, d = \frac{5}{7}$. −8

22. Determine a_{15} when $a_1 = \frac{4}{3}, d = \frac{1}{3}$. 6

In Exercises 23–30, write an expression for the general or nth term, a_n, for the arithmetic sequence.

23. 1, 2, 3, 4, … $a_n = n$ **24.** 1, 3, 5, 7, … $a_n = 2n - 1$

25. 2, 4, 6, 8, … $a_n = 2n$ **26.** 3, 6, 9, 12, … $a_n = 3n$

27. 2, 6, 10, 14, …
$a_n = 4n - 2$

28. −7, −2, 3, 8, …
$a_n = 5n - 12$

29. −3, −$\frac{3}{2}$, 0, $\frac{3}{2}$, …
$a_n = \frac{3}{2}n - \frac{9}{2}$

30. −5, −2, 1, 4, … $a_n = 3n - 8$

In Exercises 31–38, determine the sum of the terms of the arithmetic sequence. The number of terms, n, is given.

31. 1, 2, 3, 4, …, 50; $n = 50$ $s_{50} = 1275$

32. 2, 4, 6, 8, …, 100; $n = 50$ $s_{50} = 2550$

33. 1, 3, 5, 7, …, 99; $n = 50$ $s_{50} = 2500$

34. 1, 4, 7, 10, …, 100; $n = 34$ $s_{34} = 1717$

35. −10, −5, 0, 5, …, 60; $n = 15$ $s_{15} = 375$

36. 100, 90, 80, 70, …, −60; $n = 17$ $s_{17} = 340$

37. $\frac{1}{5}, \frac{2}{5}, \frac{3}{5}, \frac{4}{5}, …, \frac{24}{5}$; $n = 24$ $s_{24} = 60$

38. $-\frac{3}{4}, -\frac{1}{2}, -\frac{1}{4}, 0, …, \frac{17}{4}$; $n = 21$ $s_{21} = 36.75$

In Exercises 39–46, write the first five terms of the geometric sequence with the first term, a_1, and common ratio, r.

39. $a_1 = 1, r = 3$
1, 3, 9, 27, 81

40. $a_1 = 3, r = 1$ 3, 3, 3, 3, 3

41. $a_1 = 5, r = 2$
5, 10, 20, 40, 80

42. $a_1 = 8, r = \frac{1}{2}$ 8, 4, 2, 1, $\frac{1}{2}$

43. $a_1 = -3, r = -1$
−3, 3, −3, 3, −3

44. $a_1 = -6, r = -2$
−6, 12, −24, 48, −96

45. $a_1 = 81, r = -\frac{1}{3}$
81, −27, 9, −3, 1

46. $a_1 = \frac{16}{15}, r = \frac{1}{2}$ $\frac{16}{15}, \frac{8}{15}, \frac{4}{15}, \frac{2}{15}, \frac{1}{15}$

In Exercises 47–54, determine the indicated term for the geometric sequence with the first term, a_1, and common ratio, r.

47. Determine a_5 when $a_1 = 7, r = 2$. 112

48. Determine a_5 when $a_1 = 2, r = 3$. 162

49. Determine a_3 when $a_1 = 3, r = \frac{1}{2}$. $\frac{3}{4}$

50. Determine a_7 when $a_1 = -3, r = -3$. −2187

51. Determine a_7 when $a_1 = -5, r = 3$. −3645

52. Determine a_8 when $a_1 = \frac{1}{2}, r = -2$. −64

53. Determine a_{10} when $a_1 = -2, r = 3$. −39,366

54. Determine a_{18} when $a_1 = -5, r = -2$. 655,360

In Exercises 55–62, write an expression for the general or nth term, a_n, for the geometric sequence.

55. 5, 25, 125, 625 ...
$a_n = 5^n$

56. 1, 5, 25, 125, ...
$a_n = 5^{n-1}$

57. −1, 1, −1, 1, ...
$a_n = (-1)(-1)^{n-1}$

58. −16, −8, −4, −2, ... *

59. 2, 1, $\frac{1}{2}$, $\frac{1}{4}$, ... *

60. −3, 6, −12, 24, ... *

61. 9, 3, 1, $\frac{1}{3}$, $\frac{1}{9}$, ... *

62. −4, −$\frac{8}{3}$, −$\frac{16}{9}$, −$\frac{32}{27}$, ... *

In Exercises 63–70, determine the sum of the first n terms of the geometric sequence for the values of a_1 and r.

63. $n = 6, a_1 = 3, r = 2$ 189

64. $n = 7, a_1 = 1, r = 3$ 1093

65. $n = 6, a_1 = -3, r = 4$ −4095

66. $n = 9, a_1 = -3, r = 5$ −1,464,843

67. $n = 11, a_1 = -7, r = 3$ −620,011

68. $n = 15, a_1 = -1, r = 2$ −32,767

69. $n = 15, a_1 = -1, r = -2$ −10,923

70. $n = 10, a_1 = 512, r = \frac{1}{2}$ 1023

Problem Solving

71. Determine the sum of the first 100 natural numbers. 5050

72. Determine the sum of the first 100 odd natural numbers. 10,000

73. Determine the sum of the first 100 even natural numbers. 10,100

74. Determine the sum of the first 50 multiples of 3. 3825

75. *Pendulum Movement* Each swing of a pendulum (from far left to far right) is 3 in. shorter than the preceding swing. The first swing is 8 ft.

   a) Find the length of the twelfth swing. 63 in.

   b) Determine the total distance traveled by the pendulum during the first 12 swings. 954 in.

76. *Clock Strikes* A clock strikes once at 1 o'clock, twice at 2 o'clock, three times at 3 o'clock, and so on. How many times does it strike over a 12-hr period? 78 times

77. *Annual Pay Raises* Rita Fernandez is given a starting salary of $35,000 and promised a $1400 raise per year after each of the next 8 years.

   a) Determine her salary during her eighth year of work.
   $44,800

   b) Determine the total salary she received over the 8 years.
   $319,200

78. *A Bouncing Ball* Each time a ball bounces, the height attained by the ball is 6 in. less than the previous height attained. If on the first bounce the ball reaches a height of 6 ft, find the height attained on the eleventh bounce. 12 in.

79. *Enrollment Increase* The current enrollment at Loras College is 8000 students. If the enrollment increases by 8% per year, determine the enrollment 10 years later.
≈ 15,992 students

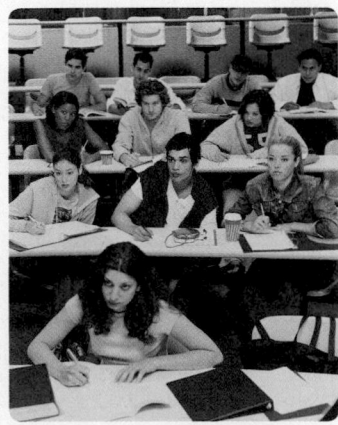

*See Instructor Answer Appendix

80. *Samurai Sword Construction* While making a traditional Japanese samurai sword, the master sword maker prepares the blade by heating a bar of iron until it is white hot. He then folds it over and pounds it smooth. Therefore, after each folding, the number of layers of steel is doubled. Assuming the sword maker starts with a bar of one layer and folds it 15 times, how many layers of steel will the finished sword contain? 32,768 layers

81. *Salary Increase* If your salary were to increase at a rate of 6% per year, find your salary during your 15th year if your original salary is $31,000. ≈ $70,088

82. *A Bouncing Ball* When dropped, a ball rebounds to four-fifths of its original height. How high will the ball rebound after the fourth bounce if it is dropped from a height of 30 ft? 12.288 ft

83. *Value of a Stock* Ten years ago, Nancy Hart purchased $2000 worth of shares in RCF, Inc. Since then, the price of the stock has roughly tripled every 2 years. Approximately how much are Nancy's shares worth today? $486,000

84. *A Baseball Game* During a baseball game, the visiting team scored 1 run in the first inning, 2 runs in the second inning, 3 runs in the third inning, 4 runs in the fourth inning, and so on. The home team scored 1 run in the first inning, 2 runs in the second inning, 4 runs in the third inning, 8 runs in the fourth inning, and so on. What is the score of the game after eight innings? Visitors 36, Home 255

Inning	1	2	3	4	5	6	7	8	9
Visitors	1	2	3	4					
Home	1	2	4	8					

Challenge Problems/Group Activities

85. A geometric sequence has $a_1 = 82$ and $r = \frac{1}{2}$; find s_6.
161.4375

86. *Sums of Interior Angles* The sums of the interior angles of a triangle, a quadrilateral, a pentagon, and a hexagon are 180°, 360°, 540°, and 720°, respectively. Use this pattern to find a formula for the general term, a_n, where a_n represents the sum of the interior angles of an n-sided polygon. $a_n = 180n - 360, n \geq 3$

87. *Divisibility by 6* Determine how many numbers between 7 and 1610 are divisible by 6. 267

88. Determine r and a_1 for the geometric sequence with $a_2 = 24$ and $a_5 = 648$. $r = 3, a_1 = 8$

89. *Total Distance Traveled by a Bouncing Ball* A ball is dropped from a height of 30 ft. On each bounce, it attains a height four-fifths of its original height (or of the previous bounce). Find the total vertical distance traveled by the ball after it has completed its fifth bounce (has therefore hit the ground six times). 191.3568 ft

Recreational Mathematics

90. *Martingale System* See the *Recreational Mathematics* box on page 274. Use the Martingale system to answer the following questions.

a) Assume a player is using a $1 standard bet and loses five times in a row. How much money should the player bet in the sixth round? How much money has the player lost at the end of the fifth round? $32, $31

b) Assume a player is using a $10 standard bet and loses five times in a row. How much money should the player bet in the sixth round? How much money has the player lost at the end of the fifth round? $320, $310

c) Assume a player is using a $1 standard bet and loses 10 times in a row. How much money should the player bet in the eleventh round? How much money has the player lost at the end of the tenth round? $1024, $1023

d) Assume a player is using a $10 standard bet and loses 10 times in a row. How much money should the player bet in the eleventh round? How much money has the player lost at the end of the tenth round? $10,240; $10,230

e) Why is this a risky strategy? *

Internet/Research Activity

91. A topic generally associated with sequences is *series*.

a) Research *series* and explain what a series is and how it differs from a sequence. Also write a formal definition of series. Give examples of different kinds of series.

b) Write the arithmetic series associated with the arithmetic sequence 1, 4, 7, 10, 13, … .

c) Write the geometric series associated with the geometric sequence 3, 6, 12, 24, 48, … .

d) What is an infinite geometric series?

e) Determine the sum of the terms of the infinite geometric series $1 + \dfrac{1}{2} + \dfrac{1}{4} + \dfrac{1}{8} + \dfrac{1}{16} + \cdots$.

▲ *The number of ancestors of a male bee is among the numbers found in the Fibonacci sequence.*

Profile in Mathematics

Fibonacci

Leonardo of Pisa (1170–1250) is considered one of the most distinguished mathematicians of the Middle Ages. He was born in Italy and was sent by his father to study mathematics with an Arab master. When he began writing, he referred to himself as Fibonacci, or "son of Bonacci," the name by which he is known today. In addition to the famous sequence bearing his name, Fibonacci is also credited with introducing the Hindu–Arabic number system into Europe. His 1202 book, *Liber Abacci* (Book of the Abacus), explained the use of this number system and emphasized the importance of the number zero.

Consider the following numbers found in nature: the number of petals on a daisy, the number of sunflower seeds in a sunflower, the number of scales on a pineapple, the number of ancestors of a male bee. In this section, we will find that all these numbers are part of a special sequence of numbers called the Fibonacci sequence.

Why *This is Important* The Fibonacci sequence and the related topic of the golden ratio appear in many places in nature and play an important role in geometry, art, and music.

Our discussion of sequences would not be complete without mentioning a sequence known as the *Fibonacci sequence*. The sequence is named after Leonardo of Pisa, also known as Fibonacci. He was one of the most distinguished mathematicians of the Middle Ages. This sequence is first mentioned in his book *Liber Abacci* (Book of the Abacus), which contained many interesting problems, such as: "A certain man put a pair of rabbits in a place surrounded on all sides by a wall. How many pairs of rabbits can be produced from that pair in a year if it is assumed that every month each pair begets a new pair which from the second month becomes productive?"

The solution to this problem (Fig. 5.10) led to the development of the sequence that bears its author's name: the Fibonacci sequence. The sequence is shown in Table 5.1. The numbers in the columns titled *Pairs of Adults* form the Fibonacci sequence.

Table 5.1

Month	Pairs of Adults	Pairs of Babies	Total Pairs
1	1	0	1
2	1	1	2
3	2	1	3
4	3	2	5
5	5	3	8
6	8	5	13
7	13	8	21
8	21	13	34
9	34	21	55
10	55	34	89
11	89	55	144
12	144	89	233

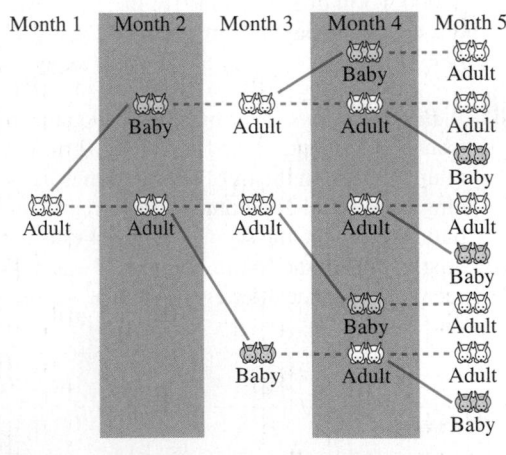

Figure 5.10

Following is the Fibonacci sequence

Fibonacci Sequence

$$1, 1, 2, 3, 5, 8, 13, 21, \ldots$$

In the Fibonacci sequence, the first and second terms are 1. The sum of these two terms is the third term. The sum of the second and third terms is the fourth term, and so on.

▲ *The head of a sunflower*

In the middle of the nineteenth century, mathematicians made a serious study of this sequence and found strong similarities between it and many natural phenomena. Fibonacci numbers appear in the seed arrangement of many species of plants and in the petal counts of various flowers. For example, when the flowering head of the sunflower matures to seed, the seeds' spiral arrangement becomes clearly visible. A typical count of these spirals may give 89 steeply curving to the right, 55 curving more shallowly to the left, and 34 again shallowly to the right. The largest known specimen to be examined had spiral counts of 144 right, 89 left, and 55 right. These numbers, like the other three mentioned, are consecutive terms of the Fibonacci sequence.

On the heads of many flowers, petals surrounding the central disk generally yield a Fibonacci number. For example, some daisies contain 21 petals, and others contain 34, 55, or 89 petals. (People who use a daisy to play the "love me, love me not" game will likely pluck 21, 34, 55, or 89 petals before arriving at an answer.)

Fibonacci numbers are also observed in the structure of pinecones and pineapples. The tablike or scalelike structures called bracts that make up the main body of the pinecone form a set of spirals that start from the cone's attachment to the branch. Two sets of oppositely directed spirals can be observed, one steep and the other more gradual. A count on the steep spiral will reveal a Fibonacci number, and a count on the gradual one will be the adjacent smaller Fibonacci number, or if not, the next smaller Fibonacci number. One investigation of 4290 pinecones from 10 species of pine trees found in California revealed that only 74 cones, or 1.7%, deviated from this Fibonacci pattern.

Like pinecone bracts, pineapple scales are patterned into spirals, and because they are roughly hexagonal in shape, three distinct sets of spirals can be counted. Generally, the number of pineapple scales in each spiral are Fibonacci numbers.

Fibonacci Numbers and Divine Proportions

In 1753, while studying the Fibonacci sequence, Robert Simson, a mathematician at the University of Glasgow, noticed that when he took the ratio of any term to the term that immediately preceded it, the value he obtained remained in the vicinity of one specific number. To illustrate this, we indicate in Table 5.2 the ratio of various pairs of sequential Fibonacci numbers.

The ratio of the 50th term to the 49th term is 1.6180. Simson proved that the ratio of the $(n + 1)$ term to the nth term as n gets larger and larger is the irrational number $(\sqrt{5} + 1)/2$, which begins $1.61803....$ This number was already well known to mathematicians at that time as the *golden number*.

Many years earlier, Bavarian astronomer and mathematician Johannes Kepler wrote that for him the golden number symbolized the Creator's intention "to create like from like." The golden number $(\sqrt{5} + 1)/2$ is frequently referred to as "phi," symbolized by the Greek letter Φ.

The ancient Greeks, in about the sixth century B.C., sought unifying principles of beauty and perfection, which they believed could be described by using mathematics. In their study of beauty, the Greeks used the term *golden ratio*. To understand the golden ratio, let's consider the line segment AB in Fig. 5.11.

Table 5.2

Numbers	Ratio
1, 1	$\dfrac{1}{1} = 1$
1, 2	$\dfrac{2}{1} = 2$
2, 3	$\dfrac{3}{2} = 1.5$
3, 5	$\dfrac{5}{3} = 1.666\ldots$
5, 8	$\dfrac{8}{5} = 1.6$
8, 13	$\dfrac{13}{8} = 1.625$
13, 21	$\dfrac{21}{13} \approx 1.615$
21, 34	$\dfrac{34}{21} \approx 1.619$
34, 55	$\dfrac{55}{34} \approx 1.618$
55, 89	$\dfrac{89}{55} \approx 1.618$

Figure 5.11

When this line segment is divided at a point C such that the ratio of the whole, AB, to the larger part, AC, is equal to the ratio of the larger part, AC, to the smaller

▲ *The Great Pyramid of Gizeh*

Figure 5.12

part, *CB*, each ratio *AB/AC* and *AC/CB* is referred to as a *golden ratio*. The proportion these ratios form, *AB/AC = AC/CB*, is called the *golden proportion*. Furthermore, each ratio in the proportion will have a value equal to the golden number, $(\sqrt{5} + 1)/2$.

$$\frac{AB}{AC} = \frac{AC}{CB} = \frac{\sqrt{5} + 1}{2} \approx 1.618$$

The Great Pyramid of Gizeh in Egypt, built about 2600 B.C., is the earliest known example of use of the golden ratio in architecture. The ratio of any of its sides of the square base (775.75 ft) to its altitude (481.4 ft) is about 1.611. Other evidence of the use of the golden ratio appears in other Egyptian buildings and tombs.

In medieval times, people referred to the golden proportion as the *divine proportion*, reflecting their belief in its relationship to the will of God.

Twentieth-century architect Le Corbusier developed a scale of proportions for the human body that he called the Modulor (Fig. 5.12). Note that the navel separates the entire body into golden proportions, as do the neck and knee.

From the golden proportion, the *golden rectangle* can be formed, as shown in Fig. 5.13.

$$\frac{\text{Length}}{\text{Width}} = \frac{a + b}{a} = \frac{a}{b} = \frac{\sqrt{5} + 1}{2}$$

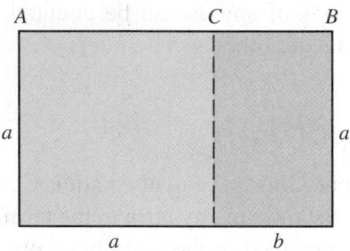

Figure 5.13

Note that when a square is cut off one end of a golden rectangle, as in Fig. 5.13, the remaining rectangle has the same properties as the original golden rectangle (creating "like from like" as Johannes Kepler had written) and is therefore itself a golden rectangle. Interestingly, the curve derived from a succession of diminishing golden rectangles, as shown in Fig. 5.14, is the same as the spiral curve of the chambered nautilus. The same curve appears on the horns of rams and some other animals. It is the same curve that is observed in the plant structures mentioned earlier: sunflowers, other flower heads, pinecones, and pineapples. You will recall that Fibonacci numbers were observed in each of these plant structures. The curve shown in Fig. 5.14 closely approximates what mathematicians call a *logarithmic spiral*.

Figure 5.14

▲ *The Parthenon*

Ancient Greek civilization used the golden rectangle in art and architecture. The main measurements of many buildings of antiquity, including the Parthenon in Athens, are governed by golden ratios and rectangles. Greek statues, vases, urns, and so on also exhibit characteristics of the golden ratio. It is for Phidas, considered the greatest of Greek sculptors, that the golden ratio was named "phi." The proportions can be found abundantly in his work.

The proportions of the golden rectangle can be found in the work of many artists, from the old masters to the moderns. For example, on page 281 the golden rectangle can be seen in the painting *Invitation to the Sideshow (La Parade de Cirque)*, 1887, by Georges Seurat, a French neoimpressionist artist.

Fibonacci and the Male Bee's Ancestors

The most frequent example given to introduce the Fibonacci sequence involves rabbits producing offspring, two at a time. Although this example makes for a nice introduction to Fibonacci sequences, it is not at all realistic. A much better example comes from the breeding practices of bees. Female or worker bees are produced when the queen bee mates with a male bee. Male bees are produced from the queen's unfertilized eggs. In essence, then, female bees have two parents, whereas male bees only have one parent. The family tree of a male bee would look like this:

From this tree, we can see that the 1 male bee (circled) has 1 parent, 2 grandparents, 3 great-grandparents, 5 great-great-grandparents, 8 great-great-great-grandparents, and so on. We see the Fibonacci sequence as we move back through the male bees' generations.

▲ Fibonacci's Garden *by Caryl Bryer Fallert*

▲ Invitation to the Sideshow (La Parade de Cirque), *1887, by Georges Seurat*

In addition to using the golden rectangle in art, several artists have used Fibonacci numbers in art. One contemporary example is the 1995 work by Caryl Bryer Fallert called *Fibonacci's Garden* which is shown in the margin. This artwork is a quilt constructed from two separate fabrics that are put together in a pattern based on the Fibonacci sequence.

Fibonacci numbers are also found in another form of art, namely music. Perhaps the most obvious link between Fibonacci numbers and music can be found on the piano keyboard. An octave (Fig. 5.15) on a keyboard has 13 keys: 8 white keys and 5 black keys (the 5 black keys are in one group of 2 and one group of 3).

5 black

C D E F G A B C

8 white
13 total

Figure 5.15

In Western music, the most complete scale, the chromatic scale, consists of 13 notes (from C to the next higher C). Its predecessor, the diatonic scale, contains 8 notes (an octave). The diatonic scale was preceded by a 5-note pentatonic scale (*penta* is Greek for "five"). Each number is a Fibonacci number. In popular music, the song "Lateralas" by the band Tool uses the Fibonacci sequence in both the time signature and the lyric arrangement. The song also contains several references to the golden ratio and to the logarithmic spiral.

The visual arts deal with what is pleasing to the eye, and musical composition deals with what is pleasing to the ear. Whereas art achieves some of its goals by using division of planes and area, music achieves some of its goals by a similar division of time, using notes of various duration and spacing. The musical intervals considered by many to be the most pleasing to the ear are the major sixth and minor sixth. A major sixth, for example, consists of the note C, vibrating at about 264[†] vibrations per second, and note A, vibrating at about 440 vibrations per second. The ratio of 440 to 264 reduces to 5 to 3, or $\frac{5}{3}$, a ratio of two consecutive Fibonacci numbers. An example of a minor sixth is E (about 330 vibrations per second) and C (about 528 vibrations per second). The ratio 528 to 330 reduces to 8 to 5, or $\frac{8}{5}$, the next ratio of two consecutive Fibonacci numbers. The vibrations of any sixth interval reduce to a similar ratio.

[†]Frequencies of notes vary in different parts of the world and change over time.

Patterns that can be expressed mathematically in terms of Fibonacci relationships have been found in Gregorian chants and works of many composers, including Bach, Beethoven, and Bartók. A number of twentieth-century musical works, including Ernst Krenek's *Fibonacci Mobile*, were deliberately structured by using Fibonacci proportions.

A number of studies have tried to explain why the Fibonacci sequence and related items are linked to so many real-life situations. It appears that the Fibonacci numbers are a part of a natural harmony that is pleasing to both the eye and the ear. In the nineteenth century, German physicist and psychologist Gustav Fechner tried to determine which dimensions were most pleasing to the eye. Fechner, along with psychologist Wilhelm Wundt, found that most people do unconsciously favor golden dimensions when purchasing greeting cards, mirrors, and other rectangular objects. This discovery has been widely used by commercial manufacturers in their packaging and labeling designs, by retailers in their store displays, and in other areas of business and advertising.

SECTION 5.8   *Exercises*

Warm Up Exercises

In Exercises 1–6, fill in the blanks with an appropriate word, phrase, or symbol(s).

1. The sequence of numbers 1, 1, 2, 3, 5, 8, 13, 21, … is known as the _____ sequence. Fibonacci

2. The irrational number $\frac{\sqrt{5}+1}{2}$ is known as the _____ number. Golden

In Exercises 3–4, use the following diagram and assume that the ratio $\frac{AB}{AC}$ is equal to the ratio $\frac{AC}{CB}$

    ●————————●————●
    A   C   B

3. Each ratio $\frac{AB}{AC}$ and $\frac{AC}{CB}$ is referred to as a Golden _____.
   Ratio

4. The proportion $\frac{AB}{AC} = \frac{AC}{CB}$ is called the Golden _____.
   Proportion

5. In medieval times, people referred to the golden proportion as the _____ proportion. Divine

6. A rectangle whose ratio of its length to its width is equal to the golden number is known as a golden _____.
   Rectangle

Practice the Skills/Problem Solving

7. **a)** To what decimal value is $(\sqrt{5}+1)/2$ approximately equal? 1.618

   b) To what decimal value is $(\sqrt{5}-1)/2$ approximately equal? 0.618

   c) By how much do the results in parts (a) and (b) differ? 1

8. The sum of any six consecutive Fibonacci numbers is always divisible by 4. Select any six consecutive Fibonacci numbers and show that for your selection this statement is true. Answers will vary.

9. The sum of any 10 consecutive Fibonacci numbers is always divisible by 11. Select any 10 consecutive Fibonacci numbers and show that for your selection this statement is true. Answers will vary.

10. The greatest common factor of any two consecutive Fibonacci numbers is 1. Show that this statement is true for the first 15 Fibonacci numbers. *

11. For any four consecutive Fibonacci numbers, the difference of the squares of the middle two numbers equals the product of the smallest and largest numbers. Select four consecutive Fibonacci numbers and show that this pattern holds for the numbers you selected. Answers will vary.

12. Twice any Fibonacci number minus the next Fibonacci number equals the second number preceding the original number. Select a number in the Fibonacci sequence and show that this pattern holds for the number selected. Answers will vary.

13. Determine the ratio of the length to width of various photographs and compare these ratios to Φ. Answers will vary.

14. Determine the ratio of the length to the width of your television screen and compare this ratio to Φ. Answers will vary.

15. Determine the ratio of the length to the width of a computer screen and compare this ratio to Φ. Answers will vary.

16. Find three physical objects whose dimensions are very close to a golden rectangle.

    a) List the articles and record the dimensions.

    b) Compute the ratios of their lengths to their widths.

    c) Find the difference between the golden ratio and the ratio you obtain in part (b)—to the nearest tenth—for each object. Answers will vary.

*See Instructor Answer Appendix

In Exercises 17–24, determine whether the sequence is a Fibonacci-type sequence (each term is the sum of the two preceding terms). If it is, determine the next two terms of the sequence.

17. 4, 5, 9, 18, 36, 72, … No

18. 4, 5, 9, 14, 23, 37, … Yes; 60, 97

19. 1, 5, 6, 11, 17, 28, … Yes; 45, 73

20. 0, π, π, 2π, 3π, 5π, … Yes; 8π, 13π

21. −1, 1, 0, 1, 1, 2, … Yes; 3, 5

22. 1, 4, 9, 16, 25, 36, … No

23. 5, 10, 15, 25, 40, 65, … Yes; 105, 170

24. $\frac{1}{4}$, $\frac{1}{4}$, $\frac{1}{2}$, $\frac{3}{4}$, $1\frac{1}{4}$, 2, … Yes; $3\frac{1}{4}$, $5\frac{1}{4}$

25. a) Select any two one-digit (nonzero) numbers and add them to obtain a third number. Continue adding the two previous terms to get a Fibonacci-type sequence. Answers will vary.

 b) Form ratios of successive terms to show how they will eventually approach the golden number. Answers will vary.

26. a) Select any three consecutive terms of a Fibonacci sequence. Subtract the product of the terms on each side of the middle term from the square of the middle term. What is the difference? Answers will vary.

 b) Repeat part (a) with three different consecutive terms of the sequence. Answers will vary.

 c) Make a conjecture about what will happen when you repeat this process for any three consecutive terms of a Fibonacci sequence.
   Answers will vary. However, you should get 1 or −1.

27. *Pascal's Triangle* One of the most famous number patterns involves *Pascal's triangle*. The Fibonacci sequence can be found by using Pascal's triangle. Can you explain how that can be done? A hint is shown.

The sums of the numbers along the diagonals (parallel to the one shown) are Fibonacci numbers.

28. *Lucas Sequence* **a)** A sequence related to the Fibonacci sequence is the *Lucas sequence*. The Lucas sequence is formed in a manner similar to the Fibonacci sequence. The first two numbers of the Lucas sequence are 1 and 3. Write the first eight terms of the Lucas sequence.
   1, 3, 4, 7, 11, 18, 29, 47

b) Complete the next two lines of the following chart.

$$1 + 2 = 3$$
$$1 + 3 = 4$$
$$2 + 5 = 7$$
$$3 + 8 = 11$$
$$5 + 13 = 18$$

8 + 21 = 29, 13 + 34 = 47

c) What do you observe about the first column in the chart in part (b)? It is the Fibonacci sequence.

Concept/Writing Exercises

29. Explain how to construct the Fibonacci sequence. *

30. Explain the relationship between the golden number, golden ratio, golden proportion, and golden rectangle.
   Answers will vary.

31. Describe three examples of where Fibonacci numbers can be found

 a) in nature. Answers will vary.

 b) in manufactured items. Answers will vary.

32. The eleventh Fibonacci number is 89. Examine the first six digits in the decimal expression of its reciprocal, $\frac{1}{89}$. What do you find?
   The decimal expansion shows several terms of the Fibonacci sequence.

33. Find the ratio of the second to the first term of the Fibonacci sequence. Then find the ratio of the third to the second term of the sequence and determine whether this ratio was an increase or decrease from the first ratio. Continue this process for 10 ratios and then make a conjecture regarding the increasing or decreasing values in consecutive ratios. *

34. A musical composition is described as follows. Explain why this piece is based on the golden ratio.

Entire Composition

34 measures	55 measures	21 measures	34 measures
Theme	Fast, Loud	Slow	Repeat of theme

The ratio of the second to the first, and the fourth to the third measures estimates the golden ratio.

Challenge Problems/Group Activities

35. *Fibonacci-Type Sequence* The following sequence represents a Fibonacci-type sequence (each term is the sum of the two preceding terms). Here x represents any natural number from 1 to 10:

$$-10, x, -10 + x, -10 + 2x, -20 + 3x, -30 + 5x, \ldots$$

For example, if $x = 2$, the first 10 terms of the sequence would be −10, 2, −8, −6, −14, −20, −34, −54, −88, −142.

Write out the first 10 terms of this Fibonacci-type sequence for x equal to the following.

a) 4 *   **b)** 5 *   **c)** 6 *   **d)** 7 *   **e)** 8 *

*See Instructor Answer Appendix

f) For values of x of 4, 5, and 6, you should have found that each term after the seventh term in the sequence was a negative number. For values of x of 7 and 8, you should have found that each term after the seventh term in the sequence was a positive number. Do you believe that for any value of x greater than or equal to 7, each term after the seventh term of the sequence will always be a positive number? Explain. Answers will vary.

36. Draw a line of length 5 in. Determine and mark the point on the line that will create the golden ratio. Explain how you determined your answer. Answers will vary.

37. The divine proportion is $(a + b)/a = a/b$ (see Fig. 5.13), which can be written $1 + (b/a) = a/b$. Now let $x = a/b$, which gives $1 + (1/x) = x$. Multiply both sides of this equation by x to get a quadratic equation and then use the quadratic formula (Section 6.9) to show that one answer is $x = (1 + \sqrt{5})/2$ (the golden ratio). Answers will vary.

38. *Pythagorean Triples* A Pythagorean triple is a set of three whole numbers, $\{a, b, c\}$, such that $a^2 + b^2 = c^2$.

For example, since $6^2 + 8^2 = (10)^2$, $\{6, 8, 10\}$ is a Pythagorean triple. The following steps show how to find Pythagorean triples using any four consecutive Fibonacci numbers. Here we will demonstrate the process with the Fibonacci numbers 3, 5, 8, and 13.

1) Determine the product of 2 and the two inner Fibonacci numbers. We have $2(5)(8) = 80$, which is the first number in the Pythagorean triple. So $a = 80$.

2) Determine the product of the two outer numbers. We have $3(13) = 39$, which is the second number in the Pythagorean triple. So $b = 39$.

3) Determine the sum of the squares of the inner two numbers. We have $5^2 + 8^2 = 25 + 64 = 89$, which is the third number in the Pythagorean triple. So $c = 89$.

This process has produced the Pythagorean triple, $\{80, 39, 89\}$. To verify,

$$(80)^2 + (39)^2 = (89)^2$$
$$6400 + 1521 = 7921$$
$$7921 = 7921$$

Use this process to produce four other Pythagorean triples. Answers will vary.

39. *Reflections* When two panes of glass are placed face to face, four interior reflective surfaces exist, labeled 1, 2, 3, and 4. If light is not reflected, it has just one path through the glass (see the figure below). If it has one reflection, it can be reflected in two ways. If it has two reflections, it can be reflected in three ways. Use this information to answer parts (a) through (c).

| 0 reflections | 1 reflection | 2 reflections |
| 1 path | 2 paths | 3 paths |

a) If a ray is reflected three times, there are five paths it can follow. Show the paths.
Answers will vary.

b) If a ray is reflected four times, there are eight paths it can follow. Show the paths.
Answers will vary.

c) How many paths can a ray follow if it is reflected five times? Explain how you determined your answer.
Answers will vary.

Internet/Research Activities

40. Write a report on the history and mathematical contributions of Fibonacci.

41. The digits 1 through 9 have evolved considerably since they appeared in Fibonacci's book *Liber Abacci*. Write a report tracing the history of the evolution of the digits 1 through 9 since Fibonacci's time.

42. Write a report indicating where the golden ratio and golden rectangle have been used in art and architecture. You may wish to include information on art and architecture related to the golden ratio and Fibonacci sequences.

CHAPTER 5   *Summary*

Important Facts and Concepts	Examples and Discussion
Section 5.1	
Fundamental Theorem of Arithmetic	Examples 2–7, pages 213–216
Every composite number can be expressed as a unique product of prime numbers.	

Sections 5.1–5.5

Sets of Numbers

Natural or counting numbers: $\{1, 2, 3, 4, \ldots\}$

Whole numbers: $\{0, 1, 2, 3, 4, \ldots\}$

Integers: $\{\ldots, -3, -2, -1, 0, 1, 2, 3, \ldots\}$

Rational numbers: Numbers of the form p/q, where p and q are integers, $q \neq 0$. Every rational number when expressed as a decimal number will be either a terminating or repeating decimal number.

Irrational number: A real number whose representation is a nonterminating, nonrepeating decimal number (not a rational number)

Real numbers: the union of the rational numbers and the irrational numbers.

Discussion pages 210, 221, 229, 244, and 252

Section 5.2

Definition of Subtraction

$a - b = a + (-b)$

Discussion page 223,
Examples 3–5, pages 223–224

Section 5.3

Fundamental Law of Rational Numbers

$\dfrac{a}{b} = \dfrac{a}{b} \cdot \dfrac{c}{c} = \dfrac{ac}{bc} \quad b \neq 0, \quad c \neq 0$

Discussion page 237,
Examples 14–16, pages 237–239

Section 5.4

Rules of Radicals

Product rule for radicals:

$\sqrt{a \cdot b} = \sqrt{a} \cdot \sqrt{b}, \quad a \geq 0, \quad b \geq 0$

Quotient rule for radicals:

$\dfrac{\sqrt{a}}{\sqrt{b}} = \sqrt{\dfrac{a}{b}}, \quad a \geq 0, \quad b > 0$

Discussion pages 245 and 247,
Examples 1–6, pages 245–248

Section 5.5

Properties of Real Numbers

Commutative property of addition: $a + b = b + a$

Commutative property of multiplication: $a \cdot b = b \cdot a$

Associative property of addition:
$(a + b) + c = a + (b + c)$

Associative property of multiplication:
$(a \cdot b) \cdot c = a \cdot (b \cdot c)$

Distributive property: $a \cdot (b + c) = ab + ac$

Discussion pages 253–256,
Examples 1–5, pages 253–256

Section 5.6

Rules of Exponents

Product rule for exponents: $a^m \cdot a^n = a^{m+n}$

Quotient rule for exponents: $\dfrac{a^m}{a^n} = a^{m-n}, \quad a \neq 0$

Zero exponent rule: $a^0 = 1, \quad a \neq 0$

Negative exponent rule: $a^{-m} = \dfrac{1}{a^m}, \quad a \neq 0$

Power rule: $(a^m)^n = a^{m \cdot n}$

Examples 1–7, pages 259–262

Scientific Notation	
Scientific notation is used to write very small or very large numbers. Each number in scientific notation is written as a number greater than or equal to 1 and less than 10 multiplied by an integer power of 10.	Discussion page 262, Examples 8–14, pages 263–266
Section 5.7	
Arithmetic Sequence	
General or nth term: $a_n = a_1 + (n-1)d$ Sum of the first n terms: $s_n = \dfrac{n(a_1 + a_n)}{2}$	Discussion page 270, Examples 1–5, pages 271–272
Geometric Sequence	
General or nth term: $a_n = a_1 r^{n-1}$ Sum of the first n terms: $s_n = \dfrac{a_1(1 - r^n)}{1 - r}, \quad r \neq 1$	Discussion page 272, Examples 6–10, pages 273–275
Section 5.8	
Fibonacci Sequence	
1, 1, 2, 3, 5, 8, 13, 21, …	Discussion pages 278–282
Golden Number	
$\dfrac{\sqrt{5} + 1}{2} \approx 1.618$	Discussion pages 278–282
Golden Proportion	
$\dfrac{a + b}{a} = \dfrac{a}{b}$	Discussion pages 278–282

CHAPTER 5   *Review Exercises*

5.1

In Exercises 1 and 2, determine whether the number is divisible by each of the following numbers: 2, 3, 4, 5, 6, 8, 9, and 10.

1. 60,060 2, 3, 4, 5, 6, 10   **2.** 400,644 2, 3, 4, 6, 9

In Exercises 3–7, determine the prime factorization of the number.

3. 588 $2^2 \cdot 3 \cdot 7^2$ **4.** 840 $2^3 \cdot 3 \cdot 5 \cdot 7$ **5.** 1452 $2^2 \cdot 3 \cdot 11^2$

In Exercises 6–9, determine the GCD and LCM of the numbers.

6. 30, 105 15; 210   **7.** 63, 108 9; 756

8. 45, 250 5; 2250   **9.** 90, 300 30; 900

10. *Train Stops* From 1912 to 1971, the Milwaukee Road Railroad Company had a train stop every 15 days in Dubuque, Iowa. During this same period, the same train also stopped in Des Moines, Iowa, every 9 days. If on April 18, 1964, the train made a stop in Dubuque and a stop in Des Moines, how many days was it until the train again stopped in both cities on the same day? 45 days

▲ *Des Moines, Iowa*

5.2

In Exercises 11–16, use a number line to evaluate the expression.

11. $6 + (-9)$ –3

12. $-2 + 5$ 3

13. $-2 + (-4)$ –6

14. $4 - 8$ –4

15. $-5 - 4$ –9

16. $-3 - (-6)$ 3

In Exercises 17–21, evaluate the expression.

17. $-2 \cdot 12$ –24

18. $(-2)(-12)$ 24

19. $\dfrac{-35}{-7}$ 5

20. $\dfrac{12}{-6}$ –2

21. $[8 \div (-4)](-3)$ 6

5.3

In Exercises 22–27, express the fraction as a terminating or repeating decimal.

22. $\dfrac{17}{20}$ 0.85

23. $\dfrac{13}{4}$ 3.25

24. $\dfrac{6}{7}$ $0.\overline{857142}$

25. $\dfrac{7}{12}$ $0.58\overline{3}$

26. $\dfrac{3}{8}$ 0.375

27. $\dfrac{11}{16}$ 0.6875

In Exercises 28–31, express the decimal number as a quotient of two integers.

28. 1.4 $\frac{14}{10} = \frac{7}{5}$

29. $0.\overline{6}$ $\frac{2}{3}$

30. $0.\overline{51}$ $\frac{51}{99}$

31. 0.083 $\frac{83}{1000}$

In Exercises 32–33, express each mixed number as an improper fraction.

32. $2\dfrac{5}{7}$ $\frac{19}{7}$

33. $-3\dfrac{1}{4}$ $-\frac{13}{4}$

In Exercises 34–35, express each improper fraction as a mixed number.

34. $\dfrac{11}{5}$ $2\frac{1}{5}$

35. $-\dfrac{136}{5}$ $-27\frac{1}{5}$

In Exercises 36–41, perform the indicated operation and reduce your answer to lowest terms.

36. $\dfrac{11}{12} - \dfrac{2}{3}$ $\frac{1}{4}$

37. $\dfrac{1}{6} + \dfrac{5}{4}$ $\frac{17}{12}$

38. $\dfrac{7}{16} \cdot \dfrac{12}{21}$ $\frac{1}{4}$

39. $\dfrac{5}{9} \div \dfrac{6}{7}$ $\frac{35}{54}$

40. $\left(\dfrac{4}{5} + \dfrac{5}{7}\right) \div \dfrac{4}{5}$ $\frac{53}{28}$

41. $\left(\dfrac{2}{3} \cdot \dfrac{1}{7}\right) \div \dfrac{4}{7}$ $\frac{1}{6}$

42. *Cajun Turkey* A recipe for Roasted Cajun Turkey calls for $\frac{1}{8}$ teaspoon of cayenne pepper per pound of turkey.

If Jennifer Sabo is preparing a turkey that weighs $17\frac{3}{4}$ pounds, how much cayenne pepper does she need? $2\frac{7}{32}$ tsp

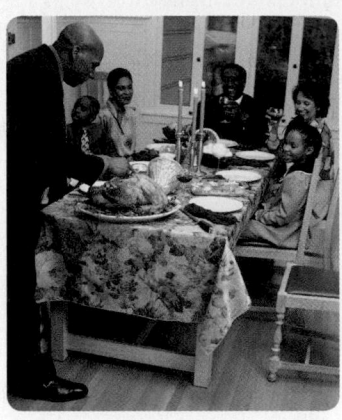

5.4

In Exercises 43–54, simplify the expression. Rationalize the denominator when necessary.

43. $\sqrt{75}$ $5\sqrt{3}$

44. $\sqrt{2} - 4\sqrt{2}$ $-3\sqrt{2}$

45. $\sqrt{8} + 6\sqrt{2}$ $8\sqrt{2}$

46. $\sqrt{3} - 7\sqrt{27}$ $-20\sqrt{3}$

47. $\sqrt{28} + \sqrt{63}$ $5\sqrt{7}$

48. $\sqrt{3} \cdot \sqrt{6}$ $3\sqrt{2}$

49. $\sqrt{8} \cdot \sqrt{6}$ $4\sqrt{3}$

50. $\dfrac{\sqrt{300}}{\sqrt{3}}$ 10

51. $\dfrac{4}{\sqrt{3}}$ $\frac{4\sqrt{3}}{3}$

52. $\dfrac{\sqrt{7}}{\sqrt{5}}$ $\frac{\sqrt{35}}{5}$

53. $3(2 + \sqrt{7})$ $6 + 3\sqrt{7}$

54. $\sqrt{3}(4 + \sqrt{6})$ $4\sqrt{3} + 3\sqrt{2}$

5.5

In Exercises 55–61, state the name of the property illustrated.

55. $3 + 8 = 8 + 3$ Commutative property of addition

56. $5 \cdot m = m \cdot 5$ Commutative property of multiplication

57. $(1 + 2) + 3 = 1 + (2 + 3)$ Associative property of addition

58. $9(x + 1) = 9 \cdot x + 9 \cdot 1$ Distributive property

59. $(3 \cdot a) \cdot b = 3 \cdot (a \cdot b)$ Associative property of multiplication

60. $a \cdot (2 + 3) = (2 + 3) \cdot a$ Commutative property of multiplication

61. $2(x + 3) = (2 \cdot x) + (2 \cdot 3)$ Distributive property

In Exercises 62–66, determine whether the set of numbers is closed under the given operation.

62. Natural numbers, subtraction No

63. Whole numbers, multiplication Yes

64. Integers, division No

65. Real numbers, subtraction Yes

66. Irrational numbers, multiplication No

5.6

In Exercises 67–72, evaluate each expression.

67. 5^3 125

68. 5^{-2} $\frac{1}{25}$

69. $\dfrac{9^5}{9^3}$ 81

70. $5^2 \cdot 5$ 125

71. 7^0 1

72. $(3^2)^2$ 81

In Exercises 73–74, write each number in scientific notation.

73. 8,200,000,000 8.2×10^9

74. 0.0000158 1.58×10^{-5}

In Exercises 75–76, express each number in decimal notation.

75. 2.8×10^5 280,000

76. 1.39×10^{-4} 0.000139

In Exercises 77–78, (a) perform the indicated operation and write your answer in scientific notation. (b) Confirm the result found in part (a) by performing the calculation on a scientific calculator.

77. $(3 \times 10^4)(2 \times 10^{-9})$ 6.0×10^{-5}

78. $\dfrac{1.5 \times 10^{-3}}{5 \times 10^{-4}}$ 3.0×10^0

In Exercises 79–81, (a) perform the indicated calculation by first converting each number to scientific notation. Write your answer in decimal notation. (b) Confirm the result found in part (a) by performing the calculation on a scientific calculator.

79. (550,000)(2,000,000) 1,100,000,000,000

80. $\dfrac{8,400,000}{70,000}$ 120

81. $\dfrac{0.000002}{0.0000004}$ 5

82. *Space Distances* The distance from Earth to the sun is about 1.49×10^{11} meters. The distance from Earth to the moon is about 3.84×10^8 meters. The distance from Earth to the sun is how many times larger than the distance from Earth to the moon? Use a scientific calculator and round your answer to the nearest whole number. ≈ 388 times

▲ *Earth*

83. *Outstanding Debt* As a result of a recent water and sewer system improvement, the city of Galena, Illinois, has an outstanding debt of $20,000,000. If the population of Galena is 3600 people, how much would each person have to contribute to pay off the outstanding debt? ≈ $5555.56

5.7

In Exercises 84–85, determine whether the sequence is arithmetic or geometric. Then determine the next two terms of the sequence.

84. 1, 5, 9, 13, … Arithmetic; 17, 21

85. $\frac{1}{2}$, 1, 2, 4, … Geometric; 8, 16

In Exercises 86–89, determine the indicated term of the sequence with the given first term, a_1, and common difference, d, or common ratio, r.

86. Determine a_9 when $a_1 = -6, d = 2$. 10

87. Determine a_{10} when $a_1 = -20, d = 5$. 25

88. Determine a_5 when $a_1 = 3, r = 2$. 48

89. Determine a_4 when $a_1 = -6, r = 2$. −48

In Exercises 90–91, determine the sum of the arithmetic sequence. The number of terms, n, is given.

90. 3, 6, 9, 12, … , 150; $n = 50$ 3825

91. 0.5, 0.75, 1.00, 1.25, … , 5.25; $n = 20$ 57.5

In Exercises 92–93, determine the sum of the first n terms of the geometric sequence for the values of a_1 and r.

92. $n = 4, a_1 = 3, r = 2$ 45

93. $n = 6, a_1 = 1, r = -2$ −21

In Exercises 94–97, first determine whether the sequence is arithmetic or geometric; then write an expression for the general or nth term, a_n.

94. 3, 6, 9, 12, … Arithmetic; $a_n = 3n$

95. 1, 4, 7, 10, … Arithmetic; $a_n = 3n - 2$

96. 2, −2, 2, −2, … Geometric; $a_n = 2(-1)^{n-1}$

97. 5, $\frac{5}{3}$, $\frac{5}{9}$, $\frac{5}{27}$, … Geometric; $a_n = 5\left(\dfrac{1}{3}\right)^{n-1}$

5.8

In Exercises 98–99, determine whether the sequence is a Fibonacci–type sequence. If so, determine the next two terms.

98. 0, 1, 1, 2, 2, 3, 3, 4, 4, … No

99. −1, 0, −1, −1, −2, −3, −5, … Yes; −8, −13

CHAPTER 5) *Test*

1. Which of the numbers 2, 3, 4, 5, 6, 8, 9, and 10 divide 48,395? 5

2. Determine the prime factorization of 414. $2 \cdot 3^2 \cdot 23$

3. Evaluate $[(-3) + 7] - (-4)$. 8

4. Evaluate $[(-70)(-5)] \div (8 - 10)$. -175

5. Convert $4\frac{5}{8}$ to an improper fraction. $\frac{37}{8}$

6. Write $\frac{5}{8}$ as a terminating or repeating decimal. 0.625

7. Express 6.45 as a quotient of two integers. $\frac{129}{20}$

8. Perform the operation and reduce the answer to lowest terms: $\frac{17}{24} - \frac{7}{12}$. $\frac{1}{8}$

9. Simplify $\sqrt{75} + \sqrt{48}$. $9\sqrt{3}$

10. Rationalize the denominator $\frac{\sqrt{2}}{\sqrt{7}}$. $\frac{\sqrt{14}}{7}$

11. Determine whether the integers are closed under the operation of multiplication. Explain your answer.
    Yes; the product of any two integers is an integer.

Name the property illustrated.

12. $(x + 3) + 5 = x + (3 + 5)$ Associative property of addition

Evaluate.

13. $\frac{4^5}{4^2}$ 64

14. $4^3 \cdot 4^2$ 1024

15. 3^{-4} $\frac{1}{81}$

16. Perform the operation by first converting the numerator and denominator to scientific notation. Write the answer in scientific notation.

$$\frac{7,200,000}{0.000009}$$ 8.0×10^{11}

17. Write an expression for the general or *n*th term, a_n, of the sequence $-2, -6, -10, -14, \ldots$. $a_n = -4n + 2$

18. Determine the sum of the terms of the arithmetic sequence. The number of terms, *n*, is given.

$$-2, -5, -8, -11, \ldots, -32; n = 11$$ -187

19. Write an expression for the general or *n*th term, a_n, of the sequence $3, 6, 12, 24, \ldots$. $a_n = 3(2)^{n-1}$

20. Write the first 10 terms of the Fibonacci sequence.
    1, 1, 2, 3, 5, 8, 13, 21, 34, 55

GROUP PROJECTS

1. *Making Rice* The amounts of ingredients needed to make 3 and 5 servings of rice are:

To Make	Rice and Water	Salt	Butter
3 servings	1 cup	$\frac{3}{8}$ tsp	$1\frac{1}{2}$ tsp
5 servings	$1\frac{2}{3}$ cup	$\frac{5}{8}$ tsp	$2\frac{1}{2}$ tsp

Find the amount of each ingredient needed to make (a) 2 servings, (b) 1 serving, and (c) 29 servings. Explain how you determined your answers.

2. *Finding Areas*

a) Determine the area of the trapezoid shown by finding the area of the three parts indicated and finding the

sum of the three areas. The necessary geometric formulas are given in Chapter 9.

b) Determine the area of the trapezoid by using the formula for the area of a trapezoid given in Chapter 9.

c) Compare your answers from parts (a) and (b). Are they the same? If not, explain why they are different.

3. *Medical Insurance* On a medical insurance policy (such as Blue Cross/Blue Shield), the policyholder may need to make copayments for prescription drugs, office visits, and procedures until the total of all copayments reaches a specified amount. Suppose that the copayment on the Gattelaro's medical policy for prescription drugs is 50% of the cost; the copayment for office visits is $10; and the copayment for all medical tests, x-rays, and other procedures is 20% of the cost. After the family's copayment totals $500 in a calendar year, all medical and prescription bills are paid in full by the insurance company. The Gattelaros had the following medical expenses from January 1 through April 30.

Date	Reason	Cost before Copayment
January 10	Office visit	$40
	Prescription	$44
February 27	Office visit	$40
	Medical tests	$188
April 19	Office visit	$40
	X-rays	$348
	Prescription	$76

a) How much had the Gattelaros paid in copayments from January 1 through April 30?

b) How much had the medical insurance company paid?

c) What is the remaining copayment that must be paid by the Gattelaros before the $500 copayment limit is reached?

4. *A Branching Plant* A plant grows for two months and then adds a new branch. Each new branch grows for two months and then adds another branch. After the second month, each branch adds a new branch every month. Assume the growth begins in January.

a) How many branches will there be in February?

b) How many branches will there be in May?

c) How many branches will there be after 12 months?

d) How is this problem similar to the problem involving rabbits that appeared in Fibonacci's book *Liber Abacci* (see page 278)?

6

Algebra, Graphs, and Functions

Why This is Important

Algebra is one of the most practical tools for solving everyday problems. You use algebra daily without realizing it. For example, you use a coordinate system when you consult a map. To evaluate how much interest you will earn in a savings account or to determine how long it will take you to travel a given distance, you use common algebraic formulas. The symbolic language of algebra makes it an excellent tool for solving problems because it allows us to write lengthy expressions in compact form. English philosopher Alfred North Whitehead explained the power of algebra when he stated, "By relieving the brain of unnecessary work, a good notation sets the mind free to concentrate on more advanced problems."

◄ Algebra is a tool for solving everyday problems such as changing a recipe to increase or decrease the number of servings.

291

▲ *You can use algebra to determine the sales tax rate when purchasing items such as tires.*

Did You Know?

Broken Bones

Imagine yourself walking down a street in Spain during the Middle Ages. You see a sign over a door: "*Algebrista y Sangrador.*" Inside, you would find a person more ready to give you a haircut than help you with your algebra. The sign translates into "Bonesetter and Bloodletter," relatively simple medical treatments administered in barbershops of the day.

The root word *al-jabr*, which the Muslims (Moors) brought to Spain along with some concepts of algebra, suggests the restoring of broken parts. The parts might be bones, or they might be mathematical expressions that are broken into separate parts and the parts moved from one side of an equation to the other and reunited in such a way as to make a solution more obvious.

Knowing the order of operations is essential to solving problems algebraically. There are many everyday problems that can be easily solved if you have an understanding of algebra. Suppose you see an advertisement for tires that states: "Purchase Michelin All-Season Tires for $135 each. This price includes mounting." You purchase four tires and have them mounted on your car. Your total price, including sales tax, comes to $583.50. What is the sales tax rate? In this section, we will discuss how to use algebra to answer questions like the one above.

Why *This is Important* This is just one type of problem that can be solved algebraically. In this section and chapter you will see many more real-life applications of algebra.

Algebra is a generalized form of arithmetic. The word *algebra* is derived from the Arabic word *al-jabr* (meaning "reunion of broken parts"), which was the title of a book written by the mathematician Muhammed ibn-Musa al Khwarizmi in about A.D. 825.

Algebra uses letters of the alphabet called *variables* to represent numbers. Often the letters x and y are used to represent variables. However, any letter may be used as a variable. A symbol that represents a specific quantity is called a *constant*.

Multiplication of numbers and variables may be represented in several different ways in algebra. Because the "times" sign might be confused with the variable x, a dot between two numbers or variables indicates multiplication. Thus, $3 \cdot 4$ means 3 times 4, and $x \cdot y$ means x times y. Placing two letters or a number and a letter next to one another, with or without parentheses, also indicates multiplication. Thus, $3x$ means 3 times x, xy means x times y, and $(x)(y)$ means x times y.

An *algebraic expression* (or simply an *expression*) is a collection of variables, numbers, parentheses, and operation symbols. Some examples of algebraic expressions are

$$x, \qquad x + 2, \qquad 3(2x + 3), \qquad \frac{3x + 1}{2x - 3}, \qquad \text{and} \qquad x^2 + 7x + 3$$

Two algebraic expressions joined by an equal sign form an *equation*. Some examples of equations are

$$x + 2 = 4, \qquad 3x + 4 = 1, \qquad \text{and} \qquad x + 3 = 2x$$

The *solution to an equation* is the number or numbers that replace the variable to make the equation a true statement. For example, the solution to the equation $x + 3 = 4$ is 1. When we find the solution to an equation, we *solve the equation*.

We can determine if any number is a solution to an equation by *checking the solution*. To check the solution, we substitute the number for the variable in the equation. If the resulting statement is a true statement, that number is a solution to the equation. If the resulting statement is a false statement, the number is not a solution to the equation. To check the number 1 in the equation $x + 3 = 4$, we do the following.

$$x + 3 = 4$$
$$1 + 3 = 4 \qquad \text{Substitute 1 for } x.$$
$$4 = 4 \qquad \text{True}$$

The same number is obtained on both sides of the equal sign, so 1 is the solution. For the equation $x + 3 = 4$, the only solution is 1. Any other value of x would result in the check being a false statement.

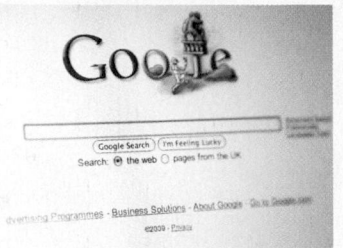
To *evaluate an expression* means to find the value of the expression for a given value of the variable. To evaluate expressions and solve equations, you must have an understanding of exponents. Exponents (Section 5.6) are used to abbreviate repeated multiplication. For example, the expression 5^2 means $5 \cdot 5$. The 2 in the expression 5^2 is the *exponent*, and the 5 is the *base*. We read 5^2 as "5 to the second power" or "5 squared," and 5^2 means $5 \cdot 5$ or 25.

In general, the number b to the nth power, written b^n, means

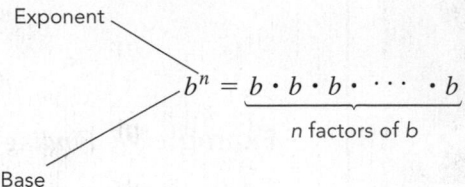

An exponent refers only to its base. In the expression -5^2, the base is 5. In the expression $(-5)^2$, the base is -5.

$$-5^2 = -(5)^2 = -1(5)^2 = -1(5)(5) = -25$$
$$(-5)^2 = (-5)(-5) = 25$$

Note that $-5^2 \neq (-5)^2$ since $-25 \neq 25$.

Order of Operations

To evaluate an expression or to check the solution to an equation, we need to know the *order of operations* to follow. For example, suppose we want to evaluate the expression $2 + 3x$ when $x = 4$. Substituting 4 for x, we obtain $2 + 3 \cdot 4$. What is the value of $2 + 3 \cdot 4$? Does it equal 20, or does it equal 14? Some standard rules, called the order of operations, have been developed to ensure that there is only one correct answer. In mathematics, unless parentheses indicate otherwise, always perform multiplication before addition. Thus, the correct answer is 14.

$$2 + 3 \cdot 4 = 2 + (3 \cdot 4) = 2 + 12 = 14$$

The order of operations for evaluating an expression is as follows.

TIMELY TIP

Some students use the phrase "*Please Excuse My Dear Aunt Sally*" or the word "PEMDAS" (Parentheses, Exponents, Multiplication, Division, Addition, Subtraction) to remind them of the order of operations. Remember: Multiplication and division are of the same order, and addition and subtraction are of the same order.

PROCEDURE **ORDER OF OPERATIONS**

1. First, perform all operations within parentheses or other grouping symbols (according to the following order).

2. Next, perform all exponential operations (that is, raising to powers or finding roots).

3. Next, perform all multiplications and divisions from left to right.

4. Finally, perform all additions and subtractions from left to right.

Example 1 *Evaluating an Expression*

Evaluate the expression $-x^2 + 4x + 16$ for $x = 3$.

Solution Substitute 3 for each x and use the order of operations to evaluate the expression.

$$-x^2 + 4x + 16$$
$$= -(3)^2 + 4(3) + 16$$
$$= -9 + 12 + 16$$
$$= 3 + 16$$
$$= 19 \qquad \blacksquare$$

Example 2 *Finding the Height*

A diver jumps from a platform diving board that is 32 feet above water. The height of the diver above water, in feet, t seconds after jumping from the platform, can be determined by the expression $-16t^2 + 20t + 32$. Determine the diver's height above the water 2 seconds after jumping from the platform.

Solution Substitute 2 for each t.

$$-16t^2 + 20t + 32$$
$$= -16(2)^2 + 20(2) + 32$$
$$= -16(4) + 20(2) + 32$$
$$= -64 + 40 + 32$$
$$= -24 + 32$$
$$= 8$$

The diver is 8 feet above water 2 seconds after jumping from the platform. $\qquad \blacksquare$

Example 3 *Substituting for Two Variables*

Evaluate $-3x^2 + 2xy - 2y^2$ when $x = 2$ and $y = 3$.

Solution Substitute 2 for each x and 3 for each y; then evaluate using the order of operations.

$$-3x^2 + 2xy - 2y^2$$
$$= -3(2)^2 + 2(2)(3) - 2(3)^2$$
$$= -3(4) + 2(2)(3) - 2(9)$$
$$= -12 + 12 - 18$$
$$= 0 - 18$$
$$= -18 \qquad \blacksquare$$

Example 4 *Is 2 a Solution?*

Determine whether 2 is a solution to the equation $3x^2 + 7x - 11 = 15$.

Solution To determine whether 2 is a solution to the equation, substitute 2 for each x in the equation. Then evaluate the left-hand side of the equation using the order of operations. If the left-hand side of the equation equals 15, then both sides of the equation have the same value and 2 is a solution. When checking the solution, we use $\overset{?}{=}$, which means we are not sure if the statement is true.

$$3x^2 + 7x - 11 = 15$$
$$3(2)^2 + 7(2) - 11 \overset{?}{=} 15 \quad \text{Substitute 2 for } x.$$
$$3(4) + 14 - 11 \overset{?}{=} 15$$
$$12 + 14 - 11 \overset{?}{=} 15$$
$$26 - 11 \overset{?}{=} 15$$
$$15 = 15 \quad \text{True}$$

Because 2 makes the equation a true statement, 2 is a solution to the equation. ■

SECTION 6.1 *Exercises*

Warm Up Exercises

In Exercises 1–8, fill in the blank with an appropriate word, phrase, or symbol(s).

1. A letter of the alphabet used to represent numbers is called a(n) _____ . Variable

2. A symbol that represents a specific quantity is called a(n) _____ . Constant

3. A collection of variables, numbers, parentheses, and operation symbols is called an algebraic _____ . Expression

4. For the expression 4^5 the base is _____ . 4

5. For the expression 8^3 the exponent is _____ . 3

6. The number or numbers that replace the variable to make an equation a true statement is called the _____ to the equation. Solution

7. To find the value of an expression for a given value of the variable means to _____ an expression. Evaluate

8. To evaluate $8 + 16 \div 4$, we perform the operation of _____ first. Division

Practice the Skills

In Exercises 9–28, evaluate the expression for the given value(s) of the variable(s).

9. x^2, $x = -6$ 36
10. x^2, $x = 5$ 25
11. $-x^2$, $x = -4$ −16
12. $-x^2$, $x = -2$ −4
13. $-2x^3$, $x = -7$ 686
14. $-x^3$, $x = -4$ 64
15. $x - 7$, $x = 4$ −3
16. $8x - 3$, $x = \frac{5}{2}$ 17
17. $-3x + 7$, $x = -2$ 13
18. $4x - 3$, $x = -1$ −7

19. $x^2 - 5x + 12$, $x = 3$ 6
20. $-x^2 + 3x - 10$, $x = -2$ −20
21. $\frac{1}{2}x^2 - 5x + 2$, $x = \frac{2}{3}$ $-\frac{10}{9}$
22. $\frac{2}{3}x^2 + x - 1$, $x = \frac{1}{2}$ $-\frac{1}{3}$
23. $8x^3 - 4x^2 + 7$, $x = \frac{1}{2}$ 7
24. $-x^2 + 5xy$, $x = 2$, $y = -3$ −34
25. $3x^2 - xy + 2y^2$, $x = -2$, $y = 1$ 16
26. $3x^2 + \frac{2}{5}xy - \frac{1}{5}y^2$, $x = 2$, $y = 5$ 11
27. $4x^2 - 10xy + 3y^2$, $x = 2$, $y = -1$ 39
28. $(2x - y)^2$, $x = 4$, $y = -2$ 100

In Exercises 29–38, determine whether the value(s) is (are) a solution to the equation.

29. $5x + 2 = 17$, $x = 3$ Yes
30. $6x - 3 = -27$, $x = -4$ Yes
31. $x - 3y = 0$, $x = 6$, $y = 3$ No
32. $4x + 2y = -2$, $x = -2$, $y = 3$ Yes
33. $-x^2 + 3x + 6 = 5$, $x = 2$ No
34. $-2x^2 + x + 5 = 20$, $x = 3$ No
35. $3x^2 + 2x = 40$, $x = -4$ Yes
36. $y = x^2 + 3x - 6$, $x = -1$, $y = -8$ Yes
37. $y = -x^2 + 3x - 1$, $x = 3$, $y = -1$ Yes
38. $y = x^3 - 3x^2 + 1$, $x = 2$, $y = -3$ Yes

Problem Solving

39. *Cost of Reimbursement* When employees travel out of town on company business, the cost for reimbursement can be determined by the expression 0.55x, where x is the number of miles driven. Determine the cost of reimbursement if an employee drives 120 miles on company business. $66

40. *8 Trillion Calculations* If a computer can do a calculation in 0.000002 sec, the time required to do n calculations can be determined by the expression 0.000002n. Determine the number of seconds needed for the computer to do 8 trillion (8,000,000,000,000) calculations. 16,000,000 sec

41. *Electronic Filing* The graph shows the number of tax-payers, in millions, filing their taxes electronically for the years 2004 through 2009. The number of taxpayers, in millions, filing their taxes electronically per year can be approximated by the expression 6.8x + 61, where x is the number of years since 2004. For example, the year 2005 would correspond to x = 1. Assuming this trend continues, use the expression to approximate the number of taxpayers who will file their taxes electronically in 2012. 115.4 million taxpayers

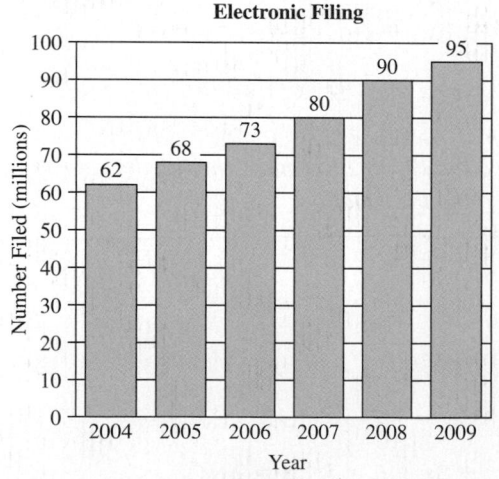

Electronic Filing

Source: *Internal Revenue Service*

42. *Cost of a Tour* The cost, in dollars, for Crescent City Tours to provide a tour for x people can be determined by the expression 220 + 2.75x. Determine the cost for Crescent City Tours to provide a tour for 75 people. $426.25

43. *Drying Time* The time, in minutes, needed for clothes hanging on a line outdoors to dry, at a specific temperature and wind speed, depends on the humidity, h. The time can be approximated by the expression $2h^2 + 80h + 40$, where h is the percent humidity expressed as a decimal number. Find the length of time required for clothing to dry if there is 60% humidity. 88.72 min

44. *Stopping Distance* A typical car's stopping distance, in feet, on wet pavement can be approximated by the expression $0.08s^2 + 0.24s - 7.10$, where s is the speed of the car, in miles per hour (mph), before braking and $60 \leq s \leq 80$ miles per hour. Use the expression to approximate the car's stopping distance on wet pavement if the speed of the car before braking is 72 mph. 424.9 feet

45. *Grass Growth* The rate of growth of grass, in inches per week, depends on a number of factors, including rainfall and temperature. For a certain area, this rate can be approximated by the expression $0.2R^2 + 0.003RT + 0.0001T^2$, where R is the weekly rainfall, in inches, and T is the average weekly temperature, in degrees Fahrenheit. Find the amount of growth of grass for a week in which the rainfall is 2 in. and the average temperature is 70°F. 1.71 in.

Concept/Writing Exercises

46. Explain why $(-1)^n = 1$ for any even number n. *

47. Does $(x + y)^2 = x^2 + y^2$? Complete the table and state your conclusion.

x	y	$(x + y)^2$	$x^2 + y^2$
2	3		
−2	−3		
−2	3		
2	−3		

The two expressions are not equal.

48. Suppose n represents any natural number. Explain why 1^n equals 1. $1^n = 1$ for all natural numbers because 1 multiplied by itself any number of times will always be 1.

49. a) Explain why $-x^2$ will always be a negative number for any nonzero real number selected for x. Answers will vary.

b) Explain why $(-x)^2$ will always be a positive number for any nonzero real number selected for x. Answers will vary.

Internet/Research Activity

50. When were exponents first used? Write a paper explaining how exponents were first used and when mathematicians began writing them in the present form.

SECTION 6.2 — Linear Equations in One Variable

While attending college, you work part time at a clothing store. You receive a weekly salary plus a commission on all clothing you sell. A linear equation can be written to determine your weekly salary based upon your weekly sales. In fact, many real-life situations can be expressed as linear equations.

Why *This is Important* Being able to solve equations algebraically will be very useful when solving application problems in this and later sections of this chapter and throughout life.

▲ *A linear equation can be used to determine a salespersons weekly salary based upon weekly sales.*

In Section 6.1, we stated that two algebraic expressions joined by an equal sign form an equation. The solution to some equations, such as $x + 3 = 4$, can be easily found by trial and error. Solving more difficult equations such as $60 = 0.51x + 40.1$ or $2x - 3 = 4(x + 3)$, however, requires us to understand some basic properties of equations.

The parts that are added or subtracted in an algebraic expression are called *terms*. The expression $0.51x + 40.1$ contains two terms: $0.51x$ and $+ 40.1$. The expression $4x - 3y - 5$ contains three terms: $4x$, $-3y$, and -5. The $+$ and $-$ signs that break the expression into terms are part of the terms. When listing the terms of an expression, however, it is not necessary to include the $+$ sign at the beginning of the term.

The numerical part of a term is called its *numerical coefficient* or, simply, its *coefficient*. In the term $4x$, the 4 is the numerical coefficient. In the term $-4y$, the -4 is the numerical coefficient.

Like terms are terms that have the same variables with the same exponents on the variables. *Unlike terms* have different variables or different exponents on the variables.

Like Terms	Unlike Terms
$2x$, $7x$ (same variable, x)	$2x$, 9 (only first term has a variable)
$-8y$, $3y$ (same variable, y)	$5x$, $6y$ (different variables)
-4, 10 (both constants)	x, 8 (only first term has a variable)
$-5x^2$, $6x^2$ (same variable with same exponent)	$2x^3$, $3x^2$ (different exponents)

To *simplify an expression* means to combine like terms by using the commutative, associative, and distributive properties discussed in Chapter 5. For convenience, we list these properties below.

Properties of the Real Numbers

$a(b + c) = ab + ac$	Distributive property
$a + b = b + a$	Commutative property of addition
$ab = ba$	Commutative property of multiplication
$(a + b) + c = a + (b + c)$	Associative property of addition
$(ab)c = a(bc)$	Associative property of multiplication

Example 1 *Combining Like Terms*

Combine like terms in each expression.

a) $8x + 4x$ b) $7y - 5y$

c) $x + 12 - 3x + 7$ d) $-2x + 4 - 6y - 11 - 5y + 3x$

Solution

a) We use the distributive property (in reverse) to combine like terms.

$$8x + 4x = (8 + 4)x \qquad \text{Distributive property}$$
$$= 12x$$

b) $7y - 5y = (7 - 5)y = 2y$

c) $x + 12 - 3x + 7 = x - 3x + 12 + 7 \qquad$ Rearrange terms; place like terms together.
$$= -2x + 19 \qquad \text{Combine like terms.}$$

d) $-2x + 4 - 6y - 11 - 5y + 3x$
$$= -2x + 3x - 6y - 5y + 4 - 11 \qquad \text{Rearrange terms; place like terms together.}$$
$$= x - 11y - 7 \qquad \text{Combine like terms.} \qquad ■$$

We are able to rearrange the terms of an expression, as was done in Example 1(c) and (d) by the commutative and associative properties that were discussed in Section 5.5.

The order of the terms in an expression is not crucial. However, when listing the terms of an expression, we generally list the terms in alphabetical order, with the constant, the term without a variable, last.

Solving Equations

Recall that to solve an equation means to find the value or values for the variable that make(s) the equation true. In this section, we discuss solving *linear (or first-degree) equations.* A linear equation in one variable is one in which the exponent on the variable is 1. Examples of linear equations are $5x - 1 = 3$ and $2x + 4 = 6x - 5$.

Equivalent equations are equations that have the same solution. The equations $2x - 5 = 1, 2x = 6,$ and $x = 3$ are all equivalent equations since they all have the same solution, 3. When we solve an equation, we write the given equation as a series of simpler equivalent equations until we obtain an equation of the form $x = c$, where c is some real number.

To solve any equation, we have to *isolate the variable.* That means getting the variable by itself on one side of the equal sign. The four properties of equality that we are about to discuss are used to isolate the variable. The first is the addition property.

Addition Property of Equality
If $a = b$, then $a + c = b + c$ for all real numbers $a, b,$ and c.

The addition property of equality indicates that the same number can be added to both sides of an equation without changing the solution.

Example 2 *Using the Addition Property of Equality*

Determine the solution to the equation $x - 9 = 15$.

Solution   To isolate the variable, add 9 to both sides of the equation.

$$x - 9 = 15$$
$$x - 9 + 9 = 15 + 9$$
$$x + 0 = 24$$
$$x = 24$$

CHECK:
$$x - 9 = 15$$
$$24 - 9 \stackrel{?}{=} 15 \qquad \text{Substitute 24 for } x.$$
$$15 = 15 \qquad \text{True} \qquad ■$$

In Example 2, we showed the step $x + 0 = 24$. This step is usually done mentally, and the step is usually not listed.

Subtraction Property of Equality

If $a = b$, then $a - c = b - c$ for all real numbers a, b, and c.

The subtraction property of equality indicates that the same number can be subtracted from both sides of an equation without changing the solution.

Example 3 *Using the Subtraction Property of Equality*

Determine the solution to the equation $x + 11 = 19$.

Solution To isolate the variable, subtract 11 from both sides of the equation.

$$x + 11 = 19$$
$$x + 11 - 11 = 19 - 11$$
$$x = 8$$

Note in Example 3 that we did not subtract 19 from both sides of the equation, because doing so would not result in getting x on one side of the equal sign by itself. Now we discuss the multiplication property.

Multiplication Property of Equality

If $a = b$, then $a \cdot c = b \cdot c$ for all real numbers a, b, and c, where $c \neq 0$.

The multiplication property of equality indicates that both sides of the equation can be multiplied by the same nonzero number without changing the solution.

Example 4 *Using the Multiplication Property of Equality*

Determine the solution to $\dfrac{x}{4} = 8$.

Solution To solve this equation, multiply both sides of the equation by 4.

$$\frac{x}{4} = 8$$

$$4\left(\frac{x}{4}\right) = 4(8)$$

$$\frac{\overset{1}{4}x}{\underset{1}{4}} = 32$$

$$1x = 32$$

$$x = 32$$

In Example 4, we showed the steps $\dfrac{4x}{4} = 32$ and $1x = 32$. Usually, we will not illustrate these steps.

Division Property of Equality

If $a = b$, then $\dfrac{a}{c} = \dfrac{b}{c}$ for all real numbers a, b, and c, $c \neq 0$.

The division property of equality indicates that both sides of an equation can be divided by the same nonzero number without changing the solution. Note that the divisor, c, cannot be 0 because division by 0 is not permitted.

Example 5 *Using the Division Property of Equality*

Solve the equation $7x = 35$.

Solution To solve this equation, divide both sides of the equation by 7.

$$7x = 35$$

$$\frac{7x}{7} = \frac{35}{7}$$

$$x = 5$$

An *algorithm* is a general procedure for accomplishing a task. The following general procedure is an algorithm for solving linear (or first-degree) equations. Sometimes the solution to an equation may be found more easily by using a variation of this general procedure. Remember that the primary objective in solving any equation is to isolate the variable.

PROCEDURE   **A GENERAL PROCEDURE FOR SOLVING LINEAR EQUATIONS**

1. If the equation contains fractions, multiply both sides of the equation by the lowest common denominator (or least common multiple). This step will eliminate all fractions from the equation.

2. Use the distributive property to remove parentheses when necessary.

3. Combine like terms on the same side of the equal sign when possible.

4. Use the addition or subtraction property to collect all terms with a variable on one side of the equal sign and all constants on the other side of the equal sign. It may be necessary to use the addition or subtraction property more than once. This process will eventually result in an equation of the form $ax = b$, where a and b are real numbers.

5. Solve for the variable using the division or multiplication property. The result will be an answer in the form $x = c$, where c is a real number.

Example 6 *Using the General Procedure*

Solve the equation $2x - 9 = 19$.

Solution Our goal is to isolate the variable; therefore, we start by getting the term $2x$ by itself on one side of the equation.

$$2x - 9 = 19$$

$2x - 9 + 9 = 19 + 9$ Add 9 to both sides of the equation (addition property) (Step 4).

$$2x = 28$$

$\dfrac{2x}{2} = \dfrac{28}{2}$ Divide both sides of the equation by 2 (division property) (Step 5).

$$x = 14$$

A check will show that 14 is the solution to $2x - 9 = 19$.

Example 7 *Solving a Linear Equation*

Solve the equation $4 = 5 + 2(t + 1)$ for t.

Solution Our goal is to isolate the variable t. To do so, follow the general procedure for solving equations.

$$4 = 5 + 2(t + 1)$$

$$4 = 5 + 2t + 2 \qquad \text{Distributive property (Step 2)}$$

$$4 = 2t + 7 \qquad \text{Combine like terms (Step 3).}$$

$$4 - 7 = 2t + 7 - 7 \qquad \text{Subtraction property (Step 4)}$$

$$-3 = 2t$$

$$\frac{-3}{2} = \frac{2t}{2} \qquad \text{Division property (Step 5)}$$

$$-\frac{3}{2} = t$$

Example 8 *Solving an Equation Containing Fractions*

Solve the equation $\dfrac{2x}{3} + \dfrac{1}{3} = \dfrac{3}{4}$.

Solution When an equation contains fractions, we generally begin by multiplying each term of the equation by the lowest common denominator, LCD (see page 237 in Chapter 5). In this example, the LCD is 12 because 12 is the smallest number that is divisible by both 3 and 4.

$$12\left(\frac{2x}{3} + \frac{1}{3}\right) = 12\left(\frac{3}{4}\right) \qquad \text{Multiply both sides of the equation by the LCD (Step 1).}$$

$$12\left(\frac{2x}{3}\right) + 12\left(\frac{1}{3}\right) = 12\left(\frac{3}{4}\right) \qquad \text{Distributive property (Step 2)}$$

$$\overset{4}{\cancel{12}}\left(\frac{2x}{\cancel{3}}\right) + \overset{4}{\cancel{12}}\left(\frac{1}{\cancel{3}}\right) = \overset{3}{\cancel{12}}\left(\frac{3}{\cancel{4}}\right) \qquad \text{Divide out common factors.}$$

$$8x + 4 = 9$$

$$8x + 4 - 4 = 9 - 4 \qquad \text{Subtraction property (Step 4)}$$

$$8x = 5$$

$$\frac{8x}{8} = \frac{5}{8} \qquad \text{Division property (Step 5)}$$

$$x = \frac{5}{8}$$

A check will show that $\frac{5}{8}$ is the solution to the equation. You could have worked the problem without first multiplying both sides of the equation by the LCD. Try it! ∎

Example 9 *Variables on Both Sides of the Equation*

Solve the equation $6x + 8 = 10x + 12$.

Solution Note that the equation has an x on both sides of the equal sign. In equations of this type, you might wonder what to do first. It actually does not matter as long as you do not forget the goal of isolating the variable x. Let's collect the terms containing a variable on the left-hand side of the equation.

$$6x + 8 = 10x + 12$$

$$6x + 8 - 8 = 10x + 12 - 8 \qquad \text{Subtraction property (Step 4)}$$

$$6x = 10x + 4$$

$$6x - 10x = 10x - 10x + 4 \qquad \text{Subtraction property (Step 4)}$$

$$-4x = 4$$

$$\frac{-4x}{-4} = \frac{4}{-4} \qquad \text{Division property (Step 5)}$$

$$x = -1$$

In the solution to Example 9, the terms containing the variable were collected on the left-hand side of the equal sign. Now work Example 9, collecting the terms with the variable on the right-hand side of the equal sign. If you do so correctly, you will get the same result.

Example 10 *Solving an Equation Containing Decimals*

Solve the equation $4x - 0.48 = 0.8x + 4$ and check your solution.

Solution This equation may be solved with the decimals, or you may multiply each term by 100 and eliminate the decimals. We will solve the equation with the decimals.

$$4x - 0.48 = 0.8x + 4$$

$$4x - 0.48 + 0.48 = 0.8x + 4 + 0.48 \qquad \text{Addition property}$$

$$4x = 0.8x + 4.48$$

$$4x - 0.8x = 0.8x - 0.8x + 4.48 \qquad \text{Subtraction property}$$

$$3.2x = 4.48$$

$$\frac{3.2x}{3.2} = \frac{4.48}{3.2} \qquad \text{Division property}$$

$$x = 1.4$$

CHECK:
$$4x - 0.48 = 0.8x + 4$$

$$4(1.4) - 0.48 \stackrel{?}{=} 0.8(1.4) + 4 \qquad \text{Substitute 1.4 for each } x \text{ in the equation.}$$

$$5.6 - 0.48 \stackrel{?}{=} 1.12 + 4$$

$$5.12 = 5.12 \qquad \text{True}$$

In Chapter 5, we explained that $a - b$ can be expressed as $a + (-b)$. We use this principle in Example 11.

Example 11 *Using the Definition of Subtraction*

Solve $12 = 2(3r - 4) - 4r$ for r.

TIMELY TIP
Remember that the goal in solving an equation is to get the variable alone on one side of the equal sign by using the general procedure for solving equations.

Solution Our goal is to isolate the variable r. To do so, follow the general procedure for solving equations.

$$12 = 2(3r - 4) - 4r$$

$$12 = 2[3r + (-4)] - 4r \qquad \text{Definition of subtraction}$$

$$12 = 2(3r) + 2(-4) - 4r \qquad \text{Distributive property}$$

$$12 = 6r - 8 - 4r$$

$$12 = 2r - 8 \qquad \text{Combine like terms.}$$

$$12 + 8 = 2r - 8 + 8 \qquad \text{Addition property}$$

$$20 = 2r$$

$$\frac{20}{2} = \frac{2r}{2} \qquad \text{Division property}$$

$$10 = r \qquad\blacksquare$$

So far, every equation has had exactly one solution. Some equations, however, have no solution, and others have more than one solution. Example 12 illustrates an equation that has no solution, and Example 13 illustrates an equation that has an infinite number of solutions.

Example 12 *An Equation with No Solution*

Solve $2(x - 4) + x + 5 = 5x - 2(x + 4)$.

Solution

$$2(x - 4) + x + 5 = 5x - 2(x + 4)$$

$$2x - 8 + x + 5 = 5x - 2x - 8 \qquad \text{Distributive property}$$

$$3x - 3 = 3x - 8 \qquad \text{Combine like terms.}$$

$$3x - 3x - 3 = 3x - 3x - 8 \qquad \text{Subtraction property}$$

$$-3 = -8 \qquad \text{False}$$

During the process of solving an equation, if you obtain a false statement like $-3 = -8$, or $5 = 0$, the equation has *no solution*. An equation that has no solution is called a *contradiction*. The equation $2(x - 4) + x + 5 = 5x - 2(x + 4)$ is a contradiction and thus has no solution. $\blacksquare$

Example 13 *An Equation with Infinitely Many Solutions*

Solve $2(x + 4) - 3(x - 5) = -x + 23$.

Solution

$$2(x + 4) - 3(x - 5) = -x + 23$$

$$2x + 8 - 3x + 15 = -x + 23 \qquad \text{Distributive property}$$

$$-x + 23 = -x + 23 \qquad \text{Combine like terms.}$$

Note that at this point both sides of the equation are the same. Every real number will satisfy this equation. This equation has an infinite number of solutions. An equation of this type is called an *identity*. When solving an equation, you can tell that the equation is an identity if you notice that the same expression appears on both sides of the equal sign. The solution to any linear equation with one variable that is an identity is *all real numbers*. If you continue to solve an equation that is an identity, you will end up with $0 = 0$, as follows.

$$-x + 23 = -x + 23$$

$$-x + x + 23 = -x + x + 23 \qquad \text{Addition property}$$

$$23 = 23 \qquad \text{Combine like terms.}$$

$$23 - 23 = 23 - 23 \qquad \text{Subtraction property}$$

$$0 = 0 \qquad \text{True for any value of } x$$

Proportions

A *ratio* is a quotient of two quantities. An example is the ratio of 2 to 5, which can be written $2 : 5$ or $\frac{2}{5}$ or 2/5. Ratios are used in proportions.

> **Definition: Proportion**
> A **proportion** is a statement of equality between two ratios.

An example of a proportion is $\dfrac{a}{b} = \dfrac{c}{d}$, where $b \neq 0$ and $d \neq 0$. Consider the proportion

$$\frac{x + 2}{5} = \frac{x + 5}{8}$$

We can solve this proportion by first multiplying both sides of the equation by the LCD, 40.

$$\frac{x + 2}{5} = \frac{x + 5}{8}$$

$$\overset{8}{\cancel{40}}\left(\frac{x + 2}{\cancel{5}}\right) = \overset{5}{\cancel{40}}\left(\frac{x + 5}{\cancel{8}}\right) \qquad \text{Multiplication property}$$

$$8(x + 2) = 5(x + 5)$$

$$8x + 16 = 5x + 25$$

$$3x + 16 = 25$$

$$3x = 9$$

$$x = 3$$

A check will show that 3 is the solution.

Proportions can often be solved more easily by using cross multiplication.

> **Cross Multiplication**
> If $\dfrac{a}{b} = \dfrac{c}{d}$, then $ad = bc$, where $b \neq 0, d \neq 0$.

Let's use cross multiplication to solve the proportion $\dfrac{x+2}{5} = \dfrac{x+5}{8}$.

$$\frac{x+2}{5} = \frac{x+5}{8}$$

$$8(x+2) = 5(x+5) \quad \text{Cross multiplication}$$

$$8x + 16 = 5x + 25$$

$$3x + 16 = 25$$

$$3x = 9$$

$$x = 3$$

Notice we obtained the same answer as we did by multiplying both sides of the equation by the LCD, 40.

Many practical application problems can be solved using proportions.

PROCEDURE   TO SOLVE APPLICATION PROBLEMS USING PROPORTIONS

1. Represent the unknown quantity by a variable.

2. Set up the proportion by listing the given ratio on the left-hand side of the equal sign and the unknown and other given quantity on the right-hand side of the equal sign. When setting up the right-hand side of the proportion, the same respective quantities should occupy the same respective positions on the left and right. For example, an acceptable proportion might be

$$\frac{\text{miles}}{\text{hour}} = \frac{\text{miles}}{\text{hour}}$$

3. Once the proportion is properly written, drop the units and use cross multiplication to solve the equation.

4. Answer the question or questions asked using the appropriate units.

Example 14 *Water Usage*

The cost for water in the city of Tucson, Arizona is $1.75 per 750 gallons (gal) of water used. What is the water bill if 30,000 gallons are used?

Solution This problem may be solved by setting up a proportion. One proportion that can be used is

$$\frac{\text{cost of 750 gal}}{750 \text{ gal}} = \frac{\text{cost of 30,000 gal}}{30,000 \text{ gal}}$$

The unknown quantity is the cost for 30,000 gallons of water, so we will call this quantity x. The proportion then becomes

$$\text{Given ratio} \begin{cases} \dfrac{1.75}{750} = \dfrac{x}{30,000} \end{cases}$$

Now we solve for x by using cross multiplication.

$$(1.75)(30,000) = 750x$$

$$52,500 = 750x$$

$$\frac{52,500}{750} = \frac{750x}{750}$$

$$\$70 = x$$

The cost of 30,000 gallons of water is $70.

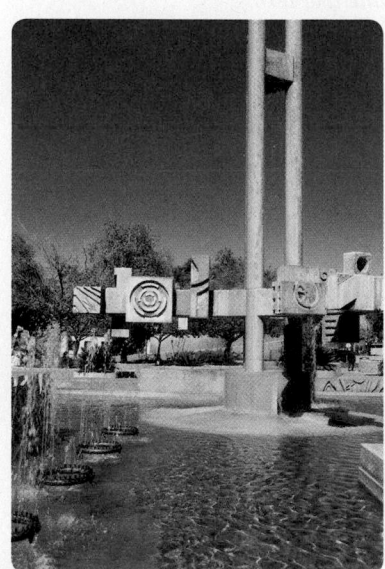

▲ *Tucson, AZ*

Example **15** *Determining the Amount of Insulin*

Insulin comes in 10-cubic-centimeter (cc) vials labeled in the number of units of insulin per cubic centimeter of fluid. A vial of insulin marked U40 has 40 units of insulin per cubic centimeter of fluid. If a patient needs 30 units of insulin, how much fluid should be drawn into the syringe from the U40 vial?

Solution The unknown quantity, x, is the number of cubic centimeters of fluid to be drawn into the syringe. Following is one proportion that can be used to find that quantity.

$$\text{Given ratio} \begin{cases} \dfrac{40 \text{ units}}{1 \text{ cc}} = \dfrac{30 \text{ units}}{x \text{ cc}} \end{cases}$$

$$40x = 30(1)$$
$$40x = 30$$
$$x = \frac{30}{40} = 0.75$$

The nurse or doctor putting the insulin in the syringe should draw 0.75 cc of the fluid. ∎

SECTION 6.2 *Exercises*

Warm Up Exercises

In Exercises 1–12, fill in the blank with an appropriate word, phrase, or symbol(s).

1. The parts that are added or subtracted in an algebraic expression are called _____. Terms

2. Terms that have the same variables with the same exponents on the variables are called _____ terms. Like

3. The numerical part of a term is called its numerical _____. Coefficient

4. An equation in which the highest exponent on the variable is a 1, is called a(n) _____ equation. Linear

5. To combine like terms by using the commutative, associative, and distributive properties means to _____ an expression. Simplify

6. A general procedure for accomplishing a task is called a(n) _____. Algorithm

7. A quotient of two quantities is called a(n) _____. Ratio

8. A statement of equality between two ratios is called a(n) _____. Proportion

9. An equation that has an infinite number of solutions is called a(n) _____. Identity

10. An equation that has no solution is called a(n) _____. Contradiction

11. When solving an equation, getting a variable by itself on one side of the equal sign means to _____ the variable. Isolate

12. Equations that have the same solution are called _____ equations. Equivalent

Practice the Skills

In Exercises 13–36, combine like terms.

13. $5x + 3x$ $8x$

14. $7x - 2x$ $5x$

15. $-8x - 3x + 12$ $-11x + 12$

16. $-6x + 2x + 21$ $-4x + 21$

17. $7x + 3y - 4x + 8y$ $3x + 11y$

18. $x - 4x + 3$ $-3x + 3$

19. $-3x + 2 - 5x$ $-8x + 2$

20. $-3x + 4x - 2 + 5$ $x + 3$

21. $2 - 3x - 2x + 1$ $-5x + 3$

22. $-0.2x + 1.7x - 4$ $1.5x - 4$

23. $6.2x - 8.3 + 7.1x$ $13.3x - 8.3$

24. $4s + 3t + 8 - 2t$ $4s + t + 8$

25. $\frac{2}{3}x + \frac{1}{6}x - 5$ $\frac{5}{6}x - 5$

26. $\frac{1}{5}x - \frac{1}{3}x - 4$ $-\frac{2}{15}x - 4$

27. $7x - 4y - 8y + 6x + 2$ $13x - 12y + 2$

28. $2p - 4q - 3p + 4q - 15$ $-p - 15$

29. $2(s + 3) + 6(s - 4) + 1$ $8s - 17$

30. $6(r - 3) - 2(r + 5) + 10$ $4r - 18$

31. $0.2(x + 4) + 1.2(x - 3)$ $1.4x - 2.8$

32. $0.9(2.3x - 2) + 1.7(3.2x - 5)$ _7.51x − 10.3_

33. $\dfrac{3}{5}(x + 1) - \dfrac{3}{10}x$ _$\frac{3}{10}x + \frac{3}{5}$_

34. $\dfrac{2}{3}(3x + 9) - \dfrac{1}{4}(2x + 5)$ _$\frac{3}{2}x + \frac{19}{4}$_

35. $\dfrac{1}{4}x + \dfrac{4}{5} - \dfrac{2}{3}x$ _$-\frac{5}{12}x + \frac{4}{5}$_ **36.** $n - \dfrac{3}{4} + \dfrac{5}{9}n - \dfrac{1}{6}$ _$\frac{14}{9}n - \frac{11}{12}$_

In Exercises 37–62, solve the equation.

37. $y - 4 = 13$ _17_

38. $y + 6 = 12$ _6_

39. $21 = -2t + 9$ _−6_

40. $12 = 3x + 6$ _2_

41. $\dfrac{3}{x} = \dfrac{7}{8}$ _$\frac{24}{7}$_

42. $\dfrac{x - 1}{5} = \dfrac{x + 5}{15}$ _4_

43. $\dfrac{1}{2}x + \dfrac{1}{3} = \dfrac{2}{3}$ _$\frac{2}{3}$_

44. $\dfrac{1}{2}y + \dfrac{1}{3} = \dfrac{1}{4}$ _$-\frac{1}{6}$_

45. $0.9x - 1.2 = 2.4$ _4_

46. $5x + 0.050 = -0.732$
_−0.1564_

47. $6t - 8 = 4t - 2$ _3_

48. $6t - 7 = 8t + 9$ _−8_

49. $\dfrac{x}{4} + 2x = \dfrac{1}{3}$ _$\frac{4}{27}$_

50. $\dfrac{r}{3} + 2r = 7$ _3_

51. $\dfrac{x - 3}{2} = \dfrac{x + 4}{3}$ _17_

52. $\dfrac{x - 5}{4} = \dfrac{x - 9}{3}$ _21_

53. $2(x + 3) - 4 = 2(x - 4)$ _No solution_

54. $3(x + 2) + 2(x - 1) = 5x - 7$ _No solution_

55. $4(x - 4) + 12 = 4(x - 1)$ _All real numbers_

56. $6(t + 2) - 14 = 6t - 2$ _All real numbers_

57. $\dfrac{1}{3}(x + 3) = \dfrac{2}{5}(x + 2)$ _3_ **58.** $\dfrac{2}{3}(x - 4) = \dfrac{1}{4}(x + 1)$ _7_

59. $3x + 2 - 6x = -x - 15 + 8 - 5x$ _−3_

60. $6x + 8 - 22x = 28 + 14x - 10 + 12x$ _$-\frac{5}{21}$_

61. $5(3n + 1) = 2(5n - 4) + 6n$ _13_

62. $4(t - 3) + 8 = 4(2t - 6)$ _5_

Problem Solving

In Exercises 63 and 64, use the water rate for Columbus, Ohio, which is $1.98 per 750 gallons of water.

63. *Water Bill* What is the water bill if a resident of Columbus uses 27,000 gal? _$71.28_

64. *Limiting the Cost* How many gallons of water can a customer use if the water bill is not to exceed $200?
≈75,757 gallons

65. *Paint* A gallon of paint covers 825 ft². How much paint is needed to paint a house with a surface area of 6600 ft²?
8 gallons

▲ *See Exercise 65*

66. *Watching Television* Nielson Media Research determines the number of people who watch a television show. One rating point means that about 1,102,000 households watched the show. The top-rated television show for the week of February 14, 2011, was *American Idol*—with a rating of 21.0. About how many households watched *American Idol* that week? _≈ 23,142,000 households_

67. *Fajitas* A recipe for six servings of beef fajitas requires 16 oz of beef sirloin.

a) If the recipe were to be made for nine servings, how many ounces of beef sirloin would be needed? _24 oz_

b) How many servings of beef fajitas can be made with 32 oz of beef sirloin? _12 servings_

68. *Topsoil* A 40-pound bag of topsoil will cover a surface area of 12 ft².

a) How many pounds of topsoil are needed to cover a surface area of 480 ft²? _1600 lb_

b) How many bags of topsoil must be purchased to cover a surface area of 480 ft²? _40 bags_

69. *Speed Limit* When Jacob Abbott crossed over from Niagara Falls, New York, to Niagara Falls, Canada, he saw a sign that said 50 miles per hour (mph) is equal to 80 kilometers per hour (kph).

▲ *Niagara Falls, Canada*

a) How many kilometers per hour are equal to 1 mph? _1.6 kph_

b) On a stretch of the Queen Elizabeth Way, the speed limit is 90 kph. What is the speed limit in miles per hour? _56.25 mph_

70. *The Proper Dosage* A doctor asks a nurse to give a patient 250 milligrams (mg) of the drug Simethicone. The drug is available only in a solution whose concentration is 40 mg Simethicone per 0.6 milliliter (mℓ) of solution. How many milliliters of solution should the nurse give the patient? _3.75 mℓ_

Amount of Insulin *In Exercises 71 and 72, how much insulin (in cc) would be given for the following doses? (Refer to Example 15 on page 306.)*

71. 15 units of insulin from a vial marked U40 0.375 cc

72. 35 units of insulin from a vial marked U40 0.875 cc

73. a) Summarize the procedure to use to solve an equation.
Answers will vary.

b) Solve the equation $2(x + 3) = 4x + 3 - 5x$ with the procedure you outlined in part (a). -1

Challenge Problems/Group Activities

74. *Depth of a Submarine* The pressure, P, in pounds per square inch (psi) exerted on an object x ft below the sea is given by the formula $P = 14.70 + 0.43x$. The 14.70 represents the weight in pounds of the column of air (from sea level to the top of the atmosphere) standing over a 1 in. by 1 in. square of seawater. The $0.43x$ represents the weight in pounds of a column of water 1 in. by 1 in. by x ft (see Fig. 6.1).

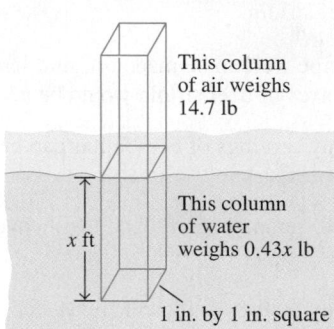

This column of air weighs 14.7 lb

This column of water weighs $0.43x$ lb

x ft

1 in. by 1 in. square

Figure 6.1

a) A submarine is built to withstand a pressure of 148 psi. How deep can that submarine go? 310 ft

b) If the pressure gauge in the submarine registers a pressure of 128.65 psi, how deep is the submarine?
265 ft below see level

75. a) *Gender Ratios* If the ratio of males to females in a class is 2 : 3, what is the ratio of males to all the students in the class? 2 : 5

b) If the ratio of males to females in a class is $m : n$, what is the ratio of males to all the students in the class?
$m : (m + n)$

76. Determine whether the given equations are equivalent.

a) $\dfrac{x}{3} = \dfrac{x + 2}{6}$, $6x = 3x + 6$ Yes

b) $2x - 9 = 19$, $\dfrac{2x - 9}{4} = \dfrac{19}{4}$ Yes

Internet/Research Activities

77. Ratio and proportion are used in many different ways in everyday life. Submit two articles from newspapers, magazines, or the Internet in which ratios and/or proportions are used. Write a brief summary of each article explaining how ratio and/or proportion were used.

78. Write a report explaining how the ancient Egyptians used equations. Include in your discussion the forms of the equations used.

SECTION 6.3   Formulas

▲ *A formula is used to determine the amount of carpet needed to cover the floor of a room.*

Suppose you need to purchase new carpet for your family room, which is in the shape of a rectangle. To determine the amount of carpet required, you would need to determine the area of the room by multiplying the length of the room by the width of the room. In this section, we will discuss a special kind of equation called a *formula*. Formulas are used to evaluate and determine the solution to many real world problems.

Why **This is Important** Using a formula can help us determine many quantities, such as how much carpet to purchase for a room and the interest you must pay when borrowing money.

A *formula* is an equation that typically has a real-life application. To *evaluate* a formula, substitute the given values for their respective variables and then evaluate using the order of operations given in Section 6.1. Many of the formulas given in this section are discussed in greater detail in other parts of the book.

Example 1 *Simple Interest*

The simple interest formula,* interest = principal × rate × time, or $i = prt$, is used to find the interest you must pay on a simple interest loan when you borrow principal, p, at simple interest rate, r, in decimal form, for time, t. Chris Campbell borrows \$5000 at a simple interest rate of 6.5% for 3 years.

a) How much will Chris Campbell pay in interest at the end of 3 years?

b) What is the total amount he will repay the bank at the end of 3 years?

Solution

a) Substitute the values of p, r, and t into the formula; then evaluate.

$$i = prt$$
$$= 5000(0.065)(3)$$
$$= 975$$

Thus, Chris must pay \$975 interest.

b) The total he must pay at the end of 3 years is the principal, \$5000, plus the \$975 interest, for a total of \$5975. ∎

Example 2 *Volume of an Ice-Cream Box*

The formula for the volume of a rectangular box† is volume = length × width × height, or $V = lwh$. Use the formula $V = lwh$ to find the width of a rectangular box of ice cream if $l = 7$ in., $h = 3.5$ in., and $V = 122.5$ in³.

Solution We substitute the appropriate values into the volume formula and solve for the desired quantity, w.

$$V = lwh$$
$$122.5 = (7)w(3.5)$$
$$122.5 = 24.5w$$
$$\frac{122.5}{24.5} = \frac{24.5w}{24.5}$$
$$5 = w$$

Therefore, the width of the ice-cream box is 5 in. ∎

In Example 1, we used the formula $i = prt$. In Example 2, we used the formula $V = lwh$. In these examples, we used a mathematical equation to represent real phenomena. When we represent real phenomena, such as finding simple interest, mathematically we say we have created a *mathematical model* or simply a *model* to represent the situation. A model may be a single formula, an equation, or a system of many equations. By using models we gain insight into real-life situations, such as how much interest you will accumulate in your savings account. We will use mathematical models throughout this chapter and elsewhere in the text. In some exercises in this and the next chapter, when you are asked to determine an equation to represent a real-life situation, we will sometimes write the word *modeling* in the instructions.

Many formulas contain Greek letters, such as μ (mu), σ (sigma), Σ (capital sigma), δ (delta), Δ (capital delta), ϵ (epsilon), π (pi), θ (theta), and λ (lambda).

---

*The simple interest formula is discussed in Section 11.2.

†The volume formula is discussed in Section 9.4.

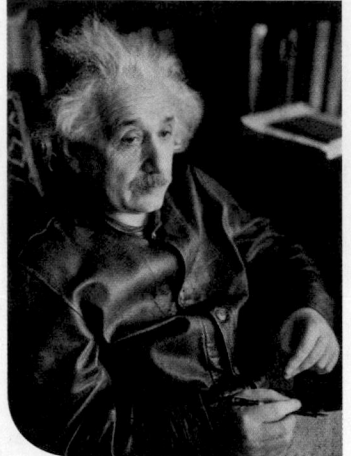
Example 3 *A Statistics Formula*

A formula used in the study of statistics to find a standard score (or z-score) is

$$z = \frac{\bar{x} - \mu}{\frac{\sigma}{\sqrt{n}}}$$

Find the value of z when $\bar{x}$ (read "x bar") $= 120$, $\mu = 100$, $\sigma = 16$, and $n = 4$.

Solution

$$z = \frac{\bar{x} - \mu}{\frac{\sigma}{\sqrt{n}}} = \frac{120 - 100}{\frac{16}{\sqrt{4}}} = \frac{20}{\frac{16}{2}} = \frac{20}{8} = 2.5$$

Some formulas contain *subscripts*. Subscripts are numbers (or letters) placed below and to the right of variables. They are used to help clarify a formula. For example, if two different amounts are used in a problem, they may be symbolized as A and A_0, or A_1 and A_2. Subscripts are read using the word *sub*; for example, A_0 is read "A sub zero" and A_1 is read "A sub one."

Solving for a Variable in a Formula or Equation

Often in mathematics and science courses, you are given a formula or an equation expressed in terms of one variable and asked to express it in terms of a different variable. For example, you may be given the formula $P = i^2 r$ and asked to solve the formula for r. To do so, treat each of the variables, except the one you are solving for, as if it were a constant. Then solve for the variable desired, using the properties previously discussed. Examples 4 through 6 show how to do this task.

When graphing equations in Section 6.7, you will sometimes have to solve the equation for the variable y, as is done in Example 4.

Example 4 *Solving for a Variable in an Equation*

Solve the equation $2x + 5y - 10 = 0$ for y.

Solution We need to isolate the term containing the variable y. Begin by moving the constant, -10, and the term $2x$ to the right-hand side of the equation.

$$2x + 5y - 10 = 0$$
$$2x + 5y - 10 + 10 = 0 + 10 \qquad \text{Addition property}$$
$$2x + 5y = 10$$
$$-2x + 2x + 5y = -2x + 10 \qquad \text{Subtraction property}$$
$$5y = -2x + 10$$
$$\frac{5y}{5} = \frac{-2x + 10}{5} \qquad \text{Division property}$$
$$y = \frac{-2x + 10}{5}$$
$$y = -\frac{2x}{5} + \frac{10}{5}$$
$$y = -\frac{2}{5}x + 2$$

■

Note that once you have found $y = \frac{-2x + 10}{5}$, you have solved the equation for y. The solution can also be expressed in the form $y = -\frac{2}{5}x + 2$. This form of the equation is convenient for graphing equations, as will be explained in Section 6.7. Example 4 can also be solved by moving the y term to the right-hand side of the equal sign. Do so now and note that you obtain the same answer.

Example 5 *Solving for a Variable in a Formula*

An important formula used in statistics is

$$z = \frac{x - \mu}{\sigma}$$

Solve this formula for x.

Solution To isolate the term x, use the general procedure for solving linear equations given in Section 6.2. Treat each letter, except x, as if it were a constant.

$$z = \frac{x - \mu}{\sigma}$$

$$z \cdot \sigma = \frac{x - \mu}{\sigma} \cdot \sigma \qquad \text{Multiply both sides of the equation by } \sigma.$$

$$z\sigma = x - \mu$$

$$z\sigma + \mu = x - \mu + \mu \qquad \text{Add } \mu \text{ to both sides of the equation.}$$

$$z\sigma + \mu = x$$

$$\text{or} \quad x = z\sigma + \mu \qquad \blacksquare$$

Example 6 *The Tax-Free Yield Formula*

A formula that may be important to you now or sometime in the future is the tax-free yield formula, $T_f = T_a(1 - F)$. This formula can be used to convert a taxable yield, T_a, into its equivalent tax-free yield, T_f, where F is the federal income tax bracket of the individual. A taxable yield is an interest rate for which income tax is paid on the interest made. A tax-free yield is an interest rate for which income tax does not have to be paid on the interest made.

a) For someone in a 25% tax bracket, find the equivalent tax-free yield of a 4% taxable investment.

b) Solve this formula for T_a. That is, write a formula for taxable yield in terms of tax-free yield.

Solution

a) $T_f = T_a(1 - F)$

$$= 0.04(1 - 0.25) = 0.04(0.75) = 0.03, \quad \text{or} \quad 3\%$$

Thus, a taxable investment of 4% is equivalent to a tax-free investment of 3% for a person in a 25% income tax bracket.

b) $\qquad T_f = T_a(1 - F)$

$$\frac{T_f}{1 - F} = \frac{T_a(1 - F)}{1 - F} \qquad \text{Divide both sides of the equation by } 1 - F.$$

$$\frac{T_f}{1 - F} = T_a, \quad \text{or} \quad T_a = \frac{T_f}{1 - F} \qquad \blacksquare$$

SECTION 6.3
Exercises

Warm Up Exercises

In Exercises 1–2, fill in the blank with an appropriate word, phrase, or symbol(s).

1. An equation that typically has a real-life application is called a(n) _____ . Formula

2. Numbers or letters that are placed below and to the right of variables are called _____ . Subscripts

Practice the Skills

In Exercises 3–34, use the formula to determine the value of the indicated variable for the values given. Use a calculator when one is needed. When necessary, round answers to the nearest hundredth.

3. $A = bh$; determine A when $b = 12$ and $h = 4$ (geometry). 48

4. $P = a + b + c$; determine P when $a = 25, b = 53$, and $c = 32$ (geometry). 110

5. $P = 2l + 2w$; determine P when $l = 12$ and $w = 16$ (geometry). 56

6. $F = ma$; determine m when $F = 40$ and $a = 5$ (physics). 8

7. $K = \frac{1}{2}mv^2$; determine m when $v = 30$ and $K = 4500$ (physics). 10

8. $p = i^2r$; determine r when $p = 62,500$ and $i = 5$ (electronics). 2500

9. $S = \pi r(r + h)$; determine S when $r = 8, \pi = 3.14$, and $h = 2$ (geometry). 251.2

10. $B = \frac{703w}{h^2}$; determine B when $w = 130$ and $h = 67$ (body mass index). 20.36

11. $z = \frac{x - \mu}{\sigma}$; determine μ when $z = 2.5, x = 42.1$, and $\sigma = 2$ (statistics). 37.1

12. $S = 4lw + 2wh$; determine l when $S = 336, h = 9$, and $w = 8$ (geometry). 6

13. $T = \frac{PV}{k}$; determine P when $T = 80, V = 20$, and $k = 0.5$ (physics). 2

14. $m = \frac{a + b + c}{3}$; determine a when $m = 85, b = 77$, and $c = 92$ (statistics). 86

15. $A = P(1 + rt)$; determine P when $A = 3600, r = 0.04$, and $t = 5$ (economics). 3000

16. $V = -\frac{1}{2}at^2$; determine a when $V = 2304$ and $t = 12$ (physics). −32

17. $V = \pi r^2h$; determine h when $V = 942, \pi = 3.14$, and $r = 5$ (geometry). 12

18. $F = \frac{9}{5}C + 32$; determine F when $C = 7$ (temperature conversion). 44.6

19. $C = \frac{5}{9}(F - 32)$; determine C when $F = 77$ (temperature conversion). 25

20. $K = \frac{F - 32}{1.8} + 273.1$; determine K when $F = 100$ (chemistry). 310.88

21. $m = \frac{y_2 - y_1}{x_2 - x_1}$; determine m when $y_2 = 8, y_1 = -4, x_2 = -3$, and $x_1 = -5$ (mathematics). 6

22. $z = \frac{\bar{x} - \mu}{\frac{\sigma}{\sqrt{n}}}$; determine z when $\bar{x} = 66, \mu = 60, \sigma = 15$, and $n = 25$ (statistics). 2

23. $S = R - rR$; determine R when $S = 186$ and $r = 0.07$ (for determining sale price when an item is discounted). 200

24. $S = C + rC$; determine C when $S = 115$ and $r = 0.15$ (for determining selling price when an item is marked up). 100

25. $E = a_1p_1 + a_2p_2 + a_3p_3$; determine E when $a_1 = 5, p_1 = 0.2, a_2 = 7, p_2 = 0.6, a_3 = 10$, and $p_3 = 0.2$ (probability). 7.2

26. $x = \frac{-b + \sqrt{b^2 - 4ac}}{2a}$; determine x when $a = 2, b = -5$, and $c = -12$ (mathematics). 4

27. $s = -16t^2 + v_0t + s_0$; determine s when $t = 4, v_0 = 30$, and $s_0 = 150$ (physics). 14

28. $R = O + (V - D)r$; determine O when $R = 670, V = 100, D = 10$, and $r = 4$ (economics). 310

29. $P = \frac{f}{1 + i}$; determine f when $i = 0.08$ and $P = 3000$ (investment banking). 3240

30. $c = \sqrt{a^2 + b^2}$; determine c when $a = 5$ and $b = 12$ (geometry). 13

31. $R_T = \dfrac{R_1 R_2}{R_1 + R_2}$; determine R_T when $R_1 = 100$ and $R_2 = 200$ (electronics). 66.67

32. $P = \dfrac{nRT}{V}$; determine V when $P = 12, n = 10, R = 60$, and $T = 8$ (chemistry). 400

33. $S_n = \dfrac{a_1(1 - r^n)}{1 - r}$; determine S_n when $a_1 = 10, r = 1/2$, and $n = 4$ (mathematics). 18.75

34. $A = P\left(1 + \dfrac{r}{n}\right)^{nt}$; determine A when $P = 100, r = 6\%$, $n = 1$, and $t = 3$ (banking). 119.10

In Exercises 35–44, solve the equation for y.

35. $5x - 4y = 14$ *

36. $7x - 3y = 23$ *

37. $8x + 7y = 21$ *

38. $-9x + 4y = 11$ *

39. $2x - 3y + 6 = 0$ *

40. $10x - 3y = 0$ $y = \frac{10}{3}x$

41. $-2x + 3y + z = 15$ *

42. $5x + 3y - 2z = 22$ *

43. $9x + 4z = 7 + 8y$ *

44. $2x - 3y + 5z = 0$ *

In Exercises 45–64, solve for the variable indicated.

45. $A = lw$, for w $w = \frac{A}{l}$

46. $V = lwh$ for w $w = \frac{V}{lh}$

47. $p = a + b + c$ for a $a = p - b - c$

48. $p = a + b + s_1 + s_2$ for s_1 $s_1 = p - a - b - s_2$

49. $V = \frac{1}{3}Bh$ for B $B = \frac{3V}{h}$

50. $V = \pi r^2 h$ for h $h = \frac{V}{\pi r^2}$

51. $C = 2\pi r$ for r $r = \frac{C}{2\pi}$

52. $y = mx + b$ for m $m = \frac{y - b}{x}$

53. $y = mx + b$ for b $b = y - mx$

54. $V = \frac{1}{3}\pi r^2 h$ for h $h = \frac{3V}{\pi r^2}$

55. $P = 2l + 2w$ for w $w = \frac{P - 2l}{2}$

56. $A = \frac{1}{2}bh$ for b $b = \frac{2A}{h}$

57. $L = \dfrac{c + 2d}{4}$ for d $d = \frac{4L - c}{2}$

58. $\dfrac{w_1}{w_2} = \dfrac{f_2 - f}{f - f_1}$ for w_1 *

59. $r = \dfrac{2gm}{c^2}$ for m $m = \frac{c^2 r}{2g}$

60. $\dfrac{P_1 V_1}{T_1} = \dfrac{P_2 V_2}{T_2}$ for V_2 *

61. $F = \frac{9}{5}C + 32$ for C $C = \frac{5}{9}(F - 32)$

62. $C = \frac{5}{9}(F - 32)$ for F $F = \frac{9}{5}C + 32$

63. $S = \pi r^2 + \pi rs$ for s $s = \frac{S - \pi r^2}{\pi r}$

64. $A = \frac{1}{2}h(b_1 + b_2)$ for b_2 $b_2 = \frac{2A}{h} - b_1$

Problem Solving

In Exercises 65–69, when appropriate, round answers to the nearest hundredth.

65. **Driving Time** A family is planning to drive 549 miles from their home in Lincoln, Nebraska, to Mount Rushmore National Park. They plan to drive at an average speed of 61 miles per hour. How much time will they spend driving? 9 hr

▲ Mount Rushmore, South Dakota

66. **Savings Account** Christine Chu borrowed $4500 from a bank at a simple interest rate of 2.5% for one year.

   a) Determine how much interest Christine paid at the end of 1 year. $112.50

   b) Determine the total amount Christine will repay the bank at the end of 1 year. $4612.50

67. **Interest on a Loan** Jeff Hubbard borrowed $800 from his brother for 2 years. At the end of 2 years, he repaid the $800 plus $128 in interest. What simple interest rate did he pay? 8%

68. **Volume of a Bucket** Determine the volume of a cylindrical bucket in cubic inches if the bucket's radius is 5 in. and the height is 12 in. The formula for the volume of a cylinder is $V = \pi r^2 h$. Use the π key on your calculator. ≈ 942.48 in.^{3}

69. **Body Mass Index** A person's body mass index (BMI) is found by the formula $B = \dfrac{703w}{h^2}$, where w is the person's weight, in pounds, and h is the person's height, in inches. John Bass is 6 ft tall and weighs 200 lb.

   a) Determine his BMI. ≈ 27.12

   b) If John would like to have a BMI of 26, how much weight would he need to gain or lose? lose ≈ 8.27 lb

Challenge Problem/Group Activity

70. Determine the volume of the block shown in Fig. 6.2, excluding the hole. The formula for the volume of a rectangular solid is $V = lwh$. The formula for the volume of a cylinder is $V = \pi r^2 h$. ≈ 1051.47 in.^{3}

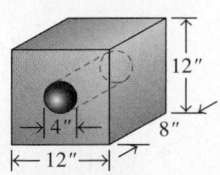

Figure 6.2

*See Instructor Answer Appendix

▲ *An equation can be used to represent the base salary and the commission earned by a sales representative.*

Suppose your weekly salary as a sales representative consists of a weekly base salary of $400 and a 6% commission on the total dollar amount of all sales you make. How many dollars in sales would you need to make in a week to earn a total of $1000 a week? To answer this question you must first express the written problem as a mathematical equation. Then you can use the general procedure for solving linear equations discussed in Section 6.2 to obtain the answer. In this section, we will explain how to write mathematical equations to represent word problems.

Why **This Is Important** Being able to express a real-life problem as a mathematical equation is necessary in order to solve application problems like the one above.

One reason to study algebra is that it can be used to solve everyday problems. In this section, we will do two things: (1) show how to translate a written problem into a mathematical equation and (2) show how linear equations can be used in solving everyday problems. We begin by illustrating how English phrases can be written as mathematical expressions. When writing a mathematical expression, we may use any letter to represent the variable. In the following illustrations, we use the letter x.

Phrase	Mathematical expression
Six more than a number	$x + 6$
A number increased by 3	$x + 3$
Four less than a number	$x - 4$
A number decreased by 9	$x - 9$
Twice a number	$2x$
Four times a number	$4x$
3 decreased by a number	$3 - x$
The difference between a number and 5	$x - 5$

Sometimes the phrase that must be converted to a mathematical expression involves more than one operation.

Phrase	Mathematical expression
Four less than 3 times a number	$3x - 4$
Ten more than twice a number	$2x + 10$
The sum of 5 times a number and 3	$5x + 3$
Eight times a number, decreased by 7	$8x - 7$

The word *is* often represents the equal sign.

Phrase	Mathematical equation
Six more than a number is 10.	$x + 6 = 10$
Five less than a number is 20.	$x - 5 = 20$
Twice a number, decreased by 6 is 12.	$2x - 6 = 12$
A number decreased by 13 is 6 times the number.	$x - 13 = 6x$

The following is a general procedure for solving word problems.

> **PROCEDURE   TO SOLVE A WORD PROBLEM**
>
> 1. Read the problem carefully at least twice to be sure that you understand it.
> 2. If possible, draw a sketch to help visualize the problem.
> 3. Determine which quantity you are being asked to find. Choose a letter to represent this unknown quantity. Write down exactly what this letter represents.
> 4. Write the word problem as an equation.
> 5. Solve the equation for the unknown quantity.
> 6. Answer the question or questions asked.
> 7. Check the solution.

This general procedure for solving word problems is illustrated in Examples 1 through 4. In these examples, the equations we obtain are mathematical models of the given situations.

Example 1 *House Cleaning Service*

A professional house cleaning service charges a base fee of $20 plus $32.50 per hour to clean the Munoz's house. If the Munoz's total bill for house cleaning services from this company was $117.50 before taxes, how many hours did it take to clean their house?

Solution In this problem, the unknown quantity is the number of hours it took to clean the Munoz's house. Let's select n to represent the number of hours. Then we construct an equation using the given information that will allow us to solve for n.

Let

$$n = \text{number of hours}$$

Then

$$\$32.50n = \text{cost for cleaning } n \text{ hours at } \$32.50 \text{ per hour}$$
$$\text{Base charge} + \text{hourly charge} = \text{total bill}$$
$$\$20 + \$32.50n = \$117.50$$

Now solve the equation.

$$20 + 32.50n = 117.50$$
$$20 - 20 + 32.50n = 117.50 - 20$$
$$32.50n = 97.5$$
$$\frac{32.50n}{32.50} = \frac{97.5}{32.50}$$
$$n = 3$$

Therefore, it took 3 hours to clean the Munoz's house.

CHECK: The check is made with the information given in the original problem.

$$\text{Total bill} = \text{base charge} + \text{hourly charge}$$
$$= 20 + 32.50(3)$$
$$= 20 + 97.50$$
$$= 117.50$$

Therefore, this answer checks.   ■

Example 2 *Dividing Land*

Mark IV Construction Company purchased 100 acres of land to be split into three parcels of land on which to build houses. One parcel of land will be three times as large as each of the other two. How many acres of land will each parcel contain?

Solution   Two parcels will contain the same number of acres, and the third parcel will contain three times that amount.

Let

$$x = \text{number of acres in the first parcel}$$
$$x = \text{number of acres in the second parcel}$$
$$3x = \text{number of acres in the third parcel}$$

Then

$$x + x + 3x = \text{total amount of land}$$
$$x + x + 3x = 100$$
$$5x = 100$$
$$x = 20$$

Thus, two parcels will contain 20 acres of land. The third parcel will contain 3(20), or 60, acres of land. A check in the original problem will verify that this answer is correct.   ∎

Example 3 *Dimensions of an Exercise Area*

Dr. Christine Seidel, a veterinarian, wants to fence in a large rectangular region in the yard behind her office for exercising dogs that are boarded overnight. She has 130 ft of fencing to use for the perimeter of the region. What should the dimensions of the region be if she wants the length to be 15 ft greater than the width?

Solution   The formula for finding the perimeter of a rectangle is $P = 2l + 2w$, where P is the perimeter, l is the length, and w is the width. A diagram, such as the one shown below, is often helpful in solving problems of this type.

Let w equal the width of the region. The length is 15 ft more than the width, so $l = w + 15$. The total distance around the region P, is 130 ft.

Substitute the known quantities in the formula.

$$P = 2l + 2w$$
$$130 = 2(w + 15) + 2w$$
$$130 = 2w + 30 + 2w$$
$$130 = 4w + 30$$
$$100 = 4w$$
$$25 = w$$

The width of the region is 25 ft and the length of the region is $25 + 15 = 40$ ft.   ∎

In shopping and other daily activities, we are occasionally asked to solve problems using percents. The word *percent* means "per hundred." Thus, for example, 7% means 7 per hundred, or $\frac{7}{100}$. When $\frac{7}{100}$ is converted to a decimal number, we obtain 0.07. Thus, 7% = 0.07.

Let's look at one example involving percent. (See Section 11.1 for a more detailed discussion of percent.)

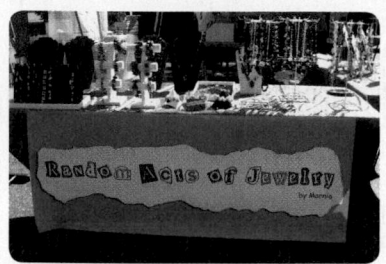

Example 4 *Craft Show*

Kim Stappenbeck is selling her homemade jewelry at a craft show. Determine the cost of a necklace before tax if the total cost of a necklace, including an 8% sales tax, is to be $34.56.

Solution We are asked to find the cost of a necklace before sales tax.

Let

$$x = \text{cost of the necklace before sales tax}$$

Then

$$0.08x = 8\% \text{ of the cost of the necklace (the sales tax)}$$

$$\text{Cost of the necklace before tax} + \text{tax on the necklace} = 34.56$$
$$x + 0.08x = 34.56$$
$$1.08x = 34.56$$
$$\frac{1.08x}{1.08} = \frac{34.56}{1.08}$$
$$x = \frac{34.56}{1.08}$$
$$x = 32$$

Thus, the cost of the necklace before tax is $32. ∎

SECTION 6.4 *Exercises*

Practice the Skills

In Exercises 1– 4, write the mathematical expression as a phrase. (There are several acceptable answers.)

1. $x + 5$ 5 more than x

2. $x - 2$ 2 less than x

3. $2x - 3$
2 times x, decreased by 3

4. $3x + 5$ 5 more than 3 times x

In Exercises 5–16, write the phrase as a mathematical expression.

5. 5 less than x $x - 5$

6. 2 more than y $y + 2$

7. 4 increased by 3 times z $4 + 3z$

8. 6 times x, decreased by 1 $6x - 1$

9. The product of 8 and w, increased by 9 $8w + 9$

10. 5 less than twice a number $2x - 5$

11. 6 more than 4 times x $4x + 6$

12. 8 increased by 5 times x $8 + 5x$

13. 12 decreased by s, divided by 4 $\frac{12 - s}{4}$

14. The sum of 8 and t, divided by 2 $\frac{8 + t}{2}$

15. Three times the sum of a number and 7 $3(x + 7)$

16. The quotient of 8 and y, decreased by 3 times x $\frac{8}{y} - 3x$

In Exercises 17–28, write an equation and solve.

17. 7 more than a number is 15. $x + 7 = 15; 8$

18. A number decreased by 3 is 8. $x - 3 = 8; 11$

19. The difference between a number and 4 is 20.
$x - 4 = 20; 24$

20. Seven multiplied by a number is 56. $7x = 56$; 8

21. Ten less than four times a number is 42. $4x - 10 = 42$; 13

22. Fourteen increased by 6 times a number is 32.
$14 + 6x = 32$; 3

23. Twelve more than 4 times a number is 32. $4x + 12 = 32$; 5

24. Eight less than 3 times a number is 6 times the number, increased by 10. $3x - 8 = 6x + 10$; -6

25. A number increased by 6 is 3 less than twice the number.
$x + 6 = 2x - 3$; 9

26. A number divided by 4 is 12 less than the number.
$\frac{x}{4} = x - 12$; 16

27. A number increased by 10 is 2 times the sum of the number and 3. $x + 10 = 2(x + 3)$; 4

28. Three times the difference of a number and 4 is 6 more than the number. $3(x - 4) = x + 6$; 9

Problem Solving

In Exercises 29–48, set up an equation that can be used to solve the problem. Solve the equation and determine the desired value(s).

29. MODELING—*Reimbursed Expenses* When sales representatives for Pfizer Pharmaceuticals drive to out-of-town meetings that require an overnight stay, they receive $150 for lodging plus $0.50 per mile driven. How many miles did Joe Kotaska drive if Pfizer reimbursed him $255 for an overnight trip? $150 + 0.50x = 255$; 210 miles

30. MODELING—*Sales Commission* Tito Sanchez receives a weekly salary of $400 at Anderson's Appliances. He also receives a 6% commission on the total dollar amount of all sales he makes. What must his total sales be in a week if he is to make a total of $790? $400 + 0.06x = 790$; $6500

31. MODELING—*Jet Skiing* At Action Water Sports of Ocean City, Maryland, the cost of renting a Jet Ski is $42 per half hour, which includes a 5% sales tax. Determine the cost of a half hour Jet Ski rental before tax.
$x + 0.05x = 42$; $40 per half hour

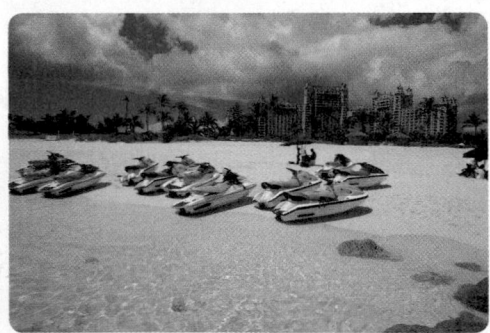

32. MODELING—*Plumbing Supplies* Home Depot has a sale offering 10% off of all plumbing supplies. If Amanda Miller spent $46.98 on plumbing supplies before tax, what was the price of the plumbing supplies she purchased before the discount? $x - 0.10x = 46.98$; $52.20

33. MODELING—*Copying* Ronnie McNeil pays 8¢ to make a copy of a page at a copy shop. She is considering purchasing a photocopy machine that is on sale for $250, including tax. How many copies would Ronnie have to make in the copy shop for her cost to equal the purchase price of the photocopy machine she is considering buying?
$0.08x = 250$; 3125 copies

34. MODELING—*Investment* Marty Faegan received an inheritance of $12,000. If he wants to invest three times as much money in stocks as in mutual funds, how much money should Marty invest in mutual funds and in stocks? $x + 3x = 12,000$; $3000 in mutual funds and $9000 in stocks

35. MODELING—*Scholarship Donation* Each year, Andrea Choi donates a total of $1000 for scholarships at Mercer County Community College. This year, she wants the amount she donates for scholarships for liberal arts to be three times the amount she donates for scholarships for business. Determine the amount she will donate for each type of scholarship. $x + 3x = 1000$; $250 for business, $750 for liberal arts

36. MODELING—*Homeowners Association* Cross Creek Townhouses Homeowners Association needs to charge each homeowner a supplemental assessment to help pay for some unexpected repairs to the townhouses. The association has $2000 in its reserve fund that it will use to help pay for the repairs. How much must the association charge each of the 50 homeowners if the total cost for the repairs is $13,350? $2000 + 50x = 13,350$; $227

37. MODELING—*Floor Area* The total floor space in three barns is 45,000 ft^2. The two smaller ones have the same area, and the largest one has three times the area of the smaller ones.

a) Determine the floor space for each barn.
$x + x + 3x = 45,000$; 9000 ft^2, 9000 ft^2, 27,000 ft^2

b) Can merchandise that takes up 8500 ft^2 of floor space fit into either of the smaller barns? Yes

38. MODELING—*Dimensions of a Deck* Jim Yuhas is building a rectangular deck and wants the length to be 3 ft greater than the width. What will be the dimensions of the deck if the perimeter is to be 54 ft?
$2w + 2(w + 3) = 54$; width: 12 ft, length: 15 ft

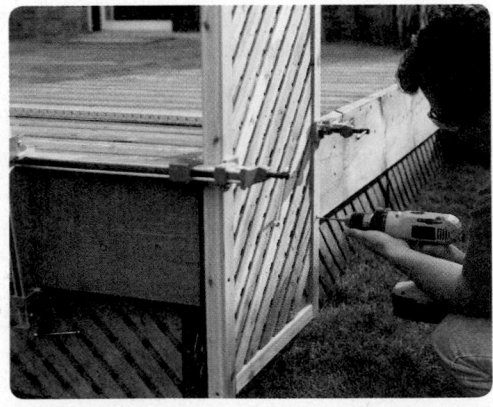

39. MODELING—*Endangered and Threatened Mammals* According to the U.S. Fish and Wildlife Service, in the United States in 2009 the number of species of endangered

mammals was 10 more than 4 times the number of species of threatened mammals. The sum of the number of species of endangered mammals and the number of species of threatened mammals was 85. Determine the number of species of endangered mammals and the number of species of threatened mammal. $x + (4x + 10) = 85$; 15 species of threatened mammals, 70 species of endangered mammals

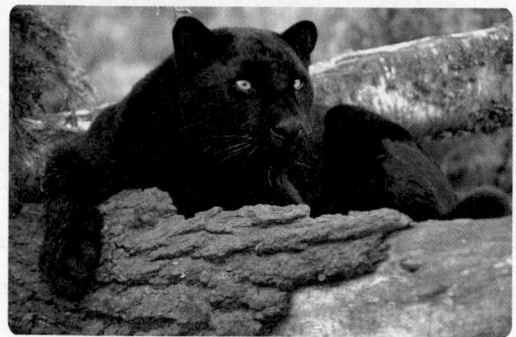

▲ *The panther is an endangered mammal.*

40. MODELING—*Counting Calories* According to *The Step Diet Book*, the number of steps it takes for a 150-lb person to burn off the calories from eating a cheeseburger and drinking a 12-oz soda is 11,040. The number of steps it takes to burn off the calories from eating a cheeseburger is 690 more than twice the number of steps it takes to burn off the calories from drinking a 12-oz soda. Determine the number of steps needed for a 150-lb person to burn off the calories from eating a cheeseburger, and from drinking a 12-oz soda. $x + (2x + 690) = 11,040$; soda: 3450 steps, cheeseburger: 7590 steps

41. MODELING—*Hurricanes* Since 1966, the total number of hurricanes formed in the Atlantic Ocean in the months of September and November is 127. The number of September hurricanes is seven more than five times the number of November hurricanes. Determine the number of hurricanes formed in September and the number of hurricanes formed in November. $x + (5x + 7) = 127$; 20 total hurricanes in November, 107 total hurricanes in September

42. MODELING—*Boat Purchase* The Nguyen's purchased a boat. If the total cost—including a 6% sales tax—was $18,232, determine the cost of the boat before tax. $x + 0.06x = 18,232$; $17,200

43. MODELING—*Enclosing Two Pens* Chuck Salvador has 140 ft of fencing in which he wants to build two connecting, adjacent square pens (see the figure). What will be the dimensions if the length of the entire enclosed region is to be twice the width? $3w + 2(2w) = 140$; width: 20 ft, length: 40 ft

44. MODELING—*Dimensions of a Bookcase* A bookcase with three shelves, as shown in the diagram on the top right, is to be built by a woodworking student. If the height of the bookcase is to be 2 ft longer than the length of a shelf and the total amount of wood to be used is 32 ft, find the dimensions of the bookcase. $4l + 2(l + 2) = 32$; length: 4 ft 8 in., height: 6 ft 8 in.

▲ *See Exercise 44*

45. MODELING—*Laundry Cost* The cost of doing the family laundry for a month at a local laundromat is $70. A new washer and dryer cost a total of $760. How many months would it take for the cost of doing the laundry at the laundromat to equal the cost of a new washer and dryer? $70x = 760$; ≈11 months

46. MODELING—*Car Antitheft System* Sandy Chang can save $92 per year off the price of her auto insurance premium by purchasing and installing a LoJack antitheft system. If the system costs $644, in how many years would the system pay for itself? $92x = 644$; 7 years

47. MODELING—*Airfare* Rachel James has been told that with her half-off airfare coupon, her airfare from New York to San Diego will be $257. The $257 includes a 7% tax *on the regular fare*. On the way to the airport, Rachel realizes that she has lost her coupon. What will her regular fare be before tax? $\frac{r}{2} + 0.07r = 257$; $450.88

48. MODELING—*Golf Membership* Malcolm Nulton has two options for membership to a golf club. Option A has an annual cost of $3300 for unlimited golf. Option B has an annual cost of $1500 plus $40 for each round of golf. How many rounds of golf would Malcolm have to play in a year for the two options to cost the same? $3300 = 1500 + 40x$; 45 rounds

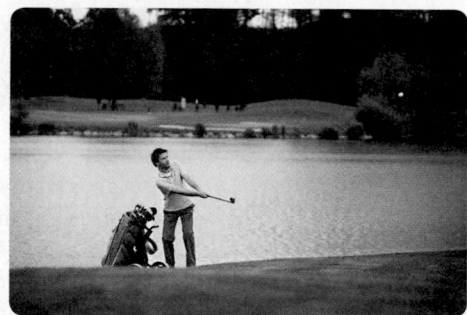

Challenge Problems/Group Activities

49. *Income Tax* Some states allow a husband and wife to file individual tax returns (on a single form) even though they have filed a joint federal tax return. It is usually to the tax-payers' advantage to do so when both husband and wife work. The smallest amount of tax owed (or the largest refund) will occur when the husband's and wife's taxable incomes are the same.

Mr. McAdams's 2011 taxable income was $34,200, and Mrs. McAdams's taxable income for that year was $36,400. The McAdams's total tax deduction for the year was $3640. This deduction can be divided between Mr. and Mrs. McAdams any way they wish. How should the $3640 be divided between them to result in each individual having the same taxable income and therefore the greatest tax refund? Deduct $720 from Mr. McAdams's income and $2920 from Mrs. McAdams's income.

50. Write each equation as a sentence. There are many correct answers.

   a) $x + 3 = 13$ A number increased by 3 is 13.

   b) $3x + 5 = 8$ 3 times a number, increased by 5 is 8.

   c) $3x - 8 = 7$ 3 times a number, decreased by 8 is 7.

51. Show that the sum of any three consecutive integers is 3 less than 3 times the largest. *

52. *Auto Insurance* A driver education course at the East Lake School of Driving costs $45 but saves those under

25 years of age 10% of their annual insurance premiums until they are 25. Dan has just turned 18, and his insurance costs $100.00 per month.

   a) When will the amount saved from insurance equal the price of the course? 4.5 months

   b) Including the cost of the course, when Dan turns 25, how much will he have saved? $795

Recreational Mathematics

53. The relationship between Fahrenheit temperature (F) and Celsius temperature (C) is shown by the formula $F = \frac{9}{5}C + 32$. At what temperature will a Fahrenheit thermometer read the same as a Celsius thermometer? −40°

*See Instructor Answer Appendix

▲ *The computer in your stereo system uses the concept of variation when it automatically balances the sound.*

Suppose you purchase a new surround sound stereo system. When you set up the system, you place a microphone at the place you typically sit when watching television. The computer within the receiver then generates a series of sounds, and automatically adjusts the volume of all the speakers in the system to give the best balance of sounds from the speakers. Because the sound you hear from each speaker is dependent on (or varies with) your distance from the speaker, the computer is using a concept called variation when activating your sound system.

Why **This is Important** As you will see by the examples in this section, variation can be used to solve a wide variety of real-life problems.

Direct Variation

Many scientific formulas are expressed as variation equations. A *variation equation* is an equation that relates one variable to one or more other variables through the operations of multiplication or division (or both operations). There are essentially four types of variation problems: direct, inverse, joint, and combined variation.

In *direct variation*, the values of the two related variables increase together or decrease together; that is, as one increases so does the other, and as one decreases so does the other.

Consider a car traveling at 40 miles an hour. The car travels 40 miles in 1 hour, 80 miles in 2 hours, and 120 miles in 3 hours. Note that, as the time increases, the distance traveled increases, and, as the time decreases, the distance traveled decreases.

The formula used to calculate distance traveled is

$$\text{Distance} = \text{rate} \cdot \text{time}$$

Since the rate is a constant 40 miles per hour, the formula can be written

$$d = 40t$$

We say that distance *varies directly* as time or that distance is *directly proportional* to time.

The preceding equation is an example of direct variation.

> **Direct Variation**
>
> If a variable y varies directly with a variable x, then
>
> $$y = kx$$
>
> where k is the **constant of proportionality** (or the variation constant).

Examples 1 through 4 illustrate direct variation.

Example 1   *Direct Variation in Electronics*

The resistance of a wire, R, varies directly as its length, L. Write an equation for the resistance of a wire, R, if the constant of proportionality is 0.008.

Solution

$$R = kL \qquad \text{R varies directly as L.}$$

$$R = 0.008L \qquad \text{Constant of proportionality, } k, \text{ is 0.008.}$$

∎

Example 2   *Direct Variation in Medicine*

The recommended dosage, d, of the antibiotic drug vancomycin is directly proportional to a person's weight, w.

a) Write this variation as an equation.

b) Find the recommended dosage, in milligrams, for Doug Kulzer, who weighs 192 lb. Assume the constant of proportionality for the dosage is 18.

Solution

a) $d = kw$

b) $d = 18(192) = 3456$

The recommended dosage for Doug Kulzer is 3456 mg.

∎

In certain variation problems, the constant of proportionality, k, may not be known. In such cases, we can often find it by substituting the given values in the variation formula and solving for k.

Example 3   *Finding the Constant of Proportionality*

Suppose w varies directly as the square of y. If w is 60 when y is 20, find the constant of proportionality.

Solution Since w varies directly as the *square of y*, we begin with the formula $w = ky^2$. Since the constant of proportionality is not given, we must find k using the given information. Substitute 60 for w and 20 for y.

$$w = ky^2$$

$$60 = k(20)^2$$

$$60 = 400k$$

$$\frac{60}{400} = \frac{400k}{400}$$

$$0.15 = k$$

Thus, the constant of proportionality is 0.15.

∎

Example 4   *Using the Constant of Proportionality*

The area, a, of a picture projected on a movie screen varies directly as the square of the distance, d, from the projector to the screen. If a projector at a distance of 25 feet projects a picture with an area of 100 square feet, what is the area of the projected picture when the projector is at a distance of 40 feet?

Solution   We begin with the formula $a = kd^2$. Since the constant of proportionality is not given, we must determine k, using the given information.

$$a = kd^2$$
$$100 = k(25)^2$$
$$100 = k(625)$$
$$\frac{100}{625} = k$$
$$0.16 = k$$

We now use $k = 0.16$ to determine a when $d = 40$.

$$a = kd^2$$
$$a = 0.16d^2$$
$$a = 0.16(40)^2$$
$$a = 0.16(1600)$$
$$a = 256 \text{ ft}^2$$

Thus, the area of a projected picture is 256 ft^2 when the projector is at a distance of 40 ft.   ∎

Inverse Variation

A second type of variation is *inverse variation*. When two quantities vary inversely, as one quantity increases the other quantity decreases, and vice versa.

To explain inverse variation, we use the formula distance = rate · time. If we solve for time, we get time = distance/rate. Assume the distance is fixed at 100 miles; then

$$\text{time} = \frac{100}{\text{rate}}$$

At 100 miles per hour, it would take 1 hour to cover this distance. At a rate of 50 miles an hour, it would take 2 hours. At a rate of 25 miles an hour, it would take 4 hours. Note that as the rate (or speed) decreases, the time increases and vice versa.

The preceding equation can be written

$$t = \frac{100}{r}$$

This equation is an example of an inverse variation equation. The time and rate are inversely proportional. The constant of proportionality in this case is 100.

> **Inverse Variation**
>
> If a variable y varies inversely with a variable x, then
>
> $$y = \frac{k}{x}$$
>
> where k is the constant of proportionality.

Two quantities *vary inversely*, or are *inversely proportional*, when as one quantity increases the other quantity decreases and vice versa. Examples 5 and 6 illustrate inverse variation.

Example **5** *Inverse Variation in Illuminance*

The illuminance, I, of a light source varies inversely as the square of the distance, d, from the source. If the illuminance is 80 units at a distance of 5 meters, determine the equation that expresses the relationship between the illuminance and the distance.

Solution Since the illuminance varies inversely as the square of the distance, the general form of the equation is

$$I = \frac{k}{d^2}$$

To determine k, we substitute the given values for I and d.

$$80 = \frac{k}{5^2}$$
$$80 = \frac{k}{25}$$
$$(80)(25) = k$$
$$2000 = k$$

Thus, the equation is $I = \dfrac{2000}{d^2}$

Example **6** *Using the Constant of Proportionality*

Suppose y varies inversely as x. If $y = 9$ when $x = 12$, determine y when $x = 4$.

Solution First write the inverse variation equation. Then solve for k.

$$y = \frac{k}{x}$$
$$9 = \frac{k}{12}$$
$$108 = k$$

Now substitute 108 for k in $y = \dfrac{k}{x}$ and determine y when $x = 4$.

$$y = \frac{108}{x} = \frac{108}{4} = 27$$

Thus, when x is 4, y is 27.

Joint Variation

One quantity may vary directly as a product of two or more other quantities. This type of variation is called *joint variation*.

Joint Variation
If a variable y varies jointly with variables x and z, then

$$y = kxz$$

where k is the constant of proportionality.

Example 7 *Joint Variation in Geometry*

The area, A, of a triangle varies jointly as its base, b, and height, h. If the area of a triangle is 48 in.^{2} when its base is 12 in. and its height is 8 in., find the area of a triangle whose base is 15 in. and whose height is 20 in.

Solution   First write the joint variation, then substitute the known values and solve for k.

$$A = kbh$$
$$48 = k(12)(8)$$
$$48 = k(96)$$
$$\frac{48}{96} = k$$
$$\tfrac{1}{2} = k$$

Now solve for the area of the given triangle.

$$A = kbh$$
$$= \tfrac{1}{2}(15)(20)$$
$$= 150 \text{ in.}^2$$

∎

Summary of Variation Equations

Direct	Inverse	Joint
$y = kx$	$y = \dfrac{k}{x}$	$y = kxz$

Combined Variation

Often in real-life situations, one variable varies as a combination of variables. The following examples illustrate the use of *combined variation*.

Example 8 *Combined Variation in Engineering*

The load, L, that a horizontal beam can safely support varies jointly as the width, w, and the square of the depth, d, and inversely as the length, l. Express L in terms of w, d, l, and the constant of proportionality, k.

Solution

$$L = \frac{kwd^2}{l}$$

∎

Example 9 *Hot Dog Price, Combined Variation*

The owners of Henrietta Hots find their weekly sales of hot dogs, S, vary directly with their advertising budget, A, and inversely with their hot dog price, P. When their advertising budget is $600 and the price of a hot dog is $1.50, they sell 5600 hot dogs a week.

a) Write a variation expressing S in terms of A and P. Include the value of the constant of proportionality.

b) Find the expected sales if the advertising budget is $800 and the hot dog price is $1.75.

Solution

a) Since S varies directly as A and inversely as P, we begin with the equation

$$S = \frac{kA}{P}$$

We now find k using the known values.

$$5600 = \frac{k(600)}{1.50}$$

$$5600 = 400k$$

$$14 = k$$

Therefore, the equation for the weekly sales of hot dogs is $S = \dfrac{14A}{P}$.

b)
$$S = \frac{14A}{P}$$

$$= \frac{14(800)}{1.75}$$

$$= 6400$$

Henrietta Hots can expect to sell 6400 hot dogs a week if the advertising budget is $800 and the hot dog price is $1.75. ∎

Example 10 Combined Variation

A varies jointly as B and C and inversely as the square of D. If $A = 1$ when $B = 9$, $C = 4$, and $D = 6$, find A when $B = 8$, $C = 12$, and $D = 5$.

Solution We begin with the equation

$$A = \frac{kBC}{D^2}$$

We must first find the constant of proportionality, k, by substituting the known values for A, B, C, and D and solving for k.

$$1 = \frac{k(9)(4)}{6^2}$$

$$1 = \frac{36k}{36}$$

$$1 = k$$

Thus, the constant of proportionality equals 1. Now we find A for the corresponding values of B, C, and D.

$$A = \frac{kBC}{D^2}$$

$$A = \frac{(1)(8)(12)}{5^2} = \frac{96}{25} = 3.84$$ ∎

Warm Up Exercises

In Exercises 1–4, fill in the blank with an appropriate word, phrase, or symbol(s).

1. When one quantity increases while the other quantity decreases, it is an example of _____ variation. Inverse

2. When the values of two related variables increase together or decrease together, it is an example of _____ variation. Direct

3. A variation equation that relates one variable to two or more other variables using the operation of multiplication is called a(n) _____ variation equation. Joint

4. In the equation $y = kx$, k is called the constant of _____. Proportionality

In Exercises 5–20, use your intuition to determine whether the variation between the indicated quantities is direct or inverse.

5. The distance between two cities on a map and the actual distance between them Direct

6. The time required to fill a pool with a hose and the volume of water coming from the hose Inverse

7. The time required to boil water on a burner and the temperature of the burner Inverse

8. A person's salary and the amount of money withheld from his or her salary for federal income taxes Direct

9. The interest earned on an investment and the interest rate Direct

10. The diameter of a hose and the volume of water coming out of the hose Direct

11. The speed of a runner and the time it takes the runner to complete a 10-kilometer race Inverse

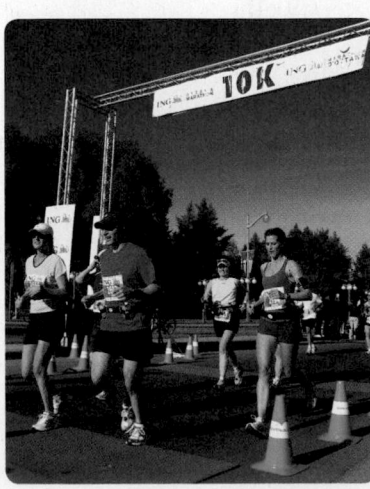

12. The time required to cool a warm room and the size of the air conditioning unit Inverse

13. The number of workers hired to install a fence and the time required to install the fence Inverse

14. The number of calories in a slice of pizza and the size of the slice Direct

15. The time required to defrost a frozen hamburger in a room and the temperature of the room Inverse

16. On Earth, the weight and mass of an object Direct

17. The number of people in line at a bank and the amount of time required for the last person to reach the teller Direct

18. The time it takes an ice cube to melt in water and the temperature of the water Inverse

19. The amount of fertilizer needed to fertilize a lawn and the area of the lawn Direct

20. The percent of light that filters through water and the depth of the water Inverse

In Exercises 21 and 22, use Exercises 5–20 as a guide.

21. Name two items that have not been mentioned in this section that vary directly. Answers will vary.

22. Name two items that have not been mentioned in this section that vary inversely. Answers will vary.

Practice the Skills

In Exercises 23–40, (a) write the variation equation and (b) determine the quantity indicated.

23. y varies directly as x. Determine y when $x = 20$ and $k = 7$. a) $y = kx$ b) 140

24. x varies inversely as y. Determine x when $y = 9$ and $k = 27$. a) $x = \frac{k}{y}$ b) 3

25. m varies inversely as the square of n. Determine m when $n = 8$ and $k = 16$. a) $m = \frac{k}{n^2}$ b) 0.25

26. r varies directly as the square of s. Determine r when $s = 2$ and $k = 13$. a) $r = ks^2$ b) 52

27. A varies directly as B and inversely as C. Determine A when $B = 5$, $C = 10$, and $k = 5$. a) $A = \frac{kB}{C}$ b) 2.5

28. M varies directly as J and inversely as C. Determine M when $J = 12$, $C = 16$, and $k = 4$. a) $M = \frac{kJ}{C}$ b) 3

29. F varies jointly as D and E. Determine F when $D = 3$, $E = 10$, and $k = 7$. a) $F = kDE$ b) 210

30. A varies jointly as R_1 and R_2 and inversely as the square of L. Determine A when $R_1 = 120$, $R_2 = 8$, $L = 5$, and $k = \frac{3}{2}$. a) $A = \frac{kR_1R_2}{L^2}$ b) 57.6

31. t varies directly as the square of d and inversely as f. If $t = 192$ when $d = 8$ and $f = 4$, determine t when $d = 10$ and $f = 6$. a) $t = \frac{kd^2}{f}$ b) 200

32. y varies directly as the square root of t and inversely as s. If $y = 12$ when $t = 36$ and $s = 2$, determine y when $t = 81$ and $s = 4$. a) $y = \frac{k\sqrt{t}}{s}$ b) 9

33. Z varies jointly as W and Y. If $Z = 12$ when $W = 9$ and $Y = 4$, determine Z when $W = 50$ and $Y = 6$. a) $Z = kWY$ b) 100

34. y varies directly as the square of R. If $y = 4$ when $R = 4$, determine y when $R = 8$. a) $y = kR^2$ b) 16

35. H varies directly as L. If $H = 12$ when $L = 40$, determine H when $L = 10$. a) $H = kL$ b) 3

36. C varies inversely as J. If $C = 7$ when $J = 0.7$, determine C when $J = 12$. a) $C = \frac{k}{J}$ b) ≈ 0.41

37. A varies directly as the square of B. If $A = 245$ when $B = 7$, determine A when $B = 12$. a) $A = kB^2$ b) 720

38. F varies jointly as M_1 and M_2 and inversely as the square of d. If $F = 20$ when $M_1 = 5$, $M_2 = 10$, and $d = 0.2$, determine F when $M_1 = 10$, $M_2 = 20$, and $d = 0.4$. a) $F = \frac{kM_1M_2}{d^2}$ b) 20

39. F varies jointly as q_1 and q_2 and inversely as the square of d. If $F = 80$ when $q_1 = 4$, $q_2 = 16$, and $d = 0.4$, determine F when $q_1 = 12$, $q_2 = 20$, and $d = 0.2$. a) $F = \frac{kq_1q_2}{d^2}$ b) 1200

40. S varies jointly as I and the square of T. If $S = 4$ when $I = 10$ and $T = 4$, determine S when $I = 4$ and $T = 6$. a) $S = kIT^2$ b) 3.6

Problem Solving

In Exercises 41–49, (a) write the variation equation and (b) determine the quantity indicated.

41. *Profit* The profit, p, from selling lawn mowers is directly proportional to n, the number of lawn mowers sold. If the profit from selling 8 lawn mowers is $600, determine the profit from selling 15 lawn mowers. a) $p = kn$ b) $1125

42. *Property Tax* The property tax, t, on a home is directly proportional to the assessed value, v, of the home. If the property tax on a home with an assessed value of $140,000 is $2100, what is the property tax on a home with an assessed value of $180,000? a) $t = kv$ b) $2700

43. *Melting an Ice Cube* The time, t, for an ice cube to melt is inversely proportional to the temperature, T, of the water in which the ice cube is placed. If it takes an ice cube 2 minutes to melt in 75°F water, how long will it take an ice cube of the same size to melt in 80°F water? a) $t = \frac{k}{T}$ b) 1.875 minutes

44. *Pressure and Volume* The volume of a gas, V, varies inversely as its pressure, P. If the volume of a gas is 6400 cubic centimeters (cc) when the pressure is 25 millimeters (mm) of mercury, determine the volume when the pressure is 200 mm of mercury. a) $V = \frac{k}{P}$ b) 800 cc

45. *Speaker Loudness* The loudness of a stereo speaker, l, measured in decibels (dB), is inversely proportional to the square of the distance, d, of the listener from the speaker. If the loudness is 20 dB when the listener is 6 ft from the speaker, what is the loudness when the listener is 3 ft from the speaker? a) $l = \frac{k}{d^2}$ b) 80 dB

46. *Distance* The distance, d, that a rock falls when dropped from a cliff varies directly as the square of time, t, the rock is falling. If a rock falls 64 feet in 2 seconds, how far will it fall in 3 seconds? a) $d = kt^2$ b) 144 ft

47. *Electrical Resistance* The electrical resistance of a wire, R, varies directly as its length, L, and inversely as its crosssectional area, A. If the resistance of a wire is 0.2 ohm when the length is 200 ft and its cross-sectional area is 0.05 in.^{2}, what is the resistance of a wire whose length is 5000 ft with a cross-sectional area of 0.01 in.^{2}? a) $R = \frac{kL}{A}$ b) 25 ohms

48. *Guitar Strings* The number of vibrations per second, v, of a guitar string varies directly as the square root of the tension, t, and inversely as the length of the string, l. If the number of vibrations per second is 5 when the tension is 225 kg and the length of the string is 0.60 m, determine

the number of vibrations per second when the tension is 196 kg and the length of the string is 0.70 m.
a) $v = \frac{k\sqrt{t}}{l}$ b) 4 vibrations per second

49. *Wattage Rating* The wattage rating of an appliance, W, varies jointly as the square of the current, I, and the resistance, R. If the wattage is 6 watts when the current is 0.2 ampere and the resistance is 150 ohms, determine the wattage when the current is 0.3 ampere and the resistance is 100 ohms. a) $W = kI^2R$ b) 9 watts

50. *Phone Calls* The number of phone calls between two cities during a given time period, N, varies directly as the populations p_1 and p_2 of the two cities and inversely to the distance, d, between them. If 100,000 calls are made between two cities 300 mi apart and the populations of the cities are 60,000 and 200,000, how many calls are made between two cities with populations of 125,000 and 175,000 that are 450 mi apart? a) $N = \frac{kp_1p_2}{d}$ b) $\approx$ 121,528 calls

Concept/Writing Exercises

51. a) If y varies directly as x and the constant of proportionality is 2, does x vary directly or inversely as y? Directly

   b) Give the new constant of proportionality as x varies directly as y. 0.5

52. a) If y varies inversely as x and the constant of proportionality is 0.3, does x vary directly or inversely as y? Inversely

   b) Give the new constant of proportionality as x varies inversely as y. Stays 0.3

53. a) Assume y varies directly as x. If x is doubled, how will it affect y? y will double.

   b) Assume y varies inversely as x. If x is doubled, how will it affect y? y will be half as large.

54. a) Assume a varies directly as b^2. If b is doubled, how will it affect a? a will be 4 times as large.

   b) Assume a varies inversely as b^2. If b is doubled, how will it affect a? a will be $\frac{1}{4}$ as large.

Challenge Problems/Group Activities

55. *Photography* An article in the magazine *Outdoor and Travel Photography* states, "If a surface is illuminated by a point-source of light, the intensity of illumination produced is inversely proportional to the square of the distance separating them. In practical terms, this means that foreground objects will be grossly overexposed if your background subject is properly exposed with a flash. Thus direct flash will not offer pleasing results if there are any intervening objects between the foreground and the subject."

   If the subject you are photographing is 4 ft from the flash and the illumination on this subject is $\frac{1}{16}$ of the light of the flash, what is the intensity of illumination on an intervening object that is 3 ft from the flash? $\frac{1}{9}$

56. *Water Cost* In a specific region of the country, the amount of a customer's water bill, W, is directly proportional to the average daily temperature for the month, T, the lawn area, A, and the square root of F, where F is the family size, and inversely proportional to the number of inches of rain, R.

   In one month, the average daily temperature is 78°F and the number of inches of rain is 5.6. If the average family of four who has a thousand square feet of lawn pays $72.00 for water for that month, estimate the water bill in the same month for the average family of six who has 1500 ft^2 of lawn. $132.27

SECTION 6.6   # Linear Inequalities

▲ *An inequality can be used to determine how many textbooks must be sold so that a bookstore's revenue is greater than its cost.*

Suppose your campus bookstore needs to determine how many textbooks for a particular course must be sold so that the bookstore's textbook revenue is greater than its cost. To determine this number, an inequality would be set up. In this section, we will discuss how to set up and how to solve an inequality.

Why *This is Important* Inequalities are used in industry in many different ways, including determining the profitability of a company.

The symbols of inequality are as follows.

Symbols of Inequality

$a < b$ means that a is less than b.
$a \leq b$ means that a is less than or equal to b.
$a > b$ means that a is greater than b.
$a \geq b$ means that a is greater than or equal to b.

An *inequality* consists of two (or more) expressions joined by an inequality sign.

Examples of inequalities

$$3 < 5, \qquad x < 2, \qquad 3x - 2 \geq 5$$

A statement of inequality can be used to indicate a set of real numbers. For example, $x < 2$ represents the set of all real numbers less than 2. Listing all these numbers is impossible, but some are $-2, -1.234, -1, -\frac{1}{2}, 0, \frac{97}{163}, 1$.

Solving Inequalities

To indicate all real numbers less than 2, we can use the number line. The number line was discussed in Chapter 5.

To indicate the solution set of $x < 2$ on the number line, we draw an open circle at 2 and a line to the left of 2 with an arrow at its end. This technique indicates that all points to the left of 2 are part of the solution set. The open circle indicates that the solution set does not include the number 2.

To indicate the solution set of $x \leq 2$ on the number line, we draw a closed (or darkened) circle at 2 and a line to the left of 2 with an arrow at its end. The closed circle indicates that the 2 is part of the solution.

Example **1** *Graphing a Less Than or Equal to Inequality*

Graph the solution set of $x \leq 1$, where x is a real number, on the number line.

Solution The numbers less than or equal to 1 are all the points on the number line to the left of 1 and 1 itself. The closed circle at 1 shows that 1 is included in the solution set.

The inequality statements $x < 2$ and $2 > x$ have the same meaning. Note that the inequality symbol points to the x in both cases. Thus, one inequality may be written in place of the other. Likewise, $x > 2$ and $2 < x$ have the same meaning. Note that the inequality symbol points to the 2 in both cases. We make use of this fact in Example 2.

Example 2 *Graphing a Less Than Inequality*

Graph the solution set of $3 < x$, where x is a real number, on the number line.

Solution We can restate $3 < x$ as $x > 3$. Both statements have identical solutions. Any number that is greater than 3 satisfies the inequality $x > 3$. The graph includes all the points to the right of 3 on the number line. To indicate that 3 is not part of the solution set, we place an open circle at 3.

We can find the solution to an inequality by adding, subtracting, multiplying, or dividing both sides of the inequality by the same number or expression. We use the procedure discussed in Section 6.2 to isolate the variable, with one important exception: ***When both sides of an inequality are multiplied or divided by a negative number, the direction of the inequality symbol is reversed.***

Example 3 *Multiplying by a Negative Number*

Solve the inequality $-x > 3$ and graph the solution set on the number line.

Solution To solve this inequality, we must eliminate the negative sign in front of the x. To do so, we multiply both sides of the inequality by -1 and change the direction of the inequality symbol.

$$-x > 3$$
$$-1(-x) < -1(3) \qquad \text{Multiply both sides of the inequality by } -1 \text{ and change the direction of the inequality symbol.}$$
$$x < -3$$

The solution set is graphed on the number line as follows.

Example 4 *Dividing by a Negative Number*

Solve the inequality $-5x < 20$ and graph the solution set on the number line.

Solution Solving the inequality requires making the coefficient of the x term 1. To do so, divide both sides of the inequality by -5 and change the direction of the inequality symbol.

$$-5x < 20$$
$$\frac{-5x}{-5} > \frac{20}{-5} \qquad \text{Divide both sides of the inequality by } -5 \text{ and change the direction of the inequality symbol.}$$
$$x > -4$$

The solution set is graphed on the number line as follows.

$x > -4$

Example 5 *Solving an Inequality*

Solve the inequality $2x + 5 > 15$ and graph the solution set on the number line.

Solution To find the solution set, isolate x on one side of the inequality symbol.

$$2x + 5 > 15$$

$$2x + 5 - 5 > 15 - 5 \quad \text{Subtract 5 from both sides of the inequality.}$$

$$2x > 10$$

$$\frac{2x}{2} > \frac{10}{2} \quad \text{Divide both sides of the inequality by 2.}$$

$$x > 5$$

Thus, the solution set to $2x + 5 > 15$ is all real numbers greater than 5.

$x > 5$

Note that in Example 5, the *direction of the inequality symbol* did not change when both sides of the inequality were divided by the positive number 2.

Example 6 *A Solution of Only Integers*

Solve the inequality $x - 1 < 3$, where x is an integer, and graph the solution set on the number line.

Solution To find the solution set, isolate x on one side of the inequality symbol.

$$x - 1 < 3$$

$$x - 1 + 1 < 3 + 1 \quad \text{Add 1 to both sides of the inequality.}$$

$$x < 4$$

Since x is an integer and is less than 4, the solution set is the set of integers less than 4, or $\{ \ldots, -2, -1, 0, 1, 2, 3 \}$. To graph the solution set, we make solid dots at the corresponding points on the number line. The ellipsis (the three dots) to the left of -3 indicate that all the integers to the left of -3 are included.

$x < 4$,
x an integer

Some linear inequalities have no solution. When solving an inequality, if you obtain a statement that is *always false*, such as $3 > 5$, the answer is *no solution*. There is no real number that makes the statement true.

Some linear inequalities have all real numbers as their solution. When solving an inequality, if you obtain a statement that is *always true*, such as $2 > 1$, the solution is *all real numbers*.

Solving Compound Inequalities

An inequality of the form $a < x < b$ is called a *compound inequality*. Consider the compound inequality $-3 < x \le 2$, which means that $-3 < x$ *and* $x \le 2$.

Example 7 *A Compound Inequality*

Graph the solution set of the inequality $-3 < x \le 2$
a) where x is an integer.   b) where x is a real number.

Solution

a) The solution set is all the integers between -3 and 2, including the 2 but not including the -3, or $\{-2, -1, 0, 1, 2\}$.

$-3 < x \le 2$,
x an integer

b) The solution set consists of all the real numbers between -3 and 2, including the 2 but not including the -3.

$-3 < x \le 2$ ■

Example 8 *Solving a Compound Inequality*

Solve the compound inequality for x and graph the solution set.

$$-4 < \frac{x+3}{2} \le 5$$

Solution To solve this compound inequality, we must isolate the x in the middle term. To do so, we use the same principles used to solve inequalities.

$$-4 < \frac{x+3}{2} \le 5$$

$$2(-4) < 2\left(\frac{x+3}{2}\right) \le 2(5) \qquad \text{Multiply each part of the inequality by 2.}$$

$$-8 < x + 3 \le 10$$

$$-8 - 3 < x + 3 - 3 \le 10 - 3 \qquad \text{Subtract 3 from each part of the inequality.}$$

$$-11 < x \le 7 \qquad\qquad\qquad\qquad\qquad ■$$

The solution set is graphed on the number line as follows.

$-11 < x \le 7$ ■

"In mathematics the art of posing problems is easier than that of solving them."

　　　　　　　Georg Cantor

Example 9 *Average Grade*

A student must have an average (the mean) on five tests that is greater than or equal to 80% but less than 90% to receive a final grade of B. Devon's grades on the first four tests were 98%, 76%, 86%, and 92%. What range of grades on the fifth test would give him a B in the course?

Solution The unknown quantity is the range of grades on the fifth test. First construct an inequality that can be used to find the range of grades on the fifth test. The average (mean) is found by adding the grades and dividing the sum by the number of tests.

Let $x =$ the fifth grade. Then

$$\text{Average} = \frac{98 + 76 + 86 + 92 + x}{5}$$

For Devon to obtain a B in this course, his average must be greater than or equal to 80 but less than 90.

$$80 \le \frac{98 + 76 + 86 + 92 + x}{5} < 90$$

$$80 \le \frac{352 + x}{5} < 90$$

$$5(80) \le \cancel{5}\left(\frac{352 + x}{\cancel{5}}\right) < 5(90) \qquad \text{Multiply the three terms of the inequality by 5.}$$

$$400 \le 352 + x < 450$$

$$400 - 352 \le 352 - 352 + x < 450 - 352 \qquad \text{Subtract 352 from all three terms.}$$

$$48 \le x < 98$$

Thus, a grade of 48% up to but not including a grade of 98% on the fifth test will result in a grade of B in this course. ∎

TIMELY TIP

Remember to change the direction of the inequality symbol when multiplying or dividing both sides of an inequality by a *negative* number.

SECTION 6.6 *Exercises*

Warm Up Exercises

In Exercises 1–8, fill in the blank with an appropriate word, phrase, or symbol(s).

1. Two or more expressions joined by an inequality sign is called a(n) _____. Inequality

2. a) $a < b$ means that a is _____ than b. Less

   b) $a > b$ means that a is _____ than b. Greater

3. An inequality of the form $a < x < b$ is called a(n) _____ inequality. Compound

4. When solving an inequality, if you obtain a statement that is always false, such as $3 > 5$, the answer is _____ solution. No

5. When solving an inequality, if you obtain a statement that is always true, such as $2 > 1$, the solution is _____ real numbers. All

6. When both sides of an inequality are multiplied or divided by a(n) _____ number, the direction of the inequality symbol is reversed. Negative

7. To indicate the solution set of $x < 5$ on the number line, we draw a(n) _____ circle at 5. Open

8. To indicate the solution set of $x \le 5$ on the number line, we draw a(n) _____ circle at 5. Closed

Practice the Skills

In Exercises 9–26, graph the solution set of the inequality, where x is a real number, on the number line.

9. $x \ge 5$ *

10. $x < 3$ *

11. $x + 7 \ge 2$ *

12. $x - 4 > -5$ *

13. $-3x \le 18$ *

14. $-4x < 12$ *

15. $\frac{x}{6} < 3$ *

16. $\frac{x}{5} > 2$ *

17. $\frac{-x}{3} \ge 3$ *

18. $\frac{-x}{2} \le -4$ *

19. $2x + 6 \ge 14$ *

20. $3x + 12 < 5x + 14$ *

21. $4(2x - 1) < 2(4x - 3)$ *

22. $-2(x - 3) \le 4x + 6$ *

23. $-1 \le x \le 3$ *

24. $-4 < x \le 1$ *

25. $2 < x - 4 \le 6$ *

26. $\frac{1}{2} < \frac{x + 4}{2} \le 4$ *

In Exercises 27–46, graph the solution set of the inequality, where x is an integer, on the number line.

27. $x > 2$ *

28. $-3 < x$ *

29. $-3x \le 27$ *

30. $3x \ge 27$ *

*See Instructor Answer Appendix

31. $x - 4 < -2$ *

32. $x + 6 > 2$ *

33. $\dfrac{x}{3} \leq -2$ *

34. $\dfrac{x}{4} \geq -3$ *

35. $-\dfrac{x}{4} \geq 2$ *

36. $\dfrac{3x}{5} \leq 3$ *

37. $-15 < -4x - 3$ *

38. $-5x - 1 < 17 - 2x$ *

39. $3(x + 4) \geq 4x + 13$ *

40. $-2(x - 1) < 3(x - 4) + 5$ *

41. $5(x + 4) - 6 \leq 2x + 8$ *

42. $-2 \leq x < 6$ *

43. $1 > -x > -6$ *

44. $-2 < 2x + 3 < 6$ *

45. $0.3 \leq \dfrac{x + 2}{10} \leq 0.5$ *

46. $-\dfrac{1}{3} < \dfrac{x - 2}{12} \leq \dfrac{1}{4}$ *

Problem Solving

47. *Indianapolis 500* The following bar graph shows the average speed, in miles per hour (mph), of the winning driver of the Indianapolis 500 for the years 2004–2010.

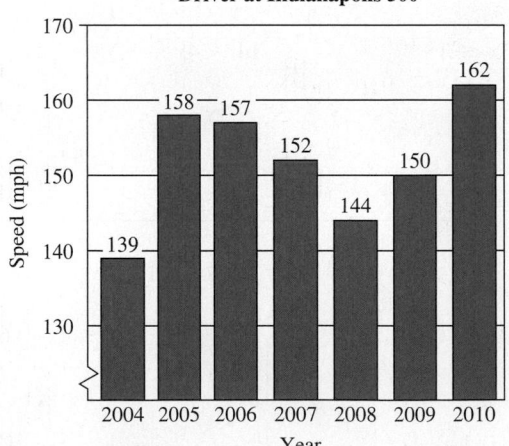

Average Speed of Winning Driver at Indianapolis 500

Source: *indianapolismotorspeedway.com*

In which years was the average speed of the winning driver

a) >150 mph? 2005, 2006, 2007, 2010

b) ≤150 mph? 2004, 2008, 2009

c) >160 mph? 2010

d) ≤140 mph? 2004

48. *Unemployment Rate* The following graph shows the unemployment rate in the United States for the years 2001–2009.

Unemployment Rate in the United States

Source: *U.S. Department of Labor*

In which years was the unemployment rate in the United States

a) > 5%
2002, 2003, 2004, 2005, 2008, 2009

b) < 5.5%
2001, 2005, 2006, 2007

c) ≥ 5.5%
2002, 2003, 2004, 2008, 2009

d) ≤ 5.0% 2001, 2006, 2007

49. *DVD Rental* Movie Mania offers two rental plans. One has an annual fee, and the other has no annual fee. The annual membership fee and the daily charge per DVD for each plan are shown in the table. Determine the maximum number of DVDs that can be rented for the no fee plan to cost less than the annual fee plan. 19 DVDs

Rental Plan	Yearly Fee	Daily Charge per DVD
Annual fee	$30	$1.49
No fee	None	$2.99

50. *Salary Plans* Bobby Exler recently accepted a sales position in Portland, Oregon. He can select between the two salary plans shown in the table. Determine the dollar amount of weekly sales that would result in Bobby earning more with Plan B than with Plan A. More than $5000

Salary Plan	Weekly Salary	Commission on Sales
Plan A	$500	6%
Plan B	$400	8%

51. *College Employment* To be eligible for financial assistance for college, Samantha Lavin can earn no more than $3200 during her summer employment. She will earn $662.50 cutting lawns. She is also earning $7.25 per hour at an evening job as a cashier at a grocery store. What is the maximum number of hours Samantha can work at the grocery store without jeopardizing her financial assistance? 350 hours

*See Instructor Answer Appendix

▲ *See Exercise 51*

52. *Anniversary* Patricia and Joe Kuby are celebrating their 75th wedding anniversary by having a party at the Diplomat Party House. They have budgeted $3000 for the party. If the party house charges a flat rate of $75 for set-up and clean-up, plus $25 per person, determine the maximum number of guests the Kubys can invite and remain within their budget. 117 guests

53. *Parking Costs* A parking garage in Richmond, Virginia, charges $1.75 for the first hour and $0.50 for each additional hour or part of an hour. What is the maximum length of time Tom Shalhoub can park in the garage if he wishes to pay no more than $4.25? 6 hours

54. *Making a Profit* For a business to realize a profit, its revenue, R, must be greater than its costs, C; that is, a profit will result only if $R > C$ (the company breaks even when $R = C$). A dry cleaning store has a weekly cost equation of $C = 0.25x + 1500$ and a weekly revenue of $R = 4x$, where x is the number of garments dry cleaned in a week. How many garments must be dry cleaned in a week for the company to make a profit? More than 400 garments

55. *Finding Velocity* The velocity, v, in feet per second, t sec after a tennis ball is projected directly upward is given by the formula $v = 84 - 32t$. How many seconds after being projected upward will the velocity be between 36 ft/sec and 68 ft/sec? $0.5 < t < 1.5$

56. *Speed Limit* The minimum speed for vehicles on a highway is 40 mph, and the maximum speed is 55 mph. If Philip Rowe has been driving nonstop along the highway for 4 hr, what range in miles could he have legally traveled? $160 \leq x \leq 220$

57. *A Grade of B* In Example 9 on page 332, what range of grades on the fifth test would result in Devon receiving a grade of B if his grades on the first four tests were 78%, 64%, 88%, and 76%? $94 \leq x \leq 100$, assuming 100 is the highest grade possible

58. *Tent Rental* The Cuhayoga Community College Planning Committee wants to rent tents for the spring job fair. Rent-a-Tent charges $325 for setup and delivery of its tents. This fee is charged regardless of the number of tents delivered and set up. In addition, Rent-a-Tent charges $125 for each tent rented. If the minimum amount the planning committee wishes to spend is $950 and the maximum amount they wish to spend is $1200, determine the minimum and maximum number of tents the committee can rent. Minimum 5, maximum 7

Challenge Problems/Group Activities

59. *Painting a House* Donovan Davis is painting the exterior of his house. The instructions on the paint can indicate that 1 gal covers from 250 to 400 ft^2. The total surface of the house to be painted is 2750 ft^2. Determine the number of gallons of paint he could use and express the answer as an inequality. $6.875 \leq x \leq 11$

60. *Final Exam* Teresa's five test grades for the semester are 86%, 78%, 68%, 92%, and 72%. Her final exam counts one-third of her final grade. What range of grades on her final exam would result in Teresa receiving a final grade of B in the course? (See Example 9.) $81.6 \leq x \leq 100$, assuming 100 is the highest grade possible

61. A student multiplied both sides of the inequality $-\frac{1}{3}x \leq 4$ by -3 and forgot to reverse the direction of the inequality symbol. What is the relation between the student's incorrect solution set and the correct solution set? Is there any number in both the correct solution set and the student's incorrect solution set? If so, what is it? The student's answer is $x \leq -12$, whereas the correct answer is $x \geq -12$. Yes, -12 is in both solution sets.

Internet/Research Activity

62. Find a newspaper or a magazine article that contains the mathematical concept of inequality.

a) From the information in the article write a statement of inequality.

b) Summarize the article and explain how you arrived at the inequality statement in part (a).

▲ *The cost of mailing a package may depend on the weight of the package.*

The profit, *p*, of a company may depend on the amount of sales, *s*. The cost, *c*, of mailing a package may depend on the weight, *w*, of the package. Real-life problems, such as these two examples, often involve two or more variables. In this section, we will discuss how to graph equations with two variables.

Why **This is Important** We see and use graphs daily. If you read a newspaper or open a magazine, you are likely to see line graphs. Also, graphs are used to display information in businesses and industry.

To be able to work with equations with two variables requires understanding the *Cartesian* (or *rectangular*) *coordinate system*, named after the French mathematician René Descartes. The rectangular coordinate system consists of two perpendicular number lines (Fig. 6.3). The horizontal line is the *x-axis*, and the vertical line is the *y-axis*. The point of intersection of the *x*-axis and *y*-axis is called the *origin*. The numbers on the axes to the right and above the origin are positive. The numbers on the axes on the left and below the origin are negative. The axes divide the plane into four parts: the first, second, third, and fourth *quadrants*.

We indicate the location of a point in the rectangular coordinate system by means of an *ordered pair* of the form (x, y). The *x*-coordinate is always placed first, and the *y*-coordinate is always placed second in the ordered pair. Consider the point illustrated in Fig. 6.4. Since the *x*-coordinate of the point is 5 and the *y*-coordinate is 3, the ordered pair that represents this point is (5, 3).

MATHEMATICS TODAY

Hollywood's Four Quadrants

A scene from the movie *Up*

Hollywood studio executives use four "quadrants" to divide up the moviegoing audience. Men 25 years and older, men younger than 25, women 25 years and older, and women younger than 25 are the age groups represented by Hollywood's four quadrants. If a studio produces a movie that appeals to all four quadrants, it is sure to have a hit movie. If the movie appeals to none of the four quadrants, the movie is sure to fail. A challenge for studio executives is to determine the core quadrant and then try to make sure no other movie geared toward the same quadrant debuts at the same time. One of the biggest hit movies of the summer of 2009 was *Up*, a movie that appealed to all four quadrants.

Figure 6.3

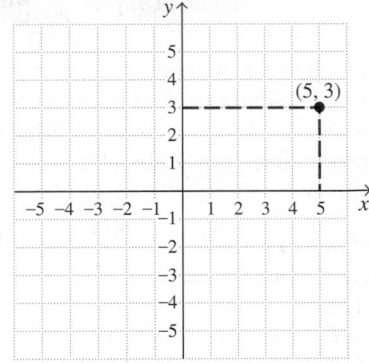

Figure 6.4

The origin is represented by the ordered pair (0, 0). Every point on the plane can be represented by one and only one ordered pair (x, y), and every ordered pair (x, y) represents one and only one point on the plane.

Example 1 *Plotting Points*

Plot the points $A(-2, 4)$, $B(-3, -1)$, $C(2, 0)$, $D(4, 2)$, and $E(0, -4)$.

Solution Point *A* has an *x*-coordinate of -2 and a *y*-coordinate of 4. Project a vertical line up from -2 on the *x*-axis and a horizontal line to the left from 4 on the

According to legend, French mathematician and philosopher René Descartes (1596–1650) did some of his best thinking in bed. He was a sickly child, and so the Jesuits who undertook his education allowed him to stay in bed each morning as long as he liked. This practice he carried into adulthood, seldom getting up before noon. One morning as he watched a fly crawl about the ceiling, near the corner of his room, he was struck with the idea that the fly's position could best be described by the connecting distances from it to the two adjacent walls. These became the coordinates of his rectangular coordinate system and were appropriately named after him (Cartesian coordinates) and not the fly.

y-axis. The two lines intersect at the point denoted *A* (Fig. 6.5). The other points are plotted in a similar manner.

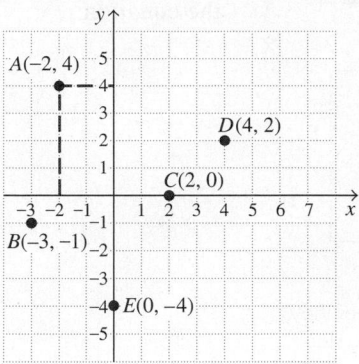

Figure 6.5

Example 2 *A Parallelogram*

The points, *A*, *B*, and *C* are three vertices of a parallelogram with two sides parallel to the *x*-axis. Plot the three points below and determine the coordinates of the fourth vertex, *D*.

$$A(1, 2) \quad B(2, 4) \quad C(7, 4)$$

Solution A parallelogram is a figure that has opposite sides that are of equal length and are parallel. (Parallel lines are two lines in the same plane that do not intersect.) The horizontal distance between points *B* and *C* is 5 units (see Fig. 6.6). Therefore, the horizontal distance between points *A* and *D* must also be 5 units. This problem has two possible solutions, as illustrated in Fig. 6.6. In each figure, we have indicated the given points in red.

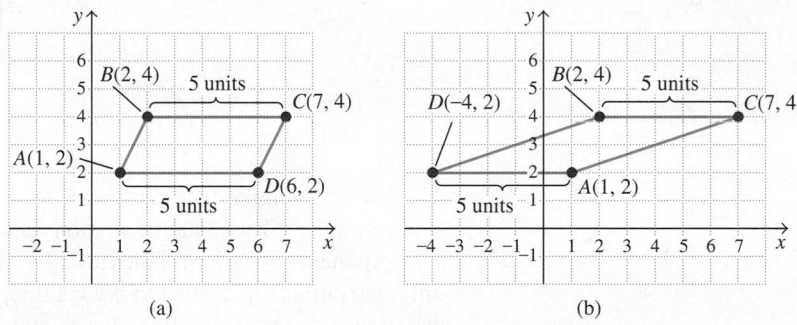

(a)   (b)

Figure 6.6

The solutions are the points (6, 2) and (−4, 2).

Graphing Linear Equations by Plotting Points

Consider the following equation in two variables: $y = x + 1$. Every ordered pair that makes the equation a true statement is a solution to, or satisfies, the equation. We can mentally find some ordered pairs that satisfy the equation $y = x + 1$ by picking some values of x and solving the equation for y. For example, suppose we let $x = 1$; then $y = 1 + 1 = 2$. The ordered pair $(1, 2)$ is a solution to the equation $y = x + 1$. We can make a chart of other ordered pairs that are solutions to the equation.

x	y	Ordered Pair
1	2	$(1, 2)$
2	3	$(2, 3)$
3	4	$(3, 4)$
4.5	5.5	$(4.5, 5.5)$
-3	-2	$(-3, -2)$

How many other ordered pairs satisfy the equation? Infinitely many ordered pairs satisfy the equation. Since we cannot list all the solutions, we show them by means of a graph. A *graph* is an illustration of all the points whose coordinates satisfy an equation.

The points $(1, 2)$, $(2, 3)$, $(3, 4)$, $(4.5, 5.5)$, and $(-3, -2)$ are plotted in Fig. 6.8. With a straightedge we can draw one line that contains all these points. This line, when extended indefinitely in either direction, passes through all the points in the plane that satisfy the equation $y = x + 1$. The arrows on the ends of the line indicate that the line extends indefinitely.

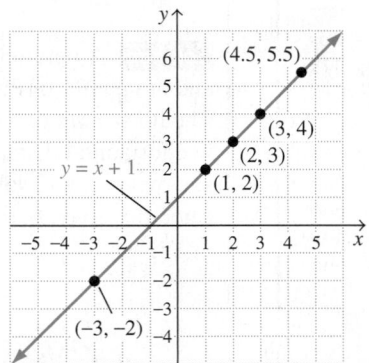

Figure 6.8

All equations of the form $ax + by = c$, $a \neq 0$ and $b \neq 0$, will be straight lines when graphed. Thus, such equations are called *linear equations in two variables*. The exponents on the variables x and y must be 1 for the equation to be linear. Since only two points are needed to draw a line, only two points are needed to graph a linear equation. It is always a good idea to plot a third point as a checkpoint. If no error has been made, all three points will be in a line, or *collinear*. One method that can be used to obtain points is to solve the equation for y, substitute values for x, and find the corresponding values of y.

Example 3 *Graphing an Equation by Plotting Points*

Graph $y = 2x + 2$.

Solution Since the equation is already solved for y, select values for x and find the corresponding values for y. The table on page 339 indicates values arbitrarily selected for x

and the corresponding values for y. The ordered pairs are $(0, 2)$, $(1, 4)$, and $(-1, 0)$. The graph is shown in Fig. 6.9.

x	y
0	2
1	4
-1	0

Figure 6.9

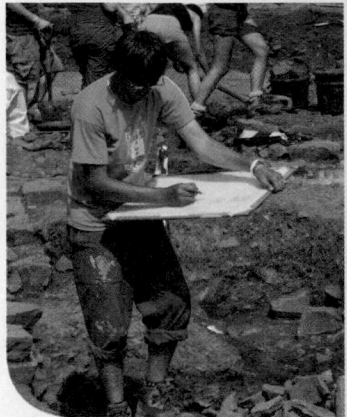

MATHEMATICS TODAY

Use of Grids

Grids have long been used in mapping. In archaeological digs, a rectangular coordinate system may be used to chart the location of each find.

Why *This is Important* Grids form the basis for plotting points when graphing equations, and also for locating cities and streets on maps.

PROCEDURE   TO GRAPH LINEAR EQUATIONS BY PLOTTING POINTS

1. Solve the equation for y.
2. Select at least three values for x and find their corresponding values of y.
3. Plot the points.
4. The points should be in a straight line. Draw a line through the set of points and place arrow tips at both ends of the line.

In Step 4 of the procedure, if the points are not in a straight line, recheck your calculations and find your error.

Graphing by Using Intercepts

Example 3 contained two special points on the graph, $(-1, 0)$ and $(0, 2)$. At these points, the line crosses the x-axis and the y-axis, respectively. The ordered pairs $(-1, 0)$ and $(0, 2)$ represent the *x-intercept* and the *y-intercept*, respectively. Another method that can be used to graph linear equations is to find the x- and y-intercepts of the graph.

PROCEDURE   FINDING THE X- AND Y-INTERCEPTS

To find the x-intercept, set $y = 0$ and solve the equation for x.

To find the y-intercept, set $x = 0$ and solve the equation for y.

A linear equation may be graphed by finding the x- and y-intercepts, plotting the intercepts, and drawing a straight line through the intercepts. When graphing by this method, you should always plot a checkpoint before drawing your graph. To obtain a checkpoint, select a nonzero value for x and find the corresponding value of y. The checkpoint should be collinear with the x- and y-intercepts.

Example 4 *Graphing an Equation by Using Intercepts*

Graph $3x + 6y = 12$ by using the x- and y-intercepts.

Solution To determine the x-intercept, set $y = 0$ and solve for x.

$$3x + 6y = 12$$
$$3x + 6(0) = 12$$
$$3x = 12$$
$$x = 4$$

The x-intercept is $(4, 0)$. To determine the y-intercept, set $x = 0$ and solve for y.

$$3x + 6y = 12$$
$$3(0) + 6y = 12$$
$$6y = 12$$
$$y = 2$$

The y-intercept is $(0, 2)$. As a checkpoint, substitute $x = 2$ and determine the corresponding value for y.

$$3x + 6y = 12$$
$$3(2) + 6y = 12$$
$$6 + 6y = 12$$
$$6y = 6$$
$$y = 1$$

The checkpoint is the ordered pair $(2, 1)$. The three points are plotted in Figure 6.10.

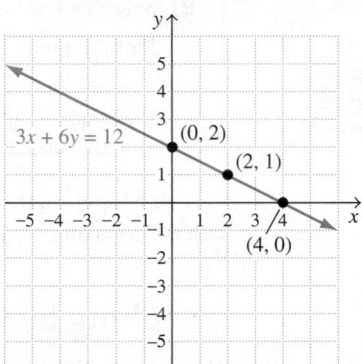

Figure 6.10

Since all three points are collinear, draw a line through the three points to obtain the graph.   ∎

Slope

Figure 6.11

Another useful concept when you are working with straight lines is slope, which is a measure of the "steepness" of a line. The *slope of a line* is a ratio of the vertical change to the horizontal change for any two points on the line. Consider Fig. 6.11. Point A has coordinates (x_1, y_1), and point B has coordinates (x_2, y_2). The vertical change between points A and B is $y_2 - y_1$. The horizontal change between points A and B is $x_2 - x_1$. Thus, the slope, which is often symbolized with the letter m, can be found as follows.

Slope of a Line

$$\textbf{Slope} = \frac{\text{vertical change}}{\text{horizontal change}}$$

$$m = \frac{y_2 - y_1}{x_2 - x_1}$$

The Greek capital letter delta, Δ, is often used to represent the words "the change in." Therefore, slope may be defined as

$$m = \frac{\Delta y}{\Delta x}$$

A line may have a positive slope, a negative slope, or a zero slope, or the slope may be undefined, as indicated in Fig. 6.12. A line with a positive slope rises from left to right, as shown in Fig. 6.12(a). A line with a negative slope falls from left to right, as shown in Fig. 6.12(b). A horizontal line, which neither rises nor falls, has a slope of zero, as shown in Fig. 6.12(c). Since a vertical line does not have any horizontal change (the x-value remains constant) and since we cannot divide by 0, the slope of a vertical line is undefined, as shown in Fig. 6.12(d).

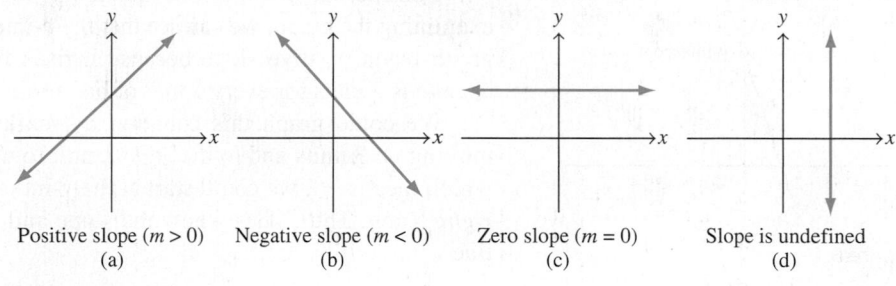

Positive slope ($m > 0$)   Negative slope ($m < 0$)   Zero slope ($m = 0$)   Slope is undefined
(a)   (b)   (c)   (d)

Figure 6.12

Example 5 *Finding the Slope of a Line*

Determine the slope of the line that passes through the points $(-1, -3)$ and $(1, 5)$.

Solution Let's begin by drawing a sketch, illustrating the points and the line. See Fig. 6.13(a).

We will let (x_1, y_1) be $(-1, -3)$ and (x_2, y_2) be $(1, 5)$. Then

$$\text{Slope} = \frac{y_2 - y_1}{x_2 - x_1} = \frac{5 - (-3)}{1 - (-1)} = \frac{5 + 3}{1 + 1} = \frac{8}{2} = \frac{4}{1} = 4$$

The slope of 4 means that there is a vertical change of 4 units for each horizontal change of 1 unit; see Fig. 6.13(b). The slope is positive, and the line rises from left to right. Note that we would have obtained the same result if we let (x_1, y_1) be $(1, 5)$ and (x_2, y_2) be $(-1, -3)$. Try this method now and see.

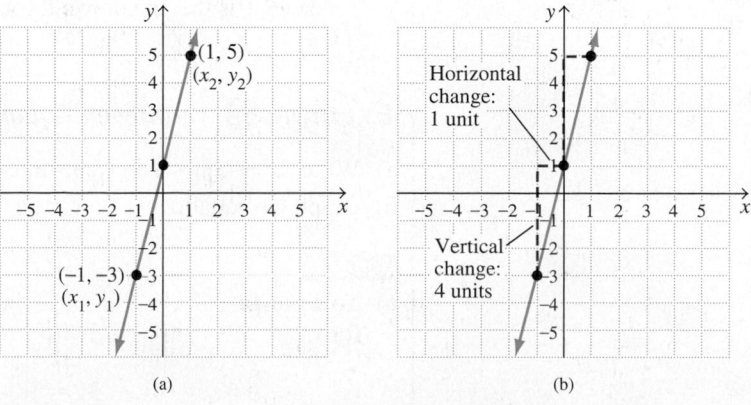

(a)   (b)

Figure 6.13

Graphing Linear Equations by Using the Slope and *y*-Intercept

A linear equation given in the form $y = mx + b$ is said to be in slope–intercept form.

> ### Slope–Intercept Form of the Equation of a Line
>
> $$y = mx + b$$
>
> where m is the slope of the line and $(0, b)$ is the y-intercept of the line.

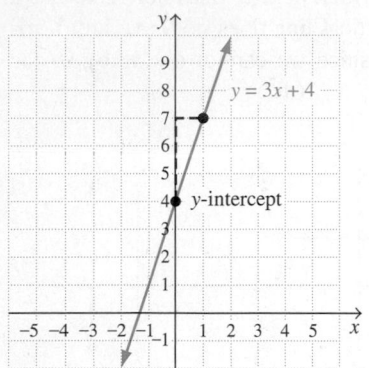

Figure 6.14

In the equation $y = mx + b$, b represents the value of y where the graph of the equation $y = mx + b$ crosses the y-axis.

Consider the graph of the equation $y = 3x + 4$, which appears in Fig. 6.14. By examining the graph, we can see that the y-intercept is $(0, 4)$. We can also see that the graph has a positive slope because it rises from left to right. Because the vertical change is 3 units for every 1 unit of horizontal change, the slope must be $\frac{3}{1}$ or 3.

We could graph this equation by marking the y-intercept at $(0, 4)$ and then moving *up* 3 units and to the *right* 1 unit to get another point. If the slope were -3, which means $\frac{-3}{1}$, we could start at the y-intercept and move *down* 3 units and to the *right* 1 unit. Thus, if we know the slope and y-intercept of a line, we can graph the line.

> **PROCEDURE**   **TO GRAPH LINEAR EQUATIONS BY USING THE SLOPE AND Y-INTERCEPT**
>
> 1. Solve the equation for y to place the equation in slope–intercept form.
> 2. Determine the slope and y-intercept from the equation.
> 3. Plot the y-intercept.
> 4. Obtain a second point using the slope.
> 5. Draw a straight line through the points.

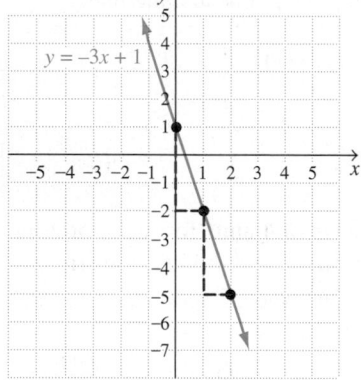

Figure 6.15

Example 6 *Graphing an Equation by Using the Slope and y-Intercept*

Graph $y = -3x + 1$ by using the slope and y-intercept.

Solution   The slope is -3 or $\frac{-3}{1}$ and the y-intercept is $(0, 1)$ (see Fig. 6.15). Plot $(0, 1)$ on the y-axis. Then plot the next point by moving *down* 3 units and to the *right* 1 unit. A third point has been plotted in the same way. The graph of $y = -3x + 1$ is the line drawn through these three points.   ■

Example 7 *Writing an Equation in Slope–Intercept Form*

a) Write $4x - 3y = 9$ in slope–intercept form.
b) Graph the equation.

Solution

a) To write $4x - 3y = 9$ in slope–intercept form, we solve the given equation for y.

$$4x - 3y = 9$$
$$4x - 4x - 3y = -4x + 9$$

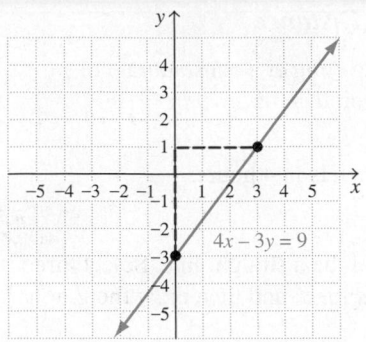

Figure 6.16

$$-3y = -4x + 9$$

$$\frac{-3y}{-3} = \frac{-4x + 9}{-3}$$

$$y = \frac{-4x}{-3} + \frac{9}{-3} \quad \text{or} \quad y = \frac{4}{3}x - 3$$

Thus, in slope–intercept form, the equation is $y = \frac{4}{3}x - 3$.

b) The y-intercept is $(0, -3)$, and the slope is $\frac{4}{3}$. Plot a point at $(0, -3)$ on the y-axis, then move *up* 4 units and to the *right* 3 units to obtain the second point (see Fig. 6.16). Draw a line through the two points. ■

Example 8 *Determining the Equation of a Line from Its Graph*

Determine the equation of the line in Fig. 6.17.

Solution If we determine the slope and the y-intercept of the line, we can write the equation using slope–intercept form, $y = mx + b$. We see from the graph that the y-intercept is $(0, 3)$; thus, $b = 3$. The slope of the line is negative because the graph falls from left to right. The change in y is 3 units for every 2-unit change in x. Thus, m, the slope of the line, is $-\frac{3}{2}$.

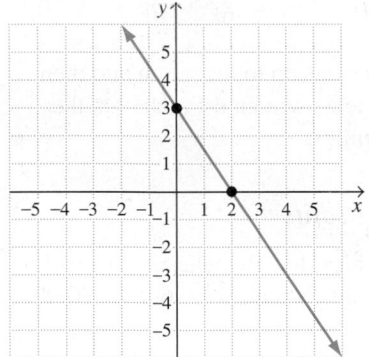

Figure 6.17

$$y = mx + b$$

$$y = -\frac{3}{2}x + 3$$

The equation of the line is $y = -\frac{3}{2}x + 3$. ■

Example 9 *Horizontal and Vertical Lines*

In the Cartesian coordinate system, graph (a) $y = 2$ and (b) $x = -3$.

Solution

a) For any value of x, the value of y is 2. Therefore, the graph will be a horizontal line through $y = 2$ (Fig. 6.18).

b) For any value of y, the value of x is -3. Therefore, the graph will be a vertical line through $x = -3$ (Fig. 6.19).

Note that the graph of $y = 2$ has a slope of 0. The slope of the graph of $x = -3$ is undefined. ■

Figure 6.18

Figure 6.19

In graphing the equations in this section, we labeled the horizontal axis the x-axis and the vertical axis the y-axis. For each equation, we can determine values for y by substituting values for x. Since the value of y depends on the value of x, we refer to y as the *dependent variable* and x as the *independent variable*. We label the *vertical axis* with the *dependent variable* and the *horizontal axis* with the *independent variable*. For the equation $C = 3n + 5$, the C is the dependent variable and n is the independent variable. Thus, to graph this equation, we label the vertical axis C and the horizontal axis n.

In many graphs, the values to be plotted on one axis are much greater than the values to be plotted on the other axis. When that occurs, we can use different scales on the horizontal and the vertical axes, as illustrated in Examples 10 and 11. The next two examples illustrate applications of graphing.

Figure 6.20

Example 10 *Using a Graph to Determine Distance*

The distance in miles, d, a car travels in t hours, traveling at a constant rate of 40 miles per hour, can be determined by the equation $d = 40t$.

a) Graph $d = 40t$, for $t \leq 6$.

b) Use the graph to estimate the distance the car travels in 4 hours.

Solution

a) Since $d = 40t$ is a linear equation, the graph will be a straight line. Select three values for t, determine the corresponding values for d, and then draw the graph (Fig 6.20).

$$d = 40t$$

			t	d
Let $t = 0$,	$d = 40(0) = 0$		0	0
Let $t = 2$,	$d = 40(2) = 80$		2	80
Let $t = 6$,	$d = 40(6) = 240$		6	240

b) By drawing a vertical line from $t = 4$ on the time axis up to the graph and then drawing a horizontal line across to the distance axis, we can estimate that the distance the car travels in 4 hours is about 160 miles.   ▪

Example 11 *Using a Graph to Determine Profits*

Javier Mungro owns a business that sells mountain bicycles. He believes the profit (or loss) from the bicycles sold can be estimated by the formula $P = 60S - 90,000$, where S is the number of bicycles sold.

a) Graph $P = 60S - 90,000$, for $S \leq 5000$ bicycles.

b) From the graph, estimate the number of bicycles that must be sold for the business to break even (Fig. 6.21).

c) From the graph, estimate the number of bicycles sold if the profit from selling bicycles is about \$150,000.

Solution

a) Select values for S and find the corresponding values of P.

S	P
0	−90,000
2000	30,000
5000	210,000

Figure 6.21

b) The break-even point is the number of bicycles that must be sold for the company to have neither a profit nor a loss. The break-even point is where the graph intercepts the horizontal, or S-axis, for that is where the profit, P, is 0. To break even, about 1500 bicycles must be sold. The actual value can be obtained by substituting 0 for P and solving the equation for S. Do this now.

c) We can estimate the answer by drawing a horizontal line from 150 on the profit axis. Since the horizontal line cuts the graph at 4000 on the S-axis, about 4000 bicycles were sold.   ▪

SECTION 6.7

Exercises

Warm Up Exercises

In Exercises 1–8, fill in the blank with an appropriate word, phrase, or symbols(s).

1. An illustration of all the points whose coordinates satisfy an equation is called a(n) _____. Graph

2. To find the *x*-intercept of the graph of a linear equation, set _____ equal to zero and solve the equation for *x*. y

3. To find the *y*-intercept of the graph of a linear equation, set _____ equal to zero and solve the equation for *y*. x

4. The ratio of the vertical change to the horizontal change for any two points on a line is called the _____ of the line. Slope

5. The three methods used to graph a linear equation given in this section are _____, _____, and _____.
   Plotting points, using intercepts, and using the slope and the *y*-intercept

6. The minimum number of points needed to graph a linear equation is _____. Two

7. In the equation $y = mx + b$, the slope of the line is represented by _____. m

8. a) The point (2, 7) is located in the _____ quadrant.
   First
   b) The point (−3, −5) is located in the _____ quadrant. Third

Practice the Skills

In Exercises 9–16, plot all the points on the same axes.

9. (3, 1) ∗   10. (−2, −4) ∗

11. (−5, −1) ∗   12. (4, 0) ∗

13. (0, 2)∗   14. (0, 0) ∗

15. (0, −5) ∗   16. $(2\frac{1}{2}, 5\frac{1}{2})$ ∗

In Exercises 17–24, plot all the points on the same axes.

17. (5, 1)∗

18. (−4, 0)∗

19. (−2, −5)∗

20. (0, −1)∗

21. (0, 2)∗

22. (−4, 5)∗

23. (4, −1)∗

24. (4.5, 3.5)∗

In Exercises 25–34 (indicated on Fig. 6.22), write the coordinates of the corresponding point.

25. (0, 2)
26. (−2, 4)
27. (−2, 0)
28. (−3, 1)
29. (−5, −3)
30. (0, −3)
31. (2, −3)
32. (4, 0)
33. (2, 2)
34. (4, 3)

Figure 6.22

In Exercises 35–42, determine which ordered pairs satisfy the given equation.

35. $x + 4y = 13$ (5, 2)   (1, 3)   (0, 5) (5, 2), (1, 3)

36. $4x − y = 4$ (0, −4)   (1, 0)   (2, −3) (0, −4), (1, 0)

37. $3x − 2y = 10$ (8, 7)   (−1, 4) $\left(\frac{10}{3}, 0\right)$ (8, 7), $\left(\frac{10}{3}, 0\right)$

38. $3y = 4x + 2$ (2, 1)   (1, 2) $\left(0, \frac{2}{3}\right)$ (1, 2), $\left(0, \frac{2}{3}\right)$

39. $6y = 3x + 6$ (1, −1),   (4, 3),   (2, 5) (4, 3)

40. $3x − 5y = −12$ (1, 3),   (−1, 2),   (−4, 0) (1, 3), (−4, 0)

41. $\frac{x}{4} + \frac{2y}{3} = 2$ (8, 0), $(1, \frac{1}{2})$,   (0, 3) (8, 0), (0, 3)

42. $\frac{x}{2} + 3y = 4$ $\left(0, \frac{4}{3}\right)$ (8, 0),   (10, −2) $\left(0, \frac{4}{3}\right)$, (8, 0)

In Exercises 43–46, graph the equation and state the slope of the line if the slope exists (see Example 9).

43. $x = 3$∗   44. $x = −2$ ∗

45. $y = 3$∗   46. $y = −4$∗

In Exercises 47–56, graph the equation by plotting points, as in Example 3.

47. $y = x + 2$ ∗   48. $y = x − 3$∗

49. $y = 3x − 1$∗   50. $y = −2x + 4$∗

51. $y + 3x = 6$∗   52. $y − 4x = 8$∗

53. $y = \frac{1}{2}x + 4$∗   54. $3y = 2x − 3$∗

55. $y = \frac{1}{3}x$∗   56. $y = −\frac{2}{3}x$∗

In Exercises 57–66, graph the equation, using the x- and y-intercepts, as in Example 4.

57. $x + y = 2$ *

58. $x - y = 4$ *

59. $2x + y = 6$ *

60. $3x - y = -6$ *

61. $2x = -4y - 8$ *

62. $y = 4x + 4$ *

63. $y = 3x + 5$ *

64. $3x + 6y = 9$ *

65. $3x - y = 5$ *

66. $6x = 3y - 9$ *

In Exercises 67–76, determine the slope of the line through the given points. If the slope is undefined, so state.

67. $(4, 7)$ and $(8, 15)$ 2

68. $(2, 3)$ and $(3, 2)$ -1

69. $(6, 5)$ and $(2, 10)$ $-\frac{5}{4}$

70. $(-5, 7)$ and $(8, 9)$ $\frac{2}{13}$

71. $(5, 1)$ and $(-3, 1)$ 0

72. $(-3, -5)$ and $(-1, -2)$ $\frac{3}{2}$

73. $(8, -3)$ and $(8, 3)$
Undefined

74. $(2, 6)$ and $(2, -3)$
Undefined

75. $(-3, -1)$ and $(8, -9)$ $-\frac{8}{11}$ **76.** $(2, 1)$ and $(-5, -9)$ $\frac{10}{7}$

In Exercises 77–86, graph the equation using the slope and y-intercept, as in Examples 6 and 7.

77. $y = x + 3$ *

78. $y = -x - 1$ *

79. $y = 3x + 1$ *

80. $y = 2x - 5$ *

81. $y = -\frac{1}{3}x + 2$ *

82. $y = \frac{1}{2}x - 2$ *

83. $7y = 4x - 7$ *

84. $3x + 2y = 6$ *

85. $3x - 2y + 6 = 0$ *

86. $3x + 4y - 8 = 0$ *

In Exercises 87–90, determine the equation of the graph.

87.

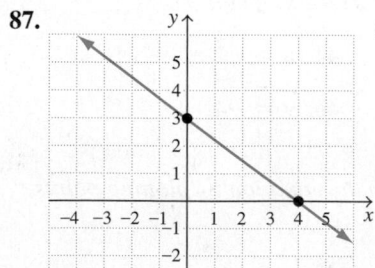

$y = -\frac{3}{4}x + 3$

88.

$y = \frac{2}{3}x + 2$

89.

$y = 3x + 2$

90.

$y = -2x + 1$

Problem Solving

In Exercises 91 and 92, points A, B, and C are three vertices of a rectangle (the points where two sides meet). Plot the three points. (a) Find the coordinates of the fourth point, D, to complete the rectangle. (b) Find the area of the rectangle; use A = lw.

91. $A(-1, 4)$, $B(4, 4)$, $C(-1, 2)$
a) $D(4, 2)$ b) $A = 10$ square units

92. $A(-4, 2)$, $B(7, 2)$, $C(7, 8)$
a) $D(-4, 8)$ b) $A = 66$ square units

In Exercises 93 and 94, points A, B, and C are three vertices of a parallelogram with sides parallel to the x-axis. Plot the three points. Find the coordinates of the fourth point, D, to complete the parallelogram. Note: There are two possible answers for point D.

93. $A(3, 2)$, $B(5, 5)$, $C(9, 5)$ $(7, 2)$ or $(-1, 2)$

94. $A(-2, 2)$, $B(3, 2)$, $C(6, -1)$ $(1, -1)$ or $(11, -1)$

In Exercises 95–98, for what value of b will the line joining the points P and Q be parallel to the indicated axis?

95. $P(2, -3)$, $Q(6, b)$;   x-axis -3

96. $P(4, 7)$, $Q(b, -2)$;   y-axis 4

97. $P(3b - 1, 5)$, $Q(8, 4)$;   y-axis 3

98. $P(-6, 2b + 3)$, $Q(7, -1)$;   x-axis -2

99. *Hanging Wallpaper* Tanisha Vizquez owns a wallpaper hanging business. Her charge, C, for hanging wallpaper is $40 plus $0.30 per square foot of wallpaper she hangs, or

*See Instructor Answer Appendix

$C = 40 + 0.30s$, where s is the number of square feet of wallpaper she hangs.

a) Graph $C = 40 + 0.30s$, for $s \le 500$. *

b) From the graph, estimate her charge if she hangs 300 square feet of wallpaper. $130

c) If her charge is $70, use the equation for C to determine how many square feet of wallpaper she hung.
   100 square feet

100. *Selling Chocolates* Ryan Stewart sells chocolate on the Internet. His monthly profit, p, in dollars, can be estimated by $p = 15n - 300$, where n is the number of dozens of chocolates he sells in a month.

   a) Graph $p = 15n - 300$, for $n \le 60$. *

   b) From the graph, estimate his profit if he sells 40 dozen chocolates in a month. $300

   c) How many dozens of chocolates must he sell in a month to break even? 20 dozens of chocolates

101. *Earning Simple Interest* When $1000 is invested in a savings account paying simple interest for a year, the interest, i, in dollars, earned can be found by the formula $i = 1000r$, where r is the rate in decimal form.

   a) Graph $i = 1000r$, for r up to and including a rate of 15%. *

   b) If the rate is 4%, what is the simple interest? $40

   c) If the rate is 6%, what is the simple interest? $60

102. *Cable Cost* The Schwimmer's cost for cable television is given by $C = 75 + 25x$, where x is the number of months of service.

   a) Graph $C = 75 + 25x$, for $x \le 50$. *

   b) From the graph, estimate the Schwimmer's cost for 30 months of cable television. $825

   c) If the Schwimmer's total cost for cable television is $975, estimate the number of months of service.
      36 months

In Exercises 103 and 104, a set of points is plotted. Also shown is a straight line through the set of points that is called the line of best fit *(or a* regression line*, as will be discussed in Chapter 13, Statistics).*

103. *Determining the Number of Defects* The top graph on the right shows the daily number of workers absent from the assembly line at J. B. Davis Corporation and

the number of defects coming off the assembly line for 8 days. (The two points indicated on the line do not represent any of the 8 days.) The line of best fit, the blue line on the graph, can be used to approximate the number of defects coming off the assembly line per day for a given number of workers absent.

a) Determine the slope of the line of best fit using the two points indicated. 2

b) Using the slope determined in part (a) and the y-intercept, $(0, 9)$, determine the equation of the line of best fit. $y = 2x + 9$

c) Using the equation you determined in part (b), determine the approximate number of defects for a day if 3 workers are absent. 15 defects

d) Using the equation you determined in part (b), approximate the number of workers absent for a day if there are 17 defects that day. 4 workers

Daily Number of Defects at J. B. Davis Corporation

104. *Determining a Test Grade* The graph below shows the hours studied and the test grades on a biology test for six students. (The two points indicated on the line do not represent any of the six students.) The line of best fit, the red line on the graph, can be used to approximate the test grade the average student receives for the number of hours he or she studies.

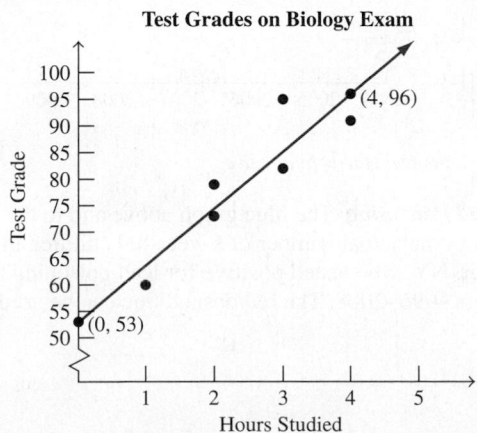

Test Grades on Biology Exam

*See Instructor Answer Appendix

a) Determine the slope of the line of best fit using the two points indicated. 10.75

b) Using the slope determined in part (a) and the y-intercept, $(0, 53)$, determine the equation of the line of best fit. $y = 10.75x + 53$

c) Using the equation you determined in part (b), determine the approximate test grade for a student who studied for 3 hours. 85.25

d) Using the equation you determined in part (b), determine the amount of time a student would need to study to receive a grade of 80 on the biology test. ≈ 2.5 hours

105. *Internet Access* The green graph shows the percentage of Americans who accessed the Internet, for the years 2004–2009. The red dashed line can be used to approximate the percentage of Americans who accessed the Internet. If we let 0 represent 2004, 1 represent 2005, and so on, then 2009 would be represented by 5. Using the ordered pairs $(0, 73.19)$ and $(5, 81.49)$,

a) determine the slope of the red dashed line. 1.66

b) determine the equation of the red dashed line, with $(0, 73.19)$ as the y-intercept. $y = 1.66x + 73.19$

c) Using the equation you determined in part (b), estimate the percentage of Americans who accessed the Internet in 2006. 76.51%

d) Using the equation you determined in part (b), determine the year in which 79.83% of Americans accessed the Internet. 4 years after 2004 or in 2008

Percentage of Americans Who Accessed the Internet

Source: *Harris Interactive*

106. *Lead Poisoning* The blue graph above and to the right shows the actual number of 6-year-old children in Rochester, NY, who tested positive for lead poisoning for the years 1996–2008. The red dashed line can be used to

approximate the number of 6-year-old children in Rochester, NY, who tested positive for lead poisoning. If we let 0 represent 1996, 1 represent 1997, and so on, then 2008 would be represented by 12. Using the ordered pairs $(0, 2747)$ and $(12, 323)$,

a) determine the slope of the red dashed line. -202

b) determine the equation of the red dashed line, with $(0, 2747)$ as the y-intercept of the graph. $y = -202x + 2747$

c) Using the equation you determined in part (b), estimate the number of 6-year-old children in Rochester, NY, who tested positive for lead poisoning in 2006. ≈ 727

d) Assuming this trend continues, use the equation you determined in part (b) to determine the year in which the number of 6-year-old children in Rochester, NY, who test positive for lead poisoning is 120. ≈ 13 years after 1996 or in 2009

Number of 6-year-olds Who Tested Positive for Lead Poisoning in Rochester, NY

Challenge Problems/Group Activities

107. a) Two lines are parallel when they do not intersect no matter how far they are extended. Explain how you can determine, without graphing the equations, whether two equations will be parallel lines when graphed.*

b) Determine whether the graphs of the equations $2x - 3y = 6$ and $4x = 6y + 6$ are parallel lines. The lines are parallel.

108. In which quadrants will the set of points that satisfy the equation $x + y = 1$ lie? Explain. Quadrants 1, 2, and 4. The graph of the line $x + y = 1$ is in quadrants 1, 2, and 4; therefore, the set of points that satisfy the equation is in these quadrants.

Internet/Research Activity

109. René Descartes is known for his contributions to algebra. Write a paper on his life and his contributions to algebra.

*See Instructor Answer Appendix

A manufacturer of gas grills needs to determine how many grills to ship to each of two stores. The manufacturer can ship at most 300 grills in total. A linear inequality in two variables can be used to represent the number of grills that can be shipped to each store. In this section, we will discuss how to solve linear inequalities in two variables.

▲ *A linear inequality in two variables may be used to represent the number of grills that can be shipped to each of two stores.*

Why *This is Important* Linear inequalities are used to express many real-life applications mathematically. Linear inequalities are also used to perform linear programming, which is a tool used in many industries.

In Section 6.6, we introduced linear inequalities in one variable. Now we will introduce linear inequalities in two variables. Some examples of linear inequalities in two variables are $2x + 3y \le 7$, $x + 7y \ge 5$, and $x - 3y < 6$.

The solution set of a linear inequality in one variable may be indicated on a number line. The solution set of a linear inequality in two variables is indicated on a coordinate plane.

An inequality that is strictly less than ($<$) or greater than ($>$) will have as its solution set a *half-plane*. A half-plane is the set of all the points on one side of a line. An inequality that is less than or equal to ($\le$) or greater than or equal to ($\ge$) will have as its solution set the set of points that consists of a half-plane and a line. To indicate that the line is part of the solution set, we draw a solid line. To indicate that the line is not part of the solution set, we draw a dashed line.

> **PROCEDURE**   **TO GRAPH LINEAR INEQUALITIES IN TWO VARIABLES**
>
> 1. Mentally substitute the equal sign for the inequality sign and plot points as if you were graphing the equation.
>
> 2. If the inequality is $<$ or $>$, draw a dashed line through the points. If the inequality is $\le$ or $\ge$, draw a solid line through the points.
>
> 3. Select a test point not on the line and substitute the x- and y-coordinates into the inequality. If the substitution results in a true statement, shade in the area on the same side of the line as the test point. If the test point results in a false statement, shade in the area on the opposite side of the line as the test point.

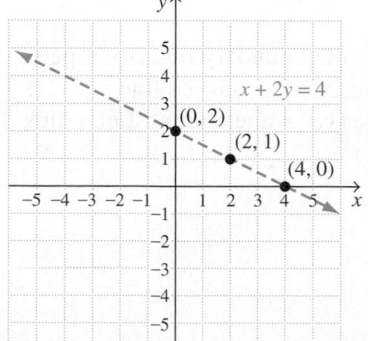

Figure 6.23

┌ **Example 1** *Graphing an Inequality*

Draw the graph of $x + 2y < 4$.

Solution To obtain the solution set, start by graphing $x + 2y = 4$. Since the original inequality is strictly "less than," draw a dashed line (Fig 6.23). The dashed line indicates that the points on the line are not part of the solution set.

The line $x + 2y = 4$ divides the plane into three parts, the line itself and two *half-planes*. The line is the boundary between the two half-planes. The points in one half-plane will satisfy the inequality $x + 2y < 4$. The points in the other half-plane will satisfy the inequality $x + 2y > 4$.

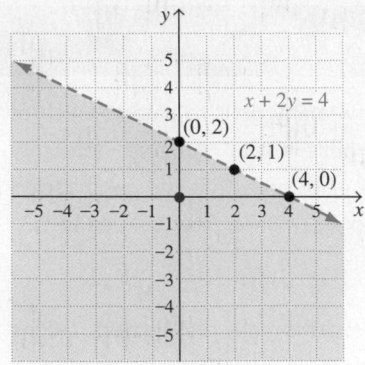

Figure 6.24

To determine the solution set to the inequality $x + 2y < 4$, pick any point on the plane that is not on the line. The simplest point to work with is the origin, $(0, 0)$. Substitute $x = 0$ and $y = 0$ into $x + 2y < 4$.

$$x + 2y < 4$$

$$\text{Is } 0 + 2(0) < 4?$$

$$0 + 0 < 4$$

$$0 < 4 \quad \text{True}$$

Since 0 is less than 4, the point $(0, 0)$ is part of the solution set. All the points on the same side of the graph of $x + 2y = 4$ as the point $(0, 0)$ are members of the solution set. We indicate that by shading the half-plane that contains $(0, 0)$. The graph is shown in Fig. 6.24. ∎

Example 2 *Graphing an Inequality*

Draw the graph of $2x - 3y \leq -6$.

Solution First draw the graph of the equation $2x - 3y = -6$. Use a solid line because the points on the boundary line are included in the solution set (see Fig. 6.25). Now pick a point that is not on the line. Take $(0, 0)$ as the test point.

$$2x - 3y \leq -6$$

$$\text{Is } 2(0) - 3(0) \leq -6?$$

$$0 \leq -6 \quad \text{False}$$

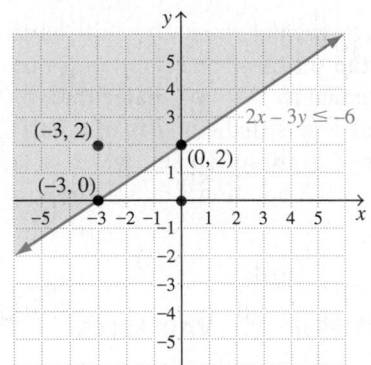

Figure 6.25

Since 0 is not less than or equal to -6 ($0 \nleq -6$), the solution set is the line and the half-plane that does not contain the point $(0, 0)$. This area is shaded in Fig. 6.25.

If you had arbitrarily selected the test point $(-3, 2)$ from the other half-plane, you would have found that the inequality would be true: $2(-3) - 3(2) \leq -6$, or $-12 \leq -6$. Because -12 is less than or equal to -6, the point $(-3, 2)$ would be in the half-plane containing the solution set. ∎

Example 3 *Graphing an Inequality*

Draw the graph of $y < x$.

Solution The inequality is strictly "less than," so the boundary line is not part of the solution set. In graphing the equation $y = x$, draw a dashed line (Fig. 6.26). Since $(0, 0)$ is *on* the line, it cannot serve as a test point. Let's pick the point $(1, -1)$.

$$y < x$$

$$-1 < 1 \quad \text{True}$$

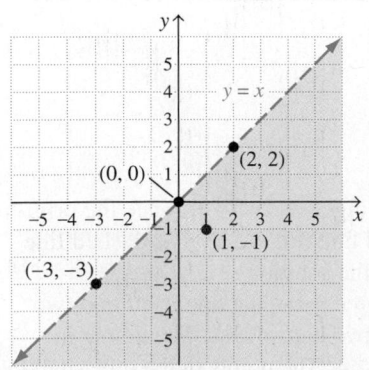

Figure 6.26

Since $-1 < 1$ is true, the solution set is the half-plane containing the point $(1, -1)$. ∎

SECTION 6.8
Exercises

Warm Up Exercises

In Exercises 1–2, fill in the blank with an appropriate word, phrase, or symbol(s).

1. The set of all points in a plane on one side of a line is called a(n) _____. Half-plane

2. a) When graphing an inequality in two variables, if the inequality contains either $<$ or $>$ use a(n) _____ line. Dashed

b) When graphing an inequality in two variables, if the inequality contains either $\leq$ or $\geq$ use a(n) _____ line. Solid

Practice the Skills

3. For each inequality, determine whether $(2, 1)$ is a solution to the inequality.

a) $4x + 2y < 10$ No

b) $4x + 2y \leq 10$ Yes

c) $4x + 2y \geq 10$ Yes

d) $4x + 2y > 10$ No

4. For each inequality, determine whether $(-2, 4)$ is a solution to the inequality.

a) $4x - 2y < -10$ Yes

b) $4x - 2y \leq -10$ Yes

c) $4x - 2y > -10$ No

d) $4x - 2y \geq -10$ No

In Exercises 5–26, draw the graph of the inequality.

5. $x \leq 2$*

6. $y \geq -1$*

7. $y > -x + 3$*

8. $y < x - 2$*

9. $y \geq 2x - 6$*

10. $y < -2x + 2$*

11. $3x - 4y > 12$*

12. $x + 2y > 4$*

13. $3x - 4y \leq 8$*

14. $4y - 3x \geq 8$*

15. $3x + 2y < 6$*

16. $-x + 2y < 2$*

17. $x + y > 0$*

18. $x + 2y \leq 0$*

19. $5x + 2y \geq 10$*

20. $y \geq -2x + 1$*

21. $y \leq 3x - 4$*

22. $3x - 2y < 12$*

23. $\frac{2}{5}x - \frac{1}{2}y \leq 1$*

24. $\frac{1}{2}x + \frac{2}{3}y \geq 1$*

25. $0.1x + 0.3y \leq 0.4$*

26. $0.2x + 0.5y \leq 0.3$*

Problem Solving

27. *Lawn Mowers* A company manufactures x walk-behind lawn mowers and y riding lawn mowers per week. The maximum number of lawn mowers the company can manufacture in a week is 25.

a) Write an inequality in two variables that represents this problem. $x + y \leq 25$

b) Graph the inequality.*

28. *Buying CDs and DVDs* Reggie Wayne is allowed to spend a maximum of $100 for purchasing x DVDs and y CDs. Each DVD costs $20, and each CD costs $10.

a) State this problem as an inequality in two variables. $20x + 10y \leq 100$

b) Graph the inequality. *

Challenge Problems/Group Activities

29. *Men's Shirts* The Tommy Hilfiger Company must ship x men's shirts to one outlet and y men's shirts to a second outlet. The maximum number of shirts the manufacturer can produce and ship is 250. We can represent this situation with the inequality $x + y \leq 250$.

a) Can x or y be negative? Explain. No, you cannot have a negative number of shirts.

b) Graph the inequality.*

c) Write one or two paragraphs interpreting the information that the graph provides. Answers will vary.

30. Which of the following inequalities have the same graph? Explain how you determined your answer.

a) $2x - y < 8$

b) $-2x + y > -8$

c) $2x - 4y < 16$

d) $y > 2x - 8$

(a), (b), and (d)

*See Instructor Answer Appendix

Solving Quadratic Equations by Using Factoring and by Using the Quadratic Formula

You are adding a brick border of uniform width around your rectangular swimming pool. If you know the surface area of the pool and the area you would like the brick border to cover, you can determine the width of the border by solving a quadratic equation. In this section, we will learn two methods that can be used to solve quadratic equations.

Why *This is Important* Quadratic equations are important in engineering, the sciences, statistics and research, and many other areas.

▲ *A quadratic equation can be used to determine the width of a border around a rectangular swimming pool.*

We begin this section by discussing binomials.

A *binomial* is an expression that contains two terms in which each exponent that appears on a variable is a whole number.

Examples of binomials

$$x + 3 \qquad x - 5$$
$$3x + 5 \qquad 4x - 2$$

To multiply two binomials, we can use the *FOIL method*. The name of the method, FOIL, is an acronym to help its users remember it as a method that obtains the products of the *F*irst, *O*uter, *I*nner, and *L*ast terms of the binomials.

$$(a + b)(c + d) = a \cdot c + a \cdot d + b \cdot c + b \cdot d$$
First   Outer   Inner   Last

After multiplying the first, outer, inner, and last terms, combine all like terms.

Example 1 *Multiplying Binomials*

Multiply $(x + 4)(x + 7)$.

Solution The FOIL method of multiplication yields

$$
\begin{aligned}
(x + 4)(x + 7) &= \overset{F}{x \cdot x} + \overset{O}{x \cdot 7} + \overset{I}{4 \cdot x} + \overset{L}{4 \cdot 7} \\
&= x^2 + 7x + 4x + 28 \\
&= x^2 + 11x + 28
\end{aligned}
$$

Note that the like terms $7x$ and $4x$ were combined to get $11x$. ∎

Example 2 *Multiplying Binomials*

Multiply $(2x + 3)(x - 1)$.

Solution

$$F \qquad O \qquad I \qquad L$$
$$(2x + 3)(x - 1) = 2x \cdot x + 2x \cdot (-1) + 3 \cdot x + 3 \cdot (-1)$$
$$= 2x^2 - 2x + 3x - 3$$
$$= 2x^2 + x - 3$$

Factoring Trinomials of the Form $x^2 + bx + c$

The expression $x^2 + 8x + 15$ is an example of a trinomial. A *trinomial* is an expression containing three terms in which each exponent that appears on a variable is a whole number.

Example 1 showed that

$$(x + 4)(x + 7) = x^2 + 11x + 28$$

Since the product of $x + 4$ and $x + 7$ is $x^2 + 11x + 28$, we say that $x + 4$ and $x + 7$ are *factors* of $x^2 + 11x + 28$. *To factor* an expression means to write the expression as a product of its factors. For example, to factor $x^2 + 11x + 28$ we write

$$x^2 + 11x + 28 = (x + 4)(x + 7)$$

Let's look at the factors more closely.

$$4 + 7 = 11$$
$$4 \cdot 7 = 28$$
$$x^2 + 11x + 28 = (x + 4)(x + 7)$$

Note that the sum of the two numbers in the factors is $4 + 7$, or 11. The 11 is the coefficient of the x-term. Also note that the product of the numbers in the two factors is $4 \cdot 7$, or 28. The 28 is the constant in the trinomial. In general, when factoring an expression of the form $x^2 + bx + c$, we need to find two numbers whose product is c and whose sum is b. When we determine the two numbers, the factors will be of the form

$$(x + \blacksquare) \ (x + \blacksquare)$$
$$\uparrow \qquad\qquad \uparrow$$
$$\text{One} \qquad \text{Other}$$
$$\text{number} \qquad \text{number}$$

Example 3 *Factoring a Trinomial*

Factor $x^2 + 6x + 8$.

Solution   We need to find two numbers whose product is 8 and whose sum is 6. Since the product is $+8$, the two numbers must both be positive or both be negative. Because the coefficient of the x-term is positive, only the positive factors of 8 need to be considered. Can you explain why? We begin by listing the positive numbers whose product is 8.

Factors of 8	Sum of Factors
1(8)	$1 + 8 = 9$
(2(4)	$2 + 4 = 6$)

Since $2 \cdot 4 = 8$ and $2 + 4 = 6$, the numbers we are seeking are 2 and 4. Thus, we write

$$x^2 + 6x + 8 = (x + 2)(x + 4)$$

Note that $(x + 4)(x - 2)$ is also an acceptable answer.

> **PROCEDURE** **TO FACTOR TRINOMIAL EXPRESSIONS OF THE FORM**
> $x^2 + bx + c$
>
> 1. Find two numbers whose product is c and whose sum is b.
>
> 2. Write factors in the form
>
> $$(x + \blacksquare) \ (x + \blacksquare)$$
> $$\uparrow \qquad \uparrow$$
> One number   Other number
> from Step 1   from Step 1
>
> 3. Check your answer by multiplying the factors using the FOIL method.

If, for example, the numbers found in Step 1 of the above procedure were 6 and -4, the factors would be written $(x + 6)(x - 4)$.

Example 4 *Factoring a Trinomial*

Factor $x^2 - 6x - 16$.

Solution We must find two numbers whose product is -16 and whose sum is -6. Begin by listing the factors of -16.

Factors of -16	Sum of Factors
$-16(1)$	$-16 + 1 = -15$
$-8(2)$	$-8 + 2 = -6$
$-4(4)$	$-4 + 4 = 0$
$-2(8)$	$-2 + 8 = 6$
$-1(16)$	$-1 + 16 = 15$

The table lists all the factors of -16. The only factors listed whose product is -16 and whose sum is -6 are -8 and 2. We listed all factors in this example so that you could see, for example, that $-8(2)$ is a different set of factors than $-2(8)$. Once you find the factors you are looking for, there is no need to go any further. The trinomial can be written in factored form as

$$x^2 - 6x - 16 = (x - 8)(x + 2) \qquad \blacksquare$$

Factoring Trinomials of the Form $ax^2 + bx + c, a \neq 1$

Now we discuss how to factor an expression of the form $ax^2 + bx + c$, where a, the coefficient of the squared term, is not equal to 1.

Consider the multiplication problem $(2x + 1)(x + 3)$.

$$(2x + 1)(x + 3) = 2x \cdot x + 2x \cdot 3 + 1 \cdot x + 1 \cdot 3$$
$$= 2x^2 + 6x + x + 3$$
$$= 2x^2 + 7x + 3$$

Since $(2x + 1)(x + 3) = 2x^2 + 7x + 3$, the factors of $2x^2 + 7x + 3$ are $2x + 1$ and $x + 3$.

Let's study the coefficients more closely.

$$\mathbf{F} = 2 \cdot 1 = 2 \quad \mathbf{O + I} = (2 \cdot 3) + (1 \cdot 1) = 7 \quad \mathbf{L} = 1 \cdot 3 = 3$$

Note that the product of the coefficient of the first terms in the multiplication of the binomials equals 2, the coefficient of the squared term. The sum of the products of the coefficients of the outer and inner terms equals 7, the coefficient of the x-term. The product of the last terms equals 3, the constant.

A procedure to factor expressions of the form $ax^2 + bx + c, a \neq 1$, follows.

PROCEDURE   **TO FACTOR TRINOMIAL EXPRESSIONS OF THE FORM** $ax^2 + bx + c, a \neq 1$

1. Write all pairs of factors of the coefficient of the squared term, a.

2. Write all pairs of factors of the constant, c.

3. Try various combinations of these factors until the sum of the products of the outer and inner terms is bx.

4. Check your answer by multiplying the factors using the FOIL method.

Example 5 *Factoring a Trinomial, a ≠ 1*

Factor $3x^2 + 17x + 10$.

Solution The only positive factors of 3 are 3 and 1. Therefore, we write

$$3x^2 + 17x + 10 = (3x \quad)(x \quad)$$

The number 10 has both positive and negative factors. However, since both the constant, 10, and the sum of the products of the outer and inner terms, 17, are positive, the two factors must be positive. Why? The positive factors of 10 are 1(10) and 2(5). The following is a list of the possible factors.

Possible Factors	Sum of Products of Outer and Inner Terms
$(3x + 1)(x + 10)$	$31x$
$(3x + 10)(x + 1)$	$13x$
$(3x + 2)(x + 5)$	$17x$ ← Correct middle term
$(3x + 5)(x + 2)$	$11x$

Thus, $3x^2 + 17x + 10 = (3x + 2)(x + 5)$.   ∎

Note that factoring problems of this type may be checked by using the FOIL method of multiplication. We will check the results to Example 5:

$$(3x + 2)(x + 5) = 3x \cdot x + 3x \cdot 5 + 2 \cdot x + 2 \cdot 5$$
$$= 3x^2 + 15x + 2x + 10$$
$$= 3x^2 + 17x + 10$$

Since we obtained the expression we started with, our factoring is correct.

Example 6 *Factoring a Trinomial, $a \neq 1$*

Factor $6x^2 - 11x - 10$.

Solution   The factors of 6 will be either $6 \cdot 1$ or $2 \cdot 3$. Therefore, the factors may be of the form $(6x \quad)(x \quad)$ or $(2x \quad)(3x \quad)$. When there is more than one set of factors for the first term, we generally try the medium-sized factors first. If that does not work, we try the other factors. Thus, we write

$$6x^2 - 11x - 10 = (2x \quad)(3x \quad)$$

The factors of -10 are $(-1)(10)$, $(1)(-10)$, $(-2)(5)$, and $(2)(-5)$. There will be eight different pairs of possible factors of the trinomial $6x^2 - 11x - 10$. Can you list them?

The correct factoring is $6x^2 - 11x - 10 = (2x - 5)(3x + 2)$.   ∎

Note that in Example 6 we first tried factors of the form $(2x \quad)(3x \quad)$. If we had not found the correct factors using them, we would have tried $(6x \quad)(x \quad)$.

Solving Quadratic Equations by Factoring

In Section 6.2, we solved linear, or first-degree, equations. In those equations, the exponent on all variables was 1. Now we deal with the *quadratic equation*. The standard form of a quadratic equation in one variable is shown in the box.

Standard Form of a Quadratic Equation

$$ax^2 + bx + c = 0, \quad a \neq 0$$

Note that in the standard form of a quadratic equation, the greatest exponent on x is 2 and the right side of the equation is equal to zero. *To solve a quadratic equation* means to find the value or values that make the equation true. In this section, we will solve quadratic equations by factoring and by the quadratic formula.

To solve a quadratic equation by factoring, set one side of the equation equal to 0 and then use the *zero-factor* property.

Zero-Factor Property

$$\text{If } a \cdot b = 0, \text{ then } a = 0 \text{ or } b = 0.$$

The zero-factor property indicates that if the product of two factors is 0, then one (or both) of the factors must have a value of 0.

Example 7 *Using the Zero-Factor Property*

Solve the equation $(x + 5)(x - 4) = 0$.

Solution   When we use the zero-factor property, either $(x + 5)$ or $(x - 4)$ must equal 0 for the product to equal 0. Thus, we set each individual factor equal to 0 and solve each resulting equation for x.

$$(x + 5)(x - 4) = 0$$
$$x + 5 = 0 \quad \text{or} \quad x - 4 = 0$$
$$x = -5 \qquad\qquad x = 4$$

Thus, the solutions are -5 and 4.

CHECK:

$$x = -5$$

$$(x + 5)(x - 4) = 0$$
$$(-5 + 5)(-5 - 4) = 0$$
$$0(-9) = 0$$
$$0 = 0 \quad \text{True}$$

$$x = 4$$

$$(x + 5)(x - 4) = 0$$
$$(4 + 5)(4 - 4) = 0$$
$$(9)(0) = 0$$
$$0 = 0 \quad \text{True} \quad \blacksquare$$

PROCEDURE   TO SOLVE A QUADRATIC EQUATION BY FACTORING

1. Use the addition or subtraction property to make one side of the equation equal to 0.
2. Factor the side of the equation not equal to 0.
3. Use the zero-factor property to solve the equation.

Examples 8 and 9 illustrate this procedure.

Example 8 *Solving a Quadratic Equation by Factoring*

Solve the equation $x^2 - 8x = -15$.

Solution   First add 15 to both sides of the equation to make the right-hand side of the equation equal to 0.

$$x^2 - 8x = -15$$
$$x^2 - 8x + 15 = -15 + 15$$
$$x^2 - 8x + 15 = 0$$

Factor the left-hand side of the equation. The object is to find two numbers whose product is 15 and whose sum is -8. Since the product of the numbers is positive and the sum of the numbers is negative, the two numbers must both be negative. The numbers are -3 and -5. Note that $(-3)(-5) = 15$ and $-3 + (-5) = -8$.

$$x^2 - 8x + 15 = 0$$
$$(x - 3)(x - 5) = 0$$

Now use the zero-factor property to find the solution.

$$x - 3 - 0 \qquad \text{or} \qquad x - 5 = 0$$
$$x = 3 \qquad\qquad\qquad x = 5$$

The solutions are 3 and 5. $\blacksquare$

Example 9 *Solving a Quadratic Equation by Factoring*

Solve the equation $3x^2 - 7x - 6 = 0$.

Solution $3x^2 - 7x - 6$ factors into $(3x + 2)(x - 3)$. Thus, we write

$$3x^2 - 7x - 6 = 0$$
$$(3x + 2)(x - 3) = 0$$
$$3x + 2 = 0 \qquad \text{or} \qquad x - 3 = 0$$
$$3x = -2 \qquad\qquad\qquad x = 3$$
$$x = -\frac{2}{3}$$

The solutions are $-\frac{2}{3}$ and 3. $\blacksquare$

TIMELY TIP

As stated on page 355, every factoring problem can be checked by multiplying the factors. If you have factored correctly, the product of the factors will be identical to the original expression that was factored. If we wished to check the factoring of Example 9, we would multiply $(3x + 2)(x - 3)$. Since the product of the factors is $3x^2 - 7x - 6$, which is the expression we started with, our factoring is correct.

Did You Know?

The Mathematics of Motion

The free fall of an object is something that has interested scientists and mathematicians for centuries. It is described by a quadratic equation. Shown here is a time-lapse photo that shows the free fall of a ball in equal time intervals. What you see can be described verbally this way: The rate of change in velocity in each interval is the same; therefore, velocity is continuously increasing and acceleration is constant.

Solving Quadratic Equations by Using the Quadratic Formula

Not all quadratic equations can be solved by factoring. When a quadratic equation cannot be easily solved by factoring, we can solve the equation with the *quadratic formula*. The quadratic formula can be used to solve any quadratic equation.

Quadratic Formula

For a quadratic equation in standard form, $ax^2 + bx + c = 0, a \neq 0$, the quadratic formula is

$$x = \frac{-b \pm \sqrt{b^2 - 4ac}}{2a}$$

In the quadratic formula, the plus or minus symbol, $\pm$, is used. If, for example, $x = 2 \pm 3$, then $x = 2 + 3 = 5$ or $x = 2 - 3 = -1$.

It is possible for a quadratic equation to have no real solution. In solving an equation, if the radicand (the expression inside the square root) is a negative number, the quadratic equation has *no real solution*.

To use the quadratic formula, first write the quadratic equation in standard form. Then determine the values for a (the coefficient of the squared term), b (the coefficient of the x term), and c (the constant). Finally, substitute the values of a, b, and c into the quadratic formula and evaluate the expression.

Example 10   *Solving a Quadratic Equation by Using the Quadratic Formula*

Solve the equation $x^2 - 5x - 14 = 0$ by using the quadratic formula.

Solution In this equation, $a = 1$, $b = -5$, and $c = -14$.

$$x = \frac{-b \pm \sqrt{b^2 - 4ac}}{2a} = \frac{-(-5) \pm \sqrt{(-5)^2 - 4(1)(-14)}}{2(1)}$$

$$= \frac{5 \pm \sqrt{25 + 56}}{2}$$

$$= \frac{5 \pm \sqrt{81}}{2}$$

$$= \frac{5 \pm 9}{2}$$

$$\frac{5 + 9}{2} = \frac{14}{2} = 7 \quad \text{or} \quad \frac{5 - 9}{2} = \frac{-4}{2} = -2$$

The solutions are 7 and −2.   ∎

Note that Example 10 can also be solved by factoring. We suggest you do so now.

Example 11   *Irrational Solutions to a Quadratic Equation*

Solve $4x^2 - 8x = -1$ by using the quadratic formula.

Solution Begin by writing the equation in standard form by adding 1 to both sides of the equation, which gives the following.

$$4x^2 - 8x + 1 = 0$$

$$a = 4, \qquad b = -8, \qquad c = 1$$

$$x = \frac{-b \pm \sqrt{b^2 - 4ac}}{2a} = \frac{-(-8) \pm \sqrt{(-8)^2 - 4(4)(1)}}{2(4)}$$

$$= \frac{8 \pm \sqrt{64 - 16}}{8}$$

$$= \frac{8 \pm \sqrt{48}}{8}$$

Since $\sqrt{48} = \sqrt{16}\sqrt{3} = 4\sqrt{3}$ (see Section 5.4), we write

$$\frac{8 \pm \sqrt{48}}{8} = \frac{8 \pm 4\sqrt{3}}{8} = \frac{\overset{1}{\cancel{4}}(2 \pm \sqrt{3})}{\underset{2}{\cancel{8}}} = \frac{2 \pm \sqrt{3}}{2}$$

The solutions are $\dfrac{2 + \sqrt{3}}{2}$ and $\dfrac{2 - \sqrt{3}}{2}$. ∎

Note that the solutions to Example 11 are irrational numbers.

Example 12 *Brick Border*

Diane Cecero and her husband recently installed an inground rectangular swimming pool measuring 40 ft by 30 ft. They want to add a brick border of uniform width around all sides of the pool. How wide can they make the brick border if they purchased enough brick to cover an area of 296 ft²?

Solution Let's make a diagram of the pool and the brick border (Fig. 6.27). Let $x =$ the uniform width of the brick border. Then the total length of the larger rectangular area, the pool plus the border, is $2x + 40$. The total width of the larger rectangular area is $2x + 30$.

The area of the brick border can be found by subtracting the area of the pool from the area of the pool plus the brick border.

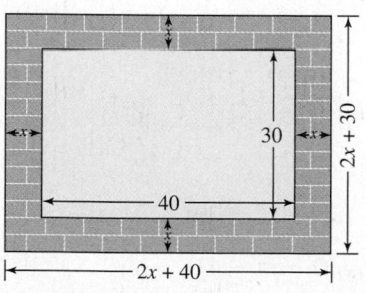

Figure 6.27

$$\text{Area of pool} = l \cdot w = (40)(30) = 1200 \text{ ft}^2$$

$$\text{Area of pool plus brick border} = l \cdot w = (2x + 40)(2x + 30)$$

$$= 4x^2 + 140x + 1200$$

$$\text{Area of the brick border} = \text{area of pool plus brick border} - \text{area of pool}$$

$$= (4x^2 + 140x + 1200) - 1200$$

$$= 4x^2 + 140x$$

The area of the brick border must be 296 ft². Therefore,

$$296 = 4x^2 + 140x$$

or

$$4x^2 + 140x - 296 = 0$$

$$4(x^2 + 35x - 74) = 0 \quad \text{Factor out 4 from each term.}$$

$$\frac{\cancel{4}}{\cancel{4}}(x^2 + 35x - 74) = \frac{0}{4} \quad \text{Divide both sides of the equation by 4.}$$

$$x^2 + 35x - 74 = 0$$

$$(x + 37)(x - 2) = 0 \quad \text{Factor trinomial.}$$

$$x + 37 = 0 \quad \text{or} \quad x - 2 = 0$$

$$x = -37 \qquad\qquad x = 2$$

Since lengths are positive, the only possible answer is $x = 2$. Thus, they can make a brick border 2 ft wide all around the pool.   ■

SECTION 6.9
Exercises

Warm Up Exercises

In Exercises 1–6, fill in the blank with an appropriate word, phrase, or symbol(s).

1. An expression that contains two terms in which each exponent that appears on a variable is a whole number is called a(n) _____. Binomial

2. An expression that contains three terms in which each exponent that appears on a variable is a whole number is called a(n) _____. Trinomial

3. When multiplying two binomials, a method that obtains the products of the first, outer, inner, and last terms is called the _____ method. FOIL

4. The property that indicates that if the product of two factors is 0, then one or both of the factors must have a value of 0 is called the _____ property. Zero-factor

5. When a quadratic equation cannot be easily solved by factoring, the equation can be solved using the _____ formula. Quadratic

6. For a quadratic equation in standard form $ax^2 + bx + c = 0, a \neq 0$, the quadratic formula is _____. $x = \frac{-b \pm \sqrt{b^2 - 4ac}}{2a}$

Practice the Skills

In Exercises 7–22, factor the trinomial. If the trinomial cannot be factored, so state.

7. $x^2 + 7x + 12$
$(x + 4)(x + 3)$

8. $x^2 + 6x + 8$
$(x + 4)(x + 2)$

9. $x^2 + x - 2$
$(x + 2)(x - 1)$

10. $x^2 + 2x - 3$
$(x + 3)(x - 1)$

11. $x^2 + 2x - 24$
$(x + 6)(x - 4)$

12. $x^2 - 6x + 8$
$(x - 4)(x - 2)$

13. $x^2 - 2x - 3$
$(x + 1)(x - 3)$

14. $x^2 - 5x - 6$
$(x - 6)(x + 1)$

15. $x^2 - 9x + 18$
$(x - 6)(x - 3)$

16. $x^2 - x - 30$
$(x + 5)(x - 6)$

17. $x^2 - 16$
$(x - 4)(x + 4)$

18. $x^2 - 64$
$(x - 8)(x + 8)$

19. $x^2 + 3x - 28$
$(x + 7)(x - 4)$

20. $x^2 + 4x - 32$
$(x - 4)(x + 8)$

21. $x^2 + 2x - 63$
$(x + 9)(x - 7)$

22. $x^2 - 2x - 48$
$(x + 6)(x - 8)$

In Exercises 23–34, factor the trinomial. If the trinomial cannot be factored, so state.

23. $2x^2 - 5x - 3$
$(2x + 1)(x - 3)$

24. $3x^2 - 13x + 4$
$(3x - 1)(x - 4)$

25. $5x^2 + 16x + 3$
$(5x + 1)(x + 3)$

26. $2x^2 - 3x - 20$
$(2x + 5)(x - 4)$

27. $5x^2 + 12x + 4$
$(5x + 2)(x + 2)$

28. $2x^2 - 9x + 10$
$(2x - 5)(x - 2)$

29. $4x^2 + 11x + 6$
$(4x + 3)(x + 2)$

30. $4x^2 + 20x + 21$
$(2x + 7)(2x + 3)$

31. $4x^2 - 11x + 6$
$(4x - 3)(x - 2)$

32. $6x^2 - 11x + 4$
$(3x - 4)(2x - 1)$

33. $8x^2 - 2x - 3$
$(4x - 3)(2x + 1)$

34. $6x^2 - 13x + 2$
$(6x - 1)(x - 2)$

In Exercises 35–38, solve each equation, using the zero-factor property.

35. $(x - 7)(x + 2) = 0$ $7, -2$

36. $(2x + 1)(x + 2) = 0$ $-\frac{1}{2}, -2$

37. $(3x + 4)(2x - 1) = 0$ $-\frac{4}{3}, \frac{1}{2}$

38. $(x - 6)(5x - 4) = 0$ $6, \frac{4}{5}$

In Exercises 39–58, solve each equation by factoring.

39. $x^2 + 10x + 21 = 0$ ₋₇, ₋₃

40. $x^2 + x - 20 = 0$ ₋₅, ₄

41. $x^2 - 9x + 8 = 0$ 8, 1

42. $x^2 - 12x + 35 = 0$ 7, 5

43. $x^2 - 15 = 2x$ 5, ₋3

44. $x^2 - 7x = -6$ 6, 1

45. $x^2 = 4x - 3$ 3, 1

46. $x^2 - 13x + 40 = 0$ 5, 8

47. $x^2 - 81 = 0$ 9, ₋9

48. $x^2 - 64 = 0$ 8, ₋8

49. $x^2 + 5x - 36 = 0$ ₋9, 4

50. $x^2 + 12x + 20 = 0$ ₋10, ₋2

51. $3x^2 + 10x = 8$ $\frac{2}{3}$, ₋4

52. $3x^2 - 5x = 2$ ₋$\frac{1}{3}$, 2

53. $5x^2 + 11x = -2$ ₋$\frac{1}{5}$, ₋2

54. $2x^2 = -5x + 3$ $\frac{1}{2}$, ₋3

55. $3x^2 - 4x = -1$ $\frac{1}{3}$, 1

56. $5x^2 + 16x + 12 = 0$ ₋$\frac{6}{5}$, ₋2

57. $6x^2 - 19x + 3 = 0$ $\frac{1}{6}$, 3

58. $4x^2 + x - 3 = 0$ $\frac{3}{4}$, ₋1

In Exercises 59–78, solve the equation, using the quadratic formula. If the equation has no real solution, so state.

59. $x^2 + 2x - 8 = 0$ ₋4, 2

60. $x^2 + 12x + 27 = 0$ ₋9, ₋3

61. $x^2 - 3x - 18 = 0$ 6, ₋3

62. $x^2 - 6x - 16 = 0$ 8, ₋2

63. $x^2 - 8x = 9$ 9, ₋1

64. $x^2 = -8x + 15$ $-4 \pm \sqrt{31}$

65. $x^2 - 2x + 3 = 0$ No real solution

66. $2x^2 - x - 3 = 0$ $\frac{3}{2}$, ₋1

67. $x^2 - 4x + 2 = 0$ $2 \pm \sqrt{2}$

68. $2x^2 - 5x - 2 = 0$ $\frac{5 \pm \sqrt{41}}{4}$

69. $3x^2 - 8x + 1 = 0$ $\frac{4 \pm \sqrt{13}}{3}$

70. $2x^2 + 4x + 1 = 0$ $\frac{-2 \pm \sqrt{2}}{2}$

71. $3x^2 - 6x - 5 = 0$ $\frac{3 \pm 2\sqrt{6}}{3}$

72. $4x^2 - 5x - 3 = 0$ $\frac{5 \pm \sqrt{73}}{8}$

73. $2x^2 + 7x + 5 = 0$ ₋1, ₋$\frac{5}{2}$

74. $3x^2 - 10x + 7 = 0$ $\frac{7}{3}$, 1

75. $3x^2 = 9x - 5$ $\frac{9 \pm \sqrt{21}}{6}$

76. $4x^2 + 7x - 1 = 0$ $\frac{-7 \pm \sqrt{65}}{8}$

77. $4x^2 + 6x = -5$ No real solution

78. $5x^2 - 4x = -2$ No real solution

Challenge Problems/Group Activities

79. *Flower Garden* Karen and Kurt Ohliger's backyard has a width of 20 meters and a length of 30 meters. Karen and Kurt want to put a rectangular flower garden in the middle of the backyard, leaving a strip of grass of uniform width around all sides of the flower garden. If they want to have 336 square meters of grass, what will be the width and length of the garden? Width = 12 m, length = 22 m

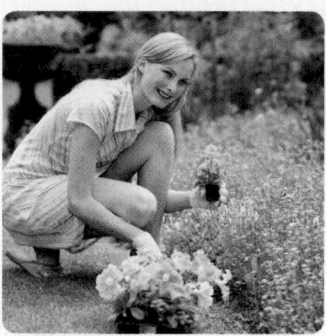

80. *Height of a Ball* A ball is projected upward from the ground. Its height h, above ground, in feet, can be determined by the equation

$$h = -16t^2 + 128t$$

where t is the number of seconds after the ball is projected. After how many seconds will the ball be 256 ft above ground? 4 seconds

81. a) Explain why solving $(x - 4)(x - 7) = 6$ by setting each factor equal to 6 is not correct. The zero-factor property cannot be used.

b) Determine the correct solution to $(x - 4)(x - 7) = 6$. $\frac{11 \pm \sqrt{33}}{2}$

82. The radicand in the quadratic formula, $b^2 - 4ac$, is called the *discriminant*. How many real number solutions will the quadratic equation have if the discriminant is (a) greater than 0, (b) equal to 0, or (c) less than zero? Explain your answer. a) Two   b) One   c) None

83. Write an equation that has solutions -1 and 3. $x^2 - 2x - 3 = 0$, other answers are possible

Internet/Research Activities

84. Italian mathematician Girolamo Cardano (1501–1576) is recognized for his skill in solving equations. Write a paper about his life and his contributions to mathematics, in particular his contribution to solving equations.

85. Chinese mathematician Foo Ling Awong, who lived during the Pong dynasty, developed a technique, other than trial and error, to factor trinomials of the form $ax^2 + bx + c, a \neq 1$. Write a paper about his life and his contributions to mathematics, in particular his technique for factoring trinomials in the form $ax^2 + bx + c, a \neq 1$. (References include history of mathematics books, encyclopedias, and the Internet.)

▲ *The relationship between the number of songs purchased from iTunes and the cost is an example of a function.*

Assume that purchasing a song from iTunes costs $1.29. Thus, purchasing one song costs 1 × $1.29, purchasing two songs costs 2 × $1.29 = $2.58, purchasing three songs costs 3 × $1.29 = $3.87, and so on. In this section we will discuss the relationships between two quantities, such as the number of songs purchased from iTunes and the cost of the songs.

Why **This is Important** Determining the relationship between two quantities is useful in many ways in real-life situations, from exchanging foreign currencies to many aspects of building a house. Functions, which we discuss in this section, express the relationship between two quantities. The concept of function is one of the most important concepts in mathematics.

*R*elations and *functions* are both extremely important mathematical concepts that we will introduce in this section. A *relation* is any set of ordered pairs. Every graph is a set of ordered pairs. Therefore, any graph will be a relation. We can indicate the relation between the number of songs purchased and the cost of the songs discussed in the section opening paragraph in a table of values.

Number of Songs	Cost
0	0.00
1	1.29
2	2.58
3	3.87
⋮	⋮
10	12.90
⋮	⋮

In general, the cost for purchasing n songs will be $1.29 times the number of songs, or $1.29n$ dollars. We can represent the cost, c, of n songs by the equation $c = 1.29n$. Since the value of c depends on the value of n, we refer to c as the *dependent variable* and n as the *independent variable*. *Note that for each value of the independent variable, n, there is one and only one value of the dependent variable, c.* An equation such as $c = 1.29n$ is called a *function*. In the equation $c = 1.29n$, the value of c depends on the value of n, so we say that "c is a function of n."

Definition: Function
A **function** is a special type of relation where each value of the independent variable corresponds to a unique value of the dependent variable.

The set of values that can be used for the independent variable is called the *domain* of the function, and the resulting set of values obtained for the dependent variable is called the *range*. The domain and range for the function $c = 1.29n$ are illustrated in Fig. 6.28 on page 363.

When we graphed equations of the form $ax + by = c$ in Section 6.7, we found that they were straight lines. For example, the graph of $y = 2x - 1$ is illustrated in Fig. 6.29 on page 363.

Figure 6.28

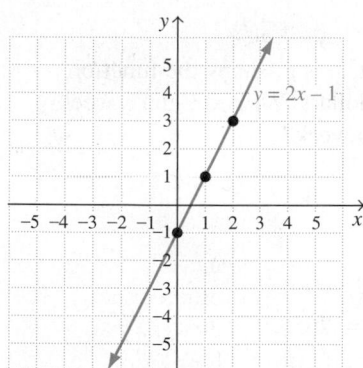

Figure 6.29

Is the equation $y = 2x - 1$ a function? To answer this question, we must ask, Does each value of x correspond to a unique value of y? The answer is yes; therefore, this equation is a function.

For the equation $y = 2x - 1$, we say that "y is a function of x" and write $y = f(x)$. The notation $f(x)$ is read "f of x." When we are given an equation that is a function, we may replace the y in the equation with $f(x)$ because $f(x)$ represents y. Thus, $y = 2x - 1$ may be written $f(x) = 2x - 1$.

To evaluate a function for a specific value of x, replace each x in the function with the given value, then evaluate. For example, to evaluate $f(x) = 2x - 1$ when $x = 8$, we do the following.

$$f(x) = 2x - 1$$
$$f(8) = 2(8) - 1 = 16 - 1 = 15$$

Thus, $f(8) = 15$. Since $f(x) = y$, when $x = 8, y = 15$. What is the domain and range of $f(x) = 2x - 1$? Because x can be any real number, the domain is the set of real numbers, symbolized $\mathbb{R}$; The range is also $\mathbb{R}$.

We can determine whether a graph represents a function by using the *vertical line test*: If a vertical line can be drawn so that it intersects the graph at more than one point, then each value of x does not have a unique value of y and the graph does not represent a function. If a vertical line cannot be made to intersect the graph in at least two different places, then the graph represents a function.

Example 1 *Using the Vertical Line Test*

Use the vertical line test to determine which of the graphs in Figure 6.30 represent functions.

Figure 6.30

Solution (a), (b), and (c) represent functions, but (d) does not.

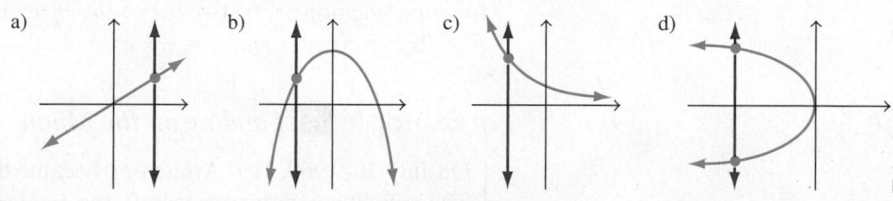

There are many real-life applications of functions. In fact, all the applications illustrated in Sections 6.2 through 6.4 are functions.

In this section, we will discuss three types of functions: linear functions, quadratic functions, and exponential functions.

Linear Functions

In Section 6.7, we graphed linear equations. The graph of any linear equation of the form $y = ax + b$ will pass the vertical line test, and so equations of the form $y = ax + b$ are *linear functions*. If we wished, we could write the linear function as $f(x) = ax + b$ since $f(x)$ means the same as y.

Example 2 *Salary as a Linear Function*

Celia Boroso's weekly salary as a real estate agent, s, is given by the function $s(x) = 100 + 0.03x$, where x is weekly sales, in dollars. What is Celia's weekly salary if she sells one house for $85,000 in a given week?

Solution Substitute 85,000 for x in the function.

$$s(x) = 100 + 0.03x$$
$$s(85,000) = 100 + 0.03(85,000)$$
$$= 100 + 2550 = 2650$$

Thus, if Celia sells one house for $85,000 in a given week, her salary for that week will be $2650. ∎

Graphs of Linear Functions

The graphs of linear functions are straight lines that will pass the vertical line test. In Section 6.7, we discussed how to graph linear equations. Linear functions can be graphed by plotting points, by using intercepts, or by using the slope and y-intercept.

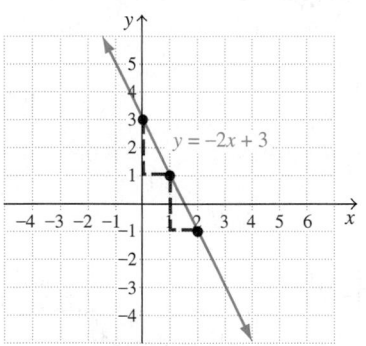

Figure 6.31

Example 3 *Graphing a Linear Function*

Graph $f(x) = -2x + 3$ by using the slope and y-intercept.

Solution Since $f(x)$ means the same as y, we can rewrite this function as $y = -2x + 3$. From Section 6.7, we know that the slope is -2 and the y-intercept is $(0, 3)$. Plot $(0, 3)$ on the y-axis. Then plot the next point by moving *down* 2 units and to the *right* 1 unit (see Fig. 6.31). A third point has been plotted in the same way. The graph of $f(x) = -2x + 3$ is the line drawn through these three points. ∎

Quadratic Functions

The standard form of a quadratic equation is $y = ax^2 + bx + c, a \neq 0$. We will learn shortly that graphs of equations of this form always pass the vertical line test and are functions. Therefore, equations of the form $y = ax^2 + bx + c, a \neq 0$, may be referred to as *quadratic functions*. We may express quadratic functions using function notation as $f(x) = ax^2 + bx + c$. Two examples of quadratic functions are $y = 2x^2 + 5x - 7$ and $y = -\frac{1}{2}x^2 + 4$.

Example 4 *Landing on the Moon*

On July 20, 1969, Neil Armstrong became the first person to walk on the moon. The velocity, v, of his spacecraft, the *Eagle*, in meters per second, was a function of time before touchdown, t, given by

$$v = f(t) = 3.2t + 0.45$$

The height of the spacecraft, h, above the moon's surface, in meters, was also a function of time before touchdown, given by

$$h = g(t) = 1.6t^2 + 0.45t$$

What was the velocity of the spacecraft and its distance from the surface of the moon

a) at 3 seconds before touchdown?   b) at touchdown (0 seconds)?

Solution

a) $v = f(t) = 3.2t + 0.45,$ $h = g(t) = 1.6t^2 + 0.45t$
   $\qquad f(3) = 3.2(3) + 0.45$ $\qquad g(3) = 1.6(3)^2 + 0.45(3)$
   $\qquad\quad = 9.6 + 0.45$ $\qquad\qquad = 1.6(9) + 1.35$
   $\qquad\quad = 10.05$ $\qquad\qquad = 14.4 + 1.35$
   $\qquad\qquad\qquad\qquad\qquad\qquad\qquad = 15.75$

The velocity 3 seconds before touchdown was 10.05 meters per second, and the height 3 seconds before touchdown was 15.75 meters.

b) $v = f(t) = 3.2t + 0.45,$ $h = g(t) = 1.6t^2 + 0.45t$
   $\qquad f(0) = 3.2(0) + 0.45$ $\qquad g(0) = 1.6(0)^2 + 0.45(0)$
   $\qquad\quad = 0 + 0.45$ $\qquad\qquad = 0 + 0$
   $\qquad\quad = 0.45$ $\qquad\qquad = 0$

The touchdown velocity was 0.45 meter per second. At touchdown, the *Eagle* is on the moon, and the distance from the surface of the moon is therefore 0 meter. ■

Graphs of Quadratic Functions

The graph of every quadratic function is a *parabola*. Two parabolas are illustrated in Fig. 6.32. Note that both graphs represent functions since they pass the vertical line test. A parabola opens upward when the coefficient of the squared term, a, is greater than 0, as shown in Figure 6.32(a). A parabola opens downward when the coefficient of the squared term, a, is less than 0, as shown in Fig. 6.32(b).

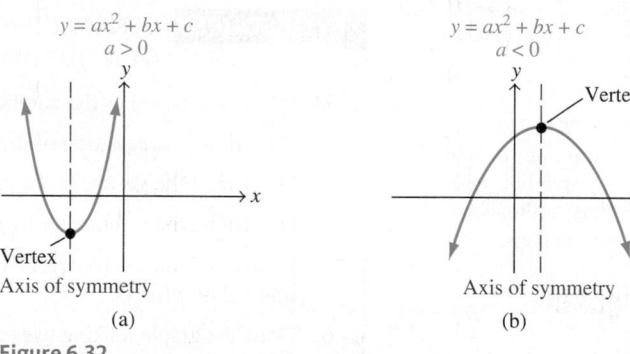

Figure 6.32

The *vertex* of a parabola is the lowest point on a parabola that opens upward and the highest point on a parabola that opens downward. Every parabola is *symmetric* with respect to a vertical line through its vertex. This line is called the *axis of symmetry* of the parabola.

Axis of Symmetry of a Parabola

The axis of symmetry of the graph of an equation of the form $y = ax^2 + bx + c$ can be determined by the following formula.

$$x = \frac{-b}{2a}$$

This formula also gives the x-coordinate of the vertex of a parabola.

Once the x-coordinate of the vertex has been determined, the y-coordinate can be found by substituting the value found for the x-coordinate into the quadratic equation and evaluating the equation. This procedure is illustrated in Example 5.

Example 5 *Describing the Graph of a Quadratic Equation*

Consider the equation $y = -2x^2 + 12x - 10$.

a) Determine whether the graph will be a parabola that opens upward or downward.

b) Determine the equation of the axis of symmetry of the parabola.

c) Determine the vertex of the parabola.

Solution

a) Since $a = -2$, which is less than 0, the parabola opens downward.

b) To find the axis of symmetry, we use the equation $x = -\frac{b}{2a}$. In the equation $y = -2x^2 + 12x - 10$, $a = -2$, $b = 12$, and $c = -10$, so

$$x = \frac{-b}{2a} = \frac{-(12)}{2(-2)} = \frac{-12}{-4} = 3$$

The equation of the axis of symmetry is $x = 3$.

c) The x-coordinate of the vertex is 3 from part (b). To find the y-coordinate, we substitute 3 for x in the equation and then evaluate.

$$\begin{aligned} y &= -2x^2 + 12x - 10 \\ &= -2(3)^2 + 12(3) - 10 \\ &= -2(9) + 36 - 10 \\ &= -18 + 36 - 10 \\ &= 8 \end{aligned}$$

Therefore, the vertex of the parabola is located at the ordered pair $(3, 8)$ on the graph. ∎

PROCEDURE   **GENERAL PROCEDURE TO SKETCH THE GRAPH OF A QUADRATIC EQUATION**

1. Determine whether the parabola opens upward or downward.

2. Determine the equation of the axis of symmetry.

3. Determine the vertex of the parabola.

4. Determine the y-intercept by substituting $x = 0$ into the equation.

5. Determine the x-intercepts (if they exist) by substituting $y = 0$ into the equation and solving for x.

6. Draw the graph, making use of the information gained in Steps 1 through 5. Remember that the parabola will be symmetric with respect to the axis of symmetry.

In Step 5, you may use either factoring or the quadratic formula to determine the x-intercepts.

Example 6 *Graphing a Quadratic Equation*

Sketch the graph of the equation $y = x^2 - 6x + 8$.

Solution We follow the steps outlined in the general procedure.

1. Since $a = 1$, which is greater than 0, the parabola opens upward.

2. Axis of symmetry: $x = \frac{-b}{2a} = \frac{-(-6)}{2(1)} = \frac{6}{2} = 3$

Thus, the axis of symmetry is $x = 3$.

3. y-coordinate of vertex:

$$y = x^2 - 6x + 8$$
$$= (3)^2 - 6(3) + 8 = 9 - 18 + 8 = -1$$

Thus, the vertex is at $(3, -1)$.

4. y-intercept:

$$y = x^2 - 6x + 8$$
$$y = (0)^2 - 6(0) + 8 = 8$$

Thus, the y-intercept is at $(0, 8)$.

5. x-intercepts:

$$0 = x^2 - 6x + 8, \text{ or } x^2 - 6x + 8 = 0$$

We can solve this equation by factoring.

$$x^2 - 6x + 8 = 0$$
$$(x - 4)(x - 2) = 0$$
$$x - 4 = 0 \quad \text{or} \quad x - 2 = 0$$
$$x = 4 \qquad\qquad x = 2$$

Thus, the x-intercepts are $(4, 0)$ and $(2, 0)$.

6. Plot the vertex $(3, -1)$, the y-intercept $(0, 8)$, and the x-intercepts $(4, 0)$ and $(2, 0)$. Then sketch the graph (Fig. 6.33).   ■

Figure 6.33

Note that the domain of the graph in Example 6, the possible x-values, is the set of all real numbers, $\mathbb{R}$. The range, the possible y-values, is the set of all real numbers greater than or equal to -1. When graphing parabolas, if you think you need additional points to graph the equation, you can always substitute values for x and find the corresponding values of y and plot those points. For example, if you substituted 1 for x, the corresponding value of y is 3. Thus, you could plot the point $(1, 3)$.

Example 7 *Domain and Range of a Quadratic Function*

a) Sketch the graph of the function $f(x) = -2x^2 + 3x + 4$.

b) Determine the domain and range of the function.

Solution

a) Since $f(x)$ means y, we can replace $f(x)$ with y to obtain $y = -2x^2 + 3x + 4$. Now graph $y = -2x^2 + 3x + 4$ using the steps outlined in the general procedure.

1. Since $a = -2$, which is less than 0, the parabola opens downward.

2. Axis of symmetry:

$$x = \frac{-b}{2a} = \frac{-(3)}{2(-2)} = \frac{-3}{-4} = \frac{3}{4}$$

Thus, the axis of symmetry is $x = \frac{3}{4}$.

3. y-coordinate of vertex:

$$y = -2x^2 + 3x + 4$$
$$= -2\left(\frac{3}{4}\right)^2 + 3\left(\frac{3}{4}\right) + 4$$
$$= -2\left(\frac{9}{16}\right) + \frac{9}{4} + 4$$
$$= -\frac{9}{8} + \frac{9}{4} + 4$$
$$= -\frac{9}{8} + \frac{18}{8} + \frac{32}{8} = \frac{41}{8} \quad \text{or} \quad 5\frac{1}{8}$$

Thus, the vertex is at $\left(\frac{3}{4}, 5\frac{1}{8}\right)$.

A ny golfer knows that a golf ball will arch in the same path going down as it did going up. Early gunners knew it, too. To hit a distant target, the cannon barrel was pointed skyward, not directly at the target. A cannonball fired at a 45° angle will travel the greatest horizontal distance. What the golfer and gunner alike were allowing for is the effect of gravity on a projectile. Projectile motion follows a parabolic path. Galileo was neither a gunner nor a golfer, but he gave us the formula that effectively describes that motion and the distance traveled by an object if it is projected at a specific angle with a specific initial velocity.

4. y-intercept: $y = -2x^2 + 3x + 4$
$$= -2(0)^2 + 3(0) + 4 = 4$$

Thus, the y-intercept is $(0, 4)$.

5. x-intercepts: $y = -2x^2 + 3x + 4$
$$0 = -2x^2 + 3x + 4 \quad \text{or} \quad -2x^2 + 3x + 4 = 0$$

This equation cannot be factored, so we will use the quadratic formula to solve it.

$$a = -2, \quad b = 3, \quad c = 4$$

$$x = \frac{-b \pm \sqrt{b^2 - 4ac}}{2a}$$

$$= \frac{-3 \pm \sqrt{3^2 - 4(-2)(4)}}{2(-2)}$$

$$= \frac{-3 \pm \sqrt{9 + 32}}{-4}$$

$$= \frac{-3 \pm \sqrt{41}}{-4}$$

Since $\sqrt{41} \approx 6.4$,

$$x \approx \frac{-3 + 6.4}{-4} \approx \frac{3.4}{-4} \approx -0.85 \quad \text{or} \quad x \approx \frac{-3 - 6.4}{-4} \approx \frac{-9.4}{-4} \approx 2.35$$

Thus, the x-intercepts are about $(-0.85, 0)$ and $(2.35, 0)$.

6. Plot the vertex $\left(\frac{3}{4}, 5\frac{1}{8}\right)$, the y-intercept $(0, 4)$, and the x-intercepts $(-0.85, 0)$ and $(2.35, 0)$. Then sketch the graph (Fig. 6.34).

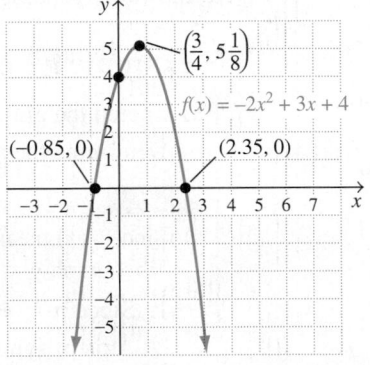

Figure 6.34

b) The domain, the values that can be used for x, is the set of all real numbers, $\mathbb{R}$. The range, the values of y, is $y \leq 5\frac{1}{8}$. ∎

When we use the quadratic formula to find the x-intercepts of a graph, if the radicand, $b^2 - 4ac$, is a negative number, the graph has no x-intercepts. The graph will lie totally above or below the x-axis.

Exponential Functions

Many real-life problems, including population growth, growth of bacteria, and decay of radioactive substances, increase or decrease at a very rapid rate. For example, the graph in Fig. 6.35 on page 369 shows the growth of the world population. Notice how the graph is increasing rapidly. This is an example in which the graph is increasing *exponentially*. The equation of a graph that increases or decreases exponentially is called an *exponential equation* or an *exponential function*. An exponential equation or exponential function is of the form $y = a^x$ or $f(x) = a^x$, where in both cases $a > 0, a \neq 1$. When graphing exponential functions we often use the form $y = a^x$, and when working with applications we often use the form $f(x) = a^x$. However, since $y = f(x)$, we can use either form to represent exponential functions.

Source: *U.S. Census Bureau*

Figure 6.35

In an exponential function, letters other than x and y may be used for the variables. The following are examples of exponential functions: $f(x) = 2^x$, $A(r) = \left(\frac{1}{2}\right)^r$ and $P(t) = 2.3^t$. Note in exponential functions that the *variable is the exponent* of some positive constant that is not equal to 1. In many real-life applications, the variable t will be used to represent time. Problems involving exponential functions can be evaluated much more easily if you use a calculator containing a $\boxed{y^x}$, $\boxed{x^y}$, or $\boxed{\wedge}$ key.

The following function, referred to as the *exponential growth* or *decay formula*, is used to solve many real-life problems.

Exponential Growth or Decay Formula

$$P(t) = P_0 a^{kt}, \qquad a > 0, \quad a \neq 1$$

In the formula, P_0 represents the original amount present, $P(t)$ represents the amount present after t years, and a and k are constants.

When $k > 0$, $P(t)$ increases as t increases and we have exponential growth. When $k < 0$, $P(t)$ decreases as t increases and we have exponential decay.

Example 8 *Using an Exponential Decay Formula*

Carbon dating is used by scientists to find the age of fossils, bones, and other items. The formula used in carbon dating is

$$P(t) = P_0 2^{-t/5600}$$

where P_0 represents the original amount of carbon 14 (C_{14}) present and $P(t)$ represents the amount of C_{14} present after t years. If 10 mg of C_{14} is present in an animal bone recently excavated, how many milligrams will be present in 3000 years?

Solution Substituting the values in the formula gives

$$
\begin{aligned}
P(t) &= P_0 2^{-t/5600} \\
&= 10(2)^{-3000/5600} \\
&\approx 10(2)^{-0.54} \qquad \text{(Recall that } \approx \text{ means "is approximately equal to.")} \\
&\approx 10(0.69) \\
&\approx 6.9 \text{ mg}
\end{aligned}
$$

Thus, in 3000 years, approximately 6.9 mg of the original 10 mg of C_{14} will remain. ∎

In Example 8, we used a calculator to evaluate $(2)^{-3000/5600}$. The steps used to find this quantity on a calculator with a $\boxed{y^x}$ key are

$$2 \boxed{y^x} \boxed{(} 3000 \boxed{+/-} \boxed{\div} 5600 \boxed{)} \boxed{=} .6898170602$$

After the $\boxed{=}$ key is pressed, the calculator displays the answer 0.6898170602. To evaluate $10(2)^{-3000/5600}$ on a scientific calculator, we can press the following keys.

$$10 \boxed{\times} 2 \boxed{y^x} \boxed{(} 3000 \boxed{+/-} \boxed{\div} 5600 \boxed{)} \boxed{=} 6.898170602$$

Notice that the answer obtained using the calculator steps shown above is a little more accurate than the answer we gave when we rounded the values before the final answer in Example 8.

Natural Exponential Functions

When the a in the exponential function $f(x) = a^x$ is replaced with a very special letter e, we get the *natural exponential function* $f(x) = e^x$. The exponential growth or decay formula is $P(t) = P_o a^{kt}$. Replacing the letter a with the letter e in the exponential growth or decay formula leads us to the *natural exponential growth or decay formula*,

> ### Natural Exponential Growth or Decay Formula
>
> $$P(t) = P_0 e^{kt} \quad a > 0, \quad a \neq 1$$

The letter e represents an irrational number called the natural base whose value is approximately 2.7183. The number e plays an important role in mathematics and is used in finding the solution to many application problems.

To evaluate $e^{0.0116(8)}$ on a calculator, as will be needed in Example 9, press[*]

$$\boxed{(} .0116 \boxed{\times} 8 \boxed{)} \boxed{inv} \boxed{ln} = 1.097242265$$

↗   ↖

Inverse   Natural
key   logarithm
key

After the $\boxed{ln}$ key is pressed, the calculator displays the answer 1.097242265.
To evaluate $7,882,590 e^{0.0116(8)}$ on a calculator, press

$$7882590 \boxed{\times} \boxed{(} .0116 \boxed{\times} 8 \boxed{)} \boxed{inv} \boxed{ln} \boxed{=} 8649110.905$$

In this calculation, after the $\boxed{=}$ key is pressed, the calculator displays the answer 8649110.905. This calculation will be used in Example 9.

Example 9 *Evaluating an Exponential Growth Function*

The population of Virginia is growing exponentially at the rate of about 1.16% per year. In 2009, the population of Virginia was about 7,882,590. Virginia's expected population, t years after 2009, is given by the formula $P(t) = 7,882,590 e^{0.0116t}$. Assuming that the population continues to grow at the same rate, determine the expected population of Virginia in 2017.

---

[*]Keys to press may vary on some calculators.

MATHEMATICS TODAY

Population Growth

Population growth during certain time periods can be described by an exponential function. Whether it is a population of bacteria, fish, flowers, or people, the same general trend emerges: a period of rapid (exponential) growth, which is then followed by a leveling-off period.

Why *This is Important* Knowing the population growth rate helps government agencies determine the number of people for whom they will need to provide future services.

Solution Since 2017 is 8 years after 2009, $t = 8$.

$$P(t) = 7{,}882{,}590e^{0.0116t}$$
$$P(7) = 7{,}882{,}590e^{0.0116(8)}$$
$$= 7{,}882{,}590e^{0.0928}$$
$$\approx 7{,}882{,}590(1.097242265)$$
$$\approx 8{,}649{,}110.905$$

Thus, in 2017, the population of Virginia is expected to be about 8,649,111 people. ∎

Example 10 *Evaluating an Exponential Decay Function*

Plutonium, a radioactive material used in most nuclear reactors, decays exponentially at a rate of 0.003% per year. If there are originally 2000 grams of plutonium, the amount of plutonium, P, remaining after t years is $P(t) = 2000e^{-0.00003t}$. How much plutonium will remain after 50 years?

Solution Substitute 50 years for t in the function, then evaluate using a calculator as described in Section 6.3.

$$P(t) = 2000e^{-0.00003t}$$
$$P(50) = 2000e^{-0.00003(50)}$$
$$= 2000e^{-0.0015}$$
$$\approx 2000(0.9985011244)$$
$$\approx 1997.0 \text{ grams}$$

Thus, after 50 years, the amount of plutonium remaining will be about 1997 grams. ∎

Graphs of Exponential Functions

What does the graph of an *exponential function* of the form $y = a^x$, $a > 0$, $a \neq 1$, look like? Examples 11 and 12 illustrate graphs of exponential functions.

Example 11 *Graphing an Exponential Function with a Base Greater Than 1*

a) Graph $y = 2^x$.

b) Determine the domain and range of the function.

Solution

a) Substitute values for x and find the corresponding values of y. The graph is shown in Fig. 6.36.

$$y = 2^x$$

$$x = -3, \qquad y = 2^{-3} = \frac{1}{2^3} = \frac{1}{8}$$

$$x = -2, \qquad y = 2^{-2} = \frac{1}{2^2} = \frac{1}{4}$$

$$x = -1, \qquad y = 2^{-1} = \frac{1}{2^1} = \frac{1}{2}$$

$$x = 0, \qquad y = 2^0 = 1$$

$$x = 1, \qquad y = 2^1 = 2$$

$$x = 2, \qquad y = 2^2 = 4$$

$$x = 3, \qquad y = 2^3 = 8$$

x	y
-3	$\frac{1}{8}$
-2	$\frac{1}{4}$
-1	$\frac{1}{2}$
0	1
1	2
2	4
3	8

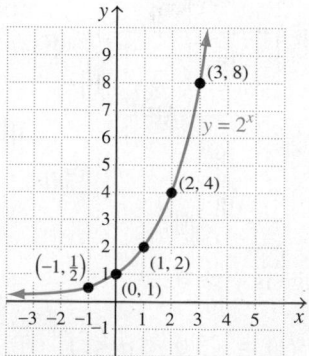

Figure 6.36

b) The domain is all real numbers, $\mathbb{R}$. The range is $y > 0$. Note that y can never have a value of 0.   ∎

All exponential functions of the form $y = a^x$, $a > 1$, will have the general shape of the graph illustrated in Fig. 6.36. Since $f(x)$ is the same as y, the graphs of functions of the form $f(x) = a^x$, $a > 1$, will also have the general shape of the graph illustrated in Fig. 6.36. Can you now predict the shape of the graph of $y = e^x$? Remember: e has a value of about 2.7183.

Example 12 *Graphing an Exponential Function with a Base Between 0 and 1*

a) Graph $y = \left(\frac{1}{2}\right)^x$.
b) Determine the domain and range of the function.

Solution

a) We begin by substituting values for x and calculating values for y. We then plot the ordered pairs and use these points to sketch the graph. To evaluate a fraction with a negative exponent, we use the fact that

$$\left(\frac{a}{b}\right)^{-x} = \left(\frac{b}{a}\right)^{x}$$

For example,

$$\left(\frac{1}{2}\right)^{-3} = \left(\frac{2}{1}\right)^{3} = 8$$

Then

$$y = \left(\frac{1}{2}\right)^{x}$$

$$x = -3, \qquad y = \left(\frac{1}{2}\right)^{-3} = 2^3 = 8$$

$$x = -2, \qquad y = \left(\frac{1}{2}\right)^{-2} = 2^2 = 4$$

$$x = -1, \qquad y = \left(\frac{1}{2}\right)^{-1} = 2^1 = 2$$

$$x = 0, \qquad y = \left(\frac{1}{2}\right)^{0} = 1$$

$$x = 1, \qquad y = \left(\frac{1}{2}\right)^{1} = \frac{1}{2}$$

$$x = 2, \qquad y = \left(\frac{1}{2}\right)^{2} = \frac{1}{4}$$

$$x = 3, \qquad y = \left(\frac{1}{2}\right)^{3} = \frac{1}{8}$$

x	y
-3	8
-2	4
-1	2
0	1
1	$\frac{1}{2}$
2	$\frac{1}{4}$
3	$\frac{1}{8}$

The graph is illustrated in Fig. 6.37.

b) The domain is the set of all real numbers, $\mathbb{R}$. The range is $y > 0$.   ∎

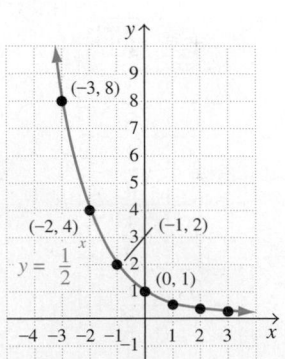

Figure 6.37

All exponential functions of the form $y = a^x$ or $f(x) = a^x$, $0 < a < 1$, will have the general shape of the graph illustrated in Fig. 6.37.

┌─
│ Example **13** *Is the Growth Exponential?*
│
│ The graph below shows the population, in millions, of people age 85 and older in
│ the United States for selected years from 1960 to 2010 and projected to 2050.
│
│ a) Does the graph approximate the graph of an exponential function?
│
│ b) Estimate the number of U.S. people age 85 and older in 2000.
│
│ **Solution**
│
│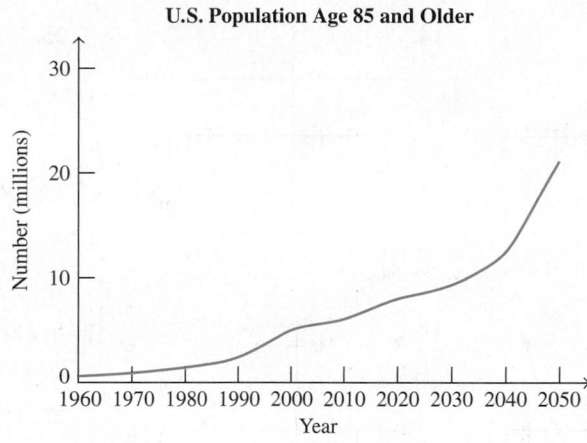
│
│ Source: *U.S. Census Bureau*
│
│ a) Yes, the graph has the approximate shape of an exponential function. A function
│   that increases rapidly with this general shape is, or approximates, an exponential
│   function.
│
│ b) From the graph, we see that there were about 5 million people in the
│   United States who were age 85 and older in 2000.   ■
└─

SECTION 6.10
Exercises

Warm Up Exercises

*In Exercises 1–8, fill in the blank with an appropriate
word, phrase, or symbol(s).*

1. Any set of ordered pairs is called a(n) _____. Relation

2. A special type of relation where each value of the
independent variable corresponds to a unique value of the
dependent variable is called a(n) _____. Function

3. The set of values that can be used for the independent
variable is called the _____ of the function. Domain

4. The set of values obtained for the dependent variable is
called the _____ of the function. Range

5. In a quadratic function of the form $f(x) = ax^2 + bx + c$,
if a is greater than 0, then the graph of $f(x)$ is a parabola
that opens _____. Upward

6. In a quadratic function of the form $f(x) = ax^2 + bx + c$,
if a is less than 0, then the graph of $f(x)$ is a parabola that
opens _____. Downward

7. The formula used to determine the equation for the axis of
symmetry of a parabola is _____. $x = -\dfrac{b}{2a}$

8. A test that is used to determine whether a graph represents
a function is called the _____ line test. Vertical

Practice the Skills

*In Exercises 9–26, determine whether the graph represents
a function. If it does represent a function, give its domain
and range.*

9.

Not a function

10.

Function, domain: $x = -2, -1, 1, 2, 3$;
range: $y = -1, 1, 2, 3$

11.

Function, domain: $\mathbb{R}$; range: $\mathbb{R}$

12.

Function, domain: $\mathbb{R}$; range: $\mathbb{R}$

13.

Not a function

14.

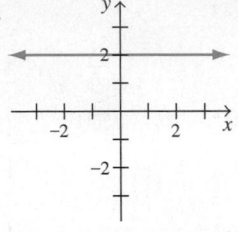

Function, domain: $\mathbb{R}$; range: $y = 2$

15.

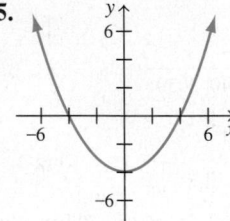

Function, domain: $\mathbb{R}$; range: $y \geq -4$

16.

Function, domain: $\mathbb{R}$; range: $y \leq 10$

17.

Not a function

18.

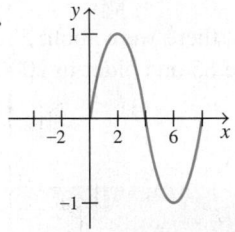

Function, domain: $0 \leq x \leq 8$;
    range: $-1 \leq y \leq 1$

19.

Function, domain: $0 \leq x < 12$;
range: $y = 1, 2, 3$

20.

Function, domain: $\mathbb{R}$; range: $\mathbb{R}$

21.

Not a function

22.

Function, domain: $\mathbb{R}$; range: $\mathbb{R}$

23.

Function, domain: $\mathbb{R}$; range $y > 0$

24.

Function, domain: $0 \leq x \leq 10$;
range: $-1 \leq y \leq 3$

25.

Not a function

26.

Function, domain: $\mathbb{R}$; range: $y \geq 0$

In Exercises 27–32, determine whether the set of ordered pairs is a function.

27. $\{(3, 7), (4, 9), (2, 1), (8, 0)\}$ Yes

28. $\{(5, -1), (6, -2), (8, -4), (10, -5)\}$ Yes

29. $\{(2, 5), (2, 7), (2, -1), (2, 2)\}$ No

30. $\{(-1, 2), (-1, 4), (-1, 6), (-1, 9)\}$ No

31. $\{(-1, -1), (0, -1), (3, -1)\}$ Yes

32. $\{(4, 2), (4, -3), (4, 5)\}$ No

In Exercises 33–46, evaluate the function for the given value of x.

33. $f(x) = x + 6, \quad x = 3$ 9

34. $f(x) = 2x - 5, \quad x = 1$ -3

35. $f(x) = -2x - 7, \quad x = -4$ 1

36. $f(x) = -5x + 3, \quad x = -1$ 8

37. $f(x) = 10x - 6, \quad x = 0$ -6

38. $f(x) = 7x - 6, \quad x = 4$ 22

39. $f(x) = x^2 - 3x + 1, \quad x = 4$ 5

40. $f(x) = x^2 - 5, \quad x = 7$ 44

41. $f(x) = -x^2 - 2x + 1, \quad x = 4$ -23

42. $f(x) = 2x^2 + 3x - 1, \quad x = 3$ 26

43. $f(x) = 4x^2 - 6x - 9, \quad x = -3$ 45

44. $f(x) = 3x^2 + 2x - 5, \quad x = -4$ 35

45. $f(x) = -5x^2 + 3x - 9, \quad x = -1$ -17

46. $f(x) = -3x^2 - 6x + 10, \quad x = -2$ 10

In Exercises 47–52, graph the function by using the slope and y-intercept.

47. $f(x) = 2x + 3$*

48. $f(x) = -x - 1$*

49. $f(x) = -3x + 2$*

50. $f(x) = 2x + 5$*

51. $f(x) = \frac{3}{2}x - 1$*

52. $f(x) = -\frac{1}{2}x + 3$*

In Exercises 53–68,

    a) *determine whether the parabola will open upward or downward.*

    b) *find the equation of the axis of symmetry.*

    c) *find the vertex.*

    d) *find the y-intercept.*

    e) *find the x-intercepts if they exist.*

    f) *sketch the graph.*

    g) *find the domain and range of the function.*

53. $y = x^2 - 1$*

54. $y = x^2 - 9$*

55. $y = -x^2 + 4$*

56. $y = -x^2 + 16$*

57. $y = -2x^2 - 8$*

58. $f(x) = -x^2 - 4$*

59. $y = 2x^2 - 3$*

60. $f(x) = -3x^2 - 6$*

61. $f(x) = x^2 + 4x - 4$*

62. $y = x^2 - 8x + 1$*

63. $y = x^2 + 5x + 6$*

64. $y = x^2 - 7x - 8$*

65. $y = -x^2 + 4x - 6$*

66. $y = -x^2 + 8x - 8$*

67. $y = -2x^2 + 3x - 2$*

68. $y = -4x^2 - 6x + 4$*

In Exercises 69–80, draw the graph of the function and state the domain and range.

69. $y = 3^x$*

70. $f(x) = 4^x$*

71. $y = \left(\frac{1}{3}\right)^x$*

72. $y = \left(\frac{1}{4}\right)^x$*

73. $f(x) = 2^x + 1$*

74. $y = 3^x - 1$*

75. $y = 4^x + 1$*

76. $y = 2^x - 1$*

77. $y = 3^{x-1}$*

78. $y = 3^{x+1}$*

79. $f(x) = 4^{x+1}$*

80. $y = 4^{x-1}$*

Problem Solving

81. *Yearly Profit* Marta Rivera is a part owner of a newly opened candy company. Marta's yearly profit, in dollars, is given by the function $p(x) = 3.5x - 15{,}000$, where x is the number of pounds of candy sold per year. If Marta sells 20,000 pounds of candy a year, determine her yearly profit. $55,000

82. *Finding Distances* The distance a car travels, $d(t)$, at a constant 60 mph is given by the function $d(t) = 60t$, where t is the time in hours. Find the distance traveled in

    a) 3 hours. 180 mi

    b) 7 hours. 420 mi

83. *U.S. Foreign-Born Population* The graph on the top of page 376 indicates the percentage of the U.S. population that was foreign-born for each decade between 1930 and 2000, and projected percentage for 2010. The function $f(x) = 0.005x^2 - 0.36x + 11.8$ can be used to estimate the percentage of the U.S. population that was foreign-born, where x is the number of years since 1930 and $0 \le x \le 80$.

    a) Use the function $f(x)$ to estimate the percentage of the U.S. population that was foreign-born in 2004. Round your answer to the nearest percent. ≈ 13%

    b) Of the years illustrated on the graph, determine the year in which the percentage of the U.S. population that was foreign-born was a minimum. 1970

    c) Determine the x-coordinate of the vertex of the graph of the function $f(x)$. Then use this value in the function $f(x)$ to estimate the minimum percentage of the U.S. population that was foreign-born. Round your answer for the vertex to the nearest whole number. Round your answer for the population to the nearest percent. $x \approx 36$; ≈ 5%

*See Instructor Answer Appendix

Percentage of U.S. Population That is Foreign-Born

Source: *Bureau of the Census, U.S. Dept. of Commerce*

84. Hourly Temperature The following graph indicates the hourly temperature, in degrees fahrenheit, in Rochester, New York, from 2 A.M. through 12 noon on Friday, February 10, 2011. The function $t(x) = 0.17x^2 - 1.75x + 15.35$ can be used to estimate the hourly temperature in Rochester, where x is the number of hours after 2 A.M on February 10, 2011 and $0 \le x \le 10$.

a) Use the function $t(x)$ to estimate the temperature in Rochester at 8 A.M. on February 10, 2011. Round your answer to the nearest degree. $\approx 11°F$

b) Use the graph to determine the hour(s) that the temperature was a minimum. 7 A.M.

c) Determine the x-coordinate of the vertex of the graph of the function $t(x)$. Then use this value in the function $t(x)$ to estimate the minimum temperature. Round your answer for the vertex to the nearest hour. Round your answer for the temperature to the nearest degree. $x \approx 5$, or about 7 a.m; $t(x) \approx 11°F$

Hourly Temperature in Rochester, NY February 10, 2011

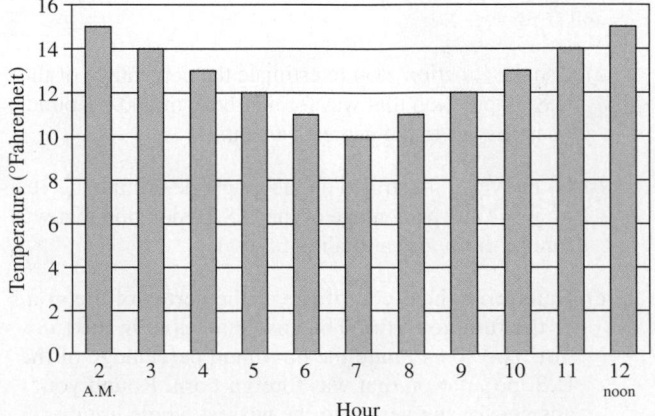

Source: *Weather.com*

85. Bacteria The number of a certain type of bacteria, y, present in a culture is determined by the equation $y = 2000(3)^x$, where x is the number of days the culture

has been growing. Find the number of bacteria present after 5 days. 486,000 bacteria

86. Adjusting for Inflation If P is the price of an item today, the price of the same item n years from today, P_n, is $P_n = P(1 + r)^n$, where r is the constant rate of inflation. Determine the price of a movie ticket 10 years from today if the price today is $8.00 and the annual rate of inflation is constant at 3%. $10.75

87. Expected Growth The town of Lockport currently has 4000 residents. The expected future population can be approximated by the function $P(x) = 4000(1.3)^{0.1x}$, where x is the number of years in the future. Determine the expected population of Lockport in

a) 10 years. 5200 people

b) 50 years. $\approx 14{,}852$ people

88. Value of an SUV The cost of a new SUV is $30,000. If it depreciates at a rate of 18% per year, the value of the SUV in t years can be approximated by the function $V(t) = 30{,}000(0.82)^t$. Determine the value of the SUV in 4 years. Round your answer to the nearest cent. $13,563.65

89. Population of China The population of China in April 2011, was about 1.34 billion people. Assume that the population of China continues to grow exponentially at the growth rate of 0.6% per year. Thus, the expected population of China, in billions of people, t years after 2011, is given by the function $P(t) = 1.34e^{0.006t}$. Determine the expected population of China in 2016. 1.38 billion people

90. Value of New York City Assume the value of the island of Manhattan has grown at an exponential rate of 8% per year since 1626 when Peter Minuit of the Dutch West India Company purchased the island for $24. The value of the island, V, at any time, t, in years after 1626, can be found by the formula $V(t) = 24e^{0.08t}$. What is the value of the island in 2012, 386 years after Minuit purchased it? Use a scientific calculator and give your answer in scientific notation as provided by your calculator. $\approx 6.18×10^{14}

91. Radioactive Decay Radium-226 is a radioactive isotope that decays exponentially at a rate of 0.0428% per year. The amount of radium-226, Rt, remaining after t years can be found by the formula $R(t) = R_0 e^{-0.000428t}$, where R_0 is the original amount present. If there are originally 10 grams of radium-226, determine the amount of radium-226 remaining after 1000 years. ≈ 6.52 grams

92. Radioactive Decay Strontium-90 is a radioactive isotope that decays exponentially at a rate of 2.8% per year. The amount of strontium-90, S, remaining after t years can be found by the function $S(t) = S_0 e^{-0.028t}$, where S_0 is the original amount present. If there are originally 1000 grams of strontium-90, determine the amount of strontium-90 remaining after 40 years. Round your answer to the nearest gram. 326 grams

93. U.S. Cellular Telephone Subscribers The graph on the top of page 377 shows the number of U.S. cellular subscribers, in thousands, for the years 1989 through 2008.

a) Does the graph approximate the graph of an exponential function? Yes

b) Estimate the number of U.S. cellular subscribers in 2008. ≈ 270,000 thousand subscribers

U.S. Cellular Telephone Subscribership

Source: *The CTIA Semi-Annual Wireless Industry Survey, 1989–2008*

94. *U.S. Gross Domestic Product* The following graph shows the U.S. gross domestic product (GDP), the market value of all goods and services produced within the United States, for every 5 years between 1965 and 2010.

a) Does the graph approximate the graph of an exponential function? Yes

b) Estimate the U.S. gross domestic product in 2005. ≈ $12,600 billion

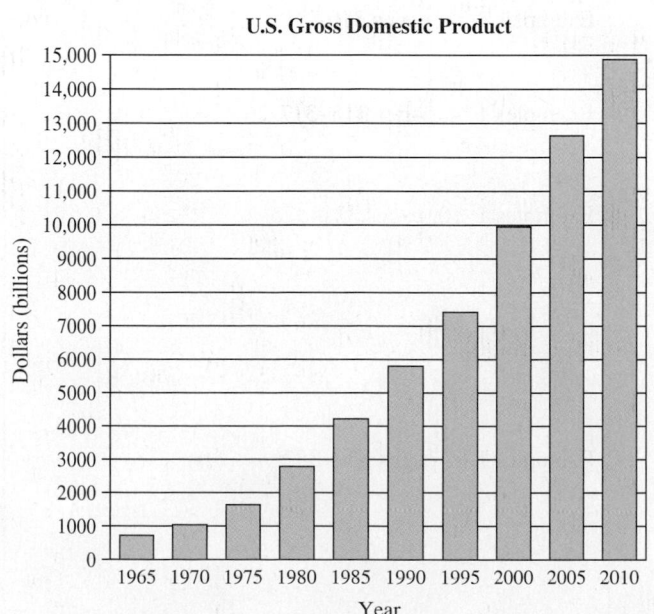

U.S. Gross Domestic Product

95. The spacing of the frets on the neck of a classical guitar is determined from the equation $d = (21.9)(2)^{(20-x)/12}$, where x = the fret number and d = the distance in centimeters of the xth fret from the bridge.

a) Determine how far the 19th fret should be from the bridge (rounded to one decimal place). 23.2 cm

b) Determine how far the 4th fret should be from the bridge (rounded to one decimal place). 55.2 cm

c) The distance of the nut from the bridge can be found by letting $x = 0$ in the given exponential equation. Find the distance from the nut to the bridge (rounded to one decimal place). 69.5 cm

Challenge Problems/Group Activities

96. *Appreciation of a House* A house initially cost $150,000. The value, V, of the house after n years if it appreciates at a constant rate of 4% per year can be determined by the function $V = f(n) = \$150{,}000(1.04)^n$.

a) Determine $f(8)$ and explain its meaning.
≈ $205,285; the value of the house after 8 years is about $205,285.

b) After how many years is the value of the house greater than $250,000? (Find by trial and error.) About 14 years

97. *Target Heart Rate* While exercising, a person's recommended target heart rate is a function of age. The recommended number of beats per minute, y, is given by the function $y = f(x) = -0.85x + 187$, where x represents a person's age in years. Determine the number of recommended heart beats per minute for the following ages and explain the results.

a) 20 170 beats per minute

b) 30 ≈ 162 beats per minute

c) 50 ≈ 145 beats per minute

d) 60 136 beats per minute

e) What is the age of a person with a recommended target heart rate of 85? 120 years of age

98. *Speed of Light* Light travels at about 186,000 miles per second through space. The distance, d, in miles that light travels in t seconds can be determined by the function $d(t) = 186,000t$.

a) Light reaches the moon from Earth in about 1.3 sec. Determine the approximate distance from Earth to the moon. 241,800 mi

b) Express the distance in miles, d, traveled by light in t minutes as a function of time, t. $d(t) = 11,160,000t$

c) Light travels from the sun to Earth in about 8.3 min. Determine the approximate distance from the sun to Earth. 92,628,000 mi

Internet/Research Activity

99. The idea of using variables in algebraic equations was introduced by the French mathematician François Viète (1540–1603). Write a paper about his life and his contributions to mathematics. In particular, discuss his work with algebra equations. References include history of mathematics books, encyclopedias, and the Internet.

CHAPTER 6) *Summary*

Important Facts and Concepts

Examples

Section 6.1

Order of Operations

Examples 1–4, pages 293–295

Section 6.2

Properties Used to Solve Equations

Addition property of equality
  If $a = b$, then $a + c = b + c$.
Subtraction property of equality
  If $a = b$, then $a - c = b - c$.
Multiplication property of equality
  If $a = b$, then $ac = bc$.
Division property of equality
  If $a = b$, then $a/c = b/c, c \neq 0$.

Examples 2–13, pages 298–304

Section 6.3

Evaluating a formula
Solving for a variable in a formula

Examples 1–3, pages 309–310
Examples 4–6, pages 310–311

Section 6.4

Applications of Linear Equations

Examples 1–4, pages 315–317

Section 6.5

Variation

Direct: $y = kx$

Inverse: $y = \dfrac{k}{x}$

Joint: $y = kxz$

Examples 1–10, pages 321–325

Section 6.6

Inequality Symbols

$a < b$ means that a is less than b.
$a \leq b$ means that a is less than or equal to b.
$a > b$ means that a is greater than b.
$a \geq b$ means that a is greater than or equal to b.

Examples 1–9, pages 329–333

Section 6.7

Intercepts

To find the x-intercept, set $y = 0$ and solve the resulting equation for x.

To find the y-intercept, set $x = 0$ and solve the resulting equation for y.

Example 4, pages 339–340

Slope

Slope (m): $m = \dfrac{y_2 - y_1}{x_2 - x_1}$

Example 5, page 341

Linear equation in two variables:

$ax + by = c, \quad a \neq 0 \quad \text{and} \quad b \neq 0$

Examples 3, 4, 6, 7, 10, 11, pages 338, 339, 342–344

Slope–intercept form of a line:

$$y = mx + b$$

Examples 6–8, pages 342–343

Section 6.8

Linear Inequalities in Two Variables

Examples 1–3, pages 349–350

Section 6.9

Quadratic equation in one variable:

$$ax^2 + bx + c = 0, \quad a \neq 0$$

Examples 8, 9, page 357

Quadratic formula:

$$x = \frac{-b \pm \sqrt{b^2 - 4ac}}{2a}$$

Examples 10, 11, pages 358–359

Zero-Factor Property

If $a \cdot b = 0$, then $a = 0$ or $b = 0$.

Example 7, page 356–357

Section 6.10

Quadratic equation (or function) in two variables:

$$y = ax^2 + bx + c, \quad a \neq 0$$

Examples 5–7, pages 366–368

Axis of symmetry of a parabola:

$$x = \frac{-b}{2a}$$

Examples 5–7, pages 366–368

Exponential function:

$$y = a^x \quad \text{or} \quad f(x) = a^x, \quad a \neq 1, \quad a > 0$$

Examples 8–12, pages 369–372

Exponential growth and decay formula:

$$P(t) = P_0 a^{kt}, a > 0, a \neq 1$$

Natural exponential function:

$$f(x) = e^x, e \approx 2.7183$$

Natural exponential growth or decay function:

$$P(t) = P_0 e^{kt}$$

Examples 9, 10, pages 370–371

CHAPTER 6) *Review Exercises*

6.1

In Exercises 1–4, evaluate the expression for the given value(s) of the variable.

1. $x^2 + 12$, $x = 3$ 21

2. $-x^2 - 8$, $x = -2$ −12

3. $4x^2 - 2x + 5$, $x = 2$ 17

4. $4x^3 - 7x^2 + 3x + 1$, $x = -1$ −13

6.2

In Exercises 5–6, combine like terms.

5. $4x - 2 + x + 9$ 5x + 7

6. $2x + 3(x - 2) + 7x$ 12x − 6

In Exercises 7–10, solve the equation for the given variable.

7. $3s + 10 = -32$ −14

8. $2t + 15 = -6t - 9$ −3

9. $\dfrac{x + 5}{2} = \dfrac{x - 3}{4}$ −13

10. $4(x - 2) = 3 + 5(x + 4)$ −31

11. *Making Oatmeal* A recipe for Hot Oats Cereal calls for 2 cups of water and for $\frac{1}{3}$ cup of dry oats. How many cups of dry oats would be used with 3 cups of water? $\frac{1}{2}$ cup

12. *Laying Blocks* A mason lays 120 blocks in 1 hr 40 min. How long will it take her to lay 300 blocks? 250 min, or 4 hr 10 min

6.3

In Exercises 13–16, use the formula to find the value of the indicated variable for the values given.

13. $F = ma$
    Determine F when $m = 40$ and $a = 5$ (physics). 200

14. $v = lwh$ 84
    Determine v when $l = 7$, $w = 4$, and $h = 3$ (*geometry*).

15. $z = \dfrac{\bar{x} - \mu}{\dfrac{\sigma}{\sqrt{n}}}$
    Determine $\bar{x}$ when $z = 2$, $\mu = 100$, $\sigma = 3$, and $n = 16$ (statistics). 101.5

16. $E = mc^2$
    Determine m when $E = 400$ and $c = 4$ (physics). 25

In Exercises 17–18, solve for y.

17. $6x - 3y = 24$ $y = 2x - 8$ 18. $2x + 9y = 17$
    $y = \dfrac{-2x + 17}{9}$ or $y = -\dfrac{2}{9}x + \dfrac{17}{9}$

In Exercises 19–22, solve for the variable indicated.

19. $A = lw$,   for w $w = \dfrac{A}{l}$

20. $P = 2l + 2w$,   for w $w = \dfrac{P - 2l}{2}$

21. $L = 2(wh + lh)$,   for l $l = \dfrac{L - 2wh}{2h}$ or $l = \dfrac{L}{2h} - w$

22. $a_n = a_1 + (n - 1)d$,   for d $d = \dfrac{a_n - a_1}{n - 1}$

6.4

In Exercises 23–26, write the phrase in mathematical terms.

23. 7 decreased by 2 times x $7 - 2x$

24. 3 times y, increased by 4 $3y + 4$

25. 10 increased by 3 times r $10 + 3r$

26. The difference between 9 divided by q and 15 $\dfrac{9}{q} - 15$

In Exercises 27–30, write an equation that can be used to solve the problems. Solve the equation and find the desired value(s).

27. Two increased by 8 times a number is 18. $2 + 8x = 18; x = 2$

28. The product of 3 and a number, increased by 8, is 6 less than the number. $3x + 8 = x - 6; x = -7$

29. Five times the difference of a number and 4 is 45. $5(x - 4) = 45; x = 13$

30. Fourteen more than 10 times a number is 8 times the sum of the number and 12. $10x + 14 = 8(x + 12); x = 41$

In Exercises 31–34, write the equation and then find the solution.

31. **MODELING** – *Investing*   Jim Lawton received an inheritance of $15,000. If he wants to invest twice as much money in mutual funds as in bonds, how much should he invest in mutual funds?
    $x + 2x = 15,000$; bonds: $5000, mutual funds: $10,000

32. **MODELING** – *Lawn Chairs*   Larry's Lawn Chair Company has fixed costs of $15,000 per month and variable costs of $9.50 per lawn chair manufactured. The company has $95,000 available to meet its total monthly expenditures. What is the maximum number of lawn chairs the company can manufacture in a month? (Fixed costs, such as rent and insurance, are those that occur regardless of the level of production. Variable costs, such as those for materials, depend on the level of production.)
    $9.50x + 15,000 = 95,000$; ≈ 8421 chairs

33. **MODELING** – *National Parks* The area of Crater Lake National Park is 4049 acres more than 5 times the area of Bryce Canyon National Park. The total area of Crater Lake National park and Bryce Canyon National Park is 219,059 acres. Determine the area, in acres, of Crater

Lake National Park and the area of Bryce Canyon National Park. $x + (5x + 4049) = 219,059$; Crater Lake National Park: 183,224 acres; Bryce Canyon National Park: 35,835 acres

▲ Carter Lake National Park, Oregon

34. MODELING – *Restaurant Profit*   John Smith owns two restaurants. His profit for a year at restaurant A is $12,000 greater than his profit at restaurant B. The total profit from both restaurants is $68,000. Determine the profit at each restaurant. $x + (x + 12,000) = 68,000$; $28,000 for B and $40,000 for A

6.5

In Exercises 35–38, find the quantity indicated.

35. s is directly proportional to t. If $s = 30$ when $t = 10$, find s when $t = 8$. 24

36. J is inversely proportional to the square of A. If $J = 25$ when $A = 2$, find J when $A = 5$. 4

37. W is directly proportional to L and inversely proportional to A. If $W = 80$ when $L = 100$ and $A = 20$, find W when $L = 50$ and $A = 40$. 20

38. z is jointly proportional to x and y and inversely proportional to the square of r. If $z = 12$ when $x = 20$, $y = 8$, and $r = 8$, find z when $x = 10$, $y = 80$, and $r = 3$. ≈ 426.7

39. *Buying Fertilizer*

   a) A 30-lb bag of fertilizer will cover an area of 2500 ft². How many pounds of fertilizer are needed to cover an area of 12,500 ft²? 150 lb

   b) How many bags of fertilizer are needed? 5 bags

40. *Property Tax*   The property tax, t, on a house is directly proportional to the assessed value, v, of the house. If the property tax on a house with an assessed value of $155,000 is $2325, what is the property tax on a house with an assessed value of $210,000? $3150

41. *Electric Bill*   An electric company charges $0.162 per kilowatt-hour (kWh). What is the electric bill if 740 kWh are used in a month? $119.88

42. *Stretching a Spring*   The length that a spring will stretch, S, varies directly with the weight, w, attached to the spring. If a spring stretches 4.2 in. when a 60-lb weight is attached, how far will the spring stretch when a 25-lb weight is attached? 1.75 in.

▲ See Exercises 42

6.6

In Exercises 43–49, graph the solution set for the set of real numbers on the real number line.

43. $8 + 9x \le 6x - 4$ *

44. $3x + 8 \ge 7x + 12$ *

45. $3(x + 9) \le 4x + 11$ *

46. $-3 \le x + 1 < 7$ *

In Exercises 47–50, graph the solution set for the set of integers on the real number line.

47. $4 + 2x > -10$ *

48. $5x + 13 \ge -22$ *

49. $-1 < x \le 9$ *

50. $-8 \le x + 2 \le 7$ *

6.7

In Exercises 51–54, graph the ordered pair in the Cartesian coordinate system.

51. $(-2, 1)$ *

52. $(2, -2)$ *

53. $(-4, 3)$ *

54. $(5, 3)$ *

In Exercises 55 and 56, points A, B, and C are vertices of a rectangle. Plot the points. Find the coordinates of the fourth point, D, to complete the rectangle. Find the area of the rectangle.

55. $A(-3, 3)$, $B(2, 3)$, $C(2, -1)$
    $D(-3, -1)$; area = 20 square units

56. $A(-3, 1)$, $B(-3, -2)$, $C(4, -2)$
    $D(4, 1)$; area = 21 square units

In Exercises 57–58, graph the equation by plotting points.

57. $x - y = 2$ *

58. $2x + 3y = 12$ *

In Exercises 59–60, graph the equation, using the x- and y-intercepts.

59. $x - 2y = 6$ *

60. $4x - 3y = 12$ *

In Exercises 61–64, find the slope of the line through the given points.

61. $(1, 3)$, $(4, 7)$ $\frac{4}{3}$

62. $(3, -1)$, $(5, -4)$ $-\frac{3}{2}$

63. $(-1, -4)$, $(2, 3)$ $\frac{7}{3}$

64. $(6, 2)$, $(6, -2)$ Undefined

*See Instructor Answer Appendix

In Exercises 65–66, graph the equation by plotting the y-intercept and then plotting a second point by making use of the slope.

65. $y = 2x - 5$ ∗

66. $2y - 4 = 3x$ ∗

In Exercises 67 and 68, determine the equation of the graph.

67.

$y = 2x + 4$

68.

$y = -x + 1$

69. *Car Wash Profit* The weekly profit, p, in dollars, at Delta Sonic Car Wash can be estimated by $p = 20n - 400$, where n is the number of cars washed in 1 week.

a) Draw a graph of weekly profit versus number of cars washed for up to and including 100 cars. ∗

b) Use the function to determine the weekly profit if 50 cars are washed. $600

c) If the weekly profit was $1000, use the function to determine how many cars were washed. 70 cars

70. MODELING—*Taxi Business Cost* Tony Li's weekly cost, C, in dollars, of operating a taxi business can be approximated by the equation $C = 0.20m + 80$, where m is the number of miles driven in a week.

a) Draw a graph of weekly cost versus the number of miles driven for up to and including 500 miles driven per week. ∗

b) If, during one week, Tony drove the taxi 150 miles, what would be the cost? $110

c) How many miles would Tony have to drive for the weekly cost to be $104? 120 miles

6.8

In Exercises 71–74, graph the inequality.

71. $2x + 3y \le 12$ ∗

72. $4x + 2y \ge 12$ ∗

73. $2x - 3y > 12$ ∗

74. $-7x - 2y < 14$ ∗

6.9

In Exercises 75–78, factor the trinomial. If the trinomial cannot be factored, so state.

75. $x^2 + 9x + 20$
$(x + 5)(x + 4)$

76. $x^2 + x - 12$
$(x + 4)(x - 3)$

77. $x^2 - 10x + 24$
$(x - 6)(x - 4)$

78. $6x^2 + 7x - 3$
$(3x - 1)(2x + 3)$

In Exercises 79–82, solve the equation by factoring.

79. $x^2 + 6x + 5 = 0$
$-1, -5$

80. $x^2 + 3x = 10$
$-5, 2$

81. $3x^2 - 17x + 10 = 0$
$\frac{2}{3}, 5$

82. $3x^2 = -7x - 2$
$-2, -\frac{1}{3}$

In Exercises 83–86, solve the equation using the quadratic formula. If the equation has no real solution, so state.

83. $x^2 - 6x - 16 = 0$
$-2, 8$

84. $2x^2 - x - 3 = 0$
$-1, \frac{3}{2}$

85. $2x^2 - 3x + 4 = 0$
No real solution

86. $x^2 - 3x - 2 = 0$
$\frac{3 \pm \sqrt{17}}{2}$

6.10

In Exercises 87–90, determine whether the graph represents a function. If it does represent a function, give its domain and range.

87.

88.

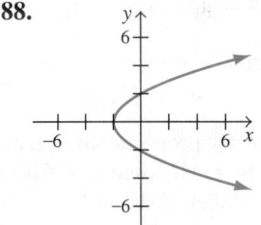

Function, domain: $x = -2, -1, 2, 3$;
range: $y = -1, 0, 2$

Not a function

89.

90.

Not a function

Function, domain: $\mathbb{R}$; range: $\mathbb{R}$

In Exercises 91–94, evaluate $f(x)$ for the given value of x.

91. $f(x) = 5x - 2$, $x = 4$ 18

92. $f(x) = -3x + 7$, $x = -3$ 16

93. $f(x) = 2x^2 - 3x + 4$, $x = 5$ 39

94. $f(x) = -4x^2 + 7x + 9$, $x = -2$ −21

∗See Instructor Answer Appendix

In Exercises 95 and 96, for each function

   a) *determine whether the parabola will open upward or downward.*

   b) *determine the equation of the axis of symmetry.*

   c) *determine the vertex.*

   d) *determine the y-intercept.*

   e) *determine the x-intercepts if they exist.*

   f) *sketch the graph.*

   g) *determine the domain and range.*

95. $y = -x^2 - 4x + 21$ *

96. $f(x) = 2x^2 + 8x + 6$ *

In Exercises 97 and 98, draw the graph of the function and state the domain and range.

97. $y = 4^x$ *   **98.** $y = \left(\dfrac{1}{2}\right)^x$ *

6.2, 6.3, 6.10

99. *Gas Mileage* The gas mileage, m, of a specific car can be estimated by the equation (or function)
$$m = 30 - 0.002n^2, \quad 20 \le n \le 80$$
where n is the speed of the car in miles per hour. Estimate the gas mileage when the car travels at 60 mph. 22.8 mpg

100. *Filtered Light* The percent of light filtering through Swan Lake, P, can be approximated by the function $P(x) = 100(0.92)^x$, where x is the depth in feet. Find the percent of light filtering through at a depth of 4.5 ft. $\approx 68.7\%$

CHAPTER 6   *Test*

1. Evaluate $3x^2 + 6x - 1$, when $x = -2$. −1

In Exercises 2 and 3, solve the equation.

2. $4x + 6 = 2(3x - 7)$ 10

3. $-2(x - 3) + 6x = 2x + 3(x - 4)$ 18

In Exercises 4 and 5, write an equation to represent the problem. Then solve the equation.

4. The product of 3 and a number, increased by 5, is 17.
   $3x + 5 = 17$; 4

5. *Salary* Mary Gilligan's salary is $350 per week plus a 6% commission of sales. How much in sales must Mary make to earn a total of $710 per week?
   $350 + 0.06x = 710$; $6000

6. Evaluate $L = ah + bh + ch$ when $a = 2, b = 5, c = 4,$ and $h = 7$. 77

7. Solve $3x + 5y = 11$ for y. $y = \dfrac{-3x + 11}{5}$ or $y = -\dfrac{3}{5}x + \dfrac{11}{5}$

8. L varies jointly as M and N and inversely as P. If $L = 12$ when $M = 8, N = 3,$ and $P = 2$, find L when $M = 10, N = 5,$ and $P = 15$. $3\frac{1}{3}$

9. For a constant area, the length, l, of a rectangle varies inversely as the width, w. If $l = 15$ ft when $w = 9$ ft, find the length of a rectangle with the same area if the width is 20 ft. 6.75 ft

10. Graph the solution set of $-5x + 14 \le 2x + 35$ on the real number line. *

11. Determine the slope of the line through the points $(-2, 8)$ and $(1, 14)$. 2

In Exercises 12 and 13, graph the equation.

12. $y = 2x - 4$ *   **13.** $2x - 3y = 15$ *

14. Graph the inequality $3y \ge 5x - 12$. *

15. Factor the following trinomial: $x^2 + 11x + 18$. If the trinomial cannot be factored, so state. $(x + 9)(x + 2)$

16. Solve the equation $x^2 + 7x = -6$ by factoring. −1, −6

17. Solve the equation $3x^2 + 2x = 8$ by using the quadratic formula. $\frac{4}{3}, -2$

18. Determine whether the graph is a function. Explain your answer. It is a function.

19. Evaluate $f(x) = -2x^2 - 8x + 7$ when $x = -2$. 15

20. For the equation $y = x^2 - 2x + 4$,

   a) determine whether the parabola will open upward or downward. Upward

   b) determine the equation of the axis of symmetry. $x = 1$

   c) determine the vertex. $(1, 3)$

   d) determine the y-intercept. $(0, 4)$

   e) determine the x-intercepts if they exist. No x-intercepts

   f) sketch the graph. *

   g) determine the domain and range of the function.
     Domain: $\mathbb{R}$; range: $y \ge 3$

*See Instructor Answer Appendix

GROUP PROJECTS

Archeology: Gaining Information From Bones

1. Archeologists have developed formulas to predict the height and, in some cases, the age at death of the deceased by knowing the lengths of certain bones in the body. The long bones of the body grow at approximately the same rate. Thus, a linear relationship exists between the length of the bones and the person's height. If the length of one of these major bones—the femur (F), the tibia (T), the humerus (H), and the radius (R)— is known, the height, h, of a person can be calculated with one of the following formulas. The relationship between bone length and height is different for males and females.

Male	Female
$h = 2.24F + 69.09$	$h = 2.23F + 61.41$
$h = 2.39T + 81.68$	$h = 2.53T + 72.57$
$h = 2.97H + 73.57$	$h = 3.14H + 64.98$
$h = 3.65R + 80.41$	$h = 3.88R + 73.51$

All measurements are in centimeters.

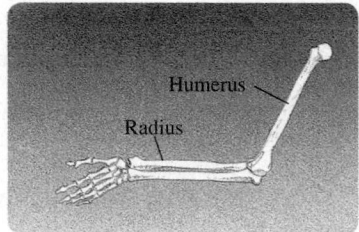

Humerus
Radius

a) Measure your humerus and use the appropriate formula to predict your height in centimeters. How close is this predicted height to your actual height? (The result is an approximation because measuring a bone covered with flesh and muscle is difficult.)

b) Determine and describe where the femur and tibia bones are located.

c) Dr. Juarez, an archeologist, had one female humerus that was 29.42 cm in length. He concluded that the height of the entire skeleton would have been 157.36 cm. Was his conclusion correct?

d) If a 21-year-old woman is 167.64 cm tall, about how long should her tibia be?

e) Sometimes the age of a person may be determined by using the fact that the height of a person, and the length of his or her long bones, decreases at the rate of 0.06 cm per year after the age of 30.

    i. At age 30, Jolene is 168 cm tall. Estimate the length of her humerus.

    ii. Estimate the length of Jolene's humerus when she is 60 years old.

f) Select six people of the same gender and measure their height and one of the bones for which an equation is given (the same bone on each person). Each measurement should be made to the nearest 0.5 cm. For each person, you will have two measurements, which can be considered an ordered pair (bone length, height). Plot the ordered pairs on a piece of graph paper, with the bone length on the horizontal axis and the height on the vertical axis. Start the scale on both axes at zero. Draw a straight line that you feel is the best approximation, or best fit, through these points. Determine where the line crosses the y-axis and the slope of the line. Your y-intercept and slope should be close to the values in the given equation for that bone. (Reference: M. Trotter and G. C. Gleser, "Estimation of Stature from Long Bones of American Whites and Negroes," *American Journal of Physical Anthropology,* 1952, 10:463–514.)

Graphing Calculator

2. The functions that we graphed in this chapter can be easily graphed with a graphing calculator (or grapher). If you do not have a graphing calculator, borrow one from your instructor or a friend.

a) Explain how you would set the domain and range. The calculator key to set the domain and range may be labeled *range* or *window*. Set the grapher with the following range or window settings:

    Xmin $= -12$, Xmax $= 12$, Xscl $= 1$,
    Ymin $= -13$, Ymax $= 6$, and Yscl $= 1$.

b) Explain how to enter a function in the graphing calculator. Enter the function $y = 3x^2 - 7x - 8$ in the calculator.

c) Graph the function you entered in part (b).

d) Learn how to use the *trace feature*. Then use it to estimate the x-intercepts. Record the estimated values for the x-intercepts.

e) Learn how to use the *zoom feature* to obtain a better approximation of the x-intercepts. Use the zoom feature twice and record the x-intercepts each time.

7

Systems of Linear Equations and Inequalities

What You Will Learn

- Solving systems of linear equations by graphing, by using the substitution method, by using the addition method, and by using matrices
- Solving systems of linear inequalities
- Adding, subtracting, and multiplying matrices
- Solving application problems using linear programming

Why This is Important

Imagine that you and a friend enter the bakery business. To make a profit in your business, you need to keep track of the cost of your materials, your overhead, the quantity of baked goods sold, the price at which you sell the baked goods, and many other items. To do so, you may need to develop and solve systems of equations.

◀ Business owners may solve systems of equations to determine under what conditions their business will be profitable.

SECTION 7.1 Systems of Linear Equations

Suppose you needed to have some landscaping work done at your home. In your local newspaper, two different landscaping services each have advertised specials. One company charges a lower consultation fee than the other company but charges a higher hourly rate for labor. How do you determine the number of hours of service needed for both services to have the same cost? How do you decide which company is less expensive for the services you need? In this section, we will introduce one way to use algebra to answer these questions.

Why *This is Important* As you will see in this section, we can often use a system of linear equations to determine the answers to real-life problems.

▲ *Solving a system of equations can help determine which of two landscaping companies offers the least expensive service.*

In algebra, it is often necessary to find the common solution to two or more linear equations. When two or more linear equations are considered simultaneously, the equations are called a *system of linear equations*. The solution to a system of linear equations may be found by a number of techniques. In this section, we illustrate how to solve a system of linear equations by graphing.

Solutions to Systems of Linear Equations

A *solution to a system of equations* is the ordered pair or ordered pairs that satisfy *all* equations in the system. A system of linear equations may have exactly one solution, no solution, or infinitely many solutions.

Example 1 *Is the Ordered Pair a Solution?*

Determine which of the ordered pairs is a solution to the following system of equations.

$$2x - y = 6$$
$$2x + y = 14$$

a) $(0, -6)$ b) $(5, 4)$ c) $(3, 8)$

Solution For the ordered pair to be a solution to the system, it must satisfy each equation in the system. Substitute the values of x and y into each equation.

a)
$2x - y = 6$	$2x + y = 14$
$2(0) - (-6) = 6$	$2(0) + (-6) = 14$
$6 = 6$ True	$-6 = 14$ False

Since $(0, -6)$ does not satisfy *both* equations, it is not a solution to the system.

b)
$2x - y = 6$	$2x + y = 14$
$2(5) - 4 = 6$	$2(5) + 4 = 14$
$6 = 6$ True	$14 = 14$ True

Since $(5, 4)$ satisfies *both* equations, it is a solution to the system.

c)
$2x - y = 6$	$2x + y = 14$
$2(3) - 8 = 6$	$2(3) + 8 = 14$
$-2 = 6$ False	$14 = 14$ True

Since $(3, 8)$ does not satisfy *both* equations, it is not a solution to the system. ∎

Solving a System of Linear Equations by Graphing

To find the solution to a system of linear equations graphically, we graph both of the equations on the same axes. The coordinates of the point or points of intersection of the graphs are the solution or solutions to the system of equations.

> **PROCEDURE** **SOLVING A SYSTEM OF EQUATIONS BY GRAPHING**
>
> 1. Determine three ordered pairs that satisfy each equation.
> 2. Plot the points that correspond to the ordered pairs and sketch the graphs of *both* equations on the same axes.
> 3. The coordinates of the point or points of intersection of the graphs are the solution or solutions to the system of equations.

When two linear equations are graphed, three situations are possible. The two lines may intersect at one point, as in Example 2; or the two lines may be parallel and not intersect, as in Example 3; or the two equations may represent the same line, as in Example 4 on page 388.

Since the solution to a system of equations may not be integer values, you may not be able to obtain the exact solution by graphing.

$x + y = 4$

x	y
0	4
1	3
4	0

$2x - y = -1$

x	y
-2	-3
1	3
0	1

Figure 7.1

Figure 7.2

TIMELY TIP

When checking the solution to a system of equations, it is important to check the solution in both equations. The ordered pair solution must satisfy *both* equations of the system.

Example 2 *A System with One Solution*

Determine the solution to the following system of equations graphically.

$$x + y = 4$$
$$2x - y = -1$$

Solution For each equation, substitute values for x and find the corresponding values for y. Three ordered pairs that satisfy $x + y = 4$ are $(0, 4), (1, 3)$, and $(4, 0)$, as shown in the left hand table above Fig. 7.1. Three ordered pairs that satisfy $2x - y = -1$ are $(-2, -3)$, $(0, 1)$, and $(1, 3)$, as shown in the right hand table above Fig. 7.1. Next, graph both $x + y = 4$ and $2x - y = -1$ on the same axis, Fig.7.1.

The graphs intersect at $(1, 3)$, which is the solution to the system of equations. This point is the only point that satisfies *both* equations.

CHECK:

$x + y = 4$	$2x - y = -1$
$1 + 3 = 4$	$2(1) - 3 = -1$
$4 = 4$ True	$2 - 3 = -1$
	$-1 = -1$ True

Fig. 7.2 shows the system of equations in Example 1, $x + y = 4$ and $2x - y = -1$, graphed on a Texas Instrument TI-84 Plus calculator.

The system of equations in Example 2 is an example of a *consistent system of equations*. A consistent system of equations is one that has at least one solution.

Example 3 *A System with No Solution*

Determine the solution to the following system of equations graphically.

$$x + y = 3$$
$$2x + 2y = -4$$

Solution Three ordered pairs that satisfy the equation $x + y = 3$ are $(0, 3)$, $(3, 0)$, and $(1, 2)$. Three ordered pairs that satisfy the equation $2x + 2y = -4$ are

Figure 7.3

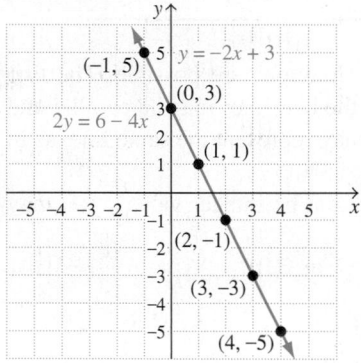

Figure 7.4

$(-2, 0)$, $(0, -2)$, and $(1, -3)$. The graphs of both equations are given in Fig. 7.3. Since the two lines are parallel, they do not intersect; therefore, the system has *no solution*. ∎

The system of equations in Example 3 has no solution. A system of equations that has no solution is called an *inconsistent system*.

Example 4 *A System with an Infinite Number of Solutions*

Determine the solution to the following system of equations graphically.

$$y = -2x + 3$$
$$2y = 6 - 4x$$

Solution Three ordered pairs that satisfy the equation $y = -2x + 3$ are $(0, 3)$, $(2, -1)$, and $(-1, 5)$. Three ordered pairs that satisfy the equation $2y = 6 - 4x$ are $(1, 1)$, $(3, -3)$, and $(4, -5)$. Graph the equations on the same axes (Fig. 7.4). Because all six points are on the same line, the two equations represent the same line. Therefore, every ordered pair that is a solution to one equation is also a solution to the other equation. Every point on the line satisfies both equations; thus, this system has an *infinite number of solutions*. Solving the second equation for y reveals that the equations are equivalent. ∎

When a system of equations has an infinite number of solutions, as in Example 4, it is called a *dependent system*. Note that because it has at least one solution, a dependent system is also a consistent system.

Figure 7.5 summarizes the three possibilities for a system of linear equations.

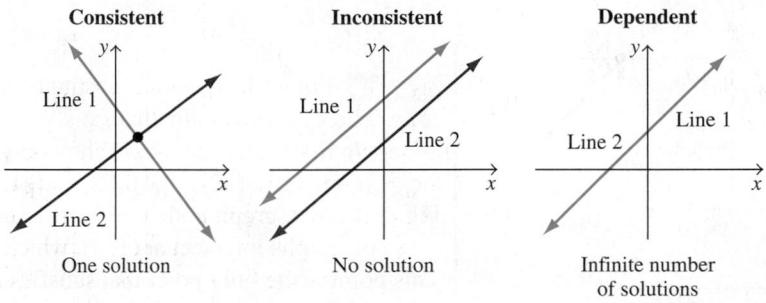

Figure 7.5

In Chapter 6, we introduced *modeling*. Recall that a *mathematical model* is an equation or system of equations that represents a real-life situation. In Examples 5 and 6, we develop equations that model a real-life situation.

Example 5 **Modeling—*A Landscape Service Application***

Tom's Tree and Landscape Service charges a consultation fee of $200 plus $50 per hour for labor for landscaping. Lawn Perfect Landscape Service charges a consultation fee of $300 plus $25 per hour for labor for landscaping.

a) Write a system of equations to represent the cost, C, of the two landscaping services, each with h hours of labor.

b) Graph both equations on the same axes and determine the number of hours needed for both services to have the same cost.

c) If the Johnsons need 7 hours of landscaping service done at their home, which service is less expensive?

TIMELY TIP

Following is a summary of the different types of systems of linear equations.

■ A *consistent system of equations* is one that has at least one solution.

■ An *inconsistent system of equations* is one that has no solution.

■ A *dependent system of equations* is one that has an infinite number of solutions.

Solution Let h = the number of hours of labor. The total cost of each service is the consultation fee plus the cost of the labor.

a) Tom's Tree and Landscape Service: $C = 200 + 50h$

  Lawn Perfect Landscape Service: $C = 300 + 25h$

b) We graphed the cost, C, versus the number of hours of labor, h, for 0 to 10 hours (Fig. 7.6). On the graph, the lines intersect at the point (4, 400). Thus, for 4 hours of service, both services would have the same cost, $400.

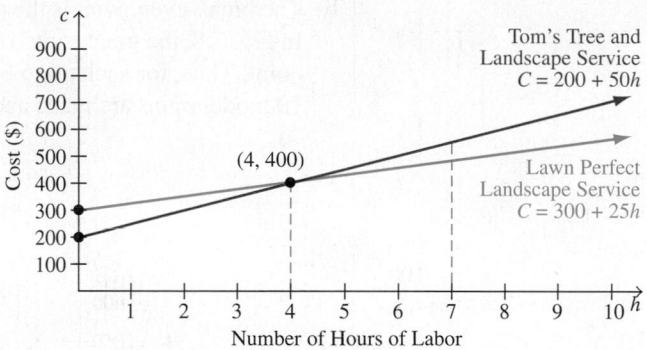

Figure 7.6

c) The graph shows that for more than 4 hours, Lawn Perfect is the least expensive service. Thus, for 7 hours, Lawn Perfect is less expensive than Tom's Tree and Landscape Service. ∎

Break-Even Analysis

Figure 7.7

Manufacturers use a technique called *break-even analysis* to determine how many units of an item must be sold for the business to "break even," that is, for its total revenue to equal its total cost. Suppose we let the horizontal axis represent the number of units manufactured and sold and the vertical axis represent dollars. Then linear equations for cost, C, and revenue, R, can both be sketched on the same axes (Fig. 7.7). Both C and R are expressed in dollars, and both are a function of the number of units. Profit, P, is the difference between revenue, R, and cost, C. Thus, $P = R - C$. If revenue is greater than cost, the company makes a profit. If cost is greater than revenue, the company has a loss.

Initially, the cost graph is higher than the revenue graph because of fixed (overhead) costs such as rent and utilities. During low levels of sales, the manufacturer suffers a loss (the cost graph is greater). During higher levels of sales, the manufacturer realizes a profit (the revenue graph is greater). The point at which the two graphs intersect is called the *break-even point*. At that number of units sold, revenue equals cost and the manufacturer breaks even.

Example 6 Modeling—*Profit and Loss in Business*

At a collectibles show, Richard Lane can sell model trains for $35. The costs for making the trains are a fixed cost of $200 and a production cost of $15 apiece.

a) Write an equation that represents Richard's revenue. Write an equation that represents Richard's cost.

b) How many model trains must Richard sell to break even?

c) Write an equation for the profit formula. Use the formula to determine Richard's profit if he sells 15 model trains.

d) How many model trains must Richard sell to make a profit of $600?

Solution

a) Let x denote the number of model trains made and sold. The revenue is given by the equation

$$R = 35x \quad (\$35 \text{ times the number of trains})$$

and the cost is given by the equation

$$C = 200 + 15x \quad (\$200 \text{ plus } \$15 \text{ times the number of trains})$$

b) The break-even point is the point at which the revenue and cost graphs intersect. In Fig. 7.8, the graphs intersect at the point (10, 350), which is the break-even point. Thus, for Richard to break even, he must sell 10 model trains. When 10 model trains are made and sold, the cost and revenue are both $350.

Figure 7.8

c) Profit is equal to the revenue minus the cost. Therefore, the profit formula is

$$P = R - C$$
$$= 35x - (200 + 15x)$$
$$= 35x - 200 - 15x$$
$$= 20x - 200$$

For 15 trains, the profit is found as follows.

$$P = 20x - 200$$
$$= 20(15) - 200 = 100$$

Richard has a profit of $100 if he sells 15 model trains. By observing the graph, we can see that if Richard sells 15 model trains, he will have a profit since at 15 trains the revenue line is greater than the cost line.

d) We can determine the number of model trains that Richard must sell to have a profit of $600 by using the profit formula. Substituting 600 for P we have

$$P = 20x - 200$$
$$600 = 20x - 200$$
$$800 = 20x$$
$$40 = x$$

Thus, Richard must sell 40 model trains to make a profit of $600. ∎

SECTION 7.1

Exercises

Warm Up Exercises

In Exercises 1–10, fill in the blank with an appropriate word, phrase, or symbol(s).

1. When two or more linear equations are considered simultaneously, the equations are called a(n) _____ of linear equations. System

2. The ordered pair or ordered pairs that satisfy all equations in a system of equations is called the _____ to the system of equations. Solution

3. A system of equations that has no solution is called a(n) _____ system of equations. Inconsistent

4. A system of equations that has at least one solution is called a(n) _____ system of equations. Consistent

5. A system of equations that has an infinite number of solutions is called a(n) _____ system of equations. Dependent

6. If the graphs of the equations in a system of linear equations are parallel lines, then the system has _____ solution(s). No

7. If the graphs of the equations in a system of linear equations intersect at only one point, then the system has _____ solution(s). One

8. If the graphs of the equations in a system of linear equations are the same line, then the system has a(n) _____ number of solutions. Infinite

9. A company makes a profit when its revenue is _____ than its cost. Greater

10. A company has a loss when its revenue is _____ than its cost. Less

Practice the Skills

In Exercises 11 and 12, determine which ordered pairs are solutions to the given system.

11. $y = 4x - 2$ $(2, 6)$ $(3, -10)$ $(1, 7)$
    $y = -x + 8$ $(2, 6)$

12. $x + 2y = 6$ $(-2, 4)$ $(2, 2)$ $(3, -9)$
    $x - y = -6$ $(-2, 4)$

In Exercises 13–16, solve the system of equations graphically.

13. $x = 1$
    $y = 3*$

14. $x = 2$
    $y = -1*$

15. $x = 4$
    $y = -3*$

16. $x = -5$
    $y = -3*$

In Exercises 17–32, solve the system of equations graphically. If the system does not have a single ordered pair as a solution, state whether the system is inconsistent or dependent.

17. $x = 2$
    $y = -x - 3*$

18. $y = 3$
    $y = x - 1*$

19. $y = 4x - 6$
    $y = -x + 9*$

20. $x + y = 4$
    $-x + y = 4*$

21. $x + 2y = 0$
    $2x - 3y = -14*$

22. $3x - y = 1$
    $4x - 3y = 3*$

23. $y = 2x - 4$
    $2x + y = 0*$

24. $y = x + 3$
    $y = -1*$

25. $x = 1$
    $x + y + 3 = 0*$

26. $2x - y = -3$
    $2x + y = -9*$

27. $3x + 2y = 6$
    $6x + 4y = 12*$

28. $2x - 3y = 12$
    $3y - 2x = 9*$

29. $y = \frac{1}{2}x + 4$
    $2y = x + 8*$

30. $y = \frac{1}{3}x - 4$
    $3y - x = 4*$

31. $y = \frac{4}{3}x - 2$
    $2x + 2y = 10*$

32. $2(x - 1) + 2y = 0$
    $3x + 2(y + 2) = 0*$

33. **a)** If the two lines in a system of equations have different slopes, how many solutions will the system have? . One unique solution; the lines intersect at one and only one point.

    b) If the two lines in a system of equations have the same slope but different y-intercepts, how many solutions will the system have? Explain. No solution; the lines do not intersect.

    c) If the two lines in a system of equations have the same slope and the same y-intercept, how many solutions will the system have? Explain. Infinitely many solutions; the lines coincide.

34. Indicate whether the graph shown represents a consistent, inconsistent, or dependent system.

    a)

    Consistent

    b)

    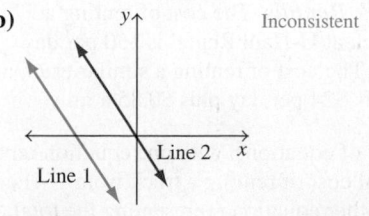

    Inconsistent

*See Instructor Answer Appendix

c)

In Exercises 35– 46, determine without graphing whether the system of equations has exactly one solution, no solution, or an infinite number of solutions. (Consider your answers to Exercise 33.)

35. $2x + y = 5$
$y = -2x + 5$
An infinite number of solutions

36. $3x + 2y = 4$
$4y = -6x + 6$ No solution

37. $3x + y = -6$
$4x - 2y = -8$
One solution

38. $x - 3y = 8$
$3x - y = 6$ One solution

39. $3x + y = 7$
$y = -3x + 9$
No solution

40. $x + 4y = 12$
$x = 4y + 3$ One solution

41. $2x - 3y = 6$
$x - \frac{3}{2}y = 3$
An infinite number of solutions

42. $x - 2y = 6$
$x + 2y = 4$ One solution

43. $3x = 6y + 5$
$y = \frac{1}{2}x - 3$
No solution

44. $3y = 6x + 4$
$-2x + y = \frac{4}{3}$
An infinite number of solutions

45. $12x - 5y = 4$
$3x + 4y = 6$ One solution

46. $4x + 7y = 2$
$4x = 6 + 7y$ One solution

Problem Solving

Two lines are perpendicular to each other when they meet at a right angle (a 90° angle). Two lines are perpendicular when their slopes are negative reciprocals. The negative reciprocal of 2 is $-\frac{1}{2}$, the negative reciprocal of $\frac{3}{5}$ is $-1/\left(\frac{3}{5}\right)$ or $-\frac{5}{3}$, and so on. If a represents any real number, except 0, its negative reciprocal is $-1/a$. Note that the product of a number and its negative reciprocal is -1. In Exercises 47–50, determine, by finding the slope of each line, whether the lines will be perpendicular to each other when graphed.

47. $4y - 2x = 15$
$3y - 5x = 9$
Not perpendicular

48. $4y - x = 6$
$y = x + 8$
Not perpendicular

49. $2x + y = 3$
$2y - x = 5$
Perpendicular

50. $6x + 5y = 3$
$-10x = 2 + 12y$
Not perpendicular

In Exercises 51–55, part of the question involves determining a system of equations that models the situation.

51. MODELING—*Truck Rentals* The cost of renting a medium-sized truck at U-Haul Rental is $30 per day plus $0.79 a mile. The cost of renting a similar truck at Discount Rentals is $24 per day plus $0.85 a mile.

a) Write a system of equations, with one equation representing the total cost of renting a truck from U-Haul for a day and the other equation representing the total cost of renting a truck from Discount Rentals for a day.*

b) Graph both equations (for up to and including 200 miles) on the same axes.*

c) Use the graph to estimate the number of miles that would need to be driven in a day for the cost of renting a truck from U-Haul to equal the cost of renting a truck from Discount. 100 miles

52. MODELING—*Landscaping Revisited* In Example 5, assume that Tom's Tree and Landscape Service charges $200 for a consultation fee plus $60 per hour for labor and that Lawn Perfect Landscape Service charges $305 for a consultation fee plus $25 per hour for labor.

a) Write the system of equations to represent the cost of the two landscaping services.*

b) Graph both equations for 0 to 10 hours on the same axes.*

c) Use the graph to estimate the number of hours of landscaping that must be used for both services to have the same cost. 3 hours

53. MODELING—*Selling Backpacks* Benjamin's Backpacks can sell backpacks for $25 per backpack. The costs for making the backpacks are a fixed cost of $400 and a production cost of $15 per backpack (see Example 6 for an example of cost and revenue equations).

a) Write the cost and revenue equations. $C = 15x + 400$
$R = 25x$

b) Graph both equations, for 0 to 50 backpacks, on the same axes.*

c) Use the graph to estimate the number of backpacks Benjamin's Backpacks must sell to break even.
40 backpacks

d) Write the profit formula. $P = 10x - 400$

e) Use the profit formula to determine whether Benjamin's Backpacks makes a profit or loss if it sells 30 backpacks. What is the profit or loss? Loss of $100

f) How many backpacks must Benjamin's Backpacks sell to realize a profit of $1000? 140 backpacks

*See Instructor Answer Appendix

54. MODELING—*Purchasing Stocks* When buying or selling stock for a customer, the Mark Demo Agency charges $40 plus 8 cents per share of stock purchased or sold. Andy Harris and Associates charges $15 plus 18 cents per share of stock purchased or sold.

a) Write a system of equations to represent the cost of purchasing or selling stock with each company.*

b) Graph both equations (for up to and including 350 shares of stock) on the same axes.*

c) Use the graph to estimate the number of shares of stock that must be purchased or sold for the total cost to be the same. 250 shares

d) If 300 shares of stock are to be purchased, which firm would be less expensive? Mark Demo Agency

55. MODELING—*Manufacturing Blu-ray Disc Players* A manufacturer sells Blu-ray Disc players for $150 per unit. Manufacturing costs consist of a fixed cost of $3850 and a production cost of $115 per unit.

a) Write the cost and revenue equations.
$C = 115x + 3850$, $R = 150x$

b) Graph both equations (for up to and including 150 units) on the same axes.*

c) Use the graph to estimate the number of units the manufacturer must sell to break even. 110 units

d) Write the profit formula. $P = 35x - 3850$

e) Use the profit formula to determine the manufacturer's profit or loss if 100 units are sold. Loss of $350

f) How many units must the manufacturer sell to make a profit of $875? 135 units

Concept/Writing Exercise

56. Explain how you can determine whether a system of two linear equations will be consistent, dependent, or inconsistent without graphing the equations.*

Challenge Problems/Group Activities

57. MODELING—*Job Offers* Hubert Hotchkiss had two job offers for sales positions. One pays a salary of $500 per week plus a 15% commission on his dollar sales volume. The second position pays a salary of $650 per week with no commission.

a) For each offer, write an equation that expresses the weekly pay. Job 1: $s = 0.15x + 500$
Job 2: $s = 650$

b) Graph the system of equations and determine the solution.*

c) For what dollar sales volume will the two offers result in the same pay? $1000

58. MODELING—*Long-Distance Calling*

a) In September 2010, an AT&T One Rate Plan charged 7 cents per minute for long-distance calls with a monthly fee of $5.95. The Sprint Nickel Anytime Plan charged 5 cents per minute for long-distance calls with a monthly fee of $8.95. Write an equation to determine the monthly cost for long-distance service with the AT&T One Rate Plan and write an equation to determine the monthly cost for long-distance service with the Sprint Nickel Anytime Plan. AT&T One Rate: $y = 0.07x + 5.95$
Sprint Nickel Anytime: $y = 0.05x + 8.95$

b) Graph the system of equations and determine the solution. *

c) After how many minutes will the cost for the two long-distance service plans be the same? 150 minutes

59. *Points of Intersection* **a)** If two lines have different slopes, what is the maximum possible number of points of intersection? One

b) If three lines all have different slopes, what is the maximum possible number of points of intersection of any two lines? Three

c) If four lines all have different slopes, what is the maximum possible number of points of intersection of any two lines? Six

d) If five lines all have different slopes, what is the maximum possible number of points of intersection of any two lines? Ten

e) Is there a pattern in the number of points of intersection? If so, explain the pattern. Use the pattern to determine the maximum possible number of points of intersection for six lines.*

Recreational Mathematics

60. Connect all the following points using exactly four straight-line segments. Do not lift your pencil off the paper.*

• • •

• • •

• • •

Internet/Research Activity

61. *The Rhind Papyrus* The Rhind Papyrus indicates that the early Egyptians used linear equations. Do research and write a paper on the symbols used in linear equations and the use of the linear equations by the early Egyptians. (References include history of mathematics books, encyclopedias, and the Internet.)

*See Instructor Answer Appendix

Solving Systems of Linear Equations by the Substitution and Addition Methods

Bill Ramierez is considering two cell phone plans. Both plans offer 300 free minutes each month. One plan charges $30 per month plus 45 cents for each additional minute after 300 minutes. The other plan charges $35 per month plus 20 cents for each additional minute after 300 minutes. How can Bill determine how long he would have to talk on the phone for the two plans to have the same cost? In this section, we will illustrate two different algebraic methods, the substitution method and the addition method, for answering this question.

▲ *Solving a system of equations may help determine which of two cell phone plans offers the least expensive service.*

Why **This is Important** Solving systems of equations may help us make financial decisions, such as which cell phone plan provides the least expensive service.

In section 7.1 we were able to estimate the solution to problems by determining what appeared to be the point of intersection of the graphs in the systems of linear equations. If an exact answer to a system of linear equations is needed, we can solve the system with algebraic methods. Two such methods are the substitution method and the addition method.

We first discuss the substitution method.

Substitution Method

> **PROCEDURE**   **PROCEDURE FOR SOLVING A SYSTEM OF EQUATIONS USING THE SUBSTITUTION METHOD**
>
> 1. Solve one of the equations for one of the variables. If possible, solve for a variable with a numerical coefficient of 1. By doing so, you may avoid working with fractions.
> 2. Substitute the expression found in Step 1 into the other equation. This step yields an equation in terms of a single variable.
> 3. Solve the equation found in Step 2 for the variable.
> 4. Substitute the value found in Step 3 into the equation you rewrote in Step 1 and solve for the remaining variable.

Examples 1, 2, and 3 illustrate the *substitution method*. These systems of equations are the same as in Examples 2, 3, and 4 in Section 7.1.

Example **1** *A Single Solution, by the Substitution Method*

Solve the following system of equations by substitution.

$$x + y = 4$$
$$2x - y = -1$$

Solution The numerical coefficients of the x- and y-terms in the equation $x + y = 4$ are both 1. Thus, we can solve this equation for either x or y. Let's solve for x in the first equation.

STEP 1.

$$x + y = 4$$
$$x + y - y = 4 - y$$
$$x = 4 - y$$

Subtract y from both sides of the equation.

STEP 2. Substitute $4 - y$ for x in the second equation.

$$2x - y = -1$$
$$2(4 - y) - y = -1$$

STEP 3. Now solve the equation for y.

$$8 - 2y - y = -1$$ Distributive property
$$8 - 3y = -1$$
$$8 - 8 - 3y = -1 - 8$$ Subtract 8 from both sides of the equation.
$$-3y = -9$$
$$\frac{-3y}{-3} = \frac{-9}{-3}$$ Divide both sides of the equation by -3.
$$y = 3$$

STEP 4. Substitute $y = 3$ in the equation solved for x and determine the value of x.

$$x = 4 - y$$
$$x = 4 - 3$$
$$x = 1$$

Thus, the solution is the ordered pair $(1, 3)$. This answer checks with the solution obtained graphically in Section 7.1, Example 2. ■

TIMELY TIP

When solving a system of equations, once you successfully solve for one of the variables, make sure you solve for the other variable. Remember that a solution to a system of equations must contain a numerical value for each variable in the system.

Example 2 *No Solution, by the Substitution Method*

Solve the following system of equations by substitution.

$$x + y = 3$$
$$2x + 2y = -4$$

Solution The numerical coefficients of the x- and y-terms in the equation $x + y = 3$ are both 1. Thus, we can solve this equation for either x or y. Let us solve for y in the first equation.

$$x + y = 3$$
$$x - x + y = 3 - x$$ Subtract x from both sides of the equation.
$$y = 3 - x$$

Now substitute $3 - x$ for y in the second equation.

$$2x + 2y = -4$$
$$2x + 2(3 - x) = -4$$
$$2x + 6 - 2x = -4$$ Distributive property
$$6 = -4$$ False

Since 6 cannot be equal to -4, there is no solution to the system of equations. Thus, the system of equations is inconsistent. This answer checks with the solution obtained graphically in Section 7.1, Example 3. ■

When solving the system in Example 2, we obtained $6 = -4$ and indicated that the system was inconsistent and that there was no solution. When solving a system of equations, if you obtain a false statement, such as $4 = 0$ or $-2 = 0$, the system is *inconsistent* and has *no solution*.

Example 3 An Infinite Number of Solutions, by the Substitution Method

Solve the following system of equations by substitution.

$$y = -2x + 3$$
$$2y = 6 - 4x$$

Solution The first equation $y = -2x + 3$ is already solved for y, so we will substitute $-2x + 3$ for y in the second equation.

$$2y = 6 - 4x$$
$$2(-2x + 3) = 6 - 4x$$
$$-4x + 6 = 6 - 4x \qquad \text{Distributive property}$$
$$4x - 4x + 6 = 6 - 4x + 4x \qquad \text{Add 4x to both sides of the equation.}$$
$$6 = 6 \qquad \text{True}$$

Since $6 = 6$, the system has an infinite number of solutions. Thus, the system of equations is dependent. This answer checks with the solution obtained in Section 7.1, Example 4. ∎

When solving Example 3, we obtained $6 = 6$ and indicated that the system was dependent and had an infinite number of solutions. When solving a system of equations, if you obtain a true statement, such as $0 = 0$ or $6 = 6$, the system is *dependent* and has an *infinite number of solutions*.

Addition Method

If neither of the equations in a system of linear equations has a variable with a coefficient of 1, it is generally easier to solve the system by using the *addition* (or *elimination*) *method*.

To solve a system of linear equations by the addition method, it is necessary to obtain two equations whose sum will be a single equation containing only one variable. To achieve this goal, we rewrite the system of equations as two equations where the coefficients of one of the variables are opposites (or additive inverses) of each other. For example, if one equation has a term of $2x$, we might rewrite the other equation so that its x term will be $-2x$. To obtain the desired equations, it might be necessary to multiply one or both equations in the original system by a number. When an equation is to be multiplied by a number, we will place brackets around the equation and place the number the equation is to be multiplied by before the brackets. For example, $4[2x + 3y = 6]$ means that each term on both sides of the equal sign in the equation $2x + 3y = 6$ is to be multiplied by 4:

$$4[2x + 3y = 6] \quad \text{gives} \quad 8x + 12y = 24$$

This notation will make our explanations much more efficient and easier for you to follow.

PROCEDURE   **SOLVING A SYSTEM OF EQUATIONS BY THE ADDITION METHOD**

1. If necessary, rewrite the equations so that the terms containing the variables appear on one side of the equal sign and the constants appear on the other side of the equal sign.

2. If necessary, multiply one or both equations by a constant(s) so that when you add the equations, the sum will be an equation containing only one variable.

3. Add the equations to obtain a single equation in one variable.

4. Solve for the variable in the equation obtained in Step 3.

5. Substitute the value found in Step 4 into either of the original equations and solve for the other variable.

Example 4 *Eliminating a Variable by the Addition Method.*

Solve the following system of equations by the addition method.

$$x + y = 4$$
$$3x - y = 8$$

Solution Since the coefficients of the y-terms, 1 and -1, are additive inverses, the sum of the y-terms will be zero when the equations are added. Thus, the sum of the two equations will contain only one variable, x. Add the two equations to obtain one equation in one variable. Then solve for the remaining variable.

$$
\begin{array}{rcl}
x + y &=& 4 \\
3x - y &=& 8 \\
\hline
4x &=& 12 \\
x &=& 3
\end{array}
$$

Now substitute 3 for x in either of the original equations to find the value of y.

$$
\begin{array}{rcl}
x + y &=& 4 \\
3 + y &=& 4 \\
y &=& 1
\end{array}
$$

The solution to the system is (3, 1). ■

Example 5 *Multiplying by -1 in the Addition Method*

Solve the following system of equations by the addition method.

$$x + 4y = 10$$
$$x + 2y = 6$$

Solution We want the sum of the two equations to have only one variable. We can eliminate the variable x by multiplying either equation by -1 and then adding the two equations. We will multiply the first equation by -1.

$$
\begin{array}{llll}
-1[x + 4y = 10] & \text{gives} & -x - 4y = -10 \\
x + 2y = 6 & & x + 2y = 6
\end{array}
$$

We now have a system of equations equivalent to the original system.

Now add the two equations.

$$
\begin{aligned}
-x - 4y &= -10 \\
\underline{x + 2y} &= \underline{6} \\
-2y &= -4 \\
y &= 2
\end{aligned}
$$

Now we solve for x by substituting 2 for y in either of the original equations.

$$
\begin{aligned}
x + 4y &= 10 \\
x + 4(2) &= 10 \\
x + 8 &= 10 \\
x &= 2
\end{aligned}
$$

The solution is (2, 2). ∎

Example 6 *Multiplying One Equation in the Addition Method.*

Solve the following system of equations by the addition method.

$$
\begin{aligned}
4x + 3y &= -1 \\
2x - y &= -13
\end{aligned}
$$

Solution We can multiply the bottom equation by 3 and then add the two equations to eliminate the variable y.

$$
\begin{array}{ccc}
4x + 3y = -1 & & 4x + 3y = -1 \\
3[2x - y = -13] & \text{gives} & 6x - 3y = -39
\end{array}
$$

$$
\begin{aligned}
4x + 3y &= -1 \\
\underline{6x - 3y} &= \underline{-39} \\
10x &= -40 \\
x &= -4
\end{aligned}
$$

Now we find y by substituting -4 for x in either of the original equations.

$$
\begin{aligned}
4x + 3y &= -1 \\
4(-4) + 3y &= -1 \\
-16 + 3y &= -1 \\
3y &= 15 \\
y &= 5
\end{aligned}
$$

The solution is $(-4, 5)$. ∎

Note that in Example 6 we could have eliminated the variable x by multiplying the bottom equation by -2, then adding the two equations. Try this method now.

Example 7 *Multiplying Both Equations*

Solve the following system of equations by the addition method.

$$
\begin{aligned}
3x - 4y &= 8 \\
2x + 3y &= 9
\end{aligned}
$$

Solution In this system, we cannot eliminate a variable by multiplying only one equation by an integer value and then adding. To eliminate a variable, we can multiply each equation by a different number. To eliminate the variable x, we can multiply the top equation by 2 and the bottom by -3 (or the top by -2 and the bottom by 3) and then add the two equations. If we want, we can instead eliminate the variable y by multiplying the top equation by 3 and the bottom by 4 and then adding the two equations. Let's eliminate the variable x.

$$2[3x - 4y = 8] \quad \text{gives} \quad 6x - 8y = 16$$
$$-3[2x + 3y = 9] \quad \text{gives} \quad -6x - 9y = -27$$

$$\begin{aligned} 6x - 8y &= 16 \\ -6x - 9y &= -27 \\ \hline -17y &= -11 \\ y &= \frac{11}{17} \end{aligned}$$

We could now find x by substituting $\frac{11}{17}$ for y in either of the original equations. Although it can be done, it gets messy. Instead, let's solve for x by eliminating the variable y from the two original equations. To do so, we multiply the first equation by 3 and the second equation by 4.

$$3[3x - 4y = 8] \quad \text{gives} \quad 9x - 12y = 24$$
$$4[2x + 3y = 9] \quad \text{gives} \quad 8x + 12y = 36$$

$$\begin{aligned} 9x - 12y &= 24 \\ 8x + 12y &= 36 \\ \hline 17x \phantom{{}- 12y} &= 60 \\ x &= \frac{60}{17} \end{aligned}$$

The solution to the system is $\left(\frac{60}{17}, \frac{11}{17} \right)$. ∎

Example 8 MODELING—*When Are Repair Costs the Same?*

Melinda Melendez needs to purchase a new radiator for her car and have it installed by a mechanic. She is considering two garages: Steve's Repair and Greg's Garage. At Steve's Repair, the parts cost $200 and the labor cost is $50 per hour. At Greg's Garage, the parts cost $375 and the labor cost is $25 per hour. How many hours would the repair need to take for the total cost at each garage to be the same?

Solution We are asked to find the number of hours the repair would need to take for each garage to have the same total cost, C. First write a system of equations to represent the total cost for each of the garages. The total cost consists of the cost of the parts and the labor cost. The labor cost depends on the number of hours of labor.

Let $x =$ the number of hours of labor.

$$\text{Total cost} = \text{cost of parts} + \text{labor cost}$$
$$\text{Steve's Repair:}\ C = 200 + 50x$$
$$\text{Greg's Garage:}\ C = 375 + 25x$$

We want to determine when the cost will be the same, so we set the two costs equal to each other (substitution method) and solve the resulting equation.

TIMELY TIP

If you obtain an equation such as $0 = 6$, or any other equation that is false when solving a system of linear equations, the system is *inconsistent* (the two equations represent parallel lines; see Fig. 7.5 on page 388) and there is no solution.

If you obtain the equation $0 = 0$ when solving a system of linear equations by either the substitution or the addition method, the system is *dependent* (both equations represent the same line; see Fig. 7.5 on page 388) and there are an infinite number of solutions.

$$200 + 50x = 375 + 25x$$

$$200 - 200 + 50x = 375 - 200 + 25x \qquad \text{Subtract 200 from both sides of the equation.}$$

$$50x = 175 + 25x$$

$$50x - 25x = 175 + 25x - 25x \qquad \text{Subtract 25x from both sides of the equation.}$$

$$25x = 175$$

$$\frac{25x}{25} = \frac{175}{25} \qquad \text{Divide both sides of the equation by 25.}$$

$$x = 7$$

Thus, for 7 hours of labor, the cost at both garages would be the same. If we construct a graph (Fig. 7.9) of the two cost equations, the point of intersection is (7, 550). If the repair were to require 7 hours of labor, the total cost at either garage would be $550.

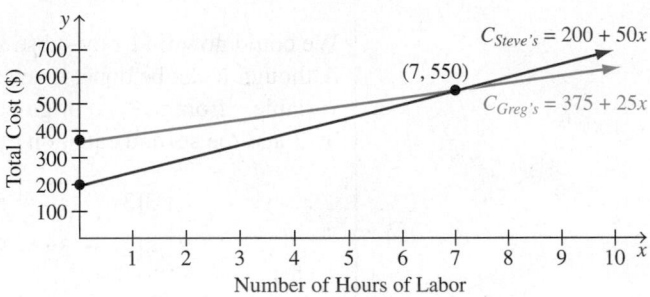

Figure 7.9

Example 9 MODELING—*A Mixture Problem*

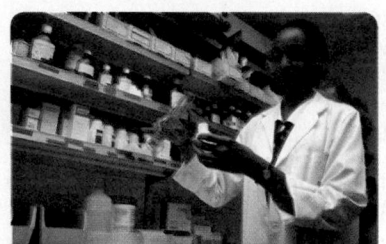

Pat Williams, a pharmacist, needs 500 milliliters (mℓ) of a 10% phenobarbital solution. She has only a 5% phenobarbital solution and a 25% phenobarbital solution available. How many milliliters of each solution should she mix to obtain the desired solution?

Solution First we set up a system of equations. The unknown quantities are the amount of 5% solution and the amount of the 25% solution that must be used. Let

$$x = \text{number of mℓ of 5\% solution}$$
$$y = \text{number of mℓ of 25\% solution}$$

We know that 500 mℓ of solution are needed. Thus,

$$x + y = 500$$

The total amount of phenobarbital in a solution is determined by multiplying the percent of phenobarbital by the number of milliliters of solution. The second equation comes from the fact that

$$\begin{pmatrix} \text{Total amount of} \\ \text{phenobarbital in} \\ \text{5\% solution} \end{pmatrix} + \begin{pmatrix} \text{total amount of} \\ \text{phenobarbital in} \\ \text{25\% solution} \end{pmatrix} = \begin{pmatrix} \text{total amount of} \\ \text{phenobarbital} \\ \text{in 10\% mixture} \end{pmatrix}$$

$$0.05x \qquad + \qquad 0.25y \qquad = \qquad 0.10(500)$$

or

$$0.05x + 0.25y = 50$$

The system of equations is

$$x + y = 500$$
$$0.05x + 0.25y = 50$$

Let's solve this system of equations by using the addition method. There are various ways of eliminating one variable. To obtain integer values in the second equation, we can multiply both sides of the equation by 100. The result will be an x-term of $5x$. If we multiply both sides of the first equation by -5, that will result in an x-term of $-5x$. By following this process, we can eliminate the x-terms from the system.

$$-5[x + y = 500] \quad \text{gives} \quad -5x - 5y = -2500$$
$$100[0.05x + 0.25y = 50] \quad \text{gives} \quad 5x + 25y = 5000$$

$$
\begin{array}{r}
-5x - 5y = -2500 \\
5x + 25y = 5000 \\
\hline
20y = 2500
\end{array}
$$

$$\frac{20y}{20} = \frac{2500}{20}$$

$$y = 125$$

Now we determine x.

$$x + y = 500$$
$$x + 125 = 500$$
$$x = 375$$

Therefore, 375 mℓ of a 5% phenobarbital solution must be mixed with 125 mℓ of a 25% phenobarbital solution to obtain 500 mℓ of a 10% phenobarbital solution. ∎

Example 9 can also be solved by using substitution. Try to do so now.

SECTION 7.2
Exercises

Warm Up Exercises

In Exercises 1–2, fill in the blank with an appropriate word, phrase, or symbol(s).

1. When solving a system of equations, if you obtain a true statement such as $0 = 0$ or $6 = 6$, the system is dependent and has a(n) _____ number of solutions.
Infinite

2. When solving a system of equations, if you obtain a false statement such as $4 = 0$ or $-2 = 0$, the system is inconsistent and has _____ solution. No

Practice the Skills

In Exercises 3–20, solve the system of equations by the substitution method. If the system does not have a single

ordered pair as a solution, state whether the system is inconsistent or dependent.

3. $y = x + 5$
   $y = -x + 7$ (1, 6)

4. $y = 4x - 2$
   $y = 3x + 1$ (3, 10)

5. $6x + 3y = 3$
   $x - 3y = 4$ (1, −1)

6. $4x - y = 2$
   $2x - y = 6$ (−2, −10)

7. $y - x = 4$ No solution;
   $x - y = 3$ inconsistent system

8. $x + y = 3$ No solution;
   $y + x = 5$ inconsistent system

9. $3y + 2x = 4$
   $3y = 6 - x$ $\left(-2, \frac{8}{3}\right)$

10. $x = 5y - 12$
    $x - y = 0$ (3, 3)

11. $y - 2x = 3$
    $2y = 4x + 6$ *

12. $y = 2$
    $y + x + 3 = 0$ (−5, 2)

13. $x = y + 3$
$x = -3$ $(-3, -6)$

14. $x + 2y = 6$
$y = 2x + 3$ $(0, 3)$

15. $y + 3x - 4 = 0$
$2x - y = 7$ $\left(\frac{11}{5}, -\frac{13}{5}\right)$

16. $x + 4y = 7$
$2x + 3y = 5$ $\left(-\frac{1}{5}, \frac{9}{5}\right)$

17. $x = 2y + 3$
$y = 3x - 1$ $\left(-\frac{1}{5}, -\frac{8}{5}\right)$

18. $x + 4y = 9$
$2x - y - 6 = 0$ $\left(\frac{11}{3}, \frac{4}{3}\right)$

19. $y = -2x + 3$
$4x + 2y = 12$
No solution; inconsistent system

20. $2x + y = 12$
$x = -\frac{1}{2}y + 6$ An infinite
number of solutions; dependent system

In Exercises 21–36, solve the system of equations by the addition method. If the system does not have a single ordered pair as a solution, state whether the system is inconsistent or dependent.

21. $4x + y = 13$
$2x - y = 5$ $(3, 1)$

22. $x + 2y = 9$
$x - 2y = -3$ $(3, 3)$

23. $x + y = 12$
$x - 2y = -3$ $(7, 5)$

24. $4x + 2y = 2$
$3x - 2y = 12$ $(2, -3)$

25. $2x - y = -4$
$-3x - y = 6$ $(-2, 0)$

26. $x + y = 6$
$-2x + y = -3$ $(3, 3)$

27. $4x + y = 6$
$3x + 2y = 7$ $(1, 2)$

28. $2x + y = 6$
$3x + y = 5$ $(-1, 8)$

29. $2x + y = 11$
$x + 3y = 18$ $(3, 5)$

30. $5x - 2y = 11$
$-3x + 2y = 1$ $\left(6, \frac{19}{2}\right)$

31. $3x - 4y = 11$
$3x + 5y = -7$ $(1, -2)$

32. $4x - 2y = 6$
$4y = 8x - 12$ *

33. $4x + y = 6$
$-8x - 2y = 13$
No solution; inconsistent system

34. $2x + 3y = 6$
$5x - 4y = -8$ $(0, 2)$

35. $2x - 4y = 4$
$3x - 2y = 4$ $\left(1, -\frac{1}{2}\right)$

36. $6x + 6y = 1$
$4x + 9y = 4$ $\left(-\frac{1}{2}, \frac{2}{3}\right)$

Problem Solving

In Exercises 37–48, write a system of equations that can be used to solve the problem. Then solve the system and determine the answer.

37. MODELING—*Owning a Business* Sosena Milion can join a small business as a full partner and receive a salary of $12,000 per year plus 15% of the year's profit, or she can join as a sales manager with a salary of $27,000 per year plus 5% of the year's profit. What must the year's profit be for her total earnings to be the same whether she joins as a full partner or as a sales manager? *

38. MODELING—*Investments* David Saxon invested $25,000 in two different corporate bonds for 1 year. One bond pays a 4.5% simple interest rate, and the other pays a 6% simple interest rate. The total annual interest David received from both bonds was $1380. Find the amount he invested in each bond. For 1 year,

the simple interest on a specific corporate bond is found by multiplying the amount invested by the simple interest rate. *

39. MODELING—*Shares of Stock* Cody Lewis owns a total of 55 shares of stock, some in LG Electronics and some in Nintendo Company. On a particular day, LG Electronics stock closed at $34.08 per share and Nintendo Company stock closed at $41.90 per share. If Cody's stock for these companies was worth $2109, how many shares of each type of stock does he own? *

40. MODELING—*Basketball Game* The Stanford University women's basketball team made 45 field goals in a recent game; some were 2-pointers and some were 3-pointers. How many 2-point baskets were made and how many 3-point baskets were made if Stanford scored 101 points? *

41. MODELING—*Chemical Mixture* Antonio Gonzalez is a chemist and needs 15 liters (ℓ) of a 25% hydrochloric acid solution. He discovers he is out of the 25% hydrochloric acid solution. He checks his supply shelf and finds he has a large supply of both 40% and 10% hydrochloric acid solutions. He decides to use the 40% and 10% solutions to make 15 ℓ of a 25% solution. How many liters of the 40% solution and of the 10% solution should he mix? *

42. MODELING—*Sets of Dishes* A restaurant manager purchased 100 sets of dishes. One design cost $30 per set, and another design cost $40 per set. If the manager spent $3200 on the dishes, how many sets of each design did she purchase? *

43. MODELING—*Choosing a Copy Service* Lori Lanier recently purchased a high-speed copier for her home office and wants to purchase a service contract on the copier. She is considering two sources for the contract. The Economy Sales and Service Company charges $18 a month plus 2 cents per copy. Office Superstore charges $24 a month but only 1.5 cents per copy. How many copies would Lori need to make for the monthly costs of both plans to be the same? *

44. MODELING—*Hardwood Floor Installation* The cost to purchase a particular type of hardwood flooring at Home Depot is $2.65 per square foot. In addition, the installation

cost is $468.75. The cost to purchase the same flooring at Hardwood Guys is $3.10 per square foot. In addition, the installation cost is $412.50. $y = 2.65x + 468.75$
$y = 3.10x + 412.50$

a) Determine the number of square feet of this flooring that Roberto Cruz must purchase for the total cost of the flooring and installation to be the same from both stores. 125 square feet

b) If Roberto needs to purchase and have installed 196 square feet of this flooring, which store would be less expensive? Home Depot

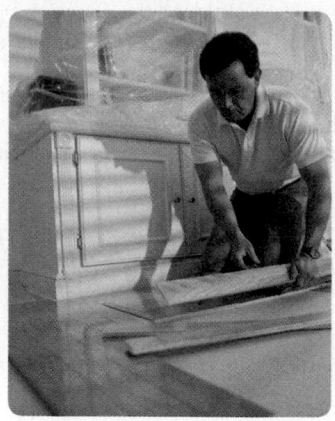

45. **MODELING—***Nut and Pretzel Mix* Dave Chwalik wants to purchase 20 pounds of party mix for a total of $30. To obtain the mixture, he will mix nuts that cost $3 per pound with pretzels that cost $1 per pound. How many pounds of each type of mix should he use? *

46. **MODELING—***Laboratory Research* Animals in an experiment are to be kept on a strict diet. Each animal is to receive, among other things, 20 g of protein and 6 g of carbohydrates. The scientist has only two food mixes of the following compositions available.

	Protein (%)	Carbohydrates (%)
Mix A	10	6
Mix B	20	2

How many grams of each mix should she use to obtain the right diet for a single animal? *

47. **MODELING—***Concert Ticket Prices* Finger Lakes Performing Arts Center sold 4600 tickets for a summer jazz concert. Covered amphitheater tickets cost $27 and lawn seats cost $14. If $104,700 in ticket sales was collected for the concert, how many tickets of each type were sold? *

48. **MODELING—***Golf Club Membership* Membership in Oakwood Country Club costs $3000 per year and entitles a member to play a round of golf for a greens fee of $18. At Pinecrest Country Club, membership costs $2500 per year and the greens fee is $20. $c = 18r + 3000$
$c = 20r + 2500$

a) How many rounds must a golfer play in a year for the costs at the two clubs to be the same? 250 rounds

b) If Tamika Johnson planned to play 30 rounds of golf in a year, which club would be the least expensive? Pinecrest

49. **MODELING—***Phone Revenue* The following graph shows that the revenue from wireless phone service has increased from 2007 through 2010. The graph also shows that the revenue from landline phone service has decreased over this time period. The revenue for wireless phone service can be modeled by the equation $y = 1.21x + 10.66$, and the revenue for landline phone service can be modeled by the equation $y = -0.88x + 18.02$, where x represents the number of years since 2000. Assuming this trend continues, use the substitution method to approximate when the revenue from wireless phone service will equal the revenue from landline phone service. 3.5 years after 2007 or in 2010

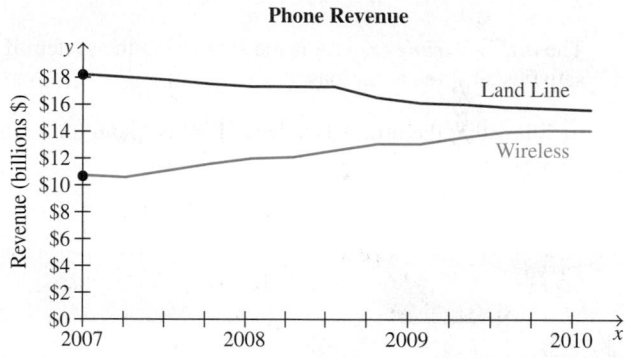

Source: SEC

50. *Salaries* Jose's salary can be modeled by the equation $y = 39,000 + 1200t$, and Charlie's salary can be modeled by the equation $y = 45,000 + 700t$, where t represents the number of years since 2002. The graph below shows Jose's salary and Charlie's salary for up to 10 years after 2002. Assuming this trend continues, use the substitution method to determine when Jose's salary will equal Charlie's salary. 12 years after 2002 or in 2014

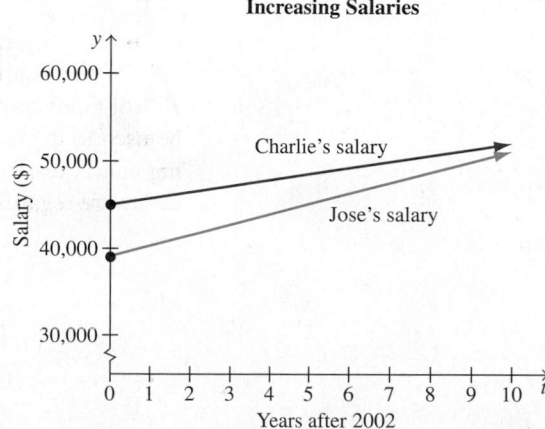

*See Instructor Answer Appendix

Challenge Problems/Group Activities

51. Solve the following system of equations for u and v by first substituting x for $\frac{1}{u}$ and y for $\frac{1}{v}$.

$$\frac{1}{u} + \frac{2}{v} = 8$$

$$\frac{3}{u} - \frac{1}{v} = 3 \quad \left(\frac{1}{2}, \frac{1}{3}\right)$$

52. Develop a system of equations that has $(6, 5)$ as its solution. Explain how you developed your system of equations. Answers will vary.

53. The substitution or addition methods can also be used to solve a system of three equations in three variables. Consider the following system.

$$x + y + z = 7$$
$$x - y + 2z = 9$$
$$-x + 2y + z = 4$$

The *ordered triple* (x, y, z) is the solution to the system if it satisfies all three equations.

a) Show that the ordered triple $(2, 1, 4)$ is a solution to the system.

b) Use the substitution or addition method to determine the solution to the system. (*Hint:* Eliminate one variable by using two equations. Then eliminate the same variable by using two different equations.) Answers will vary.

54. Construct a system of two equations that has no solution. Explain how you know the system has no solution. Answers will vary.

55. Construct a system of two equations that has an infinite number of solutions. Explain how you know the system has an infinite number of solutions. Answers will vary.

56. When solving a system of equations by the substitution method, a student obtained the equation $0 = 0$ and gave the solution as $(0, 0)$. What is the student's error? *

57. In parts (a)–(d), make up a system of linear equations whose solution will be the ordered pair given. *Hint:* It may be helpful to visualize possible graphs that have the given solution. There are many possible answers for each part.

a) $(0, 0)$ **b)** $(1, 0)$ **c)** $(0, 1)$ **d)** $(1, 1)$
Answers will vary.

*See Instructor Answer Appendix

▲ *In this section, we introduce a method to display information from a survey such as opinions of college students.*

Five hundred students at the University of Delaware were asked if they were in favor of or opposed to an increase in their student fees to pay for building a new meeting room for student clubs. Each student was also asked to indicate whether he or she was a freshman, sophomore, junior, or senior. How can the responses from the survey be displayed? In this section, we will introduce a method used to display information such as responses from a survey.

Why **This is Important** We often need an efficient way to display information such as responses from a survey or a company's current inventory.

A *matrix* is a rectangular array of elements. An array is a systematic arrangement of numbers or symbols in rows and columns. Matrices (the plural of matrix) may be used to display information and to solve systems of linear equations. The following matrix displays the responses from the survey of 500 students at the University of Delaware regarding an increase in their student fees.

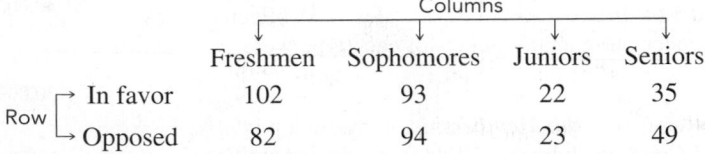

	Freshmen	Sophomores	Juniors	Seniors
In favor	102	93	22	35
Opposed	82	94	23	49

The numbers in the rows and columns of a matrix are called the *elements* of the matrix. The matrix given above contains eight elements. The *dimensions* of a matrix may be indicated with the notation $r \times s$, where r is the number of rows and s is the number of columns in the matrix. Because the matrix given on page 404 has 2 rows and 4 columns, it is a 2 by 4, written 2 × 4, matrix. In this text, from this point onward, we use brackets, [ ], to indicate a matrix. Consider the two matrices below. A matrix that contains the same number of rows and columns is called a *square matrix*. Following is an example of a 2 × 2 square matrix and a 3 × 3 square matrix.

$$\begin{bmatrix} 2 & 3 \\ 5 & 2 \end{bmatrix} \qquad \begin{bmatrix} 4 & 6 & -1 \\ 2 & 3 & 0 \\ 5 & 2 & 1 \end{bmatrix}$$

Two matrices are equal if and only if they have the same elements in the same relative positions.

Example 1 *Equal Matrices*

Given $A = B$, determine x and y.

$$A = \begin{bmatrix} 2 & 5 \\ 7 & -1 \end{bmatrix}, \qquad B = \begin{bmatrix} x & 5 \\ 7 & y \end{bmatrix}$$

Solution Since the matrices are equal, the corresponding elements must be the same, so $x = 2$ and $y = -1$. ∎

Addition of Matrices

Two matrices can be added only if they have the same dimensions (same number of rows and same number of columns). To obtain the sum of two matrices with the same dimensions, add the corresponding elements of the two matrices.

Example 2 *Adding Matrices*

Determine $A + B$ if

$$A = \begin{bmatrix} 5 & 6 \\ 2 & -3 \end{bmatrix} \quad \text{and} \quad B = \begin{bmatrix} 2 & 8 \\ 4 & 0 \end{bmatrix}$$

Solution $A + B = \begin{bmatrix} 5 & 6 \\ 2 & -3 \end{bmatrix} + \begin{bmatrix} 2 & 8 \\ 4 & 0 \end{bmatrix}$

$$= \begin{bmatrix} 5 + 2 & 6 + 8 \\ 2 + 4 & -3 + 0 \end{bmatrix} = \begin{bmatrix} 7 & 14 \\ 6 & -3 \end{bmatrix}$$ ∎

Example 3 MODELING—*Sales of Bicycles*

Peddler's Bicycle Corporation owns and operates two stores, one in Pennsylvania and one in New Jersey. The number of mountain bicycles (MB) and racing bicycles (RB) sold in each store during January through June and during July through December are indicated in the matrices that follow. We will call the matrices A and B.

	Pennsylvania		New Jersey	
	MB	RB	MB	RB
Jan.–June	515	425	520	350
July–Dec.	290	250	180	271

$$\begin{bmatrix} 515 & 425 \\ 290 & 250 \end{bmatrix} = A \qquad \begin{bmatrix} 520 & 350 \\ 180 & 271 \end{bmatrix} = B$$

Determine the total number of each type of bicycle sold by the corporation during each time period.

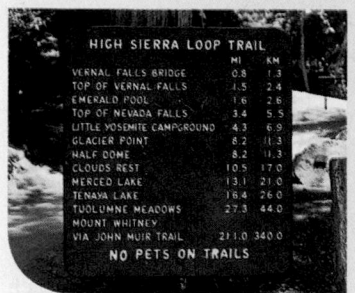

Solution To solve the problem, we add matrices A and B.

$$
\begin{array}{c}
\text{Jan.–June} \\
\text{July–Dec.}
\end{array}
\begin{array}{cc}
\quad MB & RB \\
\end{array}
\begin{bmatrix}
515 + 520 & 425 + 350 \\
290 + 180 & 250 + 271
\end{bmatrix}
=
\begin{array}{cc}
MB & RB \\
\end{array}
\begin{bmatrix}
1035 & 775 \\
470 & 521
\end{bmatrix}
$$

We can see from the sum matrix that during the period from January through June, a total of 1035 mountain bicycles and 775 racing bicycles were sold. During the period from July through December, a total of 470 mountain bicycles and 521 racing bicycles were sold. ∎

Subtraction of Matrices

Only matrices with the same dimension may be subtracted. To do so, we subtract each entry in one matrix from the corresponding entry in the other matrix.

Example 4 *Subtracting Matrices*

Determine $A - B$ if

$$
A = \begin{bmatrix} 3 & 6 \\ 5 & -1 \end{bmatrix} \quad \text{and} \quad B = \begin{bmatrix} 2 & -4 \\ 8 & -3 \end{bmatrix}
$$

Solution

$$
A - B = \begin{bmatrix} 3 & 6 \\ 5 & -1 \end{bmatrix} - \begin{bmatrix} 2 & -4 \\ 8 & -3 \end{bmatrix}
$$

$$
= \begin{bmatrix} 3 - 2 & 6 - (-4) \\ 5 - 8 & -1 - (-3) \end{bmatrix} = \begin{bmatrix} 1 & 10 \\ -3 & 2 \end{bmatrix}
$$ ∎

Multiplying a Matrix by a Real Number

A matrix may be multiplied by a real number by multiplying each entry in the matrix by the real number. Sometimes when we multiply a matrix by a real number, we call that real number a *scalar*.

Example 5 *Multiplying a Matrix by a Scalar*

For matrices A and B, determine (a) $3A$ and (b) $3A - 2B$.

$$
A = \begin{bmatrix} 1 & 4 \\ -3 & 5 \end{bmatrix}, \qquad B = \begin{bmatrix} -1 & 3 \\ 5 & 6 \end{bmatrix}
$$

Solution

a) $3A = 3\begin{bmatrix} 1 & 4 \\ -3 & 5 \end{bmatrix} = \begin{bmatrix} 3(1) & 3(4) \\ 3(-3) & 3(5) \end{bmatrix} = \begin{bmatrix} 3 & 12 \\ -9 & 15 \end{bmatrix}$

b) We determined $3A$ in part (a). Now we find $2B$.

$$
2B = 2\begin{bmatrix} -1 & 3 \\ 5 & 6 \end{bmatrix} = \begin{bmatrix} 2(-1) & 2(3) \\ 2(5) & 2(6) \end{bmatrix} = \begin{bmatrix} -2 & 6 \\ 10 & 12 \end{bmatrix}
$$

$$
3A - 2B = \begin{bmatrix} 3 & 12 \\ -9 & 15 \end{bmatrix} - \begin{bmatrix} -2 & 6 \\ 10 & 12 \end{bmatrix}
$$

$$
= \begin{bmatrix} 3 - (-2) & 12 - 6 \\ -9 - 10 & 15 - 12 \end{bmatrix} = \begin{bmatrix} 5 & 6 \\ -19 & 3 \end{bmatrix}
$$ ∎

Multiplication of Matrices

Multiplication of matrices is slightly more difficult than addition of matrices. Multiplication of matrices is possible only when the number of *columns* of the first matrix, A, is the same as the number of *rows* of the second matrix, B. We use the notation

$$A$$
$$3 \times 4$$

to indicate that matrix A has three rows and four columns. Suppose matrix A is a 3×4 matrix and matrix B is a 4×5 matrix. Then

$$
\begin{array}{cc}
A & B \\
3 \times 4 & 4 \times 5
\end{array}
$$
$$\underbrace{\qquad}_{\text{Same}}$$
Product matrix 3×5

This notation indicates that matrix A has four columns and matrix B has four rows. Therefore, we can multiply these two matrices. The product matrix will have the same number of rows as matrix A and the same number of columns as matrix B. Thus, the dimensions of the product matrix are 3×5.

Example 6 *Can These Matrices Be Multiplied?*

Determine which of the following pairs of matrices can be multiplied.

a) $A = \begin{bmatrix} 3 & 2 \\ 5 & 7 \end{bmatrix}, \quad B = \begin{bmatrix} 0 & 6 \\ 4 & 1 \end{bmatrix}$

b) $A = \begin{bmatrix} 2 & 3 \\ 5 & 6 \end{bmatrix}, \quad B = \begin{bmatrix} 2 & 4 & -1 \\ 6 & 8 & 0 \end{bmatrix}$

c) $A = \begin{bmatrix} 2 & 1 & 4 \\ 3 & 2 & 8 \end{bmatrix}, \quad B = \begin{bmatrix} 2 & 1 & 3 \\ 1 & 0 & -2 \end{bmatrix}$

Solution

a)

$$
\begin{array}{cc}
A & B \\
2 \times 2 & 2 \times 2
\end{array}
$$
$$\underbrace{\qquad}_{\text{Same}}$$

  Because matrix A has two columns and matrix B has two rows, the two matrices can be multiplied. The product is a 2×2 matrix.

b)

$$
\begin{array}{cc}
A & B \\
2 \times 2 & 2 \times 3
\end{array}
$$
$$\underbrace{\qquad}_{\text{Same}}$$

  Because matrix A has two columns and matrix B has two rows, the two matrices can be multiplied. The product is a 2×3 matrix.

c)

$$
\begin{array}{cc}
A & B \\
2 \times 3 & 2 \times 3
\end{array}
$$
$$\underbrace{\qquad}_{\text{Not same}}$$

  Because matrix A has three columns and matrix B has two rows, the two matrices cannot be multiplied.

Profile In Mathematics

James Sylvester, William Rowan Hamilton, and Arthur Cayley

James Sylvester

William Rowan Hamilton

Arthur Cayley

Three mathematicians played important roles in the development of matrix theory: James Sylvester (1814–1897), William Rowan Hamilton (1805–1865), and Arthur Cayley (1821–1895). Sylvester and Cayley cooperated in developing matrix theory. Sylvester was the first to use the term *matrix*. Hamilton, a noted physicist, astronomer, and mathematician, also used what was essentially the algebra of matrices under the name *linear and vector functions*. The mathematical concept of *vector space* grew out of Hamilton's work on the algebra of vectors.

To explain matrix multiplication, let's use matrices A and B that follow.

$$A = \begin{bmatrix} 3 & 2 \\ 5 & 7 \end{bmatrix} \quad \text{and} \quad B = \begin{bmatrix} 0 & 6 \\ 4 & 1 \end{bmatrix}$$

Since A contains two rows and B contains two columns, the product matrix will contain two rows and two columns. To multiply two matrices, we use a row–column scheme of multiplying. The numbers in the *first row* of matrix A are multiplied by the numbers in the *first column* of matrix B. These products are then added to determine the entry in the product matrix.

$$A \times B = \begin{bmatrix} 3 & 2 \\ 5 & 7 \end{bmatrix} \begin{bmatrix} 0 & 6 \\ 4 & 1 \end{bmatrix}$$

First row   First column

$$\begin{bmatrix} 3 & 2 \\ 5 & 7 \end{bmatrix} \qquad \begin{bmatrix} 0 & 6 \\ 4 & 1 \end{bmatrix}$$

$$(3 \times 0) + (2 \times 4) = 0 + 8$$
$$= 8$$

The 8 is placed in the first-row, first-column position of the product matrix. The other numbers in the product matrix are obtained similarly, as illustrated in the matrix that follows.

First row   First column   First row   Second column

$$\begin{bmatrix} 3 & 2 \\ 5 & 7 \end{bmatrix} \quad \begin{bmatrix} 0 & 6 \\ 4 & 1 \end{bmatrix} \qquad \begin{bmatrix} 3 & 2 \\ 5 & 7 \end{bmatrix} \quad \begin{bmatrix} 0 & 6 \\ 4 & 1 \end{bmatrix}$$

$$(3 \times 0) + (2 \times 4) = 8 \qquad (3 \times 6) + (2 \times 1) = 20$$

$$A \times B = \begin{bmatrix} 8 & 20 \\ 28 & 37 \end{bmatrix}$$

Second row   First column   Second row   Second column

$$\begin{bmatrix} 3 & 2 \\ 5 & 7 \end{bmatrix} \quad \begin{bmatrix} 0 & 6 \\ 4 & 1 \end{bmatrix} \qquad \begin{bmatrix} 3 & 2 \\ 5 & 7 \end{bmatrix} \quad \begin{bmatrix} 0 & 6 \\ 4 & 1 \end{bmatrix}$$

$$(5 \times 0) + (7 \times 4) = 28 \qquad (5 \times 6) + (7 \times 1) = 37$$

We can shorten the procedure as follows.

$$A \times B = \begin{bmatrix} 3 & 2 \\ 5 & 7 \end{bmatrix} \begin{bmatrix} 0 & 6 \\ 4 & 1 \end{bmatrix}$$

$$= \begin{bmatrix} 3(0) + 2(4) & 3(6) + 2(1) \\ 5(0) + 7(4) & 5(6) + 7(1) \end{bmatrix}$$

$$= \begin{bmatrix} 8 & 20 \\ 28 & 37 \end{bmatrix}$$

In general, if

$$A = \begin{bmatrix} a & b \\ c & d \end{bmatrix} \quad \text{and} \quad B = \begin{bmatrix} e & f \\ g & h \end{bmatrix}$$

then

$$A \times B = \begin{bmatrix} a & b \\ c & d \end{bmatrix} \begin{bmatrix} e & f \\ g & h \end{bmatrix} = \begin{bmatrix} ae + bg & af + bh \\ ce + dg & cf + dh \end{bmatrix}$$

When two parties pursue conflicting interests, the situation can sometimes be described and modeled in a matrix under a branch of mathematics known as *game theory*. Consider a famous problem called "the prisoner's dilemma." A pair of criminal suspects, A and B, are being held in separate jail cells and cannot communicate with each other. Each one is told that there are four possible outcomes: If both confess, each receives a 3-year sentence. If A confesses and B does not, A receives a 1-year sentence, whereas B receives a 10-year sentence. If B confesses and A does not, B receives a 1-year sentence and A receives a 10-year sentence. Finally, if neither confesses, each will be imprisoned for 2 years. (Try arranging this situation in a matrix.)

If neither prisoner knows whether the other will confess, what should each prisoner do? A study of game theory shows that it is in each prisoner's best interest to confess to the crime.

Let's do one more multiplication of matrices.

Example 7 *Multiplying Matrices*

Determine $A \times B$ if

$$A = \begin{bmatrix} 3 & 1 \\ 4 & 2 \end{bmatrix} \quad \text{and} \quad B = \begin{bmatrix} 5 & -1 & 3 \\ 2 & 8 & 0 \end{bmatrix}$$

Solution Matrix A contains two columns, and matrix B contains two rows. Thus, the matrices can be multiplied. Since matrix A contains two rows and matrix B contains three columns, the product matrix will contain two rows and three columns.

$$A \times B = \begin{bmatrix} 3 & 1 \\ 4 & 2 \end{bmatrix}\begin{bmatrix} 5 & -1 & 3 \\ 2 & 8 & 0 \end{bmatrix}$$

$$= \begin{bmatrix} 3(5) + 1(2) & 3(-1) + 1(8) & 3(3) + 1(0) \\ 4(5) + 2(2) & 4(-1) + 2(8) & 4(3) + 2(0) \end{bmatrix}$$

$$= \begin{bmatrix} 17 & 5 & 9 \\ 24 & 12 & 12 \end{bmatrix}$$

It should be noted that multiplication of matrices *is not* commutative; that is, $A \times B \neq B \times A$, except in special instances.

Square matrices have a *multiplicative identity matrix*. The multiplicative identity matrices for a 2×2 and a 3×3 matrix, denoted I, follow. Note that in any multiplicative identity matrix, 1's go diagonally from top left to bottom right and all other elements in the matrix are 0's.

$$I = \begin{bmatrix} 1 & 0 \\ 0 & 1 \end{bmatrix} \qquad I = \begin{bmatrix} 1 & 0 & 0 \\ 0 & 1 & 0 \\ 0 & 0 & 1 \end{bmatrix}$$

For any square matrix, A, $A \times I = I \times A = A$.

Example 8 *Using the Identity Matrix in Multiplication*

Use the multiplicative identity matrix for a 2×2 matrix and matrix A to show that $A \times I = A$.

$$A = \begin{bmatrix} 4 & 3 \\ 2 & 1 \end{bmatrix}$$

Solution The identity matrix is $I = \begin{bmatrix} 1 & 0 \\ 0 & 1 \end{bmatrix}$.

$$A \times I = \begin{bmatrix} 4 & 3 \\ 2 & 1 \end{bmatrix}\begin{bmatrix} 1 & 0 \\ 0 & 1 \end{bmatrix}$$

$$= \begin{bmatrix} 4(1) + 3(0) & 4(0) + 3(1) \\ 2(1) + 1(0) & 2(0) + 1(1) \end{bmatrix}$$

$$= \begin{bmatrix} 4 & 3 \\ 2 & 1 \end{bmatrix} = A$$

Verify for yourself that $I \times A = A$ as well.

Example 9 illustrates an application of multiplication of matrices.

Example 9 *A Manufacturing Application*

The Fancy Frock Company manufactures three types of women's outfits: a dress, a two-piece suit (skirt and jacket), and a three-piece suit (skirt, jacket, and a vest). On a particular day, the firm produces 20 dresses, 30 two-piece suits, and 50 three-piece suits. Each dress requires 4 units of material and 1 hour of work to produce, each two-piece suit requires 5 units of material and 2 hours of work to produce, and each three-piece suit requires 6 units of material and 3 hours to produce. Use matrix multiplication to determine the total number of units of material and the total number of hours needed for that day's production.

Solution Let matrix A represent the number of each type of women's outfits produced.

$$A = \begin{array}{ccc} \text{Dress} & \text{Two-piece} & \text{Three-piece} \\ [\ 20 & 30 & 50\ ] \end{array}$$

The units of material and time requirements for each type are indicated in matrix B.

$$B = \begin{array}{cc} \text{Material} & \text{Hours} \\ \begin{bmatrix} 4 & 1 \\ 5 & 2 \\ 6 & 3 \end{bmatrix} & \begin{array}{l} \text{Dress} \\ \text{Two-piece} \\ \text{Three-piece} \end{array} \end{array}$$

The product of A and B, or $A \times B$, will give the total number of units of material and the total number of hours of work needed for that day's production.

$$A \times B = [20 \quad 30 \quad 50] \begin{bmatrix} 4 & 1 \\ 5 & 2 \\ 6 & 3 \end{bmatrix}$$

$$= [20(4) + 30(5) + 50(6) \quad 20(1) + 30(2) + 50(3)]$$

$$= [530 \quad 230]$$

Thus, a total of 530 units of material and a total of 230 hours of work are needed that day. ∎

> **TIMELY TIP**
>
> Matrices can only be added or subtracted if they have the same dimensions.
>   Matrices can only be multiplied if the number of *columns* in the first matrix is the same as the number of *rows* in the second matrix.

SECTION 7.3 *Exercises*

Warm Up Exercises

In Exercises 1–10, fill in the blank with an appropriate word, phrase, or symbol(s).

1. A rectangular array of numbers is called a(n) _____.
Matrix

2. A matrix that contains the same number of rows and columns is called a(n) _____ matrix. Square

3. The number of columns in a 3 × 2 matrix is _____. 2

4. The number of rows in a 4 × 3 matrix is _____. 4

5. To add or subtract two matrices, the matrices must have the same _____. Dimensions

6. When multiplying a matrix by a real number, the real number is called a(n) _____. Scalar

7. Multiplication of matrices is possible only when the number of _____ of the first matrix is the same as the number of _____ of the second matrix. Columns, rows

8. The product of a square matrix A with an identity matrix I is always the square matrix _____. A

9. The multiplicative identity matrix of a 2×2 matrix is _____. *

10. The multiplicative identity matrix of a 3×3 matrix is _____. *

Practice the Skills

In Exercises 11–14, determine $A + B$.

11. $A = \begin{bmatrix} 8 & 5 \\ 7 & 1 \end{bmatrix}$, $B = \begin{bmatrix} -3 & -2 \\ 0 & 4 \end{bmatrix}$ $\begin{bmatrix} 5 & 3 \\ 7 & 5 \end{bmatrix}$

12. $A = \begin{bmatrix} 7 & 4 & -1 \\ 5 & -3 & 6 \end{bmatrix}$, $B = \begin{bmatrix} -1 & 0 & 5 \\ 2 & -3 & 0 \end{bmatrix}$ *

13. $A = \begin{bmatrix} 5 & 2 \\ -1 & 4 \\ 7 & 0 \end{bmatrix}$, $B = \begin{bmatrix} -3 & 3 \\ -4 & 0 \\ 1 & 6 \end{bmatrix}$ $\begin{bmatrix} 2 & 5 \\ -5 & 4 \\ 8 & 6 \end{bmatrix}$

14. $A = \begin{bmatrix} 2 & 6 & 3 \\ -1 & -6 & 4 \\ 3 & 0 & 5 \end{bmatrix}$, $B = \begin{bmatrix} -1 & 3 & 1 \\ 7 & -2 & 1 \\ 2 & 3 & 8 \end{bmatrix}$ *

In Exercises 15–18, determine $A - B$.

15. $A = \begin{bmatrix} 8 & 6 \\ 4 & -2 \end{bmatrix}$, $B = \begin{bmatrix} -2 & 5 \\ 9 & 1 \end{bmatrix}$ $\begin{bmatrix} 10 & 1 \\ -5 & -3 \end{bmatrix}$

16. $A = \begin{bmatrix} 10 & 1 \\ 12 & 2 \\ -3 & -9 \end{bmatrix}$, $B = \begin{bmatrix} -3 & 3 \\ 2 & 6 \\ -1 & 5 \end{bmatrix}$ $\begin{bmatrix} 13 & -2 \\ 10 & -4 \\ -2 & -14 \end{bmatrix}$

17. $A = \begin{bmatrix} -5 & 1 \\ 8 & 6 \\ 1 & -5 \end{bmatrix}$, $B = \begin{bmatrix} -6 & -8 \\ -10 & -11 \\ 3 & -7 \end{bmatrix}$ $\begin{bmatrix} 1 & 9 \\ 18 & 17 \\ -2 & 2 \end{bmatrix}$

18. $A = \begin{bmatrix} 5 & 3 & -1 \\ 7 & 4 & 2 \\ 6 & -1 & -5 \end{bmatrix}$, $B = \begin{bmatrix} 4 & 3 & 6 \\ -2 & -4 & 9 \\ 0 & -2 & 4 \end{bmatrix}$ *

In Exercises 19–24,

$$A = \begin{bmatrix} 1 & 2 \\ 0 & 5 \end{bmatrix}, \quad B = \begin{bmatrix} 3 & 2 \\ 5 & 0 \end{bmatrix}, \quad \text{and} \quad C = \begin{bmatrix} -2 & 3 \\ 4 & 0 \end{bmatrix}.$$

Determine the following.

19. $2B$ $\begin{bmatrix} 6 & 4 \\ 10 & 0 \end{bmatrix}$

20. $-3B$ $\begin{bmatrix} -9 & -6 \\ -15 & 0 \end{bmatrix}$

21. $2B + 3C$ $\begin{bmatrix} 0 & 13 \\ 22 & 0 \end{bmatrix}$

22. $2B + 3A$ $\begin{bmatrix} 9 & 10 \\ 10 & 15 \end{bmatrix}$

23. $3B - 2C$ $\begin{bmatrix} 13 & 0 \\ 7 & 0 \end{bmatrix}$

24. $4C - 2A$ $\begin{bmatrix} -10 & 8 \\ 16 & -10 \end{bmatrix}$

In Exercises 25–30, determine $A \times B$.

25. $A = \begin{bmatrix} 3 & 5 \\ 0 & 6 \end{bmatrix}$, $B = \begin{bmatrix} 4 & 2 \\ 8 & 3 \end{bmatrix}$ $\begin{bmatrix} 52 & 21 \\ 48 & 18 \end{bmatrix}$

26. $A = \begin{bmatrix} 1 & -1 \\ 2 & 6 \end{bmatrix}$, $B = \begin{bmatrix} 4 & -2 \\ -3 & -2 \end{bmatrix}$ $\begin{bmatrix} 7 & 0 \\ -10 & -16 \end{bmatrix}$

27. $A = \begin{bmatrix} 2 & 3 & -1 \\ 0 & 4 & 6 \end{bmatrix}$, $B = \begin{bmatrix} 2 \\ 4 \\ 1 \end{bmatrix}$ $\begin{bmatrix} 15 \\ 22 \end{bmatrix}$

28. $A = \begin{bmatrix} 1 & 1 \\ 1 & 1 \end{bmatrix}$, $B = \begin{bmatrix} 1 & -1 \\ -1 & 2 \end{bmatrix}$ $\begin{bmatrix} 0 & 1 \\ 0 & 1 \end{bmatrix}$

29. $A = \begin{bmatrix} 4 & 7 & 6 \\ -2 & 3 & 1 \\ 5 & 1 & 2 \end{bmatrix}$, $B = \begin{bmatrix} 1 & 0 & 0 \\ 0 & 1 & 0 \\ 0 & 0 & 1 \end{bmatrix}$ *

30. $A = \begin{bmatrix} 2 & -3 \\ 9 & 2 \end{bmatrix}$, $B = \begin{bmatrix} 1 & 2 \\ 3 & 4 \end{bmatrix}$ $\begin{bmatrix} -7 & -8 \\ 15 & 26 \end{bmatrix}$

In Exercises 31–36, determine $A + B$ and $A \times B$. If an operation cannot be performed, explain why.

31. $A = \begin{bmatrix} 1 & 3 & 0 \\ 2 & 4 & -1 \end{bmatrix}$, $B = \begin{bmatrix} 7 & -2 & 3 \\ 2 & -1 & 1 \end{bmatrix}$ *

32. $A = \begin{bmatrix} 6 & 4 & -1 \\ 2 & 3 & 4 \end{bmatrix}$, $B = \begin{bmatrix} 1 & 0 \\ 4 & -1 \end{bmatrix}$
Cannot be added; cannot be multiplied

33. $A = \begin{bmatrix} 2 & 5 & 1 \\ 8 & 3 & 6 \end{bmatrix}$, $B = \begin{bmatrix} 3 & 2 \\ 4 & 6 \\ -2 & 0 \end{bmatrix}$ *

34. $A = \begin{bmatrix} 6 & 5 \\ 4 & 3 \\ 2 & 1 \end{bmatrix}$, $B = \begin{bmatrix} 6 & 5 \\ 4 & 3 \\ 2 & 1 \end{bmatrix}$ *

35. $A = \begin{bmatrix} 1 & 2 \\ 3 & 4 \end{bmatrix}$, $B = \begin{bmatrix} -3 \\ 2 \end{bmatrix}$ Cannot be added; $\begin{bmatrix} 1 \\ -1 \end{bmatrix}$

36. $A = \begin{bmatrix} -2 & 3 \\ 6 & 7 \end{bmatrix}$, $B = \begin{bmatrix} 1 & 3 \\ 3 & -4 \end{bmatrix}$ *

In Exercises 37–39, show the commutative property of addition, $A + B = B + A$, holds for matrices A and B.

37. $A = \begin{bmatrix} 4 & -3 \\ 7 & 1 \end{bmatrix}$, $B = \begin{bmatrix} 2 & 3 \\ 6 & 7 \end{bmatrix}$ *

38. $A = \begin{bmatrix} 9 & 4 \\ 1 & 7 \end{bmatrix}$, $B = \begin{bmatrix} 2 & 0 \\ -1 & 6 \end{bmatrix}$ *

39. $A = \begin{bmatrix} 0 & -1 \\ 3 & -4 \end{bmatrix}$, $B = \begin{bmatrix} 8 & 1 \\ 3 & -4 \end{bmatrix}$ *

*See Instructor Answer Appendix

40. Create two matrices with the same dimensions, A and B, and show that $A + B = B + A$. Answers will vary.

In Exercises 41–43, show that the associative property of addition, $(A + B) + C = A + (B + C)$, holds for the matrices given.

41. $A = \begin{bmatrix} 6 & 5 \\ -1 & 3 \end{bmatrix}$, $B = \begin{bmatrix} 3 & 4 \\ -2 & 7 \end{bmatrix}$, $C = \begin{bmatrix} -2 & 4 \\ 5 & 0 \end{bmatrix}^*$

42. $A = \begin{bmatrix} 4 & 1 \\ 6 & 7 \end{bmatrix}$, $B = \begin{bmatrix} -9 & 1 \\ -7 & 2 \end{bmatrix}$, $C = \begin{bmatrix} -6 & -3 \\ 3 & 6 \end{bmatrix}^*$

43. $A = \begin{bmatrix} 7 & 4 \\ 9 & -36 \end{bmatrix}$, $B = \begin{bmatrix} 5 & 6 \\ -1 & -4 \end{bmatrix}$, $C = \begin{bmatrix} -7 & -5 \\ -1 & 3 \end{bmatrix}^*$

44. Create three matrices with the same dimensions, A, B, and C, and show that $(A + B) + C = A + (B + C)$. Answers will vary.

In Exercises 45–49, determine whether the commutative property of multiplication, $A \times B = B \times A$, holds for the matrices given.

45. $A = \begin{bmatrix} 1 & -2 \\ 4 & -3 \end{bmatrix}$, $B = \begin{bmatrix} -1 & -3 \\ 2 & 4 \end{bmatrix}$ No

46. $A = \begin{bmatrix} 3 & 1 \\ 6 & 6 \end{bmatrix}$, $B = \begin{bmatrix} 1 & 0 \\ 0 & 1 \end{bmatrix}$ Yes

47. $A = \begin{bmatrix} 4 & 2 \\ 1 & -3 \end{bmatrix}$, $B = \begin{bmatrix} 2 & 4 \\ -3 & 1 \end{bmatrix}$ No

48. $A = \begin{bmatrix} -3 & 2 \\ 6 & -5 \end{bmatrix}$, $B = \begin{bmatrix} -\frac{5}{3} & -\frac{2}{3} \\ -2 & -1 \end{bmatrix}$ Yes

49. $A = \begin{bmatrix} 3 & 2 & 1 \\ 4 & 2 & 0 \\ 0 & -2 & 5 \end{bmatrix}$, $B = \begin{bmatrix} 1 & 0 & 0 \\ 0 & 1 & 0 \\ 0 & 0 & 1 \end{bmatrix}$ Yes

50. Create two square matrices A and B with the same dimensions, and determine whether $A \times B = B \times A$.
Answers will vary. For matrices A and B, in general $A \times B \neq B \times A$.

In Exercises 51–55, show that the associative property of multiplication, $(A \times B) \times C = A \times (B \times C)$, holds for the matrices given.

51. $A = \begin{bmatrix} 1 & 3 \\ 4 & 0 \end{bmatrix}$, $B = \begin{bmatrix} 4 & 2 \\ 3 & 1 \end{bmatrix}$, $C = \begin{bmatrix} 2 & 1 \\ 3 & 0 \end{bmatrix}^*$

52. $A = \begin{bmatrix} -2 & 3 \\ 0 & 4 \end{bmatrix}$, $B = \begin{bmatrix} 4 & 0 \\ 3 & 5 \end{bmatrix}$, $C = \begin{bmatrix} 3 & 4 \\ -2 & 5 \end{bmatrix}^*$

53. $A = \begin{bmatrix} 4 & 3 \\ -6 & 2 \end{bmatrix}$, $B = \begin{bmatrix} 1 & 2 \\ 0 & 1 \end{bmatrix}$, $C = \begin{bmatrix} 4 & 3 \\ 0 & -2 \end{bmatrix}^*$

54. $A = \begin{bmatrix} -1 & -2 \\ -3 & -4 \end{bmatrix}$, $B = \begin{bmatrix} 1 & 0 \\ 0 & 1 \end{bmatrix}$, $C = \begin{bmatrix} 0 & 0 \\ 0 & 0 \end{bmatrix}^*$

55. $A = \begin{bmatrix} 3 & 4 \\ -1 & -2 \end{bmatrix}$, $B = \begin{bmatrix} 0 & 1 \\ 1 & 0 \end{bmatrix}$, $C = \begin{bmatrix} 2 & 0 \\ 3 & 0 \end{bmatrix}^*$

56. Create three matrices, A, B, and C, and show that $(A \times B) \times C = A \times (B \times C)$. Answers will vary.

Problem Solving

57. **MODELING—***High School Play* Bakersfield High School sold tickets for the musical *Grease*. Matrix A represents the number of student, adult, and senior citizen tickets sold for the matinee and evening shows on day 1. Matrix B represents the number of student, adult, and senior citizen tickets sold for the matinee and evening shows on day 2.

$$A = \begin{bmatrix} 85 & 150 & 50 \\ 95 & 162 & 41 \end{bmatrix} \begin{matrix} \text{Matinee} \\ \text{Evening} \end{matrix}$$

with columns Student, Adult, Senior citizen.

$$B = \begin{bmatrix} 73 & 130 & 45 \\ 120 & 200 & 53 \end{bmatrix} \begin{matrix} \text{Matinee} \\ \text{Evening} \end{matrix}$$

with columns Student, Adult, Senior citizen.

Use matrix addition to determine the total number of student, adult, and senior citizen tickets sold by Bakersfield High School for both days for the matinee and evening shows.*

58. **MODELING—***T-shirt Inventory* Hollister sells two types of t-shirts—male and female. Matrix A represents the stock on hand of each type and size of t-shirt at the beginning of a given day. Matrix B represents the stock on hand of each type and size of t-shirt at the end of the same given day.

$$A = \begin{bmatrix} 31 & 18 \\ 39 & 16 \\ 41 & 22 \\ 34 & 21 \end{bmatrix} \begin{matrix} \text{Small} \\ \text{Medium} \\ \text{Large} \\ \text{Extra large} \end{matrix} \quad B = \begin{bmatrix} 14 & 9 \\ 18 & 9 \\ 19 & 15 \\ 15 & 9 \end{bmatrix} \begin{matrix} \text{Small} \\ \text{Medium} \\ \text{Large} \\ \text{Extra large} \end{matrix}$$

with columns Male, Female.

Use matrix subtraction to determine the number of t-shirts sold in the given day for each size of each type.*

59. MODELING—*Supplying Muffins* A bakery supplies chocolate chip, blueberry, and coffee cake muffins to Java's Coffee Shop and to Spot Coffee Shop. Matrix A shows the number of each type of muffin, in dozens, supplied to each coffee shop in 1 week. The bakery's cost for ingredients, per dozen, for chocolate chip, blueberry, and coffee cake muffins is $3, $2, and $1.5, respectively. Matrix B represents the bakery's cost for ingredients, per dozen, for each type of muffin.

$$A = \begin{matrix} \text{Chocolate} & \text{Blue-} & \text{Coffee} \\ \text{chip} & \text{berry} & \text{cake} \\ \begin{bmatrix} 7 & 8.5 & 10 \\ 7.5 & 8 & 11 \end{bmatrix} & & \begin{matrix} \text{Java's Coffee Shop} \\ \text{Spot Coffee Shop} \end{matrix} \end{matrix}$$

$$B = \begin{bmatrix} 3 \\ 2 \\ 1.5 \end{bmatrix} \begin{matrix} \text{Chocolate chip} \\ \text{Blueberry} \\ \text{Coffee cake} \end{matrix}$$

Use matrix multiplication to determine the total weekly cost of ingredients for each shop.*

60. MODELING—*Menu Choices* The cafeteria manager at the University of Virginia recently added three new meals to the lunch menu, each consisting of a meat, a vegetable, a salad, and a dessert. The first day these new meals were offered, 35 students purchased meal 1, 28 students purchased meal 2, and 23 students purchased meal 3. Matrix A represents the number of students who purchased each type of meal. Matrix B represents the cost per serving, in cents, for each item from the three meals.

$$A = \begin{matrix} \text{Meal} & \text{Meal} & \text{Meal} \\ 1 & 2 & 3 \\ \begin{bmatrix} 35 & 28 & 23 \end{bmatrix} \end{matrix}$$

$$B = \begin{matrix} \text{Meat} & \text{Vegetable} & \text{Salad} & \text{Dessert} \\ \begin{bmatrix} 45 & 12 & 8 & 10 \\ 52 & 8 & 6 & 15 \\ 49 & 7 & 9 & 11 \end{bmatrix} & & & \begin{matrix} \text{Meal 1} \\ \text{Meal 2} \\ \text{Meal 3} \end{matrix} \end{matrix}$$

Use matrix multiplication to determine the total cost for each item. *

61. MODELING—*Cookie Company Costs* The Original Cookie Factory bakes and sells four types of cookies: chocolate chip, sugar, molasses, and peanut butter. Matrix A shows the number of units of various ingredients used in baking a dozen of each type of cookie.

$$A = \begin{matrix} \text{Sugar} & \text{Flour} & \text{Milk} & \text{Eggs} \\ \begin{bmatrix} 2 & 2 & \frac{1}{2} & 1 \\ 3 & 2 & 1 & 2 \\ 0 & 1 & 0 & 3 \\ \frac{1}{2} & 1 & 0 & 0 \end{bmatrix} & & & \begin{matrix} \text{Chocolate chip} \\ \text{Sugar} \\ \text{Molasses} \\ \text{Peanut butter} \end{matrix} \end{matrix}$$

The cost, in cents per cup or per egg, for each ingredient when purchased in small quantities and in large quantities is given in matrix B on the top of the right hand column.

$$B = \begin{matrix} \text{Large} & \text{Small} \\ \text{quantities} & \text{quantities} \\ \begin{bmatrix} 10 & 12 \\ 5 & 8 \\ 8 & 8 \\ 4 & 6 \end{bmatrix} & & \begin{matrix} \text{Sugar} \\ \text{Flour} \\ \text{Milk} \\ \text{Eggs} \end{matrix} \end{matrix}$$

Use matrix multiplication to find a matrix representing the comparative cost per item for small and large quantities purchased.*

In Exercises 62 and 63, use the information given in Exercise 61. Suppose a typical day's order consists of 40 dozen chocolate chip cookies, 30 dozen sugar cookies, 12 dozen molasses cookies, and 20 dozen peanut butter cookies.

62. a) Express these orders as a 1×4 matrix.
[40 30 12 20]

b) Use matrix multiplication to determine the amount of each ingredient needed to fill the day's order.
[180 172 50 136]

63. Use matrix multiplication to determine the cost, in dollars, under the two purchase options (small and large quantities) to fill the day's order. [36.04 47.52]

64. MODELING—*Food Prices* To raise money for a local charity, the Spanish Club at Montclair High School sold hot dogs, soft drinks, and candy bars for 3 days in the student lounge. The sales for the 3 days are summarized in matrix A.

$$A = \begin{matrix} \text{Hot} & \text{Soft} & \text{Candy} \\ \text{dogs} & \text{drinks} & \text{bars} \\ \begin{bmatrix} 52 & 50 & 75 \\ 48 & 43 & 60 \\ 62 & 57 & 81 \end{bmatrix} & & \begin{matrix} \text{Day 1} \\ \text{Day 2} \\ \text{Day 3} \end{matrix} \end{matrix}$$

The cost and revenue (in dollars) for hot dogs, soft drinks, and candy are summarized in matrix B on the next page.

*See Instructor Answer Appendix

$$B = \begin{bmatrix} 0.30 & 0.75 \\ 0.25 & 0.50 \\ 0.15 & 0.45 \end{bmatrix} \begin{matrix} \text{Hot dogs} \\ \text{Soft drinks} \\ \text{Candy bars} \end{matrix}$$

with headers Cost, Revenue

Multiply the two matrices to form a 3×2 matrix that shows the total cost and revenue for each item.*

In Exercises 65 and 66, there are many acceptable answers.

65. a) Construct two matrices A and B whose product is a 3×1 matrix.

b) For your matrices, determine $A \times B$.
Answers will vary.

66. a) Construct two matrices A and B whose product is a 4×1 matrix.

b) For your matrices, determine $A \times B$.
Answers will vary.

Two matrices whose product is the multiplicative identity matrix are said to be multiplicative inverses. That is, if $A \times B = B \times A = I$, where I is the multiplicative identity matrix, then A and B are multiplicative inverses. In Exercises 69 and 70, determine whether A and B are multiplicative inverses.

67. $A = \begin{bmatrix} 5 & -2 \\ -2 & 1 \end{bmatrix}, \quad B = \begin{bmatrix} 1 & 2 \\ 2 & 5 \end{bmatrix}$ Yes

68. $A = \begin{bmatrix} 7 & 3 \\ 2 & 1 \end{bmatrix}, \quad B = \begin{bmatrix} 1 & -3 \\ -2 & 7 \end{bmatrix}$ Yes

Challenge Problems/Group Activities

In Exercises 69 and 70, determine whether the statement is true or false. Give an example to support your answer.

69. $A - B = B - A$, where A and B are any matrices. False

70. For scalar a and matrices B and C,
$a(B + C) = aB + aC$. True

71. MODELING—*Sofa Manufacturing Costs* The number of hours of labor required to manufacture one sofa of various sizes is summarized in matrix L.

	Cutting	Assembly	Packing	
$L =$	1.4 hr	0.7 hr	0.3 hr	Small
	1.8 hr	1.4 hr	0.3 hr	Medium
	2.7 hr	2.8 hr	0.5 hr	Large

Department (header spanning Cutting, Assembly, Packing); Sofa size (bracket on Small, Medium, Large)

The hourly labor rates for cutting, assembly, and packing at the Ames City Plant and at the Bay City Plant are given in matrix C.

$$C = \begin{bmatrix} \$14 & \$12 \\ \$10 & \$9 \\ \$7 & \$5 \end{bmatrix} \begin{matrix} \text{Cutting} \\ \text{Assembly} \\ \text{Packaging} \end{matrix} \left.\right\} \text{Department}$$

with headers Plant: Ames City, Bay City

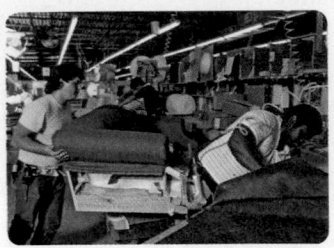

a) What is the total labor cost for manufacturing a small-sized sofa at the Ames City plant? $28.70

b) What is the total cost for manufacturing a large-sized sofa at the Bay City plant? $60.10

c) Determine the product $L \times C$ and explain the meaning of the results.*

72. Is it possible that two matrices could be added but not multiplied? If so, give an example.*

73. Is it possible that two matrices could be multiplied but not added? If so, give an example.*

Recreational Mathematics

74. Make up two matrices A and B such that

$$A + B = \begin{bmatrix} 1 & 0 \\ 0 & 1 \end{bmatrix} \text{ and } A \times B = \begin{bmatrix} 0 & 0 \\ 0 & 0 \end{bmatrix}.$$

Answers will vary.

Internet/Research Activities

75. Find an article that shows information illustrated in matrix form. Write a short paper explaining how to interpret the information provided by the matrix. Include the article with your report.

76. *Messages* The study of encoding and decoding messages is called *cryptography*. Do research on current real-life uses of cryptography and write a paper on how matrix multiplication is used to encode and decode messages. In your paper, include current real-life uses of cryptography.

*See Instructor Answer Appendix

Solving Systems of Linear Equations by Using Matrices

Full-price tickets for a concert held at your college sell for $25. Student tickets sell for $15. If you knew how many tickets were sold and the amount of money collected in ticket sales, could you determine how many full-price tickets and how many student tickets were sold? In this section we will illustrate a method for answering this question using matrices.

Why *This is Important* Matrices can be used to solve many problems that are modeled with a system of linear equations.

▲ *Matrices can be used to solve problem such as determining the number of full-price tickets and the number of student tickets sold at a concert.*

In Section 7.3, we introduced matrices. Now we will discuss the procedure to solve a system of linear equations using matrices. We will illustrate how to solve a system of two equations and two unknowns. Systems of equations containing three equations and three unknowns (called third-order systems) and higher-order systems can also be solved by using matrices, but we will not discuss third- or higher-order systems in this book.

The first step in solving a system of equations using matrices is to represent the system of equations with an *augmented matrix*. An augmented matrix consists of two smaller matrices, one for the coefficients of the variables in the equations and one for the constants in the equations. To determine the augmented matrix, first write each equation in standard form, $ax + by = c$. For the system of equations below, its augmented matrix is shown to its right.

System of equations	Augmented matrix
$a_1 x + b_1 y = c_1$	$\begin{bmatrix} a_1 & b_1 & \vert & c_1 \\ a_2 & b_2 & \vert & c_2 \end{bmatrix}$
$a_2 x + b_2 y = c_2$	

Following is another example.

System of equations	Augmented matrix
$x + 2y = 8$	$\begin{bmatrix} 1 & 2 & \vert & 8 \\ 3 & -1 & \vert & 7 \end{bmatrix}$
$3x - y = 7$	

Note that the vertical bar in the augmented matrix separates the numerical coefficients from the constants. The matrix is just a shortened way of writing the system of equations. Thus, we can solve a system of equations by using matrices in a manner very similar to solving a system of equations with the addition method.

To solve a system of equations by using matrices, we use *row transformations* to obtain new matrices that have the same solution as the original system. We will discuss three row transformation procedures.

PROCEDURE **ROW TRANSFORMATIONS**

1. Any two rows of a matrix may be interchanged (which is the same as interchanging any two equations in the system of equations).

2. All the numbers in any row may be multiplied by any nonzero real number (which is the same as multiplying both sides of an equation by any nonzero real number).

3. All the numbers in any row may be multiplied by any nonzero real number, and these products may be added to the corresponding numbers in any other row of numbers.

We use row transformations to obtain an augmented matrix whose numbers to the left of the vertical bar are the same as in the *multiplicative identity matrix*. From this type of augmented matrix, we can determine the solution to the system of equations. For example, if we get

$$\left[\begin{array}{cc|c} 1 & 0 & 3 \\ 0 & 1 & -2 \end{array}\right]$$

it tells us that $1x + 0y = 3$ or $x = 3$, and $0x + 1y = -2$ or $y = -2$. Thus, the solution to the system of equations that yielded this augmented matrix is $(3, -2)$. Now let's work an example.

Example 1 Using Row Transformations

Solve the following system of equations by using matrices.

$$x + 2y = 5$$
$$3x - y = 8$$

Solution First we write the augmented matrix.

$$\left[\begin{array}{cc|c} 1 & 2 & 5 \\ 3 & -1 & 8 \end{array}\right]$$

Our goal is to obtain a matrix of the form

$$\left[\begin{array}{cc|c} 1 & 0 & c_1 \\ 0 & 1 & c_2 \end{array}\right]$$

where c_1 and c_2 may represent any real numbers. It is generally easier to work by columns. Therefore, we will try to get the first column of the augmented matrix to be $\begin{smallmatrix}1\\0\end{smallmatrix}$ and the second column to be $\begin{smallmatrix}0\\1\end{smallmatrix}$. Since the element in the top left position is already a 1, we must work to change the 3 in the first column, second row, into a 0. We use row transformation procedure 3 to change the 3 into a 0. If we multiply the top row of numbers by -3 and add these products to the second row of numbers, the element in the first column, second row will become a 0.

$$\left[\begin{array}{cc|c} 1 & 2 & 5 \\ 3 & -1 & 8 \end{array}\right]\quad\text{Original augmented matrix}$$

The top row of numbers multiplied by -3 gives

$$1(-3),\qquad 2(-3),\qquad\text{and}\qquad 5(-3)$$

Now add these products to their respective numbers in row 2.

$$\left[\begin{array}{cc|c} 1 & 2 & 5 \\ 3 + 1(-3) & -1 + 2(-3) & 8 + 5(-3) \end{array}\right] = \left[\begin{array}{cc|c} 1 & 2 & 5 \\ 0 & -7 & -7 \end{array}\right]$$

The next step is to obtain a 1 in the second column, second row. At present, -7 is in that position. To change the -7 to a 1, we use row transformation procedure 2. If we multiply -7 by $-\frac{1}{7}$, the product will be 1. Therefore, we multiply all the numbers in the second row by $-\frac{1}{7}$ to get

$$\left[\begin{array}{cc|c} 1 & 2 & 5 \\ 0(-\frac{1}{7}) & -7(-\frac{1}{7}) & -7(-\frac{1}{7}) \end{array}\right] = \left[\begin{array}{cc|c} 1 & 2 & 5 \\ 0 & 1 & 1 \end{array}\right]$$

The next step is to obtain a 0 in the second column, first row. At present, a 2 is in that position. Multiplying the numbers in the second row by -2 and adding the products to the corresponding numbers in the first row gives a 0 in the desired position.

$$\begin{bmatrix} 1 + 0(-2) & 2 + 1(-2) & | & 5 + 1(-2) \\ 0 & 1 & | & 1 \end{bmatrix} = \begin{bmatrix} 1 & 0 & | & 3 \\ 0 & 1 & | & 1 \end{bmatrix}$$

We now have the desired augmented matrix:

$$\begin{bmatrix} 1 & 0 & | & 3 \\ 0 & 1 & | & 1 \end{bmatrix}$$

With this matrix, we see that $1x + 0y = 3$, or $x = 3$, and $0x + 1y = 1$, or $y = 1$. The solution to the system is $(3, 1)$.

CHECK:
$$\begin{array}{ll} x + 2y = 5 & 3x - y = 8 \\ 3 + 2(1) = 5 & 3(3) - 1 = 8 \\ 5 = 5 \quad \text{True} & 8 = 8 \quad \text{True} \end{array}$$

Now we give a general procedure to change an augmented matrix to the desired form.

> **PROCEDURE   TO CHANGE AN AUGMENTED MATRIX TO THE FORM**
> $$\begin{bmatrix} 1 & 0 & | & c_1 \\ 0 & 1 & | & c_2 \end{bmatrix}$$
>
> **Use row transformations to:**
> 1. Change the element in the first column, first row, to a 1.
> 2. Change the element in the first column, second row, to a 0.
> 3. Change the element in the second column, second row, to a 1.
> 4. Change the element in the second column, first row, to a 0.

Generally, when changing an element in the augmented matrix to a 1, we use Step 2 in the row transformation box on page 415. When changing an element to a 0, we use Step 3 in the row transformation box.

Example 2 *Using Matrices to Solve a System of Equations*

Solve the following system of equations using matrices.

$$\begin{aligned} 3x + 6y &= -9 \\ 4x - 2y &= 8 \end{aligned}$$

Solution First write the augmented matrix.

$$\begin{bmatrix} 3 & 6 & | & -9 \\ 4 & -2 & | & 8 \end{bmatrix}$$

To obtain a 1 in the first column, first row, multiply the numbers in the first row by $\frac{1}{3}$.

$$\begin{bmatrix} 1 & 2 & | & -3 \\ 4 & -2 & | & 8 \end{bmatrix}$$

To obtain a 0 in the first column, second row, multiply the numbers in the first row by -4 and add the products to the corresponding numbers in the second row.

$$\begin{bmatrix} 1 & 2 & | & -3 \\ 4 + 1(-4) & -2 + 2(-4) & | & 8 + (-3)(-4) \end{bmatrix} = \begin{bmatrix} 1 & 2 & | & -3 \\ 0 & -10 & | & 20 \end{bmatrix}$$

To obtain a 1 in the second column, second row, multiply the numbers in the second row by $-\frac{1}{10}$.

$$\begin{bmatrix} 1 & 2 & \Big| & -3 \\ 0\left(-\frac{1}{10}\right) & -10\left(-\frac{1}{10}\right) & \Big| & 20\left(-\frac{1}{10}\right) \end{bmatrix} = \begin{bmatrix} 1 & 2 & \Big| & -3 \\ 0 & 1 & \Big| & -2 \end{bmatrix}$$

To obtain a 0 in the second column, first row, multiply the numbers in the second row by -2 and add the products to the corresponding numbers in the first row.

$$\begin{bmatrix} 1 + 0(-2) & 2 + 1(-2) & \Big| & -3 + (-2)(-2) \\ 0 & 1 & \Big| & -2 \end{bmatrix} = \begin{bmatrix} 1 & 0 & \Big| & 1 \\ 0 & 1 & \Big| & -2 \end{bmatrix}$$

The solution to the system of equations is $(1, -2)$.   ■

Inconsistent and Dependent Systems

Assume that you solve a system of two equations and obtain an augmented matrix in which one row of numbers on the left side of the vertical line are all zeroes but a zero does not appear in the same row on the right side of the vertical line. This situation indicates that the system is inconsistent and has no solution. For example, a system of equations that yields the following augmented matrix is an inconsistent system.

$$\begin{bmatrix} 1 & 2 & \Big| & 5 \\ 0 & 0 & \Big| & 4 \end{bmatrix} \quad \text{Inconsistent system}$$

The second row of the matrix represents the equation

$$0x + 0y = 4 \quad \text{or} \quad 0 = 4$$

which is never true. This matrix represents a system of equations that has no solution.

If you obtain a matrix in which a 0 appears across an entire row, the system of equations is dependent. For example, a system of equations that yields the following matrix is a dependent system.

$$\begin{bmatrix} 1 & 5 & \Big| & -6 \\ 0 & 0 & \Big| & 0 \end{bmatrix} \quad \text{Dependent system}$$

The second row of the matrix represents the equation

$$0x + 0y = 0 \quad \text{or} \quad 0 = 0$$

which is always true. This matrix represents a system of equations that has an infinite number of solutions.

Triangularization Method

Another procedure to solve a system of two equations is to use row transformation procedures to obtain an augmented matrix of the form

$$\begin{bmatrix} 1 & a & \Big| & b \\ 0 & 1 & \Big| & c \end{bmatrix}$$

where a, b, and c represent real numbers. This procedure is called the *triangularization method* because the ones and zeroes form a triangle.

When the matrix is in this form, we can write the following system of equations.

$$1x + ay = b \qquad \text{or} \qquad x + ay = b$$
$$0x + 1y = c \qquad\qquad\qquad y = c$$

Using substitution, we can solve the system. Example 3 illustrates the triangulariza-tion method.

Example 3 *Solving a System of Equations Using the Triangularization Method*

Solve the following system of equations using the triangularization method.

$$3x + 6y = -9$$
$$4x - 2y = 8$$

Solution   In Example 2, in the process of solving the system we obtained the aug-mented matrix

$$\begin{bmatrix} 1 & 2 & | & -3 \\ 0 & 1 & | & -2 \end{bmatrix}$$

This matrix represents the following system of equations.

$$x + 2y = -3$$
$$y = -2$$

To solve for x, we substitute -2 for y in the equation

$$x + 2y = -3$$
$$x + 2(-2) = -3$$
$$x - 4 = -3$$
$$x = 1$$

Thus, the solution to the system is $(1, -2)$, as was obtained in Example 2. You may use either method when solving a system of equations with matrices unless your instructor specifies otherwise. ∎

SECTION 7.4 *Exercises*

Warm Up Exercises

In Exercises 1–4, fill in the blank with an appropriate word, phrase, or symbol(s).

1. A matrix that consists of two smaller matrices, one for the coefficients of the variables in the equations and one for the constants in the equations, is called a(n) _____ matrix. Augmented

2. To solve a system of equations by using matrices, use _____ transformations to obtain new matrices that have the same solution as the original system. Row

3. A system of linear equations that yields the augmented matrix $\begin{bmatrix} 1 & 3 & | & 5 \\ 0 & 0 & | & 2 \end{bmatrix}$ is an inconsistent system and has _____ solution. No

4. A system of linear equations that yields the augmented matrix $\begin{bmatrix} 1 & 4 & | & 8 \\ 0 & 0 & | & 0 \end{bmatrix}$ is a dependent system and has a(n) _____ number of solutions. Infinite

Practice the Skills

In Exercises 5–18, use matrices to solve the system of equations.

5. $x + 2y = 7$
 $-x + 2y = 1$ (3, 2)

6. $x - y = 1$
 $2x - y = 3$ (2, 1)

7. $x - 2y = -1$
 $2x + y = 8$ (3, 2)

8. $x + y = -1$
 $2x + 3y = -5$ (2, −3)

9. $x + y = 5$
$3x - y = 3$ (2, 3)

10. $2x - 5y = -6$
$-4x + 10y = 12$ *

11. $2x - 3y = 10$
$2x + 2y = 5$ $\left(\dfrac{7}{2}, -1\right)$

12. $x + 3y = 1$
$-3x - y = 5$ (−2, 1)

13. $5x + 2y = 7$
$4x + 4y = 8$ (1, 1)

14. $4x + 2y = -10$
$-2x + y = -7$ $\left(\dfrac{1}{2}, -6\right)$

15. $-3x + 6y = 5$
$2x - 4y = 8$
No solution; inconsistent system

16. $2x - 5y = 10$
$3x + y = 15$ (5, 0)

17. $3x + y = 13$
$x + 3y = 15$ (3, 4)

18. $4x - 3y = 7$
$-2x + 5y = 14$ $\left(\dfrac{11}{2}, 5\right)$

Problem Solving

In Exercises 19–22, use matrices to solve the problem.

19. MODELING—*Selling Game Systems* GameStop sells Xbox game systems for $300 and Wii game systems for $200. Recently the store sold a total of fifteen Xbox and Wii game systems in a single day. If the receipts for the day for the two systems totaled $3600, how many of each game system were sold? Xbox 360 systems: 6; Wii systems: 9

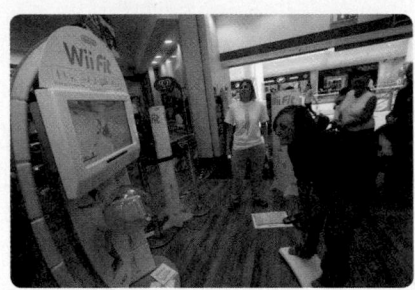

20. MODELING—*TV Dimensions* Vita Gunta just purchased a new high-definition television. She noticed that the perimeter of the screen is 124 in. The width of the screen is 8 in. greater than its height. Find the dimensions of the screen.
Width: 35 in.; height: 27 in.

21. MODELING—*On the Job* Peoplepower, Inc., a daily employment agency, charges $12 per hour for a truck driver and $10 per hour for a laborer. On a certain job, the laborer worked two more hours than the truck driver, and together they cost $196. How many hours did each work?
Truck driver: 8 hours; laborer: 10 hours

22. MODELING—*Snack Mix* If Andy DaLora buys 2 lb of caramel corn and 3 lb of mixed nuts, his total cost would be $27. If he buys 1 lb of caramel corn and 2 lb of mixed nuts, his total cost would be $17. Find the cost of 1 lb of caramel corn and 1 lb of mixed nuts.
Caramel corn: $3 per lb; mixed nuts: $7 per lb

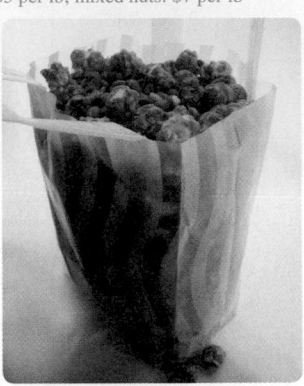

23. MODELING—*Fill in the Missing Information* Garmin sells two types of navigation systems to electronics stores. The basic system sells for $110, and the premium system sells for $145. Garmin received an order for a total of 200 navigation systems and a check for $23,750. When placing the order, the salesperson failed to specify the number of each type of system ordered. Can Garmin fill the order with the information given? If so, determine the number of basic systems and the number of premium systems the salesperson ordered.
Basic systems: 150; premium systems: 50

Internet/Research Activity

24. Do research and write a paper on the development of matrices. In your paper, cover the contributions of James Joseph Sylvester, Arthur Cayley, and William Rowan Hamilton. References include history of mathematics books, encyclopedias, and the Internet.

*See Instructor Answer Appendix

SECTION 7.5 Systems of Linear Inequalities

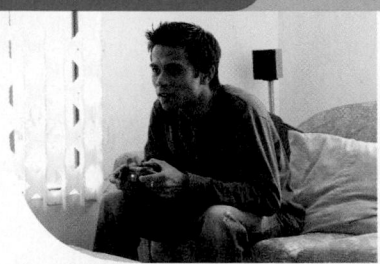

▲ *A system of inequalities may be used to determine how many game systems should be stocked to satisfy store requirements.*

Joey Barnes is the manager of a GameStop video game store. He must determine how many PlayStation 3 and how many Xbox video game systems to keep in stock. Some of the factors he needs to consider include the price of the system, the demand for each system, and the amount of money he wishes to spend on inventory. In this section we will use a system of linear inequalities to express these requirements mathematically.

Why **This is Important** Businesses often use systems of linear inequalities to make important decisions.

The solution set of a system of linear inequalities is the set of points that satisfy all inequalities in the system. The solution set of a system of linear inequalities may consist of infinitely many ordered pairs. To determine the solution set to a system of linear inequalities, graph each inequality on the same axes. The ordered pairs common to all the inequalities are the solution set to the system.

PROCEDURE   **SOLVING A SYSTEM OF LINEAR INEQUALITIES**

1. Select one of the inequalities. Replace the inequality symbol with an equal sign and draw the graph of the equation. Draw the graph with a dashed line if the inequality is $<$ or $>$ and with a solid line if the inequality is $\leq$ or $\geq$.

2. Select a test point on one side of the line and determine whether the point is a solution to the inequality. If so, shade the area on the side of the line containing the point. If the point is not a solution, shade the area on the other side of the line.

3. Repeat Steps 1 and 2 for the other inequality.

4. The intersection of the two shaded areas and any solid line common to both inequalities form the solution set to the system of inequalities.

Example 1   *Solving a System of Inequalities*

Graph the following system of inequalities and indicate the solution set.

$$x + y < 1$$
$$x - y < 5$$

Solution   Graph both inequalities on the same axes. First draw the graph of $x + y < 1$. When drawing the graph, remember to use a dashed line, since the inequality is "less than" (see Fig. 7.10a). If you have forgotten how to graph inequalities, review Section 6.8. Shade the half plane that satisfies the inequality $x + y < 1$.

 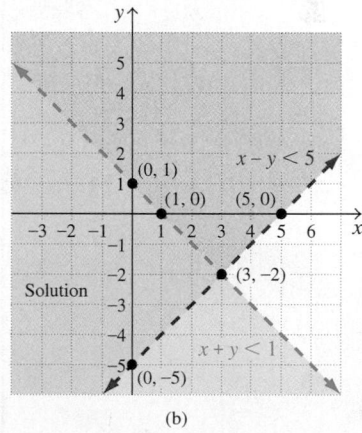

                (a)   (b)

Figure 7.10

Now, on the same axes, shade the half plane that satisfies the inequality $x - y < 5$ (see Fig. 7.10b). The solution set consists of all the points common to the two shaded half planes. These are the points in the region on the graph containing both color shadings. In Figure 7.10(b), we have indicated this region in green. Figure 7.10(b) shows that the two lines intersect at $(3, -2)$. This ordered pair can also be found by any of the algebraic methods discussed in Sections 7.2 and 7.3. The ordered pair $(3, -2)$ is not part of the solution set. ∎

Example 2 *Solving a System of Linear Inequalities*

Graph the following system of inequalities and indicate the solution set.

$$4x - 2y \geq 8$$
$$2x + 3y < 6$$

Solution Graph the inequality $4x - 2y \geq 8$. Remember to use a solid line because the inequality is "greater than or equal to"; see Fig. 7.11(a).

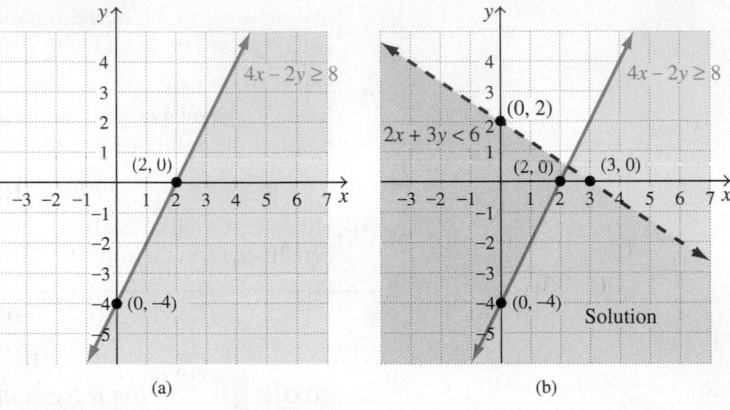

Figure 7.11

On the same set of axes, draw the graph of $2x + 3y < 6$. Use a dashed line since the inequality is "less than"; see Fig. 7.11(b). The solution is the region of the graph that contains both color shadings and the part of the solid line that satisfies the inequality $2x + 3y < 6$. Note that the point of intersection of the two lines is not a part of the solution set. ∎

Example 3 *Another System of Inequalities*

Graph the following system of inequalities and indicate the solution set.

$$x \geq -2$$
$$y < 3$$

Solution Graph the inequality $x \geq -2$; see Fig. 7.12(a). On the same axes, graph the inequality $y < 3$; see Fig. 7.12(b). The solution set is that region of the graph that is shaded in both colors and the part of the solid line that satisfies the inequality $y < 3$. The point of intersection of the two lines, $(-2, 3)$, is not part of the solution because it does not satisfy the inequality $y < 3$.

(a)

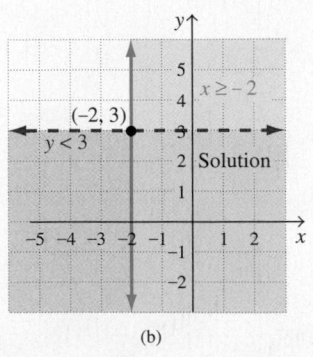
(b)

Figure 7.12 ∎

Concept Exercises

In Exercises 1–4, fill in the blank with an appropriate word, phrase, or symbol(s).

1. The set of points that satisfy all inequalities in a system of linear inequalities is called the _____ set. Solution

2. When graphing a linear inequality, if the inequality contains $<$ or $>$, draw the graph with a(n) _____ line. Dashed

3. When graphing a linear inequality, if the inequality contains $\leq$ or $\geq$, draw the graph with a(n) _____ line.
Solid

4. The solution set to a system of linear inequalities is the set of _____ pairs that are common to all the inequalities in the system. Ordered

Practice The Skills

In Exercises 5–20, graph the system of linear inequalities and indicate the solution set.

5. $y > -x + 3$
$y > 2x$ ∗

6. $y > -4x$
$y \leq -2x + 2$ ∗

7. $x + y \leq 5$
$x - y < 3$ ∗

8. $x + y < 4$
$3x + 2y \geq 6$ ∗

9. $x - y < 4$
$x + y < 5$ ∗

10. $3x - y \leq 6$
$x - y > 4$ ∗

11. $x + 2y \geq 4$
$3x - y \geq -6$ ∗

12. $x - 3y \leq 3$
$x + 2y \geq 4$ ∗

13. $y \leq 3x$
$x \geq 3y$ ∗

14. $y \leq 2$
$x - y < 1$ ∗

15. $x \geq 1$
$y \leq 1$ ∗

16. $x \leq 0$
$y \leq 0$ ∗

17. $4x + 2y > 8$
$x \geq y - 1$ ∗

18. $5y > 3x + 10$
$3y < -2x - 3$ ∗

19. $3x \geq 2y + 6$
$x \leq y + 3$ ∗

20. $3x \geq 2y + 10$
$x \leq y + 8$ ∗

Challenge Problems/Group Activities

21. MODELING—*Craft Sales* Julie Gratien makes small and large decorated bowls. It takes Julie 20 minutes to decorate a small bowl and 30 minutes to decorate a large bowl. She can spend no more than a total of 600 minutes decorating the bowls. The number of small bowls made needs to be at least twice the number of large bowls made. Julie must also make at least 10 small bowls and 5 large bowls.

a) Using x to represent the number of small bowls made and y to represent the number of large bowls made, translate the problem into a system of linear inequalities.
$20x + 30y \leq 600, x \geq 2y, x \geq 10, y \geq 5$

b) Solve the system graphically. Graph sales for small bowls on the horizontal axis and sales for large bowls on the vertical axis. ∗

c) Select a point in the solution set. Determine the sales for the two types of bowls that correspond to the point selected. One example is 15 small bowls, 7 large bowls.

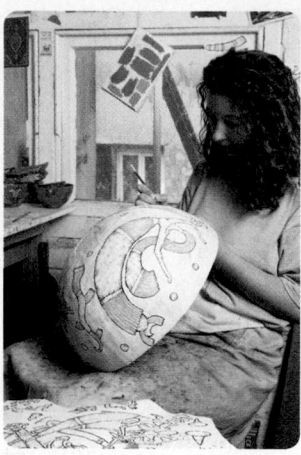

22. MODELING—*Special Diet* Ruben Gonzalez is on a special diet. He must consume fewer than 500 calories at a meal that consists of one serving of chicken and one serving of rice. The meal must contain at least 150 calories from each source.

a) Using x to represent the number of calories from chicken and y to represent the number of calories from rice, translate the problem into a system of linear inequalities. $x + y < 500, x \geq 150, y \geq 150$

b) Solve the system graphically. Graph calories from chicken on the horizontal axis and calories from rice on the vertical axis. ∗

c) There are about 180 calories in 3 oz of chicken and about 200 calories in 8 oz of rice. Select a point in the solution set. For the point selected, determine the number of ounces of chicken and the number of ounces of rice to be served. One example is (220, 220); approximately 3.7 oz of chicken, 8.8 oz of rice.

23. Write a system of linear inequalities whose solution is the second quadrant, including the axes. $x \leq 0, y \geq 0$

Concept/Writing Exercises

24. a) Do all systems of linear inequalities have solutions? Explain. No

b) Write a system of inequalities that has no solution. ∗

25. Can a system of linear inequalities have a solution set consisting of a single point? Explain. Yes. One example is $x \geq 0$, $y \geq 0, x \leq 0, y \leq 0$ which has solution (0, 0).

*See Instructor Answer Appendix

26. Can a system of linear inequalities have as its solution set all the points on the coordinate plane? Explain your answer, giving an example to support it. No. Every line divides the plane into two half planes, only one of which can be part of the solution.

27. Write a system of linear inequalities that has the ordered pair (0, 0) as its only solution. There are many possible answers. Answers will vary.

28. Write a system of linear inequalities that has the following ordered pairs as some of its solutions. There are many possible answers.

$$\ldots (-3, -3), (-2, -2), (-1, -1), (0, 0), (1, 1), (2, 2), (3, 3), \ldots$$

Answers will vary.

SECTION 7.6   Linear Programming

Anne Kress is the manager of a company that manufactures skateboards and in-line skates. She must determine the number of skateboards and in-line skates to produce in order to maximize profit. Some of the factors she needs to consider include the profit, demand, and production restrictions for each item. In this section we will use a method called linear programming to answer various questions, such as how much of an item must be produced to obtain the maximum profit.

Why *This is Important* Government, business, and industry often require decision makers to find cost-effective solutions to a variety of problems using linear programming.

▲ *Linear programming can be used to determine how many skateboards and in-line skates a company should make in order to maximize profit.*

Linear programming provides businesses and governments with a mathematical form of decision making that makes the most efficient use of time and resources. Linear programming often serves as a method of expressing the relationships in many of these problems and uses systems of linear inequalities.

The typical linear programming problem has many variables and is generally so lengthy that it is solved on a computer by a technique called the *simplex method*. The simplex method was developed in the 1940s by George B. Dantzig (see the *Profile in Mathematics* on page 426). Linear programming is used to solve problems in the social sciences, health care, land development, nutrition, military, and many other fields.

We will not discuss the simplex method in this textbook. We will merely give a brief introduction to how linear programming works. You can find a detailed explanation in books on finite mathematics.

In a linear programming problem, there are restrictions called *constraints*. Each constraint is represented as a linear inequality. The list of constraints forms a system of linear inequalities. When the system of inequalities is graphed, we often obtain a region bounded on all sides by line segments (Fig. 7.13). This region is called the *feasible region*. The points where two or more boundaries intersect are called the *vertices* of the feasible region. The points on the boundary of the region and the points inside the feasible region are the solution set for the system of inequalities.

For each linear programming problem, we will obtain a formula of the form $K = Ax + By$, called the *objective function*. The objective function is the formula for the quantity K (or some other variable) that we want to maximize or minimize. The values we substitute for x and y determine the value of K. From the information given in the problem, we determine the real number constants A and B. In a particular linear programming problem, a typical equation that might be used to find the maximum profit, P, is $P = 3x + 7y$. We would find the maximum profit by substituting the ordered pairs (x, y) of the vertices of the feasible region into the formula $P = 3x + 7y$ to see which ordered pair yields the greatest value of P and therefore the maximum profit. The ordered pair that yields the smallest value of P determines the minimum profit.

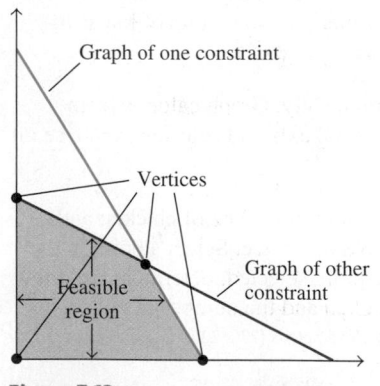

Graph of one constraint

Vertices

Graph of other constraint

Feasible region

Figure 7.13

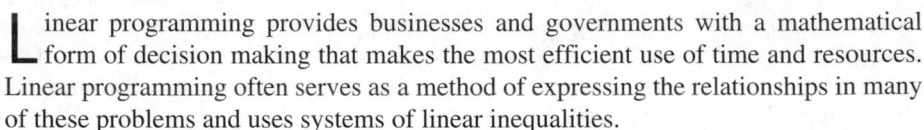

Did You Know?

The Logistics of D-Day

Winston Churchill called the invasion of Normandy "the most difficult and complicated operation that has ever taken place."

Linear programming was first used to deal with the age-old military problem of logistics: obtaining, maintaining, and transporting military equipment and personnel. George B. Dantzig developed the simplex method for the Allies of World War II to do just that. Consider the logistics of the Allied invasion of Normandy. Meteorologic experts had settled on three possible dates in June 1944. It had to be a day when low tide and first light would coincide, when the winds should not exceed 8 to 13 mph, and when visibility was not less than 3 miles. A force of 170,000 assault troops was to be assembled and moved to 22 airfields in England where 1200 air transports and 700 gliders would then take them to the coast of France to converge with 5000 ships of the D-day armada. The code name for the invasion was Operation Overlord, but it is known to most as D-day.

Linear programming is used to determine which ordered pair will yield the maximum (or minimum) value of the variable that is being maximized (or minimized). The fundamental principle of linear programming provides a rule for finding those maximum and minimum values.

Fundamental Principle of Linear Programming

If the objective function, $K = Ax + By$, is evaluated at each point in a feasible region, the maximum and minimum values of the equation occur at vertices of the region.

Linear programming is a powerful tool for finding the maximum and minimum values of an objective function. Using the fundamental principle of linear programming, we are quickly able to determine the maximum and minimum values of an objective function by using just a few of the infinitely many points in the feasible region.

Example 1 illustrates how the fundamental principle is used to solve a linear programming problem.

Example 1 MODELING—*Using the Fundamental Principle of Linear Programming*

The Ric Shaw Chair company makes two types of rocking chairs, a plain chair and a fancy chair. Each rocking chair must be assembled and then finished. The plain chair takes 4 hours to assemble and 4 hours to finish. The fancy chair takes 8 hours to assemble and 12 hours to finish. The company can provide at most 160 worker-hours of assembling and 180 worker-hours of finishing a day. If the profit on a plain chair is $40 and the profit on a fancy chair is $65, how many rocking chairs of each type should the company make per day to maximize profits? What is the maximum profit?

Solution From the information given, we know the following facts.

	Assembly Time (hr)	Finishing Time (hr)	Profit ($)
Plain chair	4	4	40.00
Fancy chair	8	12	65.00

Let

$$x = \text{the number of plain chairs made per day}$$
$$y = \text{the number of fancy chairs made per day}$$
$$40x = \text{profit on the plain chairs}$$
$$65y = \text{profit on the fancy chairs}$$
$$P = \text{the total profit}$$

The total profit is the sum of the profit on the plain chairs and the profit on the fancy chairs. Since $40x$ is the profit on the plain chairs and $65y$ is the profit on the fancy chairs, the profit formula is $P = 40x + 65y$.

The maximum profit, P, is dependent on several conditions, called *constraints*. The number of chairs manufactured each day cannot be a negative amount. This condition gives us the constraints $x \geq 0$ and $y \geq 0$. Another constraint is determined by the total number of hours allocated for assembling. Four hours are needed to assemble the plain chair, so the total number of hours per day to assemble x plain chairs is $4x$. Eight hours are required to assemble a fancy chair, so the total number of hours needed to assemble y fancy chairs is $8y$. The maximum number of hours allocated for assembling is 160 per day. Thus, the third constraint

Figure 7.14

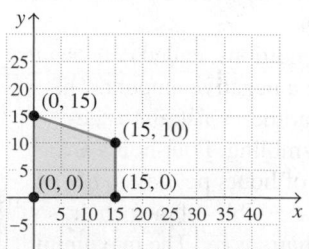

Figure 7.15

is $4x + 8y \le 160$. The final constraint is determined by the number of hours allotted for finishing. Finishing a plain chair takes 4 hours, or $4x$ hours to finish x plain chairs. Finishing a fancy chair takes 12 hours, or $12y$ hours to finish y fancy chairs. The total number of hours allotted for finishing is 180 per day. Therefore, the fourth constraint is $4x + 12y \le 180$. Thus, the four constraints are

$$x \ge 0$$
$$y \ge 0$$
$$4x + 8y \le 160$$
$$4x + 12y \le 180$$

The list of constraints is a system of linear inequalities in two variables. The solution to the system of inequalities is the set of ordered pairs that satisfy all the constraints. These points are plotted in Fig. 7.14. Note that the solution to the system consists of the colored region and the solid boundaries. The points $(0, 0)$, $(0, 15)$, $(30, 5)$, and $(40, 0)$ are the points at which the boundaries intersect. These points can also be found by the addition or substitution method described in Section 7.2.

The goal in this example is to maximize the profit. The objective function is given by the profit formula $P = 40x + 65y$. According to the fundamental principle, the maximum profit will be found at one of the vertices of the feasible region. Calculate P for each one of the vertices.

$$P = 40x + 65y$$

At $(0, 0)$, $P = 40(0) + 65(0) = 0$

At $(0, 15)$, $P = 40(0) + 65(15) = 975$

At $(30, 5)$, $P = 40(30) + 65(5) = 1525$

At $(40, 0)$, $P = 40(40) + 65(0) = 1600$

The maximum profit is at $(40, 0)$, which means that the company should manufacture 40 plain rocking chairs and no fancy rocking chairs. The maximum profit would be $1600. The minimum profit would be at $(0, 0)$, when no rocking chairs of either style were manufactured.   ■

A variation of the problem in Example 1 could be that the company knows that it cannot make more than 15 plain rocking chairs per day. With this additional constraint, we now have the following set of constraints.

$$x \ge 0$$
$$x \le 15$$
$$y \ge 0$$
$$4x + 8y \le 160$$
$$4x + 12y \le 180$$

The graph of the feasible region of these constraints is shown in Fig. 7.15.

The vertices of the feasible region are $(0, 0)$, $(0, 15)$, $(15, 10)$, and $(15, 0)$. To determine the maximum profit, we calculate P for each of these vertices:

$$P = 40x + 65y$$

At $(0, 0)$, $P = 40(0) + 65(0) = 0$

At $(0, 15)$, $P = 40(0) + 65(15) = 975$

At $(15, 10)$, $P = 40(15) + 65(10) = 1250$

At $(15, 0)$, $P = 40(15) + 65(0) = 600$

This set of constraints gives the maximum profit of $1250 when the company manufactures 15 plain rocking chairs and 10 fancy rocking chairs.

Example 2   MODELING—*Washers and Dryers, Maximizing Profit*

The Admiral Appliance Company makes washers and dryers. The company must manufacture at least one washer per day to ship to one of its customers. No more than 6 washers can be manufactured due to production restrictions. The number of dryers manufactured cannot exceed 7 per day. Also, the number of washers manufactured cannot exceed the number of dryers manufactured per day. If the profit on each washer is $20 and the profit on each dryer is $30, how many of each appliance should the company make per day to maximize profits? What is the maximum profit?

Solution Let

$$x = \text{the number of washers manufactured per day}$$
$$y = \text{the number of dryers manufactured per day}$$
$$20x = \text{the profit on washers}$$
$$30y = \text{the profit on dryers}$$
$$P = \text{the total profit}$$

The maximum profit is dependent on several constraints. The number of appliances manufactured each day cannot be a negative amount. This condition gives us the constraints $x \geq 0$ and $y \geq 0$. The company must manufacture at least one washer per day; therefore, $x \geq 1$. No more than 6 washers can be manufactured per day; therefore, $x \leq 6$. No more than 7 dryers can be manufactured per day; therefore, $y \leq 7$. The number of washers cannot exceed the number of dryers manufactured per day; therefore, $x \leq y$. Thus, the six constraints are

$$x \geq 0, y \geq 0, x \geq 1, x \leq 6, y \leq 7, x \leq y$$

In this example, the objective function is the profit formula. Since $20x$ is the profit on x washers and $30y$ is the profit on y dryers, the profit formula is $P = 20x + 30y$. Figure 7.16 shows the feasible region. The feasible region consists of the shaded region and the boundaries. The vertices of the feasible region are at $(1, 1)$, $(1, 7)$, $(6, 7)$, and $(6, 6)$.

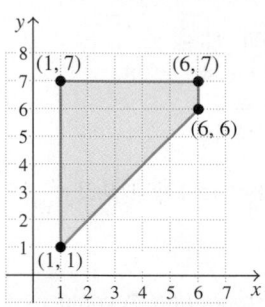

Figure 7.16

Next we calculate the value of the objective function, P, at each one of the vertices.

$$P = 20x + 30y$$

At $(1, 1)$, $P = 20(1) + 30(1) = 50$

At $(1, 7)$, $P = 20(1) + 30(7) = 230$

At $(6, 7)$, $P = 20(6) + 30(7) = 330$

At $(6, 6)$, $P = 20(6) + 30(6) = 300$

The maximum profit is at $(6, 7)$. Therefore, the company should manufacture 6 washers and 7 dryers to maximize its profit. The maximum profit is $330. ∎

Use the following steps to solve a linear programming problem.

PROCEDURE   SOLVING A LINEAR PROGRAMMING PROBLEM

1. Determine all necessary constraints.
2. Determine the objective function.
3. Graph the constraints and determine the feasible region.
4. Determine the vertices of the feasible region.
5. Determine the value of the objective function at each vertex.

The solution is determined by the values in the ordered pair of the vertex that yields the maximum or minimum value of the objective function.

Concept Exercises

In Exercises 1–6, fill in the blank with an appropriate word, phrase, or symbol(s).

1. The restrictions that are represented in a linear programming problem by linear inequalities are called the _____. Constraints

2. In a linear programming problem, the shaded region formed by graphing the system of inequalities is called the _____ region. Feasible

3. The points of intersection of the boundaries of the feasible region are called the _____. Vertices

4. The typical linear programming problem has many variables and is generally so lengthy that it is solved on a computer by a technique called the _____ method. Simplex

5. In a linear programming problem, the function used for the quantity that we want to maximize or minimize is called the _____ function. Objective

6. The maximum and minimum values of the objective function occur at the _____ of the feasible region. Vertices

Practice the Skills

Exercises 7–10 show a feasible region and its vertices. Find the maximum and minimum values of the given objective function.

7. $K = 6x + 4y$

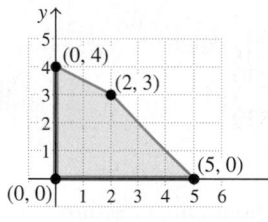

Maximum is 30 at (5, 0), minimum is 0 at (0, 0).

8. $K = 10x + 8y$

Maximum is 238 at (15, 11), minimum is 0 at (0, 0).

9. $K = 2x + 3y$

Maximum is 190 at (50, 30), minimum is 70 at (20, 10).

10. $K = 40x + 50y$

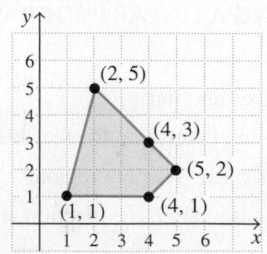

Maximum is 330 at (2, 5), minimum is 90 at (1, 1).

In Exercises 11–16, a set of constraints and a profit formula are given.

a) *Draw the graph of the constraints and find the vertices of the feasible region.*

b) *Use the vertices obtained in part (a) to determine the maximum and minimum profit.*

11. $x + y \le 5$
$2x + y \le 8$
$x \ge 0$
$y \ge 0$
$P = 4x + 3y*$

12. $x + 2y \le 6$
$3x + 2y \le 12$
$x \ge 0$
$y \ge 0$
$P = 2x + 6y*$

13. $x + y \le 4$
$x + 3y \le 6$
$x \ge 0$
$y \ge 0$
$P = 7x + 6y*$

14. $x + y \le 50$
$x + 3y \le 90$
$x \ge 0$
$y \ge 0$
$P = 20x + 40y*$

15. $2x + 3y \ge 18$
$4x + 2y \le 20$
$x \ge 1$
$y \ge 4$
$P = 2.20x + 1.65y*$

16. $x + 2y \le 14$
$7x + 4y \ge 28$
$x \ge 2$
$x \le 10$
$y \ge 1$
$P = 15.13x + 9.35y*$

Problem Solving

17. **MODELING**—*Washing Machine Production* A company manufactures two types of washers, top load and front load. The company can manufacture a maximum of 18 washers per day. It makes a profit of $20 on top load machines and $25 on front load machines. No more than 5 front load machines can be manufactured due to production restrictions. To meet consumer demand, the company must manufacture at least 2 front load machines and 2 top load machines per day.

a) List the constraints.
$x + y \le 18, y \le 5, x \ge 2, y \ge 2$

b) Determine the objective function. $P = 20x + 25y$

c) Graph the set of constraints.*

d) Determine the vertices of the feasible region.
(2, 5), (13, 5), (16, 2), (2, 2)

e) How many washing machines of each type should be made to maximize profit?
13 top load machines and 5 front load machines

f) Determine the maximum profit. $385

18. **MODELING**—*On Wheels* The Boards and Blades Company manufactures skateboards and in-line skates. The company can produce a maximum of 20 skateboards and pairs of in-line skates per day. It makes a profit of $25 on

*See Instructor Answer Appendix

a skateboard and a profit of $20 on a pair of in-line skates. The company's planners want to make at least 3 skateboards but not more than 6 skateboards per day. To keep customers happy, they must make at least 2 pairs of in-line skates per day.

a) List the constraints. $x + y \leq 20, x \geq 3, x \leq 6, y \geq 2$

b) Determine the objective function. $P = 25x + 20y$

c) Graph the set of constraints.*

d) Determine the vertices of the feasible region.
(3, 17), (6, 14), (6, 2) (3, 2)

e) How many skateboards and pairs of in-line skates should be made to maximize the profit?
Six skateboards and 14 pairs of in-line skates

f) Determine the maximum profit. $430

19. **MODELING—*Paint Production*** A paint supplier has two machines that produce both indoor paint and outdoor paint. To meet one of its contractual obligations, the company must produce at least 60 gal of indoor paint and 100 gal of outdoor paint. Machine I makes 3 gal of indoor paint and 10 gal of outdoor paint per hour. Machine II makes 4 gal of indoor paint and 5 gal of outdoor paint per hour. It costs $28 per hour to run machine I and $33 per hour to run machine II.

a) List the constraints.
$3x + 4y \geq 60, 10x + 5y \geq 100, x \geq 0, y \geq 0$

b) Determine the objective function. $C = 28x + 33y$

c) Graph the set of constraints.*

d) Determine the vertices of the feasible region.
(0, 20), (4, 12), (20, 0)

e) How many hours should each machine be operated to fulfill the contract at a minimum cost?
4 hours for Machine I and 12 hours for Machine II

f) Determine the minimum cost. $508

Challenge Problems/Group Activities

20. **MODELING—*Hot Dog Profits*** To make one package of all-beef hot dogs, a manufacturer uses 1 lb of beef; to make one package of regular hot dogs, the manufacturer uses $\frac{1}{2}$ lb each of beef and pork. The profit on the all-beef hot dogs is 40 cents per pack, and the profit on regular

hot dogs is 30 cents per pack. If there are 200 lb of beef and 150 lb of pork available, how many packs of all-beef and regular hot dogs should the manufacturer make to maximize the profit? What is the profit?*

21. **MODELING—*Car Seats and Strollers*** A company makes car seats and strollers. Each car seat and stroller passes through three processes: assembly, safety testing, and packaging. A car seat requires 1 hr in assembly, 2 hr in safety testing, and 1 hr in packaging. A stroller requires 3 hr in assembly, 1 hr in safety testing, and 1 hr in packaging. Employee work schedules allow for 24 hr per day for assembly, 16 hr per day for safety testing, and 10 hr per day for packaging. The profit for each car seat is $25, and the profit for each stroller is $35. How many units of each type should the company make per day to maximize the profit? What is the maximum profit?
Three car seats and seven strollers, $320

22. **MODELING—*Special Diet*** A dietitian prepares a special diet using two food groups, A and B. Each ounce of food group A contains 3 units of vitamin C and 1 unit of vitamin D. Each ounce of food group B contains 1 unit of vitamin C and 2 units of vitamin D. The minimum daily requirements with this diet are at least 9 units of vitamin C and at least 8 units of vitamin D. Each ounce of food group A costs 50 cents, and each ounce of food group B costs 30 cents.

a) List the constraints. $3x + y \geq 9, x + 2y \geq 8, x \geq 0, y \geq 0$

b) Determine the objective function for minimizing cost.
$C = 0.50x + 0.30y$

c) Graph the set of constraints.*

d) Determine the vertices of the feasible region.
(0, 9), (2, 3), (8, 0)

e) How many ounces of each food group should be used to meet the daily requirements and minimize the cost?
2 ounces of food group A and 3 ounces of food group B

f) Determine the minimum cost. $1.90

Internet/Research Activity

23. ***Operations research*** draws on several disciplines, including mathematics, probability theory, statistics, and economics. George B. Dantzig (see the *Profile in Mathematics* on page 426) was one of the key people in developing operations research. Write a paper on Dantzig and his contributions to operations research and linear programming.

*See Instructor Answer Appendix

CHAPTER 7 *Summary*

Important Facts and Concepts	Examples and Discussion
Section 7.1	
Solving Systems of Equations by Graphing	Discussion page 387
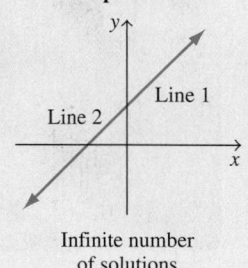	Examples 2–6, pages 387–390
Section 7.2	
Solving Systems of Equations by Algebraic Methods	
Substitution	Examples 1–3, 8, pages 394–396, 399–400
Addition (or elimination) method	Examples 4–7, 9, pages 397–399, 400–401
Section 7.3	
Multiplicative Identity Matrix	Example 8, page 409
$$\begin{bmatrix} 1 & 0 \\ 0 & 1 \end{bmatrix}, \begin{bmatrix} 1 & 0 & 0 \\ 0 & 1 & 0 \\ 0 & 0 & 1 \end{bmatrix}, \ldots$$	
Section 7.4	
Writing Augumented Metrices	
System of equations Augmented matrix	Discussion pages 415–416
$a_1 x + b_1 y = c_1$ $\quad$ $\begin{bmatrix} a_1 & b_1 & \vert & c_1 \\ a_2 & b_2 & \vert & c_2 \end{bmatrix}$ $a_2 x + b_2 y = c_2$	Examples 1–3, pages 416–419
Section 7.5	
System of Linear Inequalities	
Graph both inequalities on the same axes. The solution is the set of points that satisfy both inequalities.	Examples 1–3, Pages 421–422
Section 7.6	
Fundamental Principle of Linear Programming	
If the objective function $K = Ax + By$ is evaluated at each point in a feasible region, the maximum and minimum values of the equation occur at vertices of the region.	Discussion pages 424–425 Examples 1–2, pages 425–427

CHAPTER 7) *Review Exercises*

7.1

In Exercises 1–4, solve the system of equations graphically. If the system does not have a single ordered pair as a solution, state whether the system is inconsistent or dependent.

1. $x = 3$
$y = 2$*

2. $x + 3y = 5$
$3x - 3y = 3$*

3. $x = 3$
$x + y = 5$*

4. $x + 2y = 5$
$2x + 4y = 4$*

In Exercises 5–8, determine without graphing whether the system of equations has exactly one solution, no solution, or an infinite number of solutions.

5. $y = \frac{1}{2}x + 3$
$2y = x + 6$
An infinite number of solutions

6. $2x + y = 4$
$y = -2x + 6$ No solution

7. $4x + 3y = 9$
$2x - 3y = 9$ One solution

8. $2x - 4y = 8$
$-2x + y = 6$ One solution

7.2

In Exercises 9–12, solve the system of equations by the substitution method. If the system does not have a single ordered pair as a solution, state whether the system is inconsistent or dependent.

9. $-x + y = -2$
$x + 2y = 5$ (3, 1)

10. $x - 2y = 9$
$y = 2x - 3$ (-1, -5)

11. $2x - y = 4$
$3x - y = 2$ (-2, -8)

12. $3x + y = 1$
$3y = -9x - 4$
No solution; inconsistent

In Exercises 13–18, solve the system of equations by the addition method. If the system does not have a single ordered pair as a solution, state whether the system is inconsistent or dependent.

13. $2x + y = 2$
$-3x - y = 5$ (-7, 16)

14. $x + y = 2$
$x + 3y = -2$ (4, -2)

15. $x - 2y = 8$
$2x + y = 6$ (4, -2)

16. $4x - 8y = 16$
$x - 2y = 4$
An infinite number of solutions; dependent

17. $3x - 4y = 10$
$5x + 3y = 7$ (2, -1)

18. $3x + 4y = 6$
$2x - 3y = 4$ (2, 0)

7.3

Given $A = \begin{bmatrix} 1 & -3 \\ 2 & 4 \end{bmatrix}$ and $B = \begin{bmatrix} 4 & -3 \\ 2 & 1 \end{bmatrix}$, determine the following.

19. $A + B$ $\begin{bmatrix} 5 & -6 \\ 4 & 5 \end{bmatrix}$

20. $A - B$ $\begin{bmatrix} -3 & 0 \\ 0 & 3 \end{bmatrix}$

21. $2A$ $\begin{bmatrix} 2 & -6 \\ 4 & 8 \end{bmatrix}$

22. $2A - 3B$ $\begin{bmatrix} -10 & 3 \\ -2 & 5 \end{bmatrix}$

23. $A \times B$ $\begin{bmatrix} -2 & -6 \\ 16 & -2 \end{bmatrix}$

24. $B \times A$ $\begin{bmatrix} -2 & -24 \\ 4 & -2 \end{bmatrix}$

7.4

In Exercises 25–30, use an augmented matrix to solve the system of equations.

25. $x + 3y = 8$
$x + y = 4$ (2, 2)

26. $-x + y = 4$
$x + 3y = 4$ (-2, 2)

27. $2x + y = 3$
$3x - y = 12$ (3, -3)

28. $2x + 3y = 2$
$4x - 9y = 4$ (1, 0)

29. $x + 3y = 3$
$3x - 2y = 2$ $\left(\frac{12}{11}, \frac{7}{11} \right)$

30. $3x - 6y = -9$
$4x + 5y = 14$ (1, 2)

7.1–7.4

31. MODELING—*Borrowing Money* A company borrows $400,000 for 1 year to expand its product line. Some of the money was borrowed at a 3% simple interest rate, and the rest of the money was borrowed at a 6% simple interest rate. How much money was borrowed at each rate if the total annual interest was $16,500?
$250,000 at 3%, $150,000 at 6%

32. MODELING—*Chemistry* In chemistry class, Tom Le has an 80% acid solution and a 50% acid solution. How much of each solution should he mix to get 100 liters of a 75% acid solution?
Mix $83\frac{1}{3}\ell$ of 80% acid solution with $16\frac{2}{3}\ell$ of 50% acid solution.

33. MODELING—*Landscaping* The Garden Factory purchased 4 tons of topsoil and 3 tons of mulch for $1529. The next week the company purchased 2 tons of topsoil and 5 tons of mulch for $1405. Determine the price per ton for topsoil and the price per ton for mulch.
$245 per ton for topsoil, $183 per ton for mulch

*See Instructor Answer Appendix

34. MODELING—*Cool Air* Emily Richelieu needs to purchase a new air conditioner for the office. Model 1600A costs $950 to purchase and $32 per month to operate. Model 6070B, a more efficient unit, costs $1275 to purchase and $22 per month to operate.

a) After how many months will the total cost of both units be equal? 32.5 months

b) Which model will be the more cost effective if the life of both units is guaranteed for 10 years? Model 6070B

35. MODELING—*Minimizing Parking Costs* The cost of parking in All-Day parking lot is $5 for the first hour and $0.50 for each additional hour. Sav-a-Lot parking lot costs $4.25 for the first hour and $0.75 for each additional hour.

a) In how many hours after the first hour would the total cost of parking at All-Day and Sav-a-Lot be the same? 3 hr

b) If Mark McMahon needed to park his car for 5 hr, which parking lot would be less expensive? All-Day parking lot

7.5

In Exercises 36–39, graph the system of linear inequalities and indicate the solution set.

36. $y \leq 3x - 1$
$y > -2x + 1$*

37. $2x + y < 8$
$y \geq 2x - 1$*

38. $x + 3y \leq 6$
$2x - 7y \geq 14$*

39. $x - y > 5$
$6x + 5y \leq 30$*

7.6

40. The set of constraints and profit formula for a linear programming problem are

$$2x + 3y \leq 12$$
$$2x + y \leq 8$$
$$x \geq 0$$
$$y \geq 0$$
$$P = 5x + 3y$$

a) Draw the graph of the constraints and determine the vertices of the feasible region.*

b) Use the vertices to determine the maximum and minimum profit. Maximum is 21 at (3, 2); minimum is 0 at (0, 0).

*See Instructor Answer Appendix

CHAPTER 7) *Test*

1. From a graph, explain how you would identify a consistent system of equations, an inconsistent system of equations, and a dependent system of equations.*

2. Solve the system of equations graphically.

$$y = 2x - 12$$
$$2x + 2y = -6*$$

3. Determine without graphing whether the system of equations has exactly one solution, no solution, or an infinite number of solutions.

$$4x + 5y = 6$$
One solution
$$-3x + 5y = 13$$

Solve the system of equations by the method indicated.

4. $x + y = -1$
$2x + 3y = -5$
(substitution) (2, −3)

5. $y = 3x - 7$
$y = 5x - 3$
(substitution) (−2, −13)

6. $x + y = 6$
$4x + 4y = -8$
(substitution) No solution

7. $x - y = 4$
$2x + y = -10$
(addition) (−2, −6)

8. $4x + 3y = 5$
$2x + 4y = 10$
(addition) (−1, 3)

9. $3x + 4y = 6$
$2x - 3y = 4$
(addition) (2, 0)

10. $x + 3y = 4$
$5x + 7y = 4$
(matrices) (−2, 2)

11. $x - y = 2$
$2x - y = 4$
(matrices) (2, 0)

12. $4x + 2y = 6$
$5x + 4y = 9$
(matrices) (1, 1)

In Exercises 13–14, for $A = \begin{bmatrix} 2 & -5 \\ 1 & 3 \end{bmatrix}$ and

$B = \begin{bmatrix} -1 & -3 \\ 5 & 2 \end{bmatrix}$, *determine the following.*

13. $A + B$*

14. $A - 2B$*

In Exercises 15–16, determine $A \times B$.

15. $A = \begin{bmatrix} 2 & 1 & 0 \\ -3 & 4 & 1 \end{bmatrix}$, $B = \begin{bmatrix} 3 \\ 1 \\ 2 \end{bmatrix}$ $\begin{bmatrix} 7 \\ -3 \end{bmatrix}$

16. $A = \begin{bmatrix} 1 & 3 \\ 0 & 6 \end{bmatrix}$, $B = \begin{bmatrix} 2 & 5 \\ 8 & -1 \end{bmatrix}$ $\begin{bmatrix} 26 & 2 \\ 48 & -6 \end{bmatrix}$

*See Instructor Answer Appendix

17. Graph the system of linear inequalities and indicate the solution set.

$$y < -2x + 2$$
$$y > 3x + 2*$$

Solve Exercises 18 and 19 by using a system of equations.

18. **MODELING**—*Truck Rental* U-Haul charges a daily fee plus a mileage charge to rent a truck. Dorothy DiMento rented a truck with U-Haul and was charged $132 for 3 days rental and 150 miles driven. Elena Dilai rented the same truck and was charged $142 for 2 days rental and 400 miles driven. Determine the daily fee and the mileage charge for renting this truck.
Daily fee: $35; mileage charge: $0.18

19. **MODELING**—*Checking Accounts* The charge for maintaining a checking account at Union Bank is $6 per month plus 10 cents for each check that is written. The charge at Citrus Bank is $2 per month and 20 cents per check.

a) How many checks would a customer have to write in a month for the total charges to be the same at both banks? 40 checks

b) If Brent Pickett planned to write 14 checks per month, which bank would be the least expensive? Citrus Bank

20. The set of constraints and profit formula for a linear programming problem are

$$x + 3y \le 6$$
$$4x + 3y \le 15$$
$$x \ge 0$$
$$y \ge 0$$
$$P = 6x + 4y$$

a) Draw the graph of the constraints and determine the vertices of the feasible region.*

b) Use the vertices to determine the maximum and minimum profit. Maximum is 22.5 at (3.75, 0); minimum is 0 at (0, 0).

*See Instructor Answer Appendix

GROUP PROJECTS

1. Make up three different systems of equations that have (1, 4) as a solution. Explain how you determined your systems.

Linear Programming

2. **MODELING**—*Profit from Bookcases* The Bookholder Company manufactures two types of bookcases out of both oak and walnut. Model 01 requires 5 board feet of oak and 2 board feet of walnut. Model 02 requires 4 board feet of oak and 3 board feet of walnut. A profit of $75 is made on each Model 01 bookcase and a profit of $125 is made on each Model 02 bookcase. The company has a supply of 1000 board feet of oak and 600 board feet of walnut. The company has orders for 40 Model 01 bookcases and 50 Model 02 bookcases. These orders indicate the minimum number the company must manufacture of each model.

a) Write the set of constraints.

b) Write the objective function.

c) Graph the set of constraints.

d) Determine the number of bookcases of each type the company should manufacture in order to maximize profits.

e) Determine the maximum profit.

Create Your Own Word Problem

3. a) Write a word problem that can be solved by using a system of two equations with two unknowns.

b) For the problem in part (a), write the system of equations and find the answer.

c) Explain how you developed the problem in part (a).

8

The Metric System

What You Will Learn

- The advantages of using the metric system
- The basic units used in the metric system
- Conversions within the metric system
- Determining length, area, volume, mass, and temperature in the metric system
- Dimensional analysis and converting to and from the metric system

Why This is Important

The United States is the only major country not presently using the metric system. For example, if you travel to Canada, Mexico, or overseas, you will find that when you purchase gasoline, the amount you get is measured in liters, not gallons.

In the United States, because of the growth in technology and the increase in international trade, more and more of the products we use daily are measured in metric units. For example, soda is sold in liter bottles, medicines are measured in milligrams, and tire sizes are given in centimeters. And when you purchase a computer, the size of the hard drive, such as 500 gigabytes (500 GB), is a metric measurement. A router's speed may be 257 megabits per second (257 Mbps). As we continue to advance in our technological age, we will use more and more metric measurements.

◄ *Everywhere outside the United States you may see traffic and other signs given in metric units.*

Basic Terms and Conversions Within the Metric System

▲ *The sciences use metric measurements.*

Have you ever taken a science course? If so, you most likely worked with metric measurements. For example, in chemistry you may have worked with liter containers, and in physics you may have worked with a mass in kilograms rather than a weight in pounds. Have you ever asked yourself why the sciences use metric measurement? In this section, we will explain some benefits of using the metric system.

Why **This is Important** Most countries use the metric system for measurement. A knowledge of the metric system will help you not only at home but also when you travel to other countries.

Did You Know?

Lost in Space

The missing *Mars Climate Orbiter*

In September 1999, the United States lost a $125 million spacecraft, the *Mars Climate Orbiter*, as it approached Mars. Two spacecraft teams, one at NASA's Jet Propulsion Laboratory (JPL) and the other at a Lockheed Martin facility, were unknowingly exchanging some vital information in different measurement units. The spacecraft team at Lockheed sent some measurements to the spacecraft team at JPL using U.S. customary units. The JPL team assumed the information it received was in metric units. The mix-up in units led to the JPL scientists giving the spacecraft's computer the wrong information, which led to the spacecraft entering the Martian atmosphere, where it burned up. NASA has taken steps to prevent this error from ever happening again.

Most countries of the world use the *Système international d'unités* or *SI system*. The SI system is generally referred to as the *metric system* in the United States. The metric system was named for the Greek word *metron,* meaning "measure." The standard units in the metric system have gone through many changes since the system was first developed in France during the French Revolution. For example, one unit of measure, the meter, was first defined as one ten-millionth of the distance between the North Pole and the equator. Later, the meter was defined as 1,650,763.73 wavelengths of the orange–red line of krypton 86. Since 1893, the meter has been defined as the distance traveled by light in a vacuum in $\frac{1}{299,792,458}$ of a second.

Two systems of weights and measures exist side by side in the United States today, the *U.S. customary system* and the metric system. The metric system is used predominantly in the automotive, construction, farm equipment, computer, bottling industries, and in health-related professions. Furthermore, almost every industry that ships internationally uses at least some metric measures.

In this chapter, we will discuss the metric measurements of length, area, volume, mass, and temperature. Using the metric system has many advantages. Some of them are summarized here.

1. The metric system is the worldwide accepted standard measurement system. All industrial nations that trade internationally, except the United States, use the metric system as the official system of measurement.

2. In the metric system there is only one basic unit of measurement for each physical quantity. In the U.S. customary system, many units are often used to represent the same physical quantity. For example, when discussing length, we use inches, feet, yards, miles, and so on. Converting from one of these units to the other is often a tedious task (consider changing 12 miles to inches). In the metric system, we can make many conversions by simply moving the decimal point.

3. The SI system is based on the number 10, and there is less need for fractions because most quantities can be expressed as decimals.

▲ *A meter (top figure) is a little longer than a yard (bottom figure).*

Basic Terms

Because the official definitions of many metric terms are quite technical, we present them informally.

The *meter* (m) is commonly used to measure *length* in the metric system. One meter is a little more than a yard. A door is about 2 meters high.

The *kilogram* (kg) is commonly used to measure *mass*. (The difference between mass and weight is discussed in Section 8.3.) One kilogram is about 2.2 pounds. A newborn baby may have a mass of about 3 kilograms. The gram (g), a unit of mass derived from the kilogram, is used to measure small amounts. A nickel has a mass of about 5 grams.

The *liter* (ℓ) is commonly used to measure *volume*. One liter is a little more than a quart. The gas tank of a compact car may hold 50 liters of gasoline.

Thus,

$$1 \text{ m} \approx 1 \text{ yd}$$
$$1 \text{ kg} \approx 2.2 \text{ lb}$$
$$1 \ell \approx 1 \text{ qt}$$

The term *degree Celsius* (°C) is used to measure *temperature*. The freezing point of water is 0°C, and the boiling point of water is 100°C. The temperature on a warm day may be 30°C.

0°C = 32°F	Water freezes
22°C = 71.6°F	Comfortable room temperature
37°C = 98.6°F	Body temperature
100°C = 212°F	Water boils

Prefixes

The metric system is based on the number 10 and therefore is a decimal system. Prefixes are used to denote a multiple or part of a base unit. Table 8.1 summarizes the more commonly used prefixes and their meanings. In the table, where we mention "base units" we mean metric units without prefixes, such as meter, gram, or liter. From Table 8.1, we can determine that a *deka*meter represents 10 meters and a *centi*meter represents $\frac{1}{100}$ of a meter. Also, 1 kiloliter = 1000 liters, 1 kilogram = 1000 grams, and 1 milliliter = $\frac{1}{1000}$ liter, and so on.

Table 8.1 Metric Prefixes

Prefix	Symbol	Meaning
kilo	k	1000 × base unit
hecto	h	100 × base unit
deka	da	10 × base unit
—	—	base unit
deci	d	$\frac{1}{10}$ of base unit
centi	c	$\frac{1}{100}$ of base unit
milli	m	$\frac{1}{1000}$ of base unit

In the metric system, a comma is commonly used the way we use a decimal point (see the photo on the left, taken in Juarez, Spain), and a decimal point is used the way we use a comma (see the photo on the right, taken in Copenhagen, Denmark).

In the metric system, groups of three digits in large numbers are often separated by a space, not a comma. For example, thirty thousand is written 30 000 and nine million is written 9 000 000. Groups of three digits to the right of the decimal point are also separated by spaces. For example, 16 millionths is written 0,000 016 in many countries of the world. We will use the decimal point in this book and write 0.000 016. In this section, we will separate groups of three digits using spaces. Note, however, that the space between groups of three digits is usually omitted if there are only four digits to the left or right of the decimal point. Thus, we will write three thousand as 3000 and five ten-thousandths as 0.0005.

For scientific work that involves very large and very small quantities, the following prefixes are also used: *mega* (M) is one million times the base unit, *giga* (G) is one billion times the base unit, *tera* (T) is one trillion times the base unit, *micro* (μ, the Greek letter mu) is one millionth of the base unit, *nano* (n) is one billionth of the base unit, and *pico* (p) is one trillionth of the base unit.

In this book, the abbreviations or symbols for units of measure are not pluralized, but full names are. For example, 5 milliliters is symbolized as 5 mℓ, not 5 mℓs. Some countries that use the metric system do not use an "s" in their abbreviations, whereas others do.

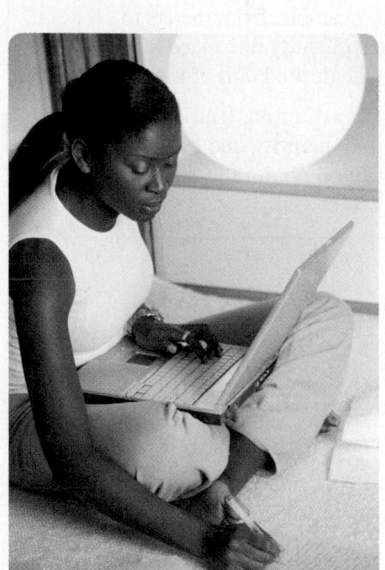

▲ *A computer's hard drive can store 500 gigabytes (500 GB) of information.*

Conversions Within the Metric System

We will use Table 8.2 to help demonstrate how to change from one metric unit to another metric unit using the meter as our base unit (for example, meters to kilometers, and so on).

The meters in Table 8.2 can be replaced by grams, liters, or any other base unit of the metric system. Regardless of which unit we choose, the procedure is the same. For purposes of explanation, we have used the meter.

Table 8.2 Changing Metric Units

Measure of length	kilometer	hectometer	dekameter	meter	decimeter	centimeter	millimeter
Symbol	km	hm	dam	m	dm	cm	mm
Number of meters	1000 m	100 m	10 m	1 m	0.1 m	0.01 m	0.001 m

Table 8.2 shows that 1 hectometer equals 100 meters and 1 millimeter is 0.001 (or $\frac{1}{1000}$) meter. The millimeter is the smallest unit in the table. A centimeter is 10 times as large as a millimeter, a decimeter is 10 times as large as a centimeter, a

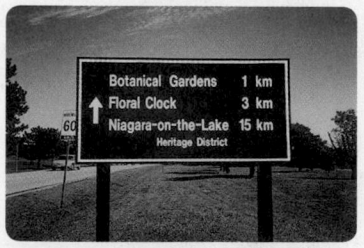

▲ *Our neighbors in Canada (and also Mexico) use the metric system. As you will learn shortly, the distance to the Botanical Gardens is about 0.6 mile and the distance to Niagara-on-the-Lake is about 9 miles from the sign.*

meter is 10 times as large as a decimeter, and so on. Because each unit is 10 times as large as the unit on its right, converting from one unit to another is simply a matter of multiplying or dividing by powers of 10.

> **PROCEDURE   CHANGING UNITS WITHIN THE METRIC SYSTEM**
>
> 1. To change from a smaller unit to a larger unit (for example, from meters to kilometers), move the decimal point in the original quantity one place to the left for each larger unit of measurement until you obtain the desired unit of measurement.
>
> 2. To change from a larger unit to a smaller unit (for example, from kilometers to meters), move the decimal point in the original quantity one place to the right for each smaller unit of measurement until you obtain the desired unit of measurement.

MATHEMATICS TODAY   Additional Metric Prefaces

Many publications about the metric system are available free from the U.S. government. You may contact the National Institute of Standards and Technology (under the U.S. Department of Customs), through the Web site at www.nist.gov/, or you may write to the institute's office (Gaithersburg, MD 20899). Two worthwhile publications are *Metric Style Guide for the News Media* and *A Brief History of Measurement Systems*. The following interesting chart was selected and modified from the latter.

Why **This is Important** We often deal with very large and very small quantities that may be stated using prefixes like giga, mega, micro, and nano. For example, a camera's memory card may contain 32 gigabytes of memory.

METRIC PREFIXES		
Multiples and Submultiples	Prefixes	Symbols
$1\ 000\ 000\ 000\ 000\ 000\ 000\ 000\ 000 = 10^{24}$	yotta	Y
$1\ 000\ 000\ 000\ 000\ 000\ 000\ 000 = 10^{21}$	zetta	Z
$1\ 000\ 000\ 000\ 000\ 000\ 000 = 10^{18}$	exa	E
$1\ 000\ 000\ 000\ 000\ 000 = 10^{15}$	peta	P
$1\ 000\ 000\ 000\ 000 = 10^{12}$	tera	T
$1\ 000\ 000\ 000 = 10^{9}$	giga	G
$1\ 000\ 000 = 10^{6}$	mega	M
$1000 = 10^{3}$	kilo	k
$100 = 10^{2}$	hecto	h
$10 = 10^{1}$	deka	da*
$1 = 10^{0}$		
$0.1 = 10^{-1}$	deci	d
$0.01 = 10^{-2}$	centi	c
$0.001 = 10^{-3}$	milli	m
$0.000\ 001 = 10^{-6}$	micro	μ
$0.000\ 000\ 001 = 10^{-9}$	nano	n
$0.000\ 000\ 000\ 001 = 10^{-12}$	pico	p
$0.000\ 000\ 000\ 000\ 001 = 10^{-15}$	femto	f
$0.000\ 000\ 000\ 000\ 000\ 001 = 10^{-18}$	atto	a
$0.000\ 000\ 000\ 000\ 000\ 000\ 001 = 10^{-21}$	zepto	z
$0.000\ 000\ 000\ 000\ 000\ 000\ 000\ 001 = 10^{-24}$	yocto	y

*Some countries use D for deka.

Example 1   *Changing Units*

a) Convert 293.7 m to km.

b) Convert 14 g to cg.

c) Convert 0.76 ℓ to mℓ.

d) Convert 240 daℓ to kℓ.

Solution

a) Table 8.2 shows that dekameters, hectometers, and kilometers are all larger units of measurements than meters. Kilometers appear three places to the left of meters in the table. Therefore, to change a measure from meters to kilometers, we must move the decimal point in the given number three places to the left, or

$$293.7 \text{ m} = 0.2937 \text{ km}$$

Note that since we are changing from a smaller unit of measurement (meter) to a larger unit of measurement (kilometer), the answer will be a smaller number of units.

b) Grams are a larger unit of measurement than centigrams. To convert grams to centigrams, we move the decimal point two places to the right, or

$$14 \text{ g} = 1400 \text{ cg}$$

Note that since we are changing from a larger unit of measurement (gram) to a smaller unit of measurement (centigram), the answer will be a larger number of units.

c) $0.76 \, \ell = 760 \text{ m}\ell$

d) $240 \text{ da}\ell = 2.40 \text{ k}\ell$ ∎

Example 2 *Two More Conversions*

a) Convert 502 mm to hectometers.

b) Convert 6.34 dam to decimeters.

Solution

a) Table 8.2 shows that hectometers are five places to the left of millimeters. Therefore, to make the conversion, we must move the decimal point in the given number five places to the left, or

$$502 \text{ mm} = 0.005\,02 \text{ hm}$$

b) Table 8.2 shows that decimeters are two places to the right of dekameters. Therefore, to make the conversion, we must move the decimal point in the given number two places to the right, or

$$6.34 \text{ dam} = 634 \text{ dm}$$ ∎

Example 3 *A Metric Road Sign*

The sign in the photo, from Italy, shows that the road narrows in 300 meters.

a) Determine the distance in kilometers.

b) Determine the distance in centimeters.

Solution

a) We must move the decimal point three places to the left to change from meters to kilometers. Therefore,

$$300 \text{ m} = 0.3 \text{ km}$$

b) We must move the decimal point two places to the right to change from meters to centimeters. Therefore,

$$300 \text{ m} = 30\,000 \text{ cm}$$ ∎

Example **4** *Comparing Lengths*

Arrange in order from smallest to largest length: 3.4 m, 3421 mm, and 104 cm.

Solution To be compared, these lengths should all be in the same units of measure. Let's convert all the measures to millimeters, the smallest units of the lengths being compared.

$$3.4 \text{ m} = 3400 \text{ mm} \qquad 3421 \text{ mm} \qquad 104 \text{ cm} = 1040 \text{ mm}$$

Since the lengths, in millimeters, from smallest to largest are 1040, 3400, 3421, the lengths arranged in order from smallest to largest are 104 cm, 3.4 m, and 3421 mm. ∎

SECTION 8.1 *Exercises*

Warm Up Exercises

In Exercises 1–16, fill in the blanks with an appropriate word, phrase, or symbol(s).

1. The name commonly used for the Système international d'unités in the United States is the _____ system. Metric

2. The name of the system of measurement primarily used in the United States today is the U.S. _____ system. Customary

3. In the metric system,

   a) the commonly used unit to measure length is the _____. Meter

   b) the commonly used unit to measure mass is the _____. Kilogram

   c) the commonly used unit to measure liquid volume is the _____, and Liter

   d) the commonly used unit to measure temperature is degrees _____. Celsius

4. Three advantages of the metric system are that

   a) it is the worldwide accepted system of _____. Measurement

   b) there is only one base unit of measurement for each physical _____, and Quantity

   c) it is based on the number _____. 10

5. In the metric system, the prefix used to indicate

   a) ten times the base unit is _____. Deka

   b) one tenth of the base unit is _____. Deci

6. In the metric system, the prefix used to indicate

   a) one hundred times the base unit is _____. Hecto

   b) one hundredth of the base unit is _____. Centi

7. In the metric system, the prefix used to indicate

   a) one thousand times the base unit is _____. Kilo

   b) one thousandth of the base unit is _____. Milli

8. In the metric system, the prefix used to indicate

   a) one million times the base unit is _____, Mega

   b) one millionth of the base unit is _____. Micro

9. 1 dam is _____ times greater than 1 dm. 100

10. 1 hm is _____ times greater than 1 cm. 10,000

11. a) The freezing point of water in the metric system is _____. 0°C

    b) The boiling point of water in the metric system is _____. 100°C

    c) Normal body temperature in the metric system is _____. 37°C

12. A kilogram is about _____ pounds. 2.2

13. a) A meter is a little longer than a _____. Yard

    b) A liter is a little more than a _____. Quart

14. The temperature on a warm day may be _____ °C. 30

15. A comfortable room temperature may be _____ °C. 22

16. A door may be _____ meters high. 2

Practice the Skills

In Exercises 17–22, match the prefix with the one letter, a–f, that gives the meaning of the prefix.

17. Kilo (d)

18. Milli (b)

19. Hecto (c)

20. Deka (e)

21. Deci (f)

22. Centi (a)

a) $\dfrac{1}{100}$ of base unit

b) $\dfrac{1}{1000}$ of base unit

c) 100 times base unit

d) 1000 times base unit

e) 10 times base unit

f) $\dfrac{1}{10}$ of base unit

23. Complete the following.

   a) 1 milligram = _____ grams 0.001

   b) 1 hectogram = _____ grams 100

   c) 1 kilogram = _____ grams 1000

   d) 1 centigram = _____ gram 0.01

   e) 1 dekagram = _____ grams 10

   f) 1 decigram = _____ gram 0.1

24. Complete the following.

   a) 1 centiliter = _____ liter 0.01

   b) 1 dekaliter = _____ liters 10

   c) 1 milliliter = _____ liter 0.001

   d) 1 deciliter = _____ liter 0.1

   e) 1 kiloliter = _____ liters 1000

   f) 1 hectoliter = _____ liters 100

In Exercises 25–30, without referring to any of the tables or your notes, give the symbol and the equivalent in grams for the unit.

25. Milligram mg; 0.001 g   **26.** Centigram cg; 0.01 g

27. Decigram dg; 0.1 g   **28.** Dekagram dag; 10 g

29. Hectogram hg; 100 g   **30.** Kilogram kg; 1000 g

Maximum Mass *In Exercises 31 and 32, use the photo taken in Canada, which shows the maximum mass for vehicles allowed on the street.*

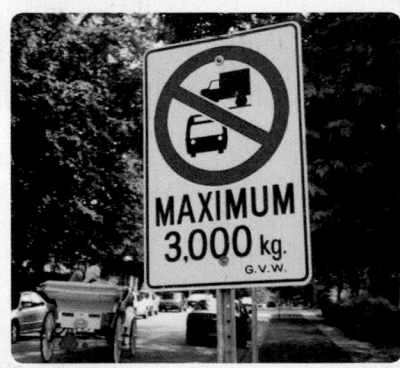

31. What is the maximum mass in grams? 3 000 000 g

32. What is the maximum mass in milligrams? 3 000 000 000 mg

In Exercises 33–38, fill in the missing values.

33. 7 m = _____ mm 7000

34. 42.9 hg = _____ g 4290

35. 0.085 hℓ = _____ kℓ 0.0085

36. 8 dam = _____ m 80

37. 186.2 cm = _____ hm 0.018 62

38. 9.32 mℓ = _____ ℓ 0.009 32

In Exercises 39–44, convert the given unit to the unit indicated.

39. 9.2 m to millimeters 9200 mm

40. 69.3 kg to hectograms 693 hg

41. 895 ℓ to milliliters 895 000 mℓ

42. 24 dm to kilometers 0.0024 km

43. 40 302 mℓ to dekaliters 4.0302 daℓ

44. 0.034 mℓ to liters 0.000 034 ℓ

In Exercises 45–50, use the photo taken in Beijing, China, that shows the distance to Xizhimen Inner Street is 500 m, and the speed limit is 80 kmph, to determine the following.

45. The distance to Xizhimen Inner Street in kilometers 0.5 km

46. The distance to Xizhimen Inner Street in centimeters 50 000 cm

47. The distance to Xizhimen Inner Street in hectometers 5 hm

48. The speed limit in meters per hour 80 000 m/hr

49. The speed limit in millimeters per hour 80 000 000 mm/hr

50. The speed limit in hectometers per hour 800 hm/hr

In Exercises 51–56, arrange the quantities in order from smallest to largest.

51. 4.4 dam, 0.52 km, 620 cm 620 cm, 4.4 dam, 0.52 km

52. 514 hm, 62 km, 680 m 680 m, 514 hm, 62 km

53. 1.4 kg, 1600 g, 16 300 dg 1.4 kg, 1600 g, 16 300 dg

54. 4.3 ℓ, 420 cℓ, 0.045 kℓ 420 cℓ, 4.3 ℓ, 0.045 kℓ

55. 2.6 km, 105 000 mm, 52.6 hm 105 000 mm, 2.6 km, 52.6 hm

56. 0.032 kℓ, 460 dℓ, 48 000 cℓ 0.032 kℓ, 460 dℓ, 48 000 cℓ

Problem Solving

57. *Who Ran Faster* Jim ran 100 m, and Bob ran 100 yd in the same length of time. Who ran faster? Explain.
Jim, 1 m > 1 yd

58. *Walking* Would you be walking faster if you walked 1 dam in 10 min or 1 hm in 10 min? Explain.
1 hm in 10 min, 1 hm > 1 dam

59. *Water Removal* One pump removes 1 daℓ of water in 1 min, and another pump removes 1 dℓ of water in 1 min. Which pump removes water faster? Explain.
The pump that removes 1 daℓ per minute, 1 daℓ > 1 dℓ

60. *Balance* If 5 kg are placed on one side of a balance and a 15 lb weight is placed on the other side, which way would the balance tip? Explain.
The side with the 15 lb would tip down, 15 lb > 5 kg

61. *Framing a Painting* This painting, including the frame, measures 74 cm by 99 cm.

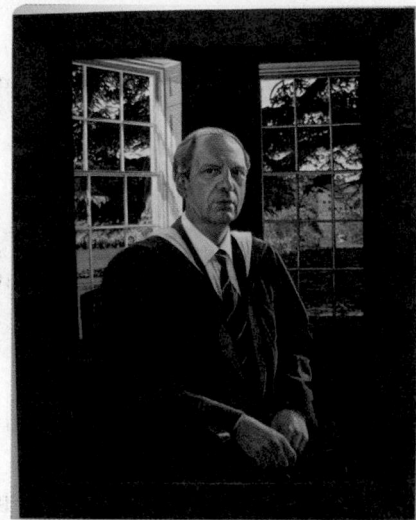

a) How many centimeters of framing were needed to frame the painting? 346 cm

b) How many millimeters of framing were needed to frame the painting? 3460 mm

62. *Calcium Tablets* Sean takes two 250-mg chewable calcium tablets each day.

a) How many milligrams of calcium will Sean take in a week? 3500 mg

b) How many grams of calcium will Sean take in a week? 3.5 g

63. *Chevy Camaro* The gas mileage of a 2010 Chevy Camaro with a 6-cylinder engine is about 12.21 kilometers per liter (km/ℓ) on the highway.

a) If John Herbert drove for 200 km on a highway, estimate the number of liters of gasoline the Camaro would use. Round your answer to the nearest tenth of a liter.
≈ 16.4 ℓ

b) What is the Camaro's gas mileage on the highway in meters per liter? ≈ 12 210 m/ℓ

64. *Track and Field* A high school has a 400-m oval track. If Patty Burgess runs around the track eight times, how many kilometers has she traveled? 3.2 km

65. *Liters of Soda* A bottle of soda contains 360 mℓ.

a) How many milliliters are contained in a six-bottle carton? 2160 mℓ

b) How many liters does the amount in part (a) equal? 2.16 ℓ

c) At $2.45 for the carton of soda, what is its cost per liter? $1.13 per liter

66. *A Home Run* A baseball diamond is a square whose sides are about 27 m in length.

a) How many meters does a batter run if he hits a home run? 108 m

b) How many kilometers? 0.108 km

c) How many millimeters? 108 000 mm

67. *Devil's Tower* The first national monument in the United States was Devil's Tower, near Sundance, Wyoming. The base of Devil's Tower is about 1558 meters above sea level, and the summit of the Tower is about 1944 meters above sea level. How high is Devil's Tower from its base to its summit in **a)** meters, **b)** kilometers, and **c)** centimeters?
a) 386 m, b) 0.386 km, c) 38 600 cm

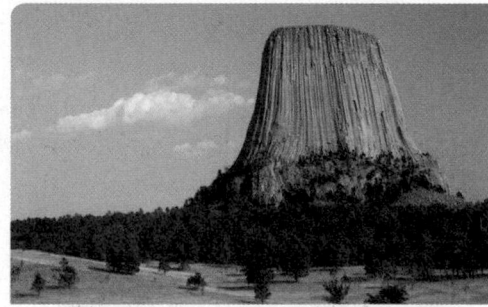

▲ *Devil's Tower in Wyoming*

68. *Tennis Stadium* This photo taken at the Roland Garros Tennis Stadium in Paris shows the distances from the Roland Garros Stadium to tennis stadiums where the other three grand slams of tennis are played.

a) How much farther is Melbourne Park (in Australia) than Flushing Meadows (in New York)? 11 120 km

b) What is the distance determined in part (a) in meters? 11 120 000 m

Challenge Exercises/Group Activities

In Exercises 69–72, fill in the blank to make a true statement.

69. 1 gigameter = _____ megameters 1000

70. 1 nanogram = _____ micrograms 0.001

71. 1 teraliter = _____ picoliters
1×10^{24} = 1 000 000 000 000 000 000 000 000

72. 1 megagram = _____ nanograms
1×10^{15} = 1 000 000 000 000 000

Large and Small Numbers One advantage of the metric system is that by using the proper prefix, you can write large and small numbers without large groups of zeroes. In Exercises 73–78, write an equivalent metric measurement without using any zeroes. For example, you can write 3000 m without zeroes as 3 km and 0.0003 hm as 3 cm.

73. 9000 cm 9 dam

74. 2000 mm 2 m

75. 0.000 06 hg 6 mg

76. 3000 dm 3 hm

77. 0.02 kℓ 2 daℓ

78. 500 cm 5 m

Recreational Mathematics

In Exercises 79–88, unscramble the word to make a metric unit of measurement.

79. magr gram

80. migradec decigram

81. rteli liter

82. raktileed dekaliter

83. terem meter

84. leritililm milliliter

85. reketolim kilometer

86. timenceret centimeter

87. greseed sulesic degrees celsius

88. togmeharc hectogram

Internet/Research Activity

89. Write a report on the development of the metric system in Europe. Indicate which individual people had the most influence in its development.

SECTION 8.2   Length, Area, and Volume

▲ *In most countries, dress sizes are given in centimeters.*

Did You Know?

**1 Yard   = 3 Feet =
36 Inches = . . .**

In the U.S. Customary system, 27 different units of length are used. How many of them can you name? Don't forget rod, mil, paris line, toise, cubit, and light-year. The different units can be found in the *CRC Handbook of Chemistry and Physics* or at the website www.hbcpnetbase.com.

When U.S. companies send their cars overseas, the gas mileage given on the car's window sticker is usually given in liters per hundred kilometers rather than miles per gallon. For example, a smart car's gas mileage may be $\frac{4.3\,\ell}{100\,\text{km}}$. Other measurements, such as the car's length and weight, are also given in metric measurements. When clothing manufacturers ship clothing overseas, the clothing sizes will be given in metric units, such as centimeters. Can you convert a pants waist size of 38 inches to centimeters? In this chapter, you will learn how to make conversions to and from the metric system.

Why *This is Important* If we export goods to other countries, our exports need to be sized in metric units. Imports from other countries, such as tires, are often sized in metric units.

This section and the next section are designed to help you *think metric*, that is, to become acquainted with day-to-day usage of metric units. In this section, we consider length, area, and volume.

Length

The basic unit of length in the metric system is the meter. In all English-speaking countries except the United States, *meter* is spelled "metre." Until 1960, the meter was officially defined by the length of a platinum bar kept in a vault in France. The modern definition of the meter is based on the speed of light, a constant that has been determined with great precision. Other commonly used units of length are the kilometer, centimeter, and millimeter. The meter, which is a little longer than 1 yard, is used to measure things that we normally measure in yards and feet. A man

▲ *Statue of Babe, at Trees of Mystery, Klamath, California. See Example 1(a).*

whose height is about 2 meters is a tall man. A tractor trailer unit (an 18-wheeler) is about 18 meters long.

The kilometer is used to measure what we normally measure in miles. For example, the distance from New York to Seattle is about 5120 kilometers. One kilometer is about 0.6 mile, and 1 mile is about 1.6 kilometers.

Centimeters and millimeters are used to measure what we normally measure in inches. The centimeter is a little less than $\frac{1}{2}$ inch (see Fig. 8.1), and the millimeter is a little less than $\frac{1}{20}$ inch. A millimeter is about the thickness of a dime. A book may measure 20 cm by 25 cm with a thickness of about 3 cm. Millimeters are often used in scientific work and other areas in which small quantities must be measured. The length of a small insect may be measured in millimeters.

Centimeters (smaller markings are millimeters)

Inches

Figure 8.1

Example 1 *Choosing an Appropriate Unit of Length*

Determine which metric unit of length you would use to express the following.

a) The height of the statue of Babe, Paul Bunion's Blue Ox, shown in the photo below in the margin.

b) The length of your nose

c) The length of a flea

d) The height of the Empire State Building

e) The diameter of a half-dollar

f) The distance between Dallas, Texas, and Chicago, Illinois.

g) The diameter of a round wastepaper basket

h) The diameter of a pencil

i) Your waist size

j) Your height

Solution

a) Meters   b) Millimeters or centimeters

c) Millimeters   d) Meters

e) Centimeters or millimeters   f) Kilometers

g) Centimeters   h) Millimeters

i) Centimeters   j) Meters or centimeters

In some parts of this solution, more than one possible answer is listed. Measurements can often be made by using more than one unit. For example, if someone asks your height, you might answer $5\frac{1}{2}$ feet or 66 inches. Both answers are correct. ■

Area

In Chapter 9, we provide formulas and discuss procedures for finding the area and volume of many geometric figures. The procedures and formulas for finding area and volume are the same regardless of whether the units are metric units or customary units. When finding areas and volumes, each side of the figure must be given in (or converted to) the same unit.

The area enclosed in a square with 1-centimeter sides (Fig. 8.2) is 1 cm × 1 cm = 1 cm². A square whose sides are 2 cm (Fig. 8.3) has an area of 2 cm × 2 cm = 2² cm² = 4 cm².

Figure 8.2   Figure 8.3

Areas are always expressed in square units, such as square centimeters, square kilometers, or square meters. When finding areas, be careful that all the numbers being multiplied are expressed in the same units.

In the metric system, the square centimeter replaces the square inch. The square meter replaces the square foot and square yard. In the future, you might purchase carpet or other floor covering by the square meter instead of by the square foot.

For measuring large land areas, the metric system uses a square unit 100 meters on each side (a square hectometer). This unit is called a *hectare* (pronounced "hectair" and symbolized ha). A hectare is about 2.5 acres. One square mile of land contains about 260 hectares. Very large units of area are measured in square kilometers. One square kilometer is about $\frac{4}{10}$ square mile.

Example 2 *Choosing an Appropriate Unit of Area*

Determine which metric unit of area you would use to measure the area of the following.

a) Yellowstone National Park (see photo)

b) The top of a kitchen table

c) The floor of the classroom

d) A person's property with an average-sized lot

e) A newspaper page

f) A baseball field

g) An ice-skating rink

h) A dime

i) A lens in eyeglasses

j) A dollar bill

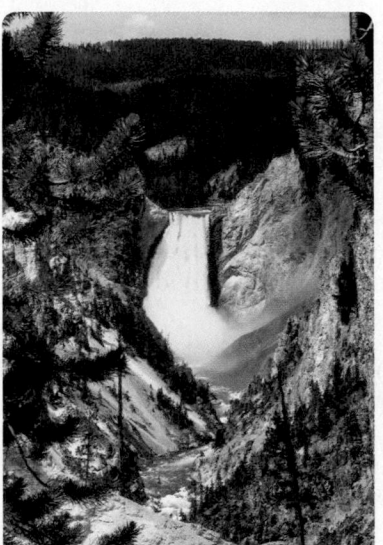

▲ *Yellowstone National Park, Wyoming; see Example 2(a).*

Solution

a) Square kilometers or hectares   b) Square meters

c) Square meters   d) Square meters or hectares

e) Square centimeters   f) Hectares or square meters

g) Square meters   h) Square millimeters or square centimeters

i) Square centimeters   j) Square centimeters   ∎

To find the area, A, of a square, we use the formula $A = s^2$, where s is the length of a side of the square. The area can also be found by the formula area = side × side. We use this information in Example 3.

1 m² or 10 000 cm²

100 cm | 1 m | 1 m | 100 cm

100 cm

Figure 8.4

Example 3 *Converting Square Meters to Square Centimeters*

A square meter is how many times larger than a square centimeter?

Solution A square meter is a square whose sides are 1 meter long. Since 1 m equals 100 cm, we can replace 1 m with 100 cm (see Fig. 8.4). The area of $1 \text{ m}^2 = 1 \text{ m} \times 1 \text{ m} = 100 \text{ cm} \times 100 \text{ cm} = 10\ 000 \text{ cm}^2$. Thus, the area of one square meter is 10,000 times larger than the area of one square centimeter. This technique can be used to convert from any square unit to a different square unit. ∎

1.1 m

1.5 m

Figure 8.5

Example 4 *Table Top*

Find the area of a rectangular table top if its length is 1.5 m and its width is 1.1 m (see Fig. 8.5).

Solution To find the area, we use the formula

$$\text{Area} = \text{length} \times \text{width}$$

or

$$A = l \times w$$

Substituting values for l and w, we have

$$A = 1.5 \text{ m} \times 1.1 \text{ m}$$
$$= 1.65 \text{ m}^2$$

Notice that the area is measured in square meters. ∎

Figure 8.6

Example 5 *A Circular Table*

A circular table has a diameter of about 76 cm (Fig. 8.6). Find the surface area of the table.

Solution The formula for the area of a circle is $A = \pi r^2$, where π is *approximately* 3.14. The radius, r, is one-half the diameter. Since the diameter is about 76 cm, the radius is about 38 cm. Substituting values for π and r, we get the following.

$$A = \pi r^2$$
$$\approx 3.14 (38 \text{ cm})^2$$
$$\approx 4534.16 \text{ cm}^2$$

Thus, the area is approximately 4534.16 square centimeters. Recall from earlier chapters that the symbol ≈ means "is approximately equal to." ∎

TIMELY TIP

Many calculators contain a $\boxed{\pi}$ key. If your calculator contains a $\boxed{\pi}$ key, you should use that key to input the value of π. If you do so, you will get a more accurate answer than if you used 3.14 for pi.

Volume

When a figure has only two dimensions—length and width—we can find its area. When a figure has three dimensions—length, width, and height—we can find its volume. The volume of an item can be considered the space occupied by the item.

In the metric system, volume may be expressed in terms of liters or cubic meters, depending on what is being measured. In all English-speaking countries except the United States, *liter* is spelled "litre."

The volume of liquids is expressed in liters. A liter is a little larger than a quart. Liters are used in place of pints, quarts, and gallons. A liter can be divided into 1000 equal parts, each of which is called a milliliter. Figure 8.7 illustrates a

Figure 8.7

graduated cylinder containing about 50 mℓ of liquid. In chemistry, 100 mℓ and other metric graduated cylinders are often used. Milliliters are used to express the volume of very small amounts of liquid. Drug dosages are often expressed in milliliters. An 8-oz cup will hold about 240 mℓ of liquid.

The kiloliter, 1000 liters, is used to represent the volume of large amounts of liquid. Tank trucks carrying gasoline to service stations hold about 10.5 kℓ of gasoline.

Cubic meters are used to express the volume of large amounts of solid and gaseous material. The volume of a dump truck's load of topsoil is measured in cubic meters. The volume of natural gas used to heat a house may soon be measured in cubic meters instead of cubic feet.

The liquid in a liter container will fit exactly in a cubic decimeter (Fig. 8.8). Note that $1 \ell = 1000$ mℓ and that $1 \text{ dm}^3 = 1000 \text{ cm}^3$. Because $1 \ell = 1 \text{ dm}^3$, 1 *mℓ must equal 1 cm³*. Other useful facts are illustrated in Table 8.3. Thus, within the metric system, conversions are much simpler than in the U.S. customary system. For example, how would you change cubic feet of water into gallons of water?

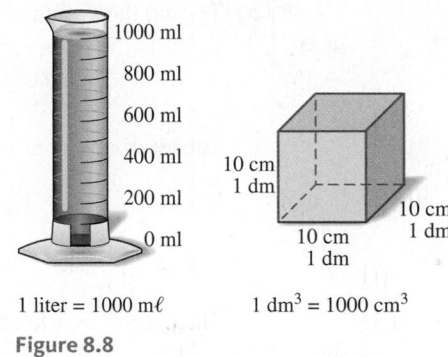

1 liter = 1000 mℓ $1 \text{ dm}^3 = 1000 \text{ cm}^3$

Figure 8.8

Table 8.3

Volume in Cubic Units		Volume in Liters
1 cm^3	=	1 mℓ
1 dm^3	=	1ℓ
1 m^3	=	1 kℓ

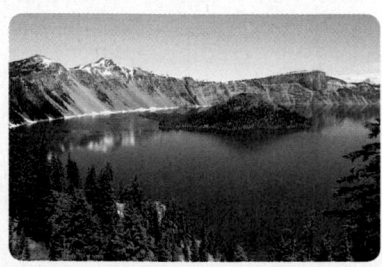

▲ *Crater Lake in Oregon. See Example 6(a).*

Example 6 *Choosing an Appropriate Unit of Volume*

Determine which metric unit of volume you would use to measure the volume of the following.

a) The water in Crater Lake (the deepest lake in the United States)

b) A carton of milk

c) A truckload of topsoil

d) A liquid drug dosage

e) Sand in a paper cup

f) A dime

g) Water in a drinking glass

h) Water in a swimming pool

i) The storage area of a sports utility vehicle with the back seats folded down or removed

j) Concrete used to lay the foundation for a basement

Solution

a) Kiloliters   b) Liters
c) Cubic meters   d) Milliliters
e) Cubic centimeters   f) Cubic millimeters
g) Milliliters   h) Kiloliters or liters or cubic meters
i) Cubic meters   j) Cubic meters   ∎

Example 7 *Swimming Pool Volume*

A swimming pool is 18 m long and 9 m wide, and it has a uniform depth of 3 m (Fig. 8.9). Find (a) the volume of the pool in cubic meters and (b) the volume of water in the pool in kiloliters.

Solution

a) To find the volume in cubic meters, we use the formula

$$V = l \times w \times h$$

Substituting values for l, w, and h we have

$$V = 18 \text{ m} \times 9 \text{ m} \times 3 \text{ m}$$
$$= 486 \text{ m}^3$$

b) Since $1 \text{ m}^3 = 1 \text{ k}\ell$, the pool will hold 486 kℓ of water.   ∎

Figure 8.9

Example 8 *Choose an Appropriate Unit*

Select the most appropriate answer. The volume of a shoe box is approximately
a) 1500 mm³.   b) 6500 ℓ.   c) 6500 cm³.

Solution A shoe box is not a liquid, so its volume is not expressed in liters. Thus, (b) is not the answer. The volume of the rectangular solid in Fig. 8.10 is approximately 1500 mm³, so (a) is not an appropriate answer. A shoe box may measure about 33 cm × 18 cm × 11 cm, or 6534 cm³. Therefore, 6500 cm³ or (c) is the most appropriate answer.   ∎

Figure 8.10

When the volume of a liquid is measured, the abbreviation cc is often used instead of cm³ to represent cubic centimeters. For example, a nurse may give a patient an injection of 3 cc or 3 mℓ of the drug ampicillin.

Example 9 *Measuring Medicine*

A nurse must give a patient 3 cc of the drug gentamicin mixed in 100 cc of a normal saline solution.
a) How many milliliters of the drug will the nurse administer?
b) What is the total volume of the drug and saline solution in milliliters?

Solution

a) Because 1 cc is equal in volume to 1 mℓ, the nurse will administer 3 mℓ of the drug.

b) The total volume is 3 + 100 or 103 cc, which is equal to 103 mℓ.   ∎

Figure 8.11

Example 10 *A Hot-Water Heater*

A hot-water heater, in the shape of a right circular cylinder, has a radius of 50 cm and a height of 148 cm. What is the capacity, in liters, of the hot-water heater?

Solution The hot-water heater is illustrated in Fig. 8.11. The formula for the volume of a right circular cylinder is $V = \pi r^2 h$, where π is approximately 3.14. Since we want the capacity in liters, we will express all the measurements in meters. The volume will then be given in cubic meters, which can be easily converted to liters. Thus, 50 cm = 0.5 m, and 148 cm = 1.48 m.

$$V = \pi r^2 h$$
$$\approx 3.14(0.5)^2(1.48)$$
$$\approx 3.14(0.25)(1.48) \approx 1.1618 \text{ m}^3$$

We want the volume in liters, so we must change the answer from cubic meters to liters.

$$1 \text{ m}^3 = 1000 \ \ell$$

So,

$$1.1618 \text{ m}^3 = 1.1618 \times 1000 = 1161.8 \ \ell$$

Therefore, the hot-water heaters capacity is about 1161.8 ℓ. ∎

Example 11 *Comparing Volume Units*

a) How many times larger is a cubic meter than a cubic centimeter?
b) How many times larger is a cubic dekameter than a cubic meter?

Solution

a) The procedure used to determine the answer is similar to that used in Example 3 in this section. First we draw a cubic meter, which is a cube 1 m long by 1 m wide by 1 m high. In Fig. 8.12, we represent each meter as 100 centimeters. The volume of the cube is its length times its width times its height, or

$$V = l \times w \times h$$
$$= 100 \text{ cm} \times 100 \text{ cm} \times 100 \text{ cm} = 1\,000\,000 \text{ cm}^3$$

Since 1 m^3 = 1 000 000 cm^3, a cubic meter is one million times larger than a cubic centimeter.

Figure 8.12

Figure 8.13

b) Work part (b) in a similar manner (Fig. 8.13). A dekameter is 10 meters. Thus,

$$V = l \times w \times h$$
$$= 10 \text{ m} \times 10 \text{ m} \times 10 \text{ m} = 1000 \text{ m}^3$$

Since 1 dam^3 = 1000 m^3, a cubic dekameter is one thousand times larger than a cubic meter. ∎

SECTION 8.2 *Exercises*

Warm Up Exercises

In Exercises 1–12, fill in the blanks with an appropriate word, phrase, or symbol (s).

1. Cubic meters, m^3, are a measure of _____. Volume

2. Millimeters, mm, are a measure of _____. Length

3. Hectares, ha, are a measure of _____. Area

4. Centimeters, cm, are a measure of _____. Length

5. Meters, m, are a measure of _____. Length

6. Liters, ℓ, are a measure of _____. Volume

7. Kiloliters, $k\ell$, are a measure of _____. Volume

8. Square meters, m^2, are a measure of _____. Area

9. Cubic centimeters, cm^3, are a measure of _____. Volume

10. Kilometers, km, are a measure of _____. Length

11. Centiliters, $c\ell$, are a measure of _____. Volume

12. Cubic kilometers, km^3, are a measure of _____. Volume

Practice the Skills

In Exercises 13–22, indicate the metric unit of measurement that you would use to express the following.

13. The length of a this book Centimeters

14. The distance between cities Kilometers

15. The diameter of a nickel Centimeters or millimeters

16. The diameter of a dinner plate Centimeters

17. The length of a newborn infant Centimeters

18. The diameter of a helicopter landing pad Meters

19. The distance between freeway exits Kilometers

20. The length of a butterfly Centimeters or millimeters

21. The distance to the moon Kilometers

22. The height of an adult male Centimeters or meters

In Exercises 23–30, choose the best answer.

23. The length of a football field, including both end zones, is about how long?

    a) 110 hm   **b)** 110 km   **c)** 110 m (c)

24. A U.S. postage stamp is about how wide and how long?

    a) 2 cm × 3 cm   **b)** 2 mm × 3 mm

    c) 2 hm × 3 hm
    (a)

25. The distance between Los Angeles and San Diego could be how far?

    a) 130 cm   **b)** 130 m   **c)** 130 km (c)

26. The longest snake, a full-grown reticulated python, may be about how long?

    a) 800 cm   **b)** 800 mm   **c)** 800 dm (a)

27. A ruler is about how wide?

    a) 4 mm   **b)** 4 cm   **c)** 4 dm (b)

28. The diameter of a coffee cup is about which of the following?

    a) 8 mm   **b)** 8 cm   **c)** 8 dm (b)

29. The world's tallest building, Burj Khalifa, in Dubai is about how tall?

    a) 828 cm   **b)** 828 km   **c)** 828 m (c)

30. The length of the New River Gorge Bridge near Fayetteville, West Virginia, is about how long?

    a) 1000 dam   **b)** 1000 m   **c)** 1000 cm (b)

▲ *New River Gorge Bridge in West Virginia*

In Exercises 31–36, (a) estimate the item in metric units and (b) measure it with a metric ruler. Record your result.

31. The width of a card from a deck of cards Answers will vary.

32. The width of a classroom door Answers will vary.

33. The length of a car Answers will vary.

34. The diameter of a can of soda Answers will vary.

35. The height of a box of cereal Answers will vary.

36. The thickness of a quarter Answers will vary.

In Exercises 37–44, indicate the metric unit of measurement you would use to express the area of the following.

37. The floor space in Walmart Square meters

38. A computer monitor's screen Square centimeters

39. A kitchen table Square centimeters or square meters

40. A building lot for a house Square meters or hectares

41. A postage stamp Square centimeters or square millimeters

42. A ceiling tile Square centimeters

43. Disney World Square kilometers or hectares

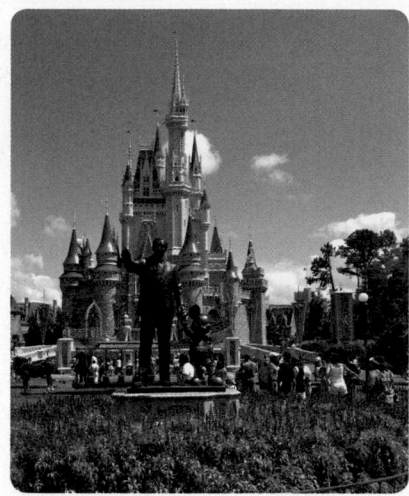

▲ *The Magic Kingdom, Disney World, Florida*

44. A professional basketball court Square meters

In Exercises 45–52, choose the best answer.

45. A credit card has an area of about

   a) 50 cm^2.   **b)** 50 mm^2.   **c)** 50 dm^2. (a)

46. The area of a city lot is about

   a) 800 m^2.   **b)** 800 hm^2.   **c)** 800 cm^2. (a)

47. The area of a city lot is about

   a) $\frac{1}{8} \text{ m}^2$.   **b)** $\frac{1}{8} \text{ ha}$.   **c)** $\frac{1}{8} \text{ km}^2$. (b)

48. The area of a floor tile is about

   a) 930 m^2.   **b)** 930 km^2.   **c)** 930 cm^2. (c)

49. The area of one side of a nickle is about

   a) 3 cm^2.   **b)** 3 m^2.   **c)** 3 mm^2. (a)

50. The area of the screen of a tabletop TV is about

   a) 1200 dm^2.   **b)** 1200 mm^2.   **c)** 1200 cm^2. (c)

51. The area of Grand Canyon National Park is about

   a) 4900 m^2.   **b)** 4900 cm^2.   **c)** 4900 km^2. (c)

52. The area of a U.S. flag is about

   a) 2.2 cm^2.   **b)** 2.2 m^2.   **c)** 2.2 km^2. (b)

In Exercises 53–58, (a) estimate the area of the item in metric units and (b) measure its dimensions in metric units and compute its area.

53. The cover of this book Answers will vary.

54. A typical photograph Answers will vary.

55. A $20 bill Answers will vary.

56. The top of your kitchen table Answers will vary.

57. A compact disk (or CD) Answers will vary.

58. The face of a penny Answers will vary.

In Exercises 59–66, determine the metric unit that would best be used to measure the volume of the following.

59. Liquid in an eye dropper Milliliters

60. Water in a hot-water heater Liters

61. Water flowing over Niagara Falls per minute Kiloliters

62. A bag of topsoil Cubic meters or cubic centimeters

63. A truckload of ready-mix concrete Cubic meters

64. Water in a bottle of water Liters or milliliters

65. Air in a hot air balloon Cubic meters

66. Air in a soccer ball Cubic centimeters

In Exercises 67–74, choose the best answer to indicate the volume of the following.

67. A shoe box

a) 7780 mm³   b) 7780 dm³   c) 7780 cm³ (c)

68. Water that could fit in a thimble

a) 3 mℓ   b) 3 ℓ   c) 3 dℓ (a)

69. Water in a 24-ft-diameter above-ground circular swimming pool

a) 55 ℓ   b) 55 mℓ   c) 55 kℓ (c)

70. Soda in a can of soda

a) 355 ℓ   b) 355 mℓ   c) 355 m³ (b)

71. A carry-on suitcase

a) 0.04 cm³   b) 0.04 mm³   c) 0.04 m³ (c)

72. Juice that can be squeezed out of an orange

a) 120 kℓ   b) 120 mℓ   c) 120 ℓ (b)

73. Air in a soccer ball

a) 5000 m³   b) 5000 cm³   c) 5000 mm³ (b)

74. Air in a balloon with a diameter of about 17 meters

a) 2600 m³   b) 2600 cm³   c) 2600 km³ (a)

In Exercises 75–78, (a) estimate the volume in metric units and (b) compute the actual volume of the item. When appropriate, use the Pi key on your calculator. Round answers to two decimal places.

75. Air in a pizza box that is 46 cm long, 46 cm wide, and 5 cm tall (Use $V = lwh$.) a) Answers will vary. b) 10 580 cm³

76. Water in a water bed that is 2 m long, 1.5 m wide, and 25 cm deep a) Answers will vary. b) 0.75 m³

77. Oil in a barrel that has a height of 1 m and a diameter of 0.5 m (Use $V = \pi r^2 h$.) a) Answers will vary. b) ≈ 0.20 m³

78. Water in a cylindrical tank that is 40 cm in diameter and 2 m high a) Answers will vary. b) ≈ 0.25 m³

In Exercises 79–82, select the best answer.

79. One liter of liquid has the equivalent volume of which of the following: a cubic centimeter, a cubic decimeter, or a cubic meter? A cubic decimeter

80. One cubic meter has the equivalent volume of which of the following liquid measures: a liter, a milliliter, or a kiloliter? A kiloliter

81. One milliliter of liquid has the equivalent volume of which of the following: a cubic centimeter, a cubic decimeter, or a cubic meter? A cubic centimeter

82. A hectare has an area of about how many acres: 2.5, 25, or 250? 2.5 acres

Problem Solving

In Exercises 83–98, when appropriate, use the π key on your calculator.

83. *Area* Use a metric ruler to measure the length and width of the sides of the rectangle. Then compute the area of the rectangle. Give your answers in metric units.

Longer side ≈ 4 cm, shorter side ≈ 2.2 cm, area ≈ 8.8 cm²

84. *Area* Use a metric ruler to find the radius of the circle. Then compute the area of the circle. Give your answers in metric units. $r ≈ 1.2$ cm, $A ≈ 4.52$ cm²

85. *Merry-Go-Round* The base of the merry-go-round (or carousel) at Hershey Park in Hershey, Pennsylvania, is a circle of radius 15.0 meters. Determine the area of the base. Use the formula $A = \pi r^2$. ≈ 706.86 m²

86. *Painting* The total area of a framed painting including the matting is 2540 cm² (see photo on top of page 453). If the length and width of the actual painting are 37 cm and 28 cm, respectively, determine the area of the matting. 1504 cm²

87. *A Walkway* A rectangular building 50 m by 70 m is surrounded by a walkway 1.5 m wide.

  a) Find the area of the region covered by the building and the walkway. 3869 m²

  b) Find the area of the walkway. 369 m²

88. *Farmland* Kim Martello has purchased a farm that is in the shape of a rectangle. The dimensions of the piece of land are 1.4 km by 3.75 km.

  a) How many square kilometers of land did she purchase? 5.25 km²

  b) If 1 km² equals 100 ha, determine the amount of land she purchased in hectares. 525 ha

89. *Children's Playground* The dimensions of a large rectangular playground are 42.4 m by 32.5 m.

  a) Determine the area of the playground in square meters. 1378 m²

  b) If 1 m² equals 0.0001 ha, determine the area of the playground in hectares. 0.1378 ha

90. *Volume of Water* **a)** What is the volume of water in a rectangular swimming pool that is 18 m long and 10 m wide and has an average depth of 2.5 m? Give your answer in cubic meters. 450 m³

  b) How many kiloliters of water will the pool hold? 450 kℓ

91. *Cost of Paint* The first coat of paint for the outside of a building requires 1 ℓ of paint for each 10 m². The second coat requires 1 ℓ for every 15 m². If the paint costs $4.75 per liter, what will be the cost of two coats of paint for the four outside walls of a rectangular building 20 m long, 12 m wide, and 6 m high? $304

92. *Volume of a saucepan* A saucepan has a diameter of 18.0 cm and a height of 9.0 cm. Determine the volume of the sauce pan in cubic centimeters. ≈2290 cm³

93. *Fish Tank Volume* A rectangular fish tank is 70 cm long, 40 cm wide, and 20 cm high.

  a) How many cubic centimeters of water will the tank hold? 56 000 cm³

  b) How many milliliters of water will the tank hold? 56 000 mℓ

  c) How many liters of water will the tank hold? 56 ℓ

94. *Hot-Water Heater* A cylindrical shaped hot-water heater has a diameter of 0.56 m and a height of 1.17 m. If the hot-water heater is filled, determine the volume of water in the hot-water heater in

  a) cubic meters. ≈0.29 m³

  b) liters. ≈290 ℓ

95. How many times larger is a square kilometer than a square hectometer? 100 times larger

96. How many times larger is a square kilometer than a square dekameter? 10,000 times larger

97. How many times larger is a cubic meter than a cubic decimeter? 1000 times larger

98. How many times larger is a cubic centimeter than a cubic millimeter? 1000 times larger

In Exercises 99–104, replace the question mark with the appropriate value.

99. 1 cm² = ? mm² 100   **100.** 1 km² = ? dam² 10 000

101. 1 cm² = ? m² 0.0001   **102.** 1 mm³ = ? dm³ 0.000 001

103. 1 m³ = ? cm³ 1 000 000   **104.** 1 hm³ = ? km³ 0.001

In Exercises 105–108, fill in the blank.

105. 419 cm³ = _____ mℓ 419

106. 435 cm³ = _____ ℓ 0.435

107. 76 kℓ = _____ m³ 76

108. 4.2 ℓ = _____ cm³ 4200

Glacier In Exercises 109–110, assume that a part of a rectangular glacier that contains 60 cubic meters of ice calves (or breaks) off and falls into the ocean.

109. When the ice that has fallen into the ocean melts, determine the approximate amount of water, in kiloliters, obtained from the ice. 60 kℓ

110. When the ice melts, determine the approximate amount of water, in cubic centimeters, obtained from the ice.
60 000 000 cm³

Challenge Problems/Group Activities

In Exercises 111 and 112, fill in the blank to make a true statement.

111. 6.7 kℓ = _____ dm³ 6700

112. 1.4 ha = _____ cm² 140 000 000

113. *Conversions* In Example 3, we illustrated how to change an area in a metric unit to an area measured with a different metric unit.

a) Using Example 3 as a guide, change 1 square mile to square inches. 4,014,489,600 sq in.

b) Is converting from one unit of area to a different unit of area generally easier in the metric system or the U.S. customary system? Explain. Answers will vary.

Recreational Mathematics

114. *Water Usage* a) How much water do we use daily? On the average, people in the United States use more water than people anywhere else in the world. Take a guess at the number of liters of water used per day per person in the United States. Answers will vary. The average use is about 590 ℓ/day.

b) Now take a guess at the number of liters used per day per person in China. .
Answers will vary. The average use is about 75 ℓ/day
Compare your answers to those given in the answer section.

Internet/Research Activity

115. *The Meter* The definition of the meter has changed several times throughout history. Write a one- to two-page report on the history of the meter, from when it was first named to the present.

SECTION 8.3   Mass and Temperature

▲ *Niagara falls in the winter.*

It is January, and you and your friends go for a visit to Niagara Falls, Canada. The thermostat in your hotel room is set on 20° Celsius. Will you need to adjust the thermostat? If the temperature outside is 15°C, how should you dress?

While watching television, you see an astronaut floating while working on the Space Station. Does this floating astronaut have any weight? Does the astronaut have any mass? In this section, we will discuss these two important metric measurements, temperature and mass.

Why **This is Important** Temperatures outside the United States are almost always given in degrees Celsius. Also, temperatures used in the sciences are measured in degrees Celsius. The concept of mass is important to all sciences.

Mass

Weight and mass are not the same. *Mass* is a measure of the amount of matter in an object. It is determined by the molecular structure of the object, and it will not change from place to place. Weight is a measure of the gravitational pull on an object. For example, the gravitational pull of Earth is about six times as great as the gravitational pull of the moon. Thus, a person on the moon weighs about $\frac{1}{6}$ as much as on Earth, even though the person's mass remains the same. In space, where there is no gravity, a person has no weight but does have mass.

Even on Earth, the gravitational pull varies from point to point. The closer you are to Earth's center, the greater the gravitational pull. Thus, a person weighs very slightly less on a mountain than in a nearby valley. Because the mass of an object does not vary with location, scientists generally use mass rather than weight.

Although weight and mass are not the same, on Earth they are proportional to each other (the greater the weight, the greater the mass). Therefore, for our purposes, we can treat weight and mass as the same.

The *kilogram* is the basic unit of mass in the metric system. It is about 2.2 pounds. The official kilogram is a cylinder of platinum–iridium alloy kept by the International Bureau of Weights and Measures, located in Sèvres, France, near Paris. (See the *Did You Know?* in the margin.)

Items that we normally measure in pounds are usually measured in kilograms in other parts of the world. For example, an average-sized man has a mass of about 75 kg.

The *gram* (a unit that is 0.001 kg) is relatively small and is used for items normally measured in ounces. A nickel has a mass of about 5 g, a cube of sugar has a mass of about 2 g, and a large paper clip has a mass of about 1 g.

The *milligram* is used extensively in the medical and scientific fields as well as in the pharmaceutical industry. Nearly all bottles of tablets are now labeled in either milligrams or grams.

The *metric tonne* (t) is used to express the mass of heavy items. One metric tonne equals 1000 kg. A metric tonne is a little larger than our customary ton of 2000 lb. The mass of a large truck may be expressed in metric tonnes.

EXAMPLE 1 *Choosing the Appropriate Unit*

Determine which metric unit you would use to express the mass of the following.

a) A 1-year-old child b) A whale c) A pair of eyeglasses

d) A box of cereal e) A laptop computer f) A spider

g) A frog h) A refrigerator

Solution

a) Kilograms b) Metric tonnes c) Grams

d) Grams e) Grams or kilograms f) Milligrams

g) Grams h) Kilograms

One kilogram of water has a volume of exactly 1 liter. In fact, 1 liter is defined to be the volume of 1 kilogram of water at a specified temperature and pressure. Thus, mass and volume are easily interchangeable in the metric system. Converting from weight to volume is not nearly as convenient in the U.S. customary system. For example, how would you change pounds of water to cubic feet or gallons of water in our customary system?

▲ *See Example 1(a)*

Figure 8.14 One cubic decimeter of water has the volume of one liter and the mass of one kilogram.

MATHEMATICS TODAY

It's a Metric World

Figure 8.16

The United States is the only westernized country not currently using the metric system as its primary system of measurement. The only countries in the world besides the United States not committed to using the metric system are Liberia and Myanmar (although Liberia and Myanmar use it in practice); see Fig. 8.16.

Why **This is Important** The European Union (EU) adopted a directive that requires all exporters to EU nations to indicate the dimensions of their products in metric units. To trade goods in many parts of the world, U.S. manufacturers must use metric measurements.

Since $1 \text{ dm}^3 = 1000 \text{ cm}^3$, $1 \ell = 1000 \text{ m}\ell$, and $1 \text{ kg} = 1000 \text{ g}$, we have the following relationship which holds for water.

$$1000 \text{ cm}^3 = 1000 \text{ m}\ell = 1000 \text{ g}$$
$$\text{or,} \quad \mathbf{1 \text{ cm}^3} = \mathbf{1 \text{ m}\ell} = \mathbf{1 \text{ g}}$$

Figure 8.14 on page 455 illustrates the relationship between volume of water in cubic decimeters, in liters, and mass in kilograms. Table 8.4 expands on this relationship between the volume and mass of water.

Table 8.4 Volume and Mass of Water

Volume in Cubic Units		Volume in Liters		Mass of Water
1 cm^3	$=$	$1 \text{ m}\ell$	$=$	1 g
1 dm^3	$=$	1ℓ	$=$	1 kg
1 m^3	$=$	$1 \text{ k}\ell$	$=$	$1 \text{ t } (1000 \text{ kg})$

EXAMPLE 2 *Volume of a Fish Tank*

A fish tank is 1 m long, 50 cm high, and 250 mm wide (Fig. 8.15).

Figure 8.15

a) Determine the number of liters of water the tank holds.

b) What is the mass of the water in kilograms?

Solution

a) We must convert all the measurements to the same units. Let's convert them all to meters: 50 cm is 0.5 m, and 250 mm is 0.25 m.

$$V = l \times w \times h$$
$$= 1 \times 0.25 \times 0.5$$
$$= 0.125 \text{ m}^3$$

Since 1 m^3 of water $= 1 \text{ k}\ell$ of water.

$$0.125 \text{ m}^3 = 0.125 \text{ k}\ell, \text{ or } 125 \ell \text{ of water}$$

Thus the tank holds 125ℓ of water.

b) Since 1ℓ of water has a mass of 1 kg, 125ℓ of water has a mass of 125 kg. Thus the water in the fish tank has a mass of 125 kg.

To convince yourself of the advantages of the metric system, do a similar problem involving the U.S. customary system of measurement, such as Challenge Problems/Group Activities Exercise 72 at the end of this section.

Temperature

The Celsius scale is used to measure temperatures in the metric system. Figure 8.17 shows a thermometer with the Fahrenheit scale on the left and the Celsius scale on the right.

The Celsius scale was named for Swedish astronomer Anders Celsius (1701–1744), who first devised it in 1742. On the Celsius scale, water freezes at 0°C and boils at 100°C. In the past, the Celsius thermometer was called a "centigrade thermometer." Recall that *centi* means $\frac{1}{100}$, and there are 100 degrees between the freezing point of water and the boiling point of water. Thus, 1°C is $\frac{1}{100}$ of this interval. Table 8.5 gives some common temperatures in both degrees Celsius (°C) and degrees Fahrenheit (°F).

Figure 8.17

Table 8.5

Celsius Temperature		Fahrenheit Temperature
−18°C	A very cold day	0°F
0°C	Freezing point of water	32°F
10°C	A warm winter day	50°F
20°C	A mild spring day	68°F
30°C	A warm summer day	86°F
37°C	Body temperature	98.6°F
100°C	Boiling point of water	212°F
177°C	Oven temperature for baking	351°F

At a temperature of −40° the Celsius and Fahrenheit temperatures are the same. That is, −40°C = −40°F.

Example 3 *Metric Temperatures*

Choose the best answer. (Refer to the dual-scale thermometer in Fig. 8.16.)

a) Chicago, Illinois, on New Year's Day might have a temperature of
   i) −10°C.   ii) 20°C.   iii) 45°C.

b) Washington, D.C., on July 4 might have a temperature of
   i) 15°C.   ii) 30°C.   iii) 40°C.

c) The oven temperature for baking a cake might be
   i) 60°C   ii) 100°C.   iii) 175°C.

Solution

a) A temperature of 20°C is possible if it is a very mild winter, but 45°C is much too hot. The best answer for a normal winter is −10°C.

b) The best estimate is 30°C. A temperature of 15°C is too chilly, and 40°C is too hot for July 4.

c) A cake bakes at temperatures well above boiling, so the only reasonable answer is 175°C. ∎

Comparing the temperatures in Table 8.5, we see that the Celsius scale has 100° from the boiling point of water to the freezing point of water and the Fahrenheit scale has 180° from the boiling point of water to the freezing point of water. Therefore, one Celsius degree represents a greater change in temperature than one Fahrenheit degree does. In fact, one Celsius degree is the same as $\frac{180}{100}$, or $\frac{9}{5}$ Fahrenheit degrees. When converting from one system to the other system, use the following formulas.

From Celsius to Fahrenheit

$$F = \frac{9}{5}C + 32$$

From Fahrenheit to Celsius

$$C = \frac{5}{9}(F - 32)$$

Example 4 *Convert to °C*

A typical setting for home thermostats is 72°F. What is the equivalent temperature on the Celsius thermometer?

Solution We use the formula $C = \frac{5}{9}(F - 32)$ to convert from °F to °C. Substituting $F = 72$ gives

$$C = \frac{5}{9}(72 - 32)$$

$$= \frac{5}{9}(40)$$

$$\approx 22.2$$

Thus, the equivalent temperature of 72°F is about 22.2°C. ∎

Example 5 *Convert to °F*

If the temperature outdoors is 28°C, what is the temperature in degrees Fahrenheit?

Solution We use the formula $F = \frac{9}{5}C + 32$ to convert from °C to °F. Substituting $C = 28$ yields

$$F = \frac{9}{5}(28) + 32$$

$$= 50.4 + 32$$

$$= 82.4$$

Thus the temperature is about 82.4°F. ∎

Did You Know?

Year of Metrification

Almost every country in the world, except for the United States, Liberia, and Myanmar, presently use the metric system. The chart below shows the official year of metrification for various countries. Space prohibits us from listing all the countries. For a more complete chart see http://lamar.colostate.edu/~hillger/internat.htm.

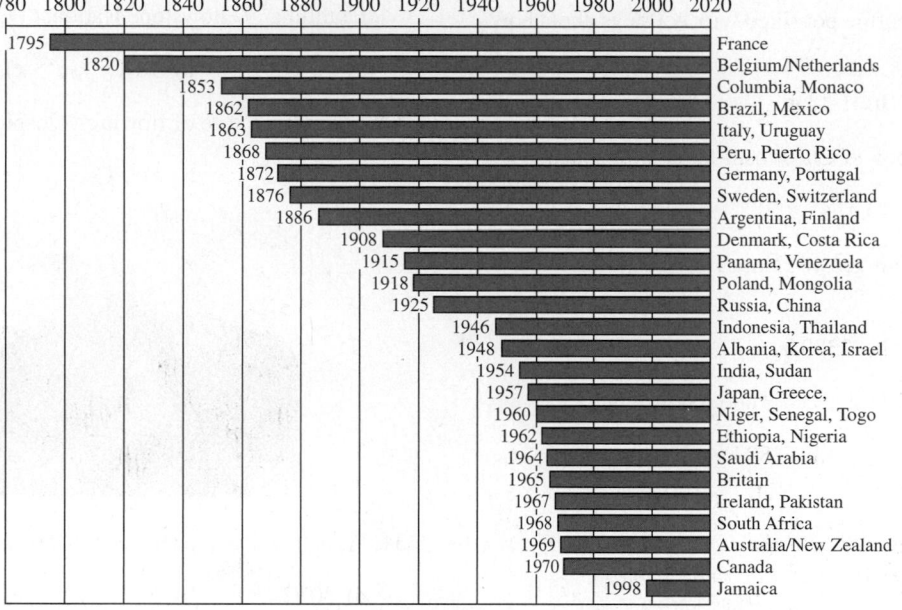

Year of Official Metrication

Advance of Metric Usage in the World

Courtesy of U. S. Metric Association (www.metric.org)

SECTION 8.3

Exercises

Warm Up Exercises

In Exercises 1–8, fill in the blanks with an appropriate word, phrase, or symbol(s).

1. The basic unit of mass in the metric system is the _____. Kilogram

2. The mass of a nickel is about 5 _____. Grams

3. A metric tonne is the unit used to express the _____ of a very heavy item, such as a dump truck. Mass

4. The metric unit that is a little more than 2.2 pounds is the _____. Kilogram

5. Temperatures in the metric system are measured in degrees _____. Celsius

6. The freezing point of water is _____ °C. 0

7. The boiling point of water is _____ °C. 100

8. Normal body temperature is _____ °C. 37

Practice the Skills

In Exercises 9–18, indicate the metric unit of measurement that would best express the mass of the following.

9. A 10-year-old boy
   Kilograms

10. A quarter
    Grams or milligrams

11. A baseball
    Grams

12. A box of cereal
    Grams

13. A new pencil
    Grams

14. A sports utility vehicle
    Metric tonnes or kilograms

15. A refrigerator
    Kilograms

16. A mosquito
    Milligrams

17. A full-grown elephant
    Kilograms or metric tonnes

18. A calculator
    Grams

▲ *See Exercise 17.*

In Exercises 19–24, select the best answer.

19. The mass of a 5-lb bag of sugar is about how much?

    a) 2.27 g   **b)** 2.27 kg   **c)** 2.27 dag (b)

20. The mass of a tea bag is about how much?

    a) 4 mg   **b)** 4 kg   **c)** 4 g (c)

21. The mass of a coffee pot filled with coffee is about how much?

    a) 1.4 mg   **b)** 1.4 kg   **c)** 1.4 g (b)

22. The mass of a box of Cheerios is about how much?

    a) 0.45 t   **b)** 0.45 g   **c)** 0.45 kg (c)

23. The mass of a full-grown rhinoceros is about how much?

    a) 2300 g   **b)** 2300 kg   **c)** 2300 dag (b)

24. The mass of a full-size car is about how much?

    a) 1 962 000 hg   **b)** 380 kg   **c)** 1.6 t (c)

In Exercises 25–28, estimate the mass of the item. If a scale with metric measure is available, find the mass.

25. Your body
Answers will vary.

26. A gallon of water
Answers will vary.

27. A telephone book
Answers will vary.

28. A tomato
Answers will vary.

In Exercises 29–38, choose the best answer. Use Table 8.5 and Fig. 8.16 to help select your answers.

29. Freezing rain is most likely to occur at a temperature of

    a) −25°C.   **b)** 32°C.   **c)** 0°C. (c)

30. The thermostat for an air conditioner was set for 70°F. This setting is closest to

    a) 2°C.   **b)** 21°C.   **c)** 52°C. (b)

31. The temperature of the water in a certain lake is 5°C. You could

    a) ice fish.

    b) dress warmly and walk along the lake.

    c) swim in the lake. (b)

32. The temperature of the water coming out of the geyser Old Faithful at Yellowstone National Park might be

    a) 50°C.   **b)** 96°C.   **c)** 3000°C. (b)

33. The temperature of flowing volcanic lava might be

    a) 50°C.   **b)** 100°C.   **c)** 1200°C. (c)

34. What might be the temperature at which a refrigerator is set?

    a) 30°C   **b)** 5°C   **c)** 0°C (b)

35. The temperature in Phoenix, Arizona, on a summer day might be

    a) 15°C   **b)** 20°C   **c)** 40°C (c)

36. What might be the temperature of an apple pie baking in the oven?

    a) 90°C   **b)** 100°C   **c)** 177°C (c)

37. The temperature of water in a hot tub might be

    a) 30°C.   **b)** 50°C.   **c)** 40°C. (c)

38. The temperature of the snow on top of Mount Rainier, Washington, might be

    a) −15°C   **b)** −5°C   **c)** 5°C (b)

▲ *Mount Rainier, Washington*

In Exercises 39–52, convert each temperature as indicated. When appropriate, give your answer to the nearest tenth of a degree.

39. $20°C =$ _____ °F
68°F

40. $-5°C =$ _____ °F 23°F

41. $92°F =$ _____ °C
$\approx 33.3°C$

42. $-10°F =$ _____ °C
$\approx -23.3°C$

43. $0°F =$ _____ °C
$\approx -17.8°C$

44. $100°F =$ _____ °C
$\approx 37.8°C$

45. $37°C =$ _____ °F
98.6°F

46. $-4°C =$ _____ °F
24.8°F

47. $17°F =$ _____ °C
$\approx -8.3°C$

48. $75°F =$ _____ °C
$\approx 23.9°C$

49. $0°C =$ _____ °F
32°F

50. $50°C =$ _____ °F
122°F

51. $-20°F =$ _____ °C
$\approx -28.9°C$

52. $425°F =$ _____ °C
$\approx 218.3°C$

In Exercises 53–58, use the following graph, which shows the daily low and high temperatures, in degrees Celsius, for the week in the outback in Australia. The week illustrated was unseasonably warm. Determine the following temperatures in degrees Fahrenheit.

THE HEAT OF THE DAY
Average January Temperature:
Maximum 22.0° Minimum 12.0°

53. The average January maximum temperature 71.6°F

54. The maximum temperature for the week 95.18°F

55. The maximum temperature on Wednesday 92.48°F

56. The maximum temperature on Saturday 90.14°F

57. The range of temperatures on Monday 64.04°F–74.30°F

58. The range of temperatures on Tuesday 71.6°F–93.2°F

Problem Solving

59. *Blueberries* As shown in the photo above and to the right, blueberries in Bologna, Italy, cost 9.00 euros per kilogram.

  a) Determine the cost, in euros, for 2.5 kilograms of blueberries. 22.5 euros

  b) If a euro has a value of $1.46, determine the cost of 1 kilogram of blueberries in U.S. dollars. $13.14

  c) If a kilogram is 2.2 pounds, determine the cost of 1 pound of blueberries in U.S. dollars. ≈ $5.97 per pound

60. *Bridge Weight Restriction* A bridge has a weight restriction of 3.5 metric tonnes (t). If the weight of an empty truck is 2.92 t and the driver and passengers together weigh 180 kilograms, how much cargo, in metric tonnes, can be added to the truck without exceeding the 3.5 t weight limit? 0.4 t

61. *Salt and Soda* A mixture of 45 g of salt and 29 g of baking soda is poured into 370 mℓ of water. What is the total mass of the mixture in grams? 444 g

62. *Jet Fuel* A jet can travel about 1 km on 17 kg of fuel. How many metric tonnes of fuel will the jet use flying nonstop between Baltimore and Los Angeles, a distance of about 4320 km? 73.44 t

63. *A Storage Tank* The dimensions of a rectangular storage tank are length 16 m, width 12 m, and height 12 m. If the tank is filled with water, determine

  a) the volume of water in the tank in cubic meters. 2304 m³

  b) the number of kiloliters of water the tank will hold.
2304 kℓ

  c) the mass of the water in metric tonnes. 2304 t

64. *A Water Heater* A hot-water heater in the shape of a right circular cylinder has a radius of 50 cm and a height of 150 cm. If the tank is filled with water, determine

  a) the volume of water in the tank in cubic meters.
≈ 1.1775 m³

  b) the number of liters of water the tank will hold. ≈1177.5 ℓ

  c) the mass of the water in kilograms. ≈1177.5 kg

65. *Earth or Space*

  a) Is a person's mass the same in space as on Earth? Explain.
Yes; mass is a measure of the amount of matter in an object.

  b) Is a person's weight the same in space as on Earth?
Explain. No; weight is a measure of gravitational force.

66. *Is There a Problem?* A temperature display at a bank flashes the temperature in degrees Fahrenheit and then flashes the temperature in degrees Celsius. If it flashes 78°F, then 20°C, is there a problem with the display? Explain.
Yes; 78°F is about 25.6°C.

In Exercises 67–70, convert as indicated.

67. 6.2 kg = _____ t   **68.** 9.52 t = _____ kg
    0.0062   9520

69. 17.4 t = _____ g   17 400 000

70. 1 460 000 mg = _____ t 0.001 46

Challenge Problems/Group Activities

71. *Gatorade* Gatorade is poured into a plastic bottle that holds 1.2 ℓ of liquid. The bottle is then placed in a freezer. When the bottle is removed from the freezer, the plastic is cut away, leaving just the frozen Gatorade.

   a) What is the approximate mass of the frozen Gatorade in grams? 1200 g

   b) What is the approximate volume of the frozen Gatorade in cubic centimeters? 1200 cm³

In Example 2, we showed how to find the volume and mass of water in a fish tank. Exercise 72 demonstrates how much more complicated solving a similar problem is in the U.S. customary system.

72. *Fish Tank* A rectangular fish tank is 1 yd long by 1.5 ft high by 15 in. wide.

   a) Determine the volume of water in the fish tank in cubic feet. 5.625 ft³

   b) Determine the weight of the water in pounds. One cubic foot of water weighs about 62.5 lb. ≈351.6 lb

   c) If 1 gal of water weighs about 8.3 lb, how many gallons will the tank hold? ≈42.4 gal

Recreational Mathematics

73. *Balance the Scale* Determine the quantity needed to replace the question mark to make the scale balance. The weight times the distance on both sides of the fulcrum (the triangle) must be the same to make the scale balance. 1500 g

74. *Interesting Facts* The 2009 *Guinness Book of World Records* provides some interesting facts.

   a) The lowest temperature ever recorded in the United States was −62.11°C on January 23, 1971, in Prospect Creek, Alaska. What is this temperature in degrees Fahrenheit? −79.8°F

   b) International Falls, Minnesota, has the lowest annual mean (average) temperature in the United States (including Alaska). Its mean annual temperature is about 2.5°C. What is this temperature in degrees Fahrenheit? 36.5°F

   c) The warmest temperature in the United States ever recorded was 56. 7°C on July 10, 1913, in Death Valley, California. What is this temperature in degrees Fahrenheit? 134.1°F

Internet/Research Activity

75. Do industries in your area export goods? If so, are they training employees to use and understand the metric system? Contact local industries that export goods and write a report on your findings.

SECTION 8.4

Dimensional Analysis and Conversions to and from the Metric System

▲ *Dimensional analysis can be used to determine how many pesos you should recieve when you convert your dollars to pesos.*

In this section we will use dimensional analysis to convert measurements from our U.S. customary system to the metric system, and vice versa. Dimensional analysis can be useful in many of your science courses, as well as in real-life situations. For example, if you drive to Mexico for a vacation, you could use dimensional analysis to determine if your 6 foot 2 inch high SUV will fit in an underground garage that accepts cars with a maximum height of 2.3 meters. Or you can use dimensional analysis to figure out how many pesos you should get when you convert your U.S. currency into Mexican currency.

Why *This is Important* As you will see by the examples, the conversion techniques discussed in this section can be used in everyday life.

You may sometimes need to change units of measurement in the metric system to equivalent units in the U.S. customary system. To do so, use *dimensional analysis*, which is a procedure used to convert from one unit of measurement to a different unit of measurement. To perform dimensional analysis, you must first understand what is meant by a unit fraction. A *unit fraction* is any fraction in which the numerator and denominator contain different units and the value of the fraction is 1. From Table 8.6, we can obtain many unit fractions involving U.S. customary units.

Table 8.6 U.S. Customary Units

1 foot = 12 inches
1 yard = 3 feet
1 mile = 5280 feet
1 pound = 16 ounces
1 ton = 2000 pounds
1 cup (liquid) = 8 fluid ounces
1 pint = 2 cups
1 quart = 2 pints
1 gallon = 4 quarts
1 minute = 60 seconds
1 hour = 60 minutes
1 day = 24 hours
1 year = 365 days

Examples of Unit Fractions

$$\frac{12 \text{ in.}}{1 \text{ ft}} \qquad \frac{1 \text{ ft}}{12 \text{ in.}} \qquad \frac{16 \text{ oz}}{1 \text{ lb}} \qquad \frac{1 \text{ lb}}{16 \text{ oz}} \qquad \frac{60 \text{ min}}{1 \text{ hr}} \qquad \frac{1 \text{ hr}}{60 \text{ min}}$$

In each of these examples, the numerator equals the denominator, so the value of the fraction is 1.

To convert an expression from one unit of measurement to a different unit, multiply the given expression by the unit fraction (or fractions) that will result in the answer having the units you are seeking. When two fractions are being multiplied and the same unit appears in the numerator of one fraction and in the denominator of the other fraction, that common unit may be divided out and eliminated. For example, suppose we want to convert 30 inches to feet. We consider the following:

$$30 \text{ in.} = ? \text{ ft}$$

Since inches are given, we will need to eliminate them. Thus, inches will need to appear in the denominator of the unit fraction. We need to convert to feet, so feet will need to appear in the numerator of the unit fraction. If we multiply a quantity in inches by a unit fraction containing feet/inches, the inches will divide out as follows, leaving feet. In the following illustration we have omitted the numbers in the unit fraction so we can concentrate on the units.

$$(\cancel{\text{in.}})\left(\frac{\text{ft}}{\cancel{\text{in.}}}\right) = \text{ft}$$

Thus, to convert 30 inches to feet, we do the following.

$$30 \text{ in.} = (30 \,\cancel{\text{in.}})\left(\frac{1 \text{ ft}}{12 \,\cancel{\text{in.}}}\right) = \frac{30}{12}\text{ft} = 2.5 \text{ ft}$$

In Examples 1 through 3, we will give examples that do not involve the metric system. After that, we will use dimensional analysis to make conversions to and from the metric system.

Example 1 *Using Dimensional Analysis*

A container contains 26 ounces of salt. Convert 26 ounces to pounds.

Solution One pound is 16 ounces. Therefore, we write

$$26 \text{ oz} = (26 \cancel{\text{ oz}})\left(\frac{1 \text{ lb}}{16 \cancel{\text{ oz}}}\right) = \frac{26}{16}\text{lb} = 1.625 \text{ lb}$$

Thus, 26 oz equals 1.625 lb.

Example 2 *Mexican Pesos*

On February 19, 2010, $1 U.S. could be exchanged for about 12.85 Mexican pesos. What was the amount in U.S. dollars of 2500 pesos?

Solution

$$2500 \text{ pesos} = 2500 \cancel{\text{ pesos}}\left(\frac{\$1.00}{12.85 \cancel{\text{ pesos}}}\right) = \frac{\$2500}{12.85} \approx \$194.55$$

Thus, 2500 pesos had a value of about $194.55.

▲ *Mexican currency*

If more than one unit needs to be changed, more than one multiplication may be needed, as illustrated in Example 3.

Example 3 *Using Several Unit Fractions*

Convert 60 miles per hour to feet per second.

Solution Let's consider the units given and where we want to end up. We are given $\frac{\text{mi}}{\text{hr}}$ and wish to end with $\frac{\text{ft}}{\text{sec}}$. Thus, we need to change miles into feet and hours into seconds. Because two units need to be changed, we will need to multiply the given quantity by two unit fractions, one for each conversion. First we show how to convert the units of measurement from miles per hour to feet per second:

$$\left(\frac{\cancel{\text{mi}}}{\cancel{\text{hr}}}\right)\left(\frac{\text{ft}}{\cancel{\text{mi}}}\right)\left(\frac{\cancel{\text{hr}}}{\text{sec}}\right) \quad \textit{gives an answer in} \quad \frac{\text{ft}}{\text{sec}}$$

Now we multiply the given quantity by the appropriate unit fractions to obtain the answer:

$$60\frac{\text{mi}}{\text{hr}} = \left(60\frac{\cancel{\text{mi}}}{\cancel{\text{hr}}}\right)\left(\frac{5280 \text{ ft}}{1 \cancel{\text{mi}}}\right)\left(\frac{1 \cancel{\text{hr}}}{3600 \text{ sec}}\right) = \frac{(60)(5280)}{(1)(3600)}\frac{\text{ft}}{\text{sec}}$$

$$= 88\frac{\text{ft}}{\text{sec}}$$

Note that $\left(60\frac{\text{mi}}{\text{hr}}\right)\left(\frac{1 \text{ hr}}{3600 \text{ sec}}\right)\left(\frac{5280 \text{ ft}}{1 \text{ mi}}\right)$ will give the same answer.

Conversions to and from the Metric System

Now we will apply dimensional analysis to the metric system.

Table 8.7 on page 465 is used in making conversions between the U.S. customary system and the metric system. The values given in Table 8.7 are often approximations. A more exact table of conversion factors may be found in many science books at your college's library or on the Internet. However, we can use this table to obtain many unit fractions.

Table 8.7 Conversions Table

Length	
1 inch (in.)	= 2.54 centimeters (cm)
1 foot (ft)	= 30 centimeters (cm)
1 yard (yd)	= 0.9 meter (m)
1 mile (mi)	= 1.6 kilometers (km)
Area	
1 square inch (in.^{2})	= 6.5 square centimeters (cm^2)
1 square foot (ft^2)	= 0.09 square meter (m^2)
1 square yard (yd^2)	= 0.8 square meter (m^2)
1 square mile (mi^2)	= 2.6 square kilometers (km^2)
1 acre	= 0.4 hectare (ha)
Volume	
1 teaspoon (tsp)	= 5 milliliters (mℓ)
1 tablespoon (tbsp)	= 15 milliliters (mℓ)
1 fluid ounce (fl oz)	= 30 milliliters (mℓ)
1 cup (c)	= 0.24 liter (ℓ)
1 pint (pt)	= 0.47 liter (ℓ)
1 quart (qt)	= 0.95 liter (ℓ)
1 gallon (gal)	= 3.8 liters (ℓ)
1 cubic foot (ft^3)	= 0.03 cubic meter (m^3)
1 cubic yard (yd^3)	= 0.76 cubic meter (m^3)
Weight (Mass)	
1 ounce (oz)	= 28 grams (g)
1 pound (lb)	= 0.45 kilogram (kg)
1 ton (T)	= 0.9 tonne (t)

Table 8.7 shows that 1 in. = 2.54 cm. From this equality, we can write the two unit fractions

$$\frac{1 \text{ in.}}{2.54 \text{ cm}} \quad \text{or} \quad \frac{2.54 \text{ cm}}{1 \text{ in.}}$$

Examples of other unit fractions from Table 8.7 are

$$\frac{1 \text{ yd}}{0.9 \text{ m}}, \quad \frac{0.9 \text{ m}}{1 \text{ yd}}, \quad \frac{1 \text{ gal}}{3.8 \, \ell}, \quad \frac{3.8 \, \ell}{1 \text{ gal}}, \quad \frac{1 \text{ lb}}{0.45 \text{ kg}}, \quad \text{and} \quad \frac{0.45 \text{ kg}}{1 \text{ lb}}$$

To change from a metric unit to a customary unit or vice versa, multiply the given quantity by the unit fraction whose product will result in the units you are seeking. For example, to convert 5 in. to centimeters, multiply 5 in. by a unit fraction with centimeters in the numerator and inches in the denominator.

$$5 \text{ in.} = (5 \text{ i\!n.})\left(\frac{2.54 \text{ cm}}{1 \text{ i\!n.}}\right)$$

$$= 5(2.54) \text{ cm}$$

$$= 12.7 \text{ cm}$$

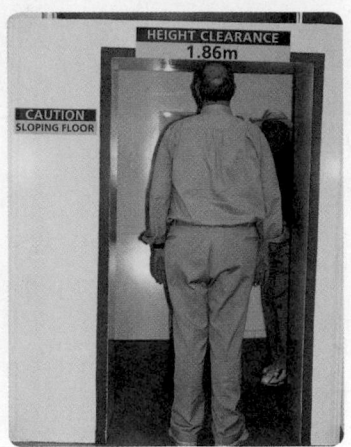

▲ *See Example 4(b)*

Example 4 *Volume and Length Conversions*

a) A recipe requires $3\frac{1}{2}$ cups of chicken broth. How many liters does this amount equal?

b) A man measures 1.86 m (see photo). What is his height in feet?

Solution

a) In Table 8.7, under the heading of volume, we see that 1 cup $=$ 0.24 ℓ. Thus, the unit fractions involving cups and liters are

$$\frac{1 \text{ cup}}{0.24 \ \ell} \quad \text{or} \quad \frac{0.24 \ \ell}{1 \text{ cup}}$$

We need to convert from cups to liters. Therefore, we use the unit fraction with cup in the denominator. Since $3\frac{1}{2}$ is 3.5 in decimal form, we write

$$3.5 \text{ cups} = 3.5 \text{ cups}\left(\frac{0.24 \ \ell}{1 \text{ cup}}\right) = (3.5)(0.24) \ \ell = 0.84 \ \ell$$

b) In Table 8.7, under the heading of length, we see that there is no conversion given from meters to feet. There are a number of ways this example could be worked. One method is to convert meters to yards and then convert yards to feet. The procedure is shown below.

$$1.86 \text{ m} = (1.86 \text{ m})\left(\frac{1 \text{ yd}}{0.9 \text{ m}}\right)\left(\frac{3 \text{ ft}}{1 \text{ yd}}\right)$$

$$= \frac{(1.86)(3)}{0.9} \text{ ft}$$

$$= 6.2 \text{ ft}$$

Thus, the man is 6.2 ft. ∎

Example 5 *Area Conversion*

An area of 54.62 hectares is for sale. Find the area in acres.

Solution   From Table 8.7, we determine that 1 acre $=$ 0.4 ha. Thus,

$$54.62 \text{ ha} = (54.62 \text{ ha})\left(\frac{1 \text{ acre}}{0.4 \text{ ha}}\right) = \frac{54.62}{0.4} \text{ acres} = 136.55 \text{ acres}$$ ∎

▲ *Jacksonville, Florida*

Example 6 *Largest City in Area*

Jacksonville, Florida, is the largest city in area in the contiguous 48 states*. Its area is 758 square miles. Determine this area in square kilometers.

Solution   We need to convert square miles to square kilometers. From Table 8.7 we find the unit fractions

$$\frac{1 \text{mi}^2}{2.6 \text{ km}^2} \quad \text{or} \quad \frac{2.6 \text{ km}^2}{1 \text{ mi}^2}$$

Since we are converting 758 square miles to square kilometers, the square miles in the unit fraction must go in the denominator. Thus we use the unit fraction $\dfrac{2.6 \text{ km}^2}{1 \text{ mi}^2}$.

$$758 \text{ mi}^2 = 758 \text{ mi}^2\left(\frac{2.6 \text{ km}^2}{1 \text{ mi}^2}\right) = 758\,(2.6)\text{km}^2 = 1970.8 \text{ km}^2$$

Therefore, the area of Jacksonville is 1970.8 square kilometers. ∎

*Yakutat, Alaska is the largest city in area in the United States.

Example 7 *Administering a Medicine*

A nurse must administer 4 cc of codeine elixir to a patient.

a) How many milliliters of the drug will be administered?

b) How many ounces is this dosage equivalent to?

Solution

a) Since 1 cc = 1 mℓ, the nurse will administer 4 mℓ of the drug.

b) Since 1 fl oz = 30 mℓ,

$$4 \text{ m}\ell = (4 \text{ m}\ell)\left(\frac{1 \text{ fl oz}}{30 \text{ m}\ell}\right) = \frac{4}{30}\text{fl oz} \approx 0.13 \text{ fl oz} \qquad \blacksquare$$

Suppose we want to convert 150 millimeters to inches. Table 8.7 does not have a conversion factor from millimeters to inches, but it does have one for inches to centimeters. Because 1 inch = 2.54 centimeters and 1 centimeter = 10 millimeters, we can reason that 1 inch = 25.4 millimeters. Therefore, unit fractions we may use are as follows.

$$\frac{1 \text{ in.}}{25.4 \text{ mm}} \qquad \text{or} \qquad \frac{25.4 \text{ mm}}{1 \text{ in.}}$$

We can solve the problem as follows.

$$150 \text{ mm} = (150 \text{ mm})\left(\frac{1 \text{ in.}}{25.4 \text{ mm}}\right) = \frac{150}{25.4}\text{in.}$$
$$\approx 5.91 \text{ in.}$$

If we wish, we can use dimensional analysis using two unit fractions to make the conversion. The procedure follows:

$$150 \text{ mm} = (150 \text{ mm})\left(\frac{1 \text{ cm}}{10 \text{ mm}}\right)\left(\frac{1 \text{ in.}}{2.54 \text{ cm}}\right) = \frac{150}{(10)(2.54)}\text{in.}$$
$$\approx 5.91 \text{ in.}$$

Example 8 *Eggplant*

The photo from Italy shows that melanzane (or eggplant) costs 2.40 euros per kilogram. If 1 euro could be converted to $1.42, determine the cost of the eggplant in U. S. dollars per pound.

Solution   In Table 8.7 we see that 1 pound = 0.45 kilogram. The two unit fractions involving pounds and kilograms are

$$\frac{1 \text{ pound}}{0.45 \text{ kilogram}} \qquad \text{or} \qquad \frac{0.45 \text{ kilogram}}{1 \text{ pound}}$$

The two unit fractions involving euros and dollars are

$$\frac{1 \text{ euro}}{\$1.42} \qquad \text{or} \qquad \frac{\$1.42}{1 \text{ euro}}$$

The conversion from euros per kilogram to U.S. dollars per pound follows.

$$2.40 \text{ euros per kilogram} = \frac{2.40 \text{ euros}}{1 \text{ kilogram}} \cdot \frac{0.45 \text{ kilogram}}{1 \text{ pound}} \cdot \frac{\$1.42}{1 \text{ euro}}$$
$$\approx \frac{\$1.53}{1 \text{ pound}} \qquad \text{or} \qquad \approx \$1.53 \text{ per pound}$$

Thus, the eggplant costs about $1.53 per pound. ∎

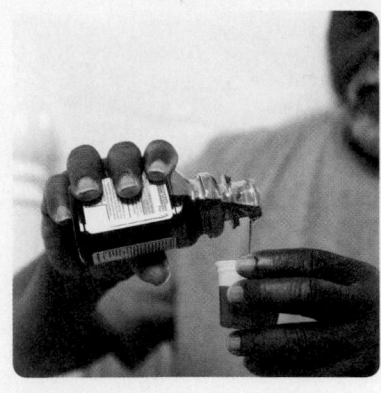

Example 9   *Understanding the Label*

The label on a bottle of Vicks Formula 44D Cough Syrup indicates that the active ingredient is dextromethorphan hydrobromide and that 5 mℓ (or 1 teaspoon) contains 10 mg of this ingredient. If the recommended dosage for adults is 3 teaspoons, determine the following.

a) How many milliliters of cough medicine should be taken?

b) How many milligrams of the active ingredient should be taken?

c) If the bottle contains 8 fluid ounces of medicine, how many milligrams of the active ingredient are in the bottle?

Solution

a) Since each teaspoon contains 5 mℓ and 3 teaspoons should be taken, 15 mℓ of the cough medicine should be taken.

$$3 \text{ tsp} = (3 \text{ tsp})\left(\frac{5 \text{ mℓ}}{1 \text{ tsp}}\right) = 15 \text{ mℓ}$$

b) Since each teaspoon contains 10 mg of the active ingredient, 30 mg of the active ingredient should be taken.

$$3 \text{ tsp} = (3 \text{ tsp})\left(\frac{10 \text{ mg}}{1 \text{ tsp}}\right) = 30 \text{ mg}$$

c) Table 8.7 shows that each fluid ounce contains 30 mℓ. Since each 5 mℓ contains 10 mg of the active ingredient, we can work the problem as follows.

$$8 \text{ fl oz} = (8 \text{ fl oz})\left(\frac{30 \text{ mℓ}}{1 \text{ fl oz}}\right)\left(\frac{10 \text{ mg}}{5 \text{ mℓ}}\right) = \frac{8(30)(10)}{5} \text{ mg} = 480 \text{ mg}$$

Therefore, there are 480 mg (or 0.48 g) of the active ingredient in the bottle of cough syrup. ∎

Example 10   *Determining Dosage by Weight*

Drug dosage is often administered according to a patient's weight. For example, 30 mg of the drug vancomycin is to be given for each kilogram of a person's weight. If Martha Greene, who weighs 136 lb, is to be given the drug, what dosage should she be given?

Solution   First we need to convert Martha's weight into kilograms. From Table 8.7, we see that 1 lb = 0.45 kg. We obtain our unit fraction from this information.

$$136 \text{ lb} = 136 \text{ lb}\left(\frac{0.45 \text{ kg}}{1 \text{ lb}}\right) = 61.2 \text{ kg}$$

Next, since 30 mg of the drug is to be given for each kilogram of a person's weight, we multiply 61.2 kg by 30 to determine the dosage.

$$\text{Amount of drug} = 61.2 \text{ kg}\left(\frac{30 \text{ mg}}{1 \text{ kg}}\right) = 1836 \text{ mg}$$

Thus, 1836 mg, or 1.836 g, of the drug should be given. ∎

MATHEMATICS TODAY   Metrics on the Moon

On Earth, only the United States, Liberia, and Myanmar (formerly Burma) still use U.S. customary units instead of metric units. And now the moon is metric, too. On January 8, 2007, NASA and 13 other international space agencies decided to use the metric system for all lunar exploration programs. All the agencies agreed that using a single measurement system would make the human habitats and vehicles placed on the moon by different space agencies more compatible with one another. That could come in handy if, say, one agency's moon base needs emergency spare parts from another agency's base. In addition, metric standardization will make it easier for countries to form new partnerships and collaborations after their lunar operations are already in place.

Why This is Important When countries collaborate on a scientific mission, such as the International Space Station, they must all use the same units of measurements. The common units of measures agreed upon for the use on the International Space Station, and other scientific areas, are those of the metric system.

SECTION 8.4   *Exercises*

Warm Up Exercises

In Exercises 1–10, fill in the blanks with an appropriate word, phrase, or symbol(s).

1. A procedure used to convert from one unit of measurement to a different unit of measurement is called _____ analysis. Dimensional

2. A fraction in which the numerator and denominator contain different units, and the value of the fraction is 1, is called a(n) _____ fraction. Unit

3. The two unit fractions that relate seconds and minutes are _____ and _____. $\frac{60 \text{ sec}}{1 \text{ min}}$, $\frac{1 \text{ min}}{60 \text{ sec}}$

4. The two unit fractions that relate feet and inches are _____ and _____. $\frac{12 \text{ in.}}{1 \text{ ft}}$, $\frac{1 \text{ ft}}{12 \text{ in.}}$

5. The two unit fractions that relate meters and centimeters are _____ and _____. $\frac{100 \text{ cm}}{1 \text{ m}}$, $\frac{1 \text{ m}}{100 \text{ cm}}$

6. The two unit fractions that relate liters and milliliters are _____ and _____. $\frac{1000 \text{ m}\ell}{1 \ell}$, $\frac{1 \ell}{1000 \text{ m}\ell}$

7. a) When converting from kilograms to pounds, you would use the unit fraction _____. $\frac{1 \text{ lb}}{0.45 \text{ kg}}$

   b) When converting from pounds to kilograms, you would use the unit fraction _____. $\frac{0.45 \text{ kg}}{1 \text{ lb}}$

8. a) When converting from centimeters to feet, you would use the unit fraction _____. $\frac{1 \text{ ft}}{30 \text{ cm}}$

   b) When converting from feet to centimeters, you would use the unit fraction _____. $\frac{30 \text{ cm}}{1 \text{ ft}}$

9. a) When converting from gallons to liters, you would use the unit fraction _____. $\frac{3.8 \ell}{1 \text{ gal}}$

   b) When converting from liters to gallons, you would use the unit fraction _____. $\frac{1 \text{ gal}}{3.8 \ell}$

10. a) When converting from square yards to square meters, you would use the unit fraction _____. $\frac{0.8 \text{ m}^2}{1 \text{ yd}^2}$

    b) When converting from square meters to square yards, you would use the unit fraction _____. $\frac{1 \text{ yd}^2}{0.8 \text{ m}^2}$

Practice the Skills

In Exercises 11–26, convert the quantity to the indicated units. When appropriate, give your answer to the nearest hundredth.

11. 82 in. to centimeters
    208.28 cm

12. 9 lb to kilograms
    4.05 kg

13. 4.2 ft to meters 1.26 m

14. 427 g to ounces 15.25 oz

15. 162 kg to pounds 360 lb

16. 20 yd^2 to square meters 16 m^2

17. 39 mi to kilometers
    62.4 km

18. 765 mm to inches 30.12 in.

19. 675 ha to acres
    1687.5 acres

20. 253 oz to grams 7084 g

21. 20.3 ℓ to pints 43.19 pints

22. 4 T to tonnes 3.6 t

23. 3.8 km^2 to square miles
    1.46 mi^2

24. 25.6 mℓ to fluid ounces
    0.85 fl oz

25. 120 lb to kilograms 54 kg

26. 6.2 acres to hectares 2.48 ha

In Exercises 27–30, use the part of the scorecard that shows the distance in meters for the first four holes of the Millbrook Resort Golf Course in Queenstown, New Zealand. Determine the distances indicated.

HOLE	BLACK Tees	BLUE Tees	HANDICAP	PAR			WHITE Tees	RED Tees
1	505	505	3	5			466	414
2	185	175	15	3			137	91
3	366	357	11	4			344	287
4	396	376	7	4			376	303

27. Hole 1, black tees, in yards ≈561.11 yd

28. Hole 2, blue tees, in yards ≈194.44 yd

29. Hole 3, white tees, in feet ≈1146.67 ft

30. Hole 4, red tees, in feet 1010 ft

Problem Solving

31. Speed Limit The photo shows that the speed limit is 50 kph. Determine the speed in miles per hour. 31.25 mph

32. How Far? Carol Ann Harle's new car traveled 105 mi on 5 gal of gasoline. How many kilometers can Carol Ann's car travel with the same amount of gasoline? 168 km

33. Buying Carpet Victoria Montoya is buying outdoor carpet for her rectangular lanai, which is 6 yd by 9 yd. The carpeting is sold in square meters. How many square meters of carpeting will she need? 43.2 m²

34. Chicago to Atlanta The distance from Chicago, Illinois, to Atlanta, Georgia, is about 717 mi. What is the distance in kilometers? 1147.2 km

35. The QEW Part of the Queen Elizabeth Way in Canada has a speed limit of 80 kph. What is the speed limit in miles per hour? 50 mph

36. Milliliters in a Glass A glass holds 8 fl oz. How many milliliters will it hold? 240 mℓ

37. Poison Dart Frog A full-grown strawberry poison dart frog has a weight of about 6 g. What is its weight in ounces? 0.21 oz

38. Swimming Pool A swimming pool holds 12,500 gal of water. What is this volume in kiloliters? 47.5 kℓ

39. Area of Tribal Park The Monument Valley Navajo Tribal Park has an area of 91,696 acres. What is its area in hectares? 36 678.4 ha

▲ *Monument Valley in Utah*

40. Building a Basement A basement is to be 50 ft long, 30 ft wide, and 8 ft high. How much dirt will have to be removed when this basement is built? Answer in cubic meters. 360 m³

41. Cost of Rice If rice costs $1.10 per kilogram, determine the cost of 1 pound of rice. $0.495 per pound

42. Weight Restriction The weight restriction on a road in Italy is 7.5 t.

a) How many tons does this weight equal? ≈8.33 T

b) How many pounds? ≈16,666.67 lb

43. Capacity of a Tank Truck A tank truck holds 34.5 kℓ of gasoline. How many gallons does it hold? ≈9078.95 gal

44. Cost per Gram A 0.25-oz bottle of Chanel perfume costs $80. What is the cost per gram? ≈$11.43 per gram

45. Car's Engine A specific car's engine has a capacity of 5.7 ℓ of oil. How many quarts of oil does the engine have? 6 qt

46. Death Valley Elevation The lowest elevation in the United States is −282 ft at Badwater in Death Valley, California. Determine this elevation in

a) centimeters. −8460 cm   **b)** meters. −84.6 m

47. Sign in Russia Using the White sign in the photo, determine the distance to the Consulate General of Sweden in

a) kilometers. 0.55 km   **b)** miles. ≈0.34 mi

48. *A Precious Stone* One gram is the same as 5 carats. David Erich's new ring contains a precious stone that is $\frac{1}{8}$ carat. Find the weight of the stone in grams. 0.025 g

49. *Square Meters to Square Feet* One meter is about 3.3 ft. Use this information to determine

    a) the equivalent of one square meter in square feet. 10.89 ft²

    b) the equivalent of one cubic meter in cubic feet. 35.937 ft³

50. *Acres to Hectares* One acre is about 0.4 hectare.

    a) Use this information to determine the equivalent of 15.3 acres in hectares. 6.12 ha

    b) If 1 hectare is 10 000 m², determine the area of the 15.3 acres in square meters. 61 200 m²

51. *Dosage for a Child* The recommended dosage of the drug codeine for pediatric patients is 1 mg per kilogram of a child's weight. What dosage of codeine should be given to April Adam, who weighs 56 lb? 25.2 mg

52. *Dosage for a Man* For each kilogram of a person's weight, 1.5 mg of the antibiotic drug gentamicin is to be administered. If Ron Gigliotti weighs 170 lb, how much of the drug should he receive? 114.75 mg

53. *Ampicillin* The recommended dosage of the drug ampicillin for pediatric patients is 200 mg per kilogram of a patient's weight. If Janine Baker weighs 76 lb, how much ampicillin should she receive? 6840 mg, or 6.84 g

54. *Medicine for a Dog* For each kilogram of weight of a dog, 5 mg of the drug bretylium is to be given. If Blaster, an Irish setter, weighs 82 lb, how much of the drug should be given? 184.5 mg

55. *Active Ingredients* The label on the bottle of Triaminic expectorant indicates that each teaspoon (5 mℓ) contains 12.5 mg of the active ingredient phenylpropanolamine hydrochloride.

    a) Determine the amount of the active ingredient in the recommended adult dosage of 2 teaspoons. 25 mg

    b) Determine the quantity of the active ingredient in a 12-oz bottle. 900 mg

56. *Stomach Ache Remedy* The label on the bottle of Maximum Strength Pepto-Bismol indicates that each tablespoon contains 236 mg of the active ingredient bismuth subsalicylate.

    a) Determine the amount of the active ingredient in the recommended dosage of 2 tablespoons. 472 mg

    b) If the bottle contains 8 fl oz, determine the quantity of the active ingredient in the bottle. 3776 mg

57. *Gibraltar* Gibraltar is a British territory that shares a 1.2-kilometer border with Spain. The territory covers an area of about 6.84 square kilometers and the Rock of Gibraltar has a maximum height of 426 meters.

    a) Determine the length of the border with Spain in miles. 0.75 mi

    b) Determine the area of the territory in square miles. ≈2.63 mi²

    c) Determine the height of the rock in feet. ≈1420 ft

▲ *Gibraltar*

58. *Disney Magic* The Disney Magic Cruise Ship is 964 feet long, has a weight of 85,000 tons, and can travel 28 mph.

    a) Determine the length of the ship in meters. 289.2 m

    b) Determine the weight in tonnes. 76 500 t

    c) Determine the speed in kilometers per hour. 44.8 kph

59. *Overseas Flight* The photo of the monitor taken during an overseas flight shows information about the location and speed of the airplane.

    a) Determine the altitude in miles. ≈6.08 mi

    b) Determine the ground speed in miles per hour. ≈ 443.13 mph

    c) Determine the headwind in miles per hour. ≈113.13 mph

    d) Determine the temperature in degrees Fahrenheit using the formula $F = \frac{9}{5}C + 32$ (see Section 8.3). −49°F

Altitude	9730 m
Ground Speed	709 km/h
Outside Air Temperature	−45 °C
Head Wind	181 km/h

60. *Peppers* Peppers in Rome, Italy, cost 2 euros (€) per kilogram.

    a) Determine the cost per pound, in euros, for the peppers. 0.9 € per pound

    b) If 1 € can be converted to $1.40 U.S., determine the cost, in U.S. dollars, of 1 pound of peppers. $1.26 per pound

61. *Saffron* The photo shows Saffron for sale in Europe.

    a) Saffron cost 7 euros (€) per 100 grams. Determine the price, in euros, of 1 kg of Saffron. 70 € per kg

    b) Determine the cost in euros of 1 pound of Saffron. 31.5 € per pound

    c) If 1 € can be converted to $1.40 U.S., determine the cost, in U.S. dollars, of 1 pound of Saffron. $44.10 per pound

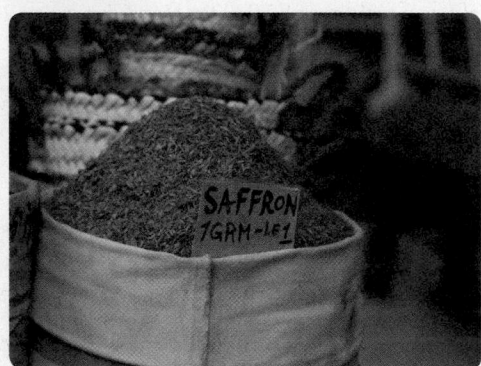

62. *Unit Fractions* On February 25, 2010, the conversion rate for the U.S. dollar was as follows. One U.S. dollar could buy 0.74 euros, 1.06 Canadian dollars, or 12.85 Mexican pesos. Using this information, determine a unit fraction to convert

    a) euros to Mexican pesos. $\frac{12.85 \text{ pesos}}{0.74 \text{ euro}} \approx \frac{17.36 \text{ pesos}}{1 \text{ euro}}$

    b) Canadian dollars to euros. $\frac{0.74 \text{ euro}}{1.06 \text{ Canadian dollars}} \approx \frac{0.70 \text{ euro}}{1 \text{ Canadian dollar}}$

    c) Canadian dollars to Mexican pesos. $\frac{12.85 \text{ pesos}}{1.06 \text{ Canadian dollars}} \approx \frac{12.12 \text{ pesos}}{1 \text{ Canadian dollar}}$

63. *Unit Fractions* An advertisement for Piaggio airplanes stated that their Avanti II had a speed of 402 knots, or 745 kilometers per hour, or 463 miles per hour. Using this information, determine a unit fraction to convert.

    a) knots to kilometers per hour. $\frac{745 \text{ kph}}{402 \text{ knots}} \approx \frac{1.85 \text{ kph}}{1 \text{ knot}}$

    b) miles per hour to knots. $\frac{402 \text{ knots}}{463 \text{ mph}} \approx \frac{0.87 \text{ k}}{1 \text{ mph}}$

    c) kilometers per hour to miles per hour. $\frac{463 \text{ mph}}{745 \text{ kph}} \approx \frac{0.62 \text{ mph}}{1 \text{ kph}}$

64. *Making Cookies* Change all the measurements in the cookie recipe to metric units. Do not forget pan size, temperature, and size of cookies.

    Magic Cookie Bar

    $\frac{1}{2}$ C graham cracker crumbs

12 oz nuts

8 oz chocolate pieces

$1\frac{1}{3}$ C flaked coconut

$1\frac{1}{3}$ C condensed milk

0.12 ℓ graham crackers, 336 g nuts, 224 g chocolate, 0.32 ℓ coconut, 0.32 ℓ milk; use 22.86 cm × 33.02 cm baking pan; bake at ≈ 176.7°C; makes about 2 doz 3.81 cm × 7.62 cm bars.

Coat the bottom of a 9 in. × 13 in. pan with melted margarine. Add rest of ingredients one by one: crumbs, nuts, chocolate, and coconut. Pour condensed milk over all. Bake at 350°F for 25 minutes. Allow to cool 15 minutes before cutting. Makes about two dozen $1\frac{1}{2}$ in. by 3 in. bars.

Challenge Problems/Group Activities

65. *Nursing Question* The following question was selected from a nursing exam. Can you answer it?

In caring for a patient after delivery, you are to give 0.2 mg Ergotrate Maleate. The ampule is labeled $\frac{1}{300}$ grain/mℓ. How much would you draw and give? (60 mg = 1 grain)

    a) 15 cc   **b)** 1.0 cc   **c)** 0.5 cc   **d)** 0.01 cc   1.0 cc, or b)

66. *How Much Beef* Paul Gosse is planning a picnic and plans on purchasing 0.18 kg of ground beef for each 100 lb of weight of guests who will be in attendance. If he expects 15 people whose average weight is 130 lb, how many pounds of beef should he purchase? 7.8 lb

67. *An Auto Engine* The displacement of automobile engines is measured in liters. A 2012 Ford Fusion SE Hybrid has a 3.0 ℓ engine.

    a) Determine the displacement of the engine in cubic centimeters. 3000 cc

    b) Determine the displacement of the engine in cubic inches. $\approx 183.07 \text{ in.}^3$

Recreational Mathematics

In Exercises 68–75, try to solve the puzzle. What is

68. 1 millionth of a mouthwash? 1 microscope

69. 2000 pounds of Chinese soup? wonton

70. 448 grams of cake? 1 pound cake

71. 1000 aches? 1 kilohurtz

72. 1 million bicycles? 2 megacycles

73. 1 million phones? 1 megaphone

74. 10 cards? 1 dekacards

75. 2000 mockingbirds? 2 kilomockingbird

CHAPTER 8) *Summary*

Important Facts and Concepts	Examples and Discussion
Section 8.1 *Metric Units and Conversions Within the Metric System*	Discussion pages 435–440 Examples 1–4, pages 438–440

Metric Units

Prefix	Symbol	Meaning
kilo	k	$1000 \times$ base unit
hecto	h	$100 \times$ base unit
deka	da	$10 \times$ base unit
—	—	base unit
deci	d	$\frac{1}{10}$ of base unit
centi	c	$\frac{1}{100}$ of base unit
milli	m	$\frac{1}{1000}$ of base unit

Section 8.2
Length, Area, Volume

Length	Discussion pages 443 and 444. Example 1, page 444
Area	Discussion pages 444–446. Examples 2–5, pages 445–446
Volume	Discussion pages 446–449. Examples 6–11, pages 447–449

Section 8.3 *Mass*	Discussion pages 454–457. Examples 1–2, pages 455–457

Water

Volume in Cubic Units		Volume in Liters		Mass of Water
1 cm^3	$=$	$1 \text{ m}\ell$	$=$	1 g
1 dm^3	$=$	1ℓ	$=$	1 kg
1 m^3	$=$	$1 \text{ k}\ell$	$=$	$1 \text{ t } (1000 \text{ kg})$

Temperature	Discussion pages 457–458. Examples 3–5, pages 457–458

$$^\circ C = \frac{5}{9}(^\circ F - 32)$$

$$^\circ F = \frac{9}{5}\,^\circ C + 32$$

Section 8.4
Dimensional Analysis

Using dimensional analysis	Discussion pages 462–464. Examples 1–3, pages 464
Using dimensional analysis with the metric system	Discussion pages 464–468. Examples 4–10, pages 466–468

CHAPTER 8) *Review Exercises*

8.1

In Exercises 1–6, indicate the meaning of the prefix.

1. Kilo
1000 × base unit

2. Centi
$\frac{1}{100}$ of base unit

3. Milli
$\frac{1}{1000}$ of base unit

4. Hecto
100 × base unit

5. Deka
10 × base unit

6. Deci
$\frac{1}{10}$ of base unit

In Exercises 7–12, change the given quantity to the quantity indicated.

7. 82 mg to grams 0.082 g

8. 3.2 ℓ to centiliters 320 cℓ

9. 0.0035 cm to millimeters 0.035 mm

10. 1 000 000 mg to kilograms 1 kg

11. 4.62 kℓ to liters 4620 ℓ

12. 192.6 dag to decigrams 19 260 dg

In Exercises 13 and 14, arrange the quantities from smallest to largest.

13. 2.67 kℓ, 3000 mℓ, 14 630 cℓ 3000 mℓ, 14 630 cℓ, 2.67 kℓ

14. 0.047 km, 4700 m, 47 000 cm 0.047 km, 47 000 cm, 4700 m

8.2, 8.3

In Exercises 15–22, indicate the metric unit of measurement that would best express the following.

15. The length of a jump rope Meters

16. The temperature of the sun's surface Degrees Celsius

17. The floor area of a department store Square meters

18. The volume of a glass of milk Milliliters or cubic centimeters

19. The length of an ant Millimeters

20. The mass of a car Kilograms or tonnes

21. The distance from Miami, Florida, to Los Angeles, California Kilometers

22. The length of the deer's ears in the following photo
Centimeters

In Exercises 23 and 24, (a) first estimate the following in metric units and then (b) measure with a metric ruler. Record your results.

23. Your waist a) Answers will vary. b) Answers will vary.

24. The length of a new pencil
a) Answers will vary. b) Answers will vary.

In Exercises 25–30, select the best answer.

25. The length of the distance between Detroit, Michigan, and Boston, Massachusetts, is about

a) 9950 m.   **b)** 9950 km.   **c)** 995 km.
(c)

26. The mass of a full-grown border collie is about

a) 600 g.   **b)** 20 kg.   **c)** 100 kg.
(b)

27. The volume of a gallon of gasoline is about

a) 0.1 kℓ.   **b)** 0.5 ℓ.   **c)** 4 ℓ.
(c)

28. The area of a large vegetable garden in a person's yard may be

a) 200 m².   **b)** 0.5 ha.   **c)** 0.02 km².
(a)

29. The temperature on a hot summer day in Florida may be

a) 34°C.   **b)** 55°C.   **c)** 25°C.
(a)

30. The height of El Capitan, a vertical peak in Yosemite National Park, is about

a) 900 cm.   **b)** 900 km.   **c)** 900 m.
(c)

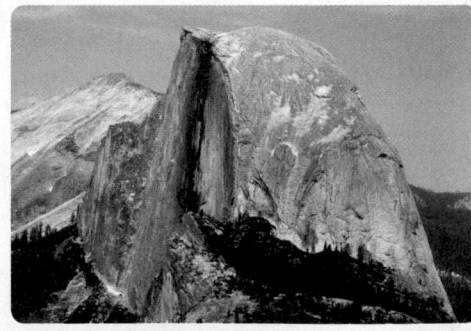

▲ *El Capitan, Yosemite National Park, California*

31. Convert 3600 kg to tonnes. 3.6 t

32. Convert 4.3 t to grams. 4 300 000 g

33. The temperature on a thermometer is 24°C. What is the Fahrenheit temperature? 75.2°F

34. If the room temperature is 68°F, what is the Celsius temperature? 20°C

35. If your outdoor thermometer shows a temperature of −6°F, what is the Celsius temperature? ≈ −21.1°C

36. If Lynn Colgin's body temperature is 39°C, what is her Fahrenheit temperature? 102.2°F

37. Measure, in centimeters, each of the line segments, then compute the area of the figure. $l = 4$ cm, $w = 1.6$ cm, $A = 6.4$ cm^2

38. Measure, in centimeters, the radius of the circle, then compute the area of the circle. $r = 1.5$ cm, $A \approx 7.07$ cm^2

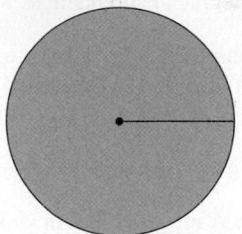

39. a) *A Hot Tubs's Volume* What is the volume of water in a full circular hot tub that has a diameter of 2 m and has a depth of 1 m? Answer in cubic meters. ≈ 3.14 m^3

   b) What is the mass of the water in kilograms? ≈ 3140 kg

40. *Computer Monitor* A rectangular computer monitor's screen measures 33.7 cm by 26.7 cm. Determine the area in

   a) square centimeters. 899.79 cm^2

   b) square meters. $0.089\,979$ m^2

41. *Volume of a Fish Tank* A small rectangular fish tank measures 80 cm long, 40 cm wide, and 30 cm high.

   a) What is its volume in cubic centimeters? $96\,000$ cm^3

   b) What is its volume in cubic meters? 0.096 m^3

   c) How many milliliters of water will the tank hold? $96\,000$ mℓ

   d) How many kiloliters of water will the tank hold? 0.096 kℓ

42. A square kilometer is a square with length and width both 1 km. How many times larger is a square kilometer than a square dekameter? $10{,}000$ times larger

8.4

In Exercises 45–58, change the given quantity to the indicated quantity. When appropriate, round answers to the nearest hundredth.

43. 86 cm = _____ in. ≈ 33.86

44. 105 kg = _____ lb ≈ 233.33

45. 83 yd = _____ m 74.7

46. 100 m = _____ yd ≈ 111.11

47. 45 mph = _____ kmph 72

48. 42 ℓ = _____ qt ≈ 44.21

49. 20 gal = _____ ℓ 76

50. 60 m^3 = _____ yd^3 ≈ 78.95

51. 96 cm^2 = _____ in.^{2} ≈ 14.77

52. 4 qt = _____ ℓ 3.8

53. 15 yd^3 = _____ m^3 11.4

54. 62 mi = _____ km 99.2

55. *Distance Traveled* The distance from Dallas, Texas, to Houston, Texas, is 241 miles. Determine this distance in kilometers. 385.6 km

56. *Natural Gas Used* The photo taken in Poland of a natural gas meter shows that 326,285 cubic meters of natural gas have been used at this location. Determine this volume in cubic yards. $429{,}322.37$ yd^3

57. *Building a Chimney* Ron Haines bought 700 bricks to build a chimney. Each brick has a mass of 1.5 kg.

   a) What is the total mass of the bricks in kilograms? 1050 kg

   b) What is the total weight of the bricks in pounds? ≈ 2333.33 lb

58. *Carpeting a Room* Irene Doo is buying new carpet for her rectangular family room. The room is 15 ft wide and 24 ft long. The carpeting is sold only in square meters. How many square meters of carpeting will she need? Round your answer to the nearest tenth of a square meter. 32.4 m^2

59. *Milk Tank* A cylindrical milk tank can store 50,000 gal of milk.

   a) Determine the volume in kiloliters. 190 kℓ

   b) Estimate the weight of the milk in kilograms. Assume that milk has the same weight as water. $190\,000$ kg

60. *The Speed Limit* The speed limit on a certain road is 65 mph. What is the speed limit in

   a) kilometers per hour? 104 kph

   b) meters per hour? $104\,000$ meters per hour

61. *A Water Tank* A rectangular tank used to test leaks in tires is 90 cm long by 70 cm wide by 40 cm deep.

   a) Determine the number of liters of water the tank holds. 252 ℓ

   b) What is the mass of the water in kilograms? 252 kg

62. *Oranges* If the cost of oranges is $3.50 per kilogram, determine the cost of 1 lb of oranges. $1.58 per pound

CHAPTER 8) *Test*

1. Change 759 cl to daℓ. 0.759 daℓ

2. Change 273 hm to cm. 2 730 000 cm

3. How many times greater is a kilometer than a dekameter? 100 times greater

4. *Jogging* A high school track is an oval that measures 400 m around. If Dave Camp jogs around the track six times, how many kilometers has he gone? 2.4 km

In Exercises 5–9, choose the best answer.

5. The width of this page is about
   a) 5 cm. b) 20 cm. c) 60 cm.
   (b)

6. The surface area of the top of a kitchen table is about
   a) 2 m². b) 200 cm². c) 2000 cm².
   (a)

7. The amount of gasoline that an automobile's gas tank can hold is about
   a) 200 ℓ. b) 20 ℓ. c) 75 ℓ.
   (c)

8. The distance that a typical car can go on a full tank of gas is about
   a) 50 m. b) 500 km. c) 5000 km.
   (b)

9. The outside temperature on a snowy day is about
   a) 18°C. b) −2°C. c) −40°C.
   (b)

10. How many times greater is a square meter than a square centimeter? 10,000 times greater

11. How many times greater is a cubic meter than a cubic centimeter? 1,000,000 times greater

12. Convert 225 oz. to grams. 6300 g

13. *Washington Monument* The Washington Monument is the world's tallest stone structure and the world's tallest obelisk. It stands about 169.29 meters tall. Determine its height in feet. 564.3 ft

14. *Natural Park* Wrangell – St. Elias National Park and Preserve in southern Alaska is the largest national park in the United States. Its area is 53,321 square kilometers. Determine the park's area in square miles. ≈20,508.1 mi²

15. Change 10°F to degrees Celsius. ≈ −12.22°C

16. Change 20°C to degrees Fahrenheit. 68°F

17. *Elevator* A sign in an elevator in France indicates that its maximum capacity is 300 kg. Determine the maximum capacity in
    a) grams. 300 000 g   b) pounds. ≈666.67 lb

18. *At the Aquarium* A rectangular fish tank at an aquarium is 20 m long by 20 m wide by 8 m deep.
    a) Determine the volume of the tank in cubic meters. 3200 m³
    b) Determine the number of liters of water the tank holds. 3 200 000 ℓ (or 3200 kℓ)
    c) Determine the weight of the water in kilograms. 3 200 000 kg

19. *Cost of Paint* The first coat of paint for the outside walls of a building requires 1 ℓ of paint for each 10 m² of wall surface. The second coat requires 1 ℓ for every 15 m². If the paint costs $3.50 per liter, what will be the cost of two coats of paint for the four outside walls of a rectangular building 20 m long, 15 m wide, and 6 m high? $245

20. *Premium Gasoline* Premium gasoline (S plomb 98) at a gas station in France costs 1.65 euros per liter, as shown in the photo.
    a) Determine the cost, per gallon, of premium gasoline in euros. 6.27 euros per gallon
    b) If one dollar could be exchanged for 0.67 euro determine the cost per gallon of the premium gasoline in U.S. dollars per gallon. ≈ $9.36 per gallon

GROUP PROJECTS

Health and Medicine

Throughout this chapter, we have shown the importance of the metric system in the medical professions. The following two questions involve applications of the metric system to medicine.

1. a) Twenty milligrams of the drug lincomycin is to be given for each kilogram of a person's weight. The drug is to be mixed with 250 cc of a normal saline solution, and the mixture is to be administered intravenously over a 1-hr period. Clyde Dexter, who weighs 196 lb, is to be given the drug. Determine the dosage of the drug he will be given.

b) At what rate per minute should the 250-cc solution be administered?

2. a) At a pharmacy, a parent asks a pharmacist why her child needs such a small dosage of a certain medicine. The pharmacist explains that a general formula may be used to estimate a child's dosage of certain medicines. The formula is

$$\text{Child's dose*} = \frac{\left(\begin{array}{c}\text{child's weight} \\ \text{in kilograms}\end{array}\right)}{67.5 \text{ kg}} \times \text{adult dose}$$

What is the amount of medicine you would give a 60-lb child if the adult dosage of the medicine is 70 mg?

b) At what weight, in pounds, would the child receive an adult dose?

3. The largest airplane in the world is the Russian-built Antonov Airlines An-225 Mriya; see photo. Below are some facts about the airplane. If the measurement is given in U.S. customary units, convert the measurement to metric units. If the measurement is given in metric units, convert the measurement to U.S. customary units.

▲ *An Antonov Airlines An–225 Mriya*

Payload: 250,000 kg 550,000 lbs
Length: 84 m 275.6 ft
Wingspan: 88.4 m 290.17 ft
Height: 18.1 m 59.3 ft
Cargo volume: 1300 m³ 43,333.33 ft³
Empty weight: 175,000 kg 385,800 lb
Maximum take-off weight: 1,323,000 lbs 600,000 kg
Take-off-run with maximum weight: 11,500 ft 3500 m
Maximum speed: 530 mph 850 kph
Range with maximum fuel: 9570 mi 15,400 km
Range with maximum payload: 2500 mi 4000 km
Service ceiling: 36,100 ft 11,000 m

---

*Consult a pediatrician before giving a child medicine.

9
Geometry

◄ *Baseballs and baseball diamonds are examples of geometric objects.*

What You Will Learn

- Points, lines, planes, and angles
- Polygons, similar figures, and congruent figures
- Perimeter and area
- Pythagorean theorem
- Circles
- Volume
- Transformational geometry, symmetry, and tessellations
- The Möbius strip, Klein bottle, and maps
- Non-Euclidean geometry and fractal geometry

Why This is Important

Many objects we encounter each day can be described in terms of geometry. Spherical baseballs hit on square baseball "diamonds," cylindrical cans of soda, and rectangular computer screens are all examples of geometric objects we frequently encounter. In addition to these items, scientists also use geometry to conduct research and create items that improve our lives. For example, the antenna on your cell phone is an example of a geometric object known as a *fractal*. In this chapter, we will study many geometric objects that we see in our everyday lives.

Points, Lines, Planes, and Angles

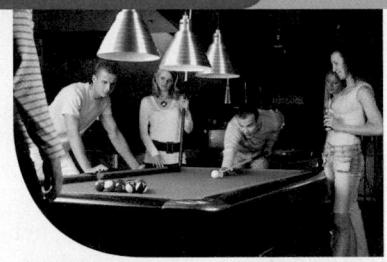

▲ *Billiard games involve many geometric concepts.*

Playing billiards involves many geometric concepts. In this section, we will introduce the geometric terms *points, lines, planes,* and *angles*. In a typical billiard game, each of these terms is evident. The billiard balls rest on specific points on the table, which is part of a plane. After being struck with a cue, the ball travels along a path that is part of a line. Angles are involved in the path the ball takes when the ball hits a table bumper or another ball. The concepts we will discuss in this section form an important basis for the study of geometry.

Why *This is Important* Geometry is used in our everyday lives to describe the world around us. An understanding of fundamental geometric concepts can help us better understand our world.

Profile In Mathematics

Euclid

Euclid (320–275 B.C.) lived in Alexandria, Egypt, and was a teacher and scholar at Alexandria's school called the *Museum*. It was here that Euclid collected and arranged many of the mathematical results known at the time. This collection of works became his 13-volume masterpiece known as *Elements*. Beginning with a list of definitions, postulates, and axioms, Euclid proved one theorem after another, using only previously proven results. This method of proof became a model of mathematical and scientific investigation that survives today. Remarkably, the geometry in *Elements* does not rely on making exact geometric measurements using a ruler or protractor. Rather, the work is developed using only an unmarked straightedge and a drawing compass. Next to the Bible, Euclid's *Elements* may be the most translated, published, and studied of all the books produced in the Western world.

Human beings recognized shapes, sizes, and physical forms long before geometry was developed. Geometry as a science is said to have begun in the Nile Valley of ancient Egypt. The Egyptians used geometry to measure land and to build pyramids and other structures.

The word *geometry* is derived from two Greek words: *ge*, meaning earth, and *metron*, meaning measure. Thus, geometry means "earth measure" or "measurement of the earth."

Unlike the Egyptians, the Greeks were interested in more than just the applied aspects of geometry. The Greeks attempted to apply their knowledge of logic to geometry. In about 600 B.C., Thales of Miletus was the first to be credited with using deductive methods to develop geometric concepts. Another outstanding Greek mathematician, Pythagoras, continued the systematic development of geometry that Thales had begun.

In about 300 B.C., Euclid (see *Profile in Mathematics* in the margin) collected and summarized much of the Greek mathematics of his time. In a set of 13 books called *Elements*, Euclid laid the foundation for plane geometry, which is also called *Euclidean geometry*.

Euclid is credited with being the first mathematician to use the *axiomatic method* in developing a branch of mathematics. First, Euclid introduced *undefined terms* such as point, line, plane, and angle. He related these to physical space by such statements as "A line is length without breadth" so that we may intuitively understand them. Because such statements play no further role in his system, they constitute primitive or undefined terms.

Second, Euclid introduced certain *definitions*. The definitions are introduced when needed and are often based on the undefined terms. Some terms that Euclid introduced and defined include triangle, right angle, and hypotenuse.

Third, Euclid stated certain primitive propositions called *postulates* (now called *axioms**) about the undefined terms and definitions. The reader is asked to accept these statements as true on the basis of their "obviousness" and their relationship with the physical world. For example, the Greeks accepted all right angles as being equal, which is Euclid's fourth postulate.

Fourth, Euclid proved, using deductive reasoning (see Section 1.1), other propositions called *theorems*. One theorem that Euclid proved is known as the Pythagorean

---

*The concept of the axiom has changed significantly since Euclid's time. Now any statement may be designated as an axiom, whether it is self-evident or not. All axioms are *accepted* as true. A set of axioms forms the foundation for a mathematical system.

theorem: "The sum of the areas of the squares constructed on the arms of a right triangle is equal to the area of the square constructed on the hypotenuse." He also proved that the sum of the angles of a triangle is 180°.

Using only 10 axioms, Euclid deduced 465 propositions (or theorems) in plane and solid geometry, number theory, and Greek geometric algebra.

Point and Line

Three basic terms in geometry are *point*, *line*, and *plane*. These three terms are not given a formal definition, but we recognize points, lines, and planes when we see them.

Let's consider some properties of a line. Assume that a line means a straight line unless otherwise stated.

1. A line is a set of points. Each point is on the line and the line passes through each point. When we wish to refer to a specific point, we will label it with a single capital letter. For example, in Fig. 9.1(a) three points are labeled *A*, *B*, and *C*, respectively.

2. Any two distinct points determine a unique line. Figure 9.1(a) illustrates a line. The arrows at both ends of the line indicate that the line continues in each direction. The line in Fig. 9.1(a) may be symbolized with any two points on the line by placing a line with a double-sided arrow above the letters that correspond to the points, such as $\overleftrightarrow{AB}$, $\overleftrightarrow{BA}$, $\overleftrightarrow{AC}$, $\overleftrightarrow{CA}$, $\overleftrightarrow{BC}$, or $\overleftrightarrow{CB}$.

3. Any point on a line separates the line into three parts: the point itself and two *half lines* (neither of which includes the point). For example, in Fig. 9.1(a) point *B* separates the line into the point *B* and two half lines. Half line *BA*, symbolized $\overset{\circ}{\rightarrow}{BA}$, is illustrated in Fig. 9.1(b). The open circle above the *B* indicates that point *B* is not included in the half line. Figure 9.1(c) illustrates half line *BC*, symbolized $\overset{\circ}{\rightarrow}{BC}$.

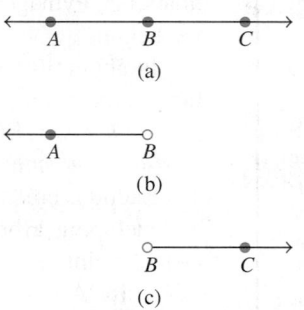

(a)

(b)

(c)

Figure 9.1

Look at the half line $\overset{\circ}{\rightarrow}{AB}$ in Fig. 9.2(b) on page 481. If the *end point*, *A*, is included with the set of points on the half line, the result is called a *ray*. Ray *AB*, symbolized $\overrightarrow{AB}$, is illustrated in Fig. 9.2(c). Ray *BA*, symbolized $\overrightarrow{BA}$, is illustrated in Fig. 9.2(d).

A *line segment* is that part of a line between two points, including the end points. Line segment *AB*, symbolized $\overline{AB}$, is illustrated in Fig. 9.2(e).

An open line segment is the set of points on a line between two points, excluding the end points. Open line segment *AB*, symbolized $\overset{\circ\,\circ}{AB}$, is illustrated in Fig. 9.2(f).

Figure 9.2(g) illustrates two half open line segments, symbolized $\overline{AB}\!\!\overset{\circ}{}$ and $\overset{\circ}{}\!\!\overline{AB}$.

Recall from Chapter 2 that the intersection (symbolized ∩) of two sets is the set of elements (points in this case) common to both sets. Consider the rays $\overrightarrow{AB}$ and $\overrightarrow{BA}$ in Fig. 9.3(a) on page 481. The intersection of $\overrightarrow{AB}$ and $\overrightarrow{BA}$ is $\overline{AB}$. Thus, $\overrightarrow{AB} \cap \overrightarrow{BA} = \overline{AB}$.

Description	Diagram	Symbol
(a) Line AB		$\overleftrightarrow{AB}$
(b) Half line AB		$\overset{\circ\longrightarrow}{AB}$
(c) Ray AB		$\overrightarrow{AB}$
(d) Ray BA		$\overleftarrow{BA}$
(e) Line segment AB		$\overline{AB}$
(f) Open line segment AB		$\overset{\circ\!-\!\circ}{AB}$
(g) Half open line segments AB		$\overline{AB}^{\circ}$ $\overset{\circ}{\overline{AB}}$

Figure 9.2

Also recall from Chapter 2 that the union (symbolized $\cup$) of two sets is the set of elements (points in this case) that belong to either of the sets or both sets. The union of $\overrightarrow{AB}$ and $\overrightarrow{BA}$ is $\overleftrightarrow{AB}$ (Fig. 9.3b). Thus, $\overrightarrow{AB} \cup \overrightarrow{BA} = \overleftrightarrow{AB}$.

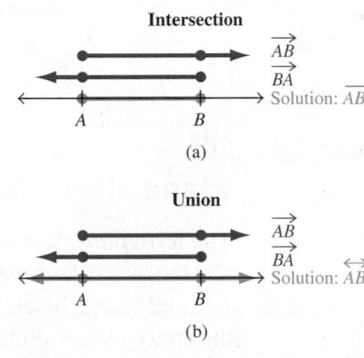

Figure 9.3

Example 1 *Unions and Intersections of Parts of a Line*

Using line AD, determine the solution to each part.

a) $\overrightarrow{AB} \cap \overrightarrow{DC}$ b) $\overrightarrow{AB} \cup \overrightarrow{DC}$ c) $\overrightarrow{AB} \cap \overrightarrow{CD}$ d) $\overrightarrow{AD} \cup \overset{\circ}{\overrightarrow{CA}}$

Solution

a) $\overrightarrow{AB} \cap \overrightarrow{DC}$

Ray AB and ray DC are shown below. The intersection of these two rays is that part of line AD that is a part of *both* ray AB *and* ray DC. The intersection of ray AB and ray DC is line segment AD.

$$\overrightarrow{AB} \cap \overrightarrow{DC} = \overline{AD}$$

b) $\overrightarrow{AB} \cup \overrightarrow{DC}$

Once again ray AB and ray DC are shown below. The union of these two rays is that part of line AD that is part of *either* ray AB *or* ray DC. The union of ray AB and ray DC is the entire line AD.

$$\overrightarrow{AB} \cup \overrightarrow{DC} = \overleftrightarrow{AD}$$

c) $\overline{AB} \cap \overrightarrow{CD}$

Line segment AB and ray CD have no points in common, so their intersection is empty.

$$\overline{AB} \cap \overrightarrow{CD} = \varnothing$$

d) $\overline{AD} \cup \overset{\circ}{\overrightarrow{CA}}$

The union of line segment AD and half line CA is ray DA (or equivalently, $\overrightarrow{DB}$ or $\overrightarrow{DC}$).

$$\overline{AD} \cup \overset{\circ}{\overrightarrow{CA}} = \overrightarrow{DA}$$

Plane

The term *plane* is one of Euclid's undefined terms. For our purposes, we can think of a plane as a two-dimensional surface that extends infinitely in both directions, like an infinitely large blackboard. Euclidean geometry is called *plane geometry* because it is the study of two-dimensional figures in a plane.

Two lines in the same plane that do not intersect are called *parallel lines*. Figure 9.4(a) illustrates two parallel lines in a plane ($\overleftrightarrow{AB}$ is parallel to $\overleftrightarrow{CD}$).

Properties of planes include the following:

1. Any three points that are not on the same line (noncollinear points) determine a unique plane (Fig. 9.4b).
2. A line in a plane divides the plane into three parts, the line and two half planes (Fig. 9.4c).
3. Any line and a point not on the line determine a unique plane.
4. The intersection of two distinct planes is a line (Fig. 9.4d).

Two planes that do not intersect are said to be *parallel planes*. For example, in Fig. 9.5 plane *ABE* is parallel to plane *GHF*.

Two lines that do not lie in the same plane and do not intersect are called *skew lines*. Figure 9.5 illustrates many skew lines (for example, $\overleftrightarrow{AB}$ and $\overleftrightarrow{CD}$).

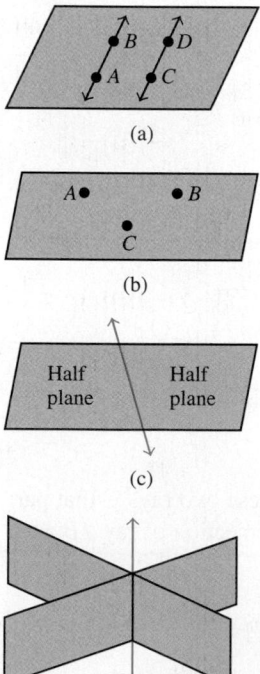

(a)

(b)

Half plane   Half plane

(c)

(d)

Figure 9.4

Figure 9.5

Angles

An *angle*, denoted $\not\subset$, is the union of two rays with a common end point (Fig. 9.6):

$$\overrightarrow{BA} \cup \overrightarrow{BC} = \measuredangle ABC \text{ (or } \measuredangle CBA)$$

An angle can be formed by the rotation of a ray about a point. An angle has an initial side and a terminal side. The initial side indicates the position of the ray prior to rotation; the terminal side indicates the position of the ray after rotation. The point common to both rays is called the *vertex* of the angle. The letter designating the vertex is always the middle one of the three letters designating an angle. The rays that make up the angle are called its *sides*.

There are several ways to name an angle. The angle in Fig. 9.6 may be denoted

$$\measuredangle ABC, \qquad \measuredangle CBA, \qquad \text{or} \qquad \measuredangle B$$

An angle divides a plane into three distinct parts: the angle itself, its interior, and its exterior. In Fig. 9.6, the angle is represented by the blue lines, the interior of the angle is shaded pink, and the exterior is shaded green.

The *measure of an angle*, symbolized m, is the amount of rotation from its initial side to its terminal side. In Fig. 9.6, the letter x represents the measure of $\measuredangle ABC$; therefore, we may write $m\measuredangle ABC = x$.

Angles can be measured in *degrees*, radians, or gradients. In this text, we will discuss only the degree unit of measurement. An angle of 45 degrees is written 45°. A *protractor* is used to measure angles. The angle shown being measured by the protractor in Fig. 9.7 is 50°.

Figure 9.7

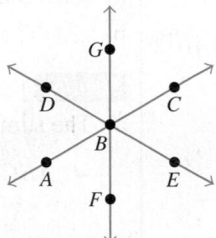

Figure 9.6

Example 2 *Union and Intersection*

Refer to Fig. 9.8. Determine the following.

Figure 9.8

a) $\overrightarrow{BC} \cup \overrightarrow{BG}$ b) $\overrightarrow{AB} \cap \overrightarrow{CB}$ c) $\overrightarrow{BE} \cap \overrightarrow{BF}$ d) $\measuredangle DBG \cap \measuredangle ABD$

Solution

a) $\overrightarrow{BC} \cup \overrightarrow{BG} = \measuredangle CBG$ or $\measuredangle GBC$ b) $\overrightarrow{AB} \cap \overrightarrow{CB} = \overline{AC}$

c) $\overrightarrow{BE} \cap \overrightarrow{BF} = \{B\}$ d) $\measuredangle DBG \cap \measuredangle ABD = \overrightarrow{BD}$

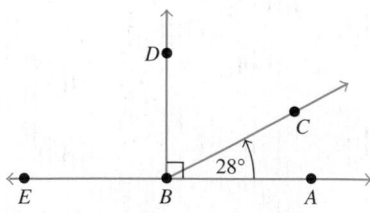

Figure 9.10

Consider a circle whose circumference is divided into 360 equal parts. If we draw a line from each mark on the circumference to the center of the circle, we get 360 wedge-shaped pieces. The measure of an angle formed by the straight sides of each wedge-shaped piece is defined to be 1°.

Angles are classified by their degree measurement, as shown in the following summary. A *right angle* has a measure of 90°, an *acute angle* has a measure less than 90°, an *obtuse angle* has a measure greater than 90° but less than 180°, and a *straight angle* has a measure of 180°.

Right Angle	Acute Angle	Obtuse Angle	Straight Angle

$x = 90°$
The symbol ∟ is used to indicate right angles.

$0° < x < 90°$ $90° < x < 180°$ $x = 180°$

Two angles in the same plane are *adjacent angles* when they have a common vertex and a common side but no common interior points. In Fig. 9.9, $\angle DBC$ and $\angle CBA$ are adjacent angles, but $\angle DBA$ and $\angle CBA$ are not adjacent angles.

Two angles are called *complementary angles* if the sum of their measures is 90°. Two angles are called *supplementary angles* if the sum of their measures is 180°.

Figure 9.9

Example 3 Determining Complementary and Supplementary Angles

In Fig. 9.10, we see that $m\angle ABC = 28°$.
a) $\angle ABC$ and $\angle CBD$ are complementary angles. Determine $m\angle CBD$.
b) $\angle ABC$ and $\angle CBE$ are supplementary angles. Determine $m\angle CBE$.

Solution

a) The sum of two complementary angles must be 90°, so

$$m\angle ABC + m\angle CBD = 90°$$
$$28° + m\angle CBD = 90°$$
$$m\angle CBD = 90° - 28° = 62°$$

Subtract 28° from each side of the equation.

b) The sum of two supplementary angles must be 180°, so

$$m\angle ABC + m\angle CBE = 180°$$
$$28° + m\angle CBE = 180°$$
$$m\angle CBE = 180° - 28° = 152°$$

Subtract 28° from each side of the equation.

Figure 9.11

Figure 9.12

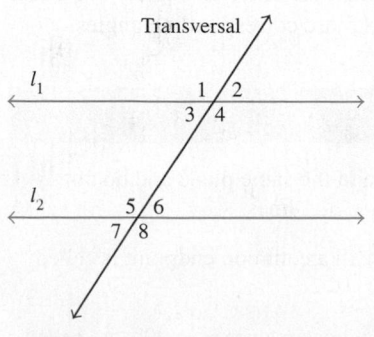

Figure 9.13

Example 4 *Determining Complementary Angles*

If $\angle ABC$ and $\angle CBD$ are complementary angles and $m\angle ABC$ is 26° less than $m\angle CBD$, determine the measure of each angle (Fig. 9.11).

Solution Let $m\angle CBD = x$. Then $m\angle ABC = x - 26$ since it is 26° less than $m\angle CBD$. Because these angles are complementary, we have

$$m\angle CBD + m\angle ABC = 90°$$
$$x + (x - 26) = 90°$$
$$2x - 26 = 90°$$
$$2x = 116°$$
$$x = 58°$$

Therefore, $m\angle CBD = 58°$ and $m\angle ABC = 58° - 26°$, or 32°. Note that $58° + 32° = 90°$, which is what we expected. ∎

Example 5 *Determining Supplementary Angles*

If $\angle ABC$ and $\angle ABD$ are supplementary and $m\angle ABC$ is five times larger than $m\angle ABD$, determine $m\angle ABC$ and $m\angle ABD$ (Fig. 9.12).

Solution Let $m\angle ABD = x$, then $m\angle ABC = 5x$. Since these angles are supplementary, we have

$$m\angle ABD + m\angle ABC = 180°$$
$$x + 5x = 180°$$
$$6x = 180°$$
$$x = 30°$$

Thus, $m\angle ABD = 30°$ and $m\angle ABC = 5(30°) = 150°$. Note that $30° + 150° = 180°$, which is what we expected. ∎

When two straight lines intersect, the nonadjacent angles formed are called *vertical angles*. In Fig. 9.13, $\angle 1$ and $\angle 3$ are vertical angles, and $\angle 2$ and $\angle 4$ are vertical angles. We can show that vertical angles have the same measure; that is, they are equal. For example, Fig. 9.13 shows that

$$m\angle 1 + m\angle 2 = 180°. \qquad \text{Why?}$$
$$m\angle 2 + m\angle 3 = 180°. \qquad \text{Why?}$$

Since $\angle 2$ has the same measure in both cases, $m\angle 1$ must equal $m\angle 3$.

Vertical Angles
Vertical angles have the same measure.

A line that intersects two different lines, l_1 and l_2, at two different points is called a *transversal*. Figure 9.14 illustrates that when two parallel lines are cut by a transversal, eight angles are formed. Angles 3, 4, 5, and 6 are called *interior angles*, and angles 1, 2, 7, and 8 are called *exterior angles*. Eight pairs of supplementary angles are formed. Can you list them?

Special names are given to the angles formed by a transversal crossing two parallel lines. We describe these angles on page 486.

Figure 9.14

Name	Description	Illustration	Pairs of Angles Meeting Criteria
Alternate interior angles	Interior angles on opposite sides of the transversal		$\angle 3$ and $\angle 6$ $\angle 4$ and $\angle 5$
Alternate exterior angles	Exterior angles on opposite sides of the transversal		$\angle 1$ and $\angle 8$ $\angle 2$ and $\angle 7$
Corresponding angles	One interior and one exterior angle on the same side of the transversal		$\angle 1$ and $\angle 5$ $\angle 2$ and $\angle 6$ $\angle 3$ and $\angle 7$ $\angle 4$ and $\angle 8$

Parallel Lines Cut by a Transversal

When two parallel lines are cut by a transversal,
1. alternate interior angles have the same measure.
2. alternate exterior angles have the same measure.
3. corresponding angles have the same measure.

Figure 9.15

Example 6 *Determining Angle Measures*

Figure 9.15 shows two parallel lines cut by a transversal. Determine the measure of $\angle 1$ through $\angle 7$.

Solution

$m\angle 6 = 49°$	$\angle 8$ and $\angle 6$ are vertical angles.
$m\angle 5 = 131°$	$\angle 8$ and $\angle 5$ are supplementary angles.
$m\angle 7 = 131°$	$\angle 5$ and $\angle 7$ are vertical angles.
$m\angle 1 = 131°$	$\angle 1$ and $\angle 7$ are alternate exterior angles.
$m\angle 4 = 49°$	$\angle 4$ and $\angle 6$ are alternate interior angles.
$m\angle 2 = 49°$	$\angle 6$ and $\angle 2$ are corresponding angles.
$m\angle 3 = 131°$	$\angle 3$ and $\angle 1$ are vertical angles.

In Example 6, the angles could have been determined in alternate ways. For example, we mentioned $m\angle 1 = 131°$ because $\angle 1$ and $\angle 7$ are alternate exterior angles. We could have also stated that $m\angle 1 = 131°$ because $\angle 1$ and $\angle 5$ are corresponding angles.

SECTION 9.1   *Exercises*

Warm Up Exercises

In Exercises 1–12, fill in the blanks with an appropriate word, phrase, or symbol(s).

1. Two lines in the same plane that do not intersect are called _____ lines. Parallel

2. Two lines that do not lie in the same plane and do not intersect are called _____ lines. Skew

3. The union of two rays with a common endpoint is called a(n) _____. Angle

4. Two angles, the sum of whose measures is 90°, are called _____ angles. Complementary

5. Two angles, the sum of whose measures is 180°, are called _____ angles. Supplementary

6. Two angles in the same plane that have a common vertex and a common side, but no common interior points, are called _____ angles. Adjacent

7. An angle whose measure is 180° is called a(n) _____ angle. Straight

8. An angle whose measure is 90° is called a(n) _____ angle. Right

9. An angle whose measure is greater than 90° but less than 180° is called a(n) _____ angle. Obtuse

10. An angle whose measure is less than 90° is called a(n) _____ angle. Acute

11. When two straight lines intersect, the nonadjacent angles formed are called _____ angles. Vertical

12. A line that intersects two different lines at two different points is called a(n) _____. Transversal

Practice the Skills

In Exercises 13–20, identify the figure as a line, half line, ray, line segment, open line segment, or half open line segment. Denote the figure by its appropriate symbol.

13. Ray, $\overrightarrow{AB}$

14.
Open line segment, $\overset{\circ}{AB}\overset{\circ}{}$

15. Half line, $\overset{\circ}{BA}\rightarrow$

16. Line segment, $\overline{AB}$

17. Ray, $\overrightarrow{BA}$

18. Line, $\overleftrightarrow{AB}$

19.
Half open line segment, $\overset{\circ}{AB}$.

20. Half line, $\overset{\circ}{AB}\rightarrow$

In Exercises 21–32, use the figure to find the following:

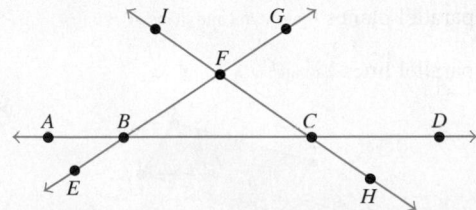

21. $\overrightarrow{AB} \cap \overrightarrow{DC}$ $\overline{AD}$

22. $\overset{\circ}{FE} \cup \overrightarrow{FG}$ $\overset{\circ}{EG}$

23. $\overset{\circ}{BC} \cup \overrightarrow{CD}$ $\overset{\circ}{BD}\overset{\circ}{}$

24. $\overrightarrow{AB} \cup \overrightarrow{BD}$ $\overline{AD}$

25. $\angle ICA \cap \overrightarrow{EG}$ $\{B, F\}$

26. $\angle IFG \cap \angle EFH$ $\{F\}$

27. $\overset{\circ}{AB} \cap \overrightarrow{HC}$ $\{C\}$

28. $\overset{\circ}{BD} \cap \overset{\circ}{CB}$ $\overset{\circ}{BC}$

29. $\overrightarrow{BC} \cup \overrightarrow{BF}$ $\angle CBF$ or $\angle FBC$

30. $\overline{BC} \cup \overline{CF} \cup \overline{FB}$ $\triangle BCF$

31. $\overset{\circ}{BD} \cup \overset{\circ}{CB}$ $\overset{\circ}{BC}$

32. $\{C\} \cap \overrightarrow{CH}$ $\varnothing$

In Exercises 33–44, use the figure to find the following.

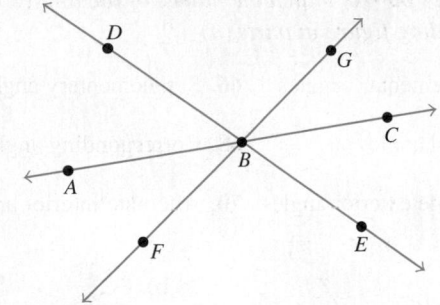

33. $\overrightarrow{DB} \cup \overrightarrow{EB}$ $\overleftrightarrow{DE}$

34. $\angle ABD \cap \angle CBG$ $\{B\}$

35. $\angle GBC \cap \angle CBE$ $\overrightarrow{BC}$

36. $\overleftrightarrow{DE} \cup \overset{\circ}{BE}$ $\overleftrightarrow{DE}$

37. $\angle ABE \cup \overset{\circ}{AB}$ $\angle ABE$

38. $\overset{\circ}{BF} \cup \overset{\circ}{BE}$ $\angle FBE$ or $\angle EBF$

39. $\overrightarrow{FG} \cap \overrightarrow{BF}$ $\overline{BF}$

40. $\overrightarrow{BE} \cup \overrightarrow{BD}$ $\overleftrightarrow{DE}$

41. $\overset{\circ}{AC} \cap \overset{\circ}{AC}$ $\overset{\circ}{AC}$

42. $\overset{\circ}{AC} \cap \overset{\circ}{BE}$ $\varnothing$

43. $\overrightarrow{EB} \cap \overset{\circ}{BE}$ $\overset{\circ}{BE}$

44. $\overrightarrow{FB} \cup \overrightarrow{BG}$ $\overrightarrow{FG}$

In Exercises 45–52, classify the angle as acute, right, straight, obtuse, or none of these angles.

45. Right

46. Acute

47. Straight

48. Straight

49. Obtuse

50. None of these angles

51. None of these angles

52. Right

In Exercises 53–58, find the complementary angle of the given angle.

53. 10°   80°

54. 15°   75°

55. $32\frac{3}{4}°$ $57\frac{1}{4}°$

56. $31\frac{2}{5}°$ $58\frac{3}{5}°$

57. 64.7°   25.3°

58. 0.01°   89.99°

In Exercises 59–64, find the supplementary angle of the given angle.

59. 80° 100°

60. 150° 30°

61. 20.5° 159.5°

62. 148.7° 31.3°

63. $43\frac{5}{7}°$ $136\frac{2}{7}°$

64. $64\frac{7}{16}°$ $115\frac{9}{16}°$

In Exercises 65–70, match the names of the angles with the corresponding figure in parts (a)–(f).

65. Complementary angles (f)

66. Supplementary angles (c)

67. Vertical angles (b)

68. Corresponding angles (d)

69. Alternate exterior angles (a)

70. Alternate interior angles (e)

a)

b)

c)

d)

e)

f)
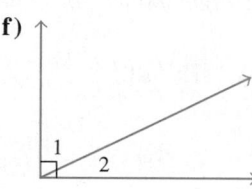

Problem Solving

71. **MODELING** - *Complementary Angles* If ∡1 and ∡2 are complementary angles and if the measure of ∡1 is five times the measure of ∡2, determine the measures of ∡1 and ∡2. $m\angle 1 = 75°, m\angle 2 = 15°$

72. **MODELING** - *Complementary Angles* The difference between the measures of two complementary angles is 22°. Determine the measures of the two angles. 56° and 34°

73. **MODELING** - *Supplementary Angles* The difference between the measures of two supplementary angles is 88°. Determine the measures of the two angles. 134° and 46°

74. **MODELING** - *Supplementary Angles* If ∡1 and ∡2 are supplementary angles and if the measure of ∡2 is 17 times the measure of ∡1, determine the measures of the two angles. $m\angle 1 = 10°, m\angle 2 = 170°$

In Exercises 75–78, parallel lines are cut by the transversal shown. Determine the measures of ∡1 through ∡7.

75. *

76. *

77. *

78. *

In Exercises 79–82, the angles are complementary angles. Determine the measures of ∡1 and ∡2.

79.

$m\angle 1 = 64°, m\angle 2 = 26°$

80.

$m\angle 1 = 16°, m\angle 2 = 74°$

81.

$m\angle 1 = 33°, m\angle 2 = 57°$

82.

$m\angle 1 = 79°, m\angle 2 = 11°$

In Exercises 83–86, the angles are supplementary angles. Determine the measures of ∡1 and ∡2.

83.

$m\angle 1 = 134°, m\angle 2 = 46°$

84.

$m\angle 1 = 156°, m\angle 2 = 24°$

85. $5x + 6$
$m\angle 1 = 29°, m\angle 2 = 151°$

86. $6x + 5$
$m\angle 1 = 25°, m\angle 2 = 155°$

The figure below suggests a number of lines and planes. The lines may be described by naming two points, and the planes may be described by naming three points. In Exercises 87–94, use the figure to name the following.

87. Two parallel planes Plane *ABG* and plane *JCD*

88. Two parallel lines $\overleftrightarrow{EF}$ and $\overleftrightarrow{DG}$

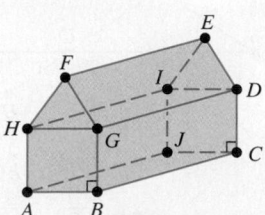

89. Two lines that intersect at right angles $\overleftrightarrow{BG}$ and $\overleftrightarrow{DG}$

90. Two planes that intersect at right angles
Plane ABG and plane BCD

91. Three planes whose intersection is a single point
Plane $AGB \cap$ plane $ABC \cap$ plane $BCD = \{B\}$

92. Three planes whose intersection is a line
Plane $HGD \cap$ plane $FGD \cap$ plane $BGD = \overleftrightarrow{GD}$

93. A line and a plane whose intersection is a point
$\overleftrightarrow{BC} \cap$ plane $ABG = \{B\}$

94. A line and a plane whose intersection is a line
$\overleftrightarrow{AB} \cap$ plane $ABG = \overleftrightarrow{AB}$

Concept/Writing Exercises

95. a) What are the four key parts in the axiomatic method used by Euclid?
Undefined terms, definitions, postulates (axioms), and theorems
  b) Discuss each of the four parts.*

96. What is the difference between an axiom and a theorem?*

97. a) How many lines can be drawn through a given point?
An infinite number
  b) How many planes can be drawn through a given point? An infinite number

98. What is the intersection of two distinct nonparallel planes? A line

99. How many planes can be drawn through a given line?
An infinite number

100. a) Will three noncollinear points A, B, and C always determine a plane? Explain. Yes

  b) Is it possible to determine more than one plane with three noncollinear points? Explain. No

  c) How many planes can be constructed through three collinear points? An infinite number

In Exercises 101–106, determine whether the statement is always true, sometimes true, or never true. Explain your answer.

101. Two lines that are both parallel to a third line must be parallel to each other. Always true. If any two lines are parallel to a third line, then they must be parallel to each other.

102. A triangle contains exactly two acute angles.*

103. Vertical angles are complementary angles. Sometimes true.
Vertical angles are only complementary when each is equal to 45°.

104. Alternate exterior angles are supplementary angles.*

105. Alternate interior angles are complementary angles.*

106. A triangle contains two obtuse angles.
Never true. The sum of two obtuse angles is greater than 180°.

Challenge Problems/Group Activities

107. Use a straightedge and a compass to construct a triangle with sides of equal length (an equilateral triangle) by doing the following:

  a) Use the straightedge to draw a line segment of any length and label the end points A and B (Fig. a).

b) Place one end of the compass at point A and the other end at point B and draw an arc as shown (Fig. b).

c) Now turn the compass around and draw another arc as shown. Label the point of intersection of the two arcs C (Fig. c).

d) Draw line segments AC and BC. This completes the construction of equilateral triangle ABC (Fig. d).
Answers will vary.

Figure a   Figure b

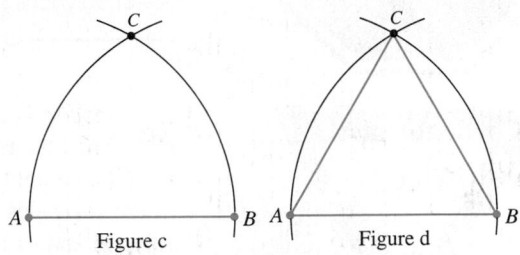

Figure c   Figure d

108. If lines l and m are parallel lines and if lines l and n are skew lines, is it true that lines m and n must also be skew? (*Hint:* Look at Fig. 9.5 on page 482.) Explain your answer and include a sketch to support your answer. No. Line m and line n may intersect.

109. Two lines are *perpendicular* if they intersect at right angles. If lines l and m are perpendicular and if lines m and n are perpendicular, is it true that lines l and n must also be perpendicular? Explain your answer and include a sketch to support your answer.
No. Line l and line n may be parallel or skew.

110. Suppose you have three distinct lines, all lying in the same plane. Find all the possible ways in which the three lines can be related. Sketch each case (four cases).*

111. If two straight lines intersect at a point, determine the sum of the measures of the 4 angles formed. 360°

112. $\angle ABC$ and $\angle CBD$ are complementary and $m\angle CBD$ is twice the $m\angle ABC$. $\angle ABD$ and $\angle DBE$ are supplementary angles.

  a) Draw a sketch illustrating $\angle ABC$, $\angle CBD$, and $\angle DBE$.*

  b) Determine $m\angle ABC$. 30°

  c) Determine $m\angle CBD$. 60°

  d) Determine $m\angle DBE$. 90°
  *See Instructor Answer Appendix

Internet/Research Activities

113. Using the Internet and other sources, write a research paper on Euclid's contributions to geometry.

114. Using the Internet and other sources, write a research paper on the three classic geometry problems of Greek antiquity (see the *Did You Know?* on page 484).

115. Search the Internet or other sources such as a geometry textbook to study the geometric constructions that use a straightedge and a compass only. Prepare a poster demonstrating five of these basic constructions.

SECTION 9.2   Polygons

▲ *The shapes of these road signs are examples of polygons.*

Figure 9.17

What shape would you use to best describe the following road signs: a stop sign, a yield sign, a speed limit sign? In this section, we will study the shapes of these and other geometric figures that can be classified as *polygons*.

Why **This is Important** Polygons appear in many aspects of our daily lives. The properties of polygons can be used in many problem-solving applications.

A *polygon* is a closed figure in a plane determined by three or more straight line segments. Examples of polygons are given in Fig. 9.16.

The straight line segments that form the polygon are called its *sides*, and a point where two sides meet is called a *vertex* (plural, *vertices*). The union of the sides of a polygon and its interior is called a *polygonal region*. A *regular polygon* is one whose sides are all the same length and whose interior angles all have the same measure. Figures 9.16(b) and (d) are regular polygons.

(a)   (b)   (c)   (d)

Figure 9.16

Polygons are named according to their number of sides. The names of some polygons are given in Table 9.1.

Table 9.1

Number of Sides	Name	Number of Sides	Name
3	Triangle	8	Octagon
4	Quadrilateral	9	Nonagon
5	Pentagon	10	Decagon
6	Hexagon	12	Dodecagon
7	Heptagon	20	Icosagon

One of the most important polygons is the triangle. The sum of the measures of the interior angles of a triangle is $180°$. To illustrate, consider triangle ABC given in Fig. 9.17. The triangle is formed by drawing two transversals through two parallel lines l_1 and l_2 with the two transversals intersecting at a point on l_1.

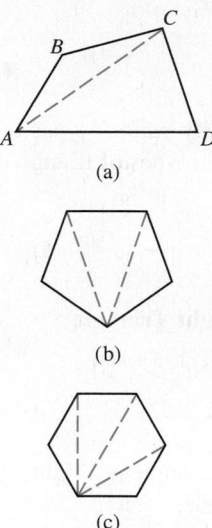

(a)

(b)

(c)

Figure 9.18

In Fig. 9.17, notice that ∡A and ∡A' are corresponding angles. Recall from Section 9.1 that corresponding angles are equal, so $m∡A = m∡A'$. Also, ∡C and ∡C' are corresponding angles; therefore, $m∡C = m∡C'$. Next, we notice that ∡B and ∡B' are vertical angles. In Section 9.1, we learned that vertical angles are equal; therefore, $m∡B = m∡B'$. Figure 9.17 shows that ∡A', ∡B', and ∡C' form a straight angle; therefore, $m∡A' + m∡B' + m∡C' = 180°$. Since $m∡A = m∡A'$, $m∡B = m∡B'$, and $m∡C = m∡C'$, we can reason that $m∡A + m∡B + m∡C = 180°$. This example illustrates that the sum of the interior angles of a triangle is 180°.

Consider the quadrilateral $ABCD$ (Fig. 9.18a). Drawing a straight line segment between any two vertices forms two triangles. Since the sum of the measures of the angles of a triangle is 180°, the sum of the measures of the interior angles of a quadrilateral is $2 \cdot 180°$, or 360°.

Now let's examine a pentagon (Fig. 9.18b). We can draw two straight line segments to form three triangles. Thus, the sum of the measures of the interior angles of a five-sided figure is $3 \cdot 180°$, or 540°. Figure 9.18(c) shows that four triangles can be drawn in a six-sided figure. Table 9.2 summarizes this information.

Table 9.2

Sides	Triangles	Sum of the Measures of the Interior Angles
3	1	$1(180°) = 180°$
4	2	$2(180°) = 360°$
5	3	$3(180°) = 540°$
6	4	$4(180°) = 720°$

If we continue this procedure, we can see that for an n-sided polygon the sum of the measures of the interior angles is $(n - 2)180°$.

Sum of the Measures of Interior Angles
The **sum** of the measures of the interior angles of an n-sided polygon is $(n - 2)180°$.

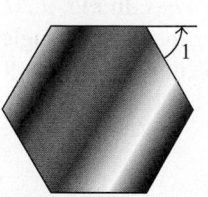

Figure 9.19

Example 1 *Angles of a Hexagon*

The surfaces of the heads of many bolts are in the shape of regular hexagons. A regular hexagon is a six-sided figure with all the sides the same length and all interior angles with the same measure. See Fig. 9.19. Determine

a) the measure of an interior angle.

b) the measure of exterior ∡1.

Solution

a) Using the formula $(n - 2)180°$, we can determine the sum of the measures of the interior angles of a hexagon as follows.

$$\text{Sum} = (6 - 2)180°$$
$$= 4(180°)$$
$$= 720°$$

The measure of an interior angle of a regular polygon can be determined by dividing the sum of the interior angles by the number of angles.

The measure of an interior angle of a regular hexagon is determined as follows:

$$\text{Measure} = \frac{720°}{6} = 120°$$

b) Since ∡1 is the supplement of an interior angle,

$$m\angle 1 = 180° - 120° = 60°$$

To discuss area in the next section, we must be able to identify various types of triangles and quadrilaterals. The following is a summary of certain types of triangles and their characteristics.

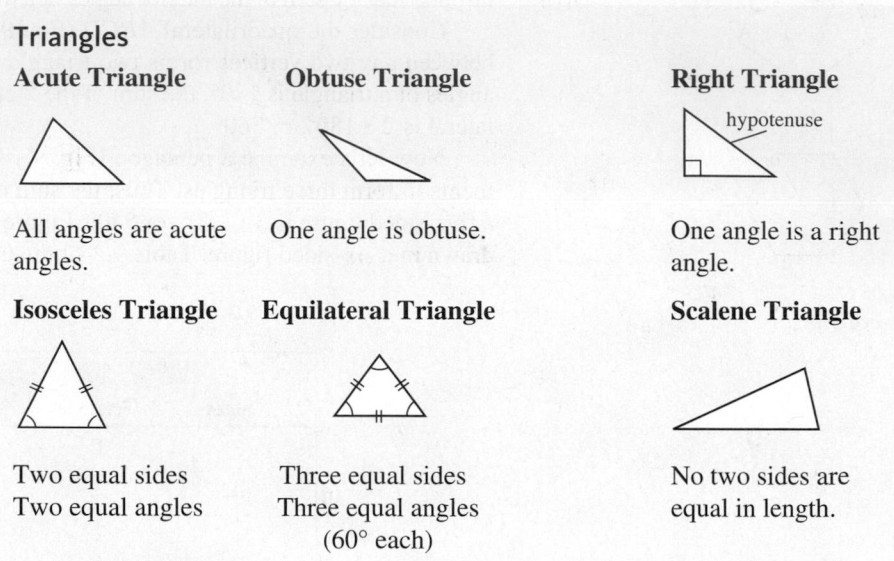

Triangles

Acute Triangle	**Obtuse Triangle**	**Right Triangle**
All angles are acute angles.	One angle is obtuse.	One angle is a right angle.
Isosceles Triangle	**Equilateral Triangle**	**Scalene Triangle**
Two equal sides Two equal angles	Three equal sides Three equal angles (60° each)	No two sides are equal in length.

Similar Figures

In everyday living, we often have to deal with geometric figures that have the "same shape" but are of different sizes. For example, an architect will make a small-scale drawing of a floor plan or a photographer will make an enlargement of a photograph. Figures that have the same shape but may be of different sizes are called *similar figures*. Two similar figures are illustrated in Fig. 9.20.

Similar figures have *corresponding angles* and *corresponding sides*. In Fig. 9.20, triangle *ABC* has angles *A*, *B*, and *C*. Their respective corresponding angles in triangle *DEF* are angles *D*, *E*, and *F*. Sides $\overline{AB}$, $\overline{BC}$, and $\overline{AC}$ in triangle *ABC* have corresponding sides $\overline{DE}$, $\overline{EF}$, and $\overline{DF}$, respectively, in triangle *DEF*.

> **Definition: Similar Figures**
> Two figures are **similar** if their corresponding angles have the same measure and the lengths of their corresponding sides are in proportion.

In Figure 9.20, ∡*A* and ∡*D* have the same measure, ∡*B* and ∡*E* have the same measure, and ∡*C* and ∡*F* have the same measure. Also, the lengths of corresponding sides of similar triangles are in proportion.

When we refer to the line segment *AB*, we place a line over the *AB* and write $\overline{AB}$. **When we refer to the *length* of a line segment, we do not place a bar above the two letters.** For example, if we write *AB* = 12, we are indicating the length of line segment $\overline{AB}$ is 12. The proportion below shows that the lengths of the corresponding sides of the similar triangles in Fig. 9.20 are in proportion.

$$\frac{AB}{DE} = \frac{BC}{EF} = \frac{AC}{DF}$$

Figure 9.20

Example 2   Similar Figures

Consider the similar figures in Fig. 9.21.

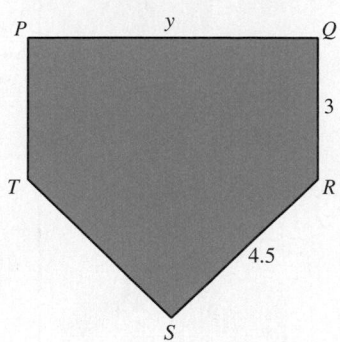

Figure 9.21

Determine

a) the length of side $\overline{BC}$.   b) the length of side $\overline{PQ}$.

Solution

a) We will represent the length of side $\overline{BC}$ with the variable x. Because the corresponding sides of similar figures must be in proportion, we can write a proportion (as explained in Section 6.2) to determine the length of side $\overline{BC}$. Corresponding sides $\overline{CD}$ and $\overline{RS}$ are known, so we use them as one ratio in the proportion. The side corresponding to $\overline{BC}$ is $\overline{QR}$.

$$\frac{BC}{QR} = \frac{CD}{RS}$$

$$\frac{x}{3} = \frac{3}{4.5}$$

Now we solve for x.

$$x \cdot 4.5 = 3 \cdot 3$$
$$4.5x = 9$$
$$x = 2$$

Thus, the length of side $\overline{BC}$ is 2 units.

b) We will represent the length of side $\overline{PQ}$ with the variable y. The side corresponding to $\overline{PQ}$ is $\overline{AB}$. We will work part (b) in a manner similar to part (a).

$$\frac{PQ}{AB} = \frac{RS}{CD}$$

$$\frac{y}{4} = \frac{4.5}{3}$$

$$y \cdot 3 = 4 \cdot 4.5$$
$$3y = 18$$
$$y = 6$$

Thus, the length of side $\overline{PQ}$ is 6 units. ∎

Example 3   Using Similar Triangles to Find the Height of a Tree

Monique Currie plans to remove a tree from her backyard. She needs to know the height of the tree. Monique is 6 ft tall and determines that when her shadow is 9 ft long, the shadow of the tree is 45 ft long (see Fig. 9.22 on page 494). How tall is the tree?

Figure 9.22

Solution We will let x represent the height of the tree. From Fig. 9.22, we can see that the triangle formed by the sun's rays, Monique, and her shadow is similar to the triangle formed by the sun's rays, the tree, and its shadow. To find the height of the tree, we will set up and solve the following proportion:

$$\frac{\text{height of the tree}}{\text{height of Monique}} = \frac{\text{length of tree's shadow}}{\text{length of Monique's shadow}}$$

$$\frac{x}{6} = \frac{45}{9}$$

$$9x = 270$$

$$x = 30$$

Therefore, the tree is 30 ft tall.   ∎

Congruent Figures

If the corresponding sides of two similar figures are the same length, the figures are called *congruent figures*. Corresponding angles of congruent figures have the same measure, and the corresponding sides are equal in length. Two congruent figures coincide when placed one upon the other.

Example 4 *Congruent Triangles*

Triangles ABC and $A'B'C'$ in Fig. 9.23 are congruent. Determine

a) the length of side $A'C'$.   b) the length of side $\overline{AB}$.

c) $m\angle C'A'B'$.   d) $m\angle ACB$.

e) $m\angle ABC$.

Figure 9.23

Solution Because $\triangle ABC$ is congruent to $\triangle A'B'C'$, we know that the corresponding side lengths are equal and corresponding angle measures are equal.

a) $A'C' = AC = 13$ b) $AB = A'B' = 10.6$

c) $m\angle C'A'B' = m\angle CAB = 60°$ d) $m\angle ACB = m\angle A'C'B' = 50°$

e) The sum of the angles of a triangle is 180°. Since $m\angle BAC = 60°$ and $m\angle ACB = 50°$, $m\angle ABC = 180° - 60° - 50° = 70°$.   ∎

Earlier we learned that *quadrilaterals* are four-sided polygons, the sum of whose interior angles is 360°. Quadrilaterals may be classified according to their characteristics, as illustrated in the summary box on page 495.

Quadrilaterals

Trapezoid	Parallelogram	Rhombus
Two sides are parallel.	Both pairs of opposite sides are parallel. Both pairs of opposite sides are equal in length.	Both pairs of opposite sides are parallel. The four sides are equal in length.

Rectangle	Square
Both pairs of opposite sides are parallel. Both pairs of opposite sides are equal in length. The angles are right angles.	Both pairs of opposite sides are parallel. The four sides are equal in length. The angles are right angles.

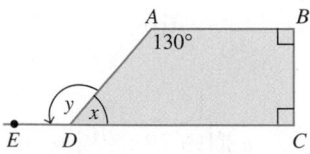

Figure 9.24

Example 5 *Angles of a Trapezoid*

Trapezoid *ABCD* is shown in Fig. 9.24.

a) Determine the measure of the interior angle, *x*.

b) Determine the measure of the exterior angle, *y*.

Solution

a) We know that each of the two right angles in trapezoid *ABCD* has a measure of 90°. We also know that the sum of the interior angles in any quadrilateral is 360°. Therefore, we have

$$m\sphericalangle DAB + m\sphericalangle ABC + m\sphericalangle BCD + m\sphericalangle x = 360°$$

$$130° + 90° + 90° + m\sphericalangle x = 360°$$

$$310° + m\sphericalangle x = 360°$$

$$m\sphericalangle x = 50°$$

Thus, the measure of the interior angle, *x*, is 50°.

b) Angle *x* and angle *y* are supplementary angles. Therefore, $m\sphericalangle x + m\sphericalangle y = 180°$ and $m\sphericalangle y = 180° - m\sphericalangle x = 180° - 50° = 130°$. Thus, the measure of the exterior angle, *y*, is 130°. ∎

Note that in Example 5 part (b) we could also have determined the measure of angle *y* as follows. By the definition of a trapezoid, sides $\overline{AB}$ and $\overline{CD}$ must be parallel. Therefore, side $\overline{AD}$ may be considered a transversal and $\sphericalangle BAD$ and $\sphericalangle ADE$ are alternate interior angles. Recall from Section 9.1 that alternate interior angles are equal. Thus, $m\sphericalangle BAD = m\sphericalangle ADE$ and $m\sphericalangle y = 130°$.

SECTION 9.2   *Exercises*

Warm Up Exercises

In Exercises 1–6, fill in the blanks with an appropriate word, phrase, or symbol(s).

1. A closed figure in a plane determined by three or more straight line segments is called a(n) _____. Polygon

2. A polygon whose sides are all the same length and whose interior angles all have the same measure is called a(n) _____ polygon. Regular

3. Two polygons are similar if their corresponding angles have the same measure and the lengths of their corresponding sides are in _____. Proportion

4. The sum of the measures of the interior angles of a triangle is _____. 180°

5. If the corresponding sides of two similar figures are the same length, the figures are called _____ figures. Congruent

6. The sum of the measures of the interior angles of a quadrilateral is _____. 360°

In Exercises 7–14, (a) name the polygon. If the polygon is a quadrilateral, give its specific name. (b) State whether or not the polygon is a regular polygon.

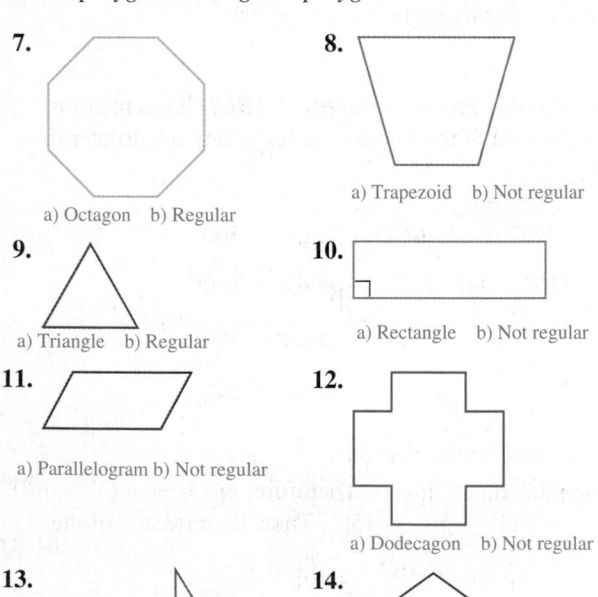

7.   a) Octagon   b) Regular

8.   a) Trapezoid   b) Not regular

9.   a) Triangle   b) Regular

10.   a) Rectangle   b) Not regular

11.   a) Parallelogram b) Not regular

12.   a) Dodecagon   b) Not regular

13.   a) Heptagon   b) Not regular

14.   a) Pentagon   b) Regular

In Exercises 15–22, identify the triangle as (a) scalene, isosceles, or equilateral and as (b) acute, obtuse, or right. The

parallel markings (the two small parallel lines) on two or more sides indicate that the marked sides are of equal length.

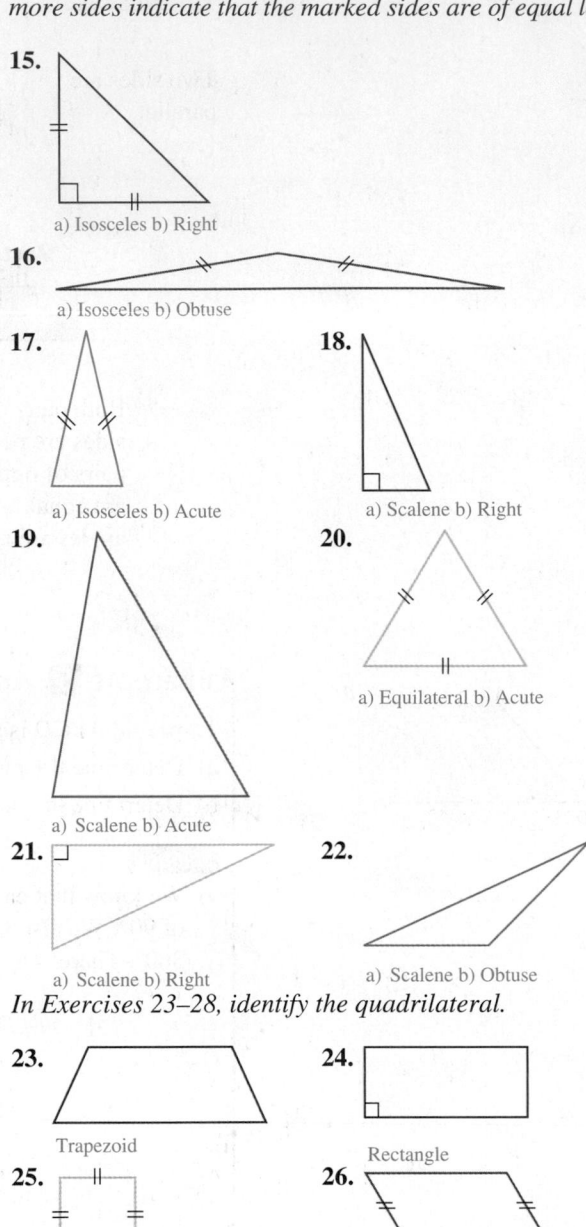

15.   a) Isosceles b) Right

16.   a) Isosceles b) Obtuse

17.   a) Isosceles b) Acute

18.   a) Scalene b) Right

19.   a) Scalene b) Acute

20.   a) Equilateral b) Acute

21.   a) Scalene b) Right

22.   a) Scalene b) Obtuse

In Exercises 23–28, identify the quadrilateral.

23.   Trapezoid

24.   Rectangle

25.   Square

26.   Parallelogram

27.   Rhombus

28.   Trapezoid

In Exercises 29–32, find the measure of ∡x.

29.   133°   37°   96°

x

30.

58°

31.

150°

32.

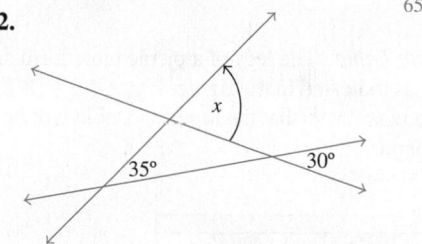

65°

In Exercises 33–34, lines l_1 and l_2 are parallel. Determine the measures of $\angle 1$ through $\angle 12$.

33.   *   **34.**   *

In Exercises 35–40, determine the sum of the measures of the interior angles of the indicated polygon.

35. Pentagon 540°   **36.** Heptagon 900°   **37.** Nonagon 1260°

38. Decagon 1440°   **39.** Icosagon 3240°   **40.** Dodecagon 1800°

In Exercises 41–46, (a) determine the measure of an interior angle of the named regular polygon. (b) If a side of the polygon is extended, determine the supplementary angle of an interior angle. See Example 1.

41. Triangle a) 60° b) 120°   **42.** Quadrilateral a) 90° b) 90°

43. Octagon a) 135° b) 45°   **44.** Nonagon a) 140° b) 40°

45. Decagon a) 144° b) 36°   **46.** Icosagon a) 162° b) 18°

In Exercises 47–52, the figures are similar. Find the length of side x and side y.

47. $x = 2, y = 1.6$

48.

$x = 30, y = 16$

49.

$x = 2\frac{2}{5}, y = 7\frac{1}{2}$

50.

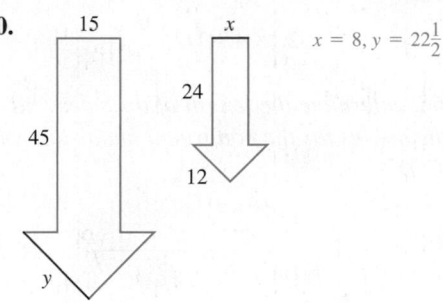

$x = 8, y = 22\frac{1}{2}$

51.

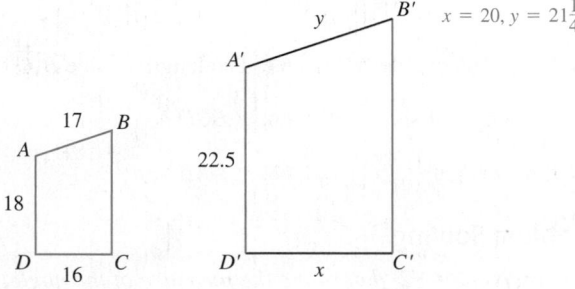

$x = 20, y = 21\frac{1}{4}$

52.

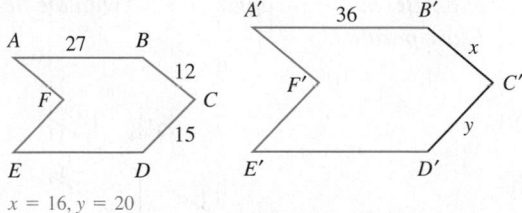

$x = 16, y = 20$

In Exercises 53–56, triangles ABC and DEC are similar figures. Determine the length of

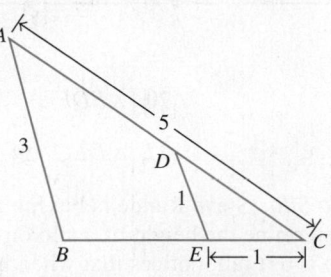

53. side $\overline{BC}$. 3   **54.** side $\overline{DC}$. $1\frac{2}{3}$

55. side $\overline{AD}$. $3\frac{1}{3}$ **56.** side $\overline{BE}$. 2

*See Instructor Answer Appendix

In Exercises 57–62, find the length of the sides and the measures of the angles for the congruent triangles ABC and A'B'C'.

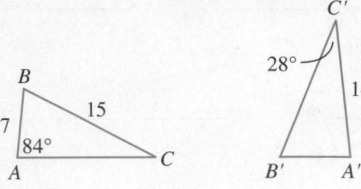

57. The length of side $\overline{AC}$ 14   **58.** The length of side $\overline{A'B'}$ 7

59. The length of side $\overline{B'C'}$ **60.** $\measuredangle B'A'C'$ 84°
15

61. $\measuredangle ACB$ 28°   **62.** $\measuredangle ABC$ 68°

In Exercises 63–68, determine the length of the sides and the measures of the angles for the congruent quadrilaterals ABCD and A'B'C'D'.

63. The length of side $\overline{AD}$ 9   **64.** The length of side $\overline{B'C'}$ 11

65. The length of side $\overline{A'B'}$ **66.** $\measuredangle BCD$ 50°
10

67. $\measuredangle A'D'C'$ 70°   **68.** $\measuredangle DAB$ 110°

Problem Solving

In Exercises 69–72, determine the measure of the angle. In the figure, $\measuredangle ABC$ makes an angle of 125° with the floor and l_1 and l_2 are parallel.

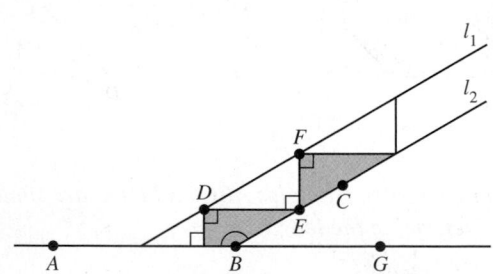

69. $\measuredangle GBC$ 55°   **70.** $\measuredangle EDF$ 55°

71. $\measuredangle DFE$ 35°   **72.** $\measuredangle DEC$ 125°

73. *Height of a Silo*   Steve Runde is buying a farm and needs to determine the height of a silo on the farm. Steve, who is 6 ft tall, notices that when his shadow is 9 ft long, the shadow of the silo is 105 ft long (see diagram above and to the right). How tall is the silo? Note that the diagram is not to scale. 70 ft

74. *Angles on a Picnic Table*   The legs of a picnic table form an isosceles triangle as indicated in the figure. If $\measuredangle ABC = 80°$, determine $m\measuredangle x$ and $m\measuredangle y$ so that the top of the table will be parallel to the ground. $m\measuredangle x = 50°, m\measuredangle y = 130°$

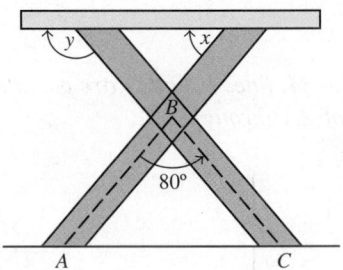

75. *Distances in Minnesota*   A triangle can be formed by drawing line segments on a map of Minnesota connecting the cities of Austin, Rochester, and St. Paul (see figure below). If the actual distance from Austin to Rochester is approximately 44 miles, use the lengths of the line segments indicated in the figure along with similar triangles to approximate

a) the actual distance from St. Paul to Austin. ≈113.14 mi

b) the actual distance from St. Paul to Rochester. ≈75.43 mi

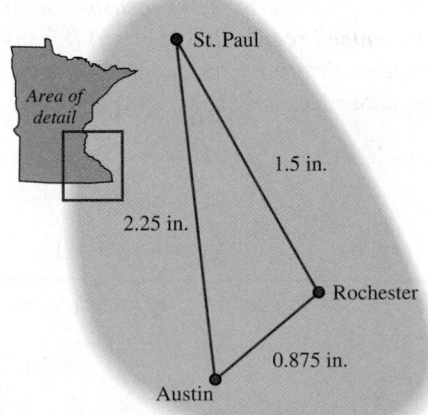

76. *Distances in Illinois* A triangle can be formed by drawing line segments on a map of Illinois connecting the cities of Rockford, Chicago, and Bloomington (see figure below). If the actual distance from Chicago to Rockford is approximately 90 miles, use the lengths of the line segments indicated in the figure along with similar triangles to approximate

a) the actual distance from Chicago to Bloomington. 135 mi

b) the actual distance from Bloomington to Rockford. 139.5 mi

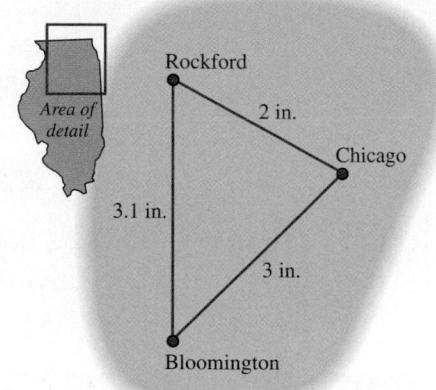

Concept/Writing Exercises

77. List six different types of triangles and in your own words describe the characteristics of each.*

78. List five different types of quadrilaterals and in your own words describe the characteristics of each.*

Challenge Problems/Group Activities

Scaling Factor In Exercises 79 and 80 we use a scaling factor. Examine the similar triangles ABC and A'B'C' in the figure below.

If we calculate the ratios $\dfrac{AB}{A'B'}$, $\dfrac{BC}{B'C'}$, *and* $\dfrac{CA}{C'A'}$, *we see that each of these ratios is equal to 2. We call this common ratio the* **scaling factor** *of* $\triangle ABC$ *with respect to* $\triangle A'B'C'$.

If we calculate the reciprocal ratios $\dfrac{A'B'}{AB}$, $\dfrac{B'C'}{BC}$, *and* $\dfrac{C'A'}{CA}$, *we see that each of these ratios is equal to* $\frac{1}{2}$. *We call this common ratio the scaling factor of* $\triangle A'B'C'$ *with respect to* $\triangle ABC$. *Every pair of similar figures has two*

scaling factors that show the relationship between the corresponding side lengths. Notice that the length of each side of $\triangle ABC$ *is two times the length of the corresponding side in* $\triangle A'B'C'$. *We can also state that the length of each side of* $\triangle A'B'C'$ *is one-half the length of the corresponding side of* $\triangle ABC$.

79. In the figure, $\triangle DEF$ is similar to $\triangle D'E'F'$. The length of the sides of $\triangle DEF$ is shown in the figure. If the scaling factor of $\triangle DEF$ with respect to $\triangle D'E'F'$ is 3, determine the length of the sides of triangle $\triangle D'E'F'$. $D'E' = 4, E'F' = 5, D'F' = 3$

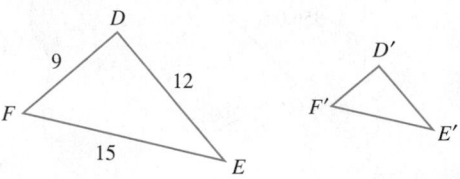

80. In the figure, quadrilateral $EFGH$ is similar to quadrilateral $E'F'G'H'$. The length of the sides of quadrilateral $EFGH$ is shown in the figure. If the scaling factor of quadrilateral $E'F'G'H'$ with respect to quadrilateral $EFGH$ is $\frac{1}{3}$, determine the length of the sides of quadrilateral $E'F'G'H'$. $E'F' = 7, F'G' = 3, G'H' = 3, E'H' = 4$

81. *Height of a Wall* You are asked to measure the height of an inside wall of a warehouse. No ladder tall enough to measure the height is available. You borrow a mirror from a salesclerk and place it on the floor. You then move away from the mirror until you can see the reflection of the top of the wall in it, as shown in the figure.

a) Explain why triangle *HFM* is similar to triangle *TBM*. (*Hint:* In the reflection of light the angle of incidence, $\angle HMF$, equals the angle of *reflection*, $\angle TMB$. Thus, $\angle HMF = \angle TMB$.)*

b) If your eyes are $5\frac{1}{2}$ ft above the floor and you are $2\frac{1}{2}$ ft from the mirror and the mirror is 20 ft from the wall, how high is the wall? 44 ft

*See Instructor Answer Appendix

Recreational Mathematics

82. *Distance Across a Lake*

a) In the figure, $m\angle CED = m\angle ABC$. Explain why triangles ABC and DEC must be similar. *

b) Determine the distance across the lake, DE. ≈ 2141.49 ft

Internet/Research Activities

83. Using the Internet and history of mathematics texts, write a paper on the history and use of the theodolite, a surveying instrument.

84. Using the Internet and other sources, write a paper on the use of geometry in the photographic process. Include discussions on the use of similar figures.

*See Instructor Answer Appendix

SECTION 9.3 | **Perimeter and Area**

▲ We will study the perimeter and area of rectangles, such as those on which volleyball games are played.

If you were to walk around the outside edge of a volleyball court, how far would you walk? If you had to place floor tiles that each measured 1 foot by 1 foot on a basketball court, how many tiles would you need? In this section, we will study the geometric concepts of perimeter and area that are used to answer these and other questions.

Why **This is Important** The concepts of area and perimeter are involved in many real-life applications of geometry. These include calculating the cost of flooring for your home, calculating the amount of fencing needed for your yard, and determining the best value when purchasing pizza!

Perimeter and Area

The *perimeter*, P, of a two-dimensional figure is the sum of the lengths of the sides of the figure. In Figs. 9.25 and 9.26, the sums of the lengths of the red line segments are the perimeters. Perimeters are measured in the same units as the sides. For example, if the sides of a figure are measured in feet, the perimeter will be measured in feet.

The *area*, A, is the region within the boundaries of the figure. The blue color in Figs. 9.25 and 9.26 indicates the areas of the figures. Area is measured in square units. For example, if the sides of a figure are measured in inches, the area of the

Figure 9.25   **Figure 9.26**

figure will be measured in square inches (in.^{2}). (See Table 8.7 on page 465 for common units of area in the U.S. customary and metric systems.)

Consider the rectangle in Fig. 9.26 on page 500. Two sides of the rectangle have length l, and two sides of the rectangle have width w. Thus, if we add the lengths of the four sides to get the perimeter, we find $P = l + w + l + w = 2l + 2w$.

Perimeter of a Rectangle

$$P = 2l + 2w$$

Figure 9.27

Consider a rectangle of length 5 units and width 3 units (Fig. 9.27). Counting the number of 1-unit by 1-unit squares within the figure, we obtain the area of the rectangle, 15 square units. The area can also be obtained by multiplying the number of units of length by the number of units of width, or 5 units $\times$ 3 units $= 15$ square units. We can find the area of a rectangle by the formula area $=$ length $\times$ width.

Area of a Rectangle

$$A = l \times w$$

Using the formula for the area of a rectangle, we can determine the formulas for the areas of other figures.

A square (Fig. 9.28) is a rectangle that contains four equal sides. Therefore, the length equals the width. If we call both the length and the width of the square s, then

$$A = l \times w, \quad \text{so} \quad A = s \times s = s^2$$

Figure 9.28

Area of a Square

$$A = s^2$$

A parallelogram with height h and base b is shown in Fig. 9.29(a).

(a)   (b)

Figure 9.29

If we were to cut off the red portion of the parallelogram on the left, Fig. 9.29(a), and attach it to the right side of the figure, the resulting figure would be a rectangle, Fig. 9.29(b). Since the area of the rectangle is $b \times h$, the area of the parallelogram is also $b \times h$.

(a)

(b)

Figure 9.30

Area of a Parallelogram

$$A = b \times h$$

Consider the triangle with height, h, and base, b, shown in Fig. 9.30(a). Using this triangle and a second identical triangle, we can construct a parallelogram, Fig. 9.30(b). The area of the parallelogram is bh. The area of the triangle is one-half that of the parallelogram. Therefore, the area of the triangle is $\frac{1}{2} \times$ base $\times$ height.

Area of a Triangle

$$A = \tfrac{1}{2}bh$$

Now consider the trapezoid shown in Fig. 9.31(a). We can partition the trapezoid into two triangles by drawing diagonal $\overline{DB}$, as in Fig. 9.31(b). One triangle has base $\overline{AB}$ (called b_2) with height $\overline{DE}$, and the other triangle has base $\overline{DC}$ (called b_1) with height $\overline{FB}$. Note that the line used to measure the height of the triangle need not be inside the triangle. Because heights $\overline{DE}$ and $\overline{FB}$ are equal, both triangles have the same height, h. The area of triangles DCB and ADB are $\tfrac{1}{2}b_1 h$ and $\tfrac{1}{2}b_2 h$, respectively. The area of the trapezoid is the sum of the areas of the triangles, $\tfrac{1}{2}b_1 h + \tfrac{1}{2}b_2 h$, which can be written $\tfrac{1}{2}h(b_1 + b_2)$.

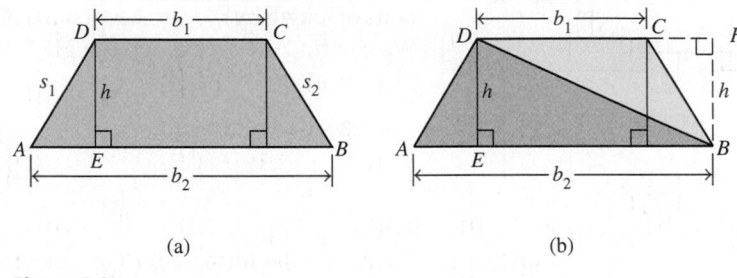

(a)   (b)

Figure 9.31

Area of a Trapezoid

$$A = \tfrac{1}{2}h(b_1 + b_2)$$

Following is a summary of the perimeters and areas of selected figures.

Perimeters and Areas

Triangle	Square	Rectangle
$P = s_1 + s_2 + s_3 \ (s_3 = b)$	$P = 4s$	$P = 2l + 2w$
$A = \tfrac{1}{2}bh$	$A = s^2$	$A = lw$

Parallelogram	Trapezoid
$P = 2b + 2w$	$P = s_1 + s_2 + b_1 + b_2$
$A = bh$	$A = \tfrac{1}{2}h(b_1 + b_2)$

Example 1 *Sodding a Lacrosse Field*

Rob Marshall wishes to replace the grass (sod) on a lacrosse field. One pallet of Bethel Farms sod costs $175 and covers 450 square feet. If the area to be covered is a rectangle with a length of 330 feet and a width of 270 feet, determine

a) the area to be covered with sod.

b) how many pallets of sod Rob needs to purchase.

c) the cost of the sod purchased.

Solution

a) The area to be covered is

$$A = l \cdot w = 330 \cdot 270 = 89{,}100 \text{ ft}^2$$

The area to be covered is in square feet because both the length and the width are measured in feet.

b) To determine the number of pallets of sod Rob needs, divide the area to be covered by the area covered by one pallet of sod.

$$\frac{\text{Area to be covered}}{\text{Area covered by one pallet}} = \frac{89{,}100}{450} = 198$$

Rob needs 198 pallets of sod.

c) The cost of 198 pallets of sod is 198 × $175, or $34,650. ∎

Pythagorean Theorem

We introduced the Pythagorean theorem in Chapter 5. Because this theorem is an important tool for finding the perimeter and area of triangles, we restate it here.

Pythagorean Theorem

The sum of the squares of the lengths of the legs of a right triangle equals the square of the length of the hypotenuse.

$$\text{leg}^2 + \text{leg}^2 = \text{hypotenuse}^2$$

Symbolically, if a and b represent the lengths of the legs and c represents the length of the hypotenuse (the side opposite the right angle), then

$$a^2 + b^2 = c^2$$

Example 2 *Crossing a Moat*

The moat surrounding a castle is 18 ft wide and the wall by the moat of the castle is 24 ft high (see Fig. 9.32). If an invading army wishes to use a ladder to cross the moat and reach the top of the wall, how long must the ladder be?

Figure 9.32

Solution The moat, the castle wall, and the ladder form a right triangle. The moat and the castle wall form the legs of the triangle (sides a and b), and the ladder forms the hypotenuse (side c). By the Pythagorean theorem,

$$c^2 = a^2 + b^2$$
$$c^2 = (18)^2 + (24)^2$$
$$c^2 = 324 + 576$$
$$c^2 = 900$$
$$\sqrt{c^2} = \sqrt{900} \qquad \text{Take the square root of both sides of the equation.}$$
$$c = 30$$

Therefore, the ladder would need to be at least 30 ft long. ∎

Circles

Circumference
$C = 2\pi r$

Radius

Area
$A = \pi r^2$

Diameter

Figure 9.33

A commonly used plane figure that is not a polygon is a *circle*. A *circle* is a set of points equidistant from a fixed point called the center. A *radius*, r, of a circle is a line segment from the center of the circle to any point on the circle (Fig. 9.33). A *diameter*, d, of a circle is a line segment through the center of a circle with both end points on the circle. Note that the diameter of the circle is twice its radius. The *circumference* is the length of the simple closed curve that forms the circle. The formulas for the area and circumference of a circle are given in the box below.

Circumference and Area of a Circle

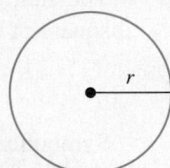

r

$$C = 2\pi r$$
$$A = \pi r^2$$

The symbol pi, π, was introduced in Chapter 5. Recall that π is approximately 3.14. However, when solving problems, you should use the $\boxed{\pi}$ key on your calculator to get a more accurate answer.

Example 3 *Comparing Pizzas*

Victoria Montoya wishes to order a large cheese pizza. She can choose among three pizza parlors in town: Antonio's, Steve's, and Dorsey's. Antonio's large cheese pizza is a round 16-in.-diameter pizza that sells for $15. Steve's large cheese pizza is a round 14-in.-diameter pizza that sells for $12. Dorsey's large cheese pizza is a square 12-in. by 12-in. pizza that sells for $10. All three pizzas have the same thickness. To get the most for her money, from which pizza parlor should Victoria order her pizza?

Solution To determine the best value, we will calculate the cost per square inch of pizza for each of the three pizzas. To do so, we will divide the cost of each pizza by its area. The areas of the two round pizzas can be determined using the formula for the area of a circle, $A = \pi r^2$. Since the radius is half the diameter,

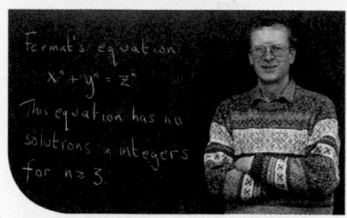
we will use $r = 8$ and $r = 7$ for Antonio's and Steve's large pizzas, respectively, and we will use the $\boxed{\pi}$ key on our calculator. The area for the square pizza can be determined using the formula for the area of a square, $A = s^2$. We will use $s = 12$.

$$\text{Area of Antonio's pizza} = \pi r^2 = \pi(8)^2 = \pi(64) \approx 201.06 \text{ in.}^2$$
$$\text{Area of Steve's pizza} = \pi r^2 = \pi(7)^2 = \pi(49) \approx 153.94 \text{ in.}^2$$
$$\text{Area of Dorsey's pizza} = s^2 = (12)^2 = 144 \text{ in.}^2$$

Now, to find the cost per square inch of pizza, we will divide the cost of the pizza by the area of the pizza.

$$\text{Cost per square inch of Antonio's pizza} \approx \frac{\$15}{201.06 \text{ in.}^2} \approx \$0.0746$$

Thus, Antonio's pizza costs about $0.0746, or about 7.5 cents, per square inch.

$$\text{Cost per square inch of Steve's pizza} \approx \frac{\$12}{153.94 \text{ in.}^2} \approx \$0.0780$$

Thus, Steve's pizza costs about $0.0780, or about 7.8 cents, per square inch.

$$\text{Cost per square inch of Dorsey's pizza} = \frac{\$10}{144 \text{ in.}^2} \approx \$0.0694$$

Thus, Dorsey's pizza costs about $0.0694, or about 6.9 cents, per square inch.

Since the cost per square inch of pizza is the lowest for Dorsey's pizza, Victoria would get the most pizza for her money by ordering her pizza from Dorsey's. ∎

Example 4 Determining the Shaded Area

Determine the shaded area. Use the $\boxed{\pi}$ key on your calculator and round your answer to the nearest hundredth.

2 ft

10 ft

Solution To determine the area of the shaded region, we will first determine the area of the parallelogram and then subtract the area of the circle. Notice that the height of the parallelogram is equal to the diameter of the circle. Since the diameter of a circle is twice its radius, the height of the parallelogram = $2 \cdot 2$ feet, or 4 feet.

$$\text{Area of the parallelogram} = bh = 10 \cdot 4 = 40 \text{ ft}^2$$
$$\text{Area of the circle} = \pi r^2 = \pi(2)^2 = \pi \cdot 4 \approx 12.57 \text{ ft}^2$$
$$\text{Area of the shaded region} = \text{Area of the parallelogram} - \text{Area of the circle}$$
$$\approx 40 - 12.57 \approx 27.43 \text{ ft}^2$$

Thus, the area of the shaded region is approximately 27.43 ft^2. ∎

Example 5 Applying Lawn Fertilizer

Altay Özgener plans to fertilize his lawn. The shapes and dimensions of his lot, house, driveway, pool, and rose garden are shown in Fig. 9.34 on page 506. One bag of fertilizer costs $29.95 and covers 5000 ft^2. Determine how many bags of fertilizer Altay needs and the total cost of the fertilizer.

Profile In Mathematics

Pierre de Fermat

P ierre de Fermat (1601–1665) is considered one of the greatest mathematicians of the seventeenth century. Fermat (pronounced Fair-MAH), however, was a lawyer by trade and considered mathematics a hobby. Although he is mostly known for his famous "last theorem" (see the *Did You Know?* on page 505), Fermat also made many contributions to mathematics through his correspondence with leading mathematicians of Europe. Although Fermat published very little himself, his letters to other mathematicians influenced virtually all branches of mathematical study in his time, including analytic geometry, calculus, probability, and number theory.

Figure 9.34

Solution   The total area of the lot is $150 \cdot 180$, or $27,000 \ \text{ft}^2$. To determine the area to be fertilized, subtract the area of house, driveway, pool, and rose garden from the total area.

$$\text{Area of house} = 60 \cdot 40 = 2400 \ \text{ft}^2$$
$$\text{Area of driveway} = 40 \cdot 16 = 640 \ \text{ft}^2$$
$$\text{Area of pool} = 20 \cdot 30 = 600 \ \text{ft}^2$$

The diameter of the rose garden is 24 ft, so its radius is 12 ft.

$$\text{Area of rose garden} = \pi r^2 = \pi(12)^2 = \pi(144) \approx 452.39 \ \text{ft}^2$$

The total area of the house, driveway, pool, and rose garden is approximately $2400 + 640 + 600 + 452.39$, or $4092.39 \ \text{ft}^2$. The area to be fertilized is $27,000 - 4092.39 \ \text{ft}^2$, or $22,907.61 \ \text{ft}^2$. The number of bags of fertilizer is found by dividing the total area to be fertilized by the number of square feet covered per bag.

The number of bags of fertilizer is $\dfrac{22,907.61}{5000}$, or about 4.58 bags. Therefore, Altay needs five bags. At \$29.95 per bag, the total cost is $5 \times \$29.95$, or \$149.75. ∎

Example 6 *Converting Between Square Feet and Square Inches*

a) Convert $1 \ \text{ft}^2$ to square inches.   b) Convert $37 \ \text{ft}^2$ to square inches.
c) Convert $432 \ \text{in}^2$ to square feet.   d) Convert $2196 \ \text{in}^2$ to square feet.

Solution

a) $1 \ \text{ft} = 12 \ \text{in.}$ Therefore, $1 \ \text{ft}^2 = 12 \ \text{in.} \times 12 \ \text{in.} = 144 \ \text{in}^2$.

b) From part (a), we know that $1 \ \text{ft}^2 = 144 \ \text{in}^2$. Therefore,
$37 \ \text{ft}^2 = 37 \times 144 \ \text{in}^2 = 5328 \ \text{in}^2$.

c) In part (b), we converted from square feet to square inches by *multiplying* the number of square feet by 144. Now, to convert from square inches to square feet we will *divide* the number of square inches by 144. Therefore,
$432 \ \text{in}^2 = \frac{432}{144} \ \text{ft}^2 = 3 \ \text{ft}^2$.

d) As in part (c), we will divide the number of square inches by 144. Therefore,
$2196 \ \text{in}^2 = \frac{2196}{144} \ \text{ft}^2 = 15.25 \ \text{ft}^2$. ∎

Example 7 *Installing Ceramic Tile*

Rebecca Williams wishes to purchase ceramic tile for her family room, which measures 30 ft $\times$ 27 ft. The cost of the tile, including installation, is $72 per square yard.

a) Find the area of Rebecca's family room in square *yards*.

b) Determine Rebecca's cost of the ceramic tile for her family room.

Solution

a) The area of the family room in square feet is $30 \cdot 27 = 810$ ft^2. Since 1 yd = 3 ft, 1 yd^2 = 3 ft $\times$ 3 ft = 9 ft^2. To find the area of the family room in square yards, divide the area in square feet by 9 ft^2.

$$\text{Area in square yards} = \frac{810}{9} = 90$$

Therefore, the area is 90 yd^2.

b) The cost of 90 yd^2 of ceramic tile, including installation, is 90 $\cdot$ $72 = $6480. ∎

When multiplying units of length, be sure that the units are the same. You can multiply feet by feet to get square feet or yards by yards to get square yards. However, you cannot get a valid answer if you multiply numbers expressed in feet by numbers expressed in yards.

SECTION 9.3 *Exercises*

Warm Up Exercises

In Exercises 1–4, fill in the blanks with an appropriate word, phrase, or symbol(s).

1. a) The sum of the lengths of the sides of a two-dimensional figure is called the _____ of the figure. Perimeter

b) The region within the boundaries of a two-dimensional figure is called the _____ of the figure. Area

2. In a right triangle, the side that is opposite the right angle is called the _____. Hypotenuse

3. A set of points equidistant from a fixed point is called a(n) _____. Circle

4. a) A line segment from the center of a circle to any point on the circle is called the _____ of the circle. Radius

b) A line segment through the center of the circle with both endpoints on the circle is called the _____ of the circle. Diameter

c) The length of the simple closed curve that forms a circle is called the _____ of the circle. Circumference

Practice the Skills

In Exercises 5–8, determine the area of the triangle.

5.

12 cm^2
4 cm
6 cm

6.
4.5 ft^2
9 ft
1 ft

7.

5 cm
7 cm
17.5 cm^2

8.
$\sqrt{3}$ m^2
$\sqrt{3}$ m
2 m

In Exercises 9–14, determine (a) the area and (b) the perimeter of the quadrilateral.

9.

5 ft
10 ft
a) 50 ft^2 b) 30 ft

10.

a) 78 in^2 b) 42 in^2

6 in.

8 in.

13 in.

11.

20 cm   27 cm

3 m

a) 6000 cm^2 b) 654 cm

12.

2 yd

6 ft

a) 36 ft^2 b) 24 ft

13.

5 in.

25 in.   2 ft   25 in.

19 in.

a) 288 in^2 b) 74 in.

14.

16 in.

13 in.   12 in.   13 in.

6 in.

a) 132 in^2 b) 48 in.

In Exercises 15–18, determine (a) the area and (b) the circumference of the circle. Use the $\boxed{\pi}$ key on your calculator and round your answer to the nearest hundredth.

15.

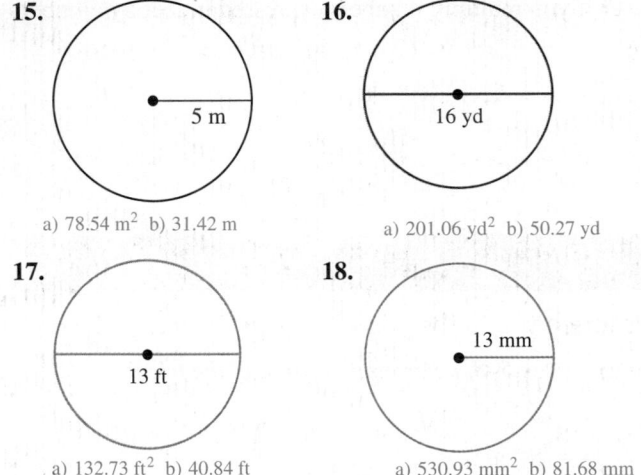

5 m

a) 78.54 m^2 b) 31.42 m

16.

16 yd

a) 201.06 yd^2 b) 50.27 yd

17.

13 ft

a) 132.73 ft^2 b) 40.84 ft

18.

13 mm

a) 530.93 mm^2 b) 81.68 mm

In Exercises 19–22, (a) use the Pythagorean theorem to determine the length of the unknown side of the triangle, (b) determine the perimeter of the triangle, and (c) determine the area of the triangle.

19.

c 15 yd

8 yd

a) 17 yd b) 40 yd c) 60 yd^2

20.

15 in.   12 in.

a

a) 9 in. b) 36 in. c) 54 in^2

21.

13 km

5 km

b

a) 12 km b) 30 km c) 30 km^2

22.

10 cm   24 cm

c

a) 26 cm b) 60 cm c) 120 cm^2

Problem Solving

In Exercises 23–32, determine the shaded area. When appropriate, use the $\boxed{\pi}$ key on your calculator and round your answer to the nearest hundredth.

23.

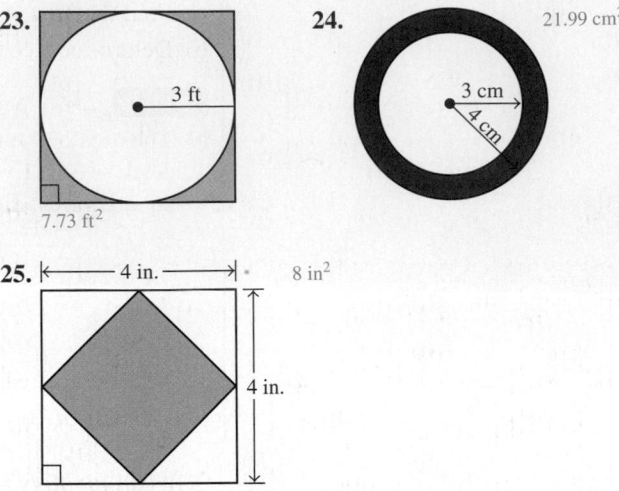

3 ft

7.73 ft^2

24.

21.99 cm^2

3 cm

4 cm

25.

⟵ 4 in. ⟶

4 in.

8 in^2

26.

⟵10 in.→

20 in.

⟵─────30 in.─────⟶

321.46 in^2

27.

9 yd   10 yd   11 yd

⟵────18 yd────⟶

90 yd^2

28.

⟵ 5 in. ⟶

⟵─── 10 in. ───⟶

29.45 in^2

29.

20 in.

4 in.

9 in.

65.73 in^2

30. **31.**

30.54 m²

56.55 mm²

32.

├─────── 24 mm ───────┤
30.90 mm²

In Exercises 33–36, one square yard equals 9 ft². Use this information to convert the following.

33. 72 ft² to square yards
8 yd²

34. 153 ft² to square yards
17 yd²

35. 14.7 yd² to square feet
132.3 ft²

36. 15.2 yd² to square feet
136.8 ft²

In Exercises 37–40, one square meter equals 10,000 cm². Use this information to convert the following.

37. 5 m² to square
centimeters 50,000 cm²

38. 0.25 m² to square
centimeters 2500 cm²

39. 8625 cm² to square
meters 0.8625 m²

40. 608 cm² to square
meters 0.0608 m²

In Exercises 41–46, Nancy Wallin has just purchased a new house that is in need of new flooring. Use the measurements given on the floor plans of Nancy's house to obtain the answer.

Second floor

First floor

41. *Cost of Hardwood Flooring* The cost of Thomasville Walnut hardwood flooring is $9.99 per square foot if Nancy installs the flooring herself or $11.99 per square foot if she has the flooring installed by the flooring company. Determine the cost for hardwood flooring in the living/dining room if

a) Nancy installs it herself. $5494.50

b) Nancy has it installed by the flooring company. $6594.50

42. *Cost of Laminate Flooring* The cost of Prestige August Oak laminate flooring is $2.29 per square foot if Nancy installs the flooring herself or $4.29 per square foot if she has the flooring installed by the flooring company. Determine the cost for the flooring in the living/dining room if

a) Nancy installs it herself. $1259.50

b) Nancy has it installed by the flooring company. $2359.50

43. *Cost of Ceramic Tile* The cost of Mohawk Porcelain ceramic tile is $8.99 per square foot. This price includes the cost of installation. Determine the cost for Nancy to have this ceramic tile installed in the kitchen and in both bathrooms. $3056.60

44. *Cost of Linoleum* The cost of Armstrong Marmorette Parchment linoleum is $2.59 per square foot. This price includes the cost of installation. Determine the cost for Nancy to have this linoleum installed in the kitchen and in both bathrooms. $880.60

45. *Cost of Berber Carpeting* The cost of Shaw Golden Wheat Berber carpeting is $7.99 per square foot. This price includes the cost of installation. Determine the cost for Nancy to have this carpeting installed in all three bedrooms. $3835.20

46. *Cost of Saxony Carpeting* The cost of DuPont Stainmaster Saxony carpeting is $6.99 per square foot. This price includes the cost of installation. Determine the cost for Nancy to have this carpeting installed in all three bedrooms. $3355.20

47. *Cost of a Lawn Service* Clarence and Rose Cohen's home lot is illustrated here. Clarence and Rose wish to hire Picture Perfect Lawn Service to cut their lawn. How much will it cost Clarence and Rose to have their lawn cut if Picture Perfect charges $0.02 per square yard? $234.21

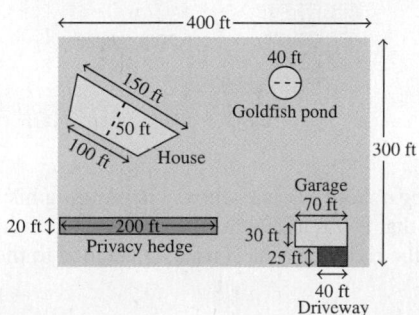

48. *Cost of a Lawn Service* Jim and Wendy Scott's home lot is illustrated here. The Scotts wish to hire a lawn service to cut their lawn. M&M Lawn Service charges $0.02 per square yard of lawn. How much will it cost the Scotts to have their lawn cut? $38.93

49. *Area of a Basketball Court* A National Basketball Association (NBA) basketball court is a rectangle that is 94 ft long and 50 ft wide.

a) If you were to walk around the outside edge of a basketball court, how far would you walk? 288 ft

b) If you had to place floor tiles that each measured 1 foot by 1 foot on a basketball court, how many tiles would you need? 4700 tiles

50. *Quartz Countertops* Larry Shedden wishes to have three Cambria Windsor quartz countertops installed in his new kitchen. The countertops are rectangular and have the following dimensions: $3\frac{1}{2}$ ft × 6 ft, $2\frac{1}{2}$ ft × 8 ft, and 3 ft × $11\frac{1}{2}$ ft. The cost of the countertops is $75 per square foot, which includes the cost of installation.

a) Determine the total area of the three countertops. 75.5 ft^2

b) Determine the total cost to have all three countertops installed. $5662.50

51. *Ladder on a Wall* Lorrie Morgan places a 29-ft ladder against the side of a building with the bottom of the ladder 20 ft away from the building (see figure). How high up on the wall does the ladder reach? 21 ft

52. *Docking a Boat* Brian Murphy is bringing his boat into a dock that is 9 ft above the water level (see figure above and to the right). If a 41-ft rope is attached to the dock on

one side and to the boat on the other side, determine the horizontal distance from the dock to the boat. 40 ft

53. *The Green Monster* In Fenway Park, home of baseball's Boston Red Sox, the left field wall is known as the *Green Monster*. The distance from home plate down the third baseline to the bottom of the wall is 310 feet (see photo). In left field, at the end of the baseline, the Green Monster is perpendicular to the ground and is 37 feet tall. Determine the distance from home plate to the top of the Green Monster along the third baseline. Round your answer to the nearest foot. 312 ft

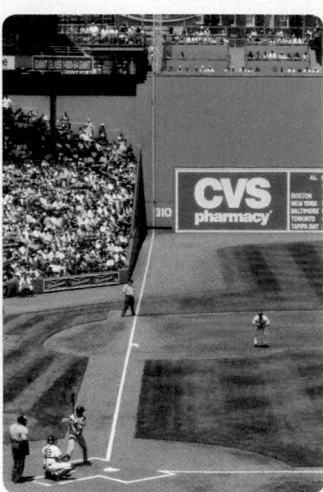

54. *Plasma Television* The screen of a plasma television is in the shape of a rectangle with a diagonal of length 43 in. If the height of the screen is 21 in., determine the width of the screen. ≈ 37.52 in.

Challenge Problems/Group Activities

55. *Doubling the Sides of a Square* In the figure below, an original square with sides of length *s* is shown. Also shown is a larger square with sides double in length, or 2*s*.

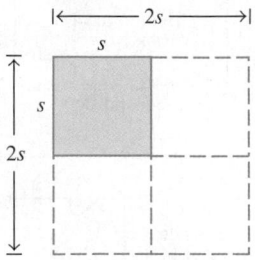

a) Express the area of the original square in terms of *s*.
$A = s^2$

b) Express the area of the larger square in terms of *s*.
$A = 4s^2$

c) How many times larger is the area of the square in part (b) than the area of the square in part (a)? Four times larger

56. *Doubling the Sides of a Parallelogram*   In the figure below, an original parallelogram with base b and height h is shown. Also shown is a larger parallelogram with base and height double in length, or $2b$ and $2h$, respectively.

a) Express the area of the original parallelogram in terms of b and h. $A = bh$

b) Express the area of the larger parallelogram in terms of b and h. $A = 4bh$

c) How many times larger is the area of the parallelogram in part (b) than the area of the parallelogram in part (a)?   Four times larger

57. *Heron's Formula*   A second formula for determining the area of a triangle (called Heron's formula) is

$$A = \sqrt{s(s - a)(s - b)(s - c)}$$

where $s = \frac{1}{2}(a + b + c)$ and a, b, and c are the lengths of the sides of the triangle. Use Heron's formula to determine the area of right triangle ABC and check your answer using the formula $A = \frac{1}{2}ab$.   24 cm²

58. *Expansion of $(a + b)^2$*   In the figure, one side of the largest square has length $a + b$. Therefore, the area of the largest square is $(a + b)^2$. Answer the following questions to find a formula for the expansion of $(a + b)^2$.

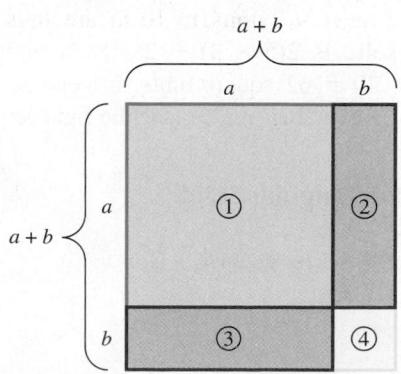

a) What is the area of the square marked ①? a^2

b) What is the area of the rectangle marked ②? ab

c) What is the area of the rectangle marked ③? ab

d) What is the area of the square marked ④? b^2

e) Add the four areas found in parts (a) through (d) to write a formula for the expansion of $(a + b)^2$. $(a + b)^2 = a^2 + 2ab + b^2$

Recreational Mathematics

59. *Sports Areas*   Use the Internet to research the official dimensions of the playing surface of your favorite sport and determine the area of the playing surface. Choices may include a basketball court, volleyball court, tennis court, racquetball court, hockey rink, football field, soccer field, lacrosse field, and a baseball diamond.   Answers will vary.

60. *Scarecrow's Error*   In the movie *The Wizard of Oz*, once the scarecrow gets his diploma he states the following: "In an isosceles triangle, the sum of the square roots of the two equal sides is equal to the square root of the third side." Discuss why this statement is incorrect.   Answers will vary.

Internet/Research Activities

For Exercises 61–63, references include the Internet, history of mathematics textbooks, and encyclopedias.

61. Research the proof of the Pythagorean theorem provided by President James Garfield. Write a brief paper and make a poster of this proof and the associated diagrams.

62. The early Babylonians and Egyptians did not know about π and had to devise techniques to approximate the area of a circle. Do research and write a paper on the techniques these societies used to approximate the area of a circle.

63. Write a paper on the contributions of Heron of Alexandria to geometry.

SECTION 9.4   Volume and Surface Area

On the label of a can of Color Place paint is the following sentence: "One gallon will cover about 400 sq. ft." This sentence refers to the two main geometric topics that we will cover in this section. *One gallon* refers to volume of the paint in the can, and *400 sq. ft* refers to the surface area that the paint will cover.

Why **This is Important** The concepts of volume and surface area have many real-life applications. These include calculating the volume of a freezer, the displacement of an engine, and the amount of paint needed to paint a room.

▲ *The amount of paint in a can refers to volume, and the amount of wall space that the paint covers refers to surface area.*

When discussing a one-dimensional figure such as a line, we can find its length. When discussing a two-dimensional figure such as a rectangle, we can find its area and its perimeter. When discussing a three-dimensional figure such as a cube, we can find its volume and its surface area. *Volume* is a measure of the capacity of a three-dimensional figure. *Surface area* is the sum of the areas of the surfaces of a three-dimensional figure. Volume refers to the amount of material that you can put *inside* a three-dimensional figure, and surface area refers to the total area that is on the *outside* surface of the figure.

Solid geometry is the study of three-dimensional solid figures, also called *space figures*. Volumes of three-dimensional figures are measured in cubic units such as cubic feet or cubic meters. Surface areas of three-dimensional figures are measured in square units such as square feet or square meters.

Rectangular Solids, Cylinders, Cones, and Spheres

Rectangular Solid

If the length of a *rectangular solid* is 5 units, the width is 2 units, and the height is 3 units, the total number of cubes is 30 (Fig. 9.35). Thus, the volume is 30 cubic units. The volume of a rectangular solid can also be found by multiplying its length times width times height; in this case, 5 units $\times$ 2 units $\times$ 3 units = 30 cubic units. In general, the volume of any rectangular solid is $V = l \times w \times h$.

The surface area of the rectangular solid in Fig. 9.35 is the sum of the area of the surfaces of the rectangular solid. Notice that each surface of the rectangular solid is a rectangle. The left and right side of the rectangular solid each has an area of 5 units $\times$ 3 units, or 15 square units. The front and back sides of the rectangular solid each has an area of 2 units $\times$ 3 units, or 6 square units. The top and bottom sides of the rectangular solid each has an area of 5 units $\times$ 2 units, or 10 square units. Therefore, the surface area of the rectangular solid is $2(5 \times 3) + 2(2 \times 3) + 2(5 \times 2) = 2(15) + 2(6) + 2(10) = 30 + 12 + 20 = 62$ square units. In general, the surface area of any rectangular solid is $SA = 2lw + 2wh + 2lh$ (see the figure to the left).

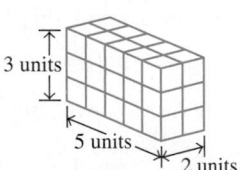

Figure 9.35

Volume and Surface Area of a Rectangular Solid

$$V = lwh \qquad SA = 2lw + 2wh + 2lh$$

Cube

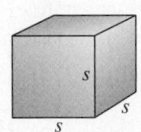

A *cube* is a rectangular solid with the same length, width, and height. If we call the length of the side of the cube s and use the volume and surface area formulas for a rectangular solid, substituting s in for l, w, and h, we obtain $V = s \cdot s \cdot s = s^3$ and $SA = 2 \cdot s \cdot s + 2 \cdot s \cdot s + 2 \cdot s \cdot s = 2s^2 + 2s^2 + 2s^2 = 6s^2$ (see the figure to the left).

Volume and Surface Area of a Cube

$$V = s^3 \qquad SA = 6s^2$$

Cylinder

Now consider the right circular cylinder shown in Fig. 9.36(a). When we use the term *cylinder* in this book, we mean a right circular cylinder. The volume of the cylinder is found by multiplying the area of the circular base, πr^2, by the height, h, to get $V = \pi r^2 h$.

The surface area of the cylinder is the sum of the area of the top, the area of the bottom, and the area of the side of the cylinder. Both the top and bottom of the cylinder are circles with an area of πr^2. To determine the area of the side of the cylinder, examine Fig. 9.36(b) and (c).

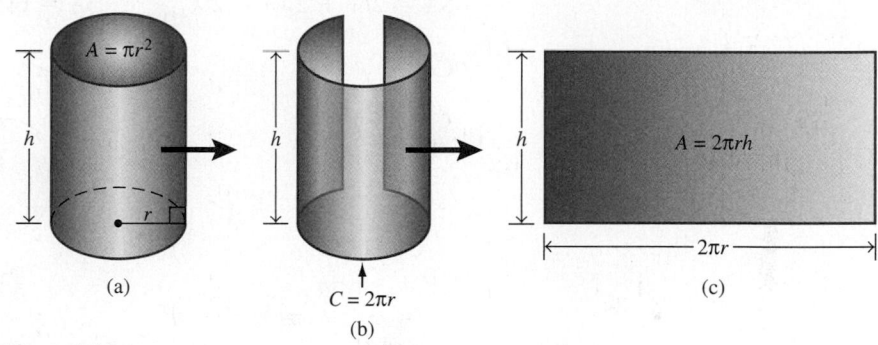

(a)   (b)   (c)

Figure 9.36

Notice how when flattened, the side of the cylinder is a rectangle whose length is the circumference of the base of the cylinder and whose width is the height of the cylinder. Thus, the side of the cylinder has an area of $2\pi r \cdot h$, or $2\pi rh$. Therefore, the surface area of the cylinder is $\pi r^2 + \pi r^2 + 2\pi rh$, or $SA = 2\pi rh + 2\pi r^2$.

Volume and Surface Area of a Cylinder

$$V = \pi r^2 h \qquad SA = 2\pi rh + 2\pi r^2$$

Figure 9.37

Now consider the right circular cone illustrated in Fig. 9.37. When we use the term *cone* in this book, we mean a right circular cone. The volume of a cone is less than the volume of a cylinder that has the same base and the same height. In fact, the volume of the cone is one-third the volume of the cylinder. The formula for the surface area of a cone is the sum of the area of the circular base of the cone, πr^2, and the area of the side of the cone, $\pi r\sqrt{r^2 + h^2}$, or $SA = \pi r^2 + \pi r\sqrt{r^2 + h^2}$. The derivation of the area of the side of the cone is beyond the scope of this book.

Volume and Surface Area of a Cone

$$V = \tfrac{1}{3}\pi r^2 h \qquad SA = \pi r^2 + \pi r\sqrt{r^2 + h^2}$$

Sphere

Baseballs, tennis balls, and so on have the shape of a *sphere*. The formulas for the volume and surface area of a sphere are as follows. The derivation of the volume and surface area of a sphere are beyond the scope of this book (see the figure to the left).

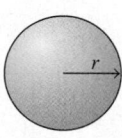

Volume and Surface Area of a Sphere

$$V = \tfrac{4}{3}\pi r^3 \qquad SA = 4\pi r^2$$

Following is a summary of the formulas for the volumes and surface areas of the three-dimensional figures we have discussed thus far.

Volumes and Surface Areas

Rectangular Solid   **Cube**   **Cylinder**

$V = lwh$ $V = s^3$ $V = \pi r^2 h$

$SA = 2lw + 2wh + 2lh$ $SA = 6s^2$ $SA = 2\pi rh + 2\pi r^2$

Cone   **Sphere**

 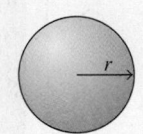

$V = \frac{1}{3}\pi r^2 h$ $V = \frac{4}{3}\pi r^3$

$SA = \pi r^2 + \pi r\sqrt{r^2 + h^2}$ $SA = 4\pi r^2$

Example 1   *Volume and Surface Area*

Determine the volume and surface area of each of the following three-dimensional figures. When appropriate, use the $\boxed{\pi}$ key on your calculator and round your answer to the nearest hundredths.

(a)   (b)

(c)   (d)

Solution

a) $V = lwh = 11 \cdot 3 \cdot 6 = 198 \text{ ft}^3$

     $SA = 2lw + 2wh + 2lh = 2 \cdot 11 \cdot 3 + 2 \cdot 3 \cdot 6 + 2 \cdot 11 \cdot 6$

        $= 66 + 36 + 132 = 234 \text{ ft}^2$

b) $V = \pi r^2 h = \pi \cdot 4^2 \cdot 8 = 128\pi \approx 402.12 \text{ in}^3$

     $SA = 2\pi rh + 2\pi r^2 = 2\pi \cdot 4 \cdot 8 + 2\pi \cdot 4^2$

        $= 64\pi + 32\pi = 96\pi \approx 301.59 \text{ in}^2$

c) $V = \frac{1}{3}\pi r^2 h = \frac{1}{3}\pi \cdot 3^2 \cdot 8 = \frac{1}{3}\pi \cdot 9 \cdot 8 = 24\pi \approx 75.40 \text{ m}^3$

$SA = \pi r^2 + \pi r \sqrt{r^2 + h^2} = \pi \cdot 3^2 + \pi \cdot 3 \cdot \sqrt{3^2 + 8^2}$
$= 9 \cdot \pi + 3 \cdot \pi \cdot \sqrt{73} \approx 108.80 \text{ m}^2$

d) $V = \frac{4}{3}\pi r^3 = \frac{4}{3} \cdot \pi \cdot 9^3 = \frac{4}{3} \cdot \pi \cdot 729 = 972\pi \approx 3053.63 \text{ cm}^3$

$SA = 4\pi r^2 = 4 \cdot \pi \cdot 9^2 = 4 \cdot \pi \cdot 81 = 324\pi \approx 1017.88 \text{ cm}^2$ ∎

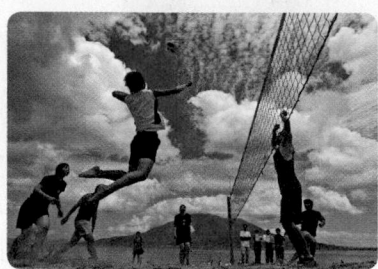

Example 2 · *Replacing a Sand Volleyball Court*

Robin Ayers is the manager at the Colony Apartments and needs to replace the sand in the rectangular sand volleyball court. The court is 30 ft wide by 60 ft long, and the sand has a uniform depth of 18 in. (see figure below). Sand sells for $27 per cubic yard.

18 in.

60 ft

30 ft

a) How many cubic yards of sand does Robin need?

b) How much will the sand cost?

Solution

a) Since we are asked to find the volume in cubic yards, we will convert each measurement to yards. There are 3 ft in a yard. Thus, 30 ft equals $\frac{30}{3}$, or 10 yd, and 60 ft equals $\frac{60}{3}$, or 20 yd. There are 36 in. in a yard, so 18 in. equals $\frac{18}{36}$, or $\frac{1}{2}$ yd. The amount of sand needed is determined using the formula for the volume of a rectangular solid, $V = l \cdot w \cdot h$. In this case, the height of the rectangular solid can be considered the depth of the sand.

$$V = l \cdot w \cdot h = 10 \cdot 20 \cdot \tfrac{1}{2} = 100 \text{ yd}^3$$

Note that since the measurements for length, width, and height are each in terms of yards, the answer is in terms of cubic yards.

b) One cubic yard of sand costs $27, so 100 yd³ will cost 100 × $27, or $2700. ∎

Example 3 · *Homecoming Float*

The basketball team at Southwestern High School is building a float for the homecoming parade. On the float is a large papier-mâché basketball that has a radius of 4.5 ft. Team members need to know the surface area of the basketball so that they can determine how much paint they will need to buy to paint the basketball.

a) Determine the surface area of the basketball.

b) If 1 quart of paint covers approximately 100 sq. ft, how many quarts of paint will team members need to buy?

Solution

a) The basketball has the shape of a sphere. We will use the formula for the surface area of a sphere: $SA = 4\pi r^2 = 4 \cdot \pi \cdot (4.5)^2 = 81\pi \approx 254.47$ sq. ft.

b) Since each quart of paint will cover about 100 sq. ft, they will need about $\frac{254.47}{100} = 2.5447$ quarts. Since you cannot buy a portion of a quart of paint, the team will need to buy 3 quarts of paint to paint the basketball. ∎

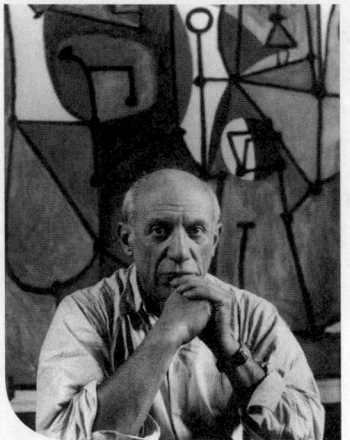
Example 4 *Silage Storage*

Gordon Langeneger has three silos on his farm. The silos are each in the shape of a right circular cylinder (see Fig. 9.38). One silo has a 12-ft diameter and is 40 ft tall. The second silo has a 14-ft diameter and is 50 ft tall. The third silo has an 18-ft diameter and is 60 ft tall.

Figure 9.38

a) What is the total capacity of the three silos in cubic feet?

b) If Gordon fills all three of his silos and then feeds his cattle 150 ft^3 of silage per day, in how many days will all three silos be empty?

Solution

a) The capacity of each silo can be determined using the formula for the volume of a right circular cylinder, $V = \pi r^2 h$. Since the radius is half the diameter, the radii for the three silos are 6 ft, 7 ft, and 9 ft, respectively. Now let's determine the volumes.

$$\text{Volume of the first silo} = \pi r^2 h = \pi \cdot 6^2 \cdot 40$$
$$= \pi \cdot 36 \cdot 40 = 1440\pi \approx 4523.89 \text{ ft}^3$$

$$\text{Volume of the second silo} = \pi r^2 h = \pi \cdot 7^2 \cdot 50$$
$$= \pi \cdot 49 \cdot 50 = 2450\pi \approx 7696.90 \text{ ft}^3$$

$$\text{Volume of the third silo} = \pi r^2 h = \pi \cdot 9^2 \cdot 60$$
$$= \pi \cdot 81 \cdot 60 = 4860\pi \approx 15{,}268.14 \text{ ft}^3$$

Therefore, the total capacity of all three silos is about

$$4523.89 + 7696.90 + 15{,}268.14 \approx 27{,}488.93 \text{ ft}^3$$

b) To find how long it takes to empty all three silos, we will divide the total capacity by 150 ft^3, the amount fed to Gordon's cattle every day.

$$\frac{27{,}488.93}{150} \approx 183.26$$

Thus, the silos will be empty in about 183 days.   ∎

Polyhedra, Prisms, and Pyramids

A *polyhedron* (plural, *polyhedra*) is a closed surface formed by the union of polygonal regions. Figure 9.39 on page 517 illustrates some polyhedra.

Each polygonal region is called a *face* of the polyhedron. The line segment formed by the intersection of two faces is called an *edge*. The point at which two or more edges intersect is called a *vertex*. In Fig. 9.39(a), there are 6 faces, 12 edges, and 8 vertices.

Polyhedra

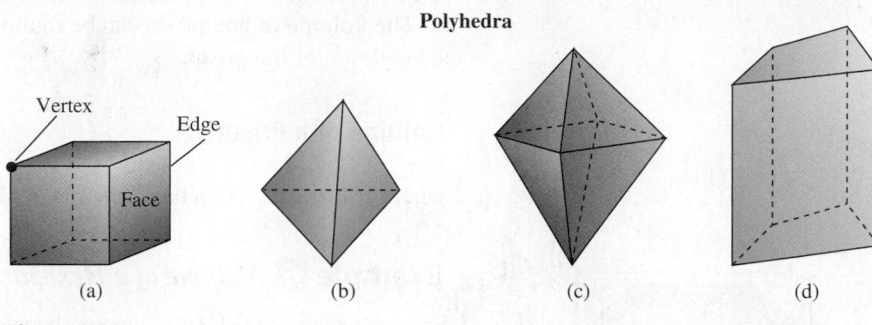

Figure 9.39

Note that:

Number of vertices − number of edges + number of faces = 2
$$8 \quad - \quad 12 \quad + \quad 6 \quad = 2$$

This formula, credited to Leonhard Euler, is true for any polyhedron.

Euler's Polyhedron Formula

Number of vertices − number of edges + number of faces = 2

We suggest that you verify that this formula holds for Fig. 9.39(b), (c), and (d).

Example 5 *Using Euler's Polyhedron Formula*

A certain polyhedron has 20 vertices and 12 faces. Determine the number of edges on the polyhedron.

Solution Since we are seeking the number of edges, we will let x represent the number of edges on the polyhedron. Next, we will use Euler's polyhedron formula to set up an equation:

Number of vertices − number of edges + number of faces = 2
$$20 \quad - \quad x \quad + \quad 12 \quad = 2$$
$$32 - x = 2$$
$$-x = -30$$
$$x = 30$$

Therefore, the polyhedron has 30 edges. ■

A *platonic solid*, also known as a *regular polyhedron*, is a polyhedron whose faces are all regular polygons of the same size and shape. There are exactly five platonic solids. All five platonic solids are illustrated in the *Did You Know?* at left.

A *prism* is a special type of polyhedron whose bases are congruent polygons and whose sides are parallelograms. These parallelogram regions are called the *lateral faces* of the prism. If all the lateral faces are rectangles, the prism is said to be a *right prism*. The prisms illustrated in Fig. 9.40 are all right prisms. When we use the word *prism* in this book, we are referring to a right prism.

Prisms

Figure 9.40

The volume of any prism can be found by multiplying the area of the base, B, by the height, h, of the prism.

> ## Volume of a Prism
> $$V = Bh$$
> where B is the area of a base and h is the height.

Example 6 Volume of a Hexagonal Prism Fish Tank

Frank Nicolzaao's fish tank is in the shape of a hexagonal prism as shown in Fig. 9.41. Use the dimensions shown in the figure and the fact that 1 gal $= 231$ in^3 to

a) determine the volume of the fish tank in cubic inches.

b) determine the volume of the fish tank in gallons (round your answer to the nearest gallon).

Solution

a) First we will need to calculate the area of the hexagonal base of the fish tank. Notice from Fig. 9.41 that by drawing a diagonal as indicated, the base can be divided into two identical trapezoids. To find the area of the hexagonal base, we will calculate the area of one of these trapezoids and then multiply by 2.

$$\text{Area of one trapezoid} = \tfrac{1}{2}h(b_1 + b_2)$$
$$= \tfrac{1}{2}(8)(16 + 8) = 96 \text{ in}^2$$
$$\text{Area of the hexagonal base} = 2(96) = 192 \text{ in}^2$$

Now to determine the volume of the fish tank, we will use the formula for the volume of a prism, $V = Bh$. We already determined that the area of the base, B, is 192 in.^{2}.

$$V = B \cdot h = 192 \cdot 24 = 4608 \text{ in}^3$$

In the above calculation, the area of the base, B, was measured in square inches and the height was measured in inches. The product of square inches and inches is cubic inches, or in.^{3}.

b) To determine the volume of the fish tank in gallons, we will divide the volume of the fish tank in cubic inches by 231.

$$V = \frac{4608}{231} \approx 19.95 \text{ gal}$$

Thus, the volume of the fish tank is approximately 20 gal. ∎

Figure 9.41

Example 7 Volumes Involving Prisms

Determine the volume of the remaining solid after the cylinder, triangular prism, and square prism have been cut from the solid (Fig. 9.42).

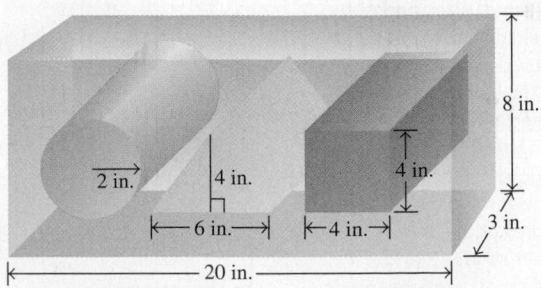

Figure 9.42

Solution To determine the volume of the remaining solid, first determine the volume of the rectangular solid. Then subtract the volume of the two prisms and the cylinder that were cut out.

$$\text{Volume of rectangular solid} = l \cdot w \cdot h$$
$$= 20 \cdot 3 \cdot 8 = 480 \text{ in}^3$$
$$\text{Volume of circular cylinder} = \pi r^2 h$$
$$= \pi (2^2)(3)$$
$$= \pi(4)(3) = 12\pi \approx 37.70 \text{ in}^3$$
$$\text{Volume of triangular prism} = \text{area of the base} \cdot \text{height}$$
$$= \tfrac{1}{2}(6)(4)(3) = 36 \text{ in}^3$$
$$\text{Volume of square prism} = s^2 \cdot h$$
$$= 4^2 \cdot 3 = 48 \text{ in}^3$$
$$\text{Volume of solid} \approx 480 - 37.70 - 36 - 48$$
$$\approx 358.30 \text{ in}^3 \qquad \blacksquare$$

Another special category of polyhedra is the *pyramid*. Unlike prisms, pyramids have only one base. The figures illustrated in Fig. 9.43 are pyramids. Note that all but one face of a pyramid intersect at a common vertex.

Pyramids

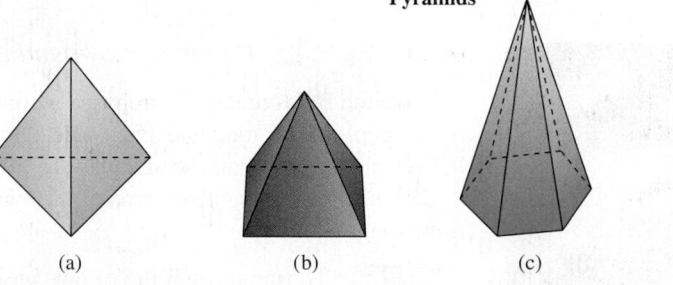

(a) (b) (c) (d)

Figure 9.43

If a pyramid is drawn inside a prism, as shown in Fig. 9.44, the volume of the pyramid is less than that of the prism. In fact, the volume of the pyramid is one-third the volume of the prism.

Figure 9.44

Volume of a Pyramid

$$V = \tfrac{1}{3}Bh$$

where B is the area of the base and h is the height.

Example 8 *Volume of a Pyramid*

Determine the volume of the pyramid shown in Fig. 9.45.

Solution First find the area of the base of the pyramid. Since the base of the pyramid is a square,

$$\text{Area of base} = s^2 = 2^2 = 4 \text{ m}^2$$

Now use this information to find the volume of the pyramid.

$$V = \tfrac{1}{3} \cdot B \cdot h$$
$$= \tfrac{1}{3} \cdot 4 \cdot 3$$
$$= 4 \text{ m}^3$$

Figure 9.45

Thus, the volume of the pyramid is 4 m^3. $\qquad \blacksquare$

Cubic Unit Conversions

In certain situations, converting volume from one cubic unit to a different cubic unit might be necessary. For example, when purchasing topsoil you might have to change the amount of topsoil from cubic feet to cubic yards prior to placing your order. Example 9 shows how that may be done.

Figure 9.46

Example 9 *Cubic Yards and Cubic Feet*

a) Convert 1 yd^3 to cubic feet. (See Fig. 9.46.)

b) Convert 8.9 yd^3 to cubic feet.

c) Convert 749.25 ft^3 to cubic yards.

Solution

a) We know that 1 yd = 3 ft. Thus, 1 yd^3 = 3 ft × 3 ft × 3 ft = 27 ft^3.

b) In part (a), we learned that 1 yd^3 = 27 ft^3. Thus, 8.9 yd^3 = 8.9 × 27 = 240.3 ft^3.

c) In part (b), we converted from cubic yards to cubic feet by *multiplying* the number of cubic yards by 27. Now, to convert from cubic feet to cubic yards we will *divide* the number of cubic feet by 27. Therefore, 749.25 ft^3 = $\frac{749.25}{27}$ yd^3 = 27.75 yd^3. ■

Example 10 *Filling in a Swimming Pool*

Madeline Bates recently purchased a home with a rectangular swimming pool. The pool is 30 ft long and 15 ft wide, and it has a uniform depth of 4.5 ft. Madeline lives in a cold climate, so she plans to fill the pool in with dirt to make a flower garden. How many cubic yards of dirt will Madeline have to purchase to fill in the swimming pool?

Solution To find the amount of dirt, we will use the formula for the volume of a rectangular solid:

$$V = lwh$$
$$= (30)(15)(4.5)$$
$$= 2025 \text{ ft}^3$$

Now we must convert this volume from cubic feet to cubic yards. In Example 9, we learned that 1 yd^3 = 27 ft^3. Therefore, 2025 ft^3 = $\frac{2025}{27}$ = 75 yd^3. Thus, Madeline needs to purchase 75 yd^3 of dirt to fill in her swimming pool. ■

SECTION 9.4 *Exercises*

Warm Up Exercises

In Exercises 1–6, fill in the blanks with an appropriate word, phrase, or symbol(s).

1. A measure of the capacity of a three-dimensional figure is called the figure's _____. Volume

2. The sum of the areas of the surfaces of a three-dimensional figure is called the figure's _____ area. Surface

3. A regular polyhedron, whose faces are all regular polygons of the same size and shape, is also called a _____ solid. Platonic

4. A polyhedron whose bases are congruent polygons and whose sides are parallelograms is called a _____. Prism

5. A prism whose sides are rectangles is called a _____ prism. Right

6. Euler's polyhedron formula states that, for any polyhedron, the number of vertices minus the number of edges plus the number of faces equals_____. 2

Practice the Skills

In Exercises 7–16, determine (a) the volume and (b) the surface area of the three-dimensional figure. When appropriate, use the $\boxed{\pi}$ key on your calculator and round your answer to the nearest hundredth.

7.

a) 64 ft³ b) 112 ft²

8. **9.**

2 yd

2 yd

2 yd

a) 8 yd³ b) 24 yd²

25 mm

6 mm

8 mm

a) 1200 mm³ b) 796 mm²

10. **11.**

a) 150.80 in³
b) 175.93 in²

13 ft

13 ft

13 ft

a) 2197 ft³ b) 1014 ft²

12 in.

2 in.

12. **13.**

24 in.

6 in.

a) 2714.34 in³ b) 1130.97 in²

3 cm

14 cm

a) 131.95 cm³ b) 163.22 cm²

14. **15.**

24 ft

10 ft

9 cm

a) 628.32 ft³ b) 463.63 ft²   a) 381.70 cm³ b) 254.47 cm²

16.

a) 1436.76 mi³ b) 615.75 mi²

|← 7 mi →|

In Exercises 17–20, determine the volume of the three-dimensional figure. When appropriate, round your answer to the nearest hundredth.

17.

750 m³

10 m

15 m

10 m

18. **19.**

8 in.

10 in.

12 in.

24 in.

8 in.

10 in.

12 in.

2400 in³

15 cm

12 cm

12 cm

720 cm³

20.

292.5 ft³

13 ft

15 ft

9 ft

Problem Solving

In Exercises 21–28, determine the volume of the shaded region. When appropriate, use the $\boxed{\pi}$ key on your calculator and round your answer to the nearest hundredth.

21.

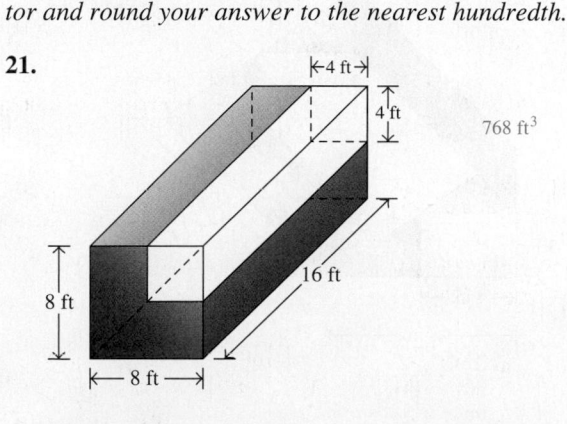

|← 4 ft →|

4 ft

768 ft³

16 ft

8 ft

|← 8 ft →|

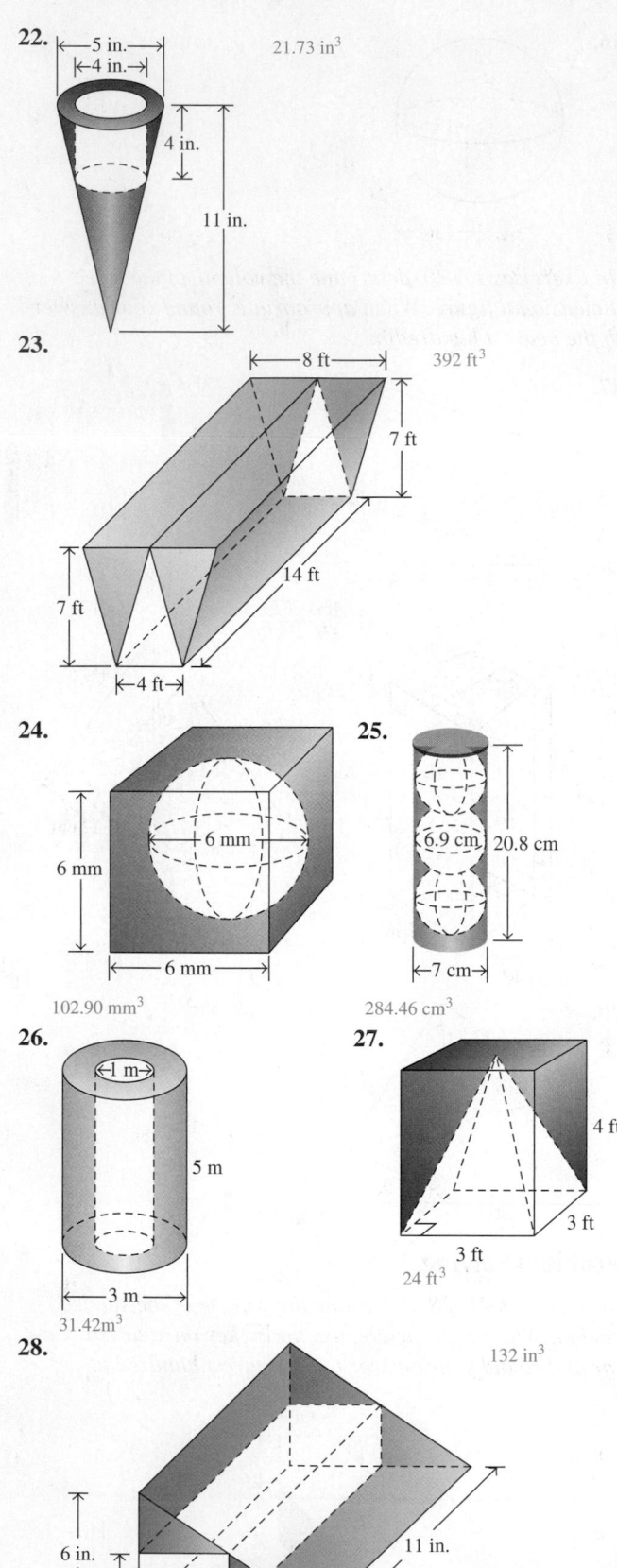

22. 21.73 in³

23. 392 ft³

24. 102.90 mm³

25. 284.46 cm³

26. 31.42m³

27. 24 ft³

28. 132 in³

In Exercises 29–32, use the fact that 1 yd³ equals 27 ft³ to make the conversion.

29. 3 yd³ to cubic feet
81 ft³

30. 7.25 yd³ to cubic feet
195.75 ft³

31. 153 ft³ to cubic yards
≈5.67 yd³

32. 2457 ft³ to cubic yards
91 yd³

In Exercises 33–36, use the fact that 1 m³ equals 1,000,000 cm³ to make the conversion.

33. 0.56 m³ to cubic centimeters 560,000 cm³

34. 17.6 m³ to cubic centimeters 17,600,000 cm³

35. 7,500,000 cm³ to cubic meters 7.5 m³

36. 7,300,000 cm³ to cubic meters 7.3 m³

37. *Playground Mulch* Bob Malena is building a backyard playground for his grandchildren and wishes to put down rubber mulch to provide safety from falls. Bob wishes to put the mulch in a pit in the shape of a rectangular solid 20 ft long, 15 ft wide, and 9 in deep.

a) Determine the volume, in cubic feet, of mulch Bob will need. 225 ft³

b) If mulch costs $11 per cubic foot, what will the cost of the mulch be? $2475

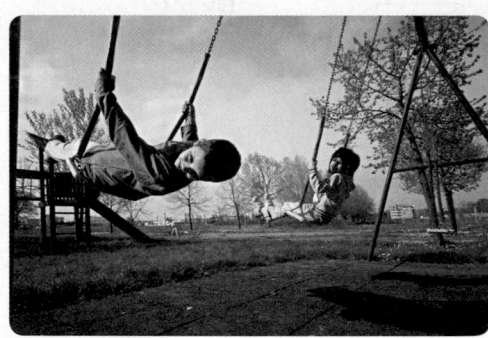

38. *Volume of a Freezer* The dimensions of the interior of an upright freezer are height 46 in., width 25 in., and depth 25 in. Determine the volume of the freezer

a) in cubic inches.
28,750 in.³

b) in cubic feet. ≈16.64 ft³

39. *CD Case* A compact disc case is a rectangular solid that is 142 mm long, 125 mm wide, and 10 mm high. Determine its surface area. 40,840 mm²

40. *Globe Surface Area* The Everest model globe has a diameter of 20 in. Determine the surface area of this globe. Round your answer to the nearest hundredth. ≈1256.64 in²

41. *Volume of a Bread Pan* A bread pan is 12 in. × 4 in. × 3 in. How many quarts does it hold, if 1 in³ ≈ 0.01736 qt? ≈2.50 qt

42. *Ice-Cream Comparison* The Louisburg Creamery packages its homemade ice cream in tubs and in boxes. The tubs are in the shape of a right cylinder with a radius of 3 in. and height of 5 in. The boxes are in the shape of a cube with each side measuring 5 in. Determine the volume of each container. Tubs ≈ 141.37 in³; boxes = 125 in³

43. *A Fish Tank*

a) How many cubic centimeters of water will a rectangular fish tank hold if the tank is 80 cm long, 50 cm wide, and 30 cm high? 120,000 cm³

b) If 1 cm³ holds 1 mℓ of liquid, how many milliliters will the tank hold? 120,000 mℓ

c) If 1 ℓ = 1000 mℓ, how many liters will the tank hold? 120 ℓ

44. *The Pyramid of Cheops* The Pyramid of Cheops in Egypt has a square base measuring 720 ft on a side. Its height is 480 ft. What is its volume? 82,944,000 ft³

45. *Engine Capacity* The engine in a 1957 Chevrolet Corvette has eight cylinders. Each cylinder is a right cylinder with a bore (diameter) of 3.875 in. and a stroke (height) of 3 in. Determine the total displacement (volume) of this engine. ≈283.04 in³

46. *Rose Garden Topsoil* Marisa Raffaele wishes to plant a rose garden in her backyard. The rose garden will be in the shape of a 9 ft by 18 ft rectangle. Marisa wishes to add a 4-in. layer of organic topsoil on top of the rectangular area. The topsoil sells for $42 per cubic yard. Determine

a) how many cubic yards of topsoil Marisa will need. 2 yd³

b) how much the topsoil will cost. $84

47. *Pool Toys* A Wacky Noodle Pool Toy, frequently referred to as a "noodle," is a cylindrical flotation device made from cell foam (see photo). One style of noodle is a cylinder that has a diameter of 2.5 in. and a length of 5.5 ft. Determine the volume of this style of noodle in

a) cubic inches. ≈323.98 in³   **b)** cubic feet. ≈0.19 ft³

48. *Comparing Cake Pans* When baking a cake, you can choose between a round pan with a 9-in. diameter and a 7 in. × 9 in. rectangular pan.

a) Determine the area of the base of each pan. Round pan base ≈63.62 in²; rectangular pan base = 63 in²

b) If both pans are 2 in. deep, determine the volume of each pan. Round pan volume ≈ 127.24 in³; rectangular pan volume = 126 in³

c) Which pan has the larger volume? Round pan

49. *Cake Icing* A bag used to apply icing to a cake is in the shape of a cone with a diameter of 3 in. and a height of 6 in. How much icing will this bag hold when full? ≈ 14.14 in³

50. *Flower Box* The flower box shown below is 4 ft long, and its ends are in the shape of a trapezoid. The upper and lower bases of the trapezoid measure 12 in. and 8 in., respectively, and the height is 9 in. Find the volume of the flower box

a) in cubic inches. 4320 in³   **b)** in cubic feet. 2.5 ft³

In Exercises 51–56, find the missing value indicated by the question mark. Use the following formula.

$$\left(\begin{array}{c}\text{Number of}\\\text{vertices}\end{array}\right) - \left(\begin{array}{c}\text{number of}\\\text{edges}\end{array}\right) + \left(\begin{array}{c}\text{number}\\\text{of faces}\end{array}\right) = 2$$

	Number of Vertices	Number of Edges	Number of Faces
51.	8	?	4 Ten edges
52.	12	16	? Six faces
53.	?	8	4 Six vertices
54.	11	?	5 Fourteen edges
55.	7	12	? Seven faces
56.	?	10	4 Eight vertices

Challenge Problems/Group Activities

57. *Earth and Moon Comparisons* The diameter of Earth is approximately 12,756.3 km. The diameter of the moon is approximately 3474.8 km. Assume that both Earth and the moon are spheres.

a) Determine the surface area of Earth. $\approx 5.11 \times 10^8\,\text{km}^2$

b) Determine the surface area of the moon. $\approx 3.79 \times 10^7\,\text{km}^2$

c) How many times larger is the surface area of Earth than the surface area of the moon? ≈ 13 times larger

d) Determine the volume of Earth. $\approx 1.09 \times 10^{12}\,\text{km}^3$

e) Determine the volume of the moon. $\sim 2.20 \times 10^{10}\,\text{km}^3$

f) How many times larger is the volume of Earth than the volume of the moon? ≈ 50 times larger

58. *Packing Orange Juice* A box is packed with six cans of orange juice. The cans are touching each other and the sides of the box, as shown. What percent of the volume of the interior of the box is not occupied by the cans? $\approx 21.46\%$

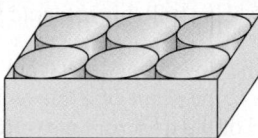

59. *Doubling the Edges of a Cube* In this exercise, we will explore what happens to the volume of a cube if we double the length of each edge of the cube.

a) Choose a number between 1 and 10 and call this number s. Answer will vary.

b) Calculate the volume of a cube with the length of each edge equal to s. Answers will vary.

c) Now double s and call this number t. Answers will vary.

d) Calculate the volume of a cube with the length of each edge equal to t. Answers will vary.

e) Repeat parts (a) through (d) for a different value of s. Answer will vary.

f) Compare the results from part (b) with the results from part (d) and explain what happens to the volume of a cube if we double the length of each edge.*

60. *Doubling the Radius of a Sphere* In this exercise, we will explore what happens to the volume of a sphere if we double the radius of the sphere.

a) Choose a number between 1 and 10 and call this number r. Answers will vary.

b) Calculate the volume of a sphere with radius r (use the $\boxed{\pi}$ key on your calculator). Answers will vary.

c) Now double r and call this number t. Answers will vary.

d) Calculate the volume of a sphere with radius t. Answers will vary.

e) Repeat parts (a) through (d) for a different value of r. Answers will vary.

f) Compare the results from part (b) with the results from part (d) and explain what happens to the volume of a sphere if we double the radius.*

61. a) Explain how to demonstrate, using the cube shown below, that
$$(a + b)^3 = a^3 + 3a^2b + 3ab^2 + b^3$$
Answers will vary.

b) What is the volume in terms of a and b of each numbered piece in the figure?*

c) An eighth piece is not illustrated. What is its volume? ab^2

Recreational Mathematics

62. *More Pool Toys* Wacky Noodle Pool Toys (see Exercise 47) come in many different shapes and sizes.

Base for part (a)   Base for part (b)

a) Determine the volume, in cubic inches, of a noodle that is in the shape of a 5.5-ft-long solid octagonal prism whose base has an area of 5 in². $330\,\text{in}^3$

b) Determine the volume, in cubic inches, of a hollow noodle that has the same shape as the noodle described in part (a) except that a right circular cylinder of diameter 0.75 in. has been removed from the center. $\approx 300.84\,\text{in}^3$

Internet/Research Activities

63. *Air-Conditioner Selection* Calculate the volume of the room in which you sleep or study. Go to a store that sells room air conditioners and find out how many cubic feet can be cooled by the different models available. Describe the model that would be the proper size for your room. What is the initial cost? How much does that model cost to operate? If you moved to a room that had twice the amount

*See Instructor Answer Appendix

of floor space and the same height, would the air conditioner you selected still be adequate? Explain.

64. Pappus of Alexandria (ca. A.D. 350) was the last of the well-known ancient Greek mathematicians. Write a paper on his life and his contributions to mathematics.

65. *Platonic Solids* Construct cardboard models of one or more of the platonic solids. Visit the Web site www.mathsnet.net/geometry/solid/platonic.html or similar Web sites for patterns to follow.

SECTION 9.5

Transformational Geometry, Symmetry, and Tessellations

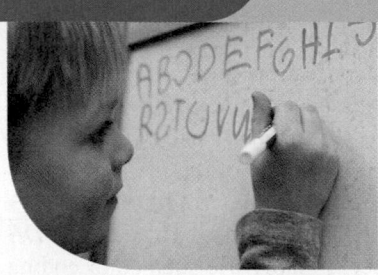

▲ *Capital letters can be used to display symmetry.*

Consider the capital letters of the alphabet. Now consider a kindergarten-age child who is practicing to write capital letters. Usually, children will write some of the letters "backwards." However, some letters cannot be made backwards. For example, the capital letter A would look the same backwards as it does forwards, but the capital letters B and C would look different backwards than they do forwards. The capital letters that appear the same forwards as they do backwards have a property called *symmetry* that we will define and study in this section. Symmetry is part of another branch of geometry known as *transformational geometry*.

Why *This is Important* Transformational geometry can be used to describe many natural phenomena in biology, physics, chemistry, and other scientific areas.

In our study of geometry, we have thus far focused on definitions, axioms, and theorems that are used in the study of *Euclidean geometry*. We will now introduce a second type of geometry called *transformational geometry*. In *transformational geometry*, we study various ways to move a geometric figure without altering the shape or size of the figure. When discussing transformational geometry, we often use the term *rigid motion*.

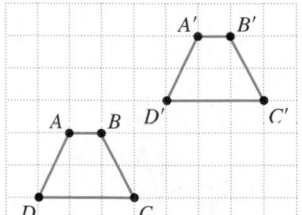

Figure 9.47

Definition: Rigid Motion or Transformation
The act of moving a geometric figure from some starting position to some ending position without altering its shape or size is called a **rigid motion** (or **transformation**).

Consider trapezoid *ABCD* in Fig. 9.47. If we move each point on this trapezoid 4 units to the right and 3 units up, the trapezoid is in the location specified by trapezoid *A'B'C'D'*. This figure illustrates one type of rigid motion. When studying rigid motions, we are concerned only about the starting and ending positions of the figure and not what happens in between. When discussing rigid motions of two-dimensional figures, we note there are four basic types of rigid motions: reflections, rotations, translations, and glide reflections. We call these four types of rigid motions the *basic rigid motions in a plane*. After we discuss the four rigid motions, we will discuss symmetry of geometric figures and tessellations.

Reflections

The first rigid motion we will study is *reflection*. In our everyday life, we are quite familiar with the concept of reflection. In transformational geometry, a reflection is an image of a geometric figure that appears on the opposite side of a designated line.

Definition: Reflection

A **reflection** is a rigid motion that moves a geometric figure to a new position such that the figure in the new position is a mirror image of the figure in the starting position. In two dimensions, the figure and its mirror image are equidistant from a line called the **reflection line** or the **axis of reflection**.

Figure 9.48 shows trapezoid $ABCD$, a reflection line l, and the reflected trapezoid $A'B'C'D'$. Notice that vertex A is 6 units to the *left* of reflection line l and that vertex A' is 6 units to the *right* of reflection line l. Next notice that vertex B is 2 units to the *left* of l and that vertex B' is 2 units to the *right* of l. A similar relationship holds true for vertices C and C' and for vertices D and D'. It is important to see that the trapezoid is not simply *moved* to the other side of the reflection line, but instead it is *reflected*. Notice in the trapezoid $ABCD$ that the longer base $\overline{BC}$ is on the *right* side of the trapezoid, but in the reflected trapezoid $A'B'C'D'$ the longer base $\overline{B'C'}$ is on the *left* side of the trapezoid. Finally, notice the colors of the sides of the two trapezoids. Side $\overline{AB}$ in trapezoid $ABCD$ and side $\overline{A'B'}$ in the reflected trapezoid are both blue. Side $\overline{BC}$ and side $\overline{B'C'}$ are both red, sides $\overline{CD}$ and $\overline{C'D'}$ are both gold, and sides $\overline{DA}$ and $\overline{D'A'}$ are both green. In this section, we will occasionally use such color coding to help you visualize the effect of a rigid transformation on a figure.

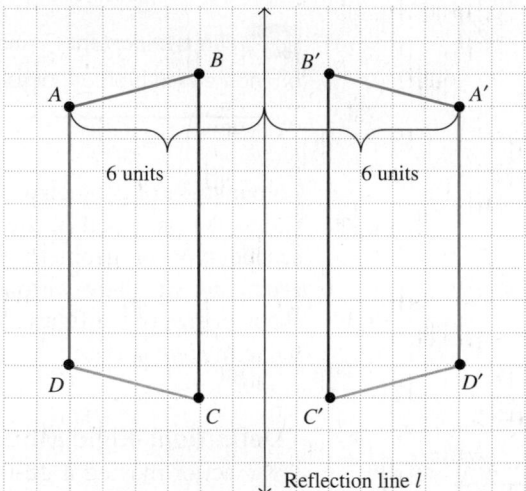

Figure 9.48

Example 1 *Reflection of a Triangle*

Construct the reflection of triangle *ABC,* shown in Fig. 9.49, about reflection line *l.*

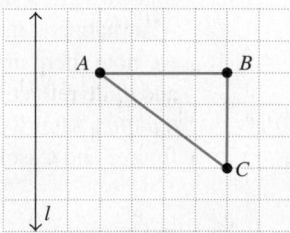

Figure 9.49

Solution The reflection of triangle ABC will be called $A'B'C'$. To determine the position of the reflection, we first examine vertex A in Fig. 9.49. Notice that vertex A is 2 units to the *right* of line l. Thus, in the reflected triangle $A'B'C'$,

Figure 9.51

Figure 9.52

Figure 9.53

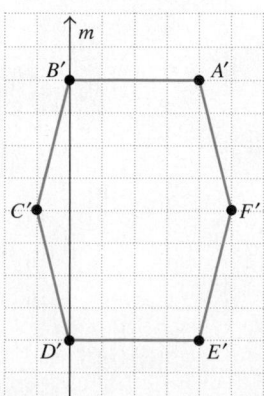

Figure 9.54

vertex A' must also be 2 units away from, but to the *left* of, reflection line l (see Fig 9.50 below). Next, notice that vertex B is 6 units to the right of line l. Thus, in the reflected triangle $A'B'C'$, vertex B' must also be 6 units away from, but to the *left* of, reflection line l. Next, notice that vertex C is 6 units to the right of line l. Thus, in the reflected triangle $A'B'C'$, vertex C' must also be 6 units away from, but to the *left* of, reflection line l. Figure 9.50 shows vertices A', B', and C'. Finally, we draw line segments between vertices A' and B', between B', and C', and between A' and C' to form the sides of the reflection triangle $A'B'$ C', as illustrated in Fig. 9.50.

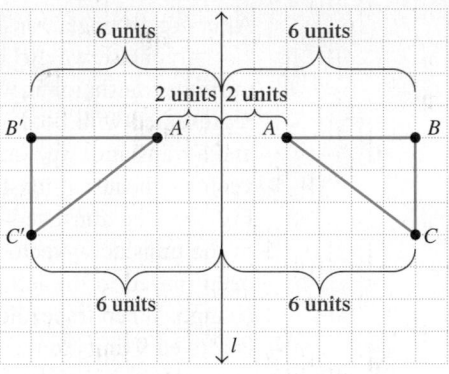

Figure 9.50

In Example 1, the reflection line did not intersect the figure being reflected. We will now study an example in which the reflection line goes directly through the figure to be reflected.

Example 2   *Reflection of a Hexagon*

Construct the reflection of hexagon *ABCDEF*, shown in Fig. 9.51, about reflection line l.

Solution From Fig. 9.51 (in the margin above), we see that vertex A in hexagon *ABCDEF* is 2 units to the left of reflection line l. Thus, vertex A' in the reflected hexagon will be 2 units to the right of l (see Fig. 9.52). Notice that vertex A' of the reflected hexagon is in the same location as vertex B of hexagon *ABCDEF* in Fig. 9.51.

We next see that vertex B in hexagon *ABCDEF* is 2 units to the right of l. Thus, vertex B' in the reflected hexagon will be 2 units to the left of l. Notice that vertex B' of the reflected hexagon is in the same location as vertex A of hexagon *ABCDEF*. We continue this process to determine the locations of vertices C', D', E', and F' of the reflected hexagon. Notice once again that each vertex of the reflected hexagon is in the same location as a vertex of hexagon *ABCDEF*. Finally, we draw the line segments to complete the reflected hexagon $A'B'C'D'E'F'$ (see Fig. 9.52). For this example, we see that other than the vertex labels, the positions of the hexagon before and after the reflection are identical.

In Example 2, the reflection line was in the center of the hexagon in the original position. As a result, the reflection line was also in the center of the reflected hexagon. In this particular case the reflected hexagon lies directly on top of the hexagon in its original position. We will revisit reflections such as that in Example 2 again when we discuss *reflective symmetry* later in this section.

Now consider hexagon *ABCDEF* in Fig. 9.53 and its reflection about line m, hexagon $A'B'C'D'E'F'$ in Fig. 9.54. Notice that the positions of the hexagon before and after the reflection, relative to line m, are not the same. Furthermore, if we line up reflection line m in Fig. 9.53 and Fig. 9.54, we would see that hexagon *ABCDEF* and hexagon $A'B'C'D'E'F'$ are in different positions.

Translations

The next rigid motion we will discuss is the *translation*. In a translation, we simply move a figure along a straight line to a new position.

Definition: Translation or Glide

A **translation** (or **glide**) is a rigid motion that moves a geometric figure by sliding it along a straight line segment in the plane. The direction and length of the line segment completely determine the translation.

After conducting a translation, we say the figure was *translated* to a new position.

A concise way to indicate the direction and the distance that a figure is moved during a translation is with a *translation vector*. In mathematics, vectors are typically represented with boldface letters. For example, in Fig. 9.55 we see trapezoid *ABCD* and a translation vector, **v**, which is pointing to the right and upward. This translation vector indicates a translation of 9 units to the right and 4 units upward. Notice that in Fig. 9.55 the translated vector appears on the right side of the polygon. The placement of the translation vector does not matter. Therefore, the translation vector could have been placed to the left, above, or below the polygon, and the translation would not change. When trapezoid *ABCD* is translated using **v**, every point on trapezoid *ABCD* is moved 9 units to the right and 4 units upward. This movement is demonstrated for vertex *A* in Fig. 9.56(a). Figure 9.56(b) shows trapezoid *ABCD* and the translated trapezoid *A'B'C'D'*. Notice in Fig. 9.56(b) that every point on trapezoid *A'B'C'D'* is 9 units to the right and 4 units up from its corresponding point on trapezoid *ABCD*.

Figure 9.55

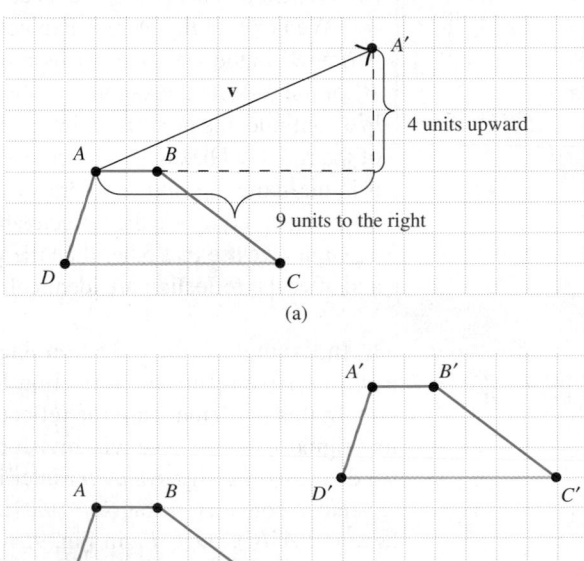

(a)

(b)

Figure 9.56

Example 3 A Translated Square

Given square *ABCD* and translation vector **v**, shown in Fig. 9.57, construct the translated square *A'B'C'D'*.

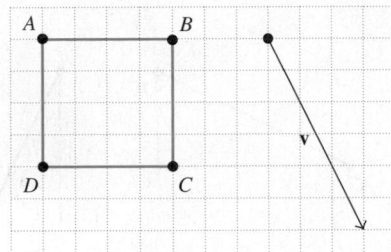

Figure 9.57

Solution The translated figure will be a square of the same size and shape as square *ABCD*. We notice that the translation vector, **v**, points 6 units downward and 3 units to the right. To determine the location of vertex *A'* of the translated square, start at vertex *A* of square *ABCD* and move down 6 units and to the right 3 units. We label this vertex *A'* (see Fig. 9.58a). We determine vertices *B', C',* and *D'* in a similar manner by moving down 6 units and to the right 3 units from vertices *B, C,* and *D,* respectively. Figure 9.58(b) shows square *ABCD* and the translated square *A'B'C'D'*. Notice in Fig. 9.58(b) that every point on square *A'B'C'D'* is 6 units down and 3 units to the right of its corresponding point on square *ABCD*.

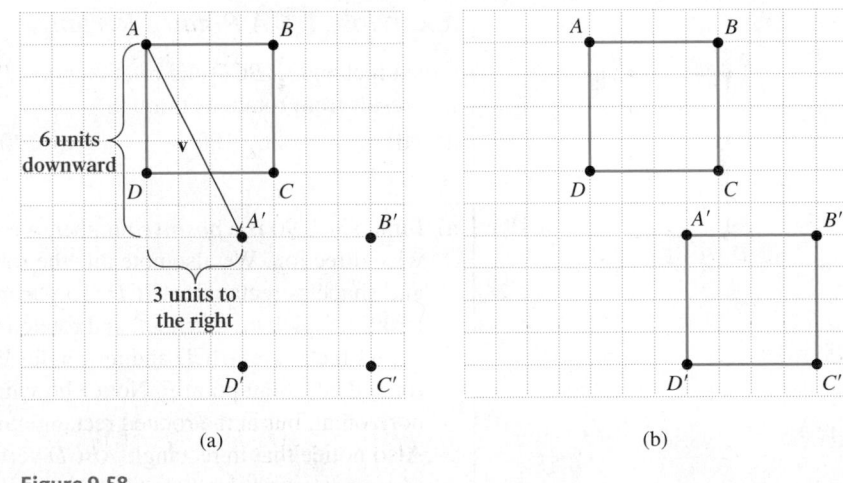

(a)   (b)

Figure 9.58

Rotations

The next rigid motion we will discuss is *rotation*. To help visualize a rotation, examine Fig. 9.59, which shows right triangle *ABC* and point *P* about which right triangle *ABC* is to be rotated.

Imagine that this page was removed from this book and attached to a bulletin board with a single pin through point *P*. Next imagine rotating the page 90° in the *counterclockwise* direction. The triangle would now appear as triangle *A'B'C'* shown in Fig. 9.60 on page 530. Next, imagine rotating the original triangle 180° in a counterclockwise direction. The triangle would now appear as triangle *A"B"C"* shown in Fig. 9.61 on page 530.

Now that we have an intuitive idea of how to determine a rotation, we give the definition of rotation.

Figure 9.59

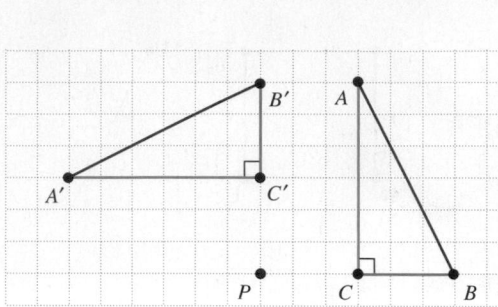

Figure 9.60

Figure 9.61

> ## Definition: Rotation
> A **rotation** is a rigid motion performed by rotating a geometric figure in the plane about a specific point, called the **rotation point** or the **center of rotation**. The angle through which the object is rotated is called the **angle of rotation**.

We will measure angles of rotation using degrees. In mathematics, generally, *counterclockwise angles have positive degree measures and clockwise angles have negative degree measures.*

Example 4 *A Rotated Rectangle*

Given rectangle *ABCD* and rotation point *P*, shown in Fig. 9.62, construct rectangles that result from rotations through

a) 90°.   b) 180°.   c) 270°.

Solution

a) First, since 90 is a *positive* number, we will rotate the figure in a counterclockwise direction. We also note that the rotated rectangle will be the same size and shape as rectangle *ABCD*. To get an idea of what the rotated rectangle will look like, pick up this book and rotate it counterclockwise 90°. Figure 9.63 shows rectangle *ABCD* and rectangle *A′B′C′D′* which is rectangle *ABCD* rotated 90° about point *P*. Notice how line segment *AB* in rectangle *ABCD* is horizontal, but in the rotated rectangle in Fig. 9.63 line segment *A′B′* is vertical. Also notice that in rectangle *ABCD* vertex *D* is 3 units to the *right* and 1 unit *above* rotation point *P*, but in the rotated rectangle, vertex *D′* is 3 units *above* and 1 unit to the *left* of rotation point *P*.

Figure 9.62

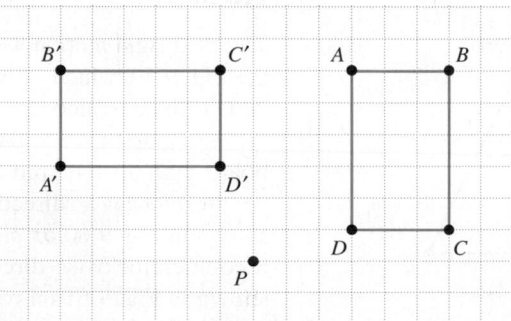

Figure 9.63

b) To gain some perspective on a 180° rotation, again pick up this book, but this time rotate the book 180° in the counterclockwise direction. The rotated rectangle $A''B''C''D''$ is shown along with the rectangle $ABCD$ in Fig. 9.64.

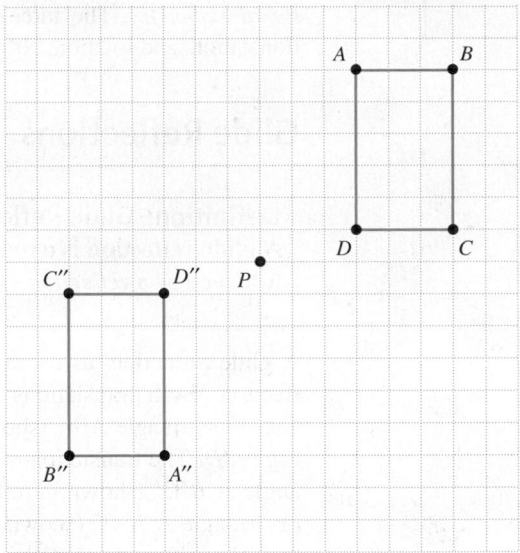

Figure 9.64

c) To gain some perspective on a 270° rotation, rotate this book 270° in the counterclockwise direction. The rotated rectangle $A'''B'''C'''D'''$ is shown along with rectangle $ABCD$ in Fig. 9.65. ∎

Thus far in our examples of rotations, the rotation point was outside the figure being rotated. We now will study an example where the rotation point is inside the figure to be rotated.

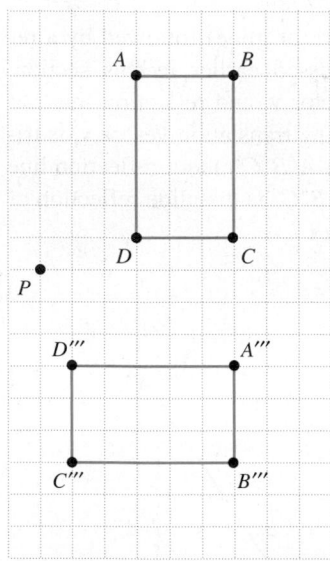

Figure 9.65

Example 5 *A Rotation Point Inside a Polygon*

Given polygon $ABCDEFGH$ and rotation point P, shown in Fig. 9.66, construct polygons that result from rotations through

a) 90°.   b) 180°.

Solution

a) We will rotate the polygon 90° in a counterclockwise direction. The resulting polygon will be the same size and shape as polygon $ABCDEFGH$. To visualize what the rotated polygon will look like, pick up this book and rotate it counterclockwise 90°. Figure 9.67 shows the polygon $ABCDEFGH$, in pale blue, and the rotated polygon $A'B'C'D'E'F'G'H'$, in deeper blue. Notice how line segments $\overline{AB}$, $\overline{CD}$, $\overline{EF}$, and $\overline{GH}$ in polygon $ABCDEFGH$ are *horizontal*, but in the rotated polygon $A'B'C'D'E'F'G'H'$, line segments $\overline{A'B'}$, $\overline{C'D'}$, $\overline{E'F'}$, and $\overline{G'H'}$ are *vertical*. Also notice in polygon $ABCDEFGH$ that line segment $\overline{GH}$ is 1 unit *above* rotation point P, but in the rotated polygon, line segment $\overline{G'H'}$ is 1 unit to the *left* of rotation point P.

b) To visualize the polygon obtained through a 180° rotation, we can pick up this book and rotate it 180° in the counterclockwise direction. Notice from Fig. 9.68 on page 532 that vertex A'' of the rotated polygon is in the same position as vertex E of polygon $ABCDEFGH$. Also notice from Fig. 9.68 that vertex B'' of the rotated polygon is in the same position as vertex F of polygon $ABCDEFGH$. In fact, each of the vertices in the rotated polygon is in the same position as a different vertex in polygon $ABCDEFGH$. From

Figure 9.66

Figure 9.67

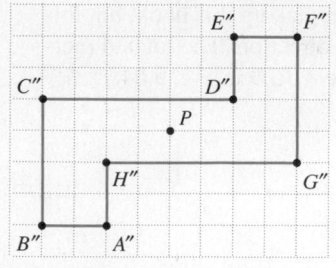

Figure 9.68

Fig. 9.68 we see that, other than vertex labels, the position of rotated polygon $A''B''C''D''E''F''G''H''$ is the same as the position of polygon $ABCDEFGH$. ∎

The polygon used in Example 5 will be discussed again later when we discuss *rotational symmetry*. The three rigid motions we have discussed thus far are reflection, translation, and rotation. Now we will discuss the fourth rigid motion, *glide reflection*.

Glide Reflections

> **Definition: Glide Reflection**
> A **glide reflection** is a rigid motion formed by performing a *translation* (or *glide*) followed by a *reflection*.

A glide reflection, as its name suggests, is a translation (or glide) followed by a reflection. Both translations and reflections were discussed earlier in this section. Consider triangle ABC (shown in blue), translation vector **v**, and reflection line l in Fig. 9.69. The translation of triangle ABC, obtained using translation vector **v**, is triangle $A'B'C'$ (shown in red). The reflection of triangle $A'B'C'$ about reflection line l is triangle $A''B''C''$ (shown in green). Thus, triangle $A''B''C''$ is the glide reflection of triangle ABC using translation vector **v** and reflection line l.

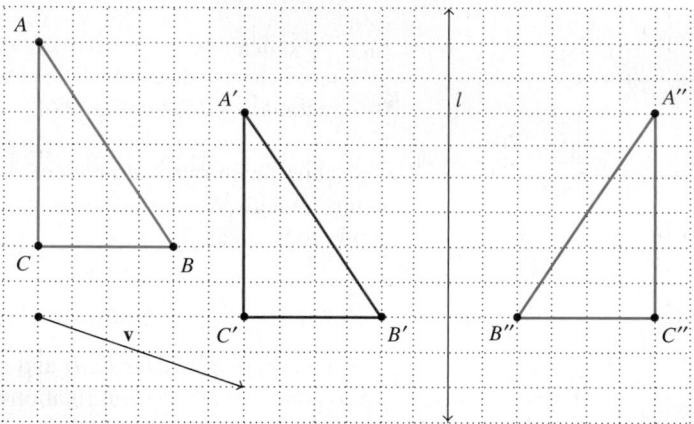

Figure 9.69

Example 6 *A Glide Reflection of a Parallelogram*

Construct a glide reflection of parallelogram $ABCD$, shown in Fig. 9.70, using translation vector **v** and reflection line l.

Solution To construct the glide reflection of parallelogram $ABCD$, first translate the parallelogram 2 units to the left and 5 units up, as indicated by translation vector **v**. This translated parallelogram is labeled $A'B'C'D'$, shown in red in Fig. 9.71(a) on page 533. Next, we will reflect parallelogram $A'B'C'D'$ about reflection line l. Parallelogram $A'B'C'D'$, shown in red, and the reflected parallelogram, labeled $A''B''C''D''$, shown in green, are shown in Fig. 9.71(b). The glide reflection of the parallelogram $ABCD$ is parallelogram $A''B''C''D''$. ∎

Figure 9.70

Symmetry

We are now ready to discuss symmetry. Our discussion of symmetry involves a rigid motion of an object.

(b)

Figure 9.71

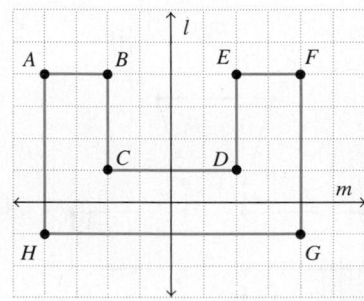

Figure 9.73

Definition: Symmetry

A **symmetry** of a geometric figure is a rigid motion that moves the figure back onto itself. That is, the beginning position and ending position of the figure must be identical.

Suppose we start with a figure in a specific position and perform a rigid motion on this figure. If the position of the figure after the rigid motion is identical to the position of the figure before the rigid motion (if the beginning and ending positions of the figure coincide), then the rigid motion is a symmetry and we say that the figure has symmetry. For a two-dimensional figure, there are four types of symmetries: reflective symmetry, rotational symmetry, translational symmetry, and glide reflective symmetry. In this textbook, however, we will discuss only reflective symmetry and rotational symmetry.

Consider the polygon and reflection line l shown in Fig. 9.72(a). If we use the rigid motion of reflection and reflect the polygon $ABCDEFGH$ about line l, we get polygon $A'B'C'D'E'F'G'H'$. Notice that the ending position of the polygon is identical to the starting position, as shown in Fig. 9.72(b). Compare Fig. 9.72(a) with Fig. 9.72(b). Although the vertex labels are different, the reflected polygon is in the same position as the polygon in the original position. Thus, we say that the polygon has *reflective symmetry* about line l. We refer to line l as a *line of symmetry*.

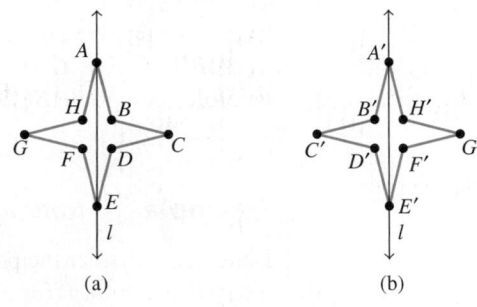

(a)   (b)

Figure 9.72

Recall Example 2 on page 527 in which hexagon $ABCDEF$ was reflected about reflection line l. Examine the hexagon in the original position (Fig. 9.51) and the hexagon in the final position after being reflected about line l (Fig. 9.52). Other than the labels of the vertices, the beginning and ending positions of the hexagon are identical. Therefore, hexagon $ABCDEF$ has reflective symmetry about line l.

Example 7 *Reflective Symmetries of Polygons*

Determine whether the polygon shown in Fig. 9.73 has reflective symmetry about each of the following lines.

a) Line l b) Line m

Solution

a) Examine the reflection of the polygon about line l as seen in Fig. 9.74(a) on page 534. Notice that other than the vertex labels, the beginning and ending positions of the polygon are identical. Thus, the polygon has reflective symmetry about line l.

b) Examine the reflection of the polygon about line m as seen in Fig. 9.74(b). Notice that the position of the reflected polygon is different from the original position of the polygon. Thus, the polygon does not have reflective symmetry about line m. ∎

(a)

(b)

Figure 9.74

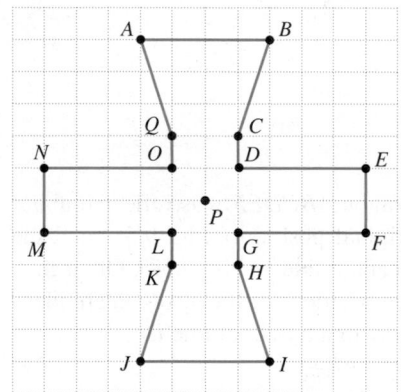

Figure 9.76

We will now discuss a second type of symmetry, rotational symmetry. Consider the polygon and rotation point P shown in Fig. 9.75(a). The rigid motion of rotation of polygon $ABCDEFGH$ through a 90° angle about point P gives polygon $A'B'C'D'E'F'G'H'$ shown in Fig. 9.75(b). Compare Fig. 9.75(a) with Fig. 9.75(b). Although the vertex labels are different, the position of the polygon before and after the rotation is identical. Thus, we say that the polygon has 90° *rotational symmetry* about point P. We refer to point P as the *point of symmetry*.

(a)   (b)

Figure 9.75

Recall Example 5 on page 531, in which polygon $ABCDEFGH$ was rotated 90° about point P in part (a) and 180° in part (b). First examine the polygon in the original position in Fig. 9.66 and the 90° rotated polygon in Fig. 9.67. Notice the position of the polygon after the 90° rotation is different from the original position of the polygon. Therefore, polygon $ABCDEFGH$ in Fig. 9.67 does not have 90° rotational symmetry about point P. Now examine the 180° rotated polygon in Fig. 9.68 on page 532. Notice that other than the vertex labels, the positions of the two polygons $ABCDEFGH$ and $A'B'C'D'E'F'G'H'$ are identical with respect to rotation about point P. Therefore, polygon $ABCDEFGH$ in Fig. 9.66 has 180° rotational symmetry about point P.

Example 8 *Rotational Symmetries*

Determine whether the polygon shown in Fig. 9.76 on page 533 has rotational symmetry about point P for rotations through each of the following angles.

a) 90°   b) 180°

Solution

a) To determine whether the polygon has 90° counterclockwise rotational symmetry about point P, we rotate the polygon 90° as shown in Fig. 9.77(a). Compare Fig. 9.77(a) with Fig. 9.76. Notice that the position of the polygon after the rotation in Fig. 9.77(a) is different than the original position of the polygon (Fig. 9.76). Therefore, the polygon does not have 90° rotational symmetry.

Figure 9.77   (a)   (b)

Symmetry can be found everywhere in nature. One type of symmetry in nature is reflective symmetry, or *bilateral* symmetry. For example, if you draw a line down the center of a maple leaf, you will often find that one half has the same shape as the other half.

Rotational symmetry, or *radial* symmetry, is also found in nature. Starfish, sand dollars, and many flowers all display rotational symmetry. For example, if you rotate a daisy 90°, 180°, or 270°, the rotated daisy will look identical to the original daisy. There are many other examples of symmetry in nature. In Exercise 63 on page 542 you are asked to find other examples of reflective symmetry and rotational symmetry.

b) To determine whether the polygon has 180° counterclockwise rotational symmetry about the point P, we rotate the polygon 180° as shown in Fig. 9.77(b) on page 534. Compare Fig. 9.77(b) with Fig. 9.76. Notice that other than vertex labels, the position of the polygon after the rotation in Fig. 9.77(b) is identical to the position of the polygon before the rotation (Fig. 9.76). Therefore, the polygon has 180° rotational symmetry. ■

Tessellations

A fascinating application of transformational geometry is the creation of *tessellations*.

> ### Definition: Tessellation or Tiling
> A **tessellation** (or **tiling**) is a pattern consisting of the repeated use of the same geometric figures to entirely cover a plane, leaving no gaps. The geometric figures used are called the **tessellating shapes** of the tessellation.

Figure 9.78 shows an example of a tessellation from ancient Egypt. Perhaps the most famous person to incorporate tessellations into his work is M. C. Escher (see *Profiles in Mathematics* on page 536).

Figure 9.78

The simplest tessellations use one single regular polygon as the tessellating shape. Recall that a *regular polygon* is one whose sides are all the same length and whose interior angles all have the same measure. A tessellation that uses one single regular polygon as the tessellating shape is called a *regular tessellation*. It can be shown that only three regular tessellations exist: those that use an equilateral triangle, a square, or a regular hexagon as the tessellating shape. Figure 9.79 shows each of these regular tessellations. Notice that each tessellation can be obtained from a single tessellating shape through the use of reflections, translations, or rotations.

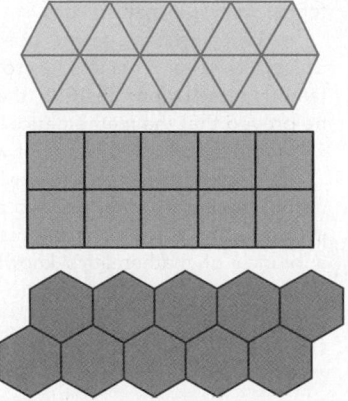

Figure 9.79

We will now learn how to create unique tessellations. We will do so by constructing a unique tessellating shape from a square. We could also construct other tessellating shapes, using an equilateral triangle or a regular hexagon. If you wish to follow along with our construction, you will need some lightweight cardboard, a ruler, cellophane tape, and a pair of scissors. We will start by measuring and cutting out a square 2 in. by 2 in. from the cardboard. We next cut the square into two parts by cutting it from top to bottom using any kind of cut. One example is shown in Fig. 9.80. We then rearrange the pieces and tape the two vertical edges together as shown in Fig. 9.81. Next we cut this new shape into two parts by cutting it from left to right using any kind of cut as shown in Fig. 9.82. We then rearrange the pieces and tape the two horizontal edges together as shown in Fig. 9.83. This completes our tessellating shape.

Figure 9.80

Figure 9.81

Figure 9.82

Figure 9.83

We now set the cardboard tessellating shape in the middle of a blank piece of paper (the tessellating shape can be rotated to any position as a starting point) and trace the outline of the shape onto the paper. Next move the tessellating shape so that it lines up with the figure already drawn and trace the outline again. Continue to do that until the page is completely covered. Once the page is covered with the tessellation, we can add some interesting colors or even some unique sketches to the tessellation. Figure 9.84 shows one tessellation created using the tessellation shape in Fig. 9.83. In Fig. 9.84, the tessellation shape was rotated about 45° counterclockwise.

An infinite number of different tessellations can be created using the method described by altering the cuts made. We could also create different tessellations using an equilateral triangle, a regular hexagon, or other types of polygons. There are also other, more complicated ways to create the tessellating shape. The Internet has many sites devoted to the creation of tessellations by hand. Many computer programs that generate tessellations are also available.

Figure 9.84

Profile In Mathematics

Maurits Cornelius Escher

In addition to being wonderfully engaging art, the work of M. C. Escher (1898–1972) also displays some of the more beautiful and intricate aspects of mathematics. Escher's work involves Euclidean, non-Euclidean (to be studied shortly), and transformational geometries. Amazingly, Escher had no formal training in mathematics.

In 1936, Escher became obsessed with tessellations, that is, with creating art that used objects to cover a plane so as to leave no gaps. Symmetry became a cornerstone of Escher's famous tessellations. In 1995, the mathematician Donald Coxeter published a paper in which he proved that the mathematics Escher displayed in the etching *Circle Limit III* (see page 557) was indeed perfectly consistent with mathematical theory.

Escher kept a notebook in which he kept background information for his artwork. In this notebook, Escher characterized all possible combinations of shapes, colors, and symmetrical properties of polygons in the plane. By doing so, Escher had unwittingly developed areas of a branch of mathematics known as *crystallography* years before any mathematician had done so!

Escher's *Self Portrait in Spherical Mirror*

SECTION 9.5 · *Exercises*

Warm Up Exercises

In Exercises 1–14, fill in the blanks with an appropriate word, phrase, or symbol(s).

1. The act of moving a geometric figure from some starting position to some ending position without altering its shape or size is called a(n) _____ motion. Rigid

2. A rigid motion that moves a geometric figure to a new position such that the new position is a mirror image of the figure in the starting position is called a(n) _____. Reflection

3. In two dimensions, the geometric figure and its reflected image are equidistant from a line called the reflection line, or the _____ of reflection. Axis

4. A rigid motion that moves a geometric figure by sliding it along a straight line segment in the plane is called a(n) _____. Translation

5. A concise way to indicate the direction and the distance that a figure is moved during a translation is with a translation _____. Vector

6. A rigid motion performed by rotating a geometric figure in the plane about a specific point is called a(n) _____. Rotation

7. The point about which a geometric figure is rotated during a rotation is called the rotation point, or the _____ of rotation. Center

8. The angle through which a geometric figure is rotated during a rotation is called the angle of _____. Rotation

9. A rigid motion formed by performing a translation followed by a reflection is called a(n) _____ reflection. Glide

10. A rigid motion that moves the geometric figure back onto itself is called a(n) _____. Symmetry

11. Rectangle *ABCD* shown below has _____ symmetry about line *l*. Reflective

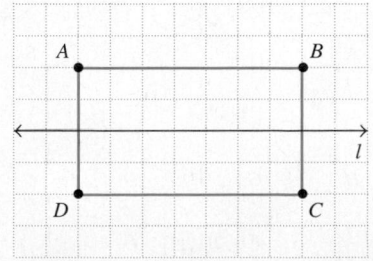

12. Rectangle *ABCD* shown below has 180° _____ symmetry about point *P*. Rotational

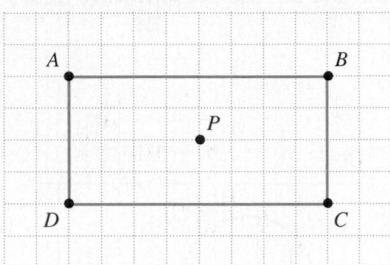

13. A pattern consisting of the repeated use of the same geometric figures to entirely cover a plane, leaving no gaps, is called a(n) _____. Tessellation

14. The geometric figures used to cover a plane are called the _____ shapes of the tessellation. Tessellating

Practice the Skills/Problem Solving

In Exercises 15–22, use the given figure and lines of reflection to construct the indicated reflections. Show the figure in the positions both before and after the reflection.

In Exercises 15 and 16, use the following figure. Construct

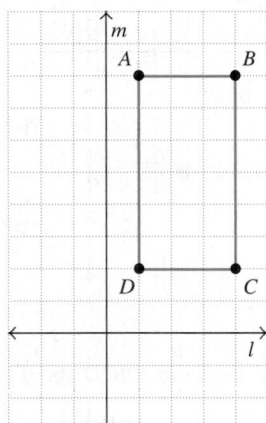

15. the reflection of rectangle *ABCD* about line *m*.*

16. the reflection of rectangle *ABCD* about line *l*.*

In Exercises 17 and 18, use the following figure. Construct

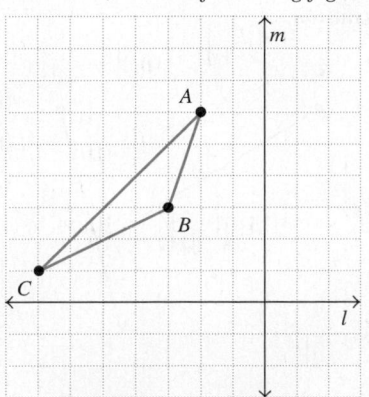

*See Instructor Answer Appendix

17. the reflection of triangle *ABC* about line *l*.*

18. the reflection of triangle *ABC* about line *m*.*

In Exercises 19 and 20, use the following figure. Construct

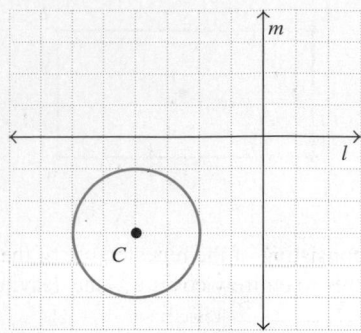

19. the reflection of circle *C* about line *l*.*

20. the reflection of circle *C* about line *m*.*

In Exercises 21 and 22, use the following figure. Construct

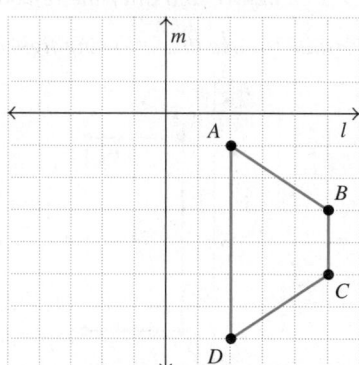

21. the reflection of trapezoid *ABCD* about line *m*.*

22. the reflection of trapezoid *ABCD* about line *l*.*

In Exercises 23–30, use the translation vectors **v** *and* **w**, *shown below, to construct the translations indicated in the exercises. Show the figure in the positions both before and after the translation.*

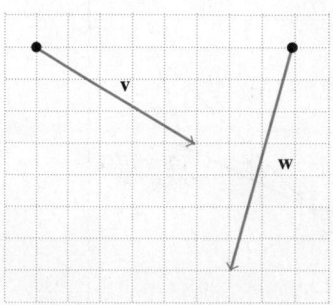

In Exercises 23 and 24, use the following figure. Construct

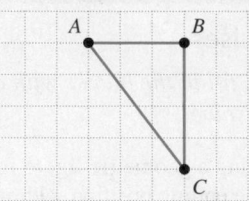

23. the translation of triangle *ABC* using translation vector **v**.*

24. the translation of triangle *ABC* using translation vector **w**.*

In Exercises 25 and 26, use the following figure. Construct

25. the translation of square *ABCD* using translation vector **w**.*

26. the translation of square *ABCD* using translation vector **v**.*

In Exercises 27 and 28, use the following figure. Construct

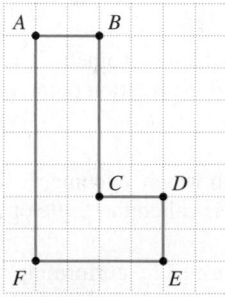

27. the translation of polygon *ABCDEF* using translation vector **v**.*

28. the translation of polygon *ABCDEF* using translation vector **w**.*

In Exercises 29 and 30, use the following figure. Construct

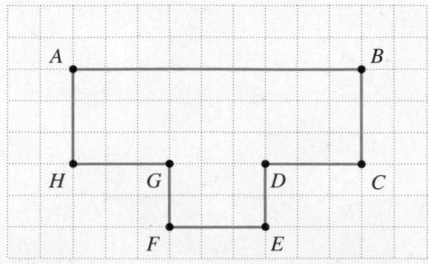

29. the translation of polygon *ABCDEFGH* using translation vector **w** (shown on page 538).*

30. the translation of polygon *ABCDEFGH* using translation vector **v** (shown on page 538).*

In Exercises 31–38, use the given figure and rotation point P to construct the indicated rotations. Show the figure in the positions both before and after the rotation.

In Exercises 31 and 32, use the following figure. Construct

31. a 90° rotation of square *ABCD* about point *P*.*

32. a 180° rotation of square *ABCD* about point *P*.*

In Exercises 33 and 34, use the following figure. Construct

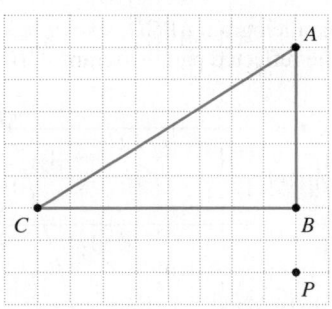

33. a 180° rotation of triangle *ABC* about point *P*.*

34. a 270° rotation of triangle *ABC* about point *P*.*

In Exercises 35 and 36, use the following figure. Construct

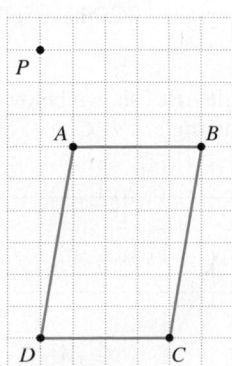

35. a 270° rotation of parallelogram *ABCD* about point *P*.*

36. a 180° rotation of parallelogram *ABCD* about point *P*.*

In Exercises 37 and 38, use the following figure. Construct

37. a 90° rotation of trapezoid *ABCD* about point *P*.*

38. a 270° rotation of trapezoid *ABCD* about point *P*.*

*In Exercises 39–46, use the given figure, translation vectors **v** and **w**, and reflection lines l and m to construct the indicated glide reflections. Show the figure in the positions before and after the glide reflection.*

In Exercises 39 and 40, use the following figure. Construct

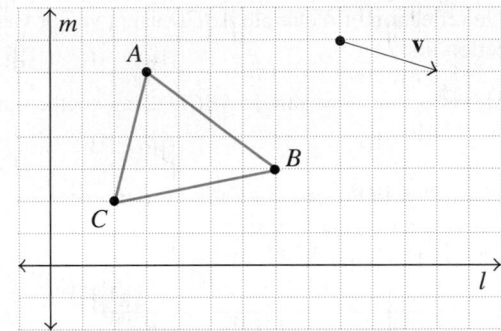

39. a glide reflection of triangle *ABC* using vector **v** and reflection line *l*.*

40. a glide reflection of triangle *ABC* using vector **v** and reflection line *m*.*

In Exercises 41 and 42, use the following figure. Construct

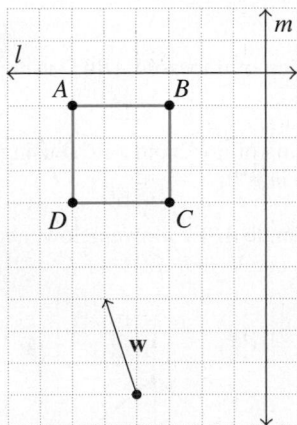

41. a glide reflection of square *ABCD* using vector **w** and reflection line *l*.*

42. a glide reflection of square *ABCD* using vector **w** and reflection line *m*.*

*See Instructor Answer Appendix

In Exercises 43 and 44, use the following figure. Construct

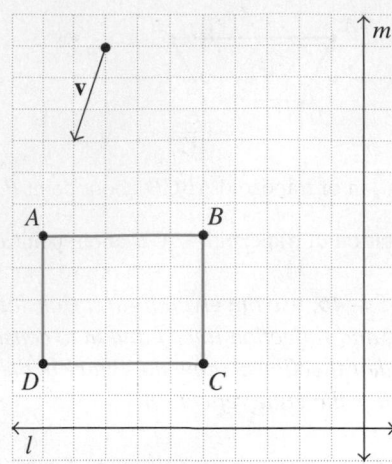

43. a glide reflection of rectangle *ABCD* using vector **v** and reflection line *l*.*

44. a glide reflection of rectangle *ABCD* using vector **v** and reflection line *m*.*

In Exercises 45 and 46, use the following figure. Construct

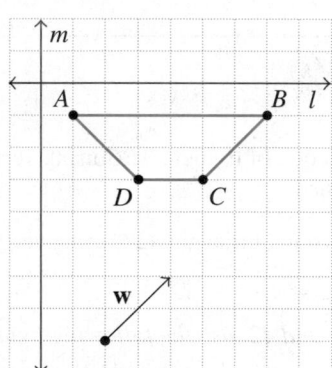

45. a glide reflection of trapezoid *ABCD* using vector **w** and reflection line *l*.*

46. a glide reflection of trapezoid *ABCD* using vector **w** and reflection line *m*.*

47. a) Reflect triangle *ABC*, shown below, about line *l*. Label the reflected triangle *A'B'C'*.*

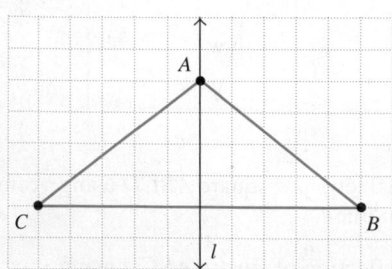

b) Other than vertex labels, is the position of triangle *A'B'C'* identical to the position of triangle *ABC*? Yes

c) Does triangle *ABC* have reflective symmetry about line *l*? Yes

48. a) Reflect rectangle *ABCD*, shown below, about line *l*. Label the reflected rectangle *A'B'C'D'*.*

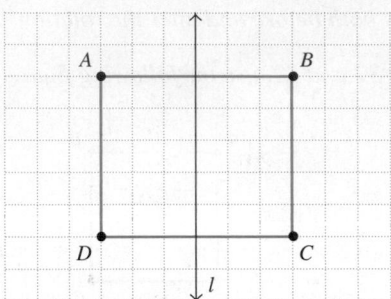

b) Other than vertex labels, is the position of rectangle *A'B'C'D'* identical to the position of rectangle *ABCD*? Yes

c) Does rectangle *ABCD* have reflective symmetry about line *l*? Yes

49. a) Reflect parallelogram *ABCD*, shown below, about line *l*. Label the reflected parallelogram *A'B'C'D'*.*

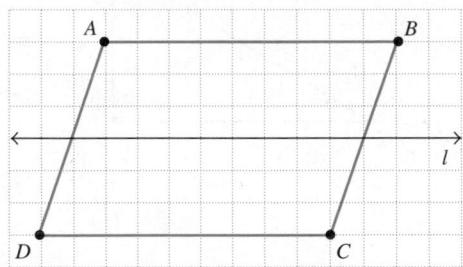

b) Other than vertex labels, is the position of parallelogram *A'B'C'D'* identical to the position of parallelogram *ABCD*? No

c) Does parallelogram *ABCD* have reflective symmetry about line *l*? No

50. a) Reflect triangle *ABC*, shown below, about line *l*. Label the reflected triangle *A'B'C'*.*

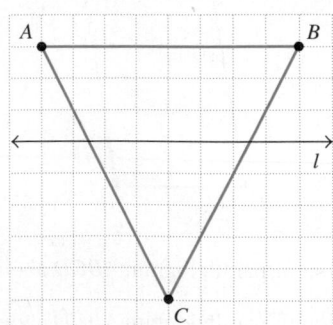

*See Instructor Answer Appendix

b) Other than vertex labels, is the position of triangle *A'B'C'* identical to the position of triangle *ABC*? No

c) Does triangle *ABC* have reflective symmetry about line *l*? No

51. a) Rotate rectangle *ABCD*, shown below, 90° about point *P*. Label the rotated rectangle *A'B'C'D'*.*

b) Other than vertex labels, is the position of rectangle *A'B'C'D'* identical to the position of rectangle *ABCD*? No

c) Does rectangle *ABCD* have 90° rotational symmetry about point *P*? No

d) Now rotate the rectangle in the original position, rectangle *ABCD*, 180° about point *P*. Label the rotated rectangle *A"B"C"D"*.*

e) Other than vertex labels, is the position of rectangle *A"B"C"D"* identical to the position of rectangle *ABCD*? Yes

f) Does rectangle *ABCD* have 180° rotational symmetry about point *P*? Yes

52. a) Rotate parallelogram *ABCD*, shown below, 90° about point *P*. Label the rotated parallelogram *A'B'C'D'*.*

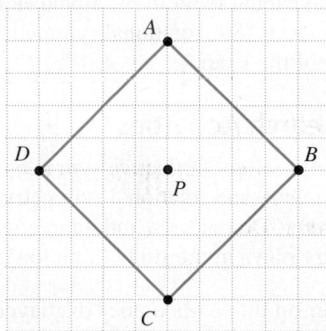

b) Other than vertex labels, is the position of parallelogram *A'B'C'D'* identical to the position of parallelogram *ABCD*? Yes

c) Does parallelogram *ABCD* have 90° rotational symmetry about point *P*? Yes

d) Now rotate the parallelogram in the original position, parallelogram *ABCD*, shown above, 180° about point *P*. Label the rotated parallelogram *A"B"C"D"*.*

e) Other than vertex labels, is the position of parallelogram *A"B"C"D"* identical to the position of parallelogram *ABCD*? Yes

f) Does parallelogram *ABCD* have 180° rotational symmetry about point *P*? Yes

53. Consider the following figure.

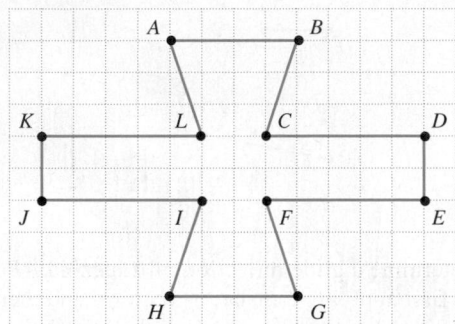

a) Insert a vertical line *m* through the figure so the figure has reflective symmetry about line *m*.*

b) Insert a horizontal line *l* through the figure so the figure has reflective symmetry about line *l*.*

c) Insert a point *P* within the figure so the figure has 180° rotational symmetry about point *P*.*

d) Is it possible to insert a point *P* within the figure so the figure has 90° rotational symmetry about point *P*? Explain your answer. No. Any 90° rotation will result in the figure being in a different position than the starting position.

54. Consider the following figure.

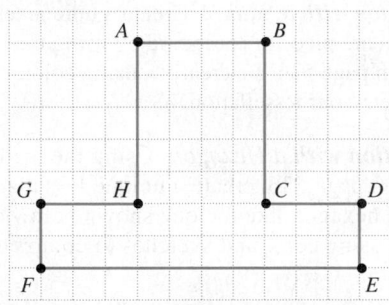

a) Insert a vertical line *m* through the figure so the figure has reflective symmetry about line *m*.*

b) Is it possible to insert a horizontal line *l* through the figure so the figure has reflective symmetry about line *l*? Explain your answer.*

c) Is it possible to insert a point *P* within the figure so the figure has 90° rotational symmetry about point *P*? Explain your answer. No. Any 90° rotation will result in the figure being in a different position than the starting position.

d) Is it possible to insert a point *P* within the figure so the figure has 180° rotational symmetry about point *P*? Explain your answer. No. Any 180° rotation will result in the figure being in a different position than the starting position.

*See Instructor Answer Appendix

Challenge Problems/Group Activities

55. *Glide Reflection, Order* Examine the figure below and then do the following:

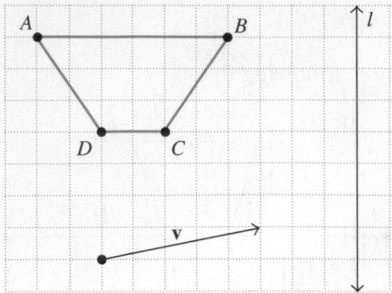

a) Determine a glide reflection of trapezoid *ABCD* by first applying translation vector **v** and then reflecting about the line *l*. Label the glide reflection $A'B'C'D'$.*

b) In this step, we will reverse the order of the translation and the reflection. First reflect trapezoid *ABCD* about the line *l* and then translate the reflection using vector **v**. Label the resulting figure $A''B''C''D''$.*

c) Is figure $A'B'C'D'$ in the same position as figure $A''B''C''D''$? No

d) What can be said about the order of the translation and the reflection used in a glide reflection? Is the figure obtained in part (a) or part (b) the glide reflection? *

56. *Tessellation with a Square* Create a unique tessellation from a square piece of cardboard by using the method described on page 536. Be creative, using color and sketches to complete your tessellation. Answers will vary.

57. *Tessellation with a Hexagon* Using the method described on page 536, create a unique tessellation using a regular hexagon like the one shown below. Be creative, using color and sketches to complete your tessellation. Answers will vary.

58. *Tessellation with an Octagon?*

Trace the regular octagon, shown below, onto a separate piece of paper.

Try to create a regular tessellation by tracing this octagon repeatedly. Attempt to cover the entire piece of paper where no two octagons overlap each other. What conclusion can you draw about using a regular octagon as a tessellating shape?
A regular octagon cannot be used as a tessellating shape.

59. *Tessellation with a Pentagon?* Repeat Exercise 58 using the regular pentagon below instead of a regular octagon.*

Recreational Mathematics

60. Examine each capital letter in the alphabet and determine which letters have reflective symmetry about a horizontal line through the center of the letter.*

61. Examine each capital letter in the alphabet and determine which letters have reflective symmetry about a vertical line through the center of the letter.*

62. Examine each capital letter in the alphabet and determine which letters have 180° rotational symmetry about a point in the center of the letter.*

Internet/Research Activities

63. In the study of biology, reflective symmetry is called *bilateral symmetry* and rotational symmetry is called *radial symmetry*. Do research and write a report on the role symmetry plays in the study of biology.

64. Write a paper on the mathematics displayed in the artwork of M. C. Escher. Include such topics as tessellations, optical illusions, perspective, and non-Euclidean geometry.

*See Instructor Answer Appendix

SECTION 9.6 Topology

Examine the outline of the map of the continental United States shown below. Now suppose you were given four crayons, each of a different color. Could you color this map with the four crayons in a way so that no two bordering states have the same color? In this section, we will discuss this question and many other questions that are relevant to the branch of mathematics known as *topology*.

Why *This is Important* Topology is used in many applications in the fields of map making (cartography), computer science, robotics, and biology.

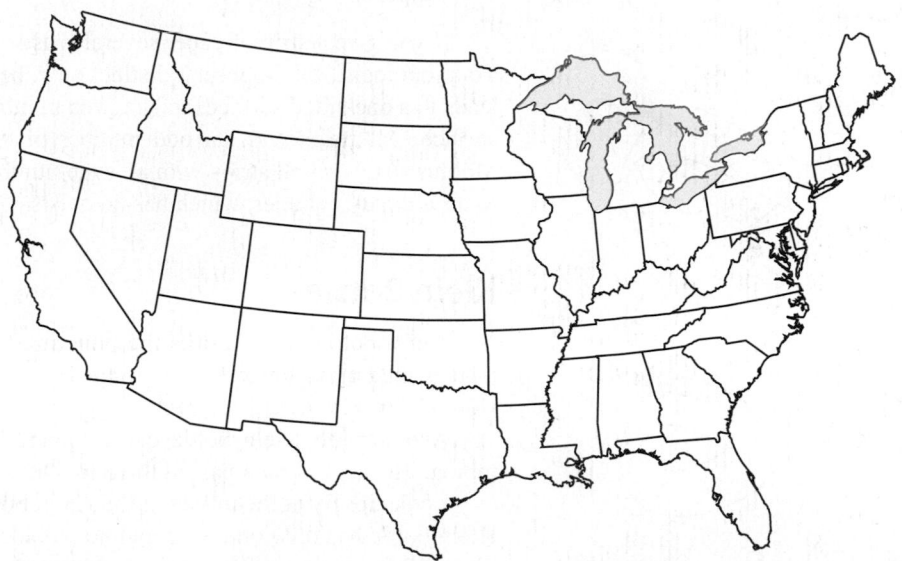

▲ *How many different colors are needed so that no two bordering states share the same color?*

The branch of mathematics called *topology* is sometimes referred to as "rubber sheet geometry" because it deals with bending and stretching of geometric figures.

One of the first pioneers of topology was the German astronomer and mathematician August Ferdinand Möbius (1790–1866). A student of Gauss, Möbius was the director of the University of Leipzig's observatory. He spent a great deal of time studying geometry and he played an essential part in the systematic development of projective geometry. He is best known for his studies of the properties of one-sided surfaces, including the one called the Möbius strip.

Möbius Strip

If you place a pencil on one surface of a sheet of paper and do not remove it from the sheet, you must cross the edge to get to the other surface. Thus, a sheet of paper has one edge and two surfaces. The sheet retains these properties even when crumpled into a ball. The *Möbius strip*, also called a *Möbius band*, is a one-sided, one-edged surface. You can construct one, as shown in Fig. 9.85, by (a) taking a strip of paper, (b) giving one end a half twist, and (c) taping the ends together.

The Möbius strip has some very interesting properties. To better understand these properties, perform the following experiments.

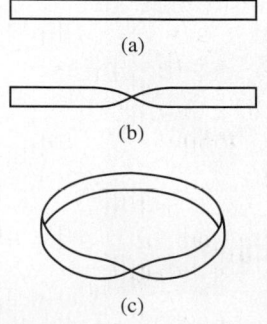

(a)

(b)

(c)

Figure 9.85

Figure 9.86

Figure 9.87

Figure 9.88

Figure 9.89

Experiment 1 Make a Möbius strip using a strip of paper and tape as illustrated in Fig. 9.85. Place the point of a felt-tip pen on the edge of the strip (Fig. 9.86). Pull the strip slowly so that the pen marks the edge; do not remove the pen from the edge. Continue pulling the strip and observe what happens.

Experiment 2 Make a Möbius strip. Place the tip of a felt-tip pen on the surface of the strip (Fig. 9.87). Pull the strip slowly so that the pen marks the surface. Continue and observe what happens.

Experiment 3 Make a Möbius strip. Use scissors to make a small slit in the middle of the strip. Starting at the slit, cut along the strip, keeping the scissors in the middle of the strip (Fig. 9.88). Continue cutting and observe what happens.

Experiment 4 Make a Möbius strip. Make a small slit at a point about one-third of the width of the strip. Cut along the strip, keeping the scissors the same distance from the edge (Fig. 9.89). Continue cutting and observe what happens.

If you give a strip of paper several twists, you get variations on the Möbius strip. To a topologist, the important distinction is between an odd number of twists, which leads to a one-sided surface, and an even number of twists, which leads to a two-sided surface. All strips with an odd number of twists are topologically the same as a Möbius strip, and all strips with an even number of twists are topologically the same as an ordinary cylinder, which has no twists.

Klein Bottle

Another topological object is the punctured *Klein bottle*; see Fig. 9.90. This object, named after Felix Klein (1849–1925), resembles a bottle but only has one side.

A punctured Klein bottle can be made by stretching a hollow piece of glass tubing. The neck is then passed through a hole and joined to the base.

Look closely at the model of the Klein bottle shown in Fig. 9.90. The punctured Klein bottle has only one edge and no outside or inside because it has just one side. Figure 9.91 shows a Klein bottle blown in glass by Alan Bennett of Bedford, England.

Imagine trying to paint a Klein bottle. You start on the "outside" of the large part and work your way down the narrowing neck. When you cross the self-intersection, you have to pretend temporarily that it is not there, so you continue to

Limericks from unknown writers:

"A mathematician confided
That a Möbius band is one-sided,
And you'll get quite a laugh
If you cut one in half
For it stays in one piece when divided."

"A mathematician named Klein
Thought the Möbius band was divine.
He said, 'If you glue
the edges of two
You'll get a weird bottle like mine.'"

Figure 9.90

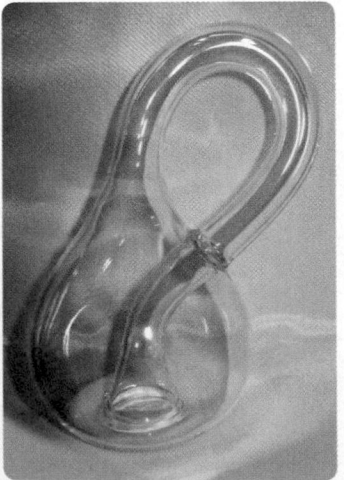

Figure 9.91 *Klein bottle,* a one-sided surface, blown in glass by Alan Bennett.

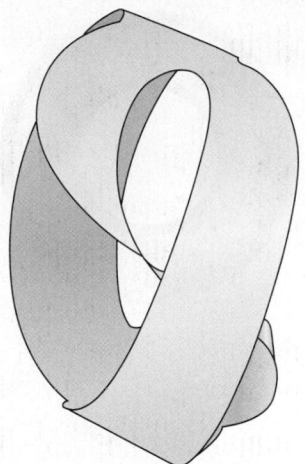
follow the neck, which is now inside the bulb. As the neck opens up, to rejoin the bulb, you find that you are now painting the inside of the bulb! What appear to be the inside and outside of a Klein bottle connect together seamlessly since it is one-sided.

If a Klein bottle is cut along a curve, the results are two (one-twist) Möbius strips; see Fig. 9.92. Thus, a Klein bottle could also be made by gluing together two Möbius strips along the edges.

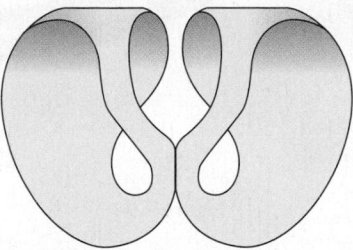

Figure 9.92 Two Möbius strips result from cutting a Klein bottle along a curve.

Maps

Mapmakers have known for a long time that regardless of the complexity of the map and whether it is drawn on a flat surface or a sphere, only four colors are needed to differentiate each country (or state) from its immediate neighbors. Thus, every map can be drawn by using only four colors, and no two countries with a common border will have the same color. Regions that meet at only one point (such as the states of Arizona, Colorado, Utah, and New Mexico) are not considered to have a common border. In Fig. 9.93(a), no two states with a common border are marked with the same color.

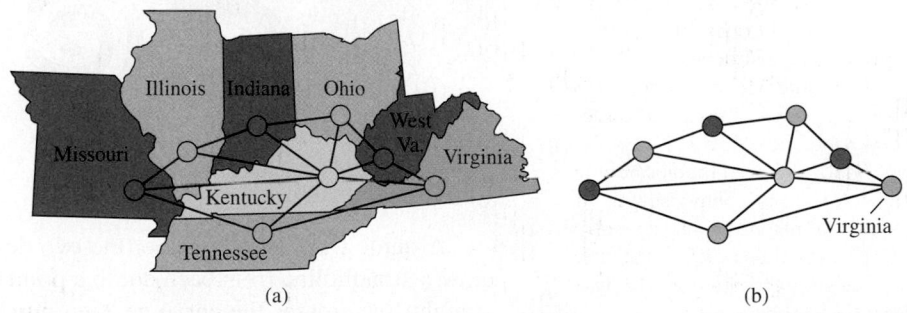

(a)   (b)

Figure 9.93

The "four-color" problem was first suggested by a student of Augustus DeMorgan in 1852. In 1976, Kenneth Appel and Wolfgang Haken of the University of Illinois—using their ingenuity, logic, and 1200 hours of computer time—succeeded in proving that only four colors are needed to draw a map. They solved the four-color map problem by reducing any map to a series of points and connecting line segments. They replaced each country with a point. They connected two countries having a common border with a straight line; see Fig. 9.93(b). They then showed that the points of any graph in the plane could be colored by using only four colors in such a way that no two points connected by the same line were the same color.

Mathematicians have shown that, on different surfaces, more than four colors may be needed to draw a map. For example, a map drawn on a Möbius strip requires a maximum of six colors, as in Fig. 9.94(a). A map drawn on a torus (the shape of a doughnut) requires a maximum of seven colors, as in Fig. 9.94(b).

(a)　　　　　　　　　　　(b)

Figure 9.94

Jordan Curves

A *Jordan curve* is a topological object that can be thought of as a circle twisted out of shape; see Fig. 9.95 (a)–(d). Like a circle, it has an inside and an outside. To get from one side to the other, at least one line must be crossed. Consider the Jordan curve in Fig. 9.95(d). Are points *A* and *B* inside or outside the curve?

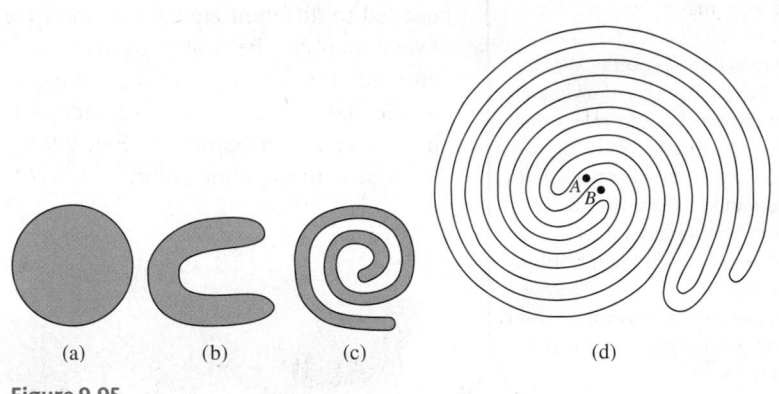

(a)　　　　(b)　　　　(c)　　　　　　(d)

Figure 9.95

A quick way to tell whether the two dots are inside or outside the curve is to draw a straight line from each dot to a point that is clearly outside the curve. If the straight line crosses the curve an even number of times, the dot is outside. If the straight line crosses the curve an odd number of times, the dot is inside the curve. Can you explain why this procedure works? Determine whether point *A* and point *B* are inside or outside the curve (see Exercises 17 and 18 at the end of this section).

Topological Equivalence

Someone once said that a topologist is a person who does not know the difference between a doughnut and a coffee cup. Two geometric figures are said to be *topologically equivalent* if one figure can be elastically twisted, stretched, bent, or shrunk into the other figure without puncturing or ripping the original figure. If a doughnut is made of elastic material, it can be stretched, twisted, bent, shrunk, and distorted until it resembles a coffee cup with a handle, as shown in Fig. 9.96 on page 547. Thus, the doughnut and the coffee cup are topologically equivalent.

Figure 9.96

In topology, figures are classified according to their *genus*. The *genus* of an object is determined by the number of holes that go *through* the object. A cup and a doughnut each have one hole and are of genus 1 (and are therefore topologically equivalent). Notice that the cup's handle is considered a hole, whereas the opening at the rim of the cup is not considered a hole. For our purposes, we will consider an object's opening a hole if you could pour liquid *through* the opening. For example, a typical bowling ball has three openings in the surface into which you can put your fingers when preparing to roll the ball, but liquid cannot be poured *through* any of these openings. Therefore, a bowling ball has genus 0 and is topologically equivalent to a marble. Figure 9.97 illustrates the genus of several objects.

Genus 0	Genus 1	Genus 2	Genus 3 or more
Marble	Doughnut	Kettle	Strainer
Bowling Ball	Coffee Cup	Scissors	Grater

Figure 9.97

SECTION 9.6   *Exercises*

Warm Up Exercises

In Exercises 1–8, fill in the blanks with an appropriate word, phrase, or symbol(s).

1. Because it deals with bending and stretching of geometric figures, topology is sometimes referred to as _____ sheet geometry. Rubber

2. A one-sided, one-edged surface is a(n) _____ strip. Möbius

3. A topological object that resembles a bottle but has only one side is a(n) _____ bottle. Klein

4. If you color a map of the United States, the maximum number of colors needed so that no two states that share a common border have the same color is _____. Four

5. A topological object that can be thought of as a circle twisted out of shape is a(n) _____ curve. Jordan

6. The number of holes that go through an object determines the _____ of the object. Genus

7. A compact disc is an example of an object that has a genus of _____. One

8. A pair of scissors is an example of an object that has a genus of _____. Two

Practice the Skills

In Exercises 9–12, color the map by using a maximum of four colors so that no two regions with a common border have the same color.

9.

Answers will vary.

10.

Answers will vary.

11.

Answers will vary.

12.

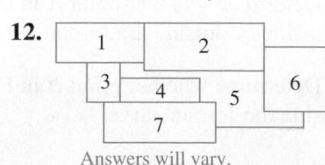

Answers will vary.

Using the Four-Color Theorem *In Exercises 13–16, maps show certain areas of the United States, Canada, and Mexico. Shade in the states (or provinces) using a maximum of four colors so that no two states (or provinces) with a common border have the same color.*

13.   Answers will vary.

14.   Answers will vary.

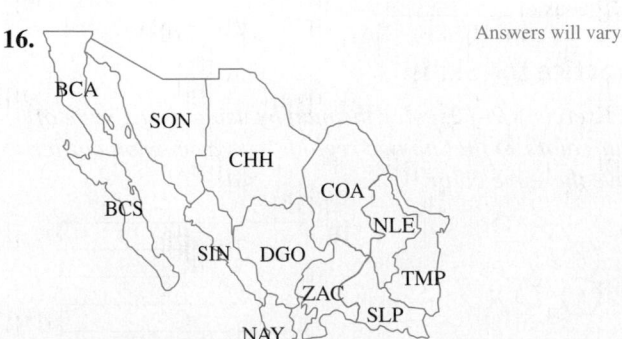

15.   Answers will vary.

16.   Answers will vary.

17. Determine whether point *A* in Fig. 9.95(d) on page 546 is inside or outside the Jordan curve. Outside

18. Determine whether point *B* in Fig. 9.95(d) is inside or outside the Jordan curve. Inside

At right is a Jordan curve. In Exercises 19–22, determine if the point is inside or outside the curve.

19. Point *A* Outside

20. Point *B* Inside

21. Point *C* Inside

22. Point *D* Outside

In Exercises 23–34, give the genus of the object. If the object has a genus larger than 5, write "larger than 5."

23.   1

24.   0

25.   5

26.   5

27.

Larger than 5

28.   0

29.   5

30.   1

31.   0

32.   0

33.

34.   0

Larger than 5

35. Name at least three objects not mentioned in this section that have

    a) genus 0. Answers will vary.   **b)** genus 1. Answers will vary.

    c) genus 2. Answers will vary.   **d)** genus 3 or more. Answers will vary.

36. Use the result of Experiment 1 on page 544 to find the number of edges on a Möbius strip. One

37. Use the result of Experiment 2 on page 544 to find the number of surfaces on a Möbius strip. One

38. How many separate strips are obtained in Experiment 3 on page 544? One

39. How many separate strips are obtained in Experiment 4 on page 544? Two

40. Make a Möbius strip. Cut it one-third of the way from the edge, as in Experiment 4 on page 544. You should get two loops, one going through the other. Determine whether either (or both) of these loops is itself a Möbius strip. The smaller one is a Möbius strip; the larger one is not.

41. a) Take a strip of paper, give it one full twist, and connect the ends. Is the result a Möbius strip with only one side? Explain. No, it has an inside and an outside.

    b) Determine the number of edges, as in Experiment 1. Two

    c) Determine the number of surfaces, as in Experiment 2. Two

    d) Cut the strip down the middle. What is the result? Two strips, one inside the other

42. Take a strip of paper, make one whole twist and another half twist, and then tape the ends together. Test by a method of your choice to determine whether this has the same properties as a Möbius strip. No, it does not.

Challenge Problems/Group Activities

43. Using clay (or glazing compound), make a doughnut. Without puncturing or tearing the doughnut, reshape it into a topologically equivalent figure, a cup with a handle. Answers will vary.

44. Using at most four colors, color the following map of the counties of New Mexico. Do not use the same color for any two counties that share a common border. Answers will vary.

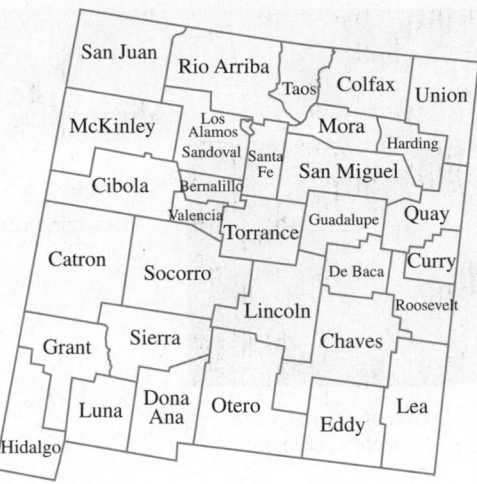

Recreational Math

45. *Topological Paper Constructions* Using paper, scissors, and tape, perform the construction described in the *Recreational Mathematics* box on page 546. Once you have completed the construction, cut along the dashed line as instructed. Set the result aside.

    In this exercise we will construct another interesting surface. We begin by constructing a "cross" shape from two strips of paper, as shown below, using scissors and tape. Note the red dashed line and the green dashed line and the ends of the strips labeled *A* or *B*.

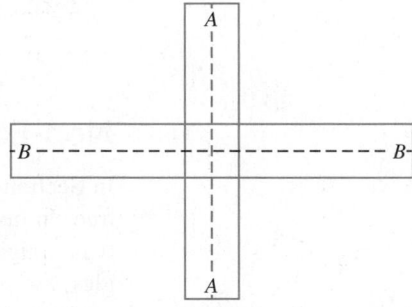

Next, using tape connect the two ends labeled *A without* twisting the ends. Then, connect the two ends labeled *B* by giving one end a half twist. The strip that connects the *B* ends should resemble a Möbius strip. Finally, cut the object first along the green dashed line and then along the red dashed line. Compare the result with that from the construction on page 546. What do you notice? Answers will vary.

Internet/Research Activities

46. Use the Internet to find a map of your state that shows the outline of all the counties within your state. Print this map and, using at most four colors, color it. Do not use the same color for any two counties that share a common border.

47. The short story *Paul Bunyan versus the Conveyor Belt* (1947) by William Hazlett Upson focuses on a conveyor belt in the shape of a Möbius strip. The story can be found in several books that include mathematical essays. Read Upson's short story and write a 200-word description of what Paul Bunyan does to the conveyor belt. Confirm the outcome of the story by repeating Paul's actions with a paper Möbius strip.

SECTION 9.7

Non-Euclidean Geometry and Fractal Geometry

▲ *Many branches of geometry are needed to accurately represent space.*

Ponder the following question: Given a line *l* and a point *P* not on the line *l*, how many lines can you draw through *P* that are parallel to *l*?

You may answer that only one line may be drawn through *P* parallel to *l*. This answer would be correct *provided* the setting of the problem is in a plane and not on the surface of a curved object. The study of this question led to the development of several new branches of geometry. It is now believed all of these branches of geometry, taken together, can be used to accurately represent space. In this section, we will study the geometry of surfaces other than the geometry of the plane.

Why **This is Important** Scientists now believe that space and time can best be represented using a combination of these different branches of geometry. In addition, many applications of the geometry described in this section are used in modem technology, such as cellular phones, computer memory, and medical imaging.

Non-Euclidean Geometry

In Section 9.1, we stated that postulates or axioms are statements to be accepted as true. In his book *Elements*, Euclid's fifth postulate was, "If a straight line falling on two straight lines makes the interior angles on the same side less than two right angles, the two straight lines, if produced indefinitely, meet on that side on which the angles are less than the two right angles."

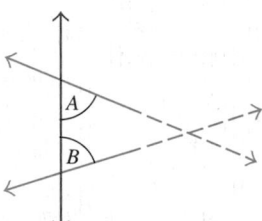

Figure 9.98

Euclid's fifth axiom may be better understood by observing Fig. 9.98. The sum of angles *A* and *B* is less than the sum of two right angles (180°). Therefore, the two lines will meet if extended.

John Playfair (1748–1819), a Scottish physicist and mathematician, wrote a geometry book that was published in 1795. In his book, Playfair gave a logically equivalent interpretation of Euclid's fifth postulate. This version is often referred to as Playfair's postulate or the Euclidean parallel postulate.

The Euclidean Parallel Postulate
Given a line and a point not on the line, one and only one line can be drawn through the given point parallel to the given line (Fig. 9.99).

Figure 9.99

The Euclidean parallel postulate may be better understood by looking at Fig. 9.99. Many mathematicians after Euclid believed that this postulate was not as self-evident as the other nine postulates given by Euclid. Others believed that this postulate could be proved from the other nine postulates and therefore was not needed at all. Of the many attempts to prove that the fifth postulate was not needed, the most noteworthy one was presented by Girolamo Saccheri (1667–1733), a Jesuit

MATHEMATICS TODAY

Mapping The Brain

Photograph courtesy of Dr. Monica K. Hurdal (mhurdal@math.fsu.edu), Dept. of Mathematics, Florida State University

Medical researchers and mathematicians are currently attempting to capture an image of the three-dimensional human brain on a two-dimensional map. In some respects, the task is like capturing the image of Earth on a two-dimensional map, but because of the many folds and fissures on the surface of the brain, the task is much more complex. Points of the brain that are at different depths can appear too close in a flat image. Therefore, to develop an accurate mapping, researchers use topology, hyperbolic geometry, and elliptical geometry to create an image known as a *conformal mapping*. Researchers use conformal mappings to precisely identify the parts of the brain that correspond to specific functions.

Why **This is Important** Medical imaging is just one application of the various branches of geometry described in this section.

priest in Italy. In the course of his elaborate chain of deductions, Saccheri proved many of the theorems of what is now called hyperbolic geometry. However, Saccheri did not realize what he had done. He believed that Euclid's geometry was the only "true" geometry and concluded that his own work was in error. Thus, Saccheri narrowly missed receiving credit for a great achievement: the founding of *non-Euclidean geometry*.

Over time, geometers became more and more frustrated at their inability to prove Euclid's fifth postulate. One of them, a Hungarian named Farkos Bolyai, in a letter to his son, Janos Bolyai, wrote, "I entreat you leave the science of parallels alone.... I have traveled past all reefs of this infernal dead sea and have always come back with a broken mast and torn sail." The son, refusing to heed his father's advice, continued to think about parallels until, in 1823, he saw the whole truth and enthusiastically declared, "I have created a new universe from nothing." He recognized that geometry branches in two directions, depending on whether Euclid's fifth postulate is applied. He recognized two different geometries and published his discovery as a 24-page appendix to a textbook written by his father. The famous mathematician George Bruce Halsted called it "the most extraordinary two dozen pages in the whole history of thought." Farkos Bolyai proudly presented a copy of his son's work to his friend Carl Friedrich Gauss, then Germany's greatest mathematician, whose reply to the father had a devastating effect on the son. Gauss wrote, "I am unable to praise this work.... To praise it would be to praise myself. Indeed, the whole content of the work, the path taken by your son, the results to which he is led, coincides almost entirely with my meditations which occupied my mind partly for the last thirty or thirty-five years." We now know from his earlier correspondence that Gauss had indeed been familiar with *hyperbolic geometry* even before Janos was born. In his letter, Gauss also indicated that it was his intention not to let his theory be published during his lifetime, but to record it so that the theory would not perish with him. It is believed that the reason Gauss did not publish his work was that he feared being ridiculed by other prominent mathematicians of his time.

At about the same time as Bolyai's publication, Nikolay Ivanovich Lobachevsky, a Russian, published a paper that was remarkably like Bolyai's, although it was quite independent of it. Lobachevsky made a deeper investigation and wrote several books. In marked contrast to Bolyai, who received no recognition during his lifetime, Lobachevsky received great praise and became a professor at the University of Kazan.

After the initial discovery, little attention was paid to the subject until 1854, when G. F. Bernhard Riemann (1826–1866), a student of Gauss, suggested a second type of non-Euclidean geometry, which is now called *spherical*, *elliptical*, or *Riemannian geometry*. The hyperbolic geometry of his predecessors was synthetic; that is, it was not based on or related to any concrete model when it was developed. Riemann's geometry was closely related to the theory of surfaces. A *model* may be considered a physical interpretation of the undefined terms that satisfies the axioms. A model may be a picture or an actual physical object.

The two types of non-Euclidean geometries we have mentioned are elliptical geometry and hyperbolic geometry. The major difference among the three geometries lies in the fifth axiom. The fifth axiom of the three geometries is summarized here.

The Fifth Axiom of Geometry

Euclidean	Elliptical	Hyperbolic
Given a line and a point not on the line, one and only one line can be drawn parallel to the given line through the given point	Given a line and a point not on the line, no line can be drawn through the given point parallel to the given line.	Given a line and a point not on the line, two or more lines can be drawn through the given point parallel to the given line.

To understand the fifth axiom of the two non-Euclidean geometries, remember that the term *line* is undefined. Thus, a line can be interpreted differently in different geometries. A model for Euclidean geometry is a plane, such as a blackboard (Fig. 9.100a). A model for elliptical geometry is a sphere (Fig. 9.100b). A model for hyperbolic geometry is a pseudosphere (Fig. 9.100c). A pseudosphere is similar to two trumpets placed bell to bell. Obviously, a line on a plane cannot be the same as a line on either of the other two figures.

(a) Plane   (b) Sphere   (c) Pseudosphere

Figure 9.100

Elliptical Geometry

A circle on the surface of a sphere is called a great circle if it divides the sphere into two equal parts. If we were to cut through a sphere along a great circle, we would have two identical pieces. If we interpret a line to be a great circle, then the two red curves in Fig. 9.101(a) are lines. Figure 9.101(a) shows that the fifth axiom of elliptical geometry is true. Two great circles on a sphere must intersect; hence, there can be no parallel lines (Fig. 9.101a).

If we were to construct a triangle on a sphere, the sum of its angles would be greater than 180° (Fig. 9.101b). The theorem "The sum of the measures of the angles of a triangle is greater than 180°" has been proven by means of the axioms of elliptical geometry. The sum of the measures of the angles varies with the area of the triangle and gets closer to 180° as the area decreases.

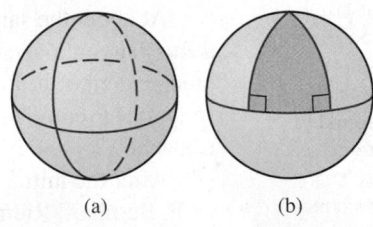

(a)   (b)

Figure 9.101

Hyperbolic Geometry

Lines in hyperbolic geometry*are represented by geodesics on the surface of a pseudosphere. A *geodesic* is the shortest and least-curved arc between two points on a surface. Figure 9.102 shows two different lines represented by geodesics on the surface of a pseudosphere. For simplicity of the diagrams, we only show one of the "bells" of the pseudosphere.

(a)   (b)

Figure 9.102

---

*A formal discussion of hyperbolic geometry is beyond the scope of this text.

Albert Einstein's general theory of relativity, published in 1916, approached space and time differently from our everyday understanding of them. Einstein's theory unites the three dimensions of space with one of time in a four-dimensional space–time continuum. His theory dealt with the path that light and objects take while moving through space under the force of gravity. Einstein conjectured that mass (such as stars and planets) caused space to be curved. The greater the mass, the greater the curvature.

To prove his conjecture, Einstein exposed himself to Riemann's non-Euclidean geometry. Einstein believed that the trajectory of a particle in space represents not a straight line but the straightest curve possible, a geodesic. Einstein's theory was confirmed by the solar eclipses of 1919 and 1922.

Space–time is now thought to be a combination of three different types of curvature: spherical (described by Riemannian geometry), flat (described by Euclidean geometry), and saddle-shaped (described by hyperbolic geometry).

"The Great Architect of the universe now appears to be a great mathematician."
British physicist Sir James Jeans

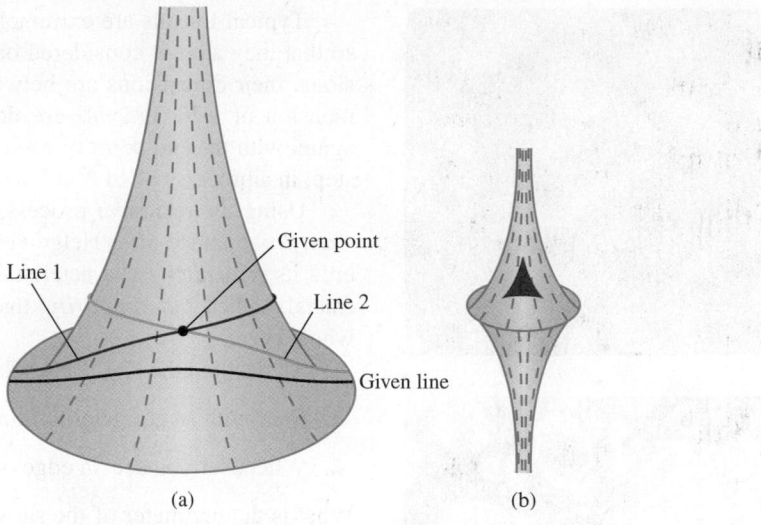

Figure 9.103

Figure 9.103(a) illustrates the fifth axiom of hyperbolic geometry. The diagram illustrates one way that, through the given point, two lines are drawn parallel to the given line. If we were to construct a triangle on a pseudosphere, the sum of the measures of the angles would be less than 180° (Fig. 9.103b). The theorem "The sum of the measures of the angles of a triangle is less than 180°" has been proven by means of the axioms of hyperbolic geometry.

We have stated that the sum of the measures of the angles of a triangle is 180°, is greater than 180°, and is less than 180°. Which statement is correct? Each statement is correct *in its own geometry.* Many theorems hold true for all three geometries; vertical angles still have the same measure, we can uniquely bisect a line segment with a straightedge and compass alone, and so on.

The many theorems based on the fifth postulate may differ in each geometry. It is important for you to realize that each theorem proved is true *in its own geometry* because each is logically deduced from the given set of axioms of the geometry. No one system is the "best" system. Euclidean geometry may appear to be the one to use in the classroom, where the blackboard is flat. In discussions involving Earth as a whole, however, elliptical geometry may be the most useful since Earth is a sphere. If the object under consideration has the shape of a saddle or pseudosphere, hyperbolic geometry may be the most useful.

Fractal Geometry

We are familiar with one-, two-, and three-dimensional figures. Many objects, however, are difficult to categorize as one-, two-, or three-dimensional. For example, how would you classify the irregular shapes we see in nature, such as a coastline, or the bark on a tree, or a mountain, or a path followed by lightning? For a long time mathematicians assumed that making realistic geometric models of natural shapes and figures was almost impossible, but the development of *fractal geometry* now makes it possible. Both color photos on the next page were made by using fractal geometry. The discovery and study of fractal geometry has been one of the most popular mathematical topics in recent times.

The word *fractal* (from the Latin word *fractus*, "broken up, fragmented") was first used in the mid-1970s by mathematician Benoit Mandelbrot to describe shapes that had several common characteristics, including some form of "self-similarity," as will be seen shortly in the Koch snowflake.

▲ *Fractal images*

Typical fractals are extremely irregular curves or surfaces that "wiggle" enough so that they are not considered one-dimensional. Fractals do not have integer dimensions; their dimensions are between 1 and 2. For example, a fractal may have a dimension of 1.26. Fractals are developed by applying the same rule over and over again, with the end point of each simple step becoming the starting point for the next step, in a process called *recursion*.

Using the recursive process, we will develop a famous fractal called the *Koch snowflake* named after Helga von Koch, a Swedish mathematician who first discovered its remarkable characteristics. The Koch snowflake illustrates a property of all fractals called *self-similarity*; that is, each smaller piece of the curve resembles the whole curve.

To develop the Koch snowflake:

1. Start with an equilateral triangle (Step 1, Fig. 9.104).

2. Whenever you see an edge —— replace it with ⌒⌒ (Steps 2–4).

What is the perimeter of the snowflake in Fig. 9.104, and what is its area? A portion of the boundary of the Koch snowflake known as the Koch curve, or the snowflake curve, is represented in Fig. 9.105.

The Koch curve consists of infinitely many pieces of the form ⌒⌒. Notice that after each step, the perimeter is $\frac{4}{3}$ times the perimeter of the previous step. Therefore, the Koch snowflake has an infinite perimeter. It can be shown that the area of the snowflake is 1.6 times the area of the starting equilateral triangle. Thus, the area of the snowflake is finite. The Koch snowflake has a finite area enclosed by an infinite boundary! This fact may seem difficult to accept, but it is true. However, the Koch snowflake, like other fractals, is not an everyday run-of-the-mill geometric shape.

Step 1   Step 2

Step 3   Step 4

Figure 9.104   **Figure 9.105**

Let us look at a few more fractals made using the recursive process. We will now construct what is known as a *fractal tree*. Start with a tree trunk (Fig. 9.106a on page 555). Draw two branches, each one a bit smaller than the trunk (Fig. 9.106b). Draw two branches from each of those branches, and continue; see Fig. 9.106(c) and (d). Ideally, we continue the process forever.

If you take a little piece of any branch and zoom in on it, it will look exactly like the original tree. Fractals are *scale independent*, which means that you cannot really tell whether you are looking at something very big or something very small because the fractal looks the same whether you are close to it or far from it.

Figure 9.106 The fractal tree

In Figs. 9.107 and 9.108, we develop two other fractals through the process of recursion. Figure 9.107 shows a fractal called the Sierpinski triangle, and Fig. 9.108 shows a fractal called the Sierpinski carpet. Both fractals are named after Waclaw Sierpinski, a Polish mathematician who is best known for his work with fractals and space-filling curves.

Figure 9.107 Sierpinski triangle

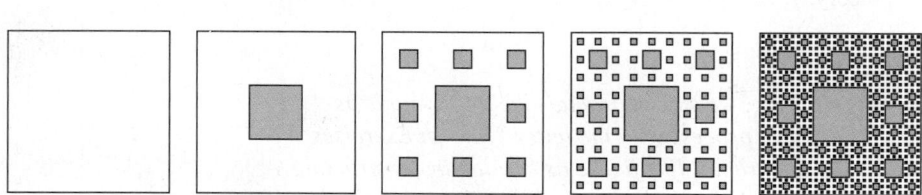

Figure 9.108 Sierpinski carpet

Fractals provide a way to study natural forms such as coastlines, trees, mountains, galaxies, polymers, rivers, weather patterns, brains, lungs, and blood supply. Fractals also help explain that which appears chaotic. The blood supply in the body is one example. The branching of arteries and veins appears chaotic, but closer inspection reveals that the same type of branching occurs for smaller and smaller blood vessels, down to the capillaries. Thus, fractal geometry provides a geometric structure for chaotic processes in nature. The study of chaotic processes is called *chaos theory*.

Fractals nowadays have a potentially important role to play in characterizing weather systems and in providing insight into various physical processes such as the occurrence of earthquakes or the formation of deposits that shorten battery life. Some scientists view fractal statistics as a doorway to unifying theories of medicine, offering a powerful glimpse of what it means to be healthy.

Fractals lie at the heart of current efforts to understand complex natural phenomena. Unraveling their intricacies could reveal the basic design principles at work in our world. Until recently, there was no way to describe fractals. Today, we are beginning to see such features everywhere. Tomorrow, we may look at the entire universe through a fractal lens.

SECTION 9.7 *Exercises*

Warm Up Exercises

In Exercises 1–8, fill in the blanks with an appropriate word, phrase, or symbol(s).

1. The fifth axiom of Euclidean geometry states that given a line and a point not on the line, one and only one line can be drawn through the given point _____ to the given line. Parallel

2. The fifth axiom of elliptical geometry states that given a line and a point not on the line, _____ line can be drawn through the given point parallel to the given line. No

3. The fifth axiom of hyperbolic geometry states that given a line and a point not on the line, _____ or more lines can be drawn through the given point parallel to the given line. Two

4. A model for Euclidean geometry is a(n) _____. Plane

5. A model for elliptical geometry is a(n) _____. Sphere

6. A model for hyperbolic geometry is a(n) _____. Pseudosphere

7. The shortest and least-curved arc between two points on a surface is a(n) _____. Geodesic

8. The study of chaotic processes is known as _____ theory. Chaos

Practice the Skills

In the following, we show a fractal-like figure made using a recursive process with the letter "M." In Exercises 9–12, use this fractal-like figure as a guide in constructing fractal-like figures with the letter given. Show three steps, as is done here.

9. I   **10.** E   **11.** H   **12.** W

13. a) Develop a fractal by beginning with a square and replacing each side —— with a ⊓. Repeat this process twice.*

b) If you continue this process, will the fractal's perimeter be finite or infinite? Explain. Infinite

c) Will the fractal's area be finite or infinite? Explain. Finite

Problem Solving/Group Activity

14. In forming the Koch snowflake in Figure 9.104 on page 554, the perimeter becomes greater at each step in the process. If each side of the original triangle is 1 unit, a general formula for the perimeter, L, of the snowflake at any step, n, may be found by the formula

$$L = 3\left(\frac{4}{3}\right)^{n-1}$$

For example, at the first step when $n = 1$, the perimeter is 3 units, which can be verified by the formula as follows:

$$L = 3\left(\frac{4}{3}\right)^{1-1} = 3\left(\frac{4}{3}\right)^{0} = 3 \cdot 1 = 3$$

At the second step, when $n = 2$, we find the perimeter as follows:

$$L = 3\left(\frac{4}{3}\right)^{2-1} = 3\left(\frac{4}{3}\right) = 4$$

Thus, at the second step the perimeter of the snowflake is 4 units.

a) Use the formula to complete the following table.*

Step	Perimeter
1	
2	
3	
4	
5	
6	

b) Use the results of your calculations to explain why the perimeter of the Koch snowflake is infinite. At each stage, the perimeter is $\frac{4}{3}$ multiplied by the previous perimeter.

c) Explain how the Koch snowflake can have an infinite perimeter, but a finite area. The area is finite because it encloses a finite region. The perimeter is infinite because it consists of an infinite number of pieces.

Concept/Writing Exercises

15. What do we mean when we say that no one axiomatic system of geometry is "best"? Each type of geometry can be used in its own frame of reference.

16. List the three types of curvature of space and the types of geometry that correspond to them. Spherical: elliptical geometry; flat: Euclidean geometry; saddle-shaped: hyperbolic geometry.

17. List at least five natural forms that appear chaotic that we can study using fractals. Coastlines, trees, mountains, galaxies, polymers, rivers, weather patterns, brains, lungs, blood supply

18. State the theorem concerning the sum of the measures of the angles of a triangle in

  a) Euclidean geometry.
    The sum of the measures of the angles of a triangle is 180°.
  b) Hyperbolic geometry.
    The sum of the measures of the angles of a triangle is less than 180°.
  c) Elliptical geometry.
    The sum of the measures of the angles of a triangle is greater than 180°.

In Exercises 19–24 describe the accomplishments of the mathematician.

19. Benoit Mandelbrot Answers will vary.

20. G. F. Bernhard Riemann Answers will vary.

21. Nikolay Ivanovich Lobachevsky Answers will vary.

22. Carl Friedrich Gauss Answers will vary.

23. Janos Bolyai Answers will vary.

24. Girolamo Saccheri Answers will vary.

Internet/Research Activities

In Exercises 25–27, references include the Internet, books on art, encyclopedias, and history of mathematics books.

25. To complete his masterpiece *Circle Limit III*, M. C. Escher studied a model of hyperbolic geometry called

the *Poincaré disk*. Write a paper on the Poincaré disk and how it was used in Escher's art. Include representations of *infinity* and the concepts of *point* and *line* in hyperbolic geometry.

▲ Escher's *Circle Limit III*

26. To transfer his two-dimensional tiling known as *Symmetry Work 45* to a sphere, M. C. Escher used the spherical geometry of Bernhard Riemann. Write a paper on Escher's use of geometry to complete this masterpiece.

27. Go to the Web site *Fantastic Fractals* at www.fantastic-fractals.com and study the information about fractals given there. Print copies, in color if a color printer is available, of the Mandlebrot set and the Julia set.

CHAPTER 9 *Summary*

Important Facts and Concepts

Examples and Discussion

Important Facts and Concepts	Examples and Discussion
Section 9.1	
Point, line, plane, ray, half line, line segment, angle, and related terms and definitions are discussed throughout Section 9.1.	Discussion, pages 480–482, Examples 1 and 2, pages 481–483
Two angles are **complementary angles** if the sum of their measures is 90°. Two angles are **supplementary angles** if the sum of their measures is 180°.	Examples 3 and 4, pages 484 and 485
Vertical angles, alternate interior angles, alternate exterior angles, and **corresponding angles** and related terms are discussed in Section 9.1	Discussion, pages 485–486, Example 6, page 486
Section 9.2	
The sum of the measures of the interior angles of an *n*-sided polygon is $(n - 2)\,180°$.	Discussion, page 491, Example 1, page 491
Two polygons are **similar** if their corresponding angles have the same measure and the lengths of their corresponding sides are in proportion.	Discussion, page 492, Examples 2–3, pages 493–494

Section 9.3
Perimeter, P, and Area, A

TRIANGLE

$P = s_1 + s_2 + s_3 \quad (s_3 = b)$

$A = \frac{1}{2}bh$

SQUARE

$P = 4s$

$A = s^2$

RECTANGLE

$P = 2l + 2w$

$A = lw$

PARALLELOGRAM

$P = 2b + 2w$

$A = bh$

TRAPEZOID

$P = s_1 + s_2 + b_1 + b_2$

$A = \frac{1}{2}h(b_1 + b_2)$

Discussion, pages 500–502, Example 1, page 502, Examples 3–5, pages 504–506

Pythagorean Theorem

$a^2 + b^2 = c^2$

Example 2, page 503

Area, A, and Perimeter, P, of a Circle

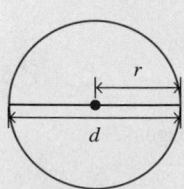

$A = \pi r^2; C = 2\pi r$ or $C = \pi d$

Discussion, page 504, Examples 3–5, pages 504–506

Section 9.4

Volume, V, and Surface Area, SA

CUBE

$V = s^3$

$SA = 6s^2$

RECTANGULAR SOLID

$V = lwh$

$SA = 2lw + 2wh + 2lh$

Discussion, pages 512–514,
Examples 1–8, pages 514–519

CYLINDER

$V = \pi r^2 h$

$SA = 2\pi rh + 2\pi r^2$

CONE

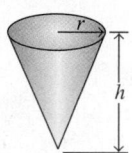

$V = \frac{1}{3}\pi r^2 h$

$SA = \pi r^2 + \pi r\sqrt{r^2 + h^2}$

SPHERE

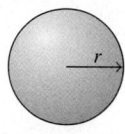

$V = \frac{4}{3}\pi r^3$

$SA = 4\pi r^2$

PYRAMID

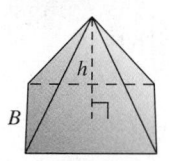

$V = \frac{1}{3}Bh$, where

B is the area of the base

PRISM

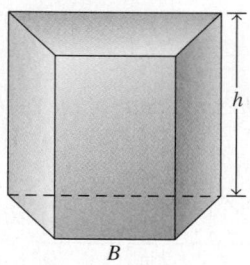

$V = Bh$, where B is the area of the base

Section 9.5

Rigid Motions

The **rigid motions: Reflections, translations, rotations,** and **glide reflections** are defined and discussed throughout Section 9.5.

Discussion, pages 525–526, 528, 529, 532,
Examples 1–6, pages 526–532

Reflective symmetry, rotational symmetry, and **tessellations** are described in Section 9.5.

Discussion, pages 532–533, Examples 7–8,
pages 533–534

Section 9.6

Topology

Möbius strip, Klein bottle, maps, Jordan curves, and **topological equivalence** are described in Section 9.6.

Discussion, pages 543–547

Section 9.7

The Fifth Axiom

Fifth axiom in Euclidean geometry: Given a line and a point not on the line, only one line can be drawn through the given point parallel to the given line.

Fifth axiom in elliptical geometry: Given a line and a point not on the line, no line can be drawn through the given point parallel to the given line.

Fifth axiom in hyperbolic geometry: Given a line and a point not on the line, two or more lines can be drawn through the given point parallel to the given line.

Discussion, pages 550–555

CHAPTER 9 Review Exercises

9.1

In Exercises 1–6, use the figure shown to determine the following.

1. $\angle ABF \cap \angle DBI$ $\overrightarrow{BF}$

2. $\overrightarrow{AB} \cap \overrightarrow{DC}$ $\overline{AD}$

3. $\overline{BF} \cup \overline{FC} \cup \overline{BC}$ $\triangle BFC$

4. $\overset{\circ\rightarrow}{BH} \cup \overset{\circ\rightarrow}{HB}$ $\overleftrightarrow{BH}$

5. $\overleftrightarrow{HI} \cap \overleftrightarrow{EG}$ $\{F\}$

6. $\overset{\circ\rightarrow}{CF} \cap \overset{\circ\rightarrow}{CG}$ $\{\ \}$

7. $m\angle A = 35.4°$. Determine the measure of the complement of $\angle A$. 54.6°

8. $m\angle B = 100.5°$. Determine the measure of the supplement $\angle B$. 79.5°

9.2

In Exercises 9–12, use the similar triangles ABC and A'B'C shown to determine the following.

9. The length of $\overline{BC}$ 10.2 in.

10. The length of $\overline{A'B'}$ 2 in.

11. $m\angle BAC$ 58°

12. $m\angle ABC$ 92°

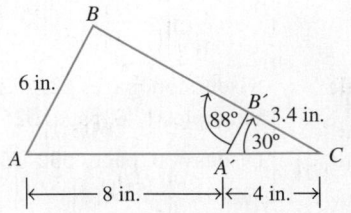

13. In the following figure, l_1 and l_2 are parallel lines. Determine $m\angle 1$ through $m\angle 6$.*

14. Determine the sum of the measures of the interior angles of an octagon. 1080°

9.3

In Exercises 15–18, determine (a) the area and (b) the perimeter of the figure.

15.
9 mi
11 mi
a) 99 mi² b) 40 mi

16.
4 in.
3.2 in. 2 in. 3.2 in.
9 in.
a) 13 in² b) 19.4 in.

17.
9 in. 7 in.
12 in.
a) 84 in² b) 42 in.

18.
3 km
4 km
(a) 6 km² b) 12 km

19. Determine (a) the area and (b) the circumference of the circle. Use the $\boxed{\pi}$ key on a calculator and round your answer to the nearest hundredth.

a) 153.94 ft² b) 43.98 ft

7 ft

*See Instructor Answer Appendix

In Exercises 20 and 21, determine the shaded area. When appropriate, use the $\boxed{\pi}$ key on your calculator and round your answer to the nearest hundredth.

20.

64.38m²

10 m

21.

12 yd

79.73 yd²

12 yd   6 yd

22. *Cost of Kitchen Tile* Determine the total cost of covering a 14-ft by 16-ft kitchen floor with ceramic tile. The cost of the tile selected is $5.25 per square foot. $1176

9.4

In Exercises 23–26, determine (a) the volume and (b) the surface area of the figure. When appropriate, use the $\boxed{\pi}$ key on your calculator and round your answer to the nearest hundredth.

23.

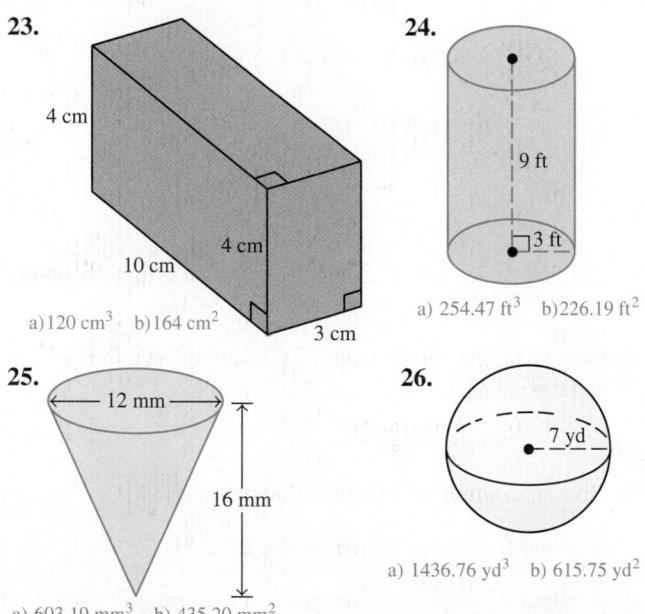

4 cm

4 cm

10 cm

3 cm

a) 120 cm³   b) 164 cm²

24.

9 ft

3 ft

a) 254.47 ft³   b) 226.19 ft²

25.

12 mm

16 mm

a) 603.19 mm³   b) 435.20 mm²

26.

7 yd

a) 1436.76 yd³   b) 615.75 yd²

In Exercises 27 and 28, determine the volume of the figure.

27.

432 m³

9 m   12 m

8 m

15 m

28.

5 ft   7 ft

6 ft   5 ft

28 ft³

In Exercises 29 and 30, determine the volume of the shaded area. When appropriate, use the $\boxed{\pi}$ key and round your answer to the nearest hundredth.

29.

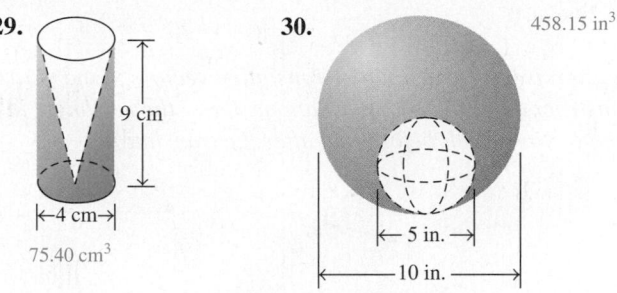

9 cm

4 cm

75.40 cm³

30.

458.15 in³

5 in.

10 in.

31. *Water Trough* Steven Dale has a water trough whose ends are trapezoids and whose sides are rectangles, as illustrated. He is afraid that the base it is sitting on will not support the weight of the trough when it is filled with water. He knows that the base will support 4800 lb.

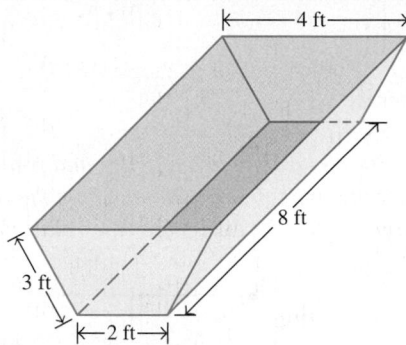

4 ft

8 ft

3 ft

2 ft

a) If the trough is filled with water, determine the number of cubic feet of water contained in the trough. ≈ 67.88 ft³

b) Determine the total weight, assuming that the trough weighs 375 lb and the water weighs 62.4 lb per cubic foot. Is the base strong enough to support the trough filled with water? 4610.7 lb; yes

c) If 1 gal of water weighs 8.3 lb, how many gallons of water will the trough hold? ≈ 510.3 gal

9.5

In Exercises 32 and 33, use the given triangle and reflection lines to construct the indicated reflections. Show the triangle in the positions both before and after the reflection.

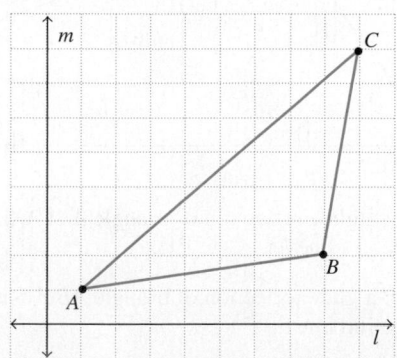

m

C

B

A

l

32. Construct the reflection of triangle *ABC* (see p. 561) about line *l*. *

33. Construct the reflection of triangle *ABC* (see p. 561) about line *m*.*

In Exercises 34 and 35, use translation vectors **v** *and* **w** *to construct the indicated translations. Show the rectangle in the positions both before and after the translation.*

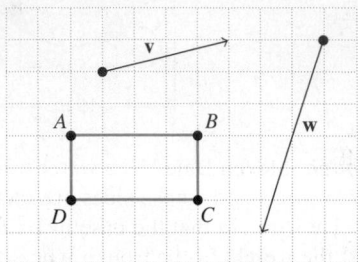

34. Construct the translation of rectangle *ABCD* using translation vector **v**.*

35. Construct the translation of rectangle *ABCD* using translation vector **w**.*

In Exercises 36–38, use the given figure and rotation point P to construct the indicated rotations. Show the trapezoid in the positions both before and after the rotation.

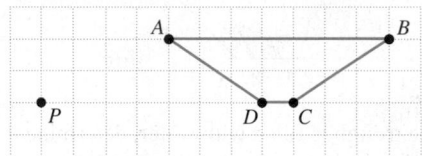

36. Construct a 90° rotation of trapezoid *ABCD* about point *P*.*

37. Construct a 180° rotation of trapezoid *ABCD* about point *P*.*

38. Construct a 270° rotation of trapezoid *ABCD* about point *P* .*

In Exercises 39 and 40, use the given figure, translation vector **v**, *and reflection lines l and m to construct the indicated glide reflections. Show the triangle in the positions both before and after the glide reflection.*

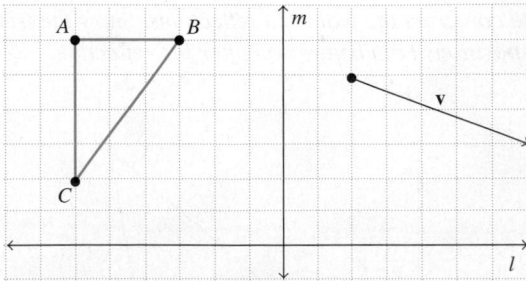

39. Construct a glide reflection of triangle *ABC* using vector **v** and reflection line *l*.*

40. Construct a glide reflection of triangle *ABC* using vector **v** and reflection line *m*.*

In Exercises 41 and 42, use the following figure to answer the following questions.

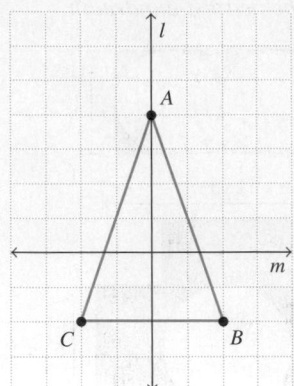

41. Does triangle *ABC* have reflective symmetry about line *l*? Explain. Yes

42. Does triangle *ABC* have reflective symmetry about line *m*? Explain. No

In Exercises 43 and 44, use the following figure to answer the following questions.

43. Does rectangle *ABCD* have 90° rotational symmetry about point *P*? Explain. No

44. Does rectangle *ABCD* have 180° rotational symmetry about point *P*? Explain. Yes

9.6

45. Give an example of an object that has

a) genus 0.
Answers will vary.

b) genus 1.
Answers will vary.

c) genus 2.
Answers will vary.

d) genus 3 or more.
Answers will vary.

46. Color the map by using a maximum of four colors so that no two regions with a common border have the same color.
Answers will vary.

*See Instructor Answer Appendix

47. Determine whether point *A* is inside or outside the Jordan curve. Outside

9.7

48. State the fifth axiom of Euclidean, elliptical, and hyperbolic geometry.*

49. Develop a fractal by beginning with a square and replacing each side —— with a ⌐⌐. Repeat this process twice.*

50. Construct a Koch snowflake by beginning with an equilateral triangle and replacing each side with a ⌃. Repeat this process twice.*

*See Instructor Answer Appendix

CHAPTER 9 Test

In Exercises 1–4, use the figure to describe the following sets of points.

1. $\overrightarrow{AF} \cap \overrightarrow{EF}$ $\overrightarrow{EF}$

2. $\overline{BC} \cup \overline{CD} \cup \overline{BD}$ $\triangle BCD$

3. $\angle EDF \cap \angle BDC$ {D}

4. $\overrightarrow{AC} \cup \overrightarrow{BA}$ $\overleftrightarrow{AC}$

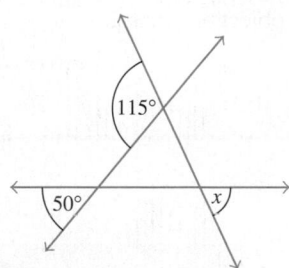

5. $m\angle A = 74.9°$. Determine the measure of the complement of $\angle A$. 15.1°

6. $m\angle B = 10.4°$. Determine the measure of the supplement of $\angle B$. 169.6°

7. In the figure, determine the measure of $\angle x$. 65°

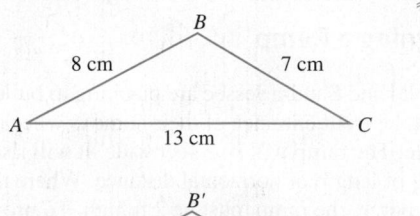

8. Determine the sum of the measures of the interior angles of a pentagon. 540°

9. Triangles *ABC* and *A'B'C'* are similar figures. Determine the length of side $\overline{B'C'}$.

≈2.69 cm

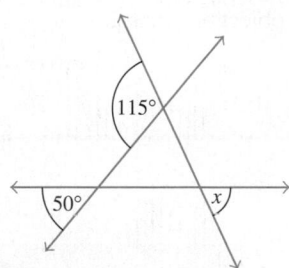

10. Right triangle *ABC* (see below) has one leg of length 12 in. and a hypotenuse of length 13 in.

a) Determine the length of the other leg. 5 in.

b) Determine the perimeter of the triangle. 30 in.

c) Determine the area of the triangle. 30 in²

11. Determine (a) the volume and (b) the surface area of a sphere of diameter 14 cm. a) 1436.76 cm³ b) 615.75 cm²

12. Determine the volume of the shaded area. Use the $\boxed{\pi}$ key on your calculator and round your answer to the nearest hundredth. 59.43 m³

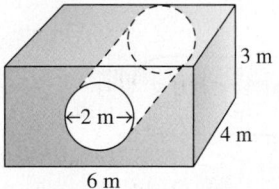

13. Determine the volume of the pyramid. 112 ft³

14. Construct a reflection of rectangle *ABCD*, shown below, about line *l*. Show the rectangle in the positions both before and after the reflection. *

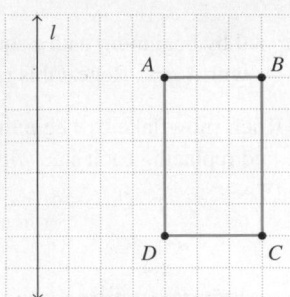

15. Construct a translation of quadrilateral *ABCD*, shown below, using translation vector **v**. Show the quadrilateral in the positions both before and after the translation.*

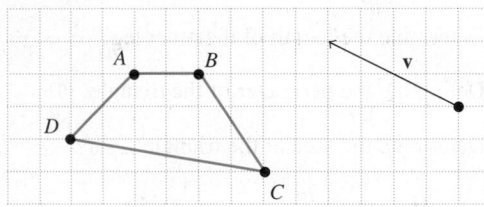

16. Construct a 180° rotation of triangle *ABC*, shown below, about rotation point *P*. Show the triangle in the positions both before and after the rotation.*

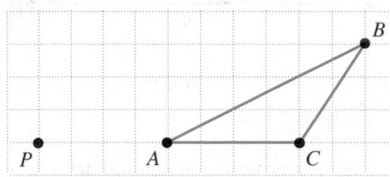

17. Construct a glide reflection of rectangle *ABCD*, shown below, using translation vector **v** and reflection line *l*. Show the rectangle in the positions both before and after the glide reflection.*

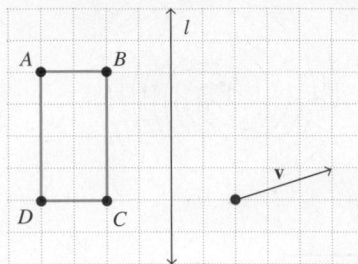

18. Use the figure below to answer the following questions.

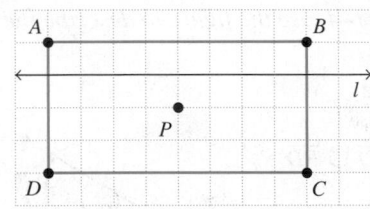

a) Does rectangle *ABCD* have reflective symmetry about line *l*? Explain. No

b) Does rectangle *ABCD* have 180° rotational symmetry about point *P*? Explain. Yes

19. What is a Möbius strip? A surface with one side and one edge

20. a) Sketch an object of genus 1. Answers will vary.

b) Sketch an object of genus 2. Answers will vary.

*See Instructor Answer Appendix

GROUP PROJECTS

Supporting a Hot Tub

1. Samantha Saraniti is thinking of buying a circular hot tub 12 ft in diameter, 4 ft deep, and weighing 475 lb. She wants to place the hot tub on a deck built to support 30,000 lb.

a) Determine the volume of the water in the hot tub in cubic feet.

b) Determine the number of gallons of water the hot tub will hold. (*Note:* 1 ft^3 ≈ 7.5 gal.)

c) Determine the weight of the water in the hot tub. (*Hint:* Fresh water weighs about 62.4 lb/ft^3.)

d) Will the deck support the weight of the hot tub and water?

e) Will the deck support the weight of the hot tub, water, and four people, whose average weight is 115 lb?

Designing a Ramp

2. David and Sandra Jessee are planning to build a ramp so that the front entrance of their home is wheelchair accessible. The ramp will be 3 feet wide. It will rise 2 in. for each foot of length of horizontal distance. Where the ramp meets the porch, the ramp must be 2 ft high. To provide stability for the ramp, the Jessees will install a slab of concrete 4 in. thick and 6 in. longer and wider than the ramp (see accompanying figure on page 565). The top of the slab will be level with the ground. The ramp may be constructed of concrete or pressure-treated lumber. You are to estimate the cost of materials for constructing the slab, the ramp of concrete, and the ramp of pressure-treated lumber.

Slab

a) Determine the length of the base of the ramp.

b) Determine the dimensions of the concrete slab on which the ramp will be set.

c) Determine the volume of the concrete in cubic yards needed to construct the slab.

d) If ready-mix concrete costs $45 per cubic yard, determine the cost of the concrete needed to construct the slab.

Concrete Ramp

e) To build the ramp of concrete, a form in the shape of the ramp must be framed. The two sides of the form are triangular, and the shape of the end, which is against the porch, is rectangular. The form will be framed from $\frac{3}{4}$-in. plywood, which comes in 4 ft $\times$ 8 ft sheets. Determine the number of sheets of plywood needed. Assume that the entire sheet(s) will be used to make the sides and the end of the form and that there is no waste.

f) If the plywood costs $18.95 for a 4 ft $\times$ 8 ft sheet, determine the cost of the plywood.

g) To brace the form, the Jessees will need two boards 2 in. $\times$ 4 in. $\times$ 8 ft (referred to as 8-ft 2 $\times$ 4's) and

six pieces of lumber 2 in. $\times$ 4 in. $\times$ 3 ft. These six pieces of lumber will be cut from 8-ft 2 $\times$ 4 boards. Determine the number of 8-ft 2 $\times$ 4 boards needed.

h) Determine the cost of the 8-ft 2 $\times$ 4 boards needed in part (g) if one board costs $2.14.

i) Determine the volume, in cubic yards, of concrete needed to fill the form.

j) Determine the cost of the concrete needed to fill the form.

k) Determine the total cost of materials for building the ramp of concrete by adding the results in parts (d), (f), (h), and (j).

Wooden Ramp

l) Determine the length of the top of the ramp.

m) The top of the ramp will be constructed of $\frac{5}{4}$-in. $\times$ 6 in. $\times$ 10 ft pressure-treated lumber. The boards will be butted end to end to make the necessary length and will be supported from underneath by a wooden frame. Determine the number of boards needed to cover the top of the ramp. The boards are laid lengthwise on the ramp.

n) Determine the cost of the boards to cover the top of the ramp if the price of a 10-ft length is $6.47.

o) To support the top of the ramp, the Jessees will need 10 pieces of 8-ft 2 $\times$ 4's. The price of a pressure-treated 8-ft 2 $\times$ 4 is $2.44. Determine the cost of the supports.

p) Determine the cost of the materials for building a wooden ramp by adding the amounts from parts (d), (n), and (o).

q) Are the materials for constructing a concrete ramp or a wooden ramp less expensive?

10

Mathematical Systems

What You Will Learn

- Mathematical systems
- Commutative and associative properties
- Closure, identity element, and inverses
- Groups and commutative groups
- Clock arithmetic
- Mathematical systems without numbers
- Modular arithmetic

Why This is Important

Mathematics plays a crucial role in the study of the interaction between many objects of interest to scientists. One branch of mathematics of particular importance to this study is group theory. Physicists and chemists rely on group theory to study the behavior of the tiniest particles that make up an atom in a scientific field known as *quantum mechanics*. Group theory can be used to predict the interactive behavior of subatomic particles within an atom, atoms within a molecule, and molecules within a chemical reaction. Group theory also plays an important role in robotics, computer graphics, weather forecasting, musical theory, and medical image analysis.

◄ *Group theory plays an important role in robotics and many other aspects of modern technology.*

Groups

▲ *The big bang theory uses groups to address questions relating to the size, structure, and future of the universe.*

How big is the universe? Is there an end to the universe? Does the universe continue to expand? Such questions are addressed by the scientific theory known as the *big bang theory*. In this section, we will introduce a mathematical structure known as a *group*. Many modern scientific theories, including the big bang theory, make use of groups and other mathematical topics discussed in this book.

Why *This is Important* The more we understand about our universe, the better prepared we are to answer questions regarding the history and future of planet Earth.

W e begin our discussion by introducing a mathematical system. As you will learn shortly, you already know and use many mathematical systems.

> **Definition: Mathematical System**
> A **mathematical system** consists of a set of elements and at least one binary operation.

> **TIMELY TIP**
> Throughout this section, we will work with many different sets of numbers, such as natural numbers, whole numbers, integers, rational numbers, and real numbers. A review of the numbers that make up each of these sets can be found on page 252–253 in Section 5.5.

In the above definition, we mention binary operation. A *binary operation* is an operation, or rule, that can be performed on two and only two elements of a set. The result is a single element. When we add *two* integers, the sum is *one* integer. When we multiply *two* integers, the product is *one* integer. Thus, addition and multiplication are both binary operations. Is finding the reciprocal of a number a binary operation? No, it is an operation on a single element of a set.

When you learned how to add integers, you were introduced to a mathematical system. The set of elements is the set of integers, and the binary operation is addition. When you learned how to multiply integers, you became familiar with a second mathematical system. The set of integers with the operation of subtraction and the set of integers with the operation of division are two other examples of mathematical systems since subtraction and division are also binary operations.

Some mathematical systems are used in solving everyday problems, such as planning work schedules. Others are more abstract and are used primarily in research, chemistry, physical structure, matter, the nature of genes, and other scientific fields.

Commutative and Associative Properties

Once a mathematical system is defined, its structure may display certain properties. Consider the set of integers

$$I = \{\dots, -3, -2, -1, 0, 1, 2, 3, \dots\}$$

Recall that the ellipsis, the three dots at each end of the set, indicates that the set continues in the same manner.

The set of integers can be studied with the operations of addition, subtraction, multiplication, and division as separate mathematical systems. For example, when we study the set of integers under the operations of addition or multiplication, we see that the commutative and associative properties hold. The general forms of the properties are shown here.

Woody Allen and Diane Keaton in *Annie Hall*

How and when will the universe end? In the Woody Allen movie *Annie Hall*, a boy (Woody Allen), having just read that the universe is expanding, becomes so worried that he can't do his homework. "Someday it will break apart," he tells his psychiatrist, "and that will be the end of everything." But his mother snaps, "You're here in Brooklyn! Brooklyn is not expanding!"

The universe could break apart. That, however, will not be for trillions of years, and life as we know it on Earth will cease long before that. Our sun, halfway through its estimated 10-billion-year lifetime, is slowly brightening. In about 1 billion years, its energy output will have increased by at least 10%, turning Earth into a Venus-like hothouse incapable of supporting life as we know it. Long before that, humans may make plans to escape to Mars, which is farther from the sun and hence cooler. Although quite some time away, scientists are already considering various scenarios to make the surface of Mars a livable habitat.

Commutative and Associative Properties

For any elements a, b, and c

	Addition	Multiplication
Commutative property	$a + b = b + a$	$a \cdot b = b \cdot a$
Associative property	$(a + b) + c = a + (b + c)$	$(a \cdot b) \cdot c = a \cdot (b \cdot c)$

The integers *are commutative* under the operations of *addition and multiplication*. For example,

Addition		*Multiplication*
$2 + 4 = 4 + 2$	and	$2 \cdot 4 = 4 \cdot 2$
$6 = 6$		$8 = 8$

The integers, however, *are not commutative* under the operations of *subtraction and division*. For example,

Subtraction		*Division*
$4 - 2 \neq 2 - 4$	and	$4 \div 2 \neq 2 \div 4$
$2 \neq -2$		$2 \neq \frac{1}{2}$

The integers *are associative* under the operations of *addition and multiplication*. For example,

Addition		*Multiplication*
$(1 + 2) + 3 = 1 + (2 + 3)$	and	$(1 \cdot 2) \cdot 3 = 1 \cdot (2 \cdot 3)$
$3 + 3 = 1 + 5$		$2 \cdot 3 = 1 \cdot 6$
$6 = 6$		$6 = 6$

The integers, however, *are not associative* under the operations of *subtraction and division*. See Exercises 21 and 22 at the end of this section.

To say that a set of elements is commutative under a given operation means that the commutative property holds for *any* elements a and b in the set. Similarly, to say that a set of elements is associative under a given operation means that the associative property holds for *any* elements a, b, and c in the set.

Consider the mathematical system consisting of the set of integers under the operation of addition. Because the set of integers is infinite, this mathematical system is an example of an *infinite mathematical system*. We will study certain properties of this mathematical system. The first property we will examine is closure.

Closure

The sum of any two integers is an integer. Therefore, the set of integers is said to be *closed*, or to satisfy the *closure property*, under the operation of addition.

Definition: Closure
If a binary operation is performed on any two elements of a set and the result is an element of the set, then that set is **closed** (or has **closure**) under the given binary operation.

Is the set of integers closed under the operation of multiplication? The answer is yes. When any two integers are multiplied, the product will be an integer.

Is the set of integers closed under the operation of subtraction? Again, the answer is yes. The difference of any two integers is an integer.

Is the set of integers closed under the operation of division? The answer is no because two integers may have a quotient that is not an integer. For example, if we select the integers 2 and 3, the quotient of 2 divided by 3 is $\frac{2}{3}$, which is not an integer. Thus, the integers are not closed under the operation of division.

We showed that the set of integers was not closed under the operation of division by finding two integers whose quotient was not an integer. A specific example illustrating that a specific property is not true is called a *counterexample*. Mathematicians and scientists often try to find a counterexample to confirm that a specific property is not always true.

Identity Element

Is there an element in the set of integers that, when added to any given integer, results in a sum that is the given integer? The answer is yes. The sum of 0 and any integer is the given integer. For example, $1 + 0 = 0 + 1 = 1$, $-4 + 0 = 0 + (-4) = -4$, and so on. For this reason, we call 0 the *additive identity element* for the set of integers. Note that for any integer a, $a + 0 = 0 + a = a$.

> **Definition: Identity Element**
> An **identity element** is an element in a set such that when a binary operation is performed on it and any given element in the set, the result is the given element.

Is there an identity element for the set of integers under the operation of multiplication? The answer is yes; it is the number 1. Note that $2 \cdot 1 = 1 \cdot 2 = 2$, $3 \cdot 1 = 1 \cdot 3 = 3$, and so on. For any integer a, $a \cdot 1 = 1 \cdot a = a$. For this reason, 1 is called the *multiplicative identity element* for the set of integers.

Inverses

What integer, when added to 4, gives a sum of 0; that is, $4 + \rule{1cm}{0.15cm} = 0$? The shaded area is to be filled in with the integer -4: $4 + (-4) = 0$. We say that -4 is the additive inverse of 4 and that 4 is the additive inverse of -4. Note that the sum of the element and its additive inverse gives the additive identity element 0. What is the additive inverse of 12? Since $12 + (-12) = 0$, -12 is the additive inverse of 12.

Other examples of integers and their additive inverses are

Element	+	Additive Inverse	=	Identity Element
0	+	0	=	0
2	+	(−2)	=	0
−5	+	5	=	0

Note that for the operation of addition, every integer a has a unique inverse, $-a$, such that $a + (-a) = -a + a = 0$.

> **Definition: Inverse**
> When a binary operation is performed on two elements in a set and the result is the identity element for the binary operation, each element is said to be the **inverse** of the other.

TIMELY TIP

Note that the set of elements need *not* be commutative for the mathematical system to be a group. Also note that *every* element in the set must have an inverse for the mathematical system to be a group.

Does every integer have an inverse under the operation of multiplication? For multiplication, the product of an integer and its inverse must yield the multiplicative identity element, 1. What is the multiplicative inverse of 2? That is, 2 times what number gives 1?

$$2 \cdot \boxed{} = 1 \qquad 2 \cdot \tfrac{1}{2} = 1$$

However, since $\frac{1}{2}$ is not an integer, 2 does not have a multiplicative inverse in the set of integers.

Group

Let's review what we have learned about the mathematical system consisting of the set of integers under the operation of addition.

1. The set of integers is *closed* under the operation of addition.
2. The set of integers has an *identity element* under the operation of addition.
3. Each element in the set of integers has an *inverse* under the operation of addition.
4. The *associative property* holds for the set of integers under the operation of addition.

The set of integers under the operation of addition is an example of a *group*. The properties of a group can be summarized as follows.

Properties of a Group

Any mathematical system that meets the following four requirements is called a **group**.
1. The set of elements is *closed* under the given operation.
2. An *identity element* exists for the set under the given operation.
3. Every element in the set has an *inverse* under the given operation.
4. The set of elements is *associative* under the given operation.

It is often very time consuming to show that the associative property holds for all cases. In many of the examples that follow, we will state that the associative property holds for the given set of elements under the given operation.

Commutative Group

The commutative property does not need to hold for a mathematical system to be a group. However, if a mathematical system meets the four requirements of a group and is also commutative under the given operation, the mathematical system is a *commutative* (or *abelian*) *group*. The abelian group is named after Niels Abel (see the *Profiles in Mathematics* in the margin).

Definition: Commutative Group

A group that satisfies the commutative property is called a **commutative group** (or **abelian group**).

Because the commutative property holds for the set of integers under the operation of addition, the set of integers under the operation of addition is not only a group, but it is also a commutative group.

Properties of a Commutative Group

A mathematical system is a **commutative group** if all five of the following conditions hold.

1. The set of elements is *closed* under the given operation.
2. An *identity element* exists for the set under the given operation.
3. Every element in the set has an *inverse* under the given operation.
4. The set of elements is *associative* under the given operation.
5. The set of elements is *commutative* under the given operation.

To determine whether a mathematical system is a group under a given operation, *check, in the following order*, whether (1) the system is closed under the given operation, (2) there is an identity element in the set for the given operation, (3) every element in the set has an inverse under the given operation, and (4) the associative property holds under the given operation. If *any* of these four requirements is *not* met, stop and state that the mathematical system is not a group. If asked to determine whether the mathematical system is a commutative group, you also need to determine whether the commutative property holds for the given operation.

Example 1 *Whole Numbers Under Addition*

Determine whether the mathematical system consisting of the set of whole numbers under the operation of addition forms a group.

Solution Recall from Chapter 5 that the set of whole numbers is $\{0, 1, 2, 3, \ldots\}$. We will check the properties required, using the operation of addition, to determine if the mathematical system is a group.

1. *Closure*: The sum of any two whole numbers is a whole number. Therefore, the set of whole numbers is closed under the operation of addition.

2. *Identity element*: The additive identity for the set of whole numbers is 0. For example, $1 + 0 = 0 + 1 = 1$, and $2 + 0 = 0 + 2 = 2$, and so on. For any whole number a, $a + 0 = 0 + a = a$. Thus, the mathematical system contains an identity element.

3. *Inverse elements*: For the mathematical system to be a group, each element must have an additive inverse *in the set*. Remember that the additive inverse of a number is the *opposite* of the number. For example, the additive inverse of 1 is -1, the additive inverse of 2 is -2, the additive inverse of 3 is -3, and so on. Since the numbers $-1, -2, -3, \ldots$ are *not* in the set of whole numbers, not every number has an inverse in the set. Therefore, this mathematical system is not a group.

Because we have already shown that the set of whole numbers under the operation of addition is not a group, there is no need to check the associative property. ∎

Example 2 *Rational Numbers Under Multiplication*

Determine whether the set of rational numbers under the operation of multiplication forms a group.

Solution Recall from Chapter 5 that the rational numbers are the set of numbers of the form $\frac{p}{q}$, where p and q are integers and $q \neq 0$. The set of rational numbers includes all fractions and integers.

1. *Closure*: The product of any two rational numbers is a rational number. Therefore, the rational numbers are closed under the operation of multiplication.

2. *Identity element*: The multiplicative identity element for the set of rational numbers is 1. Note, for example, that $3 \cdot 1 = 1 \cdot 3 = 3$, and $\frac{3}{8} \cdot 1 = 1 \cdot \frac{3}{8} = \frac{3}{8}$. For any rational number a, $a \cdot 1 = 1 \cdot a = a$.

3. *Inverse elements*: For the mathematical system to be a group under the operation of multiplication, *each and every* rational number must have a multiplicative inverse in the set of rational numbers. Remember that for the operation of multiplication, the product of a number and its inverse must give the multiplicative identity element, 1. Let's check a few rational numbers:

$$\text{Rational Number} \quad \cdot \quad \text{Inverse} \quad = \quad \text{Identity Element}$$
$$3 \quad \cdot \quad \frac{1}{3} \quad = \quad 1$$
$$\frac{2}{3} \quad \cdot \quad \frac{3}{2} \quad = \quad 1$$
$$-\frac{1}{5} \quad \cdot \quad -5 \quad = \quad 1$$

Looking at these examples you might deduce that each rational number does have an inverse. However, one rational number, 0, does not have an inverse.

$$0 \cdot ? = 1$$

Because there is no rational number that when multiplied by 0 gives 1, 0 does not have a multiplicative inverse. Since not *every* rational number has an inverse, this mathematical system is not a group.

There is no need at this point to check the associative property because we have already shown that the mathematical system of rational numbers under the operation of multiplication is not a group. ∎

Example 3 *Real Numbers Under Addition*

Determine whether the set of real numbers under the operation of addition forms a commutative group.

Solution Recall from Chapter 5 that the real numbers can be thought of as the numbers that correspond to *each* point on the real number line. The set of real numbers includes all rational numbers and all irrational numbers.

1. *Closure*: The sum of any two real numbers is a real number. Therefore, the real numbers are closed under the operation of addition.

2. *Identity element*: The additive identity element for the set of real numbers is 0. For example, $\frac{2}{3} + 0 = 0 + \frac{2}{3} = \frac{2}{3}$ and $\sqrt{5} + 0 = 0 + \sqrt{5} = \sqrt{5}$. For any real number a, $a + 0 = 0 + a = a$.

3. *Inverse elements*: For the set of real numbers under the operation of addition to be a commutative group, each and every real number must have an additive inverse in the set of real numbers. For the operation of addition, the sum of a real number and its additive inverse, or *opposite*, must be the additive identity element, 0. From Chapter 5, we saw that every real number a has an opposite $-a$ such that $a + (-a) = -a + a = 0$. Recall also that $0 + 0 = 0$; therefore, 0 is its own additive inverse. Thus, all real numbers have an additive inverse.

4. *Associative property*: From Chapter 5, we know that the real numbers are associative under the operation of addition. That is, for any real numbers a, b, and c, $(a + b) + c = a + (b + c)$.

5. *Commutative property*: From Chapter 5, we know that the real numbers are commutative under the operation of addition. That is, for any real numbers a and b, $a + b = b + a$.

Since all five properties (closure, identity element, inverse elements, associative property, and commutative property) hold, the set of real numbers under the operation of addition forms a commutative group. ∎

SECTION 10.1

Exercises

Warm Up Exercises

In Exercises 1–14, fill in the blanks with an appropriate word, phrase, or symbol(s).

1. A mathematical system consists of a set of elements and at least one _____ operation. Binary

2. A binary operation is an operation or rule that can be performed on exactly two elements of a set, with the result being a(n) _____ element. Single

3. The commutative property of addition states: $a + b =$ _____. $b + a$

4. The commutative property of multiplication states: $a \cdot b =$ _____. $b \cdot a$

5. The associative property of multiplication states: $(a \cdot b) \cdot c =$ _____. $a \cdot (b \cdot c)$

6. The associative property of addition states: $(a + b) + c =$ _____. $a + (b + c)$

7. If a binary operation is performed on any two elements of a set and the result is an element of the set, then that set is _____ under the given binary operation. Closed

8. A specific example illustrating that a property is not true is called a(n) _____. Counterexample

9. Since the sum of 0 and any integer is the given integer, we say that 0 is the additive _____ element for the set of the integers under the operation of addition. Identity

10. Since the product of 1 and any integer is the given integer, we say that 1 is the _____ identity element for the set of the integers under the operation of multiplication. Multiplicative

11. When a binary operation is performed on two elements in a set and the result is the identity element for the binary operation, each element is said to be the _____ of the other. Inverse

12. If a mathematical system possesses the following properties—closure, identity element, inverses, and the associative property—then the mathematical system is a(n) _____. Group

13. A group that also satisfies the commutative property is called a(n) _____ (or abelian) group. Commutative

14. Another name for a commutative group is a(n) _____ group. Abelian

Practice the Skills

15. Give the commutative property of multiplication and illustrate the property with an example.
    $a \cdot b = b \cdot a$ for any elements a and b; $2 \cdot 3 = 3 \cdot 2$

16. Give the commutative property of addition and illustrate the property with an example.
    $a + b = b + a$ for any elements a and b; $3 + 4 = 4 + 3$

17. Give the associative property of addition and illustrate the property with an example. $(a + b) + c = a + (b + c)$ for any elements a, b, and c; $(3 + 4) + 5 = 3 + (4 + 5)$

18. Give the associative property of multiplication and illustrate the property with an example. $(a \cdot b) \cdot c = a \cdot (b \cdot c)$ for any elements a, b, and c; $(2 \cdot 3) \cdot 4 = 2 \cdot (3 \cdot 4)$

19. Give an example to show that the commutative property does not hold for the set of integers under the operation of division. $4 \div 2 \neq 2 \div 4$
    $2 \neq \dfrac{1}{2}$

20. Give an example to show that the commutative property does not hold for the set of integers under the operation of subtraction. $7 - 3 \neq 3 - 7$
    $4 \neq -4$

21. Give an example to show that the associative property does not hold for the set of integers under the operation of subtraction. *

22. Give an example to show that the associative property does not hold for the set of integers under the operation of division. $(8 \div 4) \div 2 \neq 8 \div (4 \div 2)$
    $1 \neq 4$

Problem Solving

In Exercises 23–36, explain your answer.

23. Is the set of integers a commutative group under the operation of addition? Yes; it satisfies the five properties needed.

24. Is the set of integers a group under the operation of addition? Yes; it satisfies the four properties needed.

25. Is the set of positive integers a group under the operation of addition? No; there is no identity element.

26. Is the set of positive integers a commutative group under the operation of addition? No; there is no identity element.

27. Is the set of positive integers a group under the operation of subtraction? No; the system is not closed.

28. Is the set of negative integers a group under the operation of division? No; the system is not closed.

29. Is the set of negative integers a commutative group under the operation of addition? No; there is no identity element.

30. Is the set of integers a group under the operation of multiplication? No; not all elements have inverses. There is no inverse for any integers except 1 and -1.

31. Is the set of positive integers a commutative group under the operation of multiplication? No; not all elements have inverses.

32. Is the set of negative integers a group under the operation of multiplication? No; the system is not closed.

33. Is the set of rational numbers a group under the operation of addition? Yes; it satisfies the four properties needed.

34. Is the set of rational numbers a commutative group under the operation of multiplication?
    No; not all elements have inverses. There is no inverse for 0.

    *See Instructor Answer Appendix

35. Is the set of rational numbers a commutative group under the operation of division? No; the system is not closed. For example, $\frac{1}{0}$ is undefined.

36. Is the set of rational numbers a group under the operation of subtraction? No; it does not have an identity element and does not satisfy the associative property.

Challenge Problems/Group Activities

In Exercises 37–40, explain your answer.

37. Is the set of real numbers a group under the operation of addition? Yes; it satisfies the four properties needed.

38. Is the set of real numbers a group under the operation of multiplication? No; 0 has no inverse.

39. Is the set of irrational numbers a group under the operation of addition? No; the system is not closed. For example, $\sqrt{2} + (-\sqrt{2}) = 0$, which is rational. There is also no identity element.

40. Is the set of irrational numbers a group under the operation of multiplication?
No; the system is not closed. For example, $\sqrt{2} \cdot \sqrt{2} = 2$, which is rational.

41. Create a mathematical system with two binary operations. Select a set of elements and two binary operations so that one binary operation with the set of elements meets the requirements for a group and the other binary operation does not. Explain why the one binary operation with the set of elements is a group. For the other binary operation and the set of elements, find counterexamples to show that it is not a group. Answers will vary.

Internet/Research Activity

42. There are other classifications of mathematical systems besides groups. For example, there are *rings* and *fields*. Do research to determine the requirements that must be met for a mathematical system to be (a) a ring and (b) a field. (c) Is the set of real numbers, under the operations of addition and multiplication, a field? Ask your instructor for references to use.

Finite Mathematical Systems

▲ *Many applications make use of mathematical systems.*

Suppose you decide to use your slow cooker to cook a roast for a dinner party. You would like to eat at 6:30 P.M., and it will take 10 hours for the roast to cook. What time should you begin to cook the roast in the slow cooker? Or, suppose you need to take medicine every eight hours. You last took the medicine at 7:45 A.M. When should you take the medicine again? Questions such as these involve the use of mathematical systems that we will study in this section.

Why *This is Important* Timekeeping is just one application of *finite mathematical systems.*

In the preceding section, we presented infinite mathematical systems. In this section, we present some finite mathematical systems. A *finite mathematical system* is one whose set contains a finite number of elements.

Clock Arithmetic

Figure 10.1

Let's develop a finite mathematical system called *clock 12 arithmetic*. The set of elements in this system will be the hours on a clock: $\{1, 2, 3, 4, 5, 6, 7, 8, 9, 10, 11, 12\}$. The binary operation that we will use is addition, which we define as movement of the hour hand in a clockwise direction. Assume that it is 4 o'clock. What time will it be in 9 hours? (See Fig. 10.1.) If we add 9 hours to 4 o'clock, the clock will read 1 o'clock. Thus, $4 + 9 = 1$ in clock arithmetic. Would $9 + 4$ be the same as $4 + 9$? Yes it will because $4 + 9 = 9 + 4 = 1$.

Table 10.1 on page 575 is the addition table for clock arithmetic. Its elements are based on the definition of addition as previously illustrated. For example, the sum of 4 and 9 is 1, so we put a 1 in the table where the row to the right of the 4 intersects the column below the 9. Likewise, the sum of 11 and 10 is 9, so we put a 9 in the table where the row to the right of the 11 intersects the column below the 10.

The binary operation of this system is defined by the table. It is denoted by the symbol $+$. To determine the value of $a + b$, where a and b are any two numbers in the set, find a in the left-hand column and find b along the top row. Assume that there is a horizontal line through a and a vertical line through b; the point of intersection of these two lines is where you find the value of $a + b$. For example, $10 + 4 = 2$ has been circled in Table 10.1. Note that $4 + 10$ also equals 2, but this result will not necessarily hold for all examples in this chapter.

Table 10.1 Clock 12 Arithmetic

+	1	2	3	4	5	6	7	8	9	10	11	12
1	2	3	4	5	6	7	8	9	10	11	12	1
2	3	4	5	6	7	8	9	10	11	12	1	2
3	4	5	6	7	8	9	10	11	12	1	2	3
4	5	6	7	8	9	10	11	12	1	2	3	4
5	6	7	8	9	10	11	12	1	2	3	4	5
6	7	8	9	10	11	12	1	2	3	4	5	6
7	8	9	10	11	12	1	2	3	4	5	6	7
8	9	10	11	12	1	2	3	4	5	6	7	8
9	10	11	12	1	2	3	4	5	6	7	8	9
10	11	12	1	②	3	4	5	6	7	8	9	10
11	12	1	2	3	4	5	6	7	8	9	10	11
12	1	2	3	4	5	6	7	8	9	10	11	12

Example 1 *A Commutative Group?*

Determine whether the clock 12 arithmetic system under the operation of addition is a commutative group.

Solution Check the five requirements that must be satisfied for a commutative group.

1. *Closure*: Is the set of elements in clock 12 arithmetic closed under the operation of addition? Yes it is, since Table 10.1 contains only the elements in the set $\{1, 2, 3, 4, 5, 6, 7, 8, 9, 10, 11, 12\}$. If Table 10.1 had contained an element other than the numbers 1 through 12, the set would not have been closed under addition.

2. *Identity element*: Is there an identity element for clock 12 arithmetic? If the time is currently 4 o'clock, how many hours have to pass before it is 4 o'clock again? Twelve hours: $4 + 12 = 12 + 4 = 4$. In fact, given any hour, in 12 hours the clock will return to the starting point. Therefore, 12 is the additive identity element in clock 12 arithmetic.

   In examining Table 10.1, we see that the row of numbers next to the 12 in the left-hand column is identical to the row of numbers along the top. We also see that the column of numbers under the 12 in the top row is identical to the column of numbers on the left. The search for such a column and row is one technique for determining whether an identity element exists for a system defined by a table.

3. *Inverse elements*: Is there an inverse for the number 4 in clock 12 arithmetic for the operation of addition? Recall that the identity element in clock 12 arithmetic is 12. What number when added to 4 gives 12—that is, $4 + \blacksquare = 12$? Table 10.1 shows that $4 + 8 = 12$ and also that $8 + 4 = 12$. Thus, 8 is the additive inverse of 4, and 4 is the additive inverse of 8.

   To find the additive inverse of 7, find 7 in the left-hand column of Table 10.1. Look to the right of the 7 until you come to the identity element 12. Then determine the number at the top of this column. The number is 5. Since $7 + 5 = 5 + 7 = 12$, 5 is the inverse of 7 and 7 is the inverse of 5. The other inverses can be found in the same way. Table 10.2 shows each element in clock 12 arithmetic and its inverse. Note that each element in the set has an *inverse*.

Table 10.2 Clock 12 Inverses

Element	+	Inverse	=	Identity Element
1	+	11	=	12
2	+	10	=	12
3	+	9	=	12
4	+	8	=	12
5	+	7	=	12
6	+	6	=	12
7	+	5	=	12
8	+	4	=	12
9	+	3	=	12
10	+	2	=	12
11	+	1	=	12
12	+	12	=	12

4. *Associative property*: Now consider the associative property. Does $(a + b) + c = a + (b + c)$ for all values a, b, and c of the set? Remember to always evaluate the values within the parentheses first. Let's select some values for a, b, and c.

   Let $a = 2$, $b = 6$, and $c = 8$. Then

$$(2 + 6) + 8 = 2 + (6 + 8)$$
$$8 + 8 = 2 + 2$$
$$4 = 4 \quad \text{True}$$

   Let $a = 5$, $b = 12$, and $c = 9$. Then

$$(5 + 12) + 9 = 5 + (12 + 9)$$
$$5 + 9 = 5 + 9$$
$$2 = 2 \quad \text{True}$$

   Randomly selecting *any* elements a, b, and c of the set reveals $(a + b) + c = a + (b + c)$. Thus, the system of clock 12 arithmetic is associative under the operation of addition. Note that if there is just one set of values a, b, and c such that $(a + b) + c \neq a + (b + c)$, the system is not associative. Usually, you will not be asked to check every case to determine whether the associative property holds. *If not every element in the set appears in every row and column of the table, however, you need to check the associative property carefully.*

5. *Commutative property*: Does the commutative property hold under the given operation? Does $a + b = b + a$ for all elements a and b of the set? Let's randomly select some values for a and b to determine whether the commutative property appears to hold. Let $a = 5$ and $b = 8$; then Table 10.1 shows that

$$5 + 8 = 8 + 5$$
$$1 = 1 \quad \text{True}$$

Let $a = 9$ and $b = 6$; then

$$9 + 6 = 6 + 9$$
$$3 = 3 \quad \text{True}$$

The commutative property holds for these two specific cases. In fact, if we were to select *any* values for a and b, we would find that $a + b = b + a$. Thus, the commutative property of addition is true in clock 12 arithmetic. Note that if there is just one set of values a and b such that $a + b \neq b + a$, the system is not commutative.

This system satisfies the five properties required for a mathematical system to be a commutative group. Thus, clock 12 arithmetic under the operation of addition is a commutative, or abelian, group. ∎

One method that can be used to determine whether a system defined by a table is commutative under the given operation is to determine whether the elements in the table are symmetric about the *main diagonal*. The main diagonal is the diagonal from the upper left-hand corner to the lower right-hand corner of the table. In Table 10.3, the main diagonal is shaded in color.

If the elements are symmetric about the main diagonal, then the system is commutative. If the elements are not symmetric about the main diagonal, then the system is not commutative. If you examine the system in Table 10.3, you see that its elements are symmetric about the main diagonal because the same numbers appear in the same relative positions on opposite sides of the main diagonal. Therefore, this mathematical system is commutative.

It is possible to have groups that are not commutative. Such groups are called *noncommutative* or *nonabelian groups*. However, a *noncommutative group defined by a table must be at least a six-element by six-element table*. Nonabelian groups are illustrated in Exercises 77 through 79 at the end of this section.

Now we will look at another finite mathematical system.

Table 10.3 Symmetry about the Main Diagonal

+	0	1	2	3	4
0	0	1	2	3	4
1	1	2	3	4	0
2	2	3	4	0	1
3	3	4	0	1	2
4	4	0	1	2	3

Table 10.4 A Four-Element System

©	2	4	6	8
2	6	8	2	4
4	8	2	4	6
6	2	4	6	8
8	4	6	8	2

Example 2 *A Finite Mathematical System*

Consider the mathematical system defined by Table 10.4. Assume that the associative property holds for the given operation.

a) List the elements in the set of this mathematical system.

b) Identify the binary operation.

c) Determine whether this mathematical system is a commutative group.

Solution

a) The set of elements for this mathematical system consists of the elements found in the top row or the left-hand column of the table: $\{2, 4, 6, 8\}$.

b) The binary operation is ©.

c) We will determine whether the five requirements for a commutative group are satisfied.

1. *Closure*: All the elements in the table are in the original set of elements $\{2, 4, 6, 8\}$, so the mathematical system is closed.

2. *Identity element*: The identity is 6. Note that the row of elements to the right of the 6 is identical to the top row *and* the column of elements under the 6 is identical to the left-hand column.

3. *Inverse elements*: When an element operates on its inverse element, the result is the identity element. For this example, the identity is 6. To determine the inverse of 2, determine which element from the set, $\{2, 4, 6, \text{ or } 8\}$ replaces the shaded area in the following equation and gives a true statement:

$$2 © \blacksquare = 6$$

From Table 10.4, we see that $2 © 2 = 6$. Thus, 2 is its own inverse.

To determine the inverse of 4, determine which element replaces the shaded area in the following equation and gives a true statement:

$$4 © \blacksquare = 6$$

From Table l0.4, we see that $4 © 8 = 8 © 4 = 6$. Therefore, 4 is the inverse of 8, and 8 is the inverse of 4. The elements and their inverses are shown in Table 10.5. Note that every element in the mathematical system has an inverse.

Table 10.5 Inverses Under ©

Element	©	Inverse	=	Identity Element
2	©	2	=	6
4	©	8	=	6
6	©	6	=	6
8	©	4	=	6

4. *Associative property*: It is given that the associative property holds for this binary operation, ©. One example of the associative property is

$$(2 © 8) © 4 = 2 © (8 © 4)$$
$$4 © 4 = 2 © 6$$
$$2 = 2 \qquad \text{True}$$

5. *Commutative property*: The elements in Table 10.4 are symmetric about the main diagonal, so the commutative property holds for the operation of ©. One example of the commutative property is

$$2 © 4 = 4 © 2$$
$$8 = 8 \qquad \text{True}$$

The five necessary properties hold. Thus, the mathematical system is a commutative group.   ∎

Mathematical Systems Without Numbers

Thus far, all the systems we have discussed have been based on sets of numbers. Example 3 illustrates a mathematical system of symbols rather than numbers.

Table 10.6 A System of Symbols

·	@	P	W
@	P	W	@
P	W	@	P
W	@	P	W

Example 3 *Investigating a System of Symbols*

Use the mathematical system defined by Table 10.6 and determine

a) the set of elements.   b) the binary operation.
c) closure or nonclosure of the system.   d) the identity element.
e) the inverse of @.   f) $(@ \boxdot P) \boxdot P$ and $@ \boxdot (P \boxdot P)$.
g) $W \boxdot P$ and $P \boxdot W$.

Solution

a) The set of elements of this mathematical system is $\{@, P, W\}$.

b) The binary operation is $\boxdot$.

c) Because the table does not contain any symbols other than @, P, and W, the system is closed under $\boxdot$.

d) The identity element is W. Note that the row next to W in the left-hand column is the same as the top row and that the column under W is identical to the left-hand column. We see that

$$@ \odot W = W \odot @ = @$$
$$P \odot W = W \odot P = P$$
$$W \odot W = W$$

e) We know that

element $\odot$ inverse element $=$ identity element,

and since W is the identity element, to find the inverse of $@$ we write

$$@ \odot \blacksquare = W$$

To find the inverse of $@$, we must determine the element to replace the shaded area. Since $@ \odot P = W$ and $P \odot @ = W$, P is the inverse of $@$.

f) We first evaluate the information within parentheses.

$$(@ \odot P) \odot P = W \odot P \qquad \text{and} \qquad @ \odot (P \odot P) = @ \odot @$$
$$= P \qquad\qquad\qquad\qquad\qquad = P$$

g) $W \odot P = P$ and $P \odot W = P$

Example 4 *Is the System a Commutative Group?*

Determine whether the mathematical system defined by Table 10.7 is a commutative group. Assume that the associative property holds for the given operation.

Table 10.7

♪	α	β	γ	δ
α	δ	α	β	γ
β	α	β	γ	δ
γ	β	γ	δ	α
δ	γ	δ	α	β

Solution

1. *Closure*: The system is closed.
2. *Identity element*: The identity element is β.
3. *Inverse elements*: Each element has an inverse, as illustrated in Table 10.8.
4. *Associative property*: It is given that the associative property holds. An example illustrating the associative property is

$$(\gamma ♪ \delta) ♪ \alpha = \gamma ♪ (\delta ♪ \alpha)$$
$$\alpha ♪ \alpha = \gamma ♪ \gamma$$
$$\delta = \delta \quad \text{True}$$

Table 10.8 Inverses Under ♪

Element	♪	Inverse	=	Identity Element
α	♪	γ	=	β
β	♪	β	=	β
γ	♪	α	=	β
δ	♪	δ	=	β

5. *Commutative property*: By examining Table 10.7, we can see that the elements are symmetric about the main diagonal. Thus, the system is commutative under the given operation, ♪. One example of the commutative property is

$$\alpha ♪ \delta = \delta ♪ \alpha$$
$$\gamma = \gamma \quad \text{True}$$

All five properties are satisfied. Thus, the system is a commutative group.

Example 5 *Another System to Study*

Determine whether the mathematical system in Table 10.9 is a commutative group under the operation of ☺.

Table 10.9

☺	x	y	z
x	x	z	y
y	z	y	x
z	y	x	z

Solution

1. The system is closed.

2. No row is identical to the top row, so there is no identity element. Therefore, this mathematical system is *not a group*. There is no need to go any further, but for practice, let's look at a few more items.

3. Since there is no identity element, there can be no inverses.

4. The associative property does not hold. The following counterexample illustrates the associative property does not hold for every case.

$$(x \odot y) \odot z \neq x \odot (y \odot z)$$
$$z \odot z \neq x \odot x$$
$$z \neq x$$

5. The table is symmetric about the main diagonal. Therefore, the commutative property does hold for the operation of $\odot$.

Note that the associative property does not hold even though the commutative property does hold. This outcome can occur when there is no identity element and every element does not have an inverse, as in this example. ∎

Example 6 *Is the System a Commutative Group?*

Determine whether the mathematical system in Table 10.10 is a commutative group under the operation of ▲.

Table 10.10

▲	A	B	C
A	A	B	C
B	B	B	A
C	C	A	C

Solution

1. The system is closed.
2. There is an identity element, *A*.
3. Each element has an inverse; *A* is its own inverse, and *B* and *C* are inverses of each other.
4. Every element in the set does not appear in every row and every column of the table, so we need to check the associative property carefully. There are many specific cases in which the associative property does hold. However, the following counterexample illustrates that the associative property does not hold for every case.

$$(B \blacktriangle B) \blacktriangle C \neq B \blacktriangle (B \blacktriangle C)$$
$$B \blacktriangle C \neq B \blacktriangle A$$
$$A \neq B$$

5. The commutative property holds because there is symmetry about the main diagonal.

Since we have shown that the associative property does not hold under the operation of ▲, this system is not a group. Therefore, it cannot be a commutative group. ∎

SECTION 10.2 Exercises

Warm Up Exercises

In Exercises 1–12, fill in the blanks with an appropriate word, phrase, or symbol(s).

1. In the mathematical system of clock 12 arithmetic, under the operation of addition, the set of elements is _____.
{1, 2, 3, 4, 5, 6, 7, 8, 9, 10, 11, 12}

2. In clock 12 arithmetic, under the operation of addition, we define addition as a movement of the hour hand in a _____ direction. Clockwise

3. Since clock 12 arithmetic, under the operation of addition, contains only the elements {1, 2, 3, 4, 5, 6, 7, 8, 9, 10, 11, 12}, the mathematical system is _____. Closed

4. In clock 12 arithmetic, since $a + 12 = 12 + a = a$, for any element a, we say that 12 is the additive _____ element. Identity

5. In clock 12 arithmetic, since $1 + 11 = 11 + 1 = 12$, we say that 1 and 11 are additive _____. Inverses

6. In clock 12 arithmetic, the additive inverse of 2 is _____. 10

7. In clock 12 arithmetic, for any elements a, b, and c, $(a + b) + c = a + (b + c)$; therefore, the _____ property holds under the operation of addition. Associative

8. In clock 12 arithmetic, for any elements a and b, $a + b = b + a$; therefore, the _____ property holds under the operation of addition. Commutative

9. In clock 12 arithmetic under the operation of addition, since the system is closed, there is an identity element, each element has an inverse, and the associative and commutative properties hold, the mathematical system is a _____ group. Commutative

10. In a finite mathematical system, if every element does not appear in every row and every column of the table, you need to check the _____ property carefully. Associative

11. In a finite mathematical system, if the elements are symmetric about the main diagonal, then the system is _____.
Commutative

12. Groups that are not commutative are called noncommutative or _____ groups. Nonabelian

Practice the Skills

In Exercises 13 and 14, determine if the system is closed. Explain how you determined your answer.

13.

ψ	x	y	z
x	z	y	x
y	y	a	y
z	x	y	z

No

14.

∇	a	b	c
a	a	b	c
b	b	c	a
c	c	a	b

Yes

In Exercises 15 and 16, determine if the system has an identity element. If so, list the identity element. Explain how you determined your answer.

15.

W	A	B	C
A	C	B	A
B	B	C	B
C	A	B	C

*16.

$\ominus$	$\square$	$\odot$	$\triangle$
$\square$	$\triangle$	$\square$	$\odot$
$\odot$	$\odot$	$\triangle$	$\square$
$\triangle$	$\square$	$\odot$	$\triangle$

There is no identity element.

In Exercises 17 and 18, the identity element is C. Determine the inverse of (a) A, (b) B, and (c) C.

17.

$\oslash$	A	B	C
A	B	C	A
B	C	A	B
C	A	B	C

*18.

$\text{JL}\atop\text{7F}$	A	B	C
A	C	B	A
B	B	C	B
C	A	B	C

*

In Exercises 19 and 20, determine if the system is commutative. Explain how you determined your answer.

19.

I	P	A	L
P	L	P	A
A	P	L	A
L	A	L	P

No; the elements are not symmetric about the main diagonal.

20.

$\boxminus$	A	$\otimes$	W
A	$\otimes$	W	A
$\otimes$	W	A	$\otimes$
W	A	$\otimes$	$\otimes$

Yes; the elements are symmetric about the main diagonal.

In Exercises 21–30, use Table 10.1 on page 575 to determine the sum in clock 12 arithmetic.

21. $3 + 6$ 9

22. $7 + 6$ 1

23. $9 + 5$ 2

24. $11 + 7$ 6

25. $4 + 12$ 4

26. $12 + 12$ 12

27. $3 + (8 + 9)$ 8

28. $(8 + 7) + 6$ 9

29. $(6 + 4) + 8$ 6

30. $(6 + 10) + 12$ 4

In Exercises 31–40, determine the difference in clock 12 arithmetic by starting at the first number and counting counterclockwise on the clock the number of units given by the second number.

31. $10 - 4$ 6

32. $9 - 8$ 1

33. $2 - 4$ 10

34. $8 - 11$ 9

35. $4 - 10$ 6

36. $1 - 12$ 1

37. $6 - 10$ 8

38. $5 - 8$ 9

39. $5 - 5$ 12

40. $12 - 12$ 12

*See Instructor Answer Appendix

41. Use the following figure to develop an addition table for clock 6 arithmetic. The figure will also be used in Exercises 42–50.*

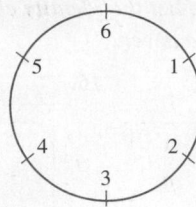

In Exercises 42–50, determine the sum or difference in clock 6 arithmetic.

42. $5 + 2$ ₁   **43.** $3 + 5$ ₂   **44.** $4 + 6$ ₄

45. $5 - 2$ ₃   **46.** $4 - 5$ ₅   **47.** $2 - 6$ ₂

48. $3 - 4$ ₅   **49.** $(3 - 5) - 6$ ₄   **50.** $2 + (1 - 3)$ ₆

51. Use the following figure to develop an addition table for clock 7 arithmetic. The figure will also be used in Exercises 52–61.*

In Exercises 52–60, determine the sum or difference in clock 7 arithmetic.

52. $4 + 4$ ₁   **53.** $3 + 6$ ₂   **54.** $6 + 7$ ₆

55. $5 + 5$ ₃   **56.** $2 - 3$ ₆   **57.** $3 - 6$ ₄

58. $2 - 4$ ₅   **59.** $(4 - 5) - 6$ ₇   **60.** $3 - (2 - 6)$ ₇

61. Determine whether clock 7 arithmetic under the operation of addition is a commutative group. Explain.
Yes; it satisfies the five required properties.

62. A mathematical system is defined by a three-element by three-element table where every element in the set appears in each row and each column. Must the mathematical system be a commutative group? Explain. No; it may not have an identity element, inverses, associative or commutative properties.

63. Consider the mathematical system defined by the following table. Assume that the associative property holds for the given operation.

£	0	2	4	6
0	0	2	4	6
2	2	4	6	0
4	4	6	0	2
6	6	0	2	4

a) What are the elements of the set in this mathematical system? $\{0, 2, 4, 6\}$

b) What is the binary operation? £

c) Is the system closed? Explain. Yes

d) Is there an identity element for the system under the given operation? If so, what is it? Yes; 0

e) Does every element in the system have an inverse? If so, give each element and its corresponding inverse.
Yes; 0–0, 2–6, 4–4, 6–2

f) Give an example to illustrate the associative property.
$(2 £ 4) £ 6 = 2 £ (4 £ 6)$

g) Is the system commutative? Give an example to verify your answer. Yes; $2 £ 6 = 6 £ 2$

h) Is the mathematical system a commutative group? Explain. Yes

In Exercises 64–66, repeat parts (a)–(h) of Exercise 63 for the mathematical system defined by the following table. Assume that the associative property holds for the given operation.

64.

®	♣	♦	♥	♠
♣	♥	♠	♣	♦
♦	♠	♣	♦	♥
♥	♣	♦	♥	♠
♠	♦	♥	♠	♣

a) $\{♣, ♦, ♥, ♠\}$ b) ®
c) Yes d) Yes; ♥
e) Yes; ♣–♣, ♦–♠,
♥–♥, ♠–♦
f) $(♣ ® ♦) ® ♥ =$
$♣ ® (♦ ® ♥)$
g) Yes; $♣ ® ♦ =$
$♦ ® ♣$
h) Yes

65.

$	*	5	L
*****	5	L	*
5	L	*	5
L	*	5	L

*

66.

�K	3	5	8	4
3	5	8	4	3
5	8	4	3	5
8	4	3	5	8
4	3	5	8	4

*

67. For the mathematical system determine

~	f	r	o	m
f	f	r	o	m
r	r	o	m	f
o	o	m	f	r
m	m	f	r	o

a) the elements in the set. $\{f, r, o, m\}$

b) the binary operation. ~

*See Instructor Answer Appendix

c) closure or nonclosure of the system. Closed

d) $(r \sim o) \sim f$ m e) $(f \sim r) \sim m$ f

f) the identity element. f g) the inverse of r. m

h) the inverse of m. r

68. a) Is the following mathematical system a group? Explain your answer. No; no identity element

b) Find an example showing that the associative property does not hold for the given set of elements.*

〰	1	2	3	4
1	2	3	4	1
2	3	4	1	2
3	4	1	2	3
4	1	4	3	2

In Exercises 69–74, for the mathematical system given, determine which of the five properties of a commutative group do not hold.

69. Not closed

‡	Δ	Φ	Γ
Δ	Δ	Φ	Γ
Φ	Φ	Γ	Δ
Γ	Γ	Δ	Π

70. *

⊗	⊡	M	🔔
⊡	⊡	M	🔔
M	M	⊡	🔔
🔔	🔔	M	⊡

71.

⊡	⊙	*	?	T	P
⊙	T	P	⊙	*	*
*	P	⊙	*	⊙	T
?	⊙	*	?	T	P
T	*	⊙	T	P	?
P	*	T	P	?	⊙

No inverse for ⊙ or for *, not associative

72.

☺	a	b	π	0	Δ
a	Δ	a	b	π	0
b	a	b	π	0	Δ
π	b	π	0	Δ	a
0	π	0	Δ	a	b
Δ	0	Δ	π	b	a

Not commutative, $\Delta \text{☺} \pi \neq \pi \text{☺} \Delta$; not associative $(a \text{☺} a) \text{☺} \Delta \neq a \text{☺} (a \text{☺} \Delta)$

73.

⇔	a	b	c	d	e
a	c	d	e	a	b
b	d	e	a	b	c
c	e	a	b	c	d
d	a	b	c	e	d
e	b	c	d	e	a

No identity element, no inverses, not associative, not commutative

74.

▽	0	1	2	3	4	5
0	0	0	0	0	0	0
1	0	1	2	3	4	5
2	0	2	4	0	2	4
3	0	3	0	3	0	3
4	0	4	2	0	4	2
5	0	5	4	3	2	1

0, 2, 3, and 4 do not have an inverse.

Problem Solving

75. a) Consider the set consisting of two elements $\{E, O\}$, where E stands for an even number and O stands for an odd number. For the operation of addition, complete the table.*

+	E	O
E		
O		

b) Determine whether this mathematical system forms a commutative group under the operation of addition. Explain your answer.
Yes, it is a commutative group; it satisfies the five properties.

76. a) Let E and O represent even numbers and odd numbers, respectively, as in Exercise 75. Complete the table for the operation of multiplication.*

×	E	O
E		
O		

b) Determine whether this mathematical system forms a commutative group under the operation of multiplication. Explain your answer. Not a group, E has no inverse.

In Exercises 77 and 78 on page 584 the tables shown are examples of noncommutative, or nonabelian, groups. For each exercise, do the following.

a) *Show that the system under the given operation is a group. (It would be very time consuming to prove that the associative property holds, but you can give some examples to show that it appears to hold.)*

*See Instructor Answer Appendix

b) *Determine a counterexample to show that the commutative property does not hold.*

77.

∞	1	2	3	4	5	6
1	5	3	4	2	6	1
2	4	6	5	1	3	2
3	2	1	6	5	4	3
4	3	5	1	6	2	4
5	6	4	2	3	1	5
6	1	2	3	4	5	6

78.

⊖	A	B	C	D	E	F
A	E	C	D	B	F	A
B	D	F	E	A	C	B
C	B	A	F	E	D	C
D	C	E	A	F	B	D
E	F	D	B	C	A	E
F	A	B	C	D	E	F

Challenge Problems/Group Activities

79. *Book Arrangements* Suppose that three books numbered 1, 2, and 3 are placed next to one another on a shelf. If we remove volume 3 and place it before volume 1, the new order of books is 3, 1, 2. Let's call this replacement R. We can write

$$R = \begin{pmatrix} 1 & 2 & 3 \\ 3 & 1 & 2 \end{pmatrix}$$

which indicates the books were switched in order from 1, 2, 3 to 3, 1, 2. Other possible replacements are S, T, U, V, and I, as indicated.

$$S = \begin{pmatrix} 1 & 2 & 3 \\ 2 & 1 & 3 \end{pmatrix} \quad T = \begin{pmatrix} 1 & 2 & 3 \\ 3 & 2 & 1 \end{pmatrix} \quad U = \begin{pmatrix} 1 & 2 & 3 \\ 1 & 3 & 2 \end{pmatrix}$$

$$V = \begin{pmatrix} 1 & 2 & 3 \\ 2 & 3 & 1 \end{pmatrix} \quad I = \begin{pmatrix} 1 & 2 & 3 \\ 1 & 2 & 3 \end{pmatrix}$$

Replacement set I indicates that the books were removed from the shelves and placed back in their original order. Consider the mathematical system with the set of elements, $\{R, S, T, U, V, I\}$ with the operation of $*$.

To evaluate $R * S$, write

$$R \qquad\qquad S$$

$$R * S = \begin{pmatrix} 1 & 2 & 3 \\ 3 & 1 & 2 \end{pmatrix} * \begin{pmatrix} 1 & 2 & 3 \\ 2 & 1 & 3 \end{pmatrix}$$

As shown in Fig. 10.2, R replaces 1 with 3 and S replaces 3 with 3 (no change), so $R * S$ replaces 1 with 3. R

replaces 2 with 1 and S replaces 1 with 2, so $R * S$ replaces 2 with 2 (no change). R replaces 3 with 2 and S replaces 2 with 1, so $R * S$ replaces 3 with 1. $R * S$ replaces 1 with 3, 2 with 2, and 3 with 1.

$$R \qquad\qquad S$$

$$1 \longrightarrow 3 \longrightarrow 3$$

$$2 \longrightarrow 1 \longrightarrow 2$$

$$3 \longrightarrow 2 \longrightarrow 1$$

$$\uparrow \quad R \quad * \quad S \quad \uparrow$$

$$R * S = \begin{pmatrix} 1 & 2 & 3 \\ 3 & 2 & 1 \end{pmatrix} = T$$

Figure 10.2

Since this result is the same as replacement set T, we write $R * S = T$.

a) Complete the table for the operation using the procedure outlined.*

*	R	S	T	U	V	I
R		T				
S						
T						
U						
V						
I						

b) Is this mathematical system a group? Explain.*

c) Is this mathematical system a commutative group? Explain. No, it is not commutative. For example, $R * S \neq S * R$

80. If a mathematical system is defined by a four-element by four-element table, how many specific cases must be illustrated to prove the set of elements is associative under the given operation? $4^3 = 64$ ways

Exercises 81–82 will help prepare you for the next section.

81. A table is shown below.

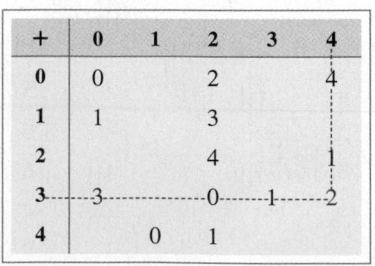

+	0	1	2	3	4
0	0		2		4
1	1		3		
2			4		1
3	3		0	1	2
4		0	1		

Fill in the blank areas of the table by performing the following operations.*

1. Add the number in the left-hand column and the number in the top row.

2. Divide this sum by 5.

3. Place the *remainder* in the cell where the number in the left-hand column and the number in the top row would meet.

For example, in the table, the number 2 is in red. This 2 is found as follows:

$$(3 + 4) \div 5 = 1, \text{remainder } 2$$

82. Using Exercise 81 as a guide, complete the following table by dividing the sum of the numbers by 6. Place the remainders in the table as explained in Exercise 81.*

+	0	1	2	3	4	5
0						
1						
2						
3						
4						
5						

Recreational Mathematics

83. *A Tiny Group* Consider the mathematical system with the single element {1} under the operation of multiplication.

a) Is this system closed? Yes

b) Does the system have an identity element? Yes; 1

c) Does 1 have an inverse? Yes; 1

d) Does the associative property hold? Yes

e) Does the commutative property hold? Yes

f) Is {1} under the operation of multiplication a commutative group? Yes

Internet/Research Activities

84. a) *Matrices* In Section 7.3, we introduced matrices. Show that 2×2 matrices under the operation of addition form a commutative group.

b) Show that 2×2 matrices under the operation of multiplication do not form a commutative group.

*See Instructor Answer Appendix

SECTION 10.3 Modular Arithmetic

▲ *When will your birthday next land on a Saturday?*

If your birthday is on a Monday this year, on what day of the week will it fall next year? What if next year is a leap year? When will your birthday next fall on a Saturday? These questions can be addressed with the type of arithmetic that we will study in this section.

Why **This is Important** Modular arithmetic is a fundamental part of many branches of mathematics. A wide variety of applications of modular arithmetic can be found in cryptography (the study of writing in secret codes), computer science, chemistry, music, and economics.

The clock arithmetic we discussed in the previous section is similar to modular arithmetic. The set of elements $\{0, 1, 2, 3, 4, 5, 6, 7, 8, 9, 10, 11\}$ together with the operation of addition is called a modulo 12 or mod 12 system. There is one difference in notation between clock 12 arithmetic and modulo 12 arithmetic. In the modulo 12 system, the symbol 12 is replaced with the symbol 0.

Modulo *m* Systems

A *modulo m system* consists of *m* elements, 0 through $m - 1$, and a binary operation. In this section, we will discuss modular arithmetic systems and their properties.

If today is Sunday, what day of the week will it be in 23 days? The answer, Tuesday, is arrived at by dividing 23 by 7. The quotient is 3 and the remainder is 2. Twenty-three days represent 3 weeks plus 2 days. Since we are interested only in the day of the week on which the twenty-third day will fall, the 3-week segment is unimportant to the answer. The remainder of 2 indicates the answer will be 2 days later than Sunday, which is Tuesday.

If we place the days of the week on a clock face as shown in Fig. 10.3, then in 23 days the hand would have made three complete revolutions and end on Tuesday. If we replace the days of the week with numbers, then a modulo 7 arithmetic system will result. See Fig. 10.4: Sunday = 0, Monday = 1, Tuesday = 2, and so on. If we start at 0 and move the hand 23 places, we will end at 2. Table 10.11 shows a modulo 7 addition table.

Table 10.11   Modular 7 Addition

+	0	1	2	3	4	5	6
0	0	1	2	3	4	5	6
1	1	2	3	4	5	6	0
2	2	3	4	5	6	0	1
3	3	4	5	6	0	1	2
4	4	5	6	0	1	2	③
5	5	6	0	1	2	3	4
6	6	0	1	2	3	4	5

Figure 10.3

Figure 10.4

If we start at 4 and add 6, we end at 3 on the clock in Fig. 10.5. This number is circled in Table 10.11. The other numbers can be obtained in the same way.

A second method of determining the sum of 4 + 6 in modulo 7 arithmetic is to divide the sum, 10, by 7 and observe the remainder.

$$10 \div 7 = 1, \quad \text{remainder } 3$$

The remainder, 3, is the sum of 4 + 6 in a modulo 7 arithmetic system.

The concept of congruence is important in modular arithmetic.

Figure 10.5

Definition: Congruent

a is **congruent** to *b* modulo *m*, written, $a \equiv b \pmod{m}$, if *a* and *b* have the same remainder when divided by *m*.

We can show, for example, that $10 \equiv 3 \pmod 7$ by dividing both 10 and 3 by 7 and observing that we obtain the same remainder in each case.

$$10 \div 7 = 1, \quad \text{remainder } 3 \qquad \text{and} \qquad 3 \div 7 = 0, \quad \text{remainder } 3$$

Since the remainders are the same, 3 in each case, 10 is congruent to 3 modulo 7, and we may write $10 \equiv 3 \pmod 7$.

Now consider $37 \equiv 5 \pmod 8$. If we divide both 37 and 5 by 8, each has the same remainder, 5.

In any modulo system, we can develop a set of *modulo classes* by placing all numbers with the same remainder in the appropriate modulo class. In a modulo 7 system, every number must have a remainder of either 0, 1, 2, 3, 4, 5, or 6. Thus, a modulo 7 system has seven modulo classes. The seven classes are presented in Table 10.12.

Every number is congruent to a number from 0 to 6 in modulo 7. For example, $24 \equiv 3 \pmod 7$ because 24 is in the same modulo class as 3.

The solution to a problem in modular arithmetic, if it exists, will always be a number from 0 through $m - 1$, where *m* is the *modulus* of the system. For example, in a modulo 7 system, because 7 is the modulus, the solution will be a number from 0 through 6.

Table 10.12   Modulo 7 Classes

0	1	2	3	4	5	6
0	1	2	3	4	5	6
7	8	9	10	11	12	13
14	15	16	17	18	19	20
21	22	23	24	25	26	27
28	29	30	31	32	33	34
⋮	⋮	⋮	⋮	⋮	⋮	⋮

Example 1 *Congruence Modulo 7*

Determine which number, from 0 through 6, the following numbers are congruent to in modulo 7.

a) 47   b) 86   c) 133

Solution We could determine the answer by listing more entries in Table 10.12. Another method of finding the answer is to divide the given number by 7 and observe the remainder. In the solutions, we will use a question mark, ?, as a place holder. The ? will represent a number from 0 through 6. When we determine the answer, we will replace the ? with the answer.

a) $47 \equiv ? \pmod 7$

To determine the value that 47 is congruent to in mod 7, divide 47 by 7 and determine the remainder.

$$\begin{array}{r} 6 \\ 7{\overline{)47}} \\ \underline{42} \\ 5 \leftarrow \text{remainder} \end{array}$$

$$47 \div 7 = 6, \text{remainder } 5$$

Thus, $47 \equiv 5 \pmod 7$.

b) $86 \equiv ? \pmod 7$

$$86 \div 7 = 12, \text{remainder } 2$$

Thus, $86 \equiv 2 \pmod 7$.

c) $133 \equiv ? \pmod 7$

$$133 \div 7 = 19, \text{remainder } 0$$

Thus, $133 \equiv 0 \pmod 7$. ∎

EXAMPLE 2 *Congruence Modulo 6*

Evaluate each of the following in modulo 6.

a) $3 + 5$ b) $5 - 2$ c) $3 \cdot 5$

Solution In each part, because we are working in modulo 6, the answer will be a number from 0 through 5.

a)
$$3 + 5 \equiv ? \pmod 6$$
$$8 \equiv ? \pmod 6$$

Since $8 \div 6 = 1$ with 2 as the remainder, $8 \equiv 2 \pmod 6$. Therefore, $3 + 5 \equiv 2 \pmod 6$.

b)
$$5 - 2 \equiv ? \pmod 6$$
$$3 \equiv ? \pmod 6$$
$$3 \equiv 3 \pmod 6$$

Remember that we want to replace the question mark with a number between 0 and 5, inclusive. Thus, $5 - 2 \equiv 3 \pmod 6$.

c)
$$3 \cdot 5 \equiv ? \pmod 6$$
$$15 \equiv ? \pmod 6$$

Since $15 \div 6 = 2$, remainder 3, $15 \equiv 3 \pmod 6$. Thus, $3 \cdot 5 \equiv 3 \pmod 6$. ∎

Note in Table 10.12 on page 586 that every number in the same modulo class differs by a multiple of the modulus, in this case a multiple of 7. Adding (or subtracting) a multiple of the modulus to (or from) a given number does not change the modulo class or congruence of the given number. For example, $3, 3 + 1(7), 3 + 2(7), 3 + 3(7), \ldots, 3 + n(7)$ are all in the same modulo class, namely, 3. We use this fact in the solution to Example 3.

EXAMPLE 3 *Using Modulo Classes in Subtraction*

Determine the positive number replacement (less than the modulus) for the question mark that makes the statement true.

a) $3 - 5 \equiv ? \,(\text{mod } 7)$ b) $? - 4 \equiv 3 \,(\text{mod } 5)$ c) $5 - ? \equiv 7 \,(\text{mod } 8)$

Solution   In each part, we wish to replace the question mark with a positive number less than the modulus. Therefore, in part (a) we wish to replace the ? with a positive number less than 7. In part (b), we wish to replace the ? with a positive number less than 5. In part (c), we wish to replace the ? with a positive number less than 8.

a) In mod 7, adding 7, or a multiple of 7, to a number results in a sum that is in the same modulo class. Thus, if we add 7, 14, 21, … to 3, the result will be a number in the same modulo class. We want to replace 3 with an equivalent mod 7 number that is greater than 5. Adding 7 to 3 yields a sum of 10, which is greater than 5.

$$3 - 5 \equiv ? \,(\text{mod } 7)$$
$$(3 + 7) - 5 \equiv ? \,(\text{mod } 7)$$
$$10 - 5 \equiv ? \,(\text{mod } 7)$$
$$5 \equiv ? \,(\text{mod } 7)$$
$$5 \equiv 5 \,(\text{mod } 7)$$

Therefore, $? = 5$ and $3 - 5 \equiv 5 \,(\text{mod } 7)$.

b) We wish to replace the ? with a number less than 5. We know that $7 - 4 \equiv 3$ mod 5 because $3 \equiv 3$ mod 5. Therefore, we need to determine what number, less than 5, the number 7 is congruent to in mod 5. If we subtract the modulus, 5, from 7, we obtain 2. Thus, 2 and 7 are in the same modular class. Therefore, $? = 2$.

$$? - 4 \equiv 3 \,(\text{mod } 5)$$
$$7 - 4 \equiv 3 \,(\text{mod } 5)$$
$$2 - 4 \equiv 3 \,(\text{mod } 5)$$

Notice in the last equivalence that if we add 5 to 2, we get $7 - 4 \equiv 3 \,(\text{mod } 5)$, which is a true statement.

c) $5 - ? \equiv 7 \,(\text{mod } 8)$

In mod 8, adding 8, or a multiple of 8, to a number results in a sum that is in the same modulo class. Thus, we can add 8 to 5 so that the statement becomes

$$(8 + 5) - ? \equiv 7 \,(\text{mod } 8)$$
$$13 - ? \equiv 7 \,(\text{mod } 8)$$

We can see that $13 - 6 = 7$. Therefore, $? = 6$ and $5 - 6 \equiv 7 \,(\text{mod } 8)$. ■

EXAMPLE 4 *Using Modulo Classes in Multiplication*

Determine all positive number replacements (less than the modulus) for the question mark that make the statement true.

a) $2 \cdot ? \equiv 3 \,(\text{mod } 5)$ b) $3 \cdot ? \equiv 0 \,(\text{mod } 6)$ c) $3 \cdot ? \equiv 2 \,(\text{mod } 6)$

Solution

a) One method of determining the solution is to replace the question mark with the numbers 0, 1, 2, 3, and 4 and then determine the equivalent modulo class of the product. We use the numbers 0–4 because we are working in modulo 5.

$$2 \cdot ? \equiv 3 \text{ (mod 5)}$$
$$2 \cdot 0 \equiv 0 \text{ (mod 5)}$$
$$2 \cdot 1 \equiv 2 \text{ (mod 5)}$$
$$2 \cdot 2 \equiv 4 \text{ (mod 5)}$$
$$2 \cdot 3 \equiv 1 \text{ (mod 5)}$$
$$2 \cdot 4 \equiv 3 \text{ (mod 5)}$$

Therefore, the question mark can be replaced with 4 since $2 \cdot 4 \equiv 3$ (mod 5).

b) Since we are working in modulo 6, replace the question mark with the numbers 0–5 and follow the procedure used in part (a).

$$3 \cdot ? \equiv 0 \text{ (mod 6)}$$
$$3 \cdot 0 \equiv 0 \text{ (mod 6)}$$
$$3 \cdot 1 \equiv 3 \text{ (mod 6)}$$
$$3 \cdot 2 \equiv 0 \text{ (mod 6)}$$
$$3 \cdot 3 \equiv 3 \text{ (mod 6)}$$
$$3 \cdot 4 \equiv 0 \text{ (mod 6)}$$
$$3 \cdot 5 \equiv 3 \text{ (mod 6)}$$

Therefore, replacing the question mark with 0, 2, or 4 results in true statements. The answers are 0, 2, and 4.

c) $3 \cdot ? \equiv 2$ (mod 6)

Examining the products in part (b) shows there are no values that satisfy the statement. The answer is "no solution." ■

Whenever a process is repetitive, modular arithmetic may be helpful in answering some questions about the process. Now let's look at an application of modular arithmetic.

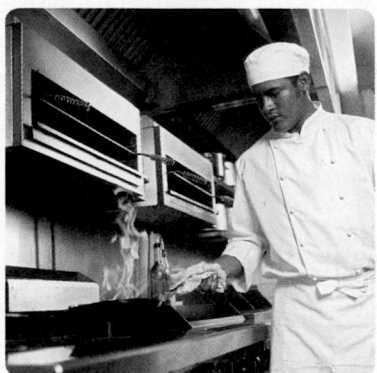

Example 5 Work Schedule

Dusty is a chef at a restaurant. His working schedule is to work for 6 days, and then he gets 2 days off. If today is the third day that Dusty has been working, determine the following.

a) Will he be working 60 days from today?

b) Will he be working 82 days from today?

c) Was he working 124 days ago?

Solution

a) Since Dusty works for 6 days and then gets 2 days off, his working schedule may be considered a modular 8 system. That is, 8, 16, 24, ... days from today will be just like today, the third day of the 8-day cycle.

   If we divide 60 by 8, we obtain

$$\begin{array}{r} 7 \\ 8\overline{)60} \\ 56 \\ \hline 4 \leftarrow \text{remainder} \end{array}$$

Therefore, in 60 days Dusty will go through 7 complete cycles and will be 4 days further into the next cycle. If we let W represent a working day and N represent a nonworking day, then Dusty's cycle may be represented as follows:

$$W \; W \; W \; W \; W \; W \; N \; N$$

    ↑ today   ↑ 4 days from today

Notice that 4 days from today will be his first nonworking day. Therefore, Dusty will not be working 60 days from today.

b) We work this part in the same way we worked part (a). Divide 82 by 8 and determine the remainder.

$$\begin{array}{r} 10 \\ 8\overline{)82} \\ 80 \\ \hline 2 \leftarrow \text{remainder} \end{array}$$

Thus, in 82 days it will be 2 days later in the cycle than it is today. Because he is currently in day 3 of his cycle, Dusty will be in day 5 of his cycle and will be working.

c) This part is worked in the same way as parts (a) and (b), but once we find the remainder we must move backward in the cycle.

$$\begin{array}{r} 15 \\ 8\overline{)124} \\ 120 \\ \hline 4 \leftarrow \text{remainder} \end{array}$$

Thus, 124 days ago was 4 days earlier in the cycle. Marking day 3 of the cycle (indicated by the word *today*) and then moving 4 days backwards brings us to the first nonworking day. The two N's shown at the beginning of the letters below are actually the end days of the previous cycle.

$$N \; N \; W \; W \; W \; W \; W \; W \; N \; N$$

  ↑ 4 days earlier than today   ↑ today

Therefore, 124 days ago Dusty was not working. ∎

Modular Arithmetic and Groups

Modular arithmetic systems under the operation of addition are commutative groups, as illustrated in Example 6.

EXAMPLE 6 *A Commutative Group*

Construct a mod 5 addition table and show that the mathematical system is a commutative group. Assume that the associative property holds for the given operation.

Solution The set of elements in modulo 5 arithmetic is $\{0, 1, 2, 3, 4\}$; the binary operation is $+$.

+	0	1	2	3	4
0	0	1	2	3	4
1	1	2	3	4	0
2	2	3	4	0	1
3	3	4	0	1	2
4	4	0	1	2	3

For this system to be a commutative group, it must satisfy the five properties of a commutative group.

1. *Closure*: Every entry in the table is a member of the set $\{0, 1, 2, 3, 4\}$, so the system is closed under addition.

2. *Identity element*: An easy way to determine whether there is an identity element is to look for a row in the table that is identical to the elements at the top of the table. Note that the row next to 0 is identical to the top of the table, which indicates that 0 *might be* the identity element. Now look at the column under the 0 at the top of the table. If this column is identical to the left-hand column, then 0 is the identity element. Since the column under 0 is the same as the left-hand column, 0 is the additive identity in modulo 5 arithmetic.

Element	+	Identity	=	Element
0	+	0	=	0
1	+	0	=	1
2	+	0	=	2
3	+	0	=	3
4	+	0	=	4

3. *Inverse elements*: Does every element have an inverse? Recall that an element plus its inverse must equal the identity element. In this example, the identity element is 0. Therefore, for each of the given elements 0, 1, 2, 3, and 4, we must find the element that when added to it results in a sum of zero. These elements will be the inverses.

Element	+	Inverse	=	Identity	
0	+	?	=	0	Since $0 + 0 \equiv 0$, 0 is its own inverse.
1	+	?	=	0	Since $1 + 4 \equiv 0$, 4 is the inverse of 1.
2	+	?	=	0	Since $2 + 3 \equiv 0$, 3 is the inverse of 2.
3	+	?	=	0	Since $3 + 2 \equiv 0$, 2 is the inverse of 3.
4	+	?	=	0	Since $4 + 1 \equiv 0$, 1 is the inverse of 4.

Note that each element has an inverse.

4. *Associative property*: It is given that the associative property holds. One example that illustrates the associative property is

$$(2 + 3) + 4 = 2 + (3 + 4)$$
$$0 + 4 = 2 + 2$$
$$4 = 4 \quad \text{True}$$

5. *Commutative property*: Is $a + b = b + a$ for *all* elements a and b of the given set? The table shows that the system is commutative because the elements are symmetric about the main diagonal. We will give one example to illustrate the commutative property.

$$4 + 2 = 2 + 4$$
$$1 = 1 \quad \text{True}$$

All five properties are satisfied. Thus, modulo 5 arithmetic under the operation of addition is a commutative group. ∎

SECTION 10.3 *Exercises*

Warm Up Exercises

In Exercises 1–6, fill in the blanks with an appropriate word, phrase, or symbol(s).

1. The elements in a modulo m system consist of the m numbers, 0 through _____. $m-1$.

2. In a modulo m system, in addition to the m elements, there is also a(n) _____ operation. Binary

3. In any modulo m system, we can develop a set of modulo classes by dividing the numbers by m and placing all numbers with the same _____ in the appropriate modulo class. Remainder

4. In a modulo m system, the number m is called the _____ of the system. Modulus

5. If a and b have the same remainder when divided by m, we say that a is _____ to b modulo m. Congruent

6. To determine the value that 45 is congruent to in modulo 7, we _____ 45 by 7 and determine the remainder. Divide

Practice the Skills

In Exercises 7–16, assume that Sunday is represented as day 0, Monday is represented as day 1, and so on. If today is Thursday (day 4), determine the day of the week it will be in the specified number of days. Assume no leap years.

7. 11 days Monday
8. 43 days Friday
9. 101 days Sunday
10. 135 days Saturday
11. 365 days Friday
12. 3 years Sunday
13. 3 years, 34 days Saturday
14. 463 days Friday
15. 400 days Friday
16. 3 years, 27 days Saturday

In Exercises 17–24, consider 12 months to be a modulo 12 system. If it is currently October, determine the month it will be in the specified number of months.

17. 19 months May
18. 73 months November
19. 2 years, 10 months August
20. 4 years, 8 months June
21. 83 months September
22. 7 years October
23. 105 months July
24. 5 years, 9 months July

In Exercises 25–36, determine what number the sum, difference, or product is congruent to in mod 5.

25. $4 + 3$ 2
26. $2 + 3$ 0
27. $1 + 2 + 3$ 1
28. $9 - 3$ 1
29. $5 - 12$ 3
30. $8 \cdot 7$ 1
31. $8 \cdot 9$ 2
32. $1 - 4$ 2
33. $4 - 8$ 1
34. $3 - 7$ 1
35. $(15 \cdot 4) - 8$ 2
36. $(4 - 9) \cdot 7$ 0

In Exercises 37–50, find the modulo class to which each number belongs for the indicated modulo system.

37. 5, mod 3 2
38. 28, mod 5 3
39. 60, mod 7 4
40. 43, mod 6 1
41. 41, mod 9 5
42. 75, mod 8 3
43. 30, mod 7 2
44. 53, mod 4 1
45. -1, mod 7 6
46. -7, mod 4 1
47. -13, mod 11 9
48. -11, mod 13 2
49. 205, mod 10 5
50. -12, mod 4 0

In Exercises 51–66, determine all positive number replacements (less than the modulus) for the question mark that make the statement true.

51. $4 + 5 \equiv ? \pmod 8$ 1
52. $? + 3 \equiv 2 \pmod 5$ 4
53. $6 + ? \equiv 2 \pmod 7$ 3
54. $4 + ? \equiv 3 \pmod 6$ 5
55. $4 - ? \equiv 5 \pmod 6$ 5
56. $2 \cdot 5 \equiv ? \pmod 7$ 3
57. $5 \cdot ? \equiv 7 \pmod 9$ 5
58. $3 \cdot ? \equiv 5 \pmod 6$ { }
59. $2 \cdot ? \equiv 1 \pmod 6$ { }
60. $3 \cdot ? \equiv 3 \pmod{12}$ 1, 5, and 9
61. $4 \cdot ? \equiv 4 \pmod{10}$ 1 and 6
62. $? - 3 \equiv 4 \pmod 8$ 7
63. $? - 8 \equiv 9 \pmod{12}$ 5
64. $6 - ? \equiv 8 \pmod 9$ 7
65. $3 \cdot ? \equiv 0 \pmod{10}$ 0
66. $4 \cdot ? \equiv 5 \pmod 8$ { }

Problem Solving

67. Presidential Elections The upcoming presidential election years are 2012, 2016, 2020, ...

a) List the next five presidential election years after 2020.
2024, 2028, 2032, 2036, 2040

b) What will be the first election year after the year 3000?
3004

c) List the election years between the years 2550 and 2575.
2552, 2556, 2560, 2564, 2568, 2572

68. Flight Schedules A pilot is scheduled to fly for 5 consecutive days and rest for 3 consecutive days. If today is the second day of her rest shift, determine whether she will be flying or resting

a) 60 days from today. Flying **b)** 90 days from today.
Flying

c) 240 days from today. **d)** Was she flying 6 days ago?
Resting Yes

e) Was she flying 20 days ago? Yes

69. Workout Schedule A golf pro's workout schedule is to give both morning and afternoon lessons for 3 days, rest for 1 day, give only morning lessons for 2 days, rest for 2 days, and then start the cycle again. If the golf pro is on his rest for 1 day part of the schedule, determine what he will be doing

a) 28 days from today. Resting (for the second of two days)

b) 60 days from today. Resting (for the second of two days)

c) 127 days from today. Morning and afternoon lessons

d) Will the golf pro have a day off 82 days from today? No

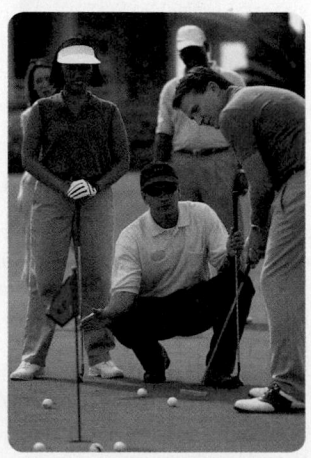

70. Physical Therapy A man has an Achilles' tendon injury and is receiving physical therapy. He must have physical therapy twice a day for 5 days, physical therapy once a day for 3 days, and then 2 days off; then the cycle begins again. If he is in his second day of his twice-a-day therapy cycle, determine what he will be doing

a) 20 days from today. **b)** 49 days from today.
Twice a day therapy Twice a day therapy

c) 103 days from today. Twice a day therapy

d) Will the man have a day off 78 days from today? Yes

71. The Weekend Off A manager of a theater has both Saturday and Sunday off every 7 weeks. It is week 2 of the 7 weeks.

a) Determine the number of weeks before he will have both Saturday and Sunday off. 5

b) Will he have both Saturday and Sunday off 25 weeks from this week? No

c) What is the first week, after 50 weeks from this week, that he will have both Saturday and Sunday off?
54 weeks from this week

72. Nursing Shifts A nurse's work pattern at Community Hospital consists of working the 7 A.M.–3 P.M. shift for 3 weeks and then the 3 P.M.–11 P.M. shift for 2 weeks.

a) If it is the third week of the pattern, what shift will the nurse be working 6 weeks from now? 3 P.M.–11 P.M.

b) If it is the fourth week of the pattern, what shift will the nurse be working 7 weeks from now? 7 A.M.–3 P.M.

c) If it is the first week of the pattern, what shift will the nurse be working 11 weeks from now? 7 A.M.–3 P.M.

73. Restaurant Rotation A waiter at a restaurant works both daytime and evening shifts. He works daytime for 5 consecutive days, then evenings for 3 consecutive days, then daytime for 4 consecutive days, then evenings for 2 consecutive days. Then the rotation starts again. If it is day 2 of the 5-day consecutive daytime shift, determine whether he will be working the daytime or evening shift

a) 20 days from today. **b)** 52 days from today. Day
Evening
c) 365 days from today. Day

74. A Truck Driver's Schedule A truck driver's routine is as follows: Drive 3 days from New York to Chicago, rest 1 day in Chicago, drive 3 days from Chicago to Los Angeles, rest 2 days in Los Angeles, drive 5 days to return to New York, rest 3 days in New York. Then the cycle begins again. If the truck driver is starting her trip to Chicago today, what will she be doing

a) 30 days from today? Driving from Los Angeles to New York

b) 70 days from today? Driving from New York to Chicago

c) 2 years from today? Resting in New York

75. a) Construct a modulo 3 addition table. *

    b) Is the system closed? Explain. Yes

    c) Is there an identity element for the system? If so, what is it? Yes, 0

    d) Does every element in the system have an inverse? If so, list the elements and their inverses. Yes; 0–0, 1–2, 2–1

    e) The associative property holds for the system. Give an example. $(1 + 2) + 2 = 1 + (2 + 2)$

    f) Does the commutative property hold for the system? Give an example. Yes; $2 + 1 = 1 + 2$

    g) Is the system a commutative group? Yes

    h) Will every modulo system under the operation of addition be a commutative group? Explain. Yes

76. Construct a modulo 8 addition table. Repeat parts (b)–(h) in Exercise 75. *

77. a) Construct a modulo 4 multiplication table. *

    b) Is the system closed under the operation of multiplication? Yes

    c) Is there an identity element in the system? If so, what is it? Yes, 1

    d) Does every element in the system have an inverse? Make a list showing the elements that have a multiplicative inverse and list the inverses. No; no inverse for 0 or for 2, inverse of 1 is 1, inverse of 3 is 3

    e) The associative property holds for the system. Give an example. $(1 \times 2) \times 3 = 1 \times (2 \times 3)$

    f) Does the commutative property hold for the system? Give an example. Yes, $2 \times 3 = 3 \times 2$

    g) Is this mathematical system a commutative group? Explain. No

78. Construct a modulo 7 multiplication table. Repeat parts (b)–(g) in Exercise 77. *

Challenge Problems/Group Activities

We have not discussed division in modular arithmetic. With what number or numbers, if any, can you replace the question marks to make the statement true? The question mark must be a number less than the modulus. Hint: Use the fact that $\frac{a}{b} \equiv c \ (mod \ m)$ means $a \equiv b \cdot c \ (mod \ m)$ and use trial and error to obtain your answer.

79. $? \div 3 \equiv 4 \ (mod \ 5)$ 2   **80.** $3 \div 4 \equiv ? \ (mod \ 7)$ 6

81. $? \div ? \equiv 1 \ (mod \ 4)$ **82.** $1 \div 2 \equiv ? \ (mod \ 5)$ 3
    1, 2, 3

In Exercises 83–85, solve for x where k is any counting number.

83. $8k \equiv x \ (mod \ 8)$ 0   **84.** $7k + 1 \equiv x \ (mod \ 7)$ 1

85. $4k - 2 \equiv x \ (mod \ 4)$ 2

86. Find the smallest positive number divisible by 5 to which 2 is congruent in modulo 6. 20

87. *Birthday Question* During a certain year, Clarence Dee's birthday is on Monday, April 18.

    a) If next year is *not* a leap year, on what day of the week will Clarence's birthday fall next year? Tuesday

    b) If next year *is* a leap year, on what day of the week will Clarence's birthday fall next year? Wednesday

88. *More Birthday Questions* During a certain leap year, Josephine Emme's birthday is on Tuesday, May 18. In how many years will Josephine's birthday fall on a

    a) Friday? 3 years   **b)** Saturday? 9 years

Recreational Math

89. *Cryptography* Read the *Recreational Mathematics* box on page 588. Using the same coding circle and a code key of the letter *e*, decipher the following message.

16	19	20	1	17	10	9	12	10
5	14	24	5	21	20	1	10	23

Knowledge is power.

90. *Rolling Wheel* The wheel shown below is to be rolled. Before the wheel is rolled, it is resting on number 0. The wheel will be rolled at a uniform rate of one complete roll every 4 minutes. In exactly 1 year (not a leap year), what number will be at the bottom of the wheel? 0

Internet/Research Activity

91. *The Enigma Cipher Machine* Do research on the Enigma ciphering machine (see the *Did You Know?* box on page 587). Write a paper on the role the machine played prior to and during World War II.

92. The concept and notation for modular systems were introduced by Carl Friedrich Gauss in 1801. Write a paper on Gauss's contribution to modular systems.

*See Instructor Answer Appendix

CHAPTER 10   *Summary*

Important Facts and Concepts	Examples and Discussion
Section 10.1	
A **mathematical system** consists of a set of elements and at least one binary operation.	Discussion, page 567
Commutative Property	
Addition: $a + b = b + a$	Discussion, pages 567–568
Multiplication: $a \cdot b = b \cdot a$	
Associative Property	
Addition: $(a + b) + c = a + (b + c)$	Discussion, pages 567–568
Multiplication: $(a \cdot b) \cdot c = a \cdot (b \cdot c)$	
Properties of a Group and a Commutative Group	
A mathematical system is a group if the first four following conditions hold, and a commutative group if all five conditions hold.	Discussion, pages 568–571, Examples 1–2, pages 571–572; Examples 1–6, pages 575–580; Example 6 pages 590–592
1. The set of elements is *closed* under the given operation.	
2. An *identity element* exists for the set.	
3. Every element in the set has an *inverse*.	
4. The set of elements is *associative* under the given operation.	
5. The set of elements is *commutative* under the given operation.	
Section 10.2, 10.3	
If the elements of a finite mathematical system are symmetric about the main diagonal, then the system is *commutative*.	Discussion, page 577, Examples 1–6, pages 575–580; Example 6, page 580
Section 10.3	
a is **congruent** to b modulo m, written $a \equiv b \ (mod \ m)$, if a and b have the same remainder when divided by m.	Discussion, pages 585–586, Examples 1-6, pages 587–591

CHAPTER 10   *Review Exercises*

10.1, 10.2

1. What is a binary operation? A binary operation is an operation that can be performed on two and only two elements of a set. The result is a single element.

2. List the parts of a mathematical system. A mathematical system consists of a set of elements and at least one binary operation.

3. Are the set of whole numbers closed under the operation of division? Explain.
   No; for example, $2 \div 3 = \frac{2}{3}$ and $\frac{2}{3}$ is not a whole number.

4. Are the set of real numbers closed under the operation of subtraction? Explain.
   Yes; the difference of any two real numbers is a real number.

Determine the sum or difference in clock 12 arithmetic.

5. $11 + 3$ 2   6. $12 + 7$ 7   7. $3 - 6$ 9

8. $4 + 7 + 9$ 8   9. $7 - 4 + 6$ 9   10. $2 - 8 - 7$ 11

11. List the properties of a group and explain what each property means. Closure, identity element, inverses, and associative property

12. What is another name for an abelian group?
    A commutative group

In Exercises 13 and 14, explain your answer.

13. Determine whether the set of integers under the operation of addition forms a group. Yes

14. Determine whether the set of integers under the operation of multiplication forms a group.
    No; no inverse for any integer except 1 and –1

15. Determine whether the set of natural numbers under the operation of addition forms a group. No; no identity element

16. Determine whether the set of rational numbers under the operation of multiplication forms a group. No; no inverse for 0

In Exercises 17–19, for the mathematical system, determine which of the five properties of a commutative group do not hold.

17.

∴	ρ	σ	ω
ρ	ρ	ω	σ
σ	ω	σ	ρ
ω	σ	ρ	ω

No identity element; no inverses

18.

?	4	#	L	P
4	P	4	#	L
#	4	#	L	P
L	#	L	P	4
P	L	P	4	L

Not every element has an inverse; not associative. For example, $(P\,?\,P)\,?\,4 \neq P\,?\,(P\,?\,4)$.

19.

□	!	?	Δ	ρ
!	?	Δ	!	ρ
?	Δ	ρ	?	!
Δ	!	?	Δ	ρ
ρ	ρ	!	ρ	Δ

Not associative. For example, $(!\,\square\,p)\,\square\,? \neq\, !\,\square\,(p\,\square\,?)$

20. Consider the following mathematical system. Assume the associative property holds for the given operation.

△	☺	●	♀	♂
☺	☺	●	♀	♂
●	●	♀	♂	☺
♀	♀	♂	☺	●
♂	♂	☺	●	♀

a) What are the elements of the set in this mathematical system? {☺, ●, ♀, ♂}

b) What is the binary operation? △

c) Is the system closed? Explain. Yes

d) Is there an identity element for the system under the given operation? Yes; ☺

e) Does every element in the system have an inverse? If so, give each element and its corresponding inverse. Yes; ☺–☺, ●–♂, ♀–♀, ♂–●

f) Give an example to illustrate the associative property. (● △ ♀) △ ♂ = ● △ (♀ △ ♂)

g) Is the system commutative? Give an example. Yes; ● △ ♂ = ♂ △ ●

h) Is this mathematical system a commutative group? Explain. Yes

10.3

In Exercises 21–30, find the modulo class to which the number belongs for the indicated modulo system.

21. 14, mod 7 0   **22.** 37, mod 6 1

23. 56, mod 9 2   **24.** 68, mod 8 4

25. 71, mod 12 11   **26.** 54, mod 4 2

27. 52, mod 12 4   **28.** 54, mod 14 12

29. 97, mod 11 9   **30.** 31, mod 20 11

In Exercises 31–40, determine all positive number replacements (less than the modulus) for the question mark that make the statement true.

31. $2 + 5 \equiv ? \pmod 6$ 1   **32.** $2 - ? \equiv 3 \pmod 7$ 6

33. $7 \cdot ? \equiv 5 \pmod 8$ 3   **34.** $5 \cdot ? \equiv 3 \pmod 8$ 7

35. $? \cdot 4 \equiv 0 \pmod 8$ **36.** $10 \cdot 7 \equiv ? \pmod{11}$ 4
0, 2, 4, 6

37. $3 - 5 \equiv ? \pmod 7$ 5   **38.** $? \cdot 7 \equiv 3 \pmod{10}$ 9

39. $? \cdot 3 = 5 \pmod 6$ **40.** $7 \cdot ? \equiv 2 \pmod 9$ 8
No solution

41. Construct a modulo 6 addition table. Then determine whether the modulo 6 system forms a commutative group under the operation of addition. *

42. Construct a modulo 4 multiplication table. Then determine whether the modulo 4 system forms a commutative group under the operation of multiplication. *

43. *Police Officer Shifts* Julie Francavilla, a police officer, has the following work pattern. She works 3 days, has 4 days off, then works 4 days, then has 3 days off, and then the pattern repeats. Assume that today is the first day of the work pattern.

a) Will Julie be working 30 days from today? Yes

b) Julie's niece is getting married 45 days from today. Will Julie have the day off? Yes

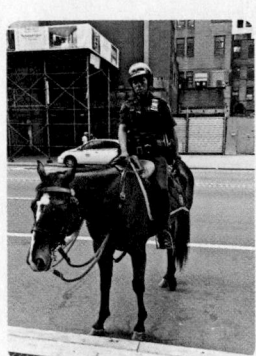

*See Instructor Answer Appendix

CHAPTER 10 *Test*

1. What is a mathematical system? A set of elements and a binary operation

2. List the requirements needed for a mathematical system to be a commutative group. Closure, identity element, inverses, associative property, commutative property

3. Is the set of integers a commutative group under the operation of addition? Explain your answer completely. Yes

4. Is the set of natural numbers a commutative group under the operation of subtraction? Explain your answer completely. No; not closed.

5. Develop a clock 5 arithmetic addition table. *

6. Is clock 5 arithmetic under the operation of addition a commutative group? Assume that the associative property holds. Explain your answer completely. Yes, it is a commutative group.

In Exercises 7 and 8, determine the following in clock 5 arithmetic.

7. $2 + 4 + 1$ 2

8. $1 - 4$ 2

9. Consider the mathematical system

□	W	S	T	R
W	T	R	W	S
S	R	W	S	T
T	W	S	T	R
R	S	T	R	W

a) What is the binary operation? □

b) Is this system closed? Explain. Yes

c) Is there an identity element for this system under the given operation? Explain. Yes, T

d) What is the inverse of the element R? S

e) What is $(T \square R) \square W$? S

In Exercises 10 and 11, determine whether the mathematical system is a commutative group. Explain your answer completely.

10.

*	a	b	c
a	a	b	c
b	b	b	a
c	c	a	d

No, not closed.

11.

?	1	2	3
1	3	1	2
2	1	2	3
3	2	3	1

Yes, it is a commutative group.

12. Determine whether the mathematical system is a commutative group. Assume that the associative property holds. Explain your answer.

○	@	$	&	%
@	%	@	$	&
$	@	$	&	%
&	$	&	%	@
%	&	%	@	$

Yes, it is a commutative group.

In Exercises 13 and 14, determine the modulo class to which the number belongs for the indicated modulo system.

13. 39, mod 4 3

14. 107, mod 11 8

In Exercises 15–19, determine all positive number replacements for the question mark, less than the modulus, that make the statement true.

15. $? + 5 \equiv 3 \pmod 6$ 4

16. $? - 3 \equiv 4 \pmod 5$ 2

17. $3 - ? \equiv 7 \pmod 9$ 5

18. $4 \cdot 2 \equiv ? \pmod 6$ 2

19. $3 \cdot ? \equiv 2 \pmod 6$ { }

20. a) Construct a modulo 5 multiplication table. *

b) Is this mathematical system a commutative group? Explain your answer completely. No; no inverse for 0.

*See Instructor Answer Appendix

GROUP PROJECTS

1. **Rotating a Square**   The square $ABCD$ below has a pin through it at point P so that the square can be rotated in a clockwise direction. The mathematical system consists of the set $\{A, B, C, D\}$ and the operation ♣. The elements of the set represent different rotations of the square clockwise, as follows.

   A = rotate about the point P clockwise 90°

   B = rotate about the point P clockwise 180°

   C = rotate about the point P clockwise 270°

   D = rotate about the point P clockwise 360°

   The operation ♣ means *followed by*. For example, A ♣ B means a clockwise rotation of 90° followed by a clockwise rotation of 180° or a clockwise rotation of 270°. Since C represents a clockwise rotation of 270°, we write A ♣ $B = C$. This result and two other results are shown in the following table.

	A	B	C	D
A		C		
B			A	
C	D			
D				

   Complete the table and determine if the mathematical system is a commutative group. Explain.

2. **Product of Zero**   In arithmetic and algebra, the statement "If $a \cdot b = 0$, then $a = 0$ or $b = 0$" is true. That is, for the product of two numbers to be 0, at least one of the factors must be 0. Can the product of two nonzero numbers equal 0 in a specific modulo system? If so, in what type of modulo systems can this result occur?

   a) Construct multiplication tables for modulo systems 3–9.

   b) Which, if any, of the multiplication tables in part (a) have products equal to 0 when neither factor is 0?

   c) Which, if any, of the multiplication tables in part (a) have products equal to 0 only when at least one factor is 0?

   d) Using the results in parts (b) and (c), can you write a conjecture as to which modulo systems have a product of 0 when neither factor is 0?

3. **Conjecture About Multiplicative Inverses**   Are there certain modulo systems where all numbers have multiplicative inverses?

   a) If you have not worked Group Projects Exercise 2, construct multiplication tables for modulo systems 3–9.

   b) Which of the multiplication tables in part (a) contain multiplicative inverses for all nonzero numbers?

   c) Which, if any, of the multiplication tables in part (a) do not contain multiplicative inverses for all nonzero numbers?

   d) Using the results in parts (b) and (c), can you write a conjecture as to which modulo systems contain multiplicative inverses for all nonzero numbers?

11

Consumer Mathematics

What You Will Learn

- Percents, fractions, and decimals
- Percent increase, percent decrease, and percent markup and markdown
- Simple interest
- Compound interest
- Present value
- Fixed and open-ended installment loans
- Mortgages
- Annuities, sinking funds, and retirement investments

Why This is Important

Managing your money takes much thought and planning. All your daily needs must be met, but at the same time you should consider your long-term goals such as purchasing a house, saving for college expenses, and investing for retirement. This chapter will provide information to help you reach these important goals.

◀ Knowledge of consumer mathematics may help you reach your long-term goals.

SECTION 11.1   Percent

▲ *Daily weather reports include percents.*

Your clock radio turns on in the morning and you hear a weather report that says there is a 75% chance of rain. Based on this information, you decide to carry your umbrella to your class. In this section, we will investigate the meaning of percent and learn how percents relate to mathematics and to daily life.

Why *This is Important* Many decisions that we make every day involve applications of percent. An understanding of percent is essential in making informed decisions.

P ercent, fractions, and decimal numbers all play an important role in consumer mathematics.

Percent, Fractions, and Decimal Numbers

A basic topic necessary for understanding the material in this chapter is percent. The word *percent* comes from the Latin *per centum*, meaning "per hundred." A *percent* is simply a ratio of some number to 100. Thus, $\frac{15}{100} = 15\%$, and $\frac{x}{100} = x\%$.

Percents are useful in making comparisons. Consider Ross, who took two psychology tests. On the first test Ross answered 18 of the 20 questions correctly, and on the second test he answered 23 of 25 questions correctly. On which test did he have the higher score? One way to compare the results is to write ratios of the number of correct answers to the number of questions on the test and then convert the ratios to percents. We can find the grades in percent for each test by (a) writing a ratio of the number of correct answers to the total number of questions, (b) rewriting these ratios with a denominator of 100, and (c) expressing the ratios as percents.

$$\text{Test 1} \qquad\quad \text{(a)} \quad\; \text{(b)} \qquad \text{(c)}$$
$$\frac{\text{Number of correct answers}}{\text{Number of questions on the test}} = \frac{18}{20} = \frac{18 \times 5}{20 \times 5} = \frac{90}{100} = 90\%$$

$$\text{Test 2} \qquad\quad \text{(a)} \quad\; \text{(b)} \qquad \text{(c)}$$
$$\frac{\text{Number of correct answers}}{\text{Number of questions on the test}} = \frac{23}{25} = \frac{23 \times 4}{25 \times 4} = \frac{92}{100} = 92\%$$

By changing the results of both tests to percents, we have a common standard for comparison. The results show that Ross scored 90% on the first test and 92% on the second test. Thus, he had a higher score on the second test.

Another procedure to change a fraction to a percent follows.

PROCEDURE   **TO CHANGE A FRACTION TO A PERCENT**

1. Divide the numerator by the denominator to obtain a decimal number.
2. Multiply the decimal number by 100 (which has the effect of moving the decimal point two places to the right).
3. Add a percent sign.

The above procedure has the effect of moving the decimal point in the original number two places to the right and adding a percent sign.

Note that Steps 2 and 3 together are the equivalent of multiplying by 100%. Since 100% = 100/100 = 1, we are not changing the *value* of the number, we are simply changing the number to a percent.

MATHEMATICS TODAY

Percent Versus Percentage

When should the word *percent* be used and when should the word *percentage* be used? Although writing style manuals are not always consistent on the use of these words, a general rule is given below.

- *Percent* (or the symbol %) accompanies a specific number. The word *percent* may also be used when a question is seeking a specific percent.
  Example 1—Eighty percent of the people liked the movie.
  Example 2—More than 80% (or 80 percent) of the boxes weighed more than 1 pound.
  Example 3—If a worker's salary increased from $35,000 to $38,000 what is the percent increase?
- *Percentage* is used without a specific number.
  Example 4—A large percentage of the population has had their flu shot.
  Example 5—The percentage of the population that has been exposed to the virus is between 60% and 70%.
  Some style manuals state that the word *percent* can be used in place of the word *percentage* on tables and graphs, and other places where space is limited. Also, in the United States, *percent* is usually written as one word, but in Europe and elsewhere it is often written using two words, per cent. Note, too, that, when writing a percent at the beginning of a sentence, as in Example 1 above, the words should be written out.

Why **This is Important** This information may be helpful if you need to write reports for school or for your job.

Example 1 *Converting Fractions to Percents*

Change each of the following fractions to a percent.

a) $\dfrac{67}{100}$ b) $\dfrac{11}{20}$ c) $\dfrac{15}{16}$

Solution For each fraction, follow the three steps in the procedure box on page 600.

a) 1. $67 \div 100 = 0.67$ 2. $0.67 \times 100 = 67$ 3. 67%

Thus, $\dfrac{67}{100} = 67\%$.

b) 1. $11 \div 20 = 0.55$ 2. $0.55 \times 100 = 55$ 3. 55%

Thus, $\dfrac{11}{20} = 55\%$.

c) 1. $15 \div 16 = 0.9375$ 2. $0.9375 \times 100 = 93.75$ 3. 93.75%

Thus, $\dfrac{15}{16} = 93.75\%$. ∎

In future examples, when changing a fraction to a percent, we will follow the three-step procedure given on page 600 without listing the individual steps. We will do this in Examples 4 and 5. To change a decimal number to a percent, follow this procedure.

PROCEDURE **TO CHANGE A DECIMAL NUMBER TO A PERCENT**

1. Multiply the decimal number by 100.
2. Add a percent sign.

The procedure for changing a decimal number to a percent is equivalent to moving the decimal point two places to the right and adding a percent sign.

Example 2 *Converting Decimal Numbers to Percents*

Change each of the following decimal numbers to a percent.

a) 0.14   b) 0.893   c) 0.7625

Solution

a) $0.14 = (0.14 \times 100)\% = 14\%$. Thus, $0.14 = 14\%$.
b) $0.893 = (0.893 \times 100)\% = 89.3\%$. Thus, $0.893 = 89.3\%$.
c) $0.7625 = (0.7625 \times 100)\% = 76.25\%$. Thus, $0.7625 = 76.25\%$. ∎

To change a number given as a percent to a decimal number, follow this procedure.

PROCEDURE **TO CHANGE A PERCENT TO A DECIMAL NUMBER**

1. Divide the number by 100.
2. Remove the percent sign.

The procedure for changing a number given as a percent to a decimal number is equivalent to moving the decimal point two places to the left and removing the percent sign. Another way to remember that is: Percent means per hundred (or to *divide by 100*).

Example 3 *Converting a Percent to a Decimal Number*

a) Change 35% to a decimal number.

b) Change 69.8% to a decimal number.

c) Change $\frac{1}{2}$% to a decimal number.

Solution

a) $35\% = \dfrac{35}{100} = 0.35$. Thus, $35\% = 0.35$.

b) $69.8\% = \dfrac{69.8}{100} = 0.698$. Thus, $69.8\% = 0.698$.

c) $\dfrac{1}{2}\% = 0.5\% = \dfrac{0.5}{100} = 0.005$. Thus, $\dfrac{1}{2}\% = 0.005$. ■

Example 4 *California Population*

In 2009 about 307,006,550 people lived in the United States, and of these people, about 36,961,664 people lived in California. Determine the percentage of people living in the United States in 2009 who lived in California. (Source: *United States Census Bureau.*)

Solution To determine the percentage of people who lived in California, divide the California population, 36,961,664, by the United States population, 307,006,550. Then move the decimal two places to the right and add a percent sign:

$$\text{Percentage of people who lived in California} = \tfrac{36,961,664}{307,006,550} \approx 0.1204 \approx 12.04\%$$

Thus, in 2009, about 12.04% of people who lived in the United States lived in California. ■

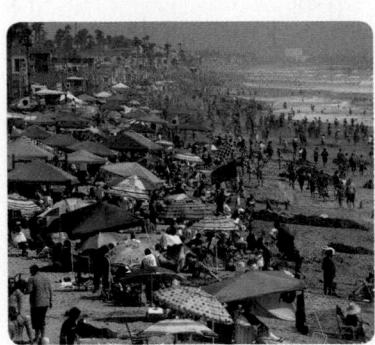

▲ *Oceanside, CA.*

Example 5 *Cherry Production*

According to the U.S. Department of Agriculture, in 2010 the United States produced about 195 million pounds of cherries. Of these cherries, 140 million pounds were produced in Michigan, 24 million pounds were produced in Utah, 16 million pounds were produced in Washington, and 15 million pounds were produced in other states. Determine the percentage of cherries produced in each of the following: Michigan, Utah, Washington, and other states.

Solution To determine each percentage, divide the number of cherries produced in each state by the total number of cherries produced in the United States. Because all the numbers given are in millions of pounds, we will calculate the percentage using the number of millions of pounds.

$$\text{Percent of cherries produced in Michigan} = \tfrac{140}{195} \approx 0.7179 \approx 71.8\%$$
$$\text{Percent of cherries produced in Utah} = \tfrac{24}{195} \approx 0.1231 \approx 12.3\%$$
$$\text{Percent of cherries produced in Washington} = \tfrac{16}{195} \approx 0.0821 \approx 8.2\%$$
$$\text{Percent of cherries produced in other states} = \tfrac{15}{195} \approx 0.0769 \approx 7.7\%$$

The sum of the percents, 71.8% + 12.3% + 8.2% + 7.7%, equals 100%. ■

Percent Change

The percent increase or decrease, or percent change, over a period of time is determined by the formula on page 603.

Percent Change

$$\textbf{Percent change} = \frac{\left(\begin{array}{c}\text{amount in}\\ \text{latest period}\end{array}\right) - \left(\begin{array}{c}\text{amount in}\\ \text{previous period}\end{array}\right)}{\text{amount in previous period}} \times 100$$

If the amount in the latest period is greater than the amount in the previous period, the answer will be positive and will indicate a percent increase. If the amount in the latest period is smaller than the amount in the previous period, the answer will be negative and will indicate a percent decrease.

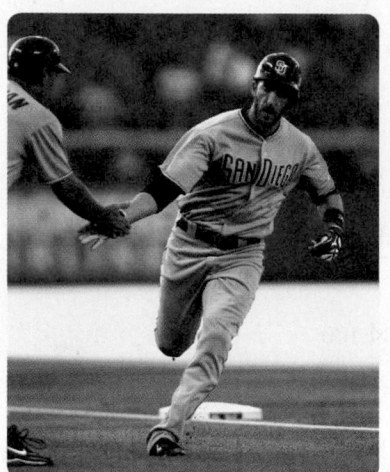

▲ San Diego Padre's rightfielder Chris Denorfia.

Example 6 *Most Improved Baseball Team*

In 2010, the Major League Baseball team with the most improved record for winning games was the San Diego Padres. In 2009, the Padres won 75 games. In 2010, the Padres won 90 games. Determine the percent increase in the number of games won by the Padres from 2009 to 2010.

Solution The previous period is 2009 and the latest period is 2010.

$$\begin{aligned}
\text{Percent change} &= \frac{\left(\begin{array}{c}\text{amount in}\\ \text{latest period}\end{array}\right) - \left(\begin{array}{c}\text{amount in}\\ \text{previous period}\end{array}\right)}{\text{amount in previous period}} \times 100\\[6pt]
&= \frac{90 - 75}{75} \times 100\\[6pt]
&= \frac{15}{75} \times 100\\[6pt]
&= 0.2 \times 100\\[6pt]
&= 20
\end{aligned}$$

Therefore, there was a 20% increase in the number of games won by the Padres from 2009 to 2010. ∎

Example 7 *Harley-Davidson Stock Price*

During the month of August 2010, the price of a share of Harley-Davidson stock fell from \$28.21 the month of to \$24.33. Determine the percent change in the price of a share of Harley-Davidson stock during August 2010.

Solution The amount in the latest period is \$24.33, and the amount in the previous period is \$28.21.

$$\begin{aligned}
\text{Percent change} &= \frac{\left(\begin{array}{c}\text{amount in}\\ \text{latest period}\end{array}\right) - \left(\begin{array}{c}\text{amount in}\\ \text{previous period}\end{array}\right)}{\text{amount in previous period}} \times 100\\[6pt]
&= \frac{24.33 - 28.21}{28.21} \times 100\\[6pt]
&= \frac{-3.88}{28.21} \times 100\\[6pt]
&\approx -0.1375 \times 100\\[6pt]
&\approx -13.75\%
\end{aligned}$$

Thus, the price of a share of Harley-Davidson stock fell about 13.75% during August 2010. ∎

Percent Markup and Markdown

A similar formula is used to calculate percent markup or markdown on cost. A positive answer indicates a markup, and a negative answer indicates a markdown.

Percent Markup or Markdown

$$\text{Percent markup (or markdown) on cost} = \frac{\text{selling price} - \text{dealer's cost}}{\text{dealer's cost}} \times 100$$

Example 8 *Determining Percent Markup*

Holdren Hardware stores pay $48.76 for glass fireplace screens. They regularly sell them for $79.88. At a sale they sell them for $69.99. Determine

a) the percent markup on the regular price.

b) the percent markup on the sale price.

Solution

a) We determine the percent markup on the regular price as follows.

$$\text{Percent markup} = \frac{\text{selling price} - \text{dealer's cost}}{\text{dealer's cost}} \times 100$$

$$= \frac{79.88 - 48.76}{48.76} \times 100$$

$$\approx 0.6382 \times 100$$

$$\approx 63.8$$

Thus, the percent markup on the regular price was about 63.8%.

b) We determine the percent markup on the sale price as follows.

$$\text{Percent markup} = \frac{69.99 - 48.76}{48.76} \times 100$$

$$\approx 0.4354 \times 100$$

$$\approx 43.5$$

Thus, the percent markup on the sale price was about 43.5%. ∎

Example 9 *Determining Percent Markdown*

To help get rid of its remaining 2012 calendars, Cardin's Pharmacy reduces the price to $4.00. If Cardin's cost per calendar was $5.00, determine the percent markdown on the calendars.

Solution We will use the same formula that we used for percent markup in Example 8.

$$\text{Percent markdown} = \frac{\text{selling price} - \text{dealer's cost}}{\text{dealer's cost}} \times 100$$

$$= \frac{4.00 - 5.00}{5.00} \times 100$$

$$= -0.20 \times 100$$

$$= -20$$

Thus, the percent markdown on the calendars was 20%. ∎

Other Percent Problems

In daily life, we may need to know how to solve any one of the following three types of problems involving percent:

1. What is a 15% tip on a restaurant bill of $45.71? The problem can be restated as

    15% of $45.71 is what number?

2. If Nancy Johnson sells a car for $19,000 and receives a commission of $475, what percent of the sale price is the commission? The problem can be restated as

    What percent of $19,000 is $475?

3. If the price of a laptop computer is reduced by 35% or $341.25, what was the original price of the computer? The problem can be restated as

    35% of what number is $341.25?

To answer these three questions, we will translate the words of the problem into an equation and then solve the equation. Some common words or phrases that we encounter are shown below, along with the symbols used when writing the equation.

Word or Phrase	Symbol in the equation
what number	x
what percent	x
is, are, was, or *were*	$=$
of	$\cdot$

To solve each problem given above, we change the percent into a decimal number and change the words of the sentence into symbols of an equation. We then solve the equation for x.

1. 15% of $45.71 is what number?

    $0.15 \cdot 45.71 = x$

    $0.15 \cdot 45.71 = x$

    $6.8565 = x$

    Since 15% of $45.71 is $6.8565, the tip would be $6.86.

2. What percent of $19,000 is $475?

    $x \cdot 19{,}000 = 475$

    $x \cdot 19{,}000 = 475$

    $19{,}000x = 475$

    $$x = \frac{475}{19{,}000} = 0.025 = 2.5\%$$

    Since 2.5% of $19,000 is $475, the commission is 2.5% of the sale price.

3. 35% of what number is $341.25?

    $0.35 \cdot x = 341.25$

    $0.35 \cdot x = 341.25$

    $0.35x = 341.25$

    $$x = \frac{341.25}{0.35} = 975$$

    Since 35% of $975 is $341.25, the original price of the computer was $975.

Example 10 *Down Payment on a Condominium Home*

Melissa Bell wishes to buy a condominium home for $189,000. To obtain the mortgage loan, she must pay 20% of the selling price as a down payment. Determine the amount of Melissa's down payment.

Solution We will let x be the amount of the down payment. This problem can be restated as "20% of the selling price is what number?" We will translate this sentence into an equation and then solve the equation.

$$\underbrace{20\% \text{ of the selling price}}_{0.20 \;\cdot\; 189{,}000} \underbrace{\text{ is }}_{=} \underbrace{\text{what number?}}_{x}$$

$$0.20 \cdot 189{,}000 = x$$
$$37{,}800 = x$$

Melissa's down payment will be $37,800.   ∎

Example 11 *Chess Membership*

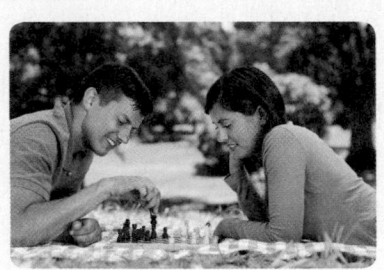

The U.S. Chess Federation (USCF) has about 74,000 members. Of these members, about 24,000 are considered *scholastic* members, meaning they are attending some level of school from kindergarten through college. What percent of USCF members are scholastic members?

Solution Let $x =$ the percent of USCF members who are scholastic members. We will translate the words of the problem into an equation and then solve this equation.

$$\underbrace{\text{What percent of}}_{x} \;\cdot\; \underbrace{\text{USCF members}}_{74{,}000} \underbrace{\text{ are }}_{=} \underbrace{\text{scholastic members?}}_{24{,}000}$$

$$x \cdot 74{,}000 = 24{,}000$$
$$74{,}000x = 24{,}000$$
$$x = \frac{24{,}000}{74{,}000} \approx 0.3243 \approx 32.4\%$$

Therefore, about 32.4% of the USCF members are scholastic members.   ∎

Example 12 *Population of Brazil*

▲ *Rio Olympic Stadium in Rio de Janeiro, Brazil.*

About 54,000,000, or about 27%, of Brazil's population is younger than 15 years old. What is the approximate population of Brazil? (Source: *CIA World Fact Book.*)

Solution Let x be the population of Brazil. This problem can be restated as "27% of what number is 54,000,000?" We will translate this sentence into an equation and then solve this equation.

$$\underbrace{27\% \text{ of}}_{0.27 \;\cdot} \underbrace{\text{what number}}_{x} \underbrace{\text{ is }}_{=} \underbrace{54{,}000{,}000?}_{54{,}000{,}000}$$

$$0.27 \cdot x = 54{,}000{,}000$$
$$0.27x = 54{,}000{,}000$$
$$x = \frac{54{,}000{,}000}{0.27} = 200{,}000{,}000$$

Thus, the population of Brazil is about 200,000,000 people.   ∎

SECTION 11.1

Exercises

Warm Up Exercises

In Exercises 1–6, fill in the blanks with an appropriate word, phrase, or symbol(s).

1. A percent is a ratio of some number to _____. 100

2. To change a fraction to a percent, first divide the numerator by the denominator to obtain a decimal number. Then multiply the decimal number by 100 and add a(n) _____ sign. Percent

3. To change a decimal number to a percent, multiply the decimal number by _____ and add a percent sign. 100

4. To change a percent to a decimal number, divide the number by 100 and _____ the percent sign. Remove

5. To compute the percent change, first determine the difference between the amount in the latest period and the amount in the previous period, then divide this difference by the amount in the _____ period. Previous

6. To compute the percent markup or markdown on cost, first find the difference between selling price and the dealer's cost, then divide this difference by the _____ cost. Dealer's

Practice the Skills

In Exercises 7–14, change the number to a percent. Express your answer to the nearest tenth of a percent.

7. $\frac{7}{10}$ 70% **8.** $\frac{4}{5}$ 80% **9.** $\frac{11}{20}$ 55.0%

10. $\frac{7}{8}$ 87.5% **11.** 0.007654 0.8% **12.** 0.5688 56.9%

13. 3.78 378.0% **14.** 13.678 1367.8%

In Exercises 15–24, change the percent to a decimal number.

15. 7% 0.07 **16.** 9.9% 0.099 **17.** 5.15% 0.0515

18. 0.75% 0.0075 **19.** $\frac{1}{4}$% 0.0025 **20.** $\frac{3}{8}$% 0.00375

21. $\frac{1}{5}$% 0.002 **22.** 135.9% 1.359 **23.** 1% 0.01

24. 0.50% 0.005

Problem Solving

For Exercises 25–67, where appropriate, round answers to the nearest tenth of a percent unless specified otherwise.

25. *Niacin* The U.S. Department of Agriculture's recommended daily allowance (USRDA) of niacin for adults is 20 mg. One serving of Cheerios provides 5 mg of niacin. What percent of the USRDA of niacin does one serving of Cheerios provide? 25%

26. *Potassium* The U.S. Department of Agriculture's recommended daily allowance (USRDA) of potassium for adults is 3500 mg. One serving of Cheerios provides 95 mg of potassium. What percent of the USRDA of potassium does one serving of Cheerios provide? 2.7%

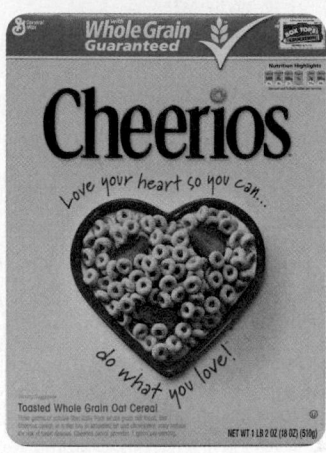

27. *Reduced Fat Milk* One serving of whole milk contains 8 g of fat. Reduced-fat milk contains 41.25% less fat per serving than whole milk. How many grams of fat does one serving of reduced-fat milk contain? 4.7 grams

28. *River Pollution* In a study of U.S. rivers, 693,905 miles of river were studied. According to the U.S. Environmental Protection Agency, it was found that 36% of the total miles of river studied had impaired water quality. How many miles of rivers had impaired quality? 249,805.8 miles

DVD Collection In Exercises 29–32, use the circle graph to answer the questions. The Lafayette County Library classifies its DVDs into one of the categories shown below. The library owns 1743 DVDs. Round your answers to the nearest whole number.

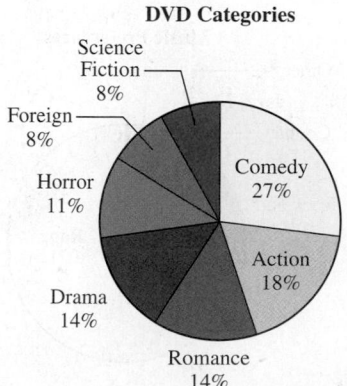

DVD Categories

29. Determine the number of comedy DVDs. 471 comedy DVDs

30. Determine the number of romance DVDs. 244 romance DVDs

31. Determine the number of horror DVDs. 192 horror DVDs

32. Determine the number of foreign DVDs. 139 foreign DVDs

Seawater Composition In Exercises 33–36, use the table to answer the questions. The elements that compose seawater, along with the corresponding percents, are shown in the table below. Round your answers to two decimal places.

Seawater Elements	
Chemical	**Percent**
Oxygen	85.84%
Hydrogen	10.82%
Chlorine	1.94%
Sodium	1.08%
Magnesium	0.13%
Other elements	0.19%

33. If a sample of seawater contains 25 mℓ, how many mℓ of oxygen are in the sample? 21.46 mℓ of oxygen

34. If a saltwater aquarium contains 55 gallons of seawater, how many gallons of hydrogen are in the aquarium? 5.95 gal of hydrogen

35. Connie Buller collects a 500-mℓ sample of seawater for her chemistry class. How many mℓ of chlorine are in the sample? 9.7 mℓ of chlorine

36. Rob Kimball collects a 6000-mℓ sample of seawater for his marine biology class. How many mℓ of magnesium are in the sample? 7.8 mℓ of magnesium

Music Preferences In Exercises 37–40, use the circle graph to answer the questions. Students at Lakewood Ranch High School were polled to determine the type of music they preferred. There were 1960 students who completed the poll. Their responses are represented in the circle graph below. Round your answers to the nearest tenth of a percent.

Music Preferences

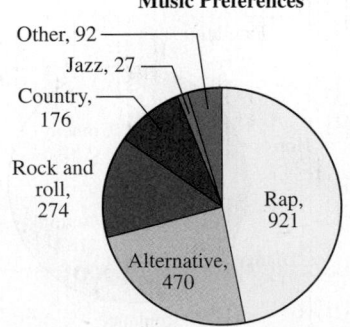

37. What percent of students preferred rap music? 47.0%

38. What percent of students preferred alternative music? 24.0%

39. What percent of students preferred rock and roll music? 14.0%

40. What percent of students preferred country music? 9.0%

41. *Russian Population* The population of Russia has been decreasing since the fall of the Soviet Union. In 1990, the population of Russia was about 148 million people. In 2010, the population of Russia was about 143 million people. Determine the percent decrease in Russia's population during this time period. 3.4% decrease

42. *United States Population* Unlike Russia (see Question 41), the population of the United States has been increasing since 1990. In 1990, the population of the United States was about 249 million. In 2010, the population of the United States was about 308 million. Determine the percent increase in the U.S. population during this time period. 23.7% increase

43. *U.S. Debt* The graph shows the federal U.S. debt, in trillions of U.S. dollars, for the years 2004–2010.

U.S. Debt

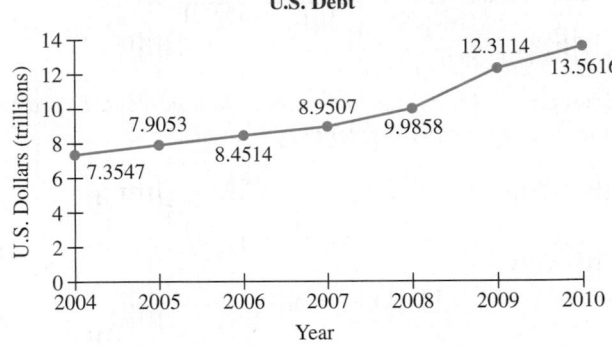

Source: *U.S. Census Bureau*

a) Determine the percent increase in the U.S. debt from 2005 to 2006. 6.9% increase

b) Determine the percent increase in the U.S. debt from 2006 to 2007. 5.9% increase

c) Determine the percent increase in the U.S. debt from 2007 to 2008. 11.6% increase

d) Determine the percent increase in the U.S. debt from 2008 to 2009. 23.3% increase

e) Determine the percent increase in the U.S. debt from 2009 to 2010. 10.2% increase

44. *United States Land Area* The graph shows the land area of the United States, in millions of square miles, for the years 1790, 1810, 1830, 1850, and 1870.

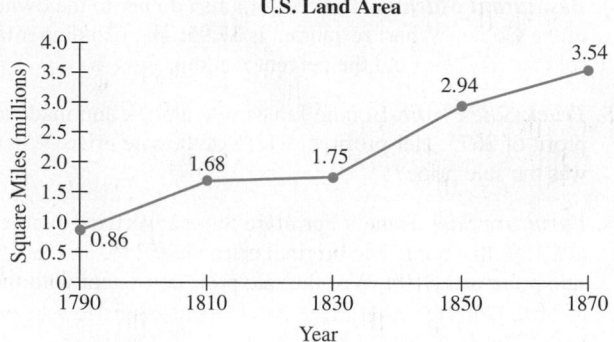

U.S. Land Area

Source: *United States Census Bureau*

a) Determine the percent increase in U.S. land area from 1790 to 1810. 95.3% increase

b) Determine the percent increase in U.S. land area from 1810 to 1830. 4.2% increase

c) Determine the percent increase in U.S. land area from 1830 to 1850. 68.0% increase

d) Determine the percent increase in U.S. land area from 1850 to 1870. 20.4% increase

45. *Dow Jones Industrial Average* The following graph shows the Dow Jones Industrial Average (DJIA) for 2000–2010 at closing on the last trading day of the year.

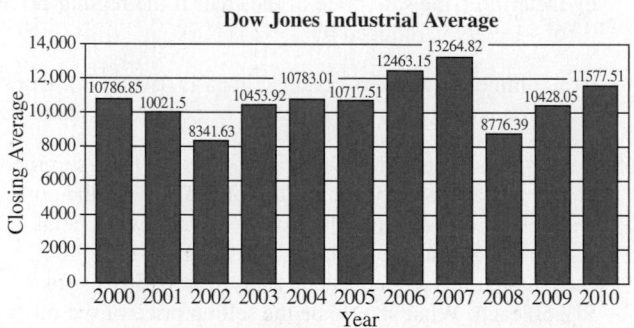

Dow Jones Industrial Average

a) Determine the percent change in the DJIA from 2000 to 2002. 22.7% decrease

b) Determine the percent change in the DJIA from 2002 to 2004. 29.3% increase

c) Determine the percent change in the DJIA from 2007 to 2008. 33.8% decrease

d) Determine the percent change in the DJIA from 2008 to 2009. 18.8% increase

e) Determine the percent change in the DJIA from 2009 to 2010. 11.0% increase

46. *Presidential Salary* The following graph shows the annual salary for the president of the United States for selected years from 1789 to 2001.

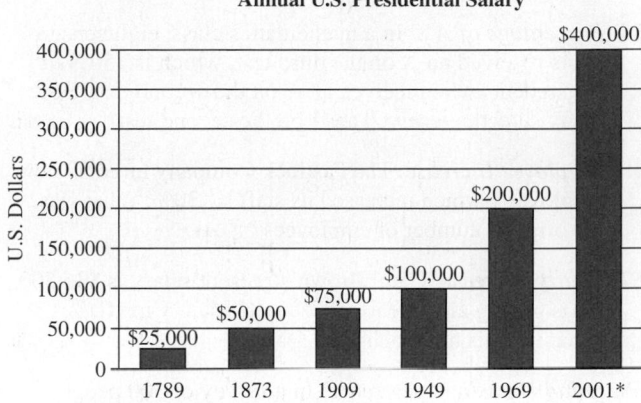

Annual U.S. Presidential Salary

Source: *Congressional Quarterly*
*As of 2011, the annual presidential salary is still $400,000.

a) Determine the percent increase in annual salary from 1789 to 1873. 100.0% increase

b) Determine the percent increase in annual salary from 1909 to 1949. 33.3% increase

c) Determine the percent increase in annual salary from 1969 to 2001. 100.0% increase

d) Determine the percent increase in annual salary from 1789 to 2001. 1500.0% increase

In Exercises 47–52, determine the answer to the question.

47. What is 15% of $45.00? $6.75

48. What is 6.5% of $150.00? $9.75

49. What percent of 96 is 24? 25%

50. What percent of 75 is 15? 20%

51. Five percent of what number is 15? 300

52. Ten percent of what number is 75? 750

53. *Tax and Tip* According to the Original Tipping Page, www.tipping.org, it is appropriate to tip waiters and waitresses 15%–20% of the total restaurant bill, *including the tax.* Mary and Keith's dinner costs $43.50 before tax, and the tax rate is 6%.

a) What is the tax on Mary and Keith's dinner? $2.61

b) What is the total bill, including tax, before the tip? $46.11

c) If Mary and Keith decide to tip 15% of the total bill, how much is the tip? $6.92

d) What is the total cost of the dinner including the tax and tip? $53.03

54. *Fishing* The Gordon and Stallard Charter Fishing Boat Company has recently increased the number of crewmembers by 25%, or 10 crewmembers. What was the original number of crewmembers? 40 crewmembers

55. *Percentage of A's* In a mathematics class, eighteen students received an A on the third test, which is 150% of the students who received an A on the second test. How many students received an A on the second test? 12 students

56. *Employee Increase* The Fastlock Company hired 57 new employees, which increased its staff by 30%. What was the original number of employees? 190 employees

57. *Salary Increase* Qami Brown's present salary is $36,500. He is getting an increase of 7% in his salary next year. What will his new salary be? $39,055

58. *Salad Dressing Preference* In a survey of 300 people, 17% prefer ranch dressing on their salad. How many people in the surveyed group prefer ranch dressing? 51 people

59. *Vacuum Cleaner Sales* A Kirby vacuum cleaner dealership sold 430 units in 2011 and 407 units in 2012. Find the percent increase or decrease in the number of units sold. 5.3% decrease

60. *Vacuum Cleaner Markup* If the Kirby dealership in Exercise 59 pays $320 for each unit and sells it for $699, what is the percent markup? 118.4% markup

61. *Increasing Farm Land* Bruce Timmerman is a farmer who recently purchased his neighbor's farm. Before the purchase, Bruce owned a total of 356 acres of land. After the purchase, Bruce owned a total of 504 acres of land. Determine the percent increase in the number of acres of land owned by Bruce. 41.6% increase

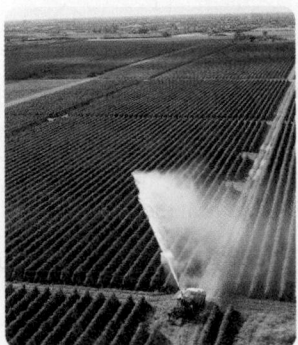

62. *Weight Loss* On January 1, Max Saindoux weighed 235 pounds and decided to diet and exercise. On June 30, Max weighed 210 pounds. Determine the percent decrease in Max's weight from January 1 to June 30. 10.6% decrease

63. *Television Sale* The regular price of a Phillips color TV is $539.62. During a sale, Hill TV is selling the TV for $439. Find the percent decrease in the price of this TV. 18.6% decrease

64. *Restaurant Markup* The cost of a fish dinner to the owner of the Golden Wharf restaurant is $7.95. The fish dinner is sold for $11.95. Find the percent markup. 50.3% markup

65. *Truck Sale Profit* Bonnie James sold a truck and made a profit of $675. Her profit was 18% of the sale price. What was the sale price? $3750

66. *Furniture Sale* Kane's Furniture Store advertised a table at a 15% discount. The original price was $115, and the sale price was $100. Was the sale price consistent with the ad? Explain. The sale price is not consistent with the ad. The sale price was $2.25 higher than it should have been.

67. *Reselling a Car* Quincy Carter purchased a used car for $1000. He decided to sell the car for 10% above his purchase price. Quincy could not sell the car so he reduced his asking price by 10%. If he sells the car at the reduced price, will he have a profit or a loss or will he break even? Explain how you arrived at your answer. He will have a loss of $10.

Challenge Problems/Group Activities

68. *Comparing Markdowns*

a) A coat is marked down 10%, and the customer is given a second discount of 15%. Is that the same as a single discount of 25%? Explain. No, the 25% discount is greater.

b) The regular price of a chair is $189.99. Determine the sale price of the chair if the regular price is reduced by 10% and this price is then reduced another 15%. $145.34

c) Determine the sale price of the chair if the regular price of $189.99 is reduced by 25%. $142.49

d) Examine the answers obtained in parts (b) and (c). Does your answer to part (a) appear to be correct? Explain. Yes

69. *Selling Ties* The Tie Shoppe paid $5901.79 for a shipment of 500 ties and wants to make a profit of 40% of the cost on the whole shipment. The store is having two special sales. At the first sale it plans to sell 100 ties for $9.00 each, and at the second sale it plans to sell 150 ties for $12.50 each. What should be the selling price of the other 250 ties for the Tie Shoppe to make a 40% profit on the whole shipment? $21.95

70. In parts (a) through (c), determine which is the greater amount and by how much.

a) $100 increased by 25% or $200 decreased by 25%. $200 decreased by 25% is greater by $25.

b) $100 increased by 50% or $200 decreased by 50%. $100 increased by 50% is greater by $50.

c) $100 increased by 100% or $200 decreased by 100%. $100 increased by 100% is greater by $200.

Internet/Research Activity

71. Find two circle graphs in newspapers, magazines, or on the Internet whose data are not given in percents. Redraw the graphs and label them with percents.

SECTION 11.2   Personal Loans and Simple Interest

▲ *A personal loan may be used to pay for emergency expenses.*

Consider the following dilemma. Your car breaks down and the mechanic tells you that the repairs will cost $450. You currently do not have the $450, but your family desperately needs to have a car. One option for you would be to borrow the money from a friend, a family member, a bank, or other lending institution. In this section, we will discuss personal loans and the cost of obtaining such loans.

Why *This is Important* Understanding the cost of borrowing money will help you make informed decisions about your personal finances.

The money a bank or other lender is willing to lend you is called the amount of *credit* extended or the *principal of the loan*. The amount of credit and the interest rate that you may obtain depend on the assurance you can give the lender that you will be able to repay the loan. Your credit is determined by your business reputation for honesty, by your earning power, and by what you can pledge as security to cover the loan. *Security* (or *collateral*) is anything of value pledged by the borrower that the lender may sell or keep if the borrower does not repay the loan. Acceptable security may be a business, a mortgage on a property, the title to an automobile, savings accounts, or stocks or bonds.

Bankers sometimes grant loans without security, but they require the signature of one or more other persons, called *cosigners*, who guarantee the loan will be repaid. For either of the two types of loans, the secured loan or the cosigner loan, the borrower (and cosigner, if there is one) must sign an agreement called a *personal note*. This document states the terms and conditions of the loan.

The most common way for individuals to borrow money is through an installment loan or using a credit card. (Installment loans and credit cards are discussed in Section 11.4.)

The concept of simple interest is essential to the understanding of installment buying. *Interest* is the money the borrower pays for the use of the lender's money. One type of interest is called simple interest. *Simple interest* is based on the entire amount of the loan for the total period of the loan. The formula used to find simple interest follows.

Simple Interest Formula

$$\text{Interest} = \text{principal} \times \text{rate} \times \text{time}$$
$$i = prt$$

In the simple interest formula, the *principal*, p, is the amount of money lent, the *rate*, r, is the rate of interest expressed as a decimal number and the *time*, t, is the number of days, months, or years for which the money will be lent. *Time is expressed in the same period as the rate.* For example, if the rate is 2% per month, the time must be expressed in months. Typically, rate means the annual rate unless otherwise stated. Principal and interest are expressed in dollars in the United States.

Ordinary Interest

The most common type of simple interest is called *ordinary interest.* For computing ordinary interest, each month has 30 days and a year has 12 months or 360 days. On the *due date* of a *simple interest note* the borrower must repay the principal plus the interest. (*Note:* Simple interest will mean ordinary interest unless stated otherwise.)

Example 1 *Air Conditioning Loan*

Sherry Tornwall needs to borrow $6200 to replace the air conditioner in her home. From her credit union, Sherry obtains a 30-month loan with an annual simple interest rate of 5.75%.

a) Calculate the simple interest she is charged on the loan.

b) Determine the amount, principal plus interest, Sherry will pay the credit union at the end of the 30 months to pay off her loan.

Solution

a) To determine the interest on the loan, we use the formula $i = prt$. We know that $p = \$6200$, $r = 5.75\%$, which written as a decimal number is 0.0575, and t in years $= \frac{30}{12} = 2.5$. We substitute the appropriate values in the simple interest formula

$$i = p \times r \times t$$
$$= \$6200 \times 0.0575 \times 2.5$$
$$= \$891.25$$

The simple interest on $6200 at 5.75% for 30 months is $891.25.

b) The amount to be repaid is equal to the principal, $6200, plus the interest, $891.25.

$$A = p + i$$
$$= \$6200 + \$891.25$$
$$= \$7091.25$$

To pay off her loan, Sherry will pay the credit union $7091.25 at the end of 30 months.

Example 2 *Determining the Annual Rate of Interest*

Philip Mahler agrees to lend $850 to his friend Joe Mahoney to help Joe travel to Cincinnati to attend a family wedding. Nine months later, Joe repaid the original $850 plus $51 interest. What annual rate of interest did Joe pay to Philip?

Solution We need to solve for the interest rate, r. Since the time is 9 months, the time in years is $\frac{9}{12}$, or 0.75. Using the formula $i = prt$, we get

$$\$51 = \$850 \times r \times 0.75$$
$$51 = 637.5r$$
$$\frac{51}{637.5} = \frac{637.5r}{637.5} \qquad \text{Divide both sides of the equation by 637.5.}$$
$$0.08 = r$$

To change this decimal number to a percent, multiply by 100 and add a percent sign. Thus the annual rate of interest paid by Joe to Philip is 8%.

Example 3 *A Pawn Loan*

To obtain money for new eyeglasses, Gilbert French decides to pawn his trumpet. Gilbert borrows $240 and after 30 days gets his trumpet back by paying the pawnbroker $288. What annual rate of interest did Gilbert pay?

Solution Gilbert paid $288 − $240 = $48 in interest, and the length of the loan is for one month, or $\frac{1}{12}$ of a year.

Using the formula $i = prt$, we get

$$\$48 = \$240 \times r \times \frac{1}{12}$$

$$48 = 20r$$

$$\frac{48}{20} = r$$

$$2.4 = r$$

The annual rate of interest as a decimal number is 2.4. To change this number to a percent, multiply the number by 100 and add a percent sign. Thus, the annual rate of interest paid is 240%.   ∎

In Examples 1, 2, and 3, we illustrated a simple interest loan, for which the interest and principal are paid on the due date of the note. There is another type of loan, the *discount note*, for which the interest is paid at the time the borrower receives the loan. The interest charged in advance is called the *bank discount*. A Federal Reserve Treasury bill is a bank discount note issued by the U.S. government. Example 4 illustrates a discount note.

Example 4 *True Interest Rate of a Discount Note*

Siegrid Cook took out a $500 loan using a 10% discount note for a period of 3 months. Determine

a) the interest she must pay to the bank on the date she receives the loan.

b) the net amount of money she receives from the bank.

c) the actual rate of interest for the loan.

Solution

a) To determine the interest, use the simple interest formula.

$$i = prt$$

$$= \$500 \times 0.10 \times \frac{3}{12}$$

$$= \$12.50$$

b) Since Siegrid must pay $12.50 interest when she first receives the loan, the net amount she receives is $500 − $12.50, or $487.50.

c) We calculate the actual rate of interest charged using the simple interest formula. In the formula for the principal, we use the amount Siegrid actually received from the bank, $487.50. For the interest, we use the interest calculated in part (a).

$$i = prt$$

$$\$12.50 = \$487.50 \times r \times \frac{3}{12}$$

$$12.50 = 121.875 \times r$$

$$\frac{12.50}{121.875} = r$$

$$0.1026 \approx r$$

Thus, the actual rate of interest is about 10.3% rather than the quoted 10%.   ∎

Example 5 *Loan Choices*

Alex Runde is the goalie for the Philadelphia Wings of the National Lacrosse League. Alex needs to purchase new goalie equipment but does not have the $1600 purchase price. The equipment dealer has two payment options. With option 1, Alex can pay $800 as a down payment and then pay $850 in 6 months. With option 2, Alex can pay $400 as a down payment and then pay $1380 in 9 months. Which payment has a higher annual simple interest rate?

Solution Before we compute the annual simple interest rates, we first need to compute the principle and the interest.

Option 1: To determine the principal of the loan, subtract the down payment from the purchase price of the equipment. Therefore, $p = \$1600 - \$800 = \$800$. To determine the interest charged, subtract the purchase price of the equipment from the total amount paid. Therefore, $i = (\$800 + \$850) - \$1600 = \$50$. To determine the time, divide 6 by 12. Therefore $t = \frac{6}{12} = 0.5$. Then we use the simple interest formula.

$$i = p \times r \times t$$
$$50 = 800 \times r \times 0.5$$
$$50 = 400r$$
$$\frac{50}{400} = r$$
$$0.125 = r$$

Option 1 has a 12.5% annual simple interest rate.

Option 2: The principal is $p = \$1600 - \$400 = \$1200$, the interest is $i = (\$400 + \$1380) - \$1600 = \$180$, and the time is $t = \frac{9}{12} = 0.75$. Then

$$i = p \times r \times t$$
$$180 = 1200 \times r \times 0.75$$
$$180 = 900r$$
$$\frac{180}{900} = r$$
$$0.2 = r$$

Option 2 has a 20.0% annual simple interest rate. Therefore, option 2 charges a higher annual simple interest rate than option 1. ∎

The United States Rule

A loan has a date of maturity, at which time the principal and interest are due. It is possible to make payments on a loan before the date of maturity. A payment that is less than the full amount owed and made prior to the due date is known as a *partial payment*. A Supreme Court decision specified the method by which these payments are credited. The procedure is called the *United States rule*.

The United States rule states that if a partial payment is made on the loan, interest is computed on the principal from the first day of the loan until the date of the partial payment. The partial payment is used to pay the interest first; then the rest of the payment is used to reduce the principal. The next time a partial payment is made, interest is calculated on the unpaid principal from the date of the previous date of payment. Again, the payment goes first to pay the interest, with the rest of the payment used to reduce the principal. An individual can make as many partial payments as he or she wishes; the procedure is repeated for each payment. The balance due on the date of maturity is found by computing interest due since the last partial payment and adding this interest to the unpaid principal.

The *Banker's rule* is used to calculate simple interest when applying the United States rule. The Banker's rule considers a year to have 360 days, and any fractional part of a year is the exact number of days of the loan.

To determine the exact number of days in a period, we can use Table 11.1 below. Example 6 on page 616 illustrates how to use the table.

Table 11.1

	31	28	31	30	31	30	31	31	30	31	30	31
Day of Month	**Jan.**	**Feb.**	**Mar.**	**Apr.**	**May**	**June**	**July**	**Aug.**	**Sept.**	**Oct.**	**Nov.**	**Dec.**
Day 1	1	32	60	91	121	152	182	213	244	274	305	335
Day 2	2	33	61	92	122	153	183	214	245	275	306	336
Day 3	3	34	62	93	123	154	184	215	246	276	307	337
Day 4	4	35	63	94	124	155	185	216	247	277	308	338
Day 5	5	36	64	95	125	156	186	217	248	278	309	339
Day 6	6	37	65	96	126	157	187	218	249	279	310	340
Day 7	7	38	66	97	127	158	188	219	250	280	311	341
Day 8	8	39	67	98	128	159	189	220	251	281	312	342
Day 9	9	40	68	99	129	160	190	221	252	282	313	343
Day 10	10	41	69	100	130	161	191	222	253	283	314	344
Day 11	11	42	70	101	131	162	192	223	254	284	315	345
Day 12	12	43	71	102	132	163	193	224	255	285	316	346
Day 13	13	44	72	103	133	164	(194)	225	256	286	317	347
Day 14	14	45	73	104	134	165	195	226	257	287	318	348
Day 15	15	46	(74)	105	135	166	196	227	258	288	319	349
Day 16	16	47	75	106	136	167	197	228	259	289	320	350
Day 17	17	48	76	107	137	168	198	229	260	290	321	351
Day 18	18	49	77	108	138	169	199	230	261	291	322	352
Day 19	19	50	78	109	139	170	200	231	262	292	323	353
Day 20	20	51	79	110	140	171	201	232	263	293	324	354
Day 21	21	52	80	111	141	172	202	233	264	294	325	355
Day 22	22	53	81	112	142	173	203	234	265	295	326	356
Day 23	23	54	82	113	143	174	204	235	266	296	327	357
Day 24	24	55	83	114	144	175	205	236	267	297	328	358
Day 25	25	56	84	115	145	176	206	237	268	298	329	359
Day 26	26	57	85	116	146	177	207	238	269	299	330	360
Day 27	27	58	86	117	147	178	208	239	270	300	331	361
Day 28	28	59	87	118	148	179	209	240	271	301	332	362
Day 29	29		88	119	149	180	210	241	272	302	333	363
Day 30	30		89	120	150	181	211	242	273	303	334	364
Day 31	31		90		151		212	243		304		365

Add 1 day for leap year if February 29 falls between the two dates under consideration.

Example 6 *Determining the Due Date of a Note*

Use Table 11.1 to determine (a) the due date of a loan made on March 15 for 120 days and (b) the number of days from April 18 to July 31.

Solution

a) To determine the due date of the loan, do the following. In Table 11.1, find Day 15 in the left column (with heading Day of Month) and then move three columns to the right (heading at the top of the column is March) to find the number 74 (circled in red). Thus, March 15 is the 74th day of the year. Add 120 to 74 since the loan will be due 120 days after March 15:

$$74 + 120 = 194$$

Thus, the due date of the note is the 194th day of the year. Find 194 (circled in blue) in Table 11.1 in the column headed July. The number in the same row as 194 in the left column is Day 13. Thus, the due date of the note is July 13.

b) To determine the number of days from April 18 to July 31, use Table 11.1 to find that April 18 is the 108th day of the year and that July 31 is the 212th day of the year. Then find the difference: $212 - 108 = 104$. Thus, the number of days from April 18 to July 31 is 104 days. ∎

Example 7 *Using the Banker's Rule*

Determine the simple interest that will be paid on a $300 loan at an interest rate of 5% for the period March 3 to May 3 using the Banker's rule.

Solution The exact number of days from March 3 to May 3 is 61. The period of time in years is 61/360. Substituting in the simple interest formula gives

$$i = prt$$
$$= \$300 \times 0.05 \times \frac{61}{360}$$
$$\approx \$2.54$$

The interest is $2.54. ∎

A borrower may wish to pay back part of the loan prior to the due date. The next example illustrates how a partial payment is credited under the United States rule. Making partial payments reduces the amount of interest paid and thus the cost of the loan.

Example 8 *Using the United States Rule*

Cathy Panik is a mathematics teacher, and she plans to attend a national conference. To pay for her airfare, on November 1, 2010, Cathy takes out a 120-day loan for $400 at an interest rate of 12.5%. Cathy uses some birthday gift money to make a partial payment of $150 on January 5, 2011. She makes a second partial payment of $100 on February 2, 2011.

a) Determine the due date of the loan.

b) Determine the interest and the amount credited to the principal on January 5.

c) Determine the interest and the amount credited to the principal on February 2.

d) Determine the amount that Cathy must pay on the due date.

Solution

a) Using Table 11.1, we see that November 1 is the 305th day of the year. Next, we note that the sum of 305 and 120 is 425. Since this due date will extend into the next year, we subtract 365 from 425 to get 60. From Table 11.1, we see that the 60th day of the year is March 1. Therefore, the loan due date is March 1, 2011. Had 2011 been a leap year, the due date would have been February 29, 2011.

b) Using Table 11.1, January 5 is the 5th day of the year and November 1 is the 305th day of the year. The number of days from November 1 to January 5 can be computed as follows: $(365 - 305) + 5 = 65$. Then, using $i = prt$ and the Banker's rule, we get

$$i = \$400 \times 0.125 \times \frac{65}{360}$$
$$\approx \$9.03$$

The interest of $9.03 that is due January 5, 2011, is deducted from the payment of $150. The remaining payment of $150 − $9.03, or $140.97, is then credited to the principal. Therefore, the adjusted principal is now $400 − $140.97, or $259.03.

Note that if that payment had been the only partial payment made, then the balance due on March 1, 2011, would be calculated by determining the interest on the balance, $259.03, for the remainder of the loan, 55 days, and adding this interest to the principal of $259.03. If this payment had been the only partial payment made, then the balance due on March 1 would be

$$\text{Balance due} = \text{principal} + \text{interest}$$
$$\approx 259.03 + \left(259.03 \times 0.125 \times \frac{55}{360} \right)$$
$$\approx 259.03 + 4.95$$
$$\approx 263.98$$

c) Since there was a second partial payment made, we use the Banker's rule to calculate the interest on the unpaid principal for the period from January 5 to February 2. According to Table 11.1, the number of days from January 5 to February 2 is $33 - 5$, or 28 days.

$$i = \$259.03 \times 0.125 \times \frac{28}{360}$$
$$\approx \$2.52$$

The interest of $2.52 that is due February 2, 2011, is deducted from the payment of $100. The remaining payment of $100 − $2.52, or $97.48, is then credited to the principal. Therefore, the new adjusted principal is now $259.03 − $97.48, or $161.55.

d) The due date of the loan is March 1. Using Table 11.1, we see that there are $60 - 33$, or 27, days from February 2 to March 1. The interest is computed on the remaining balance of $161.51 by using the simple interest formula.

$$i = \$161.55 \times 0.125 \times \frac{27}{360}$$
$$\approx \$1.51$$

Therefore, the balance due on the maturity date of the loan is the sum of the principal and the interest, $161.55 + $1.51, or $163.06. *Note:* The sum of the days in the three calculations, $65 + 28 + 27$, equals the total number of days in the loan, 120. ∎

Warm Up Exercises

In Exercises 1–8, fill in the blanks with an appropriate word, phrase, or symbol(s).

1. The money a bank or other lending institution is willing to lend you is called the amount of credit extended or the _____ of the loan. Principal

2. Anything of value pledged by the borrower that the lender may sell or keep if the borrower does not repay the loan is called the _____ or collateral. Security

3. The money the borrower pays for the use of the lender's money is called the _____. Interest

4. When using the simple interest formula, the interest rate, r, is expressed as a(n) _____ number. Decimal

5. When using the simple interest formula, time, t, is expressed in the same period as the _____. Rate

6. A payment that is less than the full amount owed and made prior to the due date is known as a(n) _____ payment. Partial

7. If a partial payment is made on a loan, interest is computed on the principal from the first day of the loan until the date of the partial payment. This is known as the _____ rule. United States

8. The Banker's rule considers a year to have _____ days. 360

Practice the Skills

In Exercises 9–18, determine the simple interest. Unless noted otherwise, assume the rate is an annual rate. Assume 360 days in a year. Round answers to the nearest cent.

9. $p = \$300$, $r = 1.5\%$, $t = 4$ years $18.00

10. $p = \$465$, $r = 2.75\%$, $t = 1.25$ years $15.98

11. $p = \$1100$, $r = 8.75\%$, $t = 90$ days $24.06

12. $p = \$2500$, $r = 3\frac{7}{8}\%$, $t = 9$ months $72.66

13. $p = \$587$, $r = 0.045\%$ per day, $t = 2$ months $15.85

14. $p = \$6742.75$, $r = 6.05\%$, $t = 90$ days $101.98

15. $p = \$2756.78$, $r = 10.15\%$, $t = 103$ days $80.06

16. $p = \$550.31$, $r = 8.9\%$, $t = 67$ days $9.12

17. $p = \$1372.11$, $r = 1\frac{3}{8}\%$ per month, $t = 6$ months $113.20

18. $p = \$41{,}864$, $r = 0.0375\%$ per day, $t = 60$ days $941.94

In Exercises 19–24, use the simple interest formula to determine the missing value. If necessary, round all dollar figures to the nearest cent.

19. $p = \$1500.00$, $r = ?$, $t = 4$ years, $i = \$336.00$ 5.6%

20. $p = ?$, $r = 2\%$, $t = 90$ days, $i = \$12.50$ $2500

21. $p = ?$, $r = 6\%$, $t = 5$ months, $i = \$175.00$ $7000

22. $p = \$800.00$, $r = 4\%$, $t = ?$, $i = \$64.00$ 2 years

23. $p = \$957.62$, $r = 6.5\%$, $t = ?$, $i = \$124.49$ 2 years

24. $p = \$1650.00$, $r = ?$, $t = 6.5$ years, $i = \$343.20$ 3.2%

Problem Solving

In Exercises 25–58, if necessary round all dollar figures to the nearest cent and round percents to the nearest hundredth of a percent.

25. *Small Business Administration Loan* Joshua Leuchter uses the Small Business Administration (SBA) Loan Program to obtain a loan to help expand his vending machine business. Joshua borrows $25,000 for 2 years with a simple interest rate of 1.5%. Determine the amount of money Joshua must repay the SBA after 2 years. $25,750

26. *Business Loan* The city of Bradenton is offering simple interest loans to start-up businesses at a rate of 3.5%. Gaetano Cannata obtains one of these loans of $6000 for 3 years to help pay for start-up costs of his restaurant, Ortygia. Determine the amount of money Gaetano must repay the city after 3 years. $6630

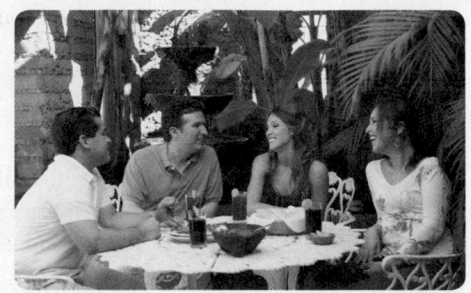

27. *Bank Personal Note* Karen Mosely borrowed $3500 from a bank for 6 months. Her friend Ms. Harris was cosigner of Karen's personal note. The bank collected $7\frac{1}{2}\%$ simple interest on the date of maturity.

a) How much did Karen pay for the use of the money? $131.25

b) Determine the amount she repaid to the bank on the due date of the note. $3631.25

28. *Bank Discount Note* Kwame Adebele borrowed $2500 for 5 months from a bank, using U.S. government bonds as security. The bank discounted the loan at 2%.

a) How much interest did Kwame pay the bank for the use of its money? $20.83

b) How much did he receive from the bank? $2479.17

c) What was the actual rate of interest he paid? 2.02%

29. *Bank Discount Note* Julie Monte borrowed $3650 from her bank for 8 months. The bank discounted the loan at 7.5%.

a) How much interest did Julie pay the bank for the use of its money? $182.50

b) How much did she receive from the bank? $3467.50

c) What was the actual rate of interest she paid? 7.89%

30. *Credit Union Loan* Enrico Montoyo wants to borrow $350 for 6 months from his credit union, using his savings account as security. The credit union's policy is that the maximum amount a person can borrow is 80% of the amount in the person's savings account. The interest rate is 2 percentage points higher than the interest rate being paid on the savings account. The current rate on the savings account is 3.25%.

a) How much money must Enrico have in his account to borrow $350? $437.50

b) What is the rate of interest the credit union will charge for the loan? 5.25%

c) Find the amount Enrico must repay in 6 months. $359.19

31. *Investing Tuition Payments* Sand Ridge School is requiring parents to pay half of the yearly tuition at the time of registration and half on the date classes begin. Registration is held 5 months prior to the beginning of school, and administrators expect 470 students to register. If annual tuition is $4500 and if the money paid at the time of registration is placed in an account paying 5.4% simple interest, how much interest will Sand Ridge School earn by the time school begins? $23,793.75

32. *A Pawn Loan* Jeffrey Kowalski wants to take his mother out for dinner on her birthday, but he doesn't get paid until the following week. To borrow money, Jeffrey pawns his watch. Based on the value of the watch, the pawnbroker loans Jeffrey $75. Fourteen days later, Jeffrey gets his watch back by paying the pawnbroker $80.25. What annual simple interest rate did the pawnbroker charge Jeffrey? 180%

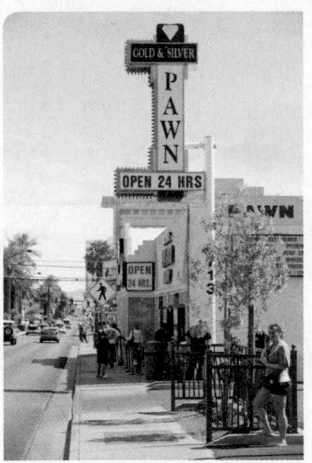

In Exercises 33–38, determine the exact time from the first date to the second date. Use Table 11.1. Assume the year is not a leap year unless otherwise indicated.

33. March 17 to November 11 239 days

34. January 17 to October 10 266 days

35. February 2 to October 31 (the loan is due in a leap year) 272 days

36. June 14 to January 24 224 days

37. August 24 to May 15 264 days

38. December 21 to April 28 128 days

In Exercises 39–42, determine the due date of the loan, using the exact time, if the loan is made on the given date for the given number of days.

39. April 15 for 100 days July 24

40. May 11 for 120 days September 8

41. November 25 for 120 days (the loan is due in a leap year) March 24

42. July 5 for 210 days January 31

In Exercises 43–52, a partial payment is made on the date(s) indicated. Use the United States rule to determine the balance due on the note at the date of maturity. (The Effective Date is the date the note was written.) Assume the year is not a leap year.

	Principal	Rate	Effective Date	Partial Payment(s)		Maturity Date
				Amount	Date(s)	
43.	$3000	4%	May 1	$1000	June 1	July 1*
44.	$6000	7%	Jan. 15	$2500	Mar. 1	Apr. 15*
45.	$2400	5.5%	Feb. 1	$1000	May 1	Aug. 31*
46.	$8500	11.5%	Sep. 1	$4250	Oct. 31	Dec. 31*
47.	$9000	6%	July 15	$4000	Dec. 27	Feb. 1*
48.	$1000	12.5%	Jan. 1	$300	Jan. 15	Feb. 15*
49.	$1800	15%	Aug. 1	$500	Sept. 1	Nov. 1*
				$500	Oct. 1	
50.	$5000	14%	Oct. 15	$800	Nov. 15	Jan. 1*
				$800	Dec. 15	
51.	$11,600	6%	Mar. 1	$2000	Aug. 1	Dec. 1*
				$4000	Nov. 15	
52.	$21,000	$4\frac{3}{8}$%	July 12	$8000	Oct. 10	Jan. 30*
				$6000	Dec. 8	

53. *Company Loan* On March 1, the Zwick Balloon Company signed a $6500 note with simple interest of $10\frac{1}{2}$% for 180 days. The company made payments of $1750 on May 1 and $2350 on July 1. How much will the company owe on the date of maturity? $2646.24

54. *Restaurant Loan* The Sweet Tooth Restaurant borrowed $3000 on a note dated May 15 with simple interest of 11%. The maturity date of the loan is September 1. The restaurant made partial payments of $875 on June 15 and $940 on August 1. Find the amount due on the maturity date of the loan. $1256.14

55. *U.S. Treasury Bills* The U.S. government borrows money by selling Treasury bills. Treasury bills are discounted notes issued by the U.S. government. On May 5, 2011, Kris Greenhalgh purchased a 182-day, $1000 U.S. Treasury bill at a 0.15% discount. On the date of maturity, Kris will receive $1000.

a) What is the date of maturity of the Treasury bill? November 3, 2011

b) How much did Kris actually pay for the Treasury bill? $999.24

c) How much interest did the U.S. government pay Kris on the date of maturity? $0.76

d) What is the actual rate of interest of the Treasury bill? (Round the answer to the nearest ten-thousandths of a percent.) 0.1504%

▲ *United States Treasury building, Washington, D.C.*

56. *U.S. Treasury Bills* On August 31, 2011, Trinity Lopez purchased a 364-day, $6000 U.S. Treasury bill at a 0.45% discount. (See Exercise 55.)

a) What is the date of maturity of the Treasury bill (2012 is a leap year)? August 29, 2012

b) How much did Trinity actually pay for the Treasury bill? $5972.70

c) How much interest did the U.S. government pay Trinity on the date of maturity? $27.30

d) What is the actual rate of interest of the Treasury bill? (Round the answer to the nearest thousandths of a percent.) 0.452%

57. *Tax Preparation Loan* Many tax preparation organizations will prepay customers' tax refunds if they pay a one-time finance charge. In essence, the customer is borrowing the money (the refund minus the finance charge) from the tax preparer, prepaying the interest (as in a discount note), and then repaying the loan with the tax refund. This procedure allows customers access to their tax refund money without having to wait. Joy Stallard had a tax refund of $743.21 due. She was able to get her tax refund immediately by paying a finance charge of $39.95. What annual simple interest rate is Joy paying for this loan assuming

a) the tax refund check would be available in 5 days? 409.01%

b) the tax refund check would be available in 10 days? 204.50%

c) the tax refund check would be available in 20 days? 102.25%

58. *Prime Interest Rate* Nick St. Louis borrowed $600 for 3 months. The banker said that Nick must repay the loan at the rate of $200 per month plus interest. The bank was charging a rate of 2% above the prime interest rate. The *prime interest rate* is the rate charged to preferred customers of the bank. During the first month the prime interest

*See Instructor Answer Appendix

rate was 4.75%, during the second month it was 5%, and during the third month it was 5.25%.

a) Find the amount Nick paid the bank at the end of the first month, at the end of the second month, and at the end of the third month.
$203.38 first month; $202.33 second month; $201.21 third month

b) What was the total amount of interest Nick paid the bank?
$6.92

Challenge Problem/Group Activity

59. *U.S. Treasury Bills* Mark Beiley purchased a 52-week U.S. Treasury bill (see Exercises 55 and 56) for $93,337. The par value (the value of the bill upon maturity) was $100,000.

a) What was the discount rate? 6.663%

b) What was the actual interest rate Mark received? ≈7.139%

c) Since U.S. Treasury bills are sold through auctions at Federal Reserve Banks, Mark did not know the purchase price of his Treasury bill until after he was notified by mail. If Mark had sent the Federal Reserve Bank a check for $100,000 to purchase the Treasury bill, how much would the Federal Reserve Bank have to rebate him upon notice of his purchase? $6663

d) On the day Mark received the rebate that was discussed in part (c), he invested it in a 1-year certificate of deposit yielding 5% interest. What is the total amount of interest he will receive from both investments? $6996.15

Recreational Mathematics

60. *Columbus Investment* On August 3, 1492, Christopher Columbus set sail on a voyage that would eventually lead him to the Americas. If on this day Columbus had invested $1 in a 5% simple interest account, determine the amount of interest the account would have earned by the following dates. Use a scientific calculator and disregard leap years in your calculations.

a) December 11, 1620 (Pilgrims land on Plymouth Rock)
$6.42

b) July 4, 1776 (Declaration of Independence) $14.20

c) December 7, 1941 (U.S. enters World War II) $22.47

d) Today's date Answers will vary.

Internet/Research Activity

61. *Loan Sources* Consider the following places where a loan may be obtained: banks, savings and loans, credit unions, and pawnshops. Write a report that includes the following information:

a) Describe the ownership of each.

b) Historically, what need is each fulfilling?

c) What are the advantages and disadvantages of obtaining a loan from each of those places listed?

SECTION 11.3   Compound Interest

▲ *Benjamin Franklin's portrait is on the $100 dollar bill.*

Albert Einstein said of compound interest, "The most powerful force in the universe is compound interest." What is this marvelous concept that warrants such a strong statement from one of the most intelligent human beings of all time? Another very intelligent person, Benjamin Franklin, described compound interest quite well when he said, "Money makes money and the money that money makes makes more money." In this section, we will introduce compound interest.

Why *This is Important* Investments that involve compound interest may play an important role in reaching some of your long-term financial goals.

Compound Interest

An *investment* is the use of money or capital for income or profit. We can divide investments into two classes: fixed investments and variable investments. In a *fixed investment*, the amount invested as principal is guaranteed and the interest is computed at a fixed rate. *Guaranteed* means that the exact amount invested will be paid back together with any accumulated interest. Examples of a fixed investment are savings accounts, money market deposit accounts, and certificates of deposit. Another fixed investment is a government savings bond. In a *variable investment*, neither the principal nor the interest is guaranteed. Examples of variable investments are stocks, mutual funds, and commercial bonds.

Simple interest, introduced earlier in the chapter, is calculated once for the period of a loan or investment using the formula $i = prt$. The interest paid on savings accounts at most banks is compound interest. A bank computes the interest periodically (for example, daily or quarterly) and adds this interest to the original principal. The interest for the following period is computed by using the new principal (original principal plus interest). In effect, the bank is computing interest on interest, which is called compound interest.

Definition: Compound Interest

Interest that is computed on the principal and any accumulated interest is called **compound interest**.

Example 1   *Computing Compound Interest*

Marjorie Thrall recently won the $1000 first prize in a raffle contest. Marjorie deposits the $1000 in a 1-year certificate of deposit paying 2.0% compounded quarterly. Find the amount, A, to which the $1000 will grow in 1 year.

Solution Compute the interest for the first quarter using the simple interest formula. Add this interest to the principal to find the amount at the end of the first quarter. In our calculation, time is $\frac{1}{4}$ of a year, or $t = 0.25$.

$$i = prt$$
$$= \$1000 \times 0.02 \times 0.25 = \$5.00$$
$$A = \$1000 + \$5 = \$1005$$

Now repeat the process for the second quarter, this time using a principal of $1005.

$$i = \$1005 \times 0.02 \times 0.25 \approx \$5.03$$
$$A = \$1005 + \$5.03 = \$1010.03$$

For the third quarter, use a principal of $1010.03.

$$i = \$1010.03 \times 0.02 \times 0.25 \approx \$5.05$$
$$A = \$1010.03 + \$5.05 = \$1015.08$$

For the fourth quarter, use a principal of $1015.08.

$$i = \$1015.08 \times 0.02 \times 0.25 \approx \$5.08$$
$$A = \$1015.08 + \$5.08 = \$1020.16$$

Hence, the $1000 grows to a final value of $1020.16 over the 1-year period.   ■

This example shows the effect of earning interest on interest, or compounding interest. In 1 year, the amount of $1000 has grown to $1020.16, compared with $1020 that would have been obtained with a simple interest rate of 2%. Thus, in 1 year alone the gain was $0.16 more with compound interest than with simple interest.

A simpler and less time-consuming way to calculate compound interest is to use the compound interest formula and a calculator.

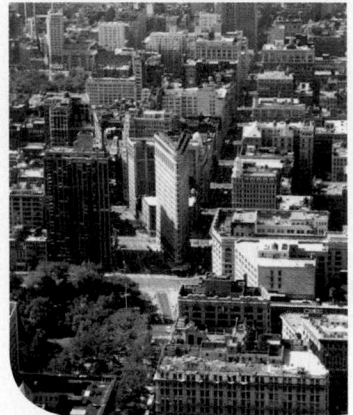
Compound Interest Formula

$$A = p\left(1 + \frac{r}{n}\right)^{nt}$$

where A is the amount that accumulates in the account, p is the principal, r is the annual interest rate as a decimal number, n is the number of compounding periods per year, and t is the time in years.

We will now use this formula to show how an investment can grow using compound interest.

Example 2 *Using the Compound Interest Formula*

Kathy Mowers invested $3000 in a savings account with an interest rate of 1.8% compounded monthly. If Kathy makes no other deposits into this account, determine the amount in the savings account after 2 years.

Solution We will use the formula for compound interest, $A = p\left(1 + \frac{r}{n}\right)^{nt}$. The principal, p, is the amount of money invested, so $p = \$3000$. The interest rate, r, is 1.8%, so $r = 0.018$. Because the interest is compounded monthly, there are 12 compounding periods per year and $n = 12$. Because the money is invested for 2 years, $t = 2$.

$$
\begin{aligned}
A &= 3000\left(1 + \frac{0.018}{12}\right)^{12 \cdot 2} \\
&= 3000(1 + 0.0015)^{24} \\
&= 3000(1.0015)^{24} \\
&\approx 3000(1.0366279) \\
&\approx 3109.88
\end{aligned}
$$

Thus, the amount in the account after 2 years would be about $3109.88. ∎

TECHNOLOGY TIP

Scientific Calculator
There are various ways to determine compound interest using a scientific calculator. In Example 2, we had to evaluate

$$3000\left(1 + \frac{0.018}{12}\right)^{12 \cdot 2}$$

To evaluate this expression on a scientific calculator, enter the following keys.

3000 $\boxed{\times}$ $\boxed{(}$ 1 $\boxed{+}$ 0.018 $\boxed{\div}$ 12 $\boxed{)}$ $\boxed{y^x}$ $\boxed{(}$ 12 $\boxed{\times}$ 2 $\boxed{)}$ $\boxed{=}$

After the $\boxed{=}$ key is pressed, the answer 3109.883655 is displayed. This answer checks with the answer obtained in Example 2.

Microsoft Excel
The software program Excel can also be used to determine compound interest. Excel is a spreadsheet, so once you insert a formula, you can change the value of the variables and the new answer will be automatically displayed. If you are not familiar with Excel, you can get help at www.office.microsoft.com.

To use Excel to determine the compound interest, set up the following columns.

	A	B	C	D	E
1	p	r	n	t	A
2	3000	0.018	12	2	

[Sheet1 / Sheet2 / Sheet3]

Ready

Then, to set up the formula in cell E2, go to the formula bar on top and enter

$$= A2*(1 + B2/C2)\wedge(C2*D2)$$

Then press the Enter key. The answer, 3109.88, will appear in cell E2.

Suppose you now wanted to determine the compound interest for $p = 6000$, $r = 0.05$, $n = 24$, and $t = 6$. If you were to change the values in cells A2 through D2 to these values respectively, the new answer, 8096.626, will now be displayed in cell E2.

Example 3 *Calculating Compound Interest*

Calculate the interest on \$650 at 8% compounded semiannually for 3 years, using the compound interest formula.

Solution Since interest is compounded semiannually, there are two periods per year. Thus, $n = 2$, $r = 0.08$, and $t = 3$. Substituting into the formula, we find the amount, A.

$$A = p\left(1 + \frac{r}{n}\right)^{nt}$$

$$= 650\left(1 + \frac{0.08}{2}\right)^{(2)(3)}$$

$$= 650(1.04)^6$$

$$\approx 650(1.2653190)$$

$$\approx \$822.46$$

Since the total amount is \$822.46 and the original principal is \$650, the interest must be \$822.46 − \$650, or \$172.46.   ■

In Example 3, the interest rate is stated as an annual rate of 8%, but the number of compounding periods per year is two. In applying the compound interest formula, the rate for one period is $r \div n$, which was 8% ÷ 2, or 4% per period.

Now we will calculate the amount, and interest, on \$1 invested at 8% compounded semiannually for 1 year. The result is

$$A = 1\left(1 + \frac{0.08}{2}\right)^{(2)(1)} = 1.0816$$

$$\text{Interest} = \text{amount} - \text{principal}$$

$$i = 1.0816 - 1$$

$$= 0.0816$$

The interest for 1 year is 0.0816. This amount written as a percent, 8.16%, is called the *effective annual yield*. *Most financial institutions refer to the effective annual yield as the annual percentage yield (APY).* If \$1 was invested at a simple interest rate of 8.16% and \$1 was invested at 8% interest compounded semiannually (equivalent to an effective yield of 8.16%), the interest from both investments would be the same.

Definition: Effective Annual Yield

The **effective annual yield** or **annual percentage yield** (**APY**) is the simple interest rate that gives the same amount of interest as a compound rate over the same period of time.

Many banks compound interest daily. When computing the effective annual yield, they use 360 for the number of periods in a year. To determine the effective annual yield for any interest rate, calculate the amount using the compound interest formula where p is $1. Then subtract $1 from that amount. The difference, written as a percent, is the effective annual yield, as illustrated in Example 4.

The sign in the margin shows interest rates and the corresponding annual percentage yields (APY) that were available for certificates of deposit (CDs) from Suncoast Schools Credit Union on December 20, 2010. To determine the effective annual yield (or the APY) for the 48-month CD, calculate the amount of interest earned on $1 for 1 year.

$$A = 1\left(1 + \frac{0.01490}{360}\right)^{360} \approx 1.0150112 \approx 1.01501$$

From this result, we subtract 1 to obtain $1.01501 - 1 = 0.01501$, or 1.501%. Confirm that the other annual percentage yields shown on the sign are correct.

Suncoast Schools Credit Union

CD Rates

Type	Rate	APY*
12 mo	0.500%	0.501%
24 mo	0.900%	0.904%
36 mo	1.290%	1.298%
48 mo	1.490%	1.501%

* Annual Percentage Yield

Example 4 *Annual Percentage Yield*

Determine the annual percentage yield or the effective annual yield for $1 invested for 1 year at the following interest rates. Round your answers to the nearest hundredth of a percent.

a) 2% compounded quarterly   b) 3% compounded monthly

Solution

a) With quarterly compounding, $n = 4$.

$$A = p\left(1 + \frac{r}{n}\right)^{nt}$$

$$= 1\left(1 + \frac{0.02}{4}\right)^{4 \cdot 1}$$

$$\approx 1.0202$$

$$i = A - 1$$

$$\approx 1.0202 - 1 \approx 0.0202$$

Thus, when the interest is 2% compounded quarterly, the annual percentage yield or the effective annual yield is about 2.02%.

b) With monthly compounding, $n = 12$.

$$A = p\left(1 + \frac{r}{n}\right)^{nt}$$

$$= 1\left(1 + \frac{0.03}{12}\right)^{12 \cdot 1}$$

$$\approx 1.0304$$

$$i = A - 1$$

$$\approx 1.0304 - 1 \approx 0.0304$$

Thus, when the interest is 3% compounded monthly, the annual percentage yield or effective annual yield is about 3.04%. ∎

▲ *Bunker Hill Community College.*

There are numerous types of savings accounts. Many savings institutions compound interest daily. Some pay interest from the day of deposit to the day of withdrawal, and others pay interest from the first of the month on all deposits made before the tenth of the month. In each of these accounts in which interest is compounded daily, interest is entered into the depositor's account only once each month or quarter. Some savings institutions will not pay any interest on a day-to-day account if the balance falls below a set amount.

Present Value

You may wonder about what amount of money you must deposit in an account today to have a certain amount of money in the future. For example, how much must you deposit in an account today at a given rate of interest so that it will accumulate to $25,000 to pay your child's college costs in 4 years? The principal, p, that would have to be invested now is called the *present value*. Following is a formula for determining the present value.

Present Value Formula

$$p = \frac{A}{\left(1 + \dfrac{r}{n}\right)^{nt}}$$

where p is the present value, or the principal to invest now, A is the amount to be accumulated in the account, r is the annual interest rate as a decimal number, n is the number of compounding periods per year, and t is the time in years.

Example 5 *Savings for College*

Will Hunting would like his daughter to attend college in 6 years when she finishes high school. Will would like to invest enough money in a certificate of deposit (CD) now to pay for his daughter's college expenses. If Will estimates that he will need $30,000 in 6 years, how much should he invest now in a CD that has a rate of 2.5% compounded quarterly?

Solution To answer this question, we will use the present value formula with $A = \$30,000$, $r = 0.025$, $n = 4$, and $t = 6$.

$$p = \frac{A}{\left(1 + \dfrac{r}{n}\right)^{nt}}$$

$$= \frac{30,000}{\left(1 + \dfrac{0.025}{4}\right)^{4 \cdot 6}}$$

$$= \frac{30,000}{(1.00625)^{24}}$$

$$\approx \frac{30,000}{1.1612920}$$

$$\approx 25,833.30$$

Will Hunting needs to invest approximately $25,833.30 now to have $30,000 in 6 years. ∎

TECHNOLOGY TIP

Scientific Calculator

To determine the present value in Example 5, we had to evaluate the expression

$$\frac{30{,}000}{\left(1 + \dfrac{0.025}{4}\right)^{4 \cdot 6}}$$

This expression can be evaluated on a scientific calculator as follows.

$$30000 \;\boxed{\div}\;\boxed{(}\; 1 \;\boxed{+}\; 0.025 \;\boxed{\div}\; 4 \;\boxed{)}\;\boxed{y^x}\;\boxed{(}\; 4 \;\boxed{\times}\; 6 \;\boxed{)}\;\boxed{=}$$

After the $\boxed{=}$ key is pressed, the answer 25833.29562 is displayed. This answer agrees with the answer obtained in Example 5.

Excel

Read the Technology Tip on compound interest on page 623. To determine the present value using Excel, enter A, r, n, t, and p in cells A1 through E1, respectively. In cells A2 through D2, enter the values of A, r, n, and t, respectively. (See the table in the Technology Tip on page 623 for an example of the row and column setup.) When cell E2 is highlighted, in the formula box at the top, enter

$$= A2/(1 + B2/C2)\wedge(C2*D2)$$

After the Enter key is pressed, the answer, 25833.30, is displayed in cell E2.

SECTION 11.3 *Exercises*

Warm Up Exercises

In Exercises 1–6, fill in the blanks with an appropriate word, phrase, or symbol(s).

1. An investment is the use of money or capital for income or _____. Profit

2. In a fixed investment the interest is computed at a fixed rate and the amount invested as principal is _____. Guaranteed

3. If neither the principal nor the interest is guaranteed, the investment is called a(n) _____ investment. Variable

4. Interest that is computed on the principal and any accumulated interest is called _____ interest. Compound

5. The effective annual yield or the annual percentage yield is the simple interest rate that gives the same amount of interest as a _____ interest rate over the same period of time. Compound

6. The principal that you would have to invest now to have a certain amount of money in the future is called the _____ value. Present

Practice the Skills

In Exercises 7–14, use the compound interest formula to compute the total amount accumulated and the interest earned. Round all answers to the nearest cent.

7. $2500 for 4 years at 1.2% compounded monthly
   $A = \$2622.86;\ i = \$122.86$

8. $7500 for 5 years at 1.6% compounded quarterly
   $A = \$8123.36;\ i = \$623.36$

9. $2000 for 4 years at 3% compounded quarterly
   $A = \$2253.98;\ i = \$253.98$

10. $5000 for 3 years at 7% compounded quarterly
    $A = \$6157.20;\ i = \$1157.20$

11. $7000 for 3 years at 5.5% compounded monthly
    $A = \$8252.64;\ i = \$1252.64$

12. $4000 for 2 years at 6% compounded semiannually
    $A = \$4502.04;\ i = \$502.04$

13. $8000 for 2 years at 4% compounded daily (use $n = 360$)
    $A = \$8666.26;\ i = \$666.26$

14. $8500 for 5 years at 4.5% compounded monthly
    $A = \$10{,}640.26;\ i = \$2140.26$

In Exercises 15–18, use the present value formula to determine the amount to be invested now, or the present value needed.

15. The desired accumulated amount is $50,000 after 10 years invested in an account with 5% interest compounded annually. $30,695.66

16. The desired accumulated amount is $75,000 after 5 years invested in an account with 4% interest compounded semiannually. $61,526.12

17. The desired accumulated amount is $100,000 after 4 years invested in an account with 4% interest compounded quarterly. $85,282.13

18. The desired accumulated amount is $15,000 after 30 years invested in an account with 3% interest compounded monthly. $6105.40

Problem Solving

In Exercises 19–44, if necessary, round all dollar figures to the nearest cent and round percents to the nearest hundredth of a percent.

19. *Little League* Braden River Little League receives a $50,000 donation for building a new snack bar and office building. The league decides to invest this money in a money market account that pays 4% interest compounded quarterly. How much will the league have in this account after 2 years? $54,142.84

20. *Contest Winnings* Mary Robinson wins $2500 in a singing contest and invests the money in a 4-year CD that pays 3% interest compounded monthly. How much money will Mary receive when she redeems the CD at the end of the 4 years? $2818.32

21. *Class Trip* To help pay for a class trip at the end of their senior year, the sophomore class at Cortez High School invests $1500 from fund-raisers in a 30-month CD paying 3.9% interest compounded monthly. Determine the amount the class will receive when it cashes in the CD after 30 months. $1653.36

22. *Investing Prize Winnings* Marcella Laddon wins third prize in the Clearinghouse Sweepstakes and receives a check for $250,000. After spending $10,000 on a vacation, she decides to invest the rest in a money market account that pays 1.5% interest compounded monthly. How much money will be in the account after 10 years? $278,814.10

23. *Investing Gifts and Scholarships* Cliff Morris just graduated from high school and has received $800 in gifts of cash from friends and relatives. In addition, Cliff received three scholarships in the amounts of $150, $300, and $1000. If Cliff takes all his gift and scholarship money and invests it in a 24-month CD paying 2% interest compounded daily, how much will he have when he cashes in the CD at the end of the 24 months? $2341.82

24. *Investing a Signing Bonus* Joe Gallegos just started a new job and has received a $5000 signing bonus. Joe decides to invest this money now so that he can buy a new car in 5 years. If Joe invests in a 5-year CD paying 3.35% interest compounded quarterly, how much money will he receive from his CD in 5 years? $5907.60

25. *Savings Account Investment* When Richard Zucker was born, his father deposited $2000 in his name in a savings account. The account was paying 5% interest compounded semiannually.

a) If the rate did not change, what was the value of the account after 15 years? $4195.14

b) If the money had been invested at 5% compounded quarterly, what would the value of the account have been after 15 years? $4214.36

26. *Investing a Prize* David Buckley won a writing contest and invested the $10,000 cash prize in a 3-year CD paying 1.29% compounded daily (use $n = 360$). What is the value of the CD after 3 years? $10,394.58

27. *Personal Loan* Brent Pickett borrowed $3000 from his brother Dave. He agreed to repay the money at the end of 2 years, giving Dave the same amount of interest that he would have received if the money had been invested at 1.75% compounded quarterly. How much money did Brent repay his brother? $3106.62

28. *Forgoing Interest* Rikki Blair borrowed $6000 from her daughter, Lynette. She repaid the $6000 at the end of 2 years. If Lynette had left the money in a bank account that paid an interest rate of $5\frac{1}{4}\%$ compounded monthly, how much interest would she have accumulated? $662.74

29. *House Down Payment* Karen Gaines invested $10,000 in a money market account with an interest rate of 1.75% compounded semiannually. Five years later, Karen withdrew the full amount to put toward the down payment on a new house. How much did Karen withdraw from the account? $10,910.27

30. *Kids Club Savings* Jean Woody opened a Kids Club savings account for her daughter at the Royal Credit Union. Jean deposited $500, and the account pays 0.25% interest compounded daily. If Jean made no further deposits or withdrawals to the account, what is the amount in the account 18 years later? $523.01

31. *Determining Effective Annual Yield* Determine the effective annual yield for $1 invested for 1 year at 3.5% compounded semiannually. 3.53%

32. *Determining Effective Annual Yield* Determine the effective annual yield for $1 invested for 1 year at 4.75% compounded monthly. 4.85%

33. *Verifying APY* Suppose you saw a sign at your local bank that said, "2.4% rate compounded monthly—2.6% Annual Percentage Yield (APY)." Is there anything wrong with the sign? Explain. Yes, the APY should be 2.43%.

34. *Verifying APY* Suppose you saw an advertisement in the newspaper for a financial planner who was recommending a certificate of deposit that paid 4.5% interest compounded quarterly. In the fine print at the bottom of the advertisement, it stated that the APY on the CD was 4.58%. Was this advertisement accurate? Explain. Yes

35. *Comparing Investments* Dave Dudley won a photography contest and received a $1000 cash prize. Will he earn more interest in 1 year if he invests his winnings in a simple interest account that pays 5% or in an account that pays 4.75% interest compounded monthly?
He will earn more interest in the account that pays the 5% simple interest.

36. *Comparing Loan Sources* Tom Angelo needs to borrow $1500 to expand his farm implement maintenance business. He learns that the local bank will lend him the money for 2 years at a rate of 10% compounded quarterly. After hearing of this rate, Tom's grandfather offers to lend him the money for 2 years with a simple interest rate of 7%. How much money will Tom save by borrowing the money from his grandfather? $117.60

37. *A New Water Tower* The village of Kieler recently completed the construction of a new water tower. The entire cost of the water tower was $925,000, and the state paid $370,000 of the total cost through the awarding of a grant. In addition, the village can delay paying the balance of the cost for 30 years (without paying any interest during the 30 years). To finance the balance, the village board will at this time assess its 598 homeowners a one-time flat fee surcharge and then invest this money in a 30-year CD paying 7.5% interest compounded monthly.

  a) What is the balance due on the water tower? $555,000

  b) How much will the village of Kieler need to invest at this time in the CD to raise the balance due in 30 years? $58,907.61

  c) What amount should each homeowner pay as a surcharge? $98.51

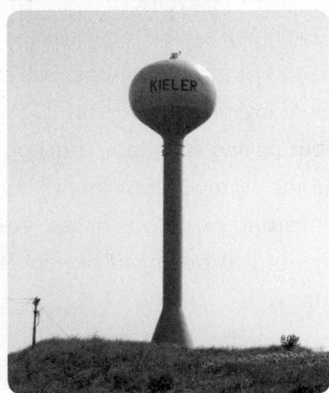

38. After seeing its neighboring village obtain a new water tower (see Exercise 37), the city board of East Dubuque begins planning to replace its water towers. The board estimates that it will need $1,750,000 to build the new water towers in 20 years. At this time, the city board plans to assess its 2753 homeowners with a one-time flat fee surcharge and then invest the money received in a CD paying 9% interest compounded daily (use $n = 360$) for 20 years.

  a) How much money will the board need to raise at this time to meet the city's water tower needs at the end of the 20 years? $289,338.14

  b) Before applying the surcharge, the city board receives a federal grant of $100,000 toward the water tower investment. Taking this grant into account, how much should the surcharge be on each homeowner? $68.78

39. *Saving for a Tractor* Jim Roznowski wants to invest some money now to buy a new tractor in the future. If he wants to have $275,000 available in 5 years, how much does he need to invest now in a CD paying 5.15% interest compounded monthly? $212,687.10

40. *Starting a New Business* Kurtis Fink's goal is to have $25,000 to start a new lawn mower repair business when he retires in 15 years. How much should Kurtis invest now in a CD that pays 2% interest compounded daily to reach his goal? $18,520.61

41. *A New Car* Adam Goldstein wishes to have $20,000 available in 18 years to purchase a new car for his son as a gift for his high school graduation. To accomplish this goal, how much should Adam invest now in a CD that pays 1.55% interest compounded daily? $15,130.89

42. *A New Roof* Rebecca Baum will need to replace the roof of her house in 5 years. How much should Rebecca invest now in a money market account that pays 2.1% interest compounded quarterly in order to have $6000 in 5 years? $5403.43

43. *Doubling the Rate* Determine the total amount and the interest paid on $1000 with interest compounded semiannually for 2 years at

a) 2%.
$1040.60, $40.60

b) 4%.
$1082.43, $82.43

c) 8%.
$1169.86, $169.86

d) Is there a predictable outcome in either the amount or the interest when the rate is doubled? Explain. No

44. *Doubling the Principal* Compute the total amount and the interest paid at 12% compounded monthly for 2 years for the following principals.

a) $100
$126.97, $26.97

b) $200
$253.95, $53.95

c) $400
$507.89, $107.89

d) Is there a predictable outcome in the interest when the principal is doubled? Explain. Yes, the interest also doubles.

Challenge Problems/Group Activities

45. *Inflation* The average cost for a loaf of bread in 2010 was $2.27. Assuming an annual inflation rate of 0.5% per year, what will be the cost for a loaf of bread in 2015? $2.33

46. *Determining the Interest Rate* For a total accumulated amount of $3586.58, a principal of $2000, and a time period of 5 years, use the compound interest formula to find *r* if interest is compounded monthly. 11.7%

47. *Rule of 72* A simple formula can help you estimate the number of years required to double your money. It's called the *rule of 72*. You simply divide 72 by the interest rate (without the percent sign). For example, with an interest rate of 4%, your money would double in approximately 72 ÷ 4, or 18 years. In (a)–(d), determine the approximate number of years it will take for $1000 to double at the given interest rate.

a) 3%
24 years

b) 6%
12 years

c) 8%
9 years

d) 12%
6 years

e) If $120 doubles in approximately 22 years, estimate the rate of interest. 3.27%

48. *Determining the Interest Rate* Richard Maruszewski borrowed $2000 from Linda Tonolli. The terms of the loan are as follows: The period of the loan is 3 years, and the rate of interest is 8% compounded semiannually. What rate of simple interest would be equivalent to the rate Linda charged Richard? 8.84% simple interest rate

Recreational Mathematics

49. *Interest Comparison* You are given a choice of taking the simple interest on $100,000 invested for 4 years at a rate of 5% or the interest on $100,000 invested for 4 years at an interest rate of 5% compounded daily. Which would you select? Explain your answer and give the difference in the two investments.*

Internet/Research Activities

50. Imagine you have $4000 to invest and you need this money to grow to $5000 by investing in a CD. Contact a local bank, a savings and loan, and a credit union to obtain CD information: the interest rate, the length of the term, and the number of times per year the CD is compounded. Find out how long it would take you to reach your goal with the institution selected. Write a report summarizing your findings.

51. Write a paper on the history of simple interest and compound interest. Answer the questions: When was simple interest first charged on loans? When was compound interest first given on investments?

*See Instructor Answer Appendix

SECTION 11.4   Installment Buying

▲ *Financial decisions may involve deciding whether to use a credit card when making a purchase.*

While you are with some friends at the mall, you spot a new pair of shoes that you really like. Although you don't have money to pay for the shoes, you do have a credit card with you. You now must make a very important decision. Do you charge the shoes to your credit card and worry about paying for them later, or do you decide that you can't afford the shoes and leave the store without them? In this section, we will look at the real cost of using a credit card to make purchases. We will also study other common types of loans frequently used to purchase big-ticket items such as cars, appliances, and home improvements.

Why **This is Important** An important part of establishing a financial plan is understanding the cost of borrowing money to make purchases. Installment loans and credit cards are two very common ways to borrow money for making such purchases.

In Section 11.2, we discussed personal notes and discounted notes. When borrowing money by either of these methods, the borrower normally repays the loan as a single payment at the end of the specified time period. There may be circumstances under which it is more convenient for the borrower to repay the loan on a weekly or monthly basis or to use some other convenient time period. One method of doing so is to borrow money on an *installment plan.*

There are two types of installment loans: fixed payment and open-end. A *fixed installment loan* is one on which you pay a fixed amount of money for a set number of payments. Examples of items purchased with fixed-payment installment loans are college tuition loans and loans for cars, boats, appliances, and furniture. These loans are generally repaid in 24, 36, 48, or 60 equal monthly payments. An *open-end installment loan* is a loan on which you can make variable payments each month. Credit cards, such as MasterCard, Visa, and Discover, are actually open-end installment loans, used to purchase items such as clothing, textbooks, and meals.

Lenders give any individual wishing to borrow money or purchase goods or services on an installment plan a credit rating to determine if the borrower is likely to repay the loan. The lending institution determines whether the applicant is a good "credit risk" by examining the individual's income, assets, liabilities, and history of repaying debts.

The advantage of installment buying is that the buyer has the use of an article while paying for it. If the article is essential, installment buying may serve a real need. A disadvantage is that some people buy more on the installment plan than they can afford. Another disadvantage is the interest the borrower pays for the loan.

To provide the borrower with a way to compare interest rates from various lenders, Congress passed the Truth in Lending Act of 1968. The law requires lending institutions to tell the borrower two things: the *annual percentage rate* and the *finance charge.* The *annual percentage rate (APR)* is the true rate of interest charged for the loan. The APR provides consumers the ability to compare loans without having to do calculations to determine the true interest rate they are being charged. The *finance charge* is the total amount of money the borrower must pay for borrowing the money. The finance charge includes the interest plus any additional fees charged to obtain the loan. *For the rest of this section, we will include the interest only when we refer to the finance charge.* In this section we will also discuss the *total installment price.* The *total installment price* is the sum of all the monthly payments and the down payment, if any.

Fixed Installment Loans

We begin our discussion of installment loans by calculating the monthly payment for a loan by using a) a table in Example 1 and b) a formula in Example 2.

Example 1 *Window Blinds*

Kristin Aiken wishes to purchase new window blinds for her house at a cost of $1500. The home improvement store has an advertised finance option of no down payment and 6% APR for 24 months.

a) Determine the finance charge.

b) Determine Kristin's monthly payment.

Solution

a) Table 11.2 on page 632 gives the finance charge per $100 of the amount financed. The table shows that the finance charge per $100 for 24 months at 6% is $6.37 (circled in red). Because Kristin is financing $1500, the number of hundreds of dollars financed is $\frac{1500}{100} = 15$. To determine the total finance charge, multiply the finance charge per $100 by the number of hundreds of dollars financed.

$$\text{Total finance charge} = \$6.37 \times 15 = \$95.55$$

Therefore, Kristin will pay a total finance charge of $95.55.

b) To determine the monthly payments, first calculate the total installment price by adding the finance charge to the purchase price.

$$\text{Total installment price} = \$1500 + \$95.55 = \$1595.55$$

Next divide the total installment price by the number of payments.

$$\text{Monthly payment} = \frac{\$1595.55}{24} \approx \$66.48$$

Kristin will have 24 monthly payments of $66.48.   ∎

Table 11.2 Annual Percentage Rate Table for Monthly Payment Plans

Number of payments	Annual Percentage Rate												
	4.0%	4.5%	5.0%	5.5%	6.0%	6.5%	7.0%	7.5%	8.0%	8.5%	9.0%	9.5%	10.0%
	(Finance charge per $100 of amount financed)												
6	1.17	1.32	1.46	1.61	1.76	1.90	2.05	2.20	2.35	2.49	2.64	2.79	2.93
12	2.18	2.45	2.73	3.00	3.28	3.56	3.83	4.11	4.39	4.66	4.94	5.22	5.50
18	3.20	3.60	4.00	4.41	4.82	5.22	5.63	6.04	6.45	6.86	7.28	7.69	8.10
24	4.22	4.75	5.29	5.83	(6.37)	6.91	7.45	8.00	8.54	9.09	9.64	10.19	10.75
30	5.25	5.92	6.59	7.26	7.94	8.61	9.30	9.98	10.66	11.35	12.04	12.74	13.43
36	6.29	7.09	7.90	8.71	9.52	10.34	11.16	11.98	12.81	13.64	14.48	15.32	16.16
48	8.38	9.46	10.54	11.63	12.73	13.83	14.94	(16.06)	17.18	18.31	19.45	20.59	21.74
60	10.50	11.86	13.23	14.61	16.00	17.40	18.81	20.23	21.66	(23.10)	24.55	26.01	27.48

The following formula can be used to directly calculate the installment payment rather than using Table 11.2

Installment Payment Formula

$$m = \frac{p\left(\dfrac{r}{n}\right)}{1 - \left(1 + \dfrac{r}{n}\right)^{-n \cdot t}}$$

In the formula, m is the installment payment, p is the amount financed, r is the annual percentage rate as a decimal number, n is the number of payments per year, and t is the time in years.

Example 2 *Using the Installment Payment Formula*

Reread Example 1. Use the installment payment formula to determine Kristin's monthly payment.

Solution In this example, Kristin is borrowing $1500, so $p = 1500$; the APR is 6%, so $r = 0.06$; she is making monthly payments, so $n = 12$; and time of the loan is 24 months, so $t = \frac{24}{12} = 2$. We substitute these values into the installment payment formula below.

$$m = \frac{p\left(\dfrac{r}{n}\right)}{1 - \left(1 + \dfrac{r}{n}\right)^{-n \cdot t}}$$

$$= \frac{1500\left(\dfrac{0.06}{12}\right)}{1 - \left(1 + \dfrac{0.06}{12}\right)^{-12 \cdot 2}}$$

$$= \frac{1500(0.005)}{1 - (1.005)^{-24}}$$

$$\approx \frac{7.5}{1 - 0.88718567}$$

$$\approx \frac{7.5}{0.11281433}$$

$$\approx 66.48$$

Thus, Kristin's monthly payment would be $66.48. Note this matches the payment calculated in Example 1. ∎

TECHNOLOGY TIP

Scientific Calculator

In Example 2 we determined the monthly payment by evaluating the following expression:

$$\frac{1500\left(\dfrac{0.06}{12}\right)}{1 - \left(1 + \dfrac{0.06}{12}\right)^{-12 \cdot 2}}$$

There are various ways to evaluate this expression on a scientific calculator. One method is to press the following sequence of keys.

(1500 (0.06 ÷ 12))) ÷ ((1 − ((1 + 0.06 ÷ 12) y^x ((+/− 12 × 2))) =

After the = key is pressed, the answer 66.48091538 is displayed.

Microsoft Excel

Read the Technology Tip on page 623. To determine the monthly payment using Excel, place the letters P, r, n, t, and m in cells A1 through E1, respectively. In cells A2 through D2, place the values 1500, 0.06, 12, and 2, respectively. In cell E2, use the formula box to add the formula

$$= (A2*(B2/C2))/(1 - (1 + B2/C2)^\wedge(-C2*D2))$$

After the Enter key is pressed, the result is as follows.

	A	B	C	D	E
1	p	r	n	t	m
2	1500	0.06	12	2	66.48092
3					

ᴵ◄ ◄ ► ►ᴵ \ Sheet1 / Sheet2 / Sheet3 / |◄

Ready

Examples 1 and 2 show that either Table 11.2 or the installment payment formula can be used to calculate a monthly payment for an installment loan. The formula has the advantage that it can be used for any APR and any number of payments, not just those used in Table 11.2. One disadvantage of the formula is that if we are given certain information about a loan and we wish to determine the APR, the calculations may be extremely difficult. For this reason, we will use Table 11.2 in Example 3 to show how to determine the APR on an installment loan.

Example 3 *Determining the APR*

Jan Ford is purchasing a boat for $25,000, including taxes. Jan decides to make a $5000 down payment and finance the balance, $20,000, through her bank. The loan officer informs her that her monthly payment will be $410.33 for 60 months.

a) Determine the finance charge.

b) Determine the APR.

Solution

a) The total installment price is the down payment plus the total monthly installment payments.

$$\text{Total installment price} = \$5000 + (60 \times \$410.33)$$
$$= \$5000 + \$24,619.80 = \$29,619.80$$

The finance charge is the total installment price minus the cash price.

$$\text{Finance charge} = \$29,619.80 - \$25,000 = \$4619.80$$

Therefore, Jan will pay a finance charge of $4619.80.

b) To determine the annual percentage rate, use Table 11.2 on page 632. First divide the finance charge by the amount financed and multiply the quotient by 100. The result is the finance charge per $100 of the amount financed.

$$\frac{\text{Finance charge}}{\text{Amount financed}} \times 100 = \frac{4619.80}{20,000} \times 100 = 0.23099 \times 100 \approx 23.10$$

Thus, Jan pays about $23.10 for each $100 being financed. To use Table 11.2, look for 60 in the far left-hand column under the heading Number of Payments. Then move across to the right until you find the value closest to $23.10. In this case, $23.10 is in the table (circled in blue). At the top of this column is the value of 8.5%. Therefore, the annual percentage rate is approximately 8.5%. ■

Much more complete APR tables similar to Table 11.2 are available at your local lending institution or on the Internet. Also available on the Internet are loan "calculators" that will calculate your payment for you if you provide the loan amount, the length of the loan, and the APR. One such loan calculator can be found at www.bankrate.com.

Example 4 *Financing a Restored Car*

Tino Garcia borrowed $9800 to purchase a classic 1966 Ford Mustang. He does not recall the APR of the loan but remembers that there are 48 payments of $237. If he did not make a down payment on the car, determine the APR.

Solution First determine the finance charge by subtracting the cash price from the total amount paid.

$$\text{Finance charge} = (237 \times 48) - 9800$$
$$= 11,376 - 9800$$
$$= \$1576$$

Now divide the finance charge by the amount of the loan and multiply this quotient by 100.

$$\frac{1576}{9800} \times 100 \approx 16.08$$

Next find 48 payments in the left column of Table 11.2. Move to the right until you find the value that is closest to 16.08. The value closest to 16.08 is 16.06 (circled in green). At the top of the column is the APR of 7.5%. Thus, the APR for Tino's loan is approximately 7.5%. ∎

In Example 4, if Tino made all 48 payments, his finance charge would be $1576. If he decides to repay the loan after making 30 payments, must he pay the total finance charge? The answer is no. By paying off his loan early, Tino is not obligated to pay the entire finance charge. The amount of the reduction of the finance charge from paying off a loan early is called the *unearned interest*. We will learn about the most common way of calculating unearned interest, the *actuarial method*. In the past, another method, called the *rule of 78s*, was also used. The rule of 78s, however, is less favorable to the consumer and is outlawed in much of the country (see the *Did You Know?* at left and Exercises 39 and 40). Now we give the formula for finding the unearned interest using the actuarial method.

Actuarial Method for Unearned Interest

$$u = \frac{n \cdot P \cdot V}{100 + V}$$

where u is the unearned interest, n is the number of remaining monthly payments (excluding the current payment), P is the monthly payment, and V is the value from the APR table that corresponds to the annual percentage rate for the number of remaining payments (excluding the current payment).

Example 5 illustrates the actuarial method for calculating unearned interest when an installment loan is paid off early.

Example 5 *Using the Actuarial Method*

In Example 4, we determined the APR of Tino's loan to be 7.5%. Instead of making his 30th payment of his 48-payment loan, Tino wishes to pay his remaining balance and terminate the loan.

a) Use the actuarial method to determine how much interest Tino will save (the unearned interest, u) by repaying the loan early.

b) What is the total amount due to pay off the loan early on the day he makes his final payment?

Solution

a) Recall from Example 4 that Tino's monthly payments are $237.00. After 30 payments have been made, 18 payments remain. Thus, $n = 18$ and $P = \$237$. To determine V, use the APR table (Table 11. 2). In the Number of Payments column, find the number of remaining payments, 18, and then look to the right until you reach the column headed by 7.5%, the APR. This row and column intersect at 6.04. Thus, $V = 6.04$. Now use the actuarial method formula to determine the unearned interest, u.

$$u = \frac{n \cdot P \cdot V}{100 + V}$$

$$= \frac{(18)(237)(6.04)}{100 + 6.04}$$

$$\approx 242.99$$

Tino will save $242.99 in interest by the actuarial method.

b) Because the remaining payments total 18($237) = $4266, Tino's remaining balance excluding his 30th monthly payment, is

$4266.00	Total of remaining payments (which includes interest)
− 242.99	Interest saved (unearned interest)
$4023.01	Balance due (excluding the 30th monthly payment)

A payment of $4023.01 plus the 30th monthly payment of $237 will terminate Tino's installment loan.

$4023.01	Balance due (excluding the 30th monthly payment)
+ 237.00	30th monthly payment
$4260.01	Total amount due

The total amount due is $4260.01.   ∎

Open-End Installment Loan

A credit card is a popular way of making purchases or borrowing money. Use of a credit card is an example of an open-end installment loan. A typical credit card charge account with a bank or store may have the terms in Table 11.3.

Table 11.3 Credit Card Terms

Type of Charge	Daily Periodic Rate*	Annual Percentage Rate*
Purchases	0.04792%	17.49%
Cash advances	0.05477%	19.99%

*These rates vary with different credit card accounts and localities.

Typically, credit card monthly statements contain the following information: balance at the beginning of the period, balance at the end of the period (or new balance), the transactions for the period, statement closing date (or billing date), payment due date, and the minimum payment due. In addition, the Credit Card Accountability Responsibility and Disclosure (CARD) Act of 2009 required credit card companies to provide additional information to their customers on their monthly statements (see *Mathematics Today*, at left). For *purchases*, there is no finance or interest charge if there is no previous balance due and you pay the entire new balance by the payment due date. The period between when a purchase is made and when the credit card company begins charging interest is called the *grace period* and is usually 20 to 25 days. However, if you use a credit card to borrow money, called a *cash advance*, there generally is no grace period and a finance charge is applied from the date you borrowed the money until the date you repay the money. When you make purchases or obtain cash advances, the minimum monthly payment will generally be any new fees and interest plus at least 1% of the outstanding principal. This sum is then rounded up to the nearest whole dollar. Credit card companies often have $20 as the lowest possible minimum monthly payment. These guidelines will vary among the different credit card companies. If you currently have a credit card, you can find out how your minimum monthly payment is calculated by reading the back of your monthly statement or by reading the literature given to you when you obtained the credit card.

Example 6 *Calculating Minimum Monthly Payments*

Mary Beth Orrange's credit card company determines her minimum monthly payment by adding any new interest owed to 1.5% of the outstanding principal. The credit card company charges an interest rate of 0.04792% per day. For Mother's Day, May 17, Mary Beth used her credit card to purchase a $1500 plasma television set for her mother. She made no other purchases in May.

a) Assuming Mary Beth owed no interest, determine Mary Beth's minimum payment due on June 1, her billing date.

b) On June 1, instead of making the minimum payment, Mary Beth makes a payment of $200. Assuming there are no additional charges or cash advances, determine Mary Beth's minimum payment due on July 1.

Solution

a) Since there is no new interest due, Mary Beth's minimum monthly payment is determined by taking 1.5% of the outstanding principal, or $0.015 \times \$1500 = \$22.50$. Rounding up to the nearest whole dollar, we determine that Mary Beth's minimum monthly payment due on June 1 is $23.

b) Mary Beth's minimum monthly payment will be the sum of the new interest charges plus 1.5% of her outstanding principal. To calculate her new interest charges, we will use the simple interest formula, $i = prt$. The principal p is $1500 − $200 = $1300, the rate r is 0.04792% per day or 0.0004792 per day, and the time t is 30 days because June has 30 days.

$$i = prt$$
$$= (\$1300)(0.0004792)(30)$$
$$\approx \$18.69$$

To determine 1.5% of the outstanding principal, multiply 0.015 by $1300 to get $19.50. Now we add the new interest to 1.5% of the outstanding principal to get $19.50 + $18.69 = $38.19. Rounding up to the nearest whole dollar, we determine that Mary Beth's minimum monthly payment due on July 1 is $39. ∎

In Example 6, Mary Beth made no additional charges during the month. When additional charges are made during the month, the finance charges on open-end installment loans or credit cards are generally calculated in one of two ways: the *previous balance method* or the *average daily balance method*. Example 7 illustrates the previous balance method, and Example 8 illustrates the average daily balance method.

With the *previous balance method*, the borrower is charged interest or a finance charge on the previous balance from the previous charge period.

Example 7 *Finance Charges Using the Previous Balance Method*

In October, Peter Collinge charged all the supplies for his Halloween party to his Visa card. On November 5, the billing date, Peter had a balance due of $275. From November 5 through December 4, he did some shopping and charged items totaling $320, and he also made a payment of $145.

a) Determine the finance charge due on December 5, Peter's next billing date, using the previous balance method. Assume that the interest rate charged is 1.3% per month.

b) Determine the new account balance on December 5.

Solution

a) The finance charge is based on the $275 balance due on November 5. To find the finance charge due on December 5, we used the simple interest formula with a time of 1 month.

$$i = \$275 \times 0.013 \times 1 \approx \$3.58$$

The finance charge due on December 5 is $3.58.

b) The balance due on December 5 is found by adding the costs of the new purchases and the calculated interest to the balance due on November 5, and then subtracting the payment made from this sum.

$$\$275 + \$320 + \$3.58 - \$145 = \$453.58$$

The balance due on December 5 is $453.58. The finance charge on January 5 is based on the December 5 balance of $453.58. ∎

Many lending institutions use the *average daily balance method* of calculating the finance charge because they believe that it is fairer to the customer. With the average daily balance method, a balance is determined each day of the billing period for which there is a transaction in the account. The average daily balance method is illustrated in Example 8.

Example 8   *Finance Charges Using the Average Daily Balance Method*

The balance on Min Zeng's credit card account on July 1, the billing date, was $375.80. The following transactions occurred during the month of July.

July 5	Payment	$150.00
July 10	Charge: Toy store	74.35
July 18	Charge: Garage	123.50
July 28	Charge: Restaurant	42.50

a) Determine the average daily balance for the billing period.

b) Determine the finance charge to be paid on August 1, Min's next billing date. Assume that the interest rate is 1.3% per month.

c) Determine the balance due on August 1.

Solution

a) To determine the average daily balance, we do the following. (i) Find the balance due for each transaction date.

July 1	$375.80				
July 5	$375.80	−	$150	=	$225.80
July 10	$225.80	+	$74.35	=	$300.15
July 18	$300.15	+	$123.50	=	$423.65
July 28	$423.65	+	$42.50	=	$466.15

(ii) Find the number of days that the balance did not change between each transaction. Count the first day in the period but not the last day. Note that the time period from July 28 through August 1, the beginning of the next billing cycle, is 4 days. (iii) Multiply the balance due by the number of days the balance did not change. (iv) Find the sum of the products.

Date	(i) Balance Due	(ii) Number of Days Balance Did Not Change	(iii) (Balance)(Days)
July 1	$375.80	4	($375.80)(4) = $1503.20
July 5	$225.80	5	($225.80)(5) = $1129.00
July 10	$300.15	8	($300.15)(8) = $2401.20
July 18	$423.65	10	($423.65)(10) = $4236.50
July 28	$466.15	4	($466.15)(4) = $1864.60
		31	(iv) Sum = $11,134.50

(v) Divide this sum by the number of days in the billing cycle (in the month). The number of days may be found by adding the days in column (ii).

$$\frac{\$11,134.50}{31} = \$359.18$$

Thus, the average daily balance is $359.18.

b) The finance charge for the month is found using the simple interest formula with the average daily balance as the principal.

$$i = \$359.18 \times 0.013 \times 1 = \$4.67$$

c) Since the finance charge for the month is $4.67, the balance owed on August 1 is $466.15 + $4.67, or $470.82. ∎

The calculations in Example 8 are tedious. These calculations, however, are made almost instantaneously with computers.

Example 9 illustrates how a credit card may be used to borrow money.

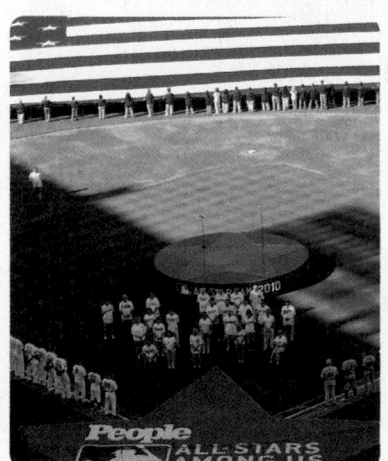

Example 9 *Using a Credit Card for a Cash Advance*

To obtain money for tickets to the Major League Baseball All-Star game, Davidson Pierre used his credit card for a cash advance of $2000. He borrowed the money on July 10 and repaid it on July 31. If Davidson is charged an interest rate of 0.05477% per day, how much did Davidson have to repay the credit card company on July 31?

Solution The amount Davidson pays is the original principal plus any accrued interest. Interest on cash advances is generally calculated for the exact number of days of the loan, starting with the day the money is obtained. The time of the loan in this case is 21 days. Using the simple interest formula, we get the following:

$$\begin{aligned} i &= prt \\ &= \$2000 \times 0.0005477 \times 21 \\ &\approx \$23.00 \end{aligned}$$

Therefore, on July 31, Davidson must repay the credit card company $2000 + $23, or $2023. ∎

Anyone purchasing a car or other costly items should consider a number of different sources for a loan. Example 10 illustrates one method of making a comparison.

Example ⑩ *Comparing Loan Sources*

Franz Helfenstein purchased carpeting costing $2400 with his credit card. When the bill comes due on February 1, Franz realizes that he can pay $350 per month until the debt is paid off. His credit card charges 1.5% interest per month.

a) Assuming Franz makes no other purchases with this credit card, how many payments are necessary to retire this debt?

b) What is the total interest Franz will pay?

c) How much money could Franz have saved by obtaining a fixed installment loan of $2400 with an annual percentage rate of 6% interest with six equal monthly payments?

Solution

a) Franz would make his first monthly payment of $350 on February 1, resulting in a new balance of $2400 − $350 = $2050. His next bill reflects the $2050 balance plus the monthly interest. He continues to make payments until the debt is retired. For each date indicated, the amount on the far right represents the amount due on that date.

February 1	$2400 − $350 = $2050
March 1	$2050 + 0.015($2050) = $2080.75; $2080.75 − $350 = $1730.75
April 1	$1730.75 + 0.015($1730.75) = $1756.71; $1756.71 − $350 = $1406.71
May 1	$1406.71 + 0.015($1406.71) = $1427.81; $1427.81 − $350 = $1077.81
June 1	$1077.81 + 0.015($1077.81) = $1093.98; $1093.98 − $350 = $743.98
July 1	$743.98 + 0.015($743.98) = $755.14; $755.14 − $350 = $405.14
August 1	$405.14 + 0.015($405.14) = $411.22; $411.22 − $350 = $61.22
September 1	$61.22 + 0.015($61.22) = $62.14

   After eight payments—seven for $350 and one for $62.14—Franz has paid off his credit card bill for his carpeting.

b) To calculate the total interest paid, we add up all his payments and then subtract the cost of the carpeting:

$$\text{Total of all payments} = 7(\$350) + \$62.14$$
$$= \$2512.14$$
$$\text{Total interest} = \$2512.14 - \$2400$$
$$= \$112.14$$

c) To determine the interest that Franz pays with the installment loan, we will use Table 11.2 on page 632. From Table 11.2, we see that a fixed installment loan with an APR of 6% for 6 months corresponds to a finance charge of $1.76 per $100 of the amount financed. So the interest, or finance charge, is

$$\text{Finance charge} = 1.76\left(\frac{2400}{100}\right)$$
$$= 1.76(24)$$
$$= \$42.24$$

Therefore, Franz would save $112.14 − $42.24 = $69.90 in interest by using an installment loan instead of a credit card. ∎

SECTION 11.4 *Exercises*

Warm Up Exercises

In Exercises 1–6, fill in the blanks with an appropriate word, phrase, or symbol(s).

1. A loan on which you pay a fixed amount of money for a set number of payments is called a fixed _____ loan. Installment

2. A loan on which you make variable payments each month is called a(n) _____ installment loan. Open-end

3. The true rate of interest charged for a loan is called the _____ percentage rate. Annual

4. The total amount of money the borrower must pay for borrowing the money is called the _____ charge. Finance

5. The sum of all the monthly payments and the down payment, if any, is called the total _____ price. Installment

6. The period between when a purchase is made and when the credit card company begins charging interest is called the _____ period. Grace

Practice the Skills

In Exercises 7–10, determine the monthly payment for the installment loan. Unless told otherwise by your instructor, you may either use Table 11.2 or the installment payment formula (see Examples 1 and 2).

	Amount Financed (P)	Annual Percentage Rate (r)	Number Payments per Year (n)	Time in Years (t)	
7.	$ 750	6%	12	2	$33.24
8.	$ 2300	9%	12	3	$73.14
9.	$15,000	5%	12	4	$345.44
10.	$38,000	4%	12	5	$699.83

Problem Solving

11. *A New Business* Landon Wallin is an auto mechanic who wishes to start his own business. He will need $4500 to purchase tools and equipment. Landon decides to finance the purchase with a 48-month fixed installment loan with an APR of 5.5%.

    a) Determine Landon's finance charge. $523.35

    b) Determine Landon's monthly payment. $104.65

12. *A New Air Conditioner* Juan Avalos paid $7000 for a new central air-conditioning unit for his house. He paid 20% as a down payment and financed the balance with a 36-month fixed installment loan with an APR of 5%.

a) Determine Juan's finance charge. $442.40

b) Determine Juan's monthly payment. $167.84

13. *Financing a New Roof* Jaime Capobianco needs a new roof on her house. The cash cost is $7500. She decides to finance the project by paying 20% down, with the balance paid in 36 monthly payments of $189.40.

    a) What finance charge will Jaime pay? $818.40

    b) What is the APR to the nearest half percent? 8.5%

14. *Financing a Computer* Ilga Ross purchased a new computer on a monthly purchase plan. The computer sold for $1495. Ilga paid 5% down and $64 a month for 24 months.

    a) What finance charge did Ilga pay? $115.75

    b) What is the APR to the nearest half percent? 7.5%

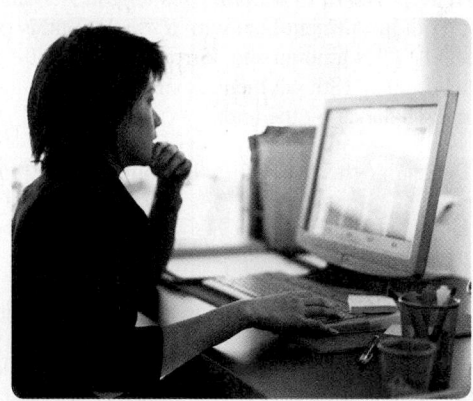

15. *Financing a New Boat* Marnie Greenhut wishes to buy a new speed boat that has a cash price of $45,000. She decides to finance the boat by paying 25% down, with the balance paid in 60 monthly payments of $636.92.

    a) What finance charge will Marnie pay? $4465.20

    b) What is the APR to the nearest half percent? 5.0%

16. *Financing Furniture* Mr. and Mrs. Chan want to buy furniture that has a cash price of $3450. On the installment plan, they must pay 25% of the cash price as a down payment and make six monthly payments of $437.

a) What finance charge will the Chans pay? $34.50

b) What is the APR to the nearest half percent? 4.5%

17. *Early Repayment of a Loan* Ray Flagg took out a 60-month fixed installment loan of $12,000 to open a new pet store. He paid no money down and began making monthly payments of $232. Ray's business does better than expected and instead of making his 24th payment, Ray wishes to repay his loan in full.

a) Determine the APR of the installment loan. 6.0%

b) How much interest will Ray save by paying off his loan early? $726.00

c) What is the total amount due to pay off the loan? $7858.00

18. *Early Repayment of a Loan* Jeslie Ann Hernandez has a 48-month installment loan with a fixed monthly payment of $83.81. The amount she borrowed was $3500. Instead of making her 18th payment, Jeslie Ann is paying the remaining balance on the loan.

a) Determine the APR of the installment loan. 7.0%

b) How much interest will Jeslie Ann save by paying off the loan early? $213.93

c) What is the total amount due to pay off the loan? $2384.18

19. *Early Repayment of a Loan* Nina Abu buys a new sport utility vehicle for $32,000. She trades in her old truck and receives $10,000, which she uses as a down payment. She finances the balance at 8% APR over 36 months. Before making her 24th payment, she decides to pay off the loan.

a) Use Table 11.2 to determine the total interest Nina would pay if all 36 payments were made. $2818.20

b) What were Nina's monthly payments? $689.39

c) How much interest will Nina save by paying off the loan early? $347.90

d) What is the total amount due to pay off the loan? $8614.17

20. *Early Repayment of a Loan* The cash price for a new washer and dryer for Toshio Nakamura's new apartment was $1250. Toshio made a $100 down payment and financed the balance on a 24-month fixed payment installment loan. The monthly payments are $50.71. Instead of making his 12th payment, Toshio decides to pay off the loan.

a) Determine the APR on the installment loan. 5.5%

b) How much interest will Toshio save by paying off the loan early? $17.72

c) What is the total amount due to pay off the loan? $641.51

21. *Credit Card Minimum Monthly Payment* Shiing Shen Chern's credit card company determines his minimum monthly payment by adding all new interest to 1% of the outstanding principal. The credit card company charges an interest rate of 0.039698% per day. On March 17, Shiing uses his credit card to purchase airline tickets for his family for $2600. He makes no other purchases during March.

a) Assuming Shiing had no new interest, determine Shiing's minimum payment due on April 1, his billing date. $26.00

b) On April 1, instead of making the minimum payment, Shiing makes a payment of $500. Assuming there are no additional charges or cash advances, determine Shiing's minimum payment due on May 1. $46.01, which rounds up to $47

22. *Credit Card Minimum Monthly Payment* Evelyn Boyd Granville's credit card company determines her minimum monthly payment by adding all new interest to 2% of the outstanding principal. The credit card company charges an interest rate of 0.04238% per day. On September 15, Evelyn uses her credit card to purchase a new picture window for her house for $3200. She makes no other purchases during September.

a) Assuming Evelyn had no new interest, determine Evelyn's minimum payment due on October 1, her billing date. $64

b) On October 1, instead of making the minimum payment, Evelyn makes a payment of $1200. Assuming there are no additional charges or cash advances, determine Evelyn's minimum payment due on November 1. $66.28, which rounds up to $67

23. *Business Expenses* Kevin Devlin's credit card company determines his minimum monthly payment by adding all new interest to 1.5% of the outstanding principal. The credit card company charges an interest rate of 0.05163% per day. On November 12, Kevin used his credit card to pay for the following business expenses: van repairs ($677), equipment maintenance ($452), office supplies ($139), and dinner with clients ($141).

a) Assuming Kevin had no new interest, determine his minimum payment due on December 1, his billing date. $21.14, which rounds up to $22

b) On December 1, instead of making his minimum payment, Kevin makes a payment of $300. Assuming there are no additional charges or cash advances, determine Kevin's minimum payment on January 1. $34.39, which rounds up to $35

24. *Vacation Expenses* Harry Waldman's credit card company determines his minimum monthly payment by adding all new interest to 2.5% of the outstanding principal. The credit card company charges an interest rate of 0.03164% per day. On August 21, while on vacation, Harry used his credit card to pay for the following expenses: airfare ($359), car rental ($273), hotel ($653), meals ($315), and surfboard rental ($225).

a) Assuming Harry had no new interest, determine Harry's minimum payment due on September 1, his billing date. $45.63, which rounds up to $46

b) On September 1, instead of making his minimum payment, Harry makes a payment of $750. Assuming there are no additional charges or cash advances, determine Harry's minimum payment on October 1. $37.08, which rounds up to $38

25. *Previous Balance Method* On the April 5 billing date, Michaelle Chappell had a balance due of $1097.86 on her credit card. From April 5 through May 4, Michaelle charged an additional $425.79 and made a payment of $800.

a) Find the finance charge on May 5, using the previous balance method. Assume that the interest rate is 1.8% per month. $19.76

b) Find the new balance on May 5. $743.41

26. *Previous Balance Method* On September 5, the billing date, Verna Brown had a balance due of $567.20 on her credit card. The transactions during the following month were

September 8	Payment	$275.00
September 21	Charge: Airline ticket	330.00
September 27	Charge: Hotel bill	190.80
October 2	Charge: Clothing	84.75

a) Find the finance charge on October 5, using the previous balance method. Assume that the interest rate is 1.1% per month. $6.24

b) Find the new balance on October 5. $903.99

27. *Previous Balance Method* On February 3, the billing date, Carol Ann Bluesky had a balance due of $124.78 on her credit card. Her bank charges an interest rate of 1.25% per month. She made the following transactions during the month.

February 8	Charge: Art supplies	$25.64
February 12	Payment	100.00
February 14	Charge: Flowers delivered	67.23
February 25	Charge: Music CD	13.90

a) Find the finance charge on March 3, using the previous balance method. $1.56

b) Find the new balance on March 3. $133.11

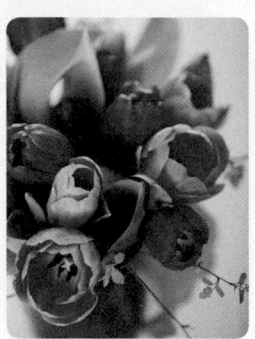

28. *Previous Balance Method* On April 15, the billing date, Gabrielle Michaelis had a balance due of $57.88 on her credit card. She is redecorating her apartment and has the following transactions.

April 16	Charge: Paint	$64.75
April 20	Payment	45.00
May 3	Charge: Curtains	72.85
May 10	Charge: Chair	135.50

a) Find the finance charge on May 15, using the previous balance method. Assume that the interest rate previous is 1.35% per month. $0.78

b) Find the new balance on May 15. $286.76

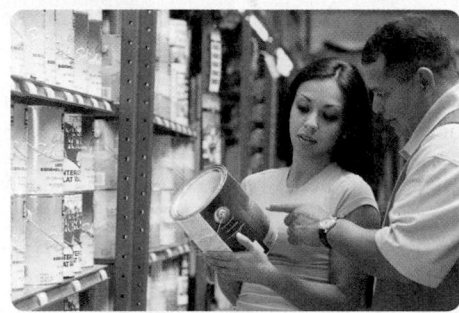

29. *Average Daily Balance Method* The balance on the Razazadas' credit card on May 12, their billing date, was $378.50. For the period ending June 12, they had the following transactions.

May 13	Charge: Toys	$129.79
May 15	Payment	50.00
June 1	Charge: Clothing	135.85
June 8	Charge: Housewares	37.63

a) Find the average daily balance for the billing period. $512.00

b) Find the finance charge to be paid on June 12. Assume an interest rate of 1.3% per month. $6.66

c) Find the balance due on June 12. $638.43

30. *Average Daily Balance Method* The Levys' credit card statement shows a balance due of $1578.25 on March 23, the billing date. For the period ending April 23, they had the following transactions.

March 26	Charge: Party supplies	$79.98
March 30	Charge: Restaurant meal	52.76
April 3	Payment	250.00
April 15	Charge: Clothing	190.52
April 22	Charge: Car repairs	190.85

a) Find the average daily balance for the billing period. $1585.37

b) Find the finance charge to be paid on April 23. Assume an interest rate of 1.3% per month. $20.61

c) Find the balance due on April 23. $1862.97

31. *Average Daily Balance Method* Refer to Exercise 27. Instead of the previous balance method, suppose that Carol Ann's bank uses the average daily balance method.

a) Find Carol Ann's average daily balance for the billing period from February 3 to March 3. Assume it is not a leap year. $121.78

b) Find the finance charge to be paid on March 3. $1.52

c) Find the balance due on March 3. $133.07

d) Compare these answers with those in Exercise 27.*

32. *Average Daily Balance Method* Refer to Exercise 26. Instead of the previous balance method, suppose Verna's bank uses the average daily balance method.

a) Find Verna's average daily balance for the billing period from September 5 to October 5. $533.06

b) Find the finance charge to be paid on October 5. $5.86

c) Find the balance due on October 5. $903.61

d) Compare these answers with those in Exercise 26.*

33. *A Cash Advance* John Richards borrowed $875 against his charge account on September 12 and repaid the loan on October 14 (32 days later). Assume that the interest rate is 0.04273% per day.

a) How much interest did John pay on the loan? $11.96

b) What amount did he pay the bank when he repaid the loan? $886.96

34. *A Cash Advance* Travis Thompson uses his credit card to obtain a cash advance of $600 to pay for his textbooks in medical school. The interest rate charged for the loan is 0.05477% per day. Travis repays the money plus the interest after 27 days.

a) Determine the interest charged for the cash advance. $8.87

b) When he repaid the loan, how much did he pay the credit card company? $608.87

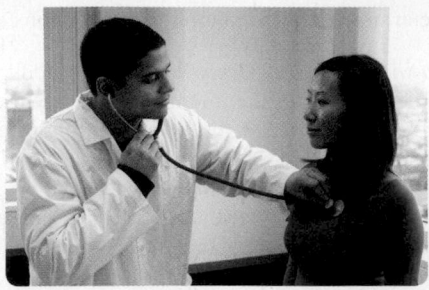

35. *Comparing Loan Sources* Grisha Stewart needs to borrow $1000 for an automobile repair. She finds that State National Bank charges 5% simple interest on the amount borrowed for the duration of the loan and requires the loan to be repaid in six equal monthly payments. Consumer's Credit Union offers loans of $1000 to be repaid in 12 monthly payments of $86.30.

a) How much interest is charged by the State National Bank? $25

b) How much interest is charged by the Consumer's Credit Union? $35.60

c) What is the APR, to the nearest half percent, on the State National Bank loan? 8.5%

d) What is the APR, to the nearest half percent, on the Consumer Credit Union loan? 6.5%

36. *Comparing Loan Options* Sara Lin wants to purchase a new television set. The purchase price is $890. If she purchases the set today and pays cash, she must take money out of her savings account. Another option is to charge the TV on her credit card, take the set home today, and pay next month. Next month she will have cash and can pay her credit card balance without paying any interest. The simple interest rate on her savings account is $5\frac{1}{4}\%$. How much is she saving by using the credit card instead of taking the money out of her savings account? $3.89

Challenge Problems/Group Activities

37. *Determining Purchase Price* Ken Tucker bought a new car, but now he cannot remember the original purchase price. His payments are $379.50 per month for 36 months. He remembers that the salesperson said the simple interest rate for the period of the loan was 6%. He also recalls he was allowed $2500 on his old car. Find the original purchase price. $14,077.97

38. *Comparing Loans* Suppose the Chans in Exercise 16 use a credit card rather than an installment plan. Assume that they make the same down payment, have no finance charge the first month, make no additional purchases on their credit card, and pay $432 per month plus the finance charge starting with the second month. The interest rate is 1.3% per month.

a) How many months will it take them to repay the loan? 6 months

b) How much interest will they pay on the loan? $83.95

c) Which method of borrowing will cost the Chans the least amount of interest, the installment loan in Exercise 16 or the credit card? The installment loan saves them $49.45

39. *Rule of 78s* When an installment loan is repaid early, there is a second method for calculating unearned interest called the *rule of 78s*. Although rarely used today, the following formula can be used to calculate unearned interest:

$$u = \frac{f \cdot k(k + 1)}{n(n + 1)}$$

where u is the unearned interest, f is the original finance charge, k is the number of remaining monthly payments (excluding the current payment), and n is the original number of payments. Joscelyn Jarrett obtained a new sport utility vehicle that had a cash price of $35,000 by paying 15% down and financing the balance with a 60-month fixed installment loan. The APR on the loan was 8.5%. Before making the 24th payment, Joscelyn decides to pay off the loan.

a) Determine the original finance charge on the 60-month loan. $6872.25

b) Determine Joscelyn's monthly payment. $610.37

c) If the actuarial method is used, determine the amount of interest Joscelyn will save by paying the loan off early. $2637.42

d) If the rule of 78s is used, determine the amount of interest Joscelyn will save by paying the loan off early. $2501.05

40. *Repayment Comparisons* Christine Biko took a world cruise that had a cash price of $23,000 by paying 10% down and financing the balance with a 48-month fixed installment loan. The APR on the loan was 6.0%. Before making the 12th payment, Christine decides to pay off the loan.

a) Determine the original finance charge on the 48-month loan. $2635.11

b) Determine Christine's monthly payment. $486.15

c) If the actuarial method is used, determine the amount of interest Christine will save by paying the loan off early. $1521.31

d) If the rule of 78s (see Exercise 39) is used, determine the amount of interest Christine will save by paying the loan off early. $1492.33

Internet/Research Activities

41. *Paying Off Your Credit Card Debt* Suppose you purchase a new wardrobe for $1000 with a credit card. You decide to pay for your new wardrobe by making the minimum monthly payment each month. You do not charge anything else to this credit card until you have the wardrobe paid off. Your credit card company determines your minimum monthly payment by adding all new interest to 1% of the outstanding principal. The credit card company charges an annual percentage rate of 18%. Go to an Internet credit card payment calculator web site such as www.bankrate.com to answer the following.

a) How long will it take you to pay off the entire credit card debt if you make the minimum monthly payments?

b) How much interest will you pay?

c) Adding the interest paid to the cash price, determine the total cost of your wardrobe.

42. Write a brief report giving the advantages and disadvantages of leasing a car. Determine all the individual costs involved with leasing a car. Indicate why you would prefer to lease or purchase a car at the present time.

43. Assume that you are married and have a child. You don't own a washer and dryer and have no money to buy the appliances. Would it be cheaper to borrow money on an installment loan and buy the appliances or to continue to go to the local coin-operated laundry for 5 years until you have saved enough to pay cash for a washer and dryer?

With the aid of parents or friends, establish how many loads of laundry you would be doing each week. Then determine the cost of doing that number of loads at a coin-operated laundry. (Don't forget the cost of transportation to and from the laundry.) Shop around for a washer and dryer, and determine the total cost on an installment plan. Don't forget to include the cost of gas, electricity, and water. This information can be obtained from a local gas and electric company. With this information, you should be able to make a decision about whether to buy now or wait 5 years.

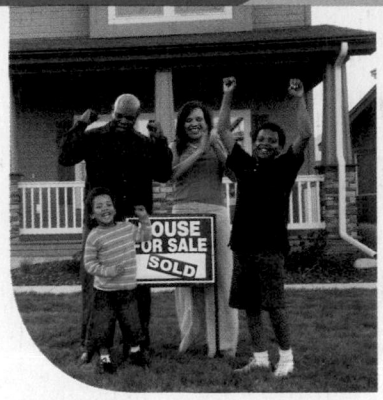

▲ *Owning your own home is part of the American dream.*

Part of the American dream is to own your own home. Owning your home means that you don't pay rent to someone else, but rather, in a way, you pay rent to yourself. Often you are also rewarded with several financial benefits. In this section, we will discuss the many advantages of owning your own home. We will also discuss the many financial obligations that must be met prior to obtaining a home loan as well as the obligations that must be met after you obtain the loan.

Why **This is Important** Learning about the costs of obtaining a mortgage can help you make wise decisions if you choose to purchase a home.

When purchasing a home, buyers usually seek a *mortgage* from a bank or other lending institution. Before approving a mortgage, which is a long-term loan, the bank will require the buyer to have a specified minimum amount for the down payment. The *down payment* is the amount of cash the buyer must pay to the seller before the lending institution will grant the buyer a mortgage. If the buyer has the down payment and meets the other criteria for the mortgage, the lending institution prepares a written agreement called the mortgage, stating the terms of the loan. The loan specifies the repayment schedule, the duration of the loan, whether the loan can be assumed by another party, and the penalty if payments are late. The party borrowing the money accepts the terms of this agreement and gives the lending institution the title or deed to the property as security.

Did You Know?

Sears Sold Houses

Courtesy of Sears, Roebuck and Co.

Sears, Roebuck and Co. started its mail-order business in the late 1880s. Its catalog, or "Consumer's Guide," was one of the most eagerly awaited publications of the time. You could order just about anything from the 1908 "Wish Book," including a line of "modern homes." The Langston, a modest two-story home, was offered for $1630. The houses were shipped in pieces by rail, assembly required.

Definition: Homeowner's Mortgage

A **homeowner's mortgage** is a long-term loan in which the property is pledged as security for payment of the difference between the down payment and the sale price.

The two most popular types of mortgage loans available today are the *conventional loan* and the *adjustable-rate loan* (or *variable-rate loan*). The major difference between the two is that the interest rate for a conventional loan is fixed for the duration of the loan, whereas the interest rate for the variable-rate loan may change every period, as specified in the loan. We will first discuss the requirements that are the same for both types of loans.

The size of the down payment required depends on who is lending the money, how old the property is, and whether or not it is easy to borrow money at that particular time. The down payment required by the lending institution can vary from 5% to 50% of the purchase price. A larger down payment is required when money is "tight," that is, when it is difficult to borrow money. Furthermore, most lending institutions tend to require larger down payments on older homes and smaller down payments on newer homes.

Lending institutions may require the buyer to pay one or more *points* for a loan at the time of the *closing* (the final step in the sale process). According to the Internal Revenue Service, *points* are interest prepaid by the buyer and may be used to reduce the stated interest rate the lender charges. One point is equal to 1% of the loan amount. This reduction in the interest rate allows the lender to reduce the size of the monthly mortgage payment, which enables more people to purchase homes. However, because points are considered interest, the rate of interest that lenders state when you are applying for a mortgage is not the annual percentage rate (APR) for the loan. Determining the APR involves a number of steps, including adding the amount paid for points to the total interest paid. The APR can then be determined using an APR table, a calculator, or an Internet Web site. Often, when shopping for a mortgage, a buyer may have two choices: pay points and get a lower interest rate, or not pay points and get a higher interest rate. Web sites such as www.hsh.com allow potential buyers to research whether paying points is to their advantage.

Conventional Loans

Example 1 illustrates purchasing a house with a conventional mortgage loan.

Example 1 *Down Payment and Points*

Patricia and Marshall Martin wish to purchase a house selling for $249,000. They plan to obtain a loan from their bank. The bank requires a 15% down payment, payable to the seller, and a payment of 2 points, payable to the bank, at the time of closing.

a) Determine the Martin's down payment.

b) Determine the amount of the Martin's mortgage.

c) Determine the cost of the 2 points paid by the Martins on their mortgage.

Solution

a) The down payment is 15% of $249,000, or

$$0.15 \times \$249,000 = \$37,350$$

b) The mortgage on the Martin's new home is the selling price minus the down payment.

$$\$249,000 - \$37,350 = \$211,650$$

c) Each point equals 1% of the mortgage amount, so 2 points equals 2% of the mortgage amount.

$$0.02 \times \$211,650 = \$4233$$

At the closing, the Martins will pay the down payment of $37,350 to the seller and the 2 points, or $4233, to the bank. ■

Banks use a formula to determine the maximum monthly payment that they believe is within the purchaser's ability to pay. A mortgage loan officer first determines the buyer's *adjusted monthly income* by subtracting from the gross monthly income (total income before any deductions) any fixed monthly payments with more than 10 months remaining (such as for a student loan, a car, furniture, or a television). The loan officer then multiplies the adjusted monthly income by 28%. (This percent, and the maximum number of payments remaining on other fixed loans, may vary in different locations.) In general, this product is the maximum monthly house payment the lending institution believes that the purchaser can afford to pay. This payment must cover principal, interest, property taxes, and insurance. Taxes and insurance are not necessarily paid to the bank; they may be paid directly to the tax collector and the insurance company. Example 2 shows how a bank uses the formula to determine whether a prospective buyer qualifies for a mortgage.

Example 2 *Qualifying for a Mortgage*

Suppose the Martin's (see Example 1) gross monthly income is $7250 and they have 23 remaining monthly payments of $225 on their car loan, 17 remaining monthly payments of $175 on their daughter's orthodontic braces, and 11

MATHEMATICS TODAY

Credit Scores

When consumers borrow money by obtaining car loans, home mortgages, or other loans or through the use of credit cards, the lender takes a risk by giving money to the borrower in exchange for the borrower's promise to repay the loan plus interest. To minimize their risk, lenders do research on borrowers to determine the likelihood the borrowers will *default*, or fail to repay the loans. Lenders often obtain this research from a *consumer credit bureau*. Credit bureaus assign a credit score to an individual after researching the individual's credit history, income, age, and other factors. A high credit score suggests that the individual is more likely to repay a loan and often enables the borrower to get lower interest rates on loans. You can find your own credit score online at www.creditscore.com. The following table shows the range of credit scores, grades, and credit outlook for these scores.

Score	Grade	Credit Outlook
901–990	A	Excellent rating; low interest rate
801–900	B	Good rating but short of excellent
701–800	C	Fair rating; moderate risk
601–700	D	Poor rating; higher risk and high interest rate
501–600	F	Lowest rating; highest risk; may not qualify for loan

Why *This is Important*
Preserving a good credit rating is essential for consumers who wish to obtain a mortgage, a credit card, or other borrowing opportunities.

remaining monthly payments of $45 on a loan used to purchase new furniture. The property taxes and homeowners' insurance on the house they wish to buy are $165 and $115 per month, respectively. Their bank will approve a loan that has a total monthly mortgage payment of principal, interest, property taxes, and homeowners' insurance that is less than or equal to 28% of their adjusted monthly income.

a) Determine 28% of the Martin's adjusted monthly income.

b) The Martins want a 30-year, $211,650 mortgage. If the interest rate is 7.0%, determine the total monthly mortgage payment (including principal, interest, property taxes, and homeowners' insurance) for this mortgage.

c) Determine whether the Martins qualify for this mortgage.

Solution

a) To determine the Martin's adjusted monthly income, subtract the sum of their monthly payments, $225 + $175 + $45 = $445, from their gross monthly income, $7250.

$7250	Gross monthly income
− 445	Monthly payments
$6805	Adjusted monthly income

Next, take 28% of the adjusted monthly income.

$$0.28 \times \$6805 = \$1905.40$$

Thus, 28% of the Martin's adjusted monthly income is $1905.40.

b) To determine the total monthly mortgage payment, we first need to determine the monthly principal and interest payments. Then we add the monthly property taxes and homeowners' insurance. We will use a table to calculate the monthly principal and interest payments the Martins will need to pay. Table 11.4 on page 649 gives monthly principal and interest payments per $1000 of mortgage. With an interest rate of 7.0% and a 30-year mortgage, the Martins would have a monthly principal and interest payment of $6.65302 (circled in blue) per thousand dollars of mortgage.

To determine the Martin's monthly principal and interest payment on their mortgage, first divide the mortgage amount by $1000, which will give the number of thousands of dollars of the mortgage.

$$\frac{\$211,650}{\$1000} = 211.65$$

Then, to determine the monthly principal and interest payment, multiply the number of thousands of dollars of mortgage, 211.65, by the value found in Table 11.4, $6.65302.

$$211.65 \times \$6.65302 \approx \$1408.11$$

Thus, the monthly principal and interest payment is $1408.11. To this amount, we add the monthly property taxes, $165, and the monthly homeowners' insurance, $115.

$$\$1408.11 + \$165 + \$115 = \$1688.11$$

Therefore, the Martins' total monthly mortgage payment is $1688.11.

c) In part (a), we determined that 28% of the Martin's adjusted monthly income is $1905.40. In part (b), we determined the Martin's total monthly mortgage payment is $1688.11. Because their total monthly mortgage payment is less than or equal to 28% of their adjusted monthly income, the Martins would most likely qualify for the mortgage.

Table 11.4 Monthly Principal and Interest Payment per $1000 of Mortgage

Rate %	Number of Years				
	10	15	20	25	30
4.0	$10.12451	$7.39688	$6.05980	$5.27837	$4.77415
4.5	10.36384	7.64993	6.32649	5.55832	5.06685
5.0	10.60655	7.90794	6.59956	5.84590	5.36822
5.5	10.85263	8.17083	6.87887	6.14087	5.67789
6.0	11.10205	8.43857	7.16431	6.44301	5.99551
6.5	11.35480	8.71107	7.45573	6.75207	6.32068
7.0	11.61085	8.98828	7.75299	7.06779	(6.65302)
7.5	11.87018	9.27012	8.05593	7.38991	6.99215
8.0	12.13276	9.55652	8.36440	7.71816	7.33765
8.5	12.39857	9.84740	8.67823	8.05227	7.68913
9.0	12.66758	10.14267	8.99726	8.39196	8.04623
9.5	12.93976	10.44225	9.32131	8.73697	8.40854
10.0	13.21507	10.74605	9.65022	9.08701	8.77572
10.5	13.49350	11.05399	9.98380	9.44182	9.14739
11.0	13.77500	11.36597	10.32188	9.80113	9.52323
11.5	14.05954	11.68190	10.66430	10.16469	9.90291
12.0	14.34709	12.00168	11.01086	10.53224	10.28613

In Example 2 we used Table 11.4 to calculate the monthly principal and interest payment on a mortgage. We may also use a formula to calculate this payment. The formula is virtually the same one we used in Section 11.4 to calculate installment payments. We will now restate this formula and use it to calculate the monthly principal and interest payments on a mortgage.

PRINCIPAL AND INTEREST PAYMENT FORMULA

$$m = \frac{p\left(\frac{r}{n}\right)}{1 - \left(1 + \frac{r}{n}\right)^{-n \cdot t}}$$

In the formula, m is the principal and interest payment, p is the amount of the mortgage, r is the interest rate as a decimal number, n is the number of mortgage payments per year, and t is the time in years.

In Example 3, we use the formula to calculate the monthly principal and interest payment for a mortgage.

Example 3 *Using the Principal and Interest Payment Formula*

Reread Example 2 on page 647. Use the principal and interest payment formula to calculate the Martin's monthly principal and interest payment. Recall that the Martins are seeking a 30-year, $211,650 mortgage with an interest rate of 7%.

Solution In this example the mortgage amount is \$211,650, so $p = 211,650$; the interest rate is 7%, so $r = 0.07$; the payments will be made monthly, so $n = 12$; and the length of the mortgage is 30 years, so $t = 30$. We substitute these values into the principal and interest formula below.

$$m = \frac{p\left(\dfrac{r}{n}\right)}{1 - \left(1 + \dfrac{r}{n}\right)^{-n \cdot t}}$$

$$= \frac{211,650\left(\dfrac{0.07}{12}\right)}{1 - \left(1 + \dfrac{0.07}{12}\right)^{-12 \cdot 30}}$$

$$\approx \frac{211,650(0.0058333333)}{1 - (1.005833333)^{-360}}$$

$$\approx \frac{1234.624993}{1 - 0.1232058683}$$

$$\approx \frac{1234.624993}{0.8767941317}$$

$$\approx 1408.112747$$

Thus, the Martins' monthly principal and interest payment is \$1408.11. Notice, this is the same payment that was found in Example 2 part (b) using Table 11.4. To see how to determine the monthly principal and interest payment on a scientific calculator, or by using Excel, see the Technology Tip on page 633. ∎

Examples 2 and 3 demonstrated that either Table 11.4 or the principal and interest formula can be used to calculate the principal and interest payment. The formula's advantage is that it can be used for any interest rate or any length of mortgage—not just those shown in Table 11.4. Principal and interest payments can also be calculated on many Web sites, such as www.bankrate.com.

What is the effect on the total monthly mortgage payments when only the period of time of the mortgage has been changed? The total monthly mortgage payments including principal, interest, property taxes, and homeowners' insurance for a 7.0% mortgage for the Martins in Example 2 would be about \$2737.44 for 10 years, \$2182.37 for 15 years, \$1920.92 for 20 years, \$1775.90 for 25 years, and \$1688.11 for 30 years. (You should verify these numbers for yourself.) Increasing the length of time decreases the monthly payment but increases the total amount of interest paid because the borrower is paying for a longer period of time (see Exercise 25 on page 656). The longer the term of the mortgage, the more expensive the total cost of the house. Although the total cost of a house with the shorter-term mortgage is less expensive overall, it is not always possible for the buyer to obtain the shorter-term mortgage. Note that based on their current adjusted monthly income, the Martins most likely would not have qualified for the 10-year, 15-year, or 20-year mortgage.

Example 4 *The Total Cost of a House*

Patricia and Marshall Martin of Examples 1, 2, and 3 purchased a house selling for \$249,000. They made a 15% down payment of \$37,350 and obtained a 30-year conventional mortgage for \$211,650 at 7.0%. They also paid 3 points at closing. Their monthly principal and interest payment on their mortgage is \$1408.11. Recall that points are considered prepaid interest.

a) Determine the total amount, including principal, interest, down payment, and points, the Martins will pay for their house over 30 years.

b) How much of the cost in part (a) is interest?

c) How much of the first mortgage payment is applied to the principal?

Solution

a) To determine the total amount the Martins will pay for their house, we first note that on a 30-year mortgage, there will be $30 \times 12 = 360$ monthly payments. We then perform the following computations.

$1408.11	Monthly principal and interest payment
$\times$ 360	Number of monthly payments
$506,919.60	Total principal and interest paid
+ 37,350.00	Down payment, from Example 1, part (a)
+ 4,233.00	2 points, from Example 1, part (c)
$548,502.60	Total cost of the house

Note that the result might not be the *exact* cost of the house because the final mortgage payment might be slightly more or less than the rest of the monthly mortgage payments.

b) To determine the amount of the interest paid over 30 years, subtract the purchase price of the house from the total price of the house.

$548,502.60	Total cost of the house
$-249,000.00	Purchase price
$299,502.60	Total interest (including the 2 points)

With this mortgage, the Martins will pay $299,502.60 in interest, including the 2 points.

c) To determine the amount of the first payment that is applied to the principal, subtract the amount of interest on the first payment from the monthly principal and interest payment. We will use the simple interest formula, $i = prt$, to determine the interest on the first payment.

$$i = prt$$
$$= \$211,650 \times 0.07 \times \frac{1}{12}$$
$$\approx \$1234.63$$

Now subtract the interest for the first month from the monthly principal and interest payment. The difference will be the amount paid on the principal for the first month.

$1408.11	Monthly principal and interest payment
$-1234.63	Interest paid for the first month
$173.48	Principal paid for the first month

Thus, the first monthly principal and interest payment consists of $1234.63 in interest and $173.48 in principal. The $173.48 is applied to reduce the outstanding balance due on the loan. Thus, the balance due on the loan after the first monthly payment is made is $211,650.00 − $173.48, or $211,476.52.   ∎

MATHEMATICS TODAY

Home Equity Loans

As you make monthly payments and pay off the principal you owe on your home, you are said to be gaining *equity* in your home. **Equity** is the difference between the appraised value of your home and your loan balance. This equity can be used as collateral in obtaining a loan. Such a loan is referred to as a **home equity loan** or a **second mortgage**. One advantage of home equity loans over other types of loans (such as installment loans) is that the interest charged on a home equity loan is often tax deductible on federal income taxes. Home equity loans are commonly used for home improvements, for bill consolidation, or to pay for college education expenses.

Why *This is Important* Home equity loans often have many advantages over other loan sources such as installment loans or credit cards.

By repeatedly using the simple interest formula month to month on the unpaid balance, you could calculate the principal and the interest for all the payments, which is a tedious task. However, a list containing the payment number, payment on the interest, payment on the principal, and balance of the loan can be prepared using a computer. Such a list is called a loan *amortization schedule*. One way to obtain an amortization schedule is by using a computer spreadsheet program. Another way is to access an amortization "calculator" program on the Internet. A part of the amortization schedule for the Martin's loan in Example 3 is given in Table 11.5. This schedule was generated from an Internet site called *Monthly Mortgage Payment Calculator (www.hsh.com).*

Table 11.5 Amortization Schedule

Annual % Rate: 7.0 Loan: $211,650 Periods: 360		Monthly Payment: $1408.11 Term: Years 30, Months 0	
Payment Number	Interest	Principal	Balance of Loan
1	$1234.63	$173.48	$211,476.52
2	$1233.61	$174.50	$211,302.01
3	$1232.60	$175.52	$211,126.49
4	$1231.57	$176.54	$210,949.95
11	$1224.24	$183.88	$209,684.99
12	$1223.16	$184.95	$209,500.04
119	$1063.49	$344.62	$181,968.54
120	$1061.48	$346.63	$181,621.91
239	$715.54	$692.57	$121,972.22
240	$711.50	$696.61	$121,275.62
359	$16.29	$1391.83	$1399.95
360	$8.17	$1399.95	$0.00

Adjustable-Rate Mortgages

Now let's consider *adjustable-rate mortgages*, ARMs (also called *variable-rate mortgages*). The rules for ARMs vary from state to state and from bank to bank, so the material presented on ARMs may not apply in your state or at your local lending institution. Generally, with adjustable-rate mortgages, the monthly mortgage payment remains the same for a 1-, 2-, or 5-year period even though the interest rate of the mortgage may change every 3 months, 6 months, or some other predetermined period. The interest rate for an adjustable-rate mortgage may be based on an index that is determined by the Federal Home Loan Bank Association or on the interest rate of a 3-month, 6-month, or 1-year Treasury bill. The interest rate of a 3-month Treasury bill may change every 3 months, the interest rate on a 6-month Treasury bill may change every 6 months, and so on. When the base is a Treasury bill, the actual interest rate charged for the mortgage is often determined by adding 3% to $3\frac{1}{2}$%, called the *add on rate* or *margin*, to the rate of the Treasury bill. Thus, if the rate of the Treasury bill is 2% and the add on rate is 3%, the interest rate charged is 5%.

Example 5   An Adjustable-Rate Mortgage

Tony and Keisha Torrence purchased a house for $115,000 with a down payment of $23,100. They obtained a 30-year adjustable-rate mortgage with the following terms. The interest rate is based on a 6-month Treasury bill. The interest rate charged is 3% above the interest rate of the 6-month Treasury bill (3% is the add on rate). The interest rate is adjusted every 6 months on the date of adjustment. The interest rate will not change more than 1% (up or down) when it is adjusted. The maximum interest rate for the duration of the loan is 12%. There is no lower limit on the interest rate. The initial mortgage interest rate is 5.5%, and the monthly payments (including principal and interest) are adjusted every 5 years.

a) Determine the initial monthly payment.

b) Determine the adjusted interest rate in 6 months if the interest rate on the Treasury bill at that time is 2%.

Solution

a) To determine the initial monthly payment of interest and principal, divide the amount of the loan, $115,000 − $23,100 = $91,900, by $1000. The result is 91.9. Now multiply the number of thousands of dollars of mortgage, 91.9, by the value found in Table 11.4 on page 649, with $r = 5.5\%$ for 30 years. The value found in the table is $5.67789.

$$\$5.67789 \times 91.9 \approx \$521.80$$

Thus, the initial monthly payment for principal and interest is $521.80. This amount will not change for the first 5 years of the mortgage.

b) The adjusted interest rate in 6 months will be the Treasury bill rate plus the add on rate.

$$2\% + 3\% = 5\%$$ ∎

In Example 5(b), note that the rate after 6 months, 5%, is lower than the initial rate of 5.5%. Since the monthly payment remains the same, the additional money paid the bank is applied to reduce the principal. The monthly interest and principal payment of $521.80 would pay off the loan in 30 years if the interest remained constant at 5.5%. What happens if the interest rate drops and stays lower than the initial 5.5% for the length of the loan? In this case, at the end of each 5-year period the bank reduces the monthly payment so that the loan will be paid off in 30 years. What happens if the interest rate increases above the initial 5.5% rate? In that case, part of, or if necessary, all the mortgage payment that would normally go toward repaying the principal would be used to meet the interest obligation. At the end of the 5-year period, the bank will increase the monthly payment so that the loan can be repaid by the end of the 30-year period. Or the bank may increase the time period of the loan beyond 30 years so that the monthly payment is affordable.

To prevent rapid increases in interest rates, some banks have a rate cap. A *rate cap* limits the maximum amount the interest rate may change. A *periodic rate cap* limits the amount the interest rate may increase in any one period. For example, your mortgage could provide that even if the index increases by 2% in 1 year, your rate can only go up 1% per year. An *aggregate rate cap* limits the interest rate increase and decrease over the entire life of the loan. If the initial interest rate is 6% and the aggregate rate cap is 2%, the interest rate could go no higher than 8% and no lower than 4% over the life of the mortgage. A *payment cap* limits the amount the monthly payment may change but does not limit changes in interest rates. If interest rates increase rapidly on a loan with a payment cap, the monthly payment may not be large enough to pay the monthly principal and interest on the loan. If that happens, the borrower could end up paying interest on interest.

Conventional mortgages and adjustable-rate mortgages are not the only methods of financing the purchase of a home. The *Mathematics Today* box on page 653 discusses some other types of mortgages that are available to consumers. More information about other types of mortgages can be found online at www.homemortgageinformation.org.

SECTION 11.5 · *Exercises*

Warm Up Exercises

In Exercises 1–6, fill in the blanks with an appropriate word, phrase, or symbol(s).

1. A long-term loan in which the property is pledged as security for payment of the difference between the down payment and the sale price is known as a homeowner's _____. Mortgage

2. The amount of cash the buyer must pay to the seller before the lending institution will grant the buyer a mortgage is known as the _____ payment. Down

3. Interest prepaid by the buyer, which may be used to reduce the stated interest rate the lender charges, are known as _____. Points

4. The final step in the real estate sale process is called the _____. Closing

5. The buyer's gross monthly income minus any fixed monthly payments with more than 10 months remaining is known as the buyer's _____ monthly income. Adjusted

6. A list containing the payment number, payment on interest, payment on principal, and the balance of the loan is called a(n) _____ schedule. Amortization

Practice the Skills

In Exercises 7–10, determine the monthly principal and interest payment for the mortgage. Unless told otherwise by your instructor, you may use either Table 11.4 or the principal and interest payment formula (See Examples 2 and 3).

	Amount Financed (P)	Annual Percentage Rate (r)	Number of Payments per Year (n)	Time in Years (t)	
7.	$85,000	6%	12	15	$717.28
8.	$112,000	9%	12	30	$901.18
9.	$285,000	5.5%	12	20	$1960.48
10.	$375,000	7.5%	12	25	$2771.22

Problem Solving

11. *Buying a House* Anna Wasilewska is buying a house selling for $175,000. To obtain her mortgage, Anna must make a 15% down payment. The current mortgage rate is 5.0%.

    a) Determine the amount of the required down payment. $26,250

    b) Determine the monthly principal and interest payment for a 30-year mortgage with a 15% down payment. $798.52

12. *Buying a House* Sadaf Din is purchasing a house selling for $215,000. To obtain her mortgage, Sadaf must make a 20% down payment. The current mortgage rate is 4.5%.

    a) Determine the amount of the required down payment. $43,000

    b) Determine the monthly principal and interest payment for a 25-year mortgage with a 20% down payment. $956.03

13. *Buying a Townhouse* Karen Guardino is purchasing a brownstone townhouse in Brooklyn for $1,750,000. The mortgage broker she is working with is requiring her to make a 15% down payment. The current mortgage rate is 6.0%.

    a) Determine the amount of the required down payment. $262,500

    b) Determine the monthly principal and interest payment for a 25-year loan with a 15% down payment. $9583.98

14. *Buying a First House* Rebecca Williams is purchasing her first house for $245,000. She is obtaining an FHA mortgage through her credit union and is required to make a 3% down payment. The current mortgage rate is 7.5%.

a) Determine the amount of the required down payment. $7350

b) Determine the monthly principal and interest payment for a 30-year loan with a 3% down payment. $1661.68

15. *Paying Points* Martha Cutler is buying a house selling for $195,000. The bank is requiring a minimum down payment of 20%. To obtain a 20-year mortgage at 6% interest, she must pay 2 points at the time of closing.

a) What is the required down payment? $39,000

b) With the 20% down payment, what is the amount of the mortgage? $156,000

c) What is the cost of the 2 points? $3120

16. *Down Payment and Points* The Nicols are buying a house selling for $245,000. They pay a down payment of $45,000 from the sale of their current house. To obtain a 15-year mortgage at 4.5% interest, the Nicols must pay 1.5 points at the time of closing.

a) What is the amount of the mortgage? $200,000

b) What is the cost of the 1.5 points? $3000

17. *Qualifying for a Mortgage* Pietr and Helga Guenther's gross monthly income is $3200. They have 25 remaining car payments of $335. The Guenthers are applying for a 15-year, $150,000 mortgage at 5% interest to buy a new house. The taxes and insurance on the house are $225 per month. Their credit union will approve a loan that has a total monthly mortgage payment of principal, interest, property taxes, and homeowners' insurance that is less than or equal to 28% of their adjusted monthly income.

a) Determine 28% of the Guenther's adjusted monthly income. $802.20

b) Determine the Guenther's total monthly mortgage payment, including principal, interest, taxes, and homeowners' insurance. $1411.19

c) Do the Guenthers qualify for this mortgage? No

18. *Qualifying for a Mortgage* Ting-Fang and Su-hua Zheng's gross monthly income is $4100. They have 18 remaining boat payments of $505. The Zhengs are applying for a 20-year, $275,000 mortgage at 9% interest to buy a new house. The taxes and insurance on the house are $425 per month. Their bank will approve a loan that has a total monthly mortgage payment of principal, interest, property taxes, and homeowners' insurance that is less than or equal to 28% of their adjusted monthly income.

a) Determine 28% of the Zheng's adjusted monthly income. $1006.60

b) Determine the Zheng's total monthly mortgage payment, including principal, interest, taxes, and insurance. $2899.25

c) Do the Zhengs qualify for this mortgage? No

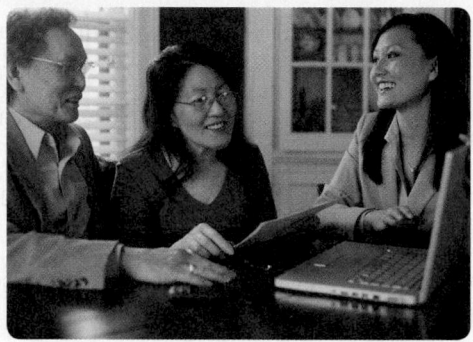

19. *A 30-Year Conventional Mortgage* Ingrid Holzner obtains a 30-year, $63,750 conventional mortgage at 8.5% on a house selling for $75,000. Her monthly payment, including principal and interest, is $490.18. She pays 0 points.

a) Determine the total amount Ingrid will pay for her house. $187,714.80

b) How much of the cost will be interest? $112,714.80

c) How much of the first payment on the mortgage is applied to the principal? $38.62

20. *A 25-Year Conventional Mortgage* Mr. and Mrs. Alan Bell obtain a 25-year, $110,000 conventional mortgage at 10.5% on a house selling for $160,000. Their monthly mortgage payment, including principal and interest, is $1038.60. They also pay 2 points at closing.

a) Determine the total amount the Bells will pay for their house. $363,780

b) How much of the cost will be interest (including the 2 points)? $203,780

c) How much of the first payment on the mortgage is applied to the principal? $76.10

21. *Evaluating a Loan Request* The Rosens found a house selling for $113,500. The taxes on the house are $1200 per year, and insurance is $320 per year. They are requesting a conventional loan from the local bank. The bank is currently requiring a 15% down payment and 3 points, and the interest rate is 10%. The Rosen's gross monthly income is $4750. They have more than 10 monthly payments remaining on a car, a boat, and furniture. The total monthly payments for these items is $420. Their bank will approve a loan that has a total monthly mortgage payment of principal, interest, property taxes, and homeowners' insurance that is less than or equal to 28% of their adjusted monthly income.

a) Determine the required down payment. $17,025

b) Determine the cost of the 3 points. $2894.25

c) Determine 28% of their adjusted monthly income. $1212.40

d) Determine the monthly payments of principal and interest for a 20-year loan. $931.00

e) Determine their total monthly payment, including homeowners' insurance and taxes. $1057.67

f) Determine whether the Rosens qualify for the 20-year loan. Yes

g) Determine how much of the first payment on the loan is applied to the principal. $127.04

22. *Evaluating a Loan Request* Kathy Fields wants to buy a condominium selling for $95,000. The taxes on the property are $1500 per year, and homeowners' insurance is $336 per year. Kathy's gross monthly income is $4000. She has 15 monthly payments of $135 remaining on her van. The bank is requiring 20% down and is charging 9.5% interest with no points. Her bank will approve a loan that has a total monthly mortgage payment of principal, interest, property taxes, and homeowners' insurance that is less than or equal to 28% of her adjusted monthly income.

a) Determine the required down payment. $19,000

b) Determine 28% of her adjusted monthly income. $1082.20

c) Determine the monthly payment of principal and interest for a 25-year loan. $664.01

d) Determine her total monthly payment, including homeowners' insurance and taxes. $817.01

e) Does Kathy qualify for the loan? Yes

f) Determine how much of the first payment on the mortgage is applied to the principal. $62.34

g) Determine the total amount she pays for the condominium with a 25-year conventional loan. (Do not include taxes or homeowners' insurance.) $218,203

h) Determine the total interest paid for the 25-year loan. $123,203

23. *Comparing Loans* The Riveras are negotiating with two banks for a mortgage to buy a house selling for $105,000. The terms at bank A are a 10% down payment, an interest rate of 10%, a 30-year conventional mortgage, and 3 points to be paid at the time of closing. The terms at bank B are a 20% down payment, an interest rate of 11.5%, a 25-year conventional mortgage, and no points. Which loan should the Riveras select for the total cost of the house to be less? Bank B

24. *Comparing Loans* Paul Westerberg is negotiating with two credit unions for a mortgage to buy a condominium selling for $525,000. The terms at Grant County Teacher's Credit Union are a 20% down payment, an interest rate of 7.5%, a 15-year mortgage, and 1 point to be paid at the time of closing. The terms at Sinnipee Consumer's Credit Union are a 15% down payment, an interest rate of 8.5%, a 20-year mortgage, and no points. Which loan should Paul select for the total cost of the down payment, points, and total mortgage payments of the house to be less?
The loan from Grant County Teacher's Credit Union

Challenge Problems/Group Activities

25. *Changing Lengths of Mortgages* Rose Hulman and her husband, George Mason, are purchasing a house for $450,000. Their bank requires them to pay a down payment of 20%. The current mortgage rate is 10%, and they are required to pay 1 point at the time of closing. Determine the total amount Rose and George will pay for their house, including principal, interest, down payment, and points (do not include taxes and homeowners' insurance) if the length of their mortgage is

a) 10 years. $664,491.60

b) 20 years. $927,379.20

c) 30 years. $1,230,933.60

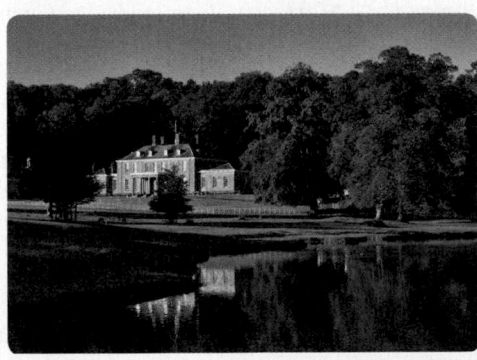

26. *Comparing Payment Frequency* Janet Samuels is purchasing a new house for $315,000. Her credit union requires her to make a 20% down payment, and the current mortgage rate is 6%. Janet is exploring different 10-year mortgage payment options. Use the principal and interest formula to determine Janet's principal and interest payment if she makes her payments

a) Monthly. $2797.72

b) Bimonthly (use $n = 24$). $1397.59

c) Weekly (use $n = 52$). $644.72

27. An Adjustable-Rate Mortgage The Simpsons purchased a house for $105,000 with a down payment of $5000. They obtained a 30-year adjustable-rate mortgage. The terms of the mortgage are as follows: The interest rate is based on a 3-month Treasury bill, the interest rate charged is 3.25% above the rate of the Treasury bill on the date of adjustment, the interest rate is adjusted every 3 months, the interest rate will not change more than 1% (up or down) when the interest rate is adjusted, the maximum interest rate that can be charged for the duration of the loan is 16%, there is no lower limit on the interest rate, the initial mortgage interest rate is 9%, and the monthly payment of interest and principal is adjusted semiannually.

a) Determine the initial monthly payment for interest and principal. $804.62

b) Determine an amortization schedule for months 1–3.*

c) Determine the interest rate for months 4–6 if the interest rate on the Treasury bill at the time is 6.13%. 9.38%

d) Determine an amortization schedule for months 4–6.*

e) Determine the interest rate for months 7–9 if the interest rate on the Treasury bill at the time is 6.21%. 9.46%

28. An Adjustable-Rate Mortgage The Bretz family purchased a house for $95,000 with a down payment of $13,000. They obtained a 30-year adjustable-rate mortgage. The terms of the mortgage are as follows: The interest rate is based on a 3-month Treasury bill, the interest rate charged is 3.25% above the rate of the Treasury bill on the date of adjustment, the interest rate is adjusted every 3 months, the interest rate will not change more than 1% (up or down) when the interest rate is adjusted, the maximum interest rate that can be charged for the duration of the loan is 16%, there is no lower limit on the interest rate, the initial mortgage interest rate is 8.5%, and the monthly payment of interest and principal is adjusted annually.

a) Determine the initial monthly payment for interest and principal. $630.51

b) Determine the interest rate in 3 months if the interest rate on the Treasury bill at the time is 5.65%. 8.9%

c) Determine the interest rate in 6 months if the interest rate on the Treasury bill at the time is 4.85%. 8.1%

29. Comparing Mortgages The Hassads are applying for a $90,000 mortgage. They can choose between a 30-year conventional mortgage and a 30-year variable-rate mortgage. The interest rate on a 30-year conventional mortgage is 9.5%. The terms of the variable-rate mortgage are 6.5% interest rate the first year, an annual cap

of 1%, and an aggregate cap of 6%. The interest rates and the mortgage payments are adjusted annually. Assume that the interest rates for the variable-rate mortgage increase by the maximum amount each year. Then the monthly mortgage payments for the variable-rate mortgage for years 1–6 are $568.86, $629.29, $692.02, $756.77, $823.27, and $891.26, respectively.

a) Knowing that they will be in the house for only 6 years, which mortgage, the conventional mortgage or the variable-rate mortgage, will be the least expensive for that period? The variable-rate mortgage

b) How much will they save by choosing the less expensive mortgage? $2149.80

Internet/Research Activity

30. Finding Your Dream Home Examine a local newspaper to find your "dream home" and note the asking price. Next contact a loan officer from your local bank, savings and loan, or credit union. Assuming you can make a 20% down payment, determine the interest rates for a 15-year and a 30-year mortgage. Use an amortization "calculator" (see page 652) with the data you obtained to print amortizations schedules. Compare the monthly payments with the 15-year mortgage to those of the 30-year mortgage. Compare the total interest costs of the 15-year mortgage with those of the 30-year mortgage. Write a report summarizing your findings.

31. Closing Costs An important part of buying a house is the closing. The exact procedures for the closing differ with individual cases and in different parts of the country. In any closing, however, both the buyer and the seller have certain expenses. To determine what is involved in the closing of a property in your community, contact a lawyer, a real estate agent, or a banker. Explain that you are a student and that your objective is to understand the procedure for closing a real estate purchase and the costs to both buyer and seller. Select a specific piece of property that is for sale. Use the asking price to determine the total closing costs to both buyer and seller. The following is a partial list of the most common closing costs. Consider them in your research.

a) Fee for title search and title insurance
b) Credit report on buyer
c) Fees to the lender for services in granting the loan
d) Fee for property survey
e) Fee for recording of the deed
f) Appraisal fee
g) Lawyer's fee
h) Escrow accounts (taxes, insurance)
i) Mortgage assumption fee

*See Instructor Answer Appendix

SECTION 11.6

Ordinary Annuities, Sinking Funds, and Retirement Investments

▲ *Saving money on a regular basis may lead to a comfortable retirement.*

In Sections 11.2 and 11.3, we studied simple and compound interest, respectively. In both sections, we answered questions involving the investment of one lump sum of money. Although such questions may be relevant to our everyday financial matters, more appropriate questions might involve investing smaller amounts of money on a regular basis over a longer period of time. For example, the Brabsons, who are planning for retirement, might ask the question: If we deposit $100 a month at 5% interest compounded monthly, how much money will we accumulate after 30 years when we're ready to retire? Also consider the Weismans, who are saving for their child's college education. They might ask the question: If we know we will need $50,000 to send our child to college in 10 years, how much should we invest each month beginning now in an account paying 6% interest compounded monthly? To answer these and similar questions, we will study two investments, the *annuity* and the *sinking fund*.

Why *This is Important* Annuities and sinking funds are an important part of a long-term investment strategy.

W e begin this section with a discussion of annuities.

Annuities

Definition: Annuity
An **annuity** is an account into which, or out of which, a sequence of scheduled payments is made.

There are many different types of annuities. An annuity may be an investment account that you have with a bank, insurance company, or financial management firm. Annuities may contain investments in stocks, bonds, mutual funds, money market accounts, and other types of investments. Annuities are often used to save for long-term goals such as saving money for college or for retirement. An annuity can also be used to provide long-term regular payments to individuals. Lottery jackpots and professional athletes' salaries are often paid out over time from annuities. Retirees may invest some of their retirement savings into an annuity and then receive monthly payments that come from that annuity. We will focus primarily on two basic types of annuities that are used as investment accounts, *ordinary annuities* and *sinking funds*. Later in this section, we will discuss other types of annuities.

Definition: Ordinary Annuity
An annuity into which equal payments are made at regular intervals, with the interest compounded at the end of each interval and with a fixed interest rate for each compounding period, is called an **ordinary annuity** or a **fixed annuity**.

For example, the Brabsons, mentioned in the opening paragraph of this section, are asking a question that may involve an ordinary annuity. They plan to make $100 payments each month into an account that pays 5% interest compounded monthly.

With an ordinary annuity, the payment period and frequency of the compounding are the same, so the Brabsons make *monthly* payments *and* the interest is compounded *monthly*. They would like to know how much money would accumulate in this annuity after 30 years. The amount of money that is present in an ordinary annuity after t years is known as the *accumulated amount* or the *future value* of an annuity.

To determine the accumulated amount of an ordinary annuity, we could make many individual calculations using the compound interest formula discussed in Section 11.3. Such calculations would be quite tedious and time consuming even with the assistance of a scientific calculator. A better way is to use a computer to generate a spreadsheet. A portion of such a spreadsheet is shown below. This spreadsheet was generated using the data from the example involving the Brabsons. Note that the Brabsons would make monthly payments for 30 years for a total of 360 payments. Also note that had the Brabsons simply put $100 in their cookie jar each month, their total amount at the end of 30 years would have been $100 × 360, or $36,000. Instead, by investing in an interest-bearing annuity, they will have accumulated $83,225.86 after 30 years.

Accumulated Amount in an Ordinary Annuity with $100 Monthly Investments with Interest Rate 5% Compounded Monthly			
Payment Number	Monthly Investment	Interest	Accumulated Amount
1	$100.00	$ —	$ 100.00
2	$100.00	$ 0.42	$ 200.42
3	$100.00	$ 0.84	$ 301.25
4	$100.00	$ 1.26	$ 402.51
5	$100.00	$ 1.68	$ 504.18
6	$100.00	$ 2.10	$ 606.28
7	$100.00	$ 2.53	$ 708.81
8	$100.00	$ 2.95	$ 811.76
9	$100.00	$ 3.38	$ 915.15
10	$100.00	$ 3.81	$ 1,018.96
⋮	⋮	⋮	⋮
351	$100.00	$328.58	$79,287.40
352	$100.00	$330.36	$79,717.76
353	$100.00	$332.16	$80,149.92
354	$100.00	$333.96	$80,583.88
355	$100.00	$335.77	$81,019.65
356	$100.00	$337.58	$81,457.23
357	$100.00	$339.41	$81,896.63
358	$100.00	$341.24	$82,337.87
359	$100.00	$343.07	$82,780.94
360	$100.00	$344.92	$83,225.86

Another way, and perhaps a more efficient way, to calculate the accumulated amount in an ordinary annuity is to use the ordinary annuity formula on page 660.

Ordinary Annuity Formula

The accumulated amount, A, of an ordinary annuity with payments of p dollars made n times per year, for t years, at interest rate r as a decimal number, compounded at the end of each payment period is given by the formula

$$A = \frac{p\left[\left(1 + \frac{r}{n}\right)^{nt} - 1\right]}{\frac{r}{n}}$$

Example 1   *Using the Ordinary Annuity Formula*

Bill and Megan Lutes are depositing $250 each quarter in an ordinary annuity that pays 4% interest compounded quarterly. Determine the accumulated amount in this annuity after 35 years.

Solution   We will use the ordinary annuity formula. The payment, p, is $250, the interest rate, r, is 4% or 0.04, the account is compounded quarterly and the payments are made quarterly, so n is 4, and the number of years, t, is 35. We substitute these values into the formula to obtain the following.

$$A = \frac{p\left[\left(1 + \frac{r}{n}\right)^{nt} - 1\right]}{\frac{r}{n}}$$

$$= \frac{250\left[\left(1 + \frac{0.04}{4}\right)^{(4\cdot35)} - 1\right]}{\frac{0.04}{4}}$$

Substitute the given values into the formula.

$$= \frac{250[1.01^{140} - 1]}{0.01}$$

To evaluate 1.01^{140}, we use the $\boxed{y^x}$ or the $\boxed{\wedge}$ key on a scientific calculator.

$$\approx \frac{250[4.027099 - 1]}{0.01}$$

We rounded 1.01^{140} to six decimal places.

$$\approx \frac{250(3.027099)}{0.01}$$

$$\approx \frac{756.77475}{0.01} \approx 75{,}677.475$$

Thus, there will be about $75,677.48 in Bill and Megan's annuity after 35 years. ■

Example 1 illustrated the power of establishing and maintaining a consistent investment plan and how using an ordinary annuity can help us save money.

TECHNOLOGY TIP

Scientific Calculator

In Example 1, we determined the accumulated amount by evaluating the expression

$$\frac{250\left[\left(1 + \frac{0.04}{4}\right)^{(4\cdot35)} - 1\right]}{\frac{0.04}{4}}$$

There are various ways to evaluate this expression on a scientific calculator. One method is to press the following sequence of keys.

$$(250 \times ((1 + 0.04 \div 4)) y^x ((4 \times$$
$$35) - 1)) \div ((0.04 \div 4)) =$$

After the $=$ key is pressed, the answer 75677.48042 is displayed.

Microsoft Excel
Read the Technology Tip on page 623. To determine the accumulated amount using Excel, place the letters p, r, n, t and A in cells A1 through E1, respectively. In cells A2 through D2, place the values for p, r, n, and t, respectively. In cell E2, use the formula box to add the formula

$$= (A2*((1 + B2/C2)\wedge(C2*D2) - 1))/(B2/C2)$$

After the Enter key is pressed, the result is as follows.

	A	B	C	D	E
1	p	r	n	t	A
2	250	0.04	4	35	75677.48

Sheet1 / Sheet2 / Sheet3 /
Ready

Next we will study a specific type of annuity called a *sinking fund*.

Sinking Funds

We now return to the second question asked at the beginning of this section. Recall that the Weismans have a goal of saving \$50,000 in 10 years for their child's college education and want to know how much they should begin to invest each month in an account paying 6% interest compounded monthly. The Weismans can help reach this goal by investing in a special kind of annuity called a *sinking fund*.

> ### Definition: Sinking Fund
> A **sinking fund** is a type of annuity in which the goal is to save a specific amount of money in a specific amount of time.

Many types of sinking funds are used for many different purposes by individuals, corporations, and governments. Historically, sinking funds were used by governments to set aside money to pay off bonds that were used to borrow large sums of money for major civic projects such as sewers, roads, or bridges. The term *sinking fund* referred to the *sinking* of the debt that was owed to repay the bonds. Our discussion of sinking funds will focus on answering questions similar to the question facing the Weismans. Because they are interested in saving a specific amount of money, \$50,000, in a specific amount of time, 10 years, their investment can be considered a sinking fund.

To determine the amount of money to be invested in a sinking fund, we can solve the ordinary annuity formula, given on page 660, for the payment, p. Solving this formula for p gives us the following formula.

Sinking Fund Payment Formula

$$p = \frac{A\left(\dfrac{r}{n}\right)}{\left(1 + \dfrac{r}{n}\right)^{nt} - 1}$$

In the formula, p is the payment needed to reach the accumulated amount, A. Payments are made n times per year, for t years, into a sinking fund with interest rate r as a decimal number, compounded n times per year.

Example 2 *Using the Sinking Fund Payment Formula*

Abigail and John Clayton would like to have $55,000 in 10 years to remodel their home. The Claytons decide to invest monthly in a sinking fund that pays 3.3% interest compounded monthly. How much should the Claytons invest in the sinking fund each month to accumulate $55,000 in 10 years?

Solution Since we are looking for how much the Claytons should invest each month to obtain an accumulated amount, we will use the sinking fund payment formula. The accumulated amount, A, is $55,000; the interest rate, r, is 3.3%, or 0.033; the payments are made monthly and the interest is compounded monthly, so n is 12; and the number of years, t, is 10.

$$
\begin{aligned}
p &= \frac{A\left(\dfrac{r}{n}\right)}{\left(1 + \dfrac{r}{n}\right)^{nt} - 1} \\[2em]
&= \frac{55{,}000\left(\dfrac{0.033}{12}\right)}{\left(1 + \dfrac{0.033}{12}\right)^{(12\cdot 10)} - 1} \\[2em]
&\approx \frac{151.25}{0.39033827} \\[1em]
&\approx 387.48442
\end{aligned}
$$

We often round to the nearest cent, or in this case, to $387.48. However, because $387.48 is slightly *less* than the answer we obtained, we will round our answer *up* to $387.49 to ensure that the Claytons reach their goal of $55,000. ∎

As we did in Example 2, *when calculating a sinking fund payment, we will round our final answers up to the nearest cent to ensure that we reach the desired accumulated amount in the sinking fund.*

TECHNOLOGY TIP

Scientific Calculator
To determine the sinking fund payment in Example 2, we evaluated the expression

$$\frac{55{,}000\left(\dfrac{0.033}{12}\right)}{\left(1 + \dfrac{0.033}{12}\right)^{(12\cdot 10)} - 1}$$

This expression can be evaluated on a scientific calculator, as follows:

55000 $\boxed{\times}$ $\boxed{(}$ 0.033 $\boxed{\div}$ 12 $\boxed{)}$ $\boxed{\div}$ $\boxed{(}$ $\boxed{(}$ $\boxed{(}$ 1 $\boxed{+}$ 0.033 $\boxed{\div}$

12 $\boxed{)}$ $\boxed{y^x}$ $\boxed{(}$ 12 $\boxed{\times}$ 10 $\boxed{)}$ $\boxed{-}$ 1 $\boxed{)}$

After the ⊟ key is pressed, the answer 387.48442 is displayed.

Microsoft Excel
Read the Technology Tip on page 660 and follow a similar procedure using the variables *A*, *r*, *n*, *t*, and, *p*, respectively. To evaluate the sinking fund payment, in cell E2 enter the formula

$$= A2*(B2/C2)/((1 + B2/C2)^{(C2*D2)} - 1)$$

After the Enter Key is pressed, the answer 387.4844 is displayed in cell E2.

In Example 2, we can check our answer by substituting $387.49 back into the ordinary annuity formula. Doing this calculation with a scientific calculator gives us an accumulated amount of about $55,000.79. If we substitute $387.48 for *A* into the ordinary annuity formula, the accumulated amount would be about $54,999.37, which is slightly short of the desired goal of $55,000.

Other Annuities

Ordinary annuities and sinking funds are not the only types of annuities. We will now briefly discuss two other common types of annuities, *variable annuities* and *immediate annuities*.

Variable Annuities

A *variable annuity* is an annuity that is invested in stocks, bonds, mutual funds, or other investments that do not provide a guaranteed interest rate. The term *variable* is used because the value of the annuity will vary depending on the performance of the investment options chosen by the investor. Like an ordinary annuity, an investor usually invests in a variable annuity by making regular periodic payments. Unlike an ordinary annuity, however, a variable annuity does not have a fixed rate of interest. Most variable annuities are investments made to save for retirement.

Immediate Annuities

An *immediate annuity* is an annuity that is established with a lump sum of money for the purpose of providing the investor with regular, usually monthly, payments for the rest of the investor's life. In exchange for giving the investment company a lump sum of money, the investor is guaranteed to receive a monthly income for the duration of the investor's life.

Other Retirement Savings Options

Annuities can be used to save for retirement, but depending on the investor's circumstances, other investment options for retirement savings may be more advantageous. We will briefly discuss several options here.

Individual Retirement Accounts

Individual retirement accounts, also known as *IRAs*, are accounts where individuals may invest up to a certain amount of money each year for the purpose of saving for retirement. IRAs have distinct tax advantages over non-IRA accounts. There are several different kinds of IRAs, but most can be classified as either a *traditional IRA* or a *Roth IRA*. A *traditional IRA* is an IRA into which *pretax* money is invested, meaning that any money invested into a traditional IRA is not subject to income taxes. However, when money is withdrawn from a traditional IRA, the money *is* subject to

▲ *It is never too early to start saving for retirement.*

income taxes. A *Roth IRA* is an IRA into which *post-tax* money is invested, meaning that the investor has already paid income taxes on the money invested. When money is withdrawn from a Roth IRA after the investor reaches retirement age, the money *is not* subject to income taxes.

401ks and 403bs

A *401k plan* is a retirement savings plan where employees of private companies can make contributions of pre–income tax dollars that are then pooled with other employees' money. These funds are then invested in a variety of stocks, bonds, money markets, and mutual funds. Although 401k plans share many of the same tax advantages as IRAs, they also have several distinct advantages. First, employees are generally allowed to invest more money annually in a 401k plan than in an IRA. Often, employees are eligible to invest up to 15% of their annual income into a 401k plan. A second advantage is that some employers will match employee contributions up to a certain limit. A *Roth 401k plan* is a retirement savings plan that differs from a 401k plan in that an investor first pays income tax on the money used to invest in a Roth 401k plan. Like a Roth IRA, money withdrawn from a Roth 401k plan after the individual reaches retirement age is not subject to income tax.

A *403b plan* is a retirement plan similar to a 401k plan, but it is available only to employees of schools, civil governments, hospitals, charities, and other not-for-profit organizations. A 403b plan shares many of the same advantages as 401k plans. One major difference, though, is that a 403b plan is not necessarily established by the employer as is a 401k plan. Rather, a 403b plan is frequently established independently by the employee with a representative of an investment or insurance company.

As you can see from this brief discussion of annuities, IRAs, 401k plans, and 403b plans, many important details can affect your decisions as you begin to invest for retirement. For more information, and for other types of retirement accounts not mentioned here, consult a financial advisor or visit a library or Internet Web site. Regardless of the source of your information, it is very important to do your own research and ask many questions prior to investing.

SECTION 11.6 *Exercises*

Warm Up Exercises

In Exercises 1–8, fill in the blanks with an appropriate word, phrase, or symbol(s).

1. An account into which, or out of which, a sequence of scheduled payments is made, is called a(n) _____.
   Annuity

2. The amount of money that is present in an ordinary annuity after *t* years is known as the accumulated amount or the _____ value of the annuity. Future

3. A type of annuity in which the goal is to save a specific amount of money in a specific amount of time is called a(n) _____ fund. Sinking

4. A variable annuity is an annuity that is invested in stocks, bonds, mutual funds, or other investments that do not provide a _____ interest rate. Guaranteed

5. An annuity that is established with a lump sum for the purpose of providing the investor with regular payments for the rest of the investor's life is called a(n) _____ annuity. Immediate

6. Accounts where individuals may invest up to a certain amount of money each year for the purpose of saving for retirement are called _____ retirement accounts. Individual

7. A retirement savings plan where employees of private companies can make contributions of pre–income tax dollars that are then pooled with other employees' money is called a _____ plan. 401k

8. A retirement plan similar to a 401k plan, but available only to employees of schools, governments, and other not-for-profit organizations, is called a _____ plan. 403b

Practice the Skills

In Exercises 9–12, use the ordinary annuity formula

$$A = \frac{p\left[\left(1 + \dfrac{r}{n}\right)^{nt} - 1\right]}{\dfrac{r}{n}}$$

to determine the accumulated amount in each annuity. Round all answers to the nearest cent.

9. $1500 invested annually for 25 years at 3% compounded annually $54,688.90

10. $800 invested semiannually for 25 years at 7% compounded semiannually $104,798.33

11. $400 invested quarterly for 35 years at 8% compounded quarterly $299,929.32

12. $200 invested monthly for 40 years at 6% compounded monthly $398,298.15

In Exercises 13–16, use the sinking fund formula

$$p = \frac{A\left(\dfrac{r}{n}\right)}{\left(1 + \dfrac{r}{n}\right)^{nt} - 1}$$

to determine the payment needed to reach the accumulated amount. To ensure that enough is invested each period, round each answer up to the next cent.

13. Semiannual payments with 2.5% interest compounded semiannually for 10 years to accumulate $7500 $332.41

14. Annual payments with 5% interest compounded annually for 20 years to accumulate $35,000 $1058.50

15. Monthly payments with 6% interest compounded monthly for 35 years to accumulate $250,000 $175.48

16. Quarterly payments with 10% interest compounded quarterly for 40 years to accumulate $1,000,000 $490.41

Problem Solving

In Exercises 17–20, round all answers to the nearest cent.

17. **Retirement Savings** To save for retirement, Jana Bryant invests $50 each month in an ordinary annuity with 3% interest compounded monthly. Determine the accumulated amount in Jana's annuity after 35 years. $37,078.18

18. **Starting a Business** To save money to start a new business, Sandra Jessee invests $200 each quarter in an ordinary annuity with 5% interest compounded quarterly. Determine the accumulated amount in Sandra's annuity after 20 years. $27,223.76

19. **Saving for Graduate School** To save for graduate school, Ena Salter invests $2000 semiannually in an ordinary annuity with 7% interest compounded semiannually. Determine the accumulated amount in Ena's annuity after 10 years. $56,559.36

20. **Grandchild's College Expenses** To save for their grandchildren's college expenses, Ken and Laura Machol invest $500 each month in an ordinary annuity with 6% interest compounded monthly. Determine the accumulated amount in the Machol's annuity after 18 years. $193,676.60

In Exercises 21–24, round all answers up to the next cent.

21. **Saving for a New Car** Erica Atalla would like to have $25,000 to buy a new car in 5 years. To accumulate $25,000 in 5 years, how much should she invest monthly in a sinking fund with 9% interest compounded monthly? $331.46

22. **Campaign Fund-Raising** Ashley Smith would like to run for Congress in 10 years and would like to have $500,000 to spend on campaign expenses. How much should she invest monthly in a sinking fund with 6% interest compounded monthly to accumulate $500,000 in 10 years? $3051.03

23. **Becoming a Millionaire** Becky Anderson would like to be a millionaire in 20 years. How much would she need to invest quarterly in a sinking fund paying 8% interest compounded quarterly to accumulate $1,000,000 in 20 years? $5160.71

24. **Repaying a Debt** The city of Corpus Christi wishes to repay a debt of $25,000,000 in 50 years. How much should the city invest semiannually in a sinking fund paying 7.5% interest compounded semiannually to accumulate $25,000,000 in 50 years? $24,223.66

Challenge Problems/Group Activities

25. *Don't Wait to Invest*   The purpose of this exercise is to demonstrate that it is much more beneficial to begin to invest for retirement early than it is to wait. We will compare the investments of two investors, Alberto and Zachary. Alberto begins to invest immediately after graduating from college, whereas Zachary waits 10 years to begin investing. For the purposes of this demonstration, we will assume that the interest rate remains the same over the entire period of time.

    a) From age 25 to 35, Alberto invests $100 per month in an annuity that pays 12% interest compounded monthly. Determine the accumulated amount in Alberto's annuity after 10 years. $23,003.87

    b) At age 35, Alberto stops making monthly payments into his annuity, but he takes the money he accumulated in his annuity and invests it in a savings account with an interest rate of 12% compounded monthly. Using the compound interest formula $A = p\left(1 + \dfrac{r}{n}\right)^{n \cdot t}$, determine the amount Alberto has in his savings account 30 years later when he retires at age 65. $826,980.88

    c) From age 35 to 65, Zachary invests $100 per month in an annuity that pays 12% interest compounded monthly. Determine the accumulated amount in Zachary's annuity after 30 years. $349,496.41

    d) Determine the total amount Alberto invested during the 10 years from age 25 to 35. $12,000

    e) Determine the total amount Zachary invested during the 30 years from age 35 to 65. $36,000

    f) Which investor has more money from the investments described here upon retirement? Alberto

Internet/Research Activities

26. *Investing in Stocks*   Using the Internet, financial magazines, books, and other resources, write a paper on investing in stocks (see the *Did You Know?* on page 659). Include in your paper a description of the following terms: *New York Stock Exchange, National Association of Securities Dealers Automated Quotations (NASDAQ), dividends,* and *capital gains.*

27. *Investing in Bonds*   Using the Internet, financial magazines, books, and other resources, write a paper on investing in bonds (see the *Did You Know?* on page 660). Include in your paper a description of the following terms: *Treasury bonds, corporate bonds,* and *municipal bonds.*

28. *Investing in Mutual Funds*   Using the Internet, financial magazines, books, and other resources, write a paper on investing in mutual funds (see the *Did You Know?* on page 661). Include in your paper a description of the following terms: *net asset value (NAV), portfolio manager,* and *expense ratios.*

29. *Financial Advisor Interview*   Annuities, IRAs, 401k plans, 403b plans, SEP accounts, and Keogh accounts are all types of investments that can be used to save for retirement. Interview a financial advisor to discuss each of these investment types. Write a paper in which you explain the differences among the different investment types and describe the advantages of each type of investment over the others.

CHAPTER 11   *Summary*

Important Facts and Concepts	Examples and Discussion
Section 11.1	
Percent Change	
$\text{Percent change} = \dfrac{\left(\begin{array}{c}\text{amount in}\\\text{latest period}\end{array}\right) - \left(\begin{array}{c}\text{amount in}\\\text{previous period}\end{array}\right)}{\text{amount in previous period}} \times 100$	Examples 6–7, page 603
Percent Markup on Cost	
$\text{Percent markup} = \dfrac{\text{selling price} - \text{dealer's cost}}{\text{dealer's cost}} \times 100$	Examples 8–9, page 604
Section 11.2	
Simple Interest Formula	
$i = prt$	Examples 1–5, pages 612–614

United States Rule

If a partial payment is made on a loan, interest is computed on the principal from the first day of the loan until the date of the partial payment. The partial payment is used to pay the interest first; then the rest of the payment is used to reduce the principal.

Discussion, page 614, Example 8, page 616

Banker's Rule

When computing interest, a year is considered to have 360 days and any fractional part of a year is the exact number of days.

Discussion, page 615, Example 7–8, page 616

Section 11.3

Compound Interest Formula

$$A = p\left(1 + \frac{r}{n}\right)^{nt}$$

Examples 2–4, pages 623–625

Present Value Formula

$$p = \frac{A}{\left(1 + \dfrac{r}{n}\right)^{nt}}$$

Example 5, page 626

Section 11.4

Installment Payment Formula

$$m = \frac{p\left(\dfrac{r}{n}\right)}{1 - \left(1 + \dfrac{r}{n}\right)^{-n \cdot t}}$$

Example 2, page 632

Actuarial Method

$$u = \frac{n \cdot P \cdot V}{100 + V}$$

Example 4, page 634

Section 11.5

Mortgage Principal and Interest Payment Formula

$$m = \frac{p\left(\dfrac{r}{n}\right)}{1 - \left(1 + \dfrac{r}{n}\right)^{-n \cdot t}}$$

Example 3, page 649

Section 11.6

Ordinary Annuity Formula

$$A = \frac{p\left[\left(1 + \dfrac{r}{n}\right)^{nt} - 1\right]}{\dfrac{r}{n}}$$

Discussion, page 660, Example 1, page 660

Sinking Fund Payment Formula

$$p = \frac{A\left(\dfrac{r}{n}\right)}{\left(1 + \dfrac{r}{n}\right)^{nt} - 1}$$

Discussion, page 662, Example 2, page 662

CHAPTER 11) *Review Exercises*

11.1

In Exercises 1–6, change the number to a percent. Round your answer to the nearest tenth of a percent.

1. $\frac{4}{5}$ 80.0%   **2.** $\frac{2}{3}$ 66.7%   **3.** $\frac{5}{8}$ 62.5%

4. 0.041 4.1%   **5.** 0.0098 0.98% ≈ 1.0%   **6.** 3.141 314.1%

In Exercises 7–12, change the percent to a decimal number.

7. 5% 0.05   **8.** 21.7% 0.217   **9.** 123% 1.23

10. $\frac{1}{4}$% 0.0025   **11.** $\frac{5}{6}$% 0.0083̄   **12.** 0.00045% 0.0000045

13. *Lambeau Field* Before undergoing renovations, the seating capacity at Lambeau Field (in Green Bay, Wisconsin) was 60,790. After the renovations were complete the seating capacity was 71,500. Determine the percent increase (to the nearest tenth of a percent) in the seating capacity of Lambeau Field. ≈ 17.6%

▲ *Lambeau Field.*

14. *Salary Increase* Charlotte Newsome had a salary of $41,500 during the first year of a new job and a salary of $42,745 during the second year. Determine the percent increase in Charlotte's salary from the first year to the second year. 3.0%

In Exercises 15–17, solve for the unknown quantity.

15. What percent of 60 is 12? 20.0%

16. Forty-four is 55% of what number? 80

17. What is 17% of 540? 91.8

18. *Tipping* At Empress Garden Restaurant, Vishnu and Krishna's bill comes to $42.79, including tax. If they wish to leave a 15% tip on the total bill, how much should they tip the waiter? $6.42

19. *Increased Membership* If the number of people in your chess club increased by 20%, or 8 people, what was the original number of people in the club? 40 people

20. *Increased Membership* The Sarasota Wheelers skateboard club had 75 members and increased the number of members to 95. What is the percent increase in the number of members? 26.7%

11.2

In Exercises 21–24, determine the missing quantity by using the simple interest formula.

21. $p = \$2500$, $r = 1.5\%$, $t = 3$ years, $i = ?$ $112.50

22. $p = \$2700$, $r = ?$, $t = 100$ days, $i = \$37.50$ 5.0%

23. $p = ?$, $r = 8\frac{1}{2}\%$, $t = 3$ years, $i = \$114.75$ $450

24. $p = \$5500$, $r = 11\frac{1}{2}\%$, $t = ?$, $i = \$316.25$ 0.5 year

25. *Wedding Loan* To pay for his daughter's wedding, Mike Hardie borrows $7500 from his friend. The loan was for 24 months and had a simple interest rate of 2.5%. Determine the amount Mike paid his friend on the date of the maturity of the loan. $7875

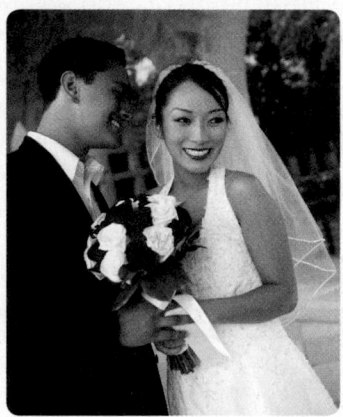

26. *A Bank Loan* Lori Holdren borrowed $3000 from her bank for 240 days at a simple interest rate of 8.1%.

   a) How much interest did she pay for the use of the money? $162

   b) How much did she pay the bank on the date of maturity? $3162

27. *A Bank Loan* Nikos Pappas borrowed $6000 for 24 months from his bank, using stock as security. The bank discounted the loan at $11\frac{1}{2}\%$.

   a) How much interest did Nikos pay the bank for the use of the money? $1380

   b) How much did he receive from the bank? $4620

   c) What was the actual rate of interest? ≈ 14.9%

28. *Savings as Security* Golda Frankl borrowed $800 for 6 months from her bank, using her savings account as security. A bank rule limits the amount that can be borrowed in this manner to 85% of the amount in the borrower's savings account. The rate of interest is 2% higher than the interest rate being paid on the savings account. The current rate on the savings account is 5.5%

a) What rate of interest will the bank charge for the loan? 7.5%

b) Determine the amount that Golda must repay in 6 months. $830

c) How much money must she have in her account to borrow $800? at least $941.18

11.3

29. *Comparing Compounding Periods* Determine the amount and the interest when $5000 is invested for 5 years at 6%

a) compounded annually. $6691.13; $1691.13

b) compounded semiannually. $6719.58; $1719.58

c) compounded quarterly. $6734.28; $1734.28

d) compounded monthly. $6744.25; $1744.25

e) compounded daily (use $n = 360$). $6749.13; $1749.13

30. *Certificate of Deposit* Jane Tanner invests $3400 in a 2-year certificate of deposit (CD) that pays 1.5% interest compounded monthly. What will be the value of the CD in 2 years? $3503.48

31. *Effective Annual Yield* Determine the effective annual yield of an investment if the interest is compounded daily at an annual rate of 5.6%. 5.76%

32. *Present Value* How many dollars must you invest today to have $40,000 in 20 years? Assume that the money earns 5.5% interest compounded quarterly. $13,415.00

11.4

33. *Repaying a Loan Early* Bill Osborn has a 48-month installment loan with a fixed monthly payment of $176.14. The amount borrowed was $7500. Instead of making his 24th payment, Bill is paying the remaining balance on the loan.

a) Determine the APR of the installment loan. 6.0%

b) How much interest will Bill save, computed by the actuarial method? $253.16

c) What is the total amount due to pay off the loan? $4150.34

34. *Repaying a Loan Early* Carter Fenton is buying a book collection that costs $4000. He is making a down payment of $500 and 24 monthly payments of $155.91.

a) Determine the APR. 6.5%

b) Instead of making his 12th payment, Carter decides to pay the total remaining balance and terminate the loan. How much will Carter save by paying off the loan early? $64.32

c) What is the total amount due to pay off the loan? $1962.51

35. *Installment Loan* Dara Holliday's cost for a new wardrobe was $3420. She made a down payment of $860 and financed the balance on a 24-month fixed payment installment loan. The monthly payments are $111.73. Instead of making her 12th payment, Dara decides to pay the total remaining balance and terminate the loan.

a) Determine the APR of the installment loan. 4.5%

b) How much interest will Dara save, computed by the actuarial method? $32.06

c) What is the total amount due to pay off the loan? $1420.43

36. *Finance Charge Comparison* On June 1, the billing date, Tim McGarry had a balance due of $485.75 on his credit card. The transactions during the month of June were

June 4	Payment	$375.00
June 8	Charge: Car repair	370.00
June 21	Charge: Airline ticket	175.80
June 28	Charge: Clothing	184.75

a) Determine the finance charge on July 1 by using the previous balance method. Assume that the interest rate is 1.3% per month. $6.31

b) Determine the new account balance on July 1 using the finance charge found in part (a). $847.61

c) Determine the average daily balance for the period. $508.99

d) Determine the finance charge on July 1 by using the average daily balance method. Assume that the interest rate is 1.3% per month. $6.62

e) Determine the new account balance on July 1 using the finance charge found in part (d). $847.92

37. Finance Charge Comparison On August 5, the billing date, Pat Schaefer had a balance due of $185.72 on her credit card. The transactions during the month of August were

August 8	Charge: Shoes	$85.75
August 10	Payment	75.00
August 15	Charge: Dry cleaning	72.85
August 21	Charge: Textbooks	275.00

a) Determine the finance charge on September 5 by using the previous balance method. Assume that the interest rate is 1.4% per month. $2.60

b) Determine the new account balance on September 5 using the finance charge found in part (a). $546.92

c) Determine the average daily balance for the period. $382.68

d) Determine the finance charge on September 5 by using the average daily balance method. Assume that the interest rate is 1.4% per month. $5.36

e) Determine the new account balance on September 5 using the finance charge found in part (d). $549.68

38. Financing an Airplane Deepankar Pal bought a new Piper Sport airplane for $140,000. He made a 40% down payment and financed the balance with the dealer on a 60-month installment loan. The monthly payments were $1624. Determine the

a) down payment. $56,000

b) amount to be financed. $84,000

c) total finance charge. $13,440

d) APR. 6.0%

39. Financing a Ski Outfit Lucille Groenke can buy a cross-country skiing outfit for $275. The store is offering the following terms: $50 down and 12 monthly payments of $19.62.

a) Determine the interest Lucille would pay. $10.44

b) Determine the APR. 8.5%

11.5

40. Building a House The Freemans have decided to build a new house. The contractor quoted them a price of $135,700. The taxes on the house will be $3450 per year, and homeowners' insurance will be $350 per year. They have applied for a conventional loan from a local bank. The bank is requiring a 25% down payment, and the interest rate on the loan is 9.5%. The Freemans' annual income is $64,000. They have more than 10 monthly payments remaining on each of the following: $218 on a car, $120 on new furniture, and $190 on a camper. Their bank will approve a loan that has a total monthly mortgage payment of principal, interest, property taxes, and homeowners' insurance that is less than or equal to 28% of their adjusted monthly income. Determine

a) the required down payment. $33,925

b) 28% of their adjusted monthly income. $1345.49

c) the monthly payment of principal and interest for a 30-year loan. $855.78

d) their total monthly payment, including insurance and taxes. $1172.45

e) Do the Freemans qualify for the mortgage? Yes

41. Thirty-Year Mortgage James Whitehead purchased a home selling for $89,900 with a 15% down payment. The period of the mortgage is 30 years, and the interest rate is 11.5% with no points. Determine the

a) amount of the down payment. $13,485

b) monthly payment of principal and interest. $756.73

c) amount of the first payment applied to the principal. $24.42

d) total cost of the house. $285,907.80

e) total interest paid. $196,007.80

42. Adjustable-Rate Mortgage The Nguyens purchased a house for $105,000 with a down payment of $26,250. They obtained a 30-year adjustable-rate mortgage. The terms of the mortgage are as follows: The interest rate is based on the 6-month Treasury bill, the interest rate charged is 3.00% above the rate of the Treasury bill on the date of adjustment, the interest rate is adjusted every 6 months, the interest rate will not change more than 1% (up or down) when the interest rate is adjusted, the maximum interest rate that can be charged for the duration of the loan is 16%, there is no lower limit on the interest rate, the initial mortgage interest rate is 7.5%, and the monthly payment of interest and principal is adjusted annually. Determine the

a) initial monthly payment for principal and interest. $550.63

b) interest rate in 6 months if the interest rate on the Treasury bill at the time is 5.00%. 8.0%

c) interest rate in 6 months if the interest rate on the Treasury bill at the time is 4.75%. 7.75%

11.6

43. Vacation Savings To save money to take an around-the-world vacation, Kim Ghiselin invests $250 monthly in an ordinary annuity with 9% interest compounded monthly. Determine the accumulated amount in Kim's annuity after 10 years. $48,378.57

44. Saving for a New Boat Raja Khoury would like to save $80,000 to buy a new Chris Craft Silver Bullet boat in 5 years. To accumulate $80,000 in 5 years, how much

should Raja invest quarterly in a sinking fund with 3.6% interest compounded quarterly? $3668.72

CHAPTER 11) *TEST*

1. Find the missing quantity by using the simple interest formula.

a) $i = ?$, $p = \$750$, $r = 2\%$, $t = 30$ months $37.50

b) $i = 351$, $p = \$2600$, $r = 4.5\%$, $t = ?$ 3 years

In Exercises 2 and 3, Patty George borrowed $1200 from a bank for 18 months to buy a new computer. The rate of simple interest charged is 9.25%.

2. How much interest did Patty pay for the use of the money? $166.50

3. What is the amount Patty repaid to the bank on the due date of the loan? $1366.50

In Exercises 4 and 5, Yolanda Fernandez received a $5400 loan with interest at 12.5% for 90 days on August 1. Yolanda made a payment of $3000 on September 15.

4. How much did she owe the bank on the date of maturity? $2523.20

5. What total amount of interest did she pay on the loan? $123.20

6. Compute the amount and the compound interest.

	Principal	Time	Rate	Compounded
a)	$7500	2 years	3%	Quarterly
b)	$2500	3 years	6.5%	Monthly

a) $7961.99; $461.99   b) $3036.68; $536.68

A New Bicycle In Exercises 7–9, Don Ransford purchases a new bike that sells for $2350. To finance it through a bank the bank will require a down payment of 15% and monthly payments of $90.79 for 24 months.

7. How much money will Don borrow from the bank? $1997.50

8. What finance charge will Don pay the bank? $181.46

9. What is the APR? 8.5%

10. Actuarial Method Gino Sedillo borrowed $7500. To repay the loan, he was scheduled to make 36 monthly installment payments of $223.10. Instead of making his 24th payment, Gino decides to pay off the loan.

a) Determine the APR of the installment loan. 4.5%

b) How much interest will Gino save (use the actuarial method)? $64.02

c) What is the total amount due to pay off the loan? $2836.28

11. *Previous Balance Method* Michael Murphy's credit card statement shows a balance due of $878.25 on March 23, the billing date. For the period ending on April 23, he had the following transactions.

March 26	Charge: Groceries	$ 95.89
March 30	Charge: Restaurant bill	68.76
April 3	Payment	450.00
April 15	Charge: Clothing	90.52
April 22	Charge: Eyeglasses	450.85

a) Determine the finance charge on April 23 by using the previous balance method. Assume that the interest rate is 1.4% per month. $12.30

b) Determine the new account balance on April 23 using the finance charge found in part (a). $1146.57

c) Determine the average daily balance for the period. $765.67

d) Determine the finance charge on April 23 by using the average daily balance method. Assume that the interest rate is 1.4% per month. $10.72

e) Determine the new account balance on April 23 using the finance charge found in part (d). $1144.99

Building a House In Exercises 12–18, the Leungs decided to build a new house. The contractor quoted them a price of $144,500, including the lot. The taxes on the house would be $3200 per year, and homeowners' insurance would cost $450 per year. They have applied for a conventional loan from a bank. The bank is requiring a 15% down payment, and the interest rate is $10\frac{1}{2}$% with 2 points. The Leung's annual income is $86,500. They have more than 10 monthly payments remaining on each of the following: $220 for a car, $175 for new furniture, and $210 on a college education loan. Their bank will approve a loan that has a total monthly mortgage payment of principal, interest, property taxes, and homeowners' insurance that is less than or equal to 28% of their adjusted monthly income.

12. What is the required down payment? $21,675

13. Determine the amount paid for points. $2456.50

14. Determine 28% of their adjusted monthly income. $1848.93

15. Determine the monthly payments of principal and interest for a 30-year loan. $1123.53

16. Determine their total monthly payments, including homeowners' insurance and taxes. $1427.70

17. Do the Leungs meet the requirements for the mortgage? Yes

18. a) Determine the total cost of the house (excluding homeowners' insurance and taxes) after 30 years. $428,602.30

b) How much of the total cost is interest, including points? $284,102.30

19. *Saving for Musical Instruments* To raise money to buy new musical instruments, the rock band *White Noise Reverie* decides to invest $400 monthly in an ordinary annuity with 3% interest compounded monthly. Determine the accumulated amount in the band's annuity after 5 years. $25,858.69

20. *Saving for a New Car* Elisa Bolotin is a freshman in high school and would like to have $15,000 in 4 years to buy a car for college. How much should she invest monthly in a sinking fund with 6% interest compounded monthly to accumulate $15,000 in 4 years? $277.28

GROUP PROJECTS

Mortgage Loan

1. The Young family is purchasing a $130,000 house with a VA mortgage. The bank is offering them a 25-year mortgage with an interest rate of 9.5%. They have $20,000 invested that could be used for a down payment. Since they do not need a down payment, Mr. Young wants to keep the money invested. Mrs. Young believes that they should make a down payment of $20,000.

a) Determine the total cost of the house with no down payment.

b) Determine the total cost of the house if they make a down payment of $20,000.

c) Mr. Young believes that the $20,000 investment will have an annual rate of return of 10% compounded quarterly. Assuming that Mr. Young is right, calculate the value of the investment in 25 years. (Use the compound interest formula on page 623.)

d) If the Youngs use the $20,000 as a down payment, their monthly payments will decrease. Determine the difference of the monthly payments in parts (a) and (b).

e) Assume that the difference in monthly payments, part (d), is invested each month at a rate of 6% compounded monthly for 25 years. Determine the value of the investment in 25 years. (Use the ordinary annuity formula on page 660.)

f) Use the information from parts (a)–(e) to analyze the problem. Would you recommend that the Youngs make the down payment of $20,000 and invest the difference in their monthly payments as in part (e) or that they do not make the down payment and keep the $20,000 invested as in part (c)? Explain.

Credit Card Terms

2. With each credit card comes a credit agreement (or security agreement) the cardholder must sign. Select two members of your group who have a major credit card (MasterCard, Visa, Discover, or American Express). If possible, one of the credit cards should be a gold or platinum card. Obtain a copy of the credit agreement signed by each cardholder and answer questions (a)–(p).

a) What are the cardholder's responsibilities?

b) What is the cardholder's maximum line of credit?

c) What restrictions apply to the use of the credit card?

d) How many days after the billing date does the cardholder have to make a payment without being charged interest?

e) What is the minimum monthly payment required, and how is it determined?

f) What is the interest rate charged on purchases?

g) How does the bank determine when to start charging interest on purchases?

h) Is there an annual fee for the credit card? If so, what is it?

i) What late charge applies if payments are not made on time?

j) What information is given on the monthly statement?

k) How is the finance charge computed?

l) What other fees, if any, may the bank charge you?

m) If the card is lost, what is the responsibility of the cardholder?

n) If the card is lost, what is the liability of the cardholder?

o) What are the advantages of a gold or platinum card over a regular card?

p) In your opinion, which of the two cards is more desirable? Explain.

12

Probability

What You Will Learn

- Empirical probability and theoretical probability
- Compound probability, conditional probability, and binomial probability
- Odds against an event and odds in favor of an event
- Expected value
- Tree diagrams
- Mutually exclusive events and independent events
- The counting principle, permutations, and combinations

Why This is Important

Each year, millions of Americans play lotteries. If you play a lottery, your hope is to beat the odds and be the person with the winning numbers. Not satisfied with leaving things to chance, mathematicians of the sixteenth, seventeenth, and eighteenth centuries invented the study of probability to determine the likelihood of an event such as winning the lottery.

Although the rules of probability were first applied to gaming, they have many other applications. The cost of your car insurance, the weather forecast, the expected number of people who will attend an outdoor concert if it is raining all involve probability. In this chapter, we will learn many of the important concepts of probability that can help us make informed decisions in our lives.

◄ *Probability is involved in all games of chance, determining the cost of car insurance, and weather forecasting.*

SECTION 12.1   The Nature of Probability

▲ *We can determine the probability of an event, such as the probability that a particular auto part will fail before the warranty expires, based on actual observations.*

How do researchers determine if a new potential drug is superior to a standard drug? How do automobile manufacturers determine the chance that a particular part will fail before the warranty expires? These and many other similar questions are answered through experimentation and observation of the results. Determining the chance of something happening in the future by observing past results is called empirical probability.

Why This is Important Understanding how to calculate probabilities based on past experience is essential to our daily lives. Empirical probability is used to determine insurance premiums and the length of a warranty. It is also used in medical and genetics research, as well as many other areas.

I n this section we introduce some basic concepts of probability including the Law of Large Numbers.

History

Probability is used in many areas, including public finance, medicine, insurance, elections, manufacturing, educational tests and measurements, genetics, weather forecasting, investments, opinion polls, the natural sciences, and games of chance. The study of probability originated from the study of games of chance. Archaeologists have found artifacts used in games of chance in Egypt dating from about 3000 B.C.

Mathematical problems relating to games of chance were studied by a number of mathematicians of the Renaissance. Italy's Girolamo Cardano (1501–1576) in his *Liber de Ludo Aleae* (book on the games of chance) presents one of the first systematic computations of probabilities. Although it is basically a gambler's manual, many consider it the first book ever written on probability. A short time later, two French mathematicians, Blaise Pascal (1623–1662) and Pierre de Fermat (1601–1665), worked together studying "the geometry of the die." In 1657, Dutch mathematician Christian Huygens (1629–1695) published *De Ratiociniis in Luno Aleae* (on ratiocination in dice games), which contained the first documented reference to the concept of mathematical expectation (see Section 12.4). Swiss mathematician Jacob Bernoulli (1654–1705), whom many consider the founder of probability theory, is said to have fused pure mathematics with the empirical methods used in statistical experiments. The works of Pierre-Simon de Laplace (1749–1827) dominated probability throughout the nineteenth century.

The Nature of Probability

Before we discuss the meaning of the word *probability* and learn how to calculate probabilities, we must introduce a few definitions.

> **Definition: Experiment**
> An **experiment** is a controlled operation that yields a set of results.

The process by which medical researchers administer experimental drugs to patients to determine their reaction is one type of experiment.

> **Definition: Outcomes**
> The possible results of an experiment are called its **outcomes**.

Profile In Mathematics

Jacob Bernoulli (1654–1705)

S wiss mathematician Jacob Bernoulli was considered a pioneer of probability theory. He was part of a famous family of mathematicians and scientists. In *Ars Conjectand*, published posthumously in 1713, he proposed that an increased degree of accuracy can be obtained by increasing the number of trials of an experiment. This theorem, called Bernoulli's theorem (of probability), is also known as the law of large numbers. Bernoulli's theorem of fluid dynamics, used in aircraft wing design, was developed by Daniel Bernoulli (1700–1782). Daniel was one of Jacob's younger brother Johann's three sons.

▲ *A die (one of a pair of dice) contains six surfaces, called faces. Each face contains a unique number of dots, from 1 to 6. The sum of the dots on opposite surfaces is 7.*

For example, the possible outcomes from administering an experimental drug may be a favorable reaction, no reaction, or an adverse reaction.

> **Definition: Event**
> An **event** is a subcollection of the outcomes of an experiment.

For example, when a die is rolled, the event of rolling a number greater than 2 can be satisfied by any one of four outcomes: 3, 4, 5, or 6. The event of rolling a 5 can be satisfied by only one outcome, the 5 itself. The event of rolling an even number can be satisfied by any of three outcomes: 2, 4, or 6.

Probability is classified as either *empirical* (experimental) or *theoretical* (mathematical). *Empirical probability* is the relative frequency of occurrence of an event and is determined by actual observations of an experiment. *Theoretical probability* is determined through a study of the possible *outcomes* that can occur for the given experiment. We will indicate the probability of an event E by $P(E)$, which is read "P of E."

Empirical Probability

In this section, we will briefly discuss empirical probability. The emphasis in the remaining sections is on theoretical probability. Following is the formula for computing empirical probability, or relative frequency.

> **Empirical Probability (Relative Frequency)**
> The empirical probability of an event, $P(E)$, can be determined by the following formula.
>
> $$P(E) = \frac{\text{number of times event } E \text{ has occurred}}{\text{total number of times the experiment has been performed}}$$

The probability of an event, whether empirical or theoretical, is always a number between 0 and 1, inclusive, and may be expressed as a decimal number or a fraction. An empirical probability of 0 indicates that the event has never occurred. An empirical probability of 1 indicates that the event has always occurred.

Example 1 *Heads Up!*

In 100 tosses of a fair coin, 44 landed heads up. Determine the empirical probability of the coin landing heads up.

Solution Let E be the event that the coin lands heads up. Then

$$P(E) = \frac{44}{100} = 0.44$$

∎

Example 2 *Blood Pressure Reduction*

A pharmaceutical company is testing a drug that is supposed to help reduce high blood pressure. The drug is given to 500 individuals with the following outcomes.

Blood pressure reduced	Blood pressure unchanged	Blood pressure increased
379	62	59

MATHEMATICS TODAY

**One Blue Eye,
One Brown Eye**

Seeing a dog or a person with different-colored eyes is unusual, but not that unusual. Features such as eye color are determined genetically, as are certain illnesses. Below is a chart listing some human genetic disorders and their rates of occurrence.

Disorder/Incidence

Cystic fibrosis:
1 out of 2500 Caucasian births

Down syndrome:
1 out of 800–1000 births

Duchenne muscular dystrophy:
1 out of 3300 male births

Fragile X syndrome:
1 out of 1500 male births
1 out of 2500 female births

Hemophilia A:
1 out of 8500 male births

Polycystic kidney disease:
1 out of 3000 births

Prader–Willi syndrome:
1 out of 12,000 births

Sickle-cell anemia:
1 out of 400–600 African-American births

Tay-Sachs disease:
1 out of 3600 Ashkenazi Jewish births

Why **This is Important** Genetics, which has its foundation in probability, is used in explaining the cause of these illnesses, and it plays an important role in research to find cures for genetic disorders.

If this drug is given to an individual, determine the empirical probability that the person's blood pressure is (a) reduced, (b) unchanged, (c) increased.

Solution

a) Let E be the event that the blood pressure is reduced.

$$P(E) = \frac{379}{500} = 0.758$$

b) Let E be the event that the blood pressure is unchanged.

$$P(E) = \frac{62}{500} = 0.124$$

c) Let E be the event that the blood pressure is increased.

$$P(E) = \frac{59}{500} = 0.118$$

Empirical probability is used when probabilities cannot be theoretically calculated. For example, life insurance companies use empirical probabilities to determine the chance of an individual in a certain profession, with certain risk factors, living to age 65.

Empirical Probability in Genetics

Using empirical probability, Gregor Mendel (1822–1884) developed the laws of heredity by crossbreeding different types of "pure" pea plants and observing the relative frequencies of the resulting offspring. These laws became the foundation for the study of genetics. For example, when he crossbred a pure yellow pea plant and a pure green pea plant, the resulting offspring (the first generation) were always yellow; see Fig. 12.1(a). When he crossbred a pure round-seeded pea plant and a pure wrinkled-seeded pea plant, the resulting offspring (the first generation) were always round; see Fig. 12.1(b).

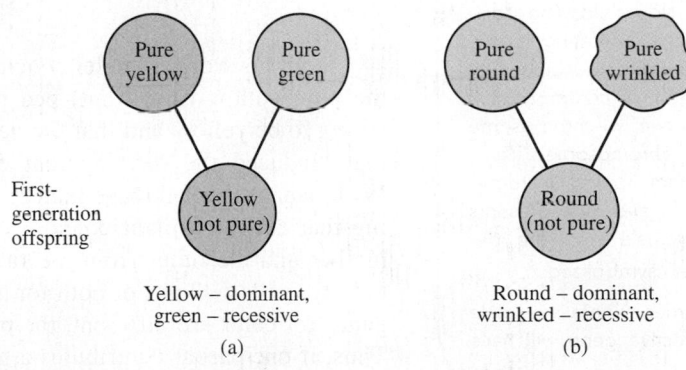

Figure 12.1

Mendel called traits such as yellow color and round seeds *dominant* because they overcame or "dominated" the other trait. He labeled the green color and the wrinkled traits *recessive*.

Mendel then crossbred the offspring of the first generation. The resulting second-generation offspring had both the dominant and the recessive traits of their grandparents; see Fig. 12.2(a) and 12.2(b) on page 678. What's more, these traits always appeared in approximately a 3 to 1 ratio of dominant to recessive.

The effect of genetic inheritance is dramatically demonstrated by the occurrence of hemophilia in some of the royal families of Europe. Great Britain's Queen Victoria (1819– 1901) was the initial carrier. The disease was subsequently introduced into the royal lines of Prussia, Russia, and Spain through the marriages of her children.

Hemophilia, a recessive sex-linked disease, keeps blood from clotting. As a result, even a minor bruise or cut can be dangerous. Females have a second gene that enables the blood to clot, which blocks the effects of the recessive carrier gene; males do not. So even though both males and females may be carriers, the disease afflicts only males.

In humans, genes are located on 23 pairs of *chromosomes*. Each parent contributes one member of each pair to a child. The gene that affects blood clotting is carried on the *x* chromosome. Females have two *x* chromosomes; males have one *x* chromosome and one *y* chromosome. Thus, on the diagram above, *xx* represents a female and *xy* represents a male. A female with the defective gene, symbolized by , will be a carrier, whereas a male with the defective gene will have hemophilia.

First-generation offspring

Yellow (not pure)   Yellow (not pure)

Round (not pure)   Round (not pure)

Second-generation offspring

Yellow or green

Round or wrinkled

Second-generation offspring – *approximately 3 yellow to every 1 green*

Second-generation offspring – *approximately 3 round to every 1 wrinkled*

(a)

(b)

Figure 12.2

Table 12.1 lists some of the actual results of Mendel's experiments with pea plants. Note that the ratio of dominant trait to recessive trait in the second-generation offspring is about 3 to 1 for each experiment. The empirical probability of the dominant trait has also been calculated. How would you find the empirical probability of the recessive trait?

Table 12.1 Second-Generation Offspring

Dominant Trait	Number with Dominant Trait	Recessive Trait	Number with Recessive Trait	Ratio of Dominant to Recessive	P (Dominant Trait)
Yellow seeds	6022	Green seeds	2001	3.01 to 1	$\frac{6022}{8023} \approx 0.75$
Round seeds	5474	Wrinkled seeds	1850	2.96 to 1	$\frac{5474}{7324} \approx 0.75$

From his work, Mendel concluded that the sex cells (now called gametes) of the pure yellow (dominant) pea plant carried some factor that caused the offspring to be yellow and that the gametes of the green variety had a variant factor that "induced the development of green plants." In 1909, Danish geneticist W. Johannsen called these factors "genes." Mendel's work led to the understanding that each pea plant contains two genes for color, one that comes from the mother and the other from the father. If the two genes are alike—for instance, both for yellow plants or both for green plants—the plant will be that color. If the genes for color are different, the plant will grow the color of the dominant gene. Thus, if one parent contributes a gene for the plant to be yellow (dominant) and the other parent contributes a gene for the plant to be green (recessive), the plant will be yellow.

The Law of Large Numbers

Most of us accept that if a "fair coin" is tossed many, many times, it will land heads up approximately half of the time. Intuitively, we can guess that the probability that a fair coin will land heads up is $\frac{1}{2}$. Does that mean that if a coin is tossed twice, it will land heads up exactly once? If a fair coin is tossed 10 times, will there necessarily be five heads? The answer is clearly no. What, then, does it mean when we state that the

"The laws of probability, so true in general, so fallacious in particular."

Edward Gibbon, 1796

probability that a fair coin will land heads up is $\frac{1}{2}$? To answer this question, let's examine Table 12.2, which shows what may occur when a fair coin is tossed a given number of times.

Table 12.2

Number of Tosses	Expected Number of Heads	Actual Number of Heads Observed	Relative Frequency of Heads
10	5	4	$\frac{4}{10} = 0.4$
100	50	45	$\frac{45}{100} = 0.45$
1000	500	546	$\frac{546}{1000} = 0.546$
10,000	5000	4852	$\frac{4852}{10,000} = 0.4852$
100,000	50,000	49,770	$\frac{49,770}{100,000} = 0.49770$

The far right column of Table 12.2, the relative frequency of heads, is a ratio of the number of heads observed to the total number of tosses of the coin. The relative frequency is the empirical probability, as defined earlier. Note that as the number of tosses increases, the relative frequency of heads gets closer and closer to $\frac{1}{2}$, or 0.5, which is what we expect.

The nature of probability is summarized by the law of large numbers.

Definition: Law of Large Numbers

The **law of large numbers** states that probability statements apply in practice to a large number of trials, not to a single trial. It is the relative frequency over the long run that is accurately predictable, not individual events or precise totals.

What does it mean to say that the probability of rolling a 2 on a die is $\frac{1}{6}$? It means that over the long run, on the average, one of every six rolls will result in a 2.

SECTION 12.1 Exercises

Warm Up Exercises

In Exercises 1–6, fill in the blank with an appropriate word, phrase, or symbol(s).

1. A controlled operation that yields a set of results is called a(n) _____. Experiment

2. The possible results of an experiment are called its _____. Outcomes

3. A subcollection of the outcomes of an experiment is called a(n) _____. Event

4. Probability is classified as either theoretical probability or _____ probability. Empirical

5. Probability determined by the relative frequency of occurrence of an event, or actual observations of an experiment is called _____ probability. Empirical

6. Probability determined through a study of the possible outcomes that can occur for a given experiment is called _____ probability. Theoretical

Practice the Skills

7. *Flip a Coin* Flip a coin 50 times and record the results. Determine the empirical probability of flipping

a) a head. Answers will vary.   **b)** a tail. Answers will vary.

c) Does the probability of flipping a head appear to be the same as flipping a tail? Answers will vary.

8. *Pair of Dice* Roll a pair of dice 60 times and record the sums. Determine the empirical probability of rolling a sum of

a) 2. Answers will vary.   **b)** 7. Answers will vary.

c) Does the probability of rolling a sum of 2 appear to be the same as the probability of rolling a sum of 7? Answers will vary.

9. *Roll a Die* Roll a die 50 times and record the results. Determine the empirical probability of rolling

a) a 1. Answers will vary.   **b)** a 4. Answers will vary.

c) Does the probability of rolling a 1 appear to be the same as the probability of rolling a 4? Explain. Answers will vary.

10. *Two Coins* Flip two coins 50 times and record the number of times exactly one head was obtained. Determine the empirical probability of flipping exactly one head. Answers will vary.

Problem Solving

11. *Boat Rentals* The last 30 boat rentals at Green Lakes Boat Rentals were 14 sunfish, 10 kayaks, and 6 rowboats. Use this information to determine the empirical probability that the next boat rental is a

a) sunfish. $\frac{7}{15}$ **b)** kayak. $\frac{1}{3}$ **c)** rowboat. $\frac{1}{5}$

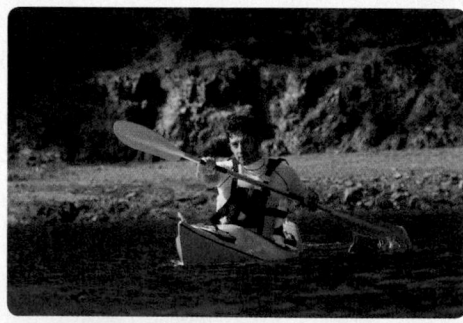

12. *Music Purchases* At the Virgin Music store in Times Square, 60 people entering the store were selected at random and were asked to choose their favorite type of music. Of the 60, 12 chose rock, 16 chose country, 8 chose classical, and 24 chose something other than rock, country, or classical. Determine the empirical probability that the next person entering the store favors

a) rock music. $\frac{1}{5}$ **b)** country music. $\frac{4}{15}$

c) something other than rock, country, or classical music. $\frac{2}{5}$

13. *Veterinarian* In a given week, a veterinarian treated the following animals.

Animal	Number Treated
Dog	45
Cat	40
Bird	15
Rabbit	5

Determine the empirical probability that the next animal she treats is

a) a dog. $\frac{3}{7}$ **b)** a cat. $\frac{8}{21}$ **c)** a rabbit. $\frac{1}{21}$

14. *Prader–Willi Syndrome* In a sample of 50,000 first-born babies, 5 were found to have Prader–Willi syndrome. Find the empirical probability that a family's first child will be born with this syndrome. $\frac{1}{10,000}$ or 0.0001

15. *Studying Abroad* The table below shows the 10 most popular destinations for U.S. college students studying abroad for the 2008–2009 school year.

Destination	Number of Students
United Kingdom	31,342
Italy	27,362
Spain	24,169
France	16,910
China	13,674
Australia	11,140
Germany	8330
Mexico	7320
Ireland	6858
Costa Rica	6363
Total	153,468

Source: *Institute of International Education*

If a student were selected at random from those who studied abroad in 2008–2009 at one of the destinations in the table, determine the empirical probability that the student studied in

a) China.*   b) Italy.*   c) Australia.*

16. *Travel Web Sites* The following table shows the number of visitors to the five most frequently visited travel Web sites in October 2010.

Web Site	Number of Visitors
Trip Advisor	24,000,000
Yahoo! Travel	23,250,000
Expedia	23,000,000
Travelocity	16,000,000
Priceline	15,000,000
Total	101,250,000

Source: ebizmba.com

Assuming this trend continues, if a person chooses to visit only one of the listed Web sites, determine the empirical probability the person will visit

a) Priceline.*   b) Expedia.*   c) Trip Advisor.*

17. *Top-Selling Video Games* The following table shows the number of video games sold worldwide for the five highest-selling video games in 2010.

▲ *Wii Fit Plus*

Title	Units Sold
Call of Duty: Black Ops	18,880,000
Wii Sports	16,600,000
Super Mario Bros.Wii	11,310,000
Wii Sports Resort	11,290,000
Wii Fit Plus	8,870,000
Total	66,950,000

Source: vgchartz.com

Assuming this trend continues, if a person chooses to purchase a video game, determine the empirical probability that the person will purchase

a) Wii Sports.*   b) Wii Fit Plus.*

c) Call of Duty: Black Ops.*

18. *Grade Distribution* Mr. Doole's grade distribution over the past 3 years for a course in college algebra is shown in the chart below.

Grade	Number
A	43
B	182
C	260
D	90
F	62
I	8

If Sue Gilligan plans to take college algebra with Mr. Doole, determine the empirical probability that she receives a grade of

a) A. $\frac{43}{645}$ b) C. $\frac{52}{129}$ c) D or higher. $\frac{115}{129}$

19. *Election* In an election for student council president at Russell Sage College, 80 students were polled and asked for whom they planned to vote. The table shows the results of the poll.

Candidate	Votes
Allison	22
Emily	18
Kimberly	20
Johanna	14
Other	6

If one student from Russell Sage College is selected at random, determine the empirical probability that the person planned to vote for

a) Allison. $\frac{11}{40}$ b) Emily. $\frac{9}{40}$

c) Kimberly. $\frac{1}{4}$ d) Johanna. $\frac{7}{40}$

e) Someone other than the four people-listed above. $\frac{3}{40}$

20. *Volunteer Hours* The graph below shows the average number of hours volunteered per week by Americans in 2009.

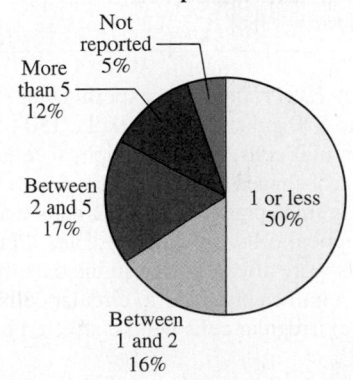

Average Number of Hours Americans Volunteered per Week

Not reported 5%
More than 5 12%
Between 2 and 5 17%
1 or less 50%
Between 1 and 2 16%

Source: CNCS (www.serve.gov)

*See Instructor Answer Appendix

If one American who participated in volunteer work is selected at random, determine the empirical probability the person volunteered

a) between 1 and 2 hours per week. 0.16

b) more than 5 hours per week. 0.12

c) between 2 and 5 hours per week. 0.17

21. *Hitting a Bull's-Eye* The pattern of hits shown on the target resulted from a marksman firing 20 rounds. For a single shot,

a) determine the empirical probability that the marksman hits the 50-point bull's-eye (the center of the target).*

b) determine the empirical probability that the marksman does not hit the bull's-eye. $\frac{14}{20} = \frac{7}{10}$

c) determine the empirical probability that the marksman scores at least 20 points. $\frac{14}{20} = \frac{7}{10}$

d) determine the empirical probability that the marksman does not score any points (the area outside the large circle).*

22. *Rock Toss* Jim Handy finds an irregularly shaped five-sided rock. He labels each side and tosses the rock 100 times. The results of his tosses are shown in the table. Determine the empirical probability that the rock will land on side 4 if tossed again. $\frac{13}{100}$

Side	1	2	3	4	5
Frequency	32	18	15	13	22

23. *Cell Biology Experiment* An experimental serum was injected into 500 guinea pigs. Initially, 150 of the guinea pigs had circular cells, 250 had elliptical cells, and 100 had irregularly shaped cells. After the serum was injected, none of the guinea pigs with circular cells were affected, 50 with elliptical cells were affected, and all those with irregular cells were affected. Determine the empirical probability that a guinea pig with (a) circular cells, (b) elliptical cells, and (c) irregular cells will be affected by injection of the serum.*

24. *Gender* In a large lecture hall there are 325 students of which 160 are male and 165 are female. If one student is

selected at random, determine the empirical probability the individual selected is

a) male. ≈ 0.49   **b)** female. ≈ 0.51

25. *Mendel's Experiment* In one of his experiments (see pages 677–678), Mendel crossbred nonpure purple flower pea plants. These purple pea plants had two traits for flowers, purple (dominant) and white (recessive). The result of this crossbreeding was 705 second-generation plants with purple flowers and 224 second-generation plants with white flowers. Determine the empirical probability of a second-generation plant having

a) white flowers.*   **b)** purple flowers.*

26. *Second-Generation Offspring* In another experiment, Mendel crossbred nonpure tall pea plants. As a result, the second-generation offspring were 787 tall plants and 277 short plants. Determine the empirical probability of a second-generation plant being

a) tall.*   **b)** short.*

Concept/Writing Exercises

27. The theoretical probability of a coin landing heads up is $\frac{1}{2}$. Does this probability mean that if a coin is flipped two times, one flip will land heads up? If not, what does it mean?*

28. To determine premiums, life insurance companies must compute the probable date of death. On the basis of a great deal of research, Mr. Duncan, age 36, is expected to live another 43.21 years. Does this determination mean that Mr. Duncan will live until he is 79.21 years old? If not, what does it mean? No, it means that the average person with traits similar to Mr. Duncan's will live another 43.21 years.

29. **a)** Explain how you would find the empirical probability of rolling a 5 on a die. Roll a die many times and then find the relative frequency of 5's to the total number of rolls.

   b) What do you believe is the empirical probability of rolling a 5? Answers will vary.

   c) Determine the empirical probability of rolling a 5 by rolling a die 40 times. Answers will vary.

30. The theoretical probability of rolling a 4 on a die is $\frac{1}{6}$. Does this probability mean that if a die is rolled six times one 4 will appear? If not, what does it mean? No, it means that if a die were rolled many times, about $\frac{1}{6}$ of the outcomes would be 4's.

Challenge Problem/Group Activity

31. **a)** *Design an Experiment* Which do you believe is used more frequently in a magazine or newspaper article, the word *a* or the word *the*? Answers will vary.

*See Instructor Answer Appendix

b) Design an experiment to determine the empirical probabilities (or relative frequencies) of the words *a* and *the* appearing in a magazine or newspaper article.
Answers will vary.

c) Perform the experiment in part (b) and determine the empirical probabilities. Answers will vary.

d) Which word, *a* or *the*, appears to occur more frequently? Answers will vary.

Recreational Mathematics

32. *Cola Preference* Can people selected at random distinguish Coke from Pepsi? Which do they prefer?

a) Design an experiment to determine the empirical probability that a person selected at random can select Coke when given samples of both Coke and Pepsi.
Answers will vary.

b) Perform the experiment in part (a) and determine the empirical probability. Answers will vary.

c) Determine the empirical probability that a person selected at random will prefer Coke over Pepsi.
Answers will vary.

Internet/Research Activities

33. Write a paper on how insurance companies use empirical probabilities in determining insurance premiums. An insurance agent may be able to direct you to a source of information.

34. Write a paper on how Gregor Mendel's use of empirical probability led to the development of the science of genetics. You may want to check with a biology professor to determine references to use.

SECTION 12.2 Theoretical Probability

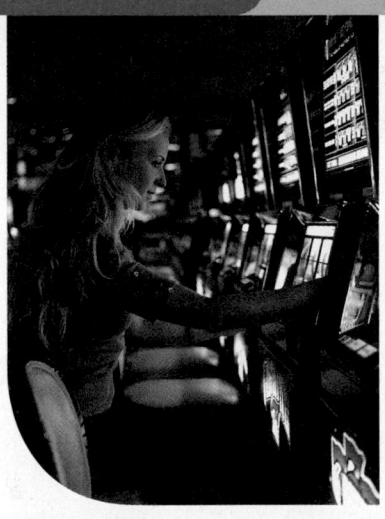

▲ *We can use probability to determine the likelihood of winning games of chance.*

Should you spend the money for a stamp to return a sweepstakes ticket? What are your chances of winning a lottery? If you go to a carnival, bazaar, or casino, which games provide the greatest chance of winning? These and similar questions can be answered once you have an understanding of theoretical probability that we will discuss in this section.

Why **This is Important** Understanding how to calculate theoretical probability is essential to many real-life applications, including games of chance. Theoretical probability is also necessary to determine the odds of an event happening, and the expected gain or loss of business ventures.

---

*R*ecall from Section 12.1 that the results of an experiment are called outcomes. When you roll a die and observe the number of points that face up, the possible outcomes are 1, 2, 3, 4, 5, and 6. It is equally likely that you will roll any one of the possible numbers.

Definition: Equally Likely Outcomes
If each outcome of an experiment has the same chance of occurring as any other outcome, we say that the outcomes are **equally likely outcomes**.

Can you think of a second set of equally likely outcomes when a die is rolled? An odd number is as likely to be rolled as an even number. Therefore, odd and even numbers are another set of equally likely outcomes.

If an event *E* has *equally likely outcomes*, the theoretical probability of event *E*, symbolized by $P(E)$, may be calculated with the following formula.

Probability
The **theoretical probability** of an event can be calculated using the following formula.

$$P(E) = \frac{\text{number of outcomes favorable to } E}{\text{total number of possible outcomes}}$$

*In the remainder of this chapter, the word **probability** will refer to **theoretical probability**.*

> **TIMELY TIP**
> To be able to do the problems in this section and the remainder of the chapter, you must have a thorough understanding of fractions. If you have forgotten how to work with fractions, we strongly suggest that you review Section 5.3 before beginning this section.

Example 1 illustrates how to use this formula.

Example 1 *Determining Probabilities*

A die is rolled. Determine the probability of rolling

a) a 5.   b) an even number.   c) a number greater than 3.

d) a 7.   e) a number less than 7.

Solution

a) There are six possible equally likely outcomes: 1, 2, 3, 4, 5, and 6. The event of rolling a 5 can occur in only one way.

$$P(5) = \frac{\text{number of outcomes that will result in a 5}}{\text{total number of possible outcomes}} = \frac{1}{6}$$

b) The event of rolling an even number can occur in three ways: 2, 4, or 6.

$$P(\text{even number}) = \frac{\text{number of outcomes that result in an even number}}{\text{total number of possible outcomes}}$$
$$= \frac{3}{6} = \frac{1}{2}$$

c) Three numbers are greater than 3, namely, 4, 5 and 6.

$$P(\text{number greater than 3}) = \frac{3}{6} = \frac{1}{2}$$

d) No outcomes will result in a 7. Thus, the event cannot occur and the probability is 0.

$$P(7) = \frac{0}{6} = 0$$

e) All the outcomes 1 through 6 are less than 7. Thus, the event must occur and the probability is 1.

$$P(\text{number less than 7}) = \frac{6}{6} = 1$$

Four important facts about probability follow.

Important Probability Facts

1. The probability of an event that cannot occur is 0.
2. The probability of an event that must occur is 1.
3. Every probability is a number between 0 and 1 inclusive; that is, $0 \leq P(E) \leq 1$.
4. The sum of the probabilities of all possible outcomes of an experiment is 1.

Example 2 *Choosing One Bird from a List*

The names of 15 birds and their food preferences are listed in Table 12.3 on page 685. Each of the 15 birds' names is listed on a slip of paper, and the 15 slips are placed in a bag. One slip is to be selected at random from the bag. Determine the probability that the slip contains the name of

a) a finch (any type listed).

b) a bird that has a high attractiveness to cracked corn.

c) a bird that has a low attractiveness to peanut kernels, *and* a low attractiveness to cracked corn, *and* a high attractiveness to black-striped sunflower seeds.

d) a bird that has a high attractiveness to either peanut kernels *or* cracked corn (or both).

Table 12.3 Birds and Their Food Preferences

Bird	Peanut Kernels	Cracked Corn	Black-Striped Sunflower Seeds
American goldfinch	L	L	H
Blue jay	H	M	H
Chickadee	M	L	H
Common grackle	M	H	H
Evening grosbeak	L	L	H
House finch	M	L	H
House sparrow	L	M	M
Mourning dove	L	M	M
Northern cardinal	L	L	H
Purple finch	L	L	H
Scrub jay	H	L	H
Song sparrow	L	L	M
Tufted titmouse	H	L	H
White-crowned sparrow	H	M	H
White-throated sparrow	H	H	H

Source: *How to Attract Birds* (Ortho Books)

Note: H = high attractiveness; M = medium attractiveness; L = low attractiveness.

Solution

a) Three of the 15 birds listed are finches (American goldfinch, house finch, and purple finch).

$$P\text{(finch)} = \frac{3}{15} = \frac{1}{5}$$

b) Two of the 15 birds listed have a high attractiveness to cracked corn (common grackle and white-throated sparrow).

$$P\text{(high attractiveness to cracked corn)} = \frac{2}{15}$$

c) Reading across the rows reveals that 4 birds have a low attractiveness to peanut kernels, a low attractiveness to cracked corn, and a high attractiveness to black-striped sunflower seeds (American goldfinch, evening grosbeak, northern cardinal, and purple finch).

$$P\left(\begin{array}{c}\text{low attractiveness to peanuts, and low to}\\\text{corn, and high to black-striped sunflower sweeds}\end{array}\right) = \frac{4}{15}$$

d) Six birds have a high attractiveness to either peanut kernels or to cracked corn (or both). They are the blue jay, common grackle, scrub jay, tufted titmouse, white-crowned sparrow, and white-throated sparrow.

$$P\text{(high attractiveness to peanut kernels or cracked corn)} = \frac{6}{15} = \frac{2}{5}$$

In any experiment, an event must either occur or not occur. *The sum of the probability that an event will occur and the probability that it will not occur is 1.* Thus, for any event *A* we conclude that

> ### The Sum of the Probabilities Equals 1
>
> $$P(A) + P(\text{not } A) = 1$$
>
> or
>
> $$P(\text{not } A) = 1 - P(A)$$

For example, if the probability that event *A* will occur is $\frac{5}{12}$, the probability that event *A* will not occur is $1 - \frac{5}{12}$, or $\frac{7}{12}$. Similarly, if the probability that event *A* will not occur is 0.3, the probability that event *A* will occur is $1 - 0.3 = 0.7$, or $\frac{7}{10}$. We make use of this concept in Example 3.

Example 3 *Selecting One Card from a Deck*

A standard deck of 52 playing cards is shown in Fig. 12.3. The deck consists of four suits: hearts, clubs, diamonds, and spades. Each suit has 13 cards, including numbered cards ace (1) through 10 and three picture (or face) cards, the jack, the queen, and the king. Hearts and diamonds are red cards; clubs and spades are black cards. There are 12 picture cards, consisting of 4 jacks, 4 queens, and 4 kings. One card is to be selected at random from the deck of cards. Determine the probability that the card selected is

a) a 7.

b) not a 7.

c) a diamond.

d) a jack *or* queen *or* king (a picture card).

e) a heart *and* a spade.

f) a card greater than 6 *and* less than 9.

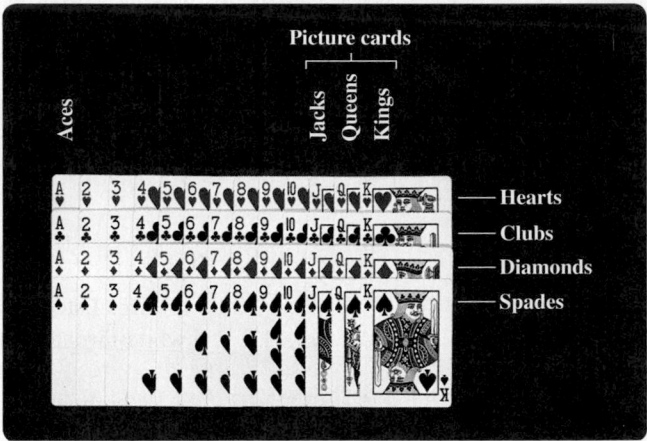

Figure 12.3

Solution

a) There are four 7's in a deck of 52 cards.

$$P(7) = \frac{4}{52} = \frac{1}{13}$$

b) $P(\text{not a } 7) = 1 - P(7) = 1 - \frac{1}{13} = \frac{12}{13}$

This probability could also have been found by noting that there are 48 cards that are not 7's in a deck of 52 cards.

$$P(\text{not a } 7) = \frac{48}{52} = \frac{12}{13}$$

c) There are 13 diamonds in the deck.

$$P(\text{diamond}) = \frac{13}{52} = \frac{1}{4}$$

d) There are 4 jacks, 4 queens, and 4 kings, or a total of 12 picture cards.

$$P(\text{jack } or \text{ queen } or \text{ king}) = \frac{12}{52} = \frac{3}{13}$$

e) The word *and* means that *both* events must occur. Since it is not possible to select one card that is both a heart and a spade the probability is 0.

$$P(\text{heart and spade}) = \frac{0}{52} = 0$$

f) The cards that are both greater than 6 and less than 9 are 7's and 8's. There are four 7's and four 8's, or a total of eight cards.

$$P(\text{greater than 6 } and \text{ less than 9}) = \frac{8}{52} = \frac{2}{13}$$ ∎

SECTION 12.2 *Exercises*

Warm Up Exercises

In Exercises 1–10, fill in the blank with an appropriate word, phrase, or symbol(s).

1. If each outcome of an experiment has the same chance of occurring as any other outcome, the outcomes are _____ likely outcomes. Equally

2. The probability of an event that cannot occur is _____. 0

3. The probability of an event that must occur is _____. 1

4. Every probability is a number between _____ and _____ inclusive. 0, 1

5. The sum of the probabilities of all possible outcomes of an experiment is _____. 1

6. For any event A, $P(A) + P(\text{not } A) =$ _____. 1

7. If the probability that an event occurs is $\frac{3}{7}$, the probability that the event does not occur is _____. $\frac{4}{7}$

8. If the probability that an event occurs is 0.2, the probability that the event does not occur is _____. 0.8

9. If the probability that an event does not occur is 0.9, the probability that the event occurs is _____. 0.1

10. If the probability that an event does not occur is $\frac{4}{9}$, the probability that the event occurs is _____. $\frac{5}{9}$

Practice the Skills

11. **Multiple-Choice Test** A multiple-choice test has five possible choices for each question.

   a) If you randomly select one of the choices, what is the probability that you select the correct answer for one particular question? $\frac{1}{5}$

   b) If you eliminate one of the five possible choices and guess from the remaining choices, what is the probability that you select the correct answer to that question? $\frac{1}{4}$

12. **Remote Control** A TV remote control has keys for channels 0 through 9. If you select one key at random,

   a) what is the probability that you press channel 6? $\frac{1}{10}$

   b) what is the probability that you press a key for an even number? $\frac{1}{2}$

   c) what is the probability that you press a key for a number less than 7? $\frac{7}{10}$

13. **Raffle** In a raffle where one number is chosen, determine the probability that you would win if you have a choice of 40 numbers to choose from. $\frac{1}{40}$

14. **Raffle** In a raffle where one number is chosen, determine the probability that you would win if you have a choice of 52 numbers to choose from. $\frac{1}{52}$

Select a Card In Exercises 15–24, one card is selected at random from a deck of cards. Determine the probability that the card selected is

15. a 5. $\frac{1}{13}$

16. a 5 or a 10. $\frac{2}{13}$

17. not a 5. $\frac{12}{13}$

18. the five of diamonds. $\frac{1}{52}$

19. a black card. $\frac{1}{2}$

20. a diamond. $\frac{1}{4}$

21. a red card or a black card. 1

22. a red card and a black card. 0

23. a card greater than 3 and less than 8. $\frac{4}{13}$

24. a king and a club. $\frac{1}{52}$

Spin the Spinner In Exercises 25–28, assume that the spinner cannot land on a line. Determine the probability that the spinner lands on (a) red, (b) green, (c) yellow, (d) blue.

25.

26.

27.

28.

Picnic In Exercises 29–32, a cooler at a picnic contains 100 cans of soda covered by ice. There are 30 cans of cola, 40 cans of orange soda, 10 cans of ginger ale, and 20 cans of root beer. The cans are all the same size and shape. If one can is selected at random from the cooler, determine the probability that the soda selected is

29. root beer. $\frac{1}{5}$

30. cola or orange soda. $\frac{7}{10}$

31. cola, root beer, or orange soda. $\frac{9}{10}$

32. ginger ale. $\frac{1}{10}$

Wheel of Fortune In Exercises 33–36, use the small replica of the Wheel of Fortune.

If the wheel is spun at random, determine the probability that the indicated sector will stop under the pointer.

33. $600 $\frac{1}{12}$

34. A number greater than $700 $\frac{1}{6}$

35. Lose a turn or Bankrupt $\frac{1}{6}$

36. $2500 or Surprise $\frac{1}{6}$

Basketballs In Exercises 37–40, 30 basketballs, including 15 Spalding, 10 Wilson, and 5 other brand-name balls, are on a basketball court. Barry Wood closes his eyes and arbitrarily picks up a ball from the court. Determine the probability that the ball selected is

37. a Spalding. $\frac{1}{2}$

38. a Wilson. $\frac{1}{3}$

39. not a Wilson. $\frac{2}{3}$

40. a Wilson or a Spalding. $\frac{5}{6}$

Traffic Light In Exercises 41–44, a traffic light is red for 25 sec, yellow for 5 sec, and green for 55 sec. What is the probability that when you reach the light,

41. the light is green. $\frac{11}{17}$

42. the light is yellow. $\frac{1}{17}$

43. the light is not red. $\frac{12}{17}$

44. the light is not green. $\frac{6}{17}$

TALLAHASSEE In Exercises 45–50, each individual letter of the word *TALLAHASSEE* is placed on a piece of paper and all 11 pieces of paper are placed in a hat. If one letter is selected at random from the hat, determine the probability that

45. the letter *S* is selected. $\frac{2}{11}$

46. the letter *S* is not selected. $\frac{9}{11}$

47. a consonant is selected. $\frac{6}{11}$

48. the letter *T* or *E* is selected. $\frac{3}{11}$

49. the letter *W* is selected. 0

50. the letter *V* is not selected. 1

National Parks In Exercises 51–54, use the list below which shows the 10 U.S. National Parks with the most visitors in 2010.

Park	Location	Visits
Great Smokey Mountains National Park	North Carolina/ Tennessee	9,463,538
Grand Canyon National Park	Arizona	4,388,386
Yosemite National Park	California	3,901,408
Yellowstone National Park	Wyoming	3,640,185
Rocky Mountain National Park	Colorado	2,955,821
Olympic National Park	Washington	2,844,563
Grand Teton National Park	Wyoming	2,669,374
Zion National Park	Utah	2,665,972
Acadia National Park	Maine	2,504,208
Cuyahoga Valley National Park	Ohio	2,492,670

Source: *National Park Service*

▲ *Grand Teton National Park, Jackson, WY*

If one of the parks in the list is selected at random, determine the probability the park

51. is located in California. $\frac{1}{10}$

52. is located in Wyoming. $\frac{1}{5}$

53. had more than 4 million visitors. $\frac{1}{5}$

54. had fewer than 3 million visitors. $\frac{3}{5}$

Dart Board In Exercises 55–58, a dart is thrown randomly and sticks on the circular dart board with 26 partitions, as shown.

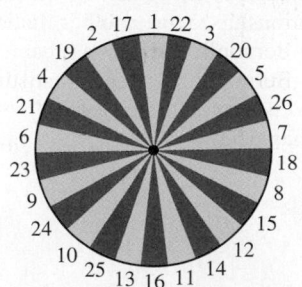

Assuming the dart cannot land on the black area or on a border between colors, determine the probability that the dart lands on

55. the area marked 15. $\frac{1}{26}$ **56.** an orange area. $\frac{1}{2}$

57. an area marked with a number greater than or equal to 22. $\frac{5}{26}$

58. an area marked with a number greater than 6 and less than or equal to 9. $\frac{3}{26}$

Car Dealership In Exercises 59–64, refer to the following table, which shows the type and manufacturer of vehicles at a specific car dealership.

	General Motors	Toyota	Total
Car	55	30	85
SUV	28	17	45
Total	83	47	130

If one person selects a vehicle at random from the dealership, determine the probability that the person selects

59. a car. $\frac{17}{26}$ **60.** an SUV. $\frac{9}{26}$

61. a vehicle manufactured by General Motors. $\frac{83}{130}$

62. a vehicle manufactured by Toyota. $\frac{47}{130}$

63. a car manufactured by General Motors. $\frac{11}{26}$

64. an SUV manufactured by General Motors. $\frac{14}{65}$

Stocking Taco Sauce In Exercises 65–70, refer to the following table, which contains information about a shopping cart full of jars of taco sauce that must be stocked on a shelf. Assume all jars are the same size and shape.

Brand	Mild	Medium	Hot	Total
Taco Bell	5	8	4	17
Ortega	2	5	3	10
Old El Paso	3	6	2	11
Other	1	2	1	4
Total	11	21	10	42

If a stock clerk selects one jar at random to place on the shelf, determine the probability he selects a jar of

65. Ortega. $\frac{5}{21}$ **66.** Old El Paso. $\frac{11}{42}$

67. a mild taco sauce. $\frac{11}{42}$ **68.** a hot taco sauce. $\frac{5}{21}$

69. Taco Bell medium taco sauce. $\frac{4}{21}$

70. Old El Paso hot taco sauce. $\frac{1}{21}$

Bean Bag Toss *In Exercises 71–76, a bean bag is randomly thrown onto the square table top shown below and does not touch a line.*

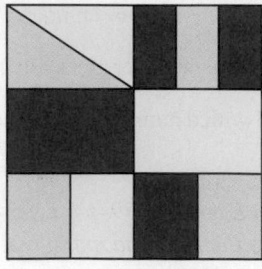

Determine the probability that the bean bag lands on

71. a red area. $\frac{13}{36}$ **72.** a green area. $\frac{11}{36}$

73. a yellow area. $\frac{1}{3}$ **74.** a red or green area. $\frac{2}{3}$

75. a yellow or green area. $\frac{23}{36}$ **76.** a red or yellow area. $\frac{25}{36}$

Challenge Problems/Group Activities

Before working Exercises 77 and 78, reread the material on genetics in Section 12.1.

77. ***Genetics*** Cystic fibrosis is an inherited disease that occurs in about 1 in every 2500 Caucasian births in North America and in about 1 in every 250,000 non-Caucasian births in North America. Let's denote the cystic fibrosis gene as *c* and a disease-free gene as *C*. Since the disease-free gene is dominant, only a person with *cc* genes will have the disease. A person who has *Cc* genes is a carrier of cystic fibrosis but does not actually have the disease. If one parent has *CC* genes and the other parent has *cc* genes, determine the probability that

   a) an offspring will inherit cystic fibrosis, that is, *cc* genes. 0

   b) an offspring will be a carrier of cystic fibrosis but not contract the disease. 1

78. ***Genetics*** Sickle-cell anemia is an inherited disease that occurs in about 1 in every 500 African-American births and about 1 in every 160,000 non–African-American births. Unlike cystic fibrosis, in which the cystic fibrosis gene is recessive, sickle-cell anemia is *codominant*. In other words, a person inheriting two sickle-cell genes will have sickle-cell anemia, whereas a person inheriting only one of the sickle-cell genes will have a mild version of sickle-cell anemia, called *sickle-cell trait*. Let's call the disease-free genes s_1 and the sickle cell gene s_2. If both parents have $s_1 s_2$ genes, determine the probability that

   a) an offspring will have sickle-cell anemia. $\frac{1}{4}$

   b) an offspring will have the sickle-cell trait. $\frac{1}{2}$

   c) an offspring will have neither sickle-cell anemia nor the sickle-cell trait. $\frac{1}{4}$

In Exercises 79 and 80, the solutions involve material that we will discuss in later sections of the chapter. Try to solve them before reading ahead.

79. ***Marbles*** A bottle contains two red and two green marbles, and a second bottle also contains two red and two green marbles. If you select one marble at random from each bottle, determine the probability (to be discussed in Section 12.6) that you obtain

   a) two red marbles. $\frac{1}{4}$ **b)** two green marbles. $\frac{1}{4}$

   c) a red marble from the first bottle and a green marble from the second bottle. $\frac{1}{4}$

80. ***Birds*** Consider Table 12.3 on page 685. Suppose you are told that one bird's name was selected at random from the birds listed and the bird selected has a low attractiveness to peanut kernels. Determine the probability (to be discussed in Section 12.7) that

   a) the bird is a sparrow. $\frac{2}{7}$

   b) the bird has a high attractiveness to cracked corn. 0

   c) the bird has a high attractiveness to black-striped sunflower seeds. $\frac{4}{7}$

Recreational Mathematics

81. ***Dice*** On a die, the sum of the dots on the opposite faces is seven. Two six-sided dice are placed together on top of one another, on a table, as shown in the figure below. The top and bottom faces of the bottom die and the bottom face of the top die cannot be seen. If you walk around the table, what is the sum of all the dots on all the visible faces of the dice? 29 dots

Internet/Research Activity

82. On page 675, we briefly discuss Jacob Bernoulli. The Bernoulli family produced several prominent mathematicians, including Jacob I, Johann I, and Daniel. Write a paper on the Bernoulli family, indicating some of the accomplishments of each of the three Bernoullis named and their relationship to one another. Indicate which Bernoulli the Bernoulli numbers are named after, which Bernoulli the Bernoulli theorem in statistics is named after, and which Bernoulli the Bernoulli theorem of fluid dynamics is named after.

Odds

The odds against winning the Fabulous Fortune lottery are about 2.6 million to 1. The odds against being audited by the IRS this year are about 47 to 1. The odds against the San Francisco Giants winning the World Series this year may be 6 to 1. We see the word *odds* daily in newspapers and magazines and often use it ourselves. Yet there is widespread misunderstanding of its meaning. In this section, we will explain the meaning of odds. We will also discuss how to determine odds against an event and how to determine odds in favor of an event.

▲ *What are the odds against the San Francisco Giants winning the World Series this year?*

Why **This is Important** Many real-life applications involve odds, including sporting events and games of chance.

Odds Against an Event

The odds given at horse races, at craps, and at all gambling games in Las Vegas and other casinos throughout the world are always *odds against* unless they are otherwise specified. The *odds against* an event is a ratio of the probability that the event will fail to occur (failure) to the probability that the event will occur (success). Thus, *to find odds you must first know or determine the probability of success and the probability of failure.*

> **Odds Against an Event**
> The following formula may be used to determine the odds against an event.
> $$\text{Odds against event} = \frac{P(\text{event fails to occur})}{P(\text{event occurs})} = \frac{P(\text{failure})}{P(\text{success})}$$

Example 1 *Rolling a 4*

Determine the odds against rolling a 4 on one roll of a die.

Solution Before we can determine the odds, we must first determine the probability of rolling a 4 (success) and the probability of not rolling a 4 (failure). When a die is rolled there are six possible outcomes: 1, 2, 3, 4, 5, and 6.

$$P(\text{rolling a 4}) = \frac{1}{6} \qquad P(\text{failure to roll a 4}) = \frac{5}{6}$$

Now that we know the probabilities of success and failure, we can determine the odds against rolling a 4.

$$\text{Odds against rolling a 4} = \frac{P(\text{failure to roll a 4})}{P(\text{rolling a 4})}$$

$$= \frac{\dfrac{5}{6}}{\dfrac{1}{6}} = \frac{5}{\cancel{6}} \cdot \frac{\cancel{6}^{1}}{1} = \frac{5}{1}$$

The ratio $\frac{5}{1}$ is commonly written as 5:1 and is read "5 to 1." Thus, the odds against rolling a 4 are 5 to 1.

TIMELY TIP
The denominators of the probabilities in an odds problem will always divide out, as was shown in Example 1.

In Example 1, we considered the possible outcomes of the die: 1, 2, 3, 4, 5, 6. Over the long run, one of every six rolls will result in a 4, and five of every six rolls will result in a number other than 4. Therefore, if a person is gambling, for each dollar bet in favor of the rolling of a 4, $5 should be bet against the rolling of a 4 if the person is to break even. The person betting in favor of the rolling of a 4 will either lose $1 (if a number other than a 4 is rolled) or win $5 (if a 4 is rolled). The person betting against the rolling of a 4 will either win $1 (if a number other than a 4 is rolled) or lose $5 (if a 4 is rolled). If this game is played for a long enough period, each player theoretically will break even.

Example 2 involves a circle graph that contains percents; see Fig. 12.4. Before we discuss Example 2, let us briefly discuss percents. Recall that probabilities are numbers between 0 and 1, inclusive. We can change a percent between 0% and 100% to a probability by writing the percent as a fraction or a decimal number. In Fig. 12.4, we see 36% in one of the sectors (or areas) of the circle. To change 36% to a probability, we can write $\frac{36}{100}$ or 0.36. Note that both the fraction and the decimal number are numbers between 0 and 1, inclusive.

Example 2 *Occupations*

The circle graph in Fig. 12.4 shows the percent of U.S. workers employed in professional, service, sales, construction, and production occupations. If one U.S. worker is selected at random, use the graph to determine the odds against the person being employed in a sales occupation.

Occupation of U.S. Workers

Source: *Bureau of Labor Statistics*

Figure 12.4

Solution From the graph, we can determine that 25%, or $\frac{25}{100}$, of U.S. workers are employed in sales occupations. Therefore, the probability that a U.S. worker is employed in a sales occupation is $\frac{25}{100}$. The probability that a U.S. worker is *not* employed in a sales occupation is $1 - \frac{25}{100} = \frac{75}{100}$.

$$\text{Odds against the person being employed in a sales occupation} = \frac{P(\text{person is not employed in a sales occupation})}{P(\text{person is employed in a sales occupation})}$$

$$= \frac{\frac{75}{100}}{\frac{25}{100}} = \frac{75}{100} \cdot \frac{100}{25} = \frac{75}{25} = \frac{3}{1}, \text{ or } 3:1$$

Thus, the odds against the person being employed in a sales occupation are 3:1. ∎

Odds in Favor of an Event

Although odds are generally given against an event, at times they may be given in favor of an event. The *odds in favor of* an event are expressed as a ratio of the probability that the event will occur to the probability that the event will fail to occur.

MATHEMATICS TODAY

Deal or No Deal

A popular television show is the NBC game show *Deal or No Deal*. A contestant chooses a brief-case from 26 briefcases. Inside each briefcase is a card indicating a specific, but unique, amount of money. As each round progresses, the contestant must either stay with the briefcase selected or make a "deal" with the "banker" to accept a cash offer in exchange for whatever dollar amount is in the chosen case. Typically, the banker's offer undervalues the remaining brief-cases, especially at the start of the game. For further information, visit www.nbc.com/Deal_or_No_Deal.

Why **This is Important** Most games of chance depend on concepts from probability.

Odds in Favor of an Event

The following formula may be used to determine the odds in favor of an event.

$$\text{Odds in favor of event} = \frac{P(\text{event occurs})}{P(\text{event fails to occur})} = \frac{P(\text{success})}{P(\text{failure})}$$

If the odds *against* an event are $a:b$, the odds *in favor of* the event are $b:a$.

Example 3 *Smartphones*

The circle graph in Fig. 12.5 shows the U.S. market share for the operating systems used in smartphones, as of December 2010. If an individual who owns a smartphone is selected at random, use the graph to determine

a) the odds against the individual owning a Google phone.

b) the odds in favor of the individual owning a Google phone.

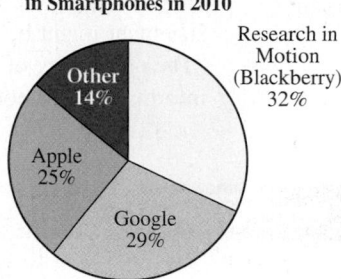

U.S. Market Share of Operating Systems Used in Smartphones in 2010

Source: ComScore

Figure 12.5

Solution

a) The graph shows that 29%, or $\frac{29}{100}$, of individuals who owned a smartphone owned a Google phone. Thus, the probability that an individual owned a Google phone is $\frac{29}{100}$. Therefore, the probability that an individual did not own a Google phone is $1 - \frac{29}{100} = \frac{71}{100}$

$$\text{Odds against an individual owning a Google phone} = \frac{P(\text{an individual did not own a Google phone})}{P(\text{an individual owned a Google phone})}$$

$$= \frac{\frac{71}{100}}{\frac{29}{100}} = \frac{71}{\cancel{100}} \cdot \frac{\overset{1}{\cancel{100}}}{29} = \frac{71}{29} \quad \text{or} \quad 71:29$$

Thus, the odds against the individual owning a Google phone are $71:29$.

b) The odds in favor of the individual owning a Google phone are $29:71$. ∎

Finding Probabilities from Odds

When odds are given, either in favor of or against a particular event, it is possible to determine the probability that the event occurs and the probability that the event does not occur. The denominators of the probabilities are found by adding the numbers in the odds statement. The numerators of the probabilities are the numbers given in the odds statements.

Example 4 *Determining Probabilities from Odds*

The odds against Robin Murphy being admitted to the college of her choice are 9:2. Determine the probability that (a) Robin is admitted and (b) Robin is not admitted.

Solution

a) We have been given odds against and have been asked to find probabilities.

$$\text{Odds against being admitted} = \frac{P(\text{fails to be admitted})}{P(\text{is admitted})}$$

Since the odds statement is 9:2, the denominators of both the probability of success and the probability of failure must be 9 + 2 or 11. To get the odds ratio of 9:2, the probabilities must be $\frac{9}{11}$ and $\frac{2}{11}$. Since odds against is a ratio of failure to success, the $\frac{9}{11}$ and $\frac{2}{11}$ represent the probabilities of failure and success, respectively. Thus, the probability that Robin is admitted (success) is $\frac{2}{11}$.

b) The probability that Robin is not admitted (failure) is $\frac{9}{11}$.   ■

Odds and probability statements are sometimes stated incorrectly. For example, consider the statement, "The odds of being selected to represent the district are 1 in 5." Odds are given using the word *to*, not *in*. Thus, there is a mistake in this statement. The correct statement might be, "The odds of being selected to represent the district are 1 to 5" or "The probability of being selected to represent the district is 1 in 5." Without additional information, it is not possible to tell which statement is the correct interpretation.

SECTION 12.3   *Exercises*

Warm Up Exercises

In Exercises 1–8, fill in the blank with an appropriate word, phrase, or symbol(s).

1. The ratio of the probability that an event will fail to occur to the probability that the event will occur is called the odds _____ an event. Against

2. The ratio of the probability that the event will occur to the probability that the event will fail to occur is called the odds _____ an event. In favor of

3. If the odds in favor of *Just in Time* winning a horse race are 1:3, then the odds against *Just in Time* winning the race are _____. 3:1

4. If the odds against winning at Monopoly are 4:1, then the odds in favor of winning at Monopoly are _____. 1:4

5. If the probability that an event will occur is $\frac{2}{3}$ then the probability that the event will not occur is $\frac{1}{3}$, and the odds in favor of the event occurring are _____. 2:1

6. If the probability that an event will fail to occur is $\frac{1}{4}$ then the probability that the event will occur is $\frac{3}{4}$ and the odds against the event occurring are _____. 1:3

7. If the odds against an event are 1:3, the probability that the event will fail to occur is _____. $\frac{1}{4}$

8. If the odds against an event are a to b, then the probability that the event occurs is _____. $\frac{b}{a+b}$

Practice the Skills/Problem Solving

9. *Dressing Up* Lila Jaquez is going to wear a blue dress and is trying to decide which pair of shoes she should wear with it. In her closet, she has 12 pairs of shoes, 5 of which go well with the dress. If Lila selects one pair of shoes at random, determine

   a) the probability that the shoes go well with the dress. $\frac{5}{12}$

   b) the probability that the shoes do not go well with the dress. $\frac{7}{12}$

   c) the odds against the shoes going well with the dress. 7:5

   d) the odds in favor of the shoes going well with the dress. 5:7

10. *Making a Donation* In her wallet, Anne Kelly has 12 bills. Six are $1 bills, two are $5 bills, three are $10 bills, and one is a $20 bill. She passes a volunteer seeking donations for the Salvation Army and decides to select one bill at random from her wallet and give it to the Salvation Army. Determine

    a) the probability that she selects a $5 bill. $\frac{1}{6}$

    b) the probability that she does not select a $5 bill. $\frac{5}{6}$

    c) the odds in favor of her selecting a $5 bill. 1:5

    d) the odds against her selecting a $5 bill. 5:1

Deal or No Deal In Exercises 11 and 12, consider the TV show Deal or No Deal. (See the Mathematics Today on page 693.) In the game show, there are 26 numbered cases, each indicating a cash prize ranging from 1 cent to $1,000,000. Contestants on the show have a series of choices to make, and each time they can either accept the cash offer made by the banker or select a case from the remaining cases. Assume that one of the remaining cases contains a $1,000,000 cash prize. Determine the odds against and the odds in favor of selecting the case containing the $1,000,000 cash prize if there are

11. seven cases remaining. 6:1, 1:6

12. four cases remaining. 3:1, 1:3

Toss a Die In Exercises 13–16, a die is tossed. Determine the odds against rolling

13. a 2. 5:1

14. an odd number. 1:1

15. a number less than 3. 4:2 or 2:1

16. a number greater than 4. 4:2 or 2:1

Deck of Cards In Exercises 17–20, a card is picked from a standard deck of cards. Determine the odds against and the odds in favor of selecting

17. a king. 12:1, 1:12

18. a heart. 3:1, 1:3

19. a picture card. 10:3, 3:10

20. a card greater than 5 (ace is low). 5:8, 8:5

Spin the Spinner In Exercises 21–24, assume that the spinner cannot land on a line. Determine the odds against the spinner landing on the color red.

21. 1:1   **22.** 2:1

23. 5:3   **24.** 5:3

25. *Students* One person is selected at random from a class of 16 men and 14 women. Determine the odds against selecting

   a) a woman. 8:7   **b)** a man. 7:8

26. *Lottery* One million tickets are sold for a lottery in which a single prize will be awarded.

a) If you purchase a ticket, determine your odds against winning. 999,999:1

b) If you purchase 10 tickets, determine your odds against winning. 999,990:10 or 99,999:1

Billiard Balls In Exercises 27–32, use the rack of 15 billiard balls shown.

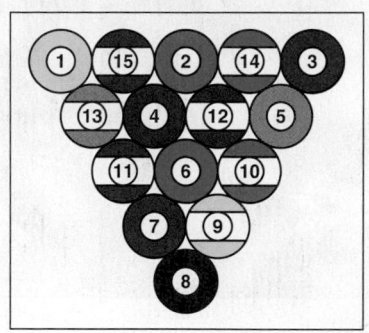

27. If one ball is selected at random, determine the odds against it containing a stripe. (Balls numbered 9 through 15 contain stripes.) 8:7

28. If one ball is selected at random, determine the odds in favor of it being a ball other than the 8 ball. 14:1

29. If one ball is selected at random, determine the odds in favor of it being an even-numbered ball. 7:8

30. If one ball is selected at random, determine the odds against it containing any red coloring (solid or striped). 13:2

31. If one ball is selected at random, determine the odds against it containing a number greater than or equal to 9. 8:7

32. If one ball is selected at random, determine the odds in favor of it containing two digits. 2:3

33. *LPGA Winnings* The chart below shows the winnings, in dollars, for the 10 golfers with the highest total LPGA winnings for the 2010 season.

Golfer	2010 Winnings
Na Yeon Choi	$1,871,166
Jiyai Shin	$1,783,127
Cristie Kerr	$1,601,552
Yani Tseng	$1,573,529
Suzann Pettersen	$1,557,175
Ai Miyazato	$1,457,384
In-Kyung Kim	$1,210,068
Song-Hee Kim	$1,208,698
Michelle Wie	$888,017
Paula Creamer	$883,870

Source: *LPGA.com*

If one of the golfers listed in the chart is selected at random, determine

a) the probability the golfer earned more than $1 million in 2010. $\frac{4}{5}$

b) the odds against the golfer earning more than $1 million in 2010. $1:4$

▲ *Paula Creamer*

34. *Rolling a Special Die* A special die used in a game contains one dot on one side, two dots on two sides, and three dots on three sides. If the die is rolled, determine

a) the probability of rolling two dots. $\frac{1}{3}$

b) the odds against rolling two dots. $4:2$ or $2:1$

35. *Medical Tests* The results of a medical test show that of 85 people selected at random who were given the test, 80 tested negative and 5 tested positive. Determine the odds against a person selected at random testing negative on the test. $1:16$

36. *A Red Marble* A box contains 9 red and 2 blue marbles. If you select one marble at random from the box, determine the odds against selecting a blue marble. $9:2$

37. *Scholarship Award* The odds in favor of Wendy White winning a scholarship are $7:4$. Determine the probability that

a) Wendy wins. $\frac{7}{11}$

b) Wendy does not win. $\frac{4}{11}$

38. *Selling a Car* The odds in favor of Sam Riveria selling his car are $3:8$. Determine the probability that Sam will

a) sell his car. $\frac{3}{11}$

b) not sell his car. $\frac{8}{11}$

39. *College Acceptance* The odds against Jason Judd getting accepted into the college his choice are $4:11$. Determine the probability that Jason gets accepted into the college of his choice. $\frac{11}{15}$

40. *Winning a Race* The odds against Paul Phillips winning the 100 yard dash are $7:2$. Determine the probability that

a) Paul wins. $\frac{2}{9}$ **b)** Paul does not win. $\frac{7}{9}$

Playing Bingo When playing bingo, 75 balls are placed in a bin and balls are selected at random. Each ball is marked with a letter and number as indicated in the following chart.

B	I	N	G	O
1–15	16–30	31–45	46–60	61–75

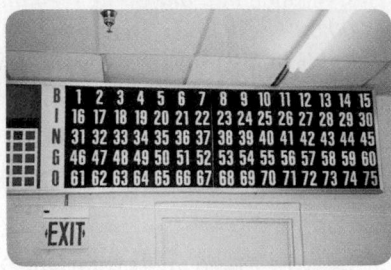

For example, there are balls marked B1, B2, up to B15; I16, I17, up to I30; and so on (see photo). In Exercises 41–46, assuming one bingo ball is selected at random, determine

41. the probability that it contains the letter G. $\frac{1}{5}$

42. the probability that it does not contain the letter G. $\frac{4}{5}$

43. the odds in favor of it containing the letter G. $1:4$

44. the odds against it containing the letter G. $4:1$

45. the odds against it being B9. $74:1$

46. the odds in favor of it being B9. $1:74$

Blood Types In Exercises 47–52, the following circle graph shows the percent of Americans with the various types of blood.

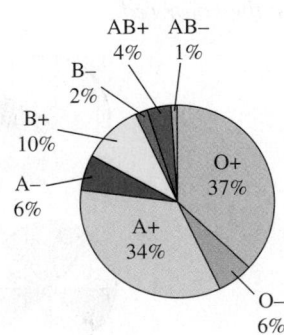

Blood Types of Americans

AB+ 4%   AB– 1%
B– 2%
B+ 10%
A– 6%
O+ 37%
A+ 34%
O– 6%

Source: *Red Cross*

If one American is selected at random, use the graph to determine

47. the probability that the person has A+ blood. 0.34

48. the probability that the person has B– blood. 0.02

49. the odds against the person having A+ blood. 33:17

50. the odds in favor of the person having B− blood. 1:49

51. the odds in favor of the person having either O+ or O−
blood. 43:57

52. the odds against the person having either A+ or O+ blood.
29:71

53. *Fixing a Car* Suppose that the probability that a mechanic
fixes a car correctly is 0.9. Determine the odds against the
mechanic fixing a car correctly. 1:9

54. *Diabetes* According to the Centers for Disease Control,
8% of Americans have diabetes. If an American is selected
at random, determine the odds in favor of this person having diabetes. 2:23

55. *Bookcase Assembly* Suppose that the probability that all
the parts needed to assemble a bookcase are included in
the carton is $\frac{7}{8}$. Determine the odds in favor of the carton
including all the needed parts. 7:1

56. *Flight Delays* Of 899,000 flights in May 2010, five were
delayed on the tarmac by more than three hours. If one of
these 899,000 flights was selected at random, determine

   a) the probability that the flight was delayed more than
three hours. $\frac{1}{179,800}$

   b) the odds against the flight being delayed more than
three hours. 179,799:1

57. *Birth Defects* Birth defects affect 1 in 33 babies born in
the United States each year.

   a) What is the probability that a baby born in the United
States will have a birth defect? $\frac{1}{33}$

   b) What are the odds against a baby born in the United
States having a birth defect? 32:1

Challenge Problems/Group Activities

58. *Odds Against* Determine the odds against an even number
or a number greater than 3 being rolled on a die. 1:2

59. *Horse Racing* Racetracks quote the approximate odds
against each horse winning on a large board called a *tote*

board. The odds quoted on a tote board for a race with five
horses is as follows.

Horse Number	Odds
2	7:2
3	2:1
4	15:1
5	7:5
6	1:1

Determine the probability of each horse winning the race.
(Do not be concerned that the sum of the probabilities is
not 1.)*

60. *Roulette* Turn to the roulette wheel illustrated on
page 707. If the wheel is spun, determine

   a) the probability that the ball lands on red. $\frac{9}{19}$

   b) the odds against the ball landing on red. 10:9

   c) the probability that the ball lands on 0 or 00. $\frac{1}{19}$

   d) the odds in favor of the ball landing on 0 or 00. 1:18

Recreational Mathematics

61. *Multiple Births* Multiple births make up about 3% of births
per year in the United States. The following illustrates the
number and type of multiple births in 2008.

Multiple Births in the United States in 2008

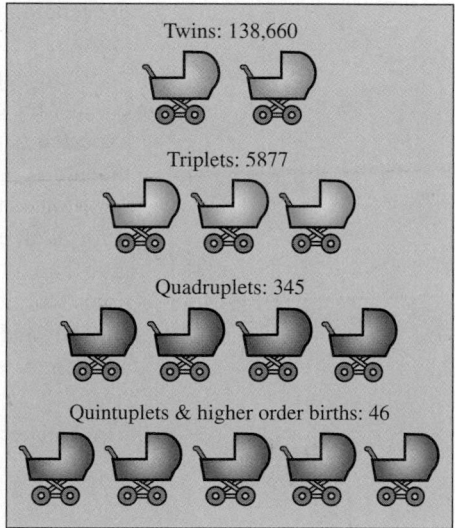

Source: *National Center for Health Services*

Using the above information, determine an estimate for the
odds against a birth being a multiple birth in 2008. ≈97:3

Internet/Research Activities

62. *State Lottery* Determine whether your state has a lottery.
If so, do research and write a paper indicating

*See Instructor Answer Appendix

a) the probability of winning the grand prize.

b) the odds against winning the grand prize.

c) Explain, using real objects such as pennies or table tennis balls, what these odds actually mean.

63. *Casino Advantages* There are many types of games of chance to choose from at casinos. The house has the advantage in each game, but the advantages differ according to the game.

a) List the games available at a typical casino.

b) List those for which the house has the smallest advantage of winning.

c) List those for which the house has the greatest advantage of winning.

SECTION 12.4   # Expected Value (Expectation)

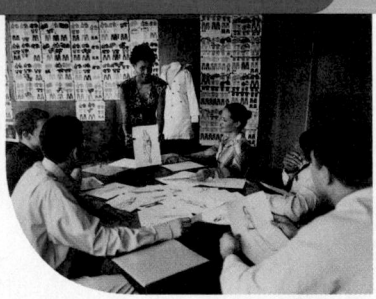

▲ *Expected value can be used to estimate the future profits of a new product.*

When a construction company estimates the number of days it will take to complete the resurfacing of a road, it will consider many things including the probability of rain, which can slow down the completion. In trying to decide whether to make a new product, such as a new cereal or new model car, a company will estimate its potential profit (or loss). When companies estimate how long it will take them to complete a task, or their expected profit, they often use expected value, or expectation, which we will discuss in this section.

Why *This is Important*   Expectation is used to make important decisions in many areas, including insurance and business ventures, and in games of chance.

Expected value, also called *expectation*, is often used to determine the expected results of an experiment or business venture *over the long term*. People use expectation to make important decisions in many different areas. For example, expectation is used in business to predict future profits of a new product. In the insurance industry, expectation is used to determine how much each insurance policy should cost for the company to make an overall profit. Expectation is also used to predict the expected gain or loss in games of chance such as the lottery, roulette, craps, and slot machines.

Consider the following situation. Tim tells Barbara that he will give her $1 if she can roll an even number on a single die. If she fails to roll an even number, she must give Tim $1. Who would win money in the long run if this game were played many times? In this situation, we would expect in the long run that half the time Tim would win $1 and half the time he would lose $1; therefore, Tim would break even. Mathematically, we could find Tim's expected gain or loss by the following procedure:

$$\text{Tim's expected gain or loss} = P\left(\begin{matrix}\text{Tim}\\\text{wins}\end{matrix}\right) \cdot \left(\begin{matrix}\text{amount}\\\text{Tim wins}\end{matrix}\right) + P\left(\begin{matrix}\text{Tim}\\\text{loses}\end{matrix}\right) \cdot \left(\begin{matrix}\text{amount}\\\text{Tim loses}\end{matrix}\right)$$

$$= \frac{1}{2}(\$1) + \frac{1}{2}(-\$1) = \$0$$

Note that the loss is written as a negative number. This procedure indicates that Tim has an expected gain or loss (or expected value) of $0. The expected value of zero indicates that he would indeed break even, as we had anticipated. Thus, the game is a *fair game*. If Tim's expected value were positive, it would indicate a gain; if negative, a loss.

The expected value, E, is calculated by multiplying the probability of an event occurring by the *net* amount gained or lost if the event occurs. If there are a number of different events and amounts to be considered, we use the following formula.

Expected Value

$$E = P_1 \cdot A_1 + P_2 \cdot A_2 + P_3 \cdot A_3 + \ldots + P_n \cdot A_n$$

The symbol P_1 represents the probability that the first event will occur, and A_1 represents the net amount won or lost if the first event occurs. P_2 is the probability of the second event, and A_2 is the net amount won or lost if the second event occurs, and so on. The sum of these products of the probabilities and their respective amounts is the expected value. The expected value is the average (or mean) result that would be obtained if the experiment were performed a great many times.

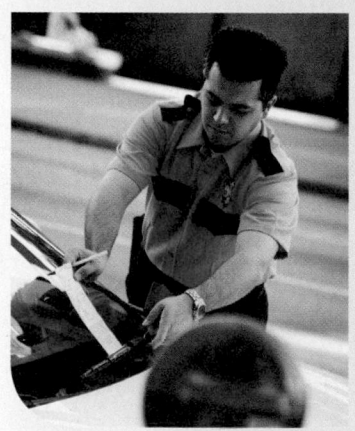

Example 1 *A Building Contract*

The Rich Walker Construction Company has just received a building contract. From past experience, Rich estimates there is a 60% chance of making a $500,000 profit, a 10% chance of breaking even, and a 30% chance of losing $200,000, depending on weather conditions and other factors. What is the expected value of the company's contract?

Solution Three amounts are to be considered: a gain of $500,000, breaking even at $0, and a loss of $200,000. The probability of gaining $500,000 is 0.6, the probability of breaking even is 0.1, and the probability of losing $200,000 is 0.3.

$$\begin{aligned}
\text{Rich's expectation} &= P_1 A_1 + P_2 A_2 + P_3 A_3 \\
&= (0.6)(\$500,000) + (0.1)(\$0) + (0.3)(-\$200,000) \\
&= \$240,000
\end{aligned}$$

Rich has an expectation, or expected average gain, of $240,000 for this contract. Thus, if the company receives similar contracts like this one, with these particular probabilities and amounts, in the long run the company would have an average gain of $240,000 per contract. However, you must remember that there is a 30% chance the company will lose $200,000 on this *particular* contract or any particular contract with these probabilities and amounts. ∎

Example 2 *Test-Taking Strategy*

Maria is taking a multiple-choice exam in which there are five possible answers for each question. The instructions indicate that she will be awarded 2 points for each correct response, that she will lose $\frac{1}{2}$ point for each incorrect response, and that no points will be added or subtracted for answers left blank.

a) If Maria does not know the correct answer to a question, is it to her advantage or disadvantage to guess at an answer?

b) If she can eliminate one of the possible choices, is it to her advantage or disadvantage to guess at the answer?

Solution

a) Let's determine the expected value if Maria guesses at an answer. Only one of five possible answers is correct.

$$P(\text{guesses correctly}) = \frac{1}{5} \qquad P(\text{guesses incorrectly}) = \frac{4}{5}$$

$$\text{Maria's expectation} = \overset{\overset{\text{Guesses}}{\text{correctly}}}{P_1 \cdot A_1} + \overset{\overset{\text{Guesses}}{\text{incorrectly}}}{P_2 \cdot A_2}$$

$$= \frac{1}{5}(2) + \frac{4}{5}\left(-\frac{1}{2}\right)$$

$$= \frac{2}{5} - \frac{2}{5} = 0$$

Thus, Maria's expectation is zero when she guesses. Therefore, over the long run she will neither gain nor lose points by guessing.

b) If Maria can eliminate one possible choice, one of four answers will be correct.

$$P(\text{guesses correctly}) = \frac{1}{4} \qquad P(\text{guesses incorrectly}) = \frac{3}{4}$$

$$\text{Maria's expectation} = \overset{\overset{\text{Guesses}}{\text{correctly}}}{P_1 \cdot A_1} + \overset{\overset{\text{Guesses}}{\text{incorrectly}}}{P_2 \cdot A_2}$$

$$= \frac{1}{4}(2) + \frac{3}{4}\left(-\frac{1}{2}\right)$$

$$= \frac{2}{4} - \frac{3}{8} = \frac{4}{8} - \frac{3}{8} = \frac{1}{8}$$

Since the expectation is a positive $\frac{1}{8}$, Maria will, on average, gain $\frac{1}{8}$ point each time she guesses when she can eliminate one possible choice. ■

Example 3 *Selling Hot Dogs*

An outdoor hot dog vendor sells an average of 50 hot dogs per day in dry weather and an average of 15 per day in wet weather. If the weather in this area is wet 20% of the time, determine the expected (average) number of hot dogs sold per day.

Solution The amounts in this example are the number of hot dogs sold. Since the weather is wet 20% of the time, it will be dry 100% − 20% = 80% of the time. When written as probabilities, 20% and 80% are 0.2 and 0.8, respectively.

$$E = P(\text{dry}) \cdot (\text{number sold}) + P(\text{wet}) \cdot (\text{number sold})$$

$$= 0.8(50) + 0.2(15)$$

$$= 40 + 3 = 43$$

Thus, the average, or expected, number of hot dogs sold per day is 43. ■

When we gave the expectation formula, we indicated that the amounts were the **net amounts**, which are the actual amounts gained or lost. Examples 4 and 5 illustrate how net amounts are used in two applications of expected value.

Example 4 *Winning a Door Prize*

When Josh Rosenberg attends a charity event, he is given a free ticket for the $50 door prize. A total of 100 tickets will be given out. Determine his expectation of winning the door prize.

Solution The probability of winning the door prize is $\frac{1}{100}$ since Josh has 1 of 100 tickets. If he wins, his net or actual winnings will be $50 since he did not pay for the ticket. The probability that Josh loses is $\frac{99}{100}$. If Josh loses, the amount he loses is $0 because he did not pay for the ticket.

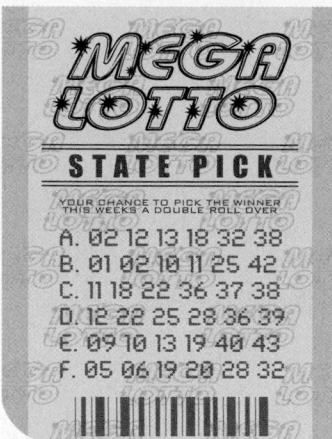
Expectation $= P(\text{Josh wins}) \cdot (\text{amount won}) + P(\text{Josh loses}) \cdot (\text{amount lost})$

$$= \frac{1}{100}(50) + \frac{99}{100}(0) = \frac{50}{100} = 0.50$$

Thus, Josh's expectation is $0.50, or 50 cents. ∎

Now we will consider a problem similar to Example 4, but this time we will assume that Josh must purchase the ticket for the door prize.

Example 5 *Winning a Door Prize*

When Josh Rosenberg attends a charity event, he is given the opportunity to purchase a ticket for the $50 door prize. The cost of the ticket is $2, and 100 tickets will be sold. Determine Josh's expectation if he purchases one ticket.

Solution As in Example 4, Josh's probability of winning is $\frac{1}{100}$. However, if he does win, his actual or net winnings will be $48. The $48 is obtained by subtracting the cost of the ticket, $2, from the amount of the door prize, $50. There is also a probability of $\frac{99}{100}$ that Josh will not win the door prize. If he does not win the door prize, he has lost the $2 that he paid for the ticket. Therefore, we must consider two amounts when we determine Josh's expectation, winning $48 and losing $2.

Expectation $= P(\text{Josh wins}) \cdot (\text{amount won}) + P(\text{Josh loses}) \cdot (\text{amount lost})$

$$= \frac{1}{100}(48) + \frac{99}{100}(-2)$$

$$= \frac{48}{100} - \frac{198}{100} = -\frac{150}{100} = -1.50$$

Josh's expectation is $−1.50 when he purchases one ticket. ∎

In Example 5, we determined that Josh's expectation was −$1.50 when he purchased one ticket. If he purchased two tickets, his expectation would be 2(−$1.50), or −$3.00. We could also compute Josh's expectation if he purchased two tickets as follows:

$$E = \frac{2}{100}(46) + \frac{98}{100}(-4) = -3.00$$

This answer, −$3.00, checks with the answer obtained by multiplying the expectation for a single ticket by 2.

Let's look at one more example in which a person must pay for a chance to win a prize. In the following example, there will be more than two amounts to consider.

Example 6 *Raffle Tickets*

One thousand raffle tickets are sold for $1 each. One grand prize of $500 and two consolation prizes of $100 will be awarded. The tickets are placed in a bin. The winning tickets will be selected from the bin. Assuming that the probability that any given ticket selected for the grand prize is $\frac{1}{1000}$ and the probability that any given ticket selected for a consolation prize is $\frac{2}{1000}$, determine

a) Irene Drew's expectation if she purchases one ticket.

b) Irene's expectation if she purchases five tickets.

Solution

a) Three amounts are to be considered: the net gain in winning the grand prize, the net gain in winning one of the consolation prizes, and the loss of the cost of the ticket. If Irene wins the grand prize, her net gain is $499 ($500 minus $1 spent for the ticket). If Irene wins one of the consolation prizes, her net gain is $99 ($100 minus $1). The probability that Irene wins the grand prize is $\frac{1}{1000}$ and the probability that she wins a consolation prize is $\frac{2}{1000}$. The probability that she does not win a prize is $1 - \frac{1}{1000} - \frac{2}{1000} = \frac{997}{1000}$.

$$E = P_1 \cdot A_1 + P_2 \cdot A_2 + P_3 \cdot A_3$$

$$= \frac{1}{1000}(\$499) + \frac{2}{1000}(\$99) + \frac{997}{1000}(-\$1)$$

$$= \frac{499}{1000} + \frac{198}{1000} - \frac{997}{1000} = -\frac{300}{1000} = -0.30$$

Thus, Irene's expectation is −$0.30 per ticket purchased.

b) On average, Irene loses 30 cents on each ticket purchased. On five tickets, her expectation is $(-\$0.30)(5)$, or −$1.50. ∎

TIMELY TIP

In any expectation problem, the sum of the probabilities of all the events should always be 1. Note in Example 6 that the sum of the probabilities is $\frac{1}{1000} + \frac{2}{1000} + \frac{997}{1000} = \frac{1000}{1000} = 1$.

Fair Price

In Example 5, we determined that Josh's expectation was −$1.50. Now let's determine how to find out how much should have been charged for a ticket so that his expectation would be $0. If Josh's expectation were to be $0, he could be expected to break even over the long run. Suppose that Josh paid 50 cents, or $0.50, for the ticket. His expectation, if paying $0.50 for the ticket, would be calculated as follows.

$$\text{Expectation} = P(\text{Josh wins}) \cdot (\text{amount won}) + P(\text{Josh loses}) \cdot (\text{amount lost})$$

$$= \frac{1}{100}(49.50) + \frac{99}{100}(-\$0.50)$$

$$= \frac{49.50}{100} - \frac{49.50}{100} = 0$$

Thus, if Josh paid 50 cents per ticket, his expectation would be $0. The 50 cents, in this case, is called the fair price of the ticket. The *fair price* is the amount to be paid that will result in an expected value of $0. The fair price may be found by adding the *cost to play* to the *expected value*.

Fair Price

To determine the fair price, use the following formula.

Fair price = expected value + cost to play

In Example 5, the cost to play was $2 and the expected value was determined to be −$1.50. The fair price for a ticket in Example 5 may be found as follows.

Fair price = expected value + cost to play
$$= -1.50 + 2.00 = 0.50$$

We obtained a fair price of $0.50. If the tickets were sold for the fair price of $0.50 each, Josh's expectation would be $0, as shown above. Can you now find the fair price that Irene should pay for a raffle ticket in Example 6? In Example 6, the cost of a ticket was $1 and we determined that the expected value was −$0.30.

Fair price = expected value + cost to play
$$= -\$0.30 + \$1.00 = \$0.70$$

Thus, the fair price for a ticket in Example 6 is $0.70, or 70 cents. Verify for yourself now that if the tickets were sold for $0.70, the expectation would be $0.00.

┌─────
│ **Example 7** *Expectation and Fair Price*
│
│ At a game of chance, the expected value is found to be −$1.50, and the cost to
│ play the game is $4.00. Determine the fair price to play the game.
│
│ **Solution** We use the formula
│
│ $$\text{Fair price} = \text{expected value} + \text{cost to play}$$
│ $$= -1.50 + 4.00$$
│ $$= 2.50$$
│
│ Thus, the fair price to play this game would be $2.50. If the cost to play was $2.50
│ instead of $4.00, the expected value would be $0.   ∎
└─────

SECTION 12.4 *Exercises*

Warm Up Exercises

In Exercises 1–4, fill in the blank with an appropriate word, phrase, or symbol(s).

1. The expected gain or loss of an experiment over the long run is called the _____ value. Expected

2. In an experiment, if an individual expects to have a loss in the long run, the expected value is _____. Negative

3. In an experiment, if an individual expects to have a gain in the long run, the expected value is _____. Positive

4. In an experiment, if an individual expects to break even in the long run, the expected value is _____. 0

Practice the Skills/Problem Solving

5. *Expected Attendance* For an outdoor art and craft show, event organizers estimate that 60,000 people will attend if it is not raining. If it is raining, event organizers estimate that 21,000 people will attend. On the day of the show, meteorologists predict a 70% chance of rain. Determine the expected number of people who will attend this show. 32,700 people

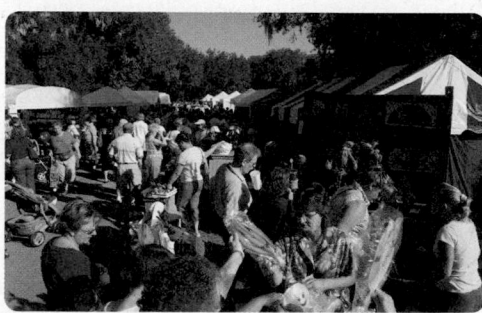

6. *A New Business* In a proposed business venture, Stephanie Morrison estimates that there is a 60% chance she will make $80,000 and a 40% chance she will lose $20,000. Determine Stephanie's expected value. $40,000

7. *Basketball* Shenise Johnson is a star player for the University of Miami Hurricanes women's basketball team. She has injured her ankle, and it is doubtful that she will be able to play in an upcoming game. If Shenise can play, the coach estimates that the Hurricanes will score 78 points. If Shenise is not able to play, the coach estimates that they will score 62 points. The team doctor estimates that there is a 50% chance Shenise will play. Determine the number of points the team can expect to score. 70 points

▲ *Shenise Johnson (left)*

8. *Career Fair Attendance* For a Nursing and Allied Health Care Career Fair, organizers estimate that 50 people will attend if it does not rain and 65 will attend if it rains. The weather forecast indicates that there is a 40% chance it will not rain and a 60% chance it will rain on the day of the career fair. Determine the expected number of people who will attend the fair. 59 people

9. *TV Shows* The Fox television network is scheduling its fall lineup of shows. For the Tuesday night 8 P.M. slot, Fox has selected the show *Glee*. If its rival network CBS schedules the show *NCIS* during the same time slot, Fox estimates that *Glee* will get 1.2 million viewers. However, if CBS schedules the show *Survivor* during that time slot, Fox estimates that *Glee* will get 1.6 million viewers. Fox believes

that the probability that CBS will show *NCIS* is 0.4 and the probability that CBS will show *Survivor* is 0.6. Determine the expected number of viewers for the show *Glee*.
1.44 million viewers

10. Seattle Greenery In July in Seattle, the grass grows $\frac{1}{2}$ in. a day on a sunny day and $\frac{1}{4}$ in. a day on a cloudy day. In Seattle in July, 75% of the days are sunny and 25% are cloudy.

a) Determine the expected amount of grass growth on a typical day in July in Seattle. $\frac{7}{16}$ in., or 0.4375 in.

b) Determine the expected total grass growth in the month of July in Seattle. $\frac{217}{16}$ in., or 13.5625 in.

11. Investment Club The Triple L investment club is considering purchasing a certain stock. After considerable research, the club members determine that there is a 70% chance of making $10,000, a 10% chance of breaking even, and a 20% chance of losing $7500. Determine the expectation of this purchase. $5500

12. Clothing Sale At a special clothing sale at the Crescent Oaks Country Club, after the cashier rings up your purchase, you select a slip of paper from a box. The slip of paper indicates the dollar amount, either $5 or $10, that is deducted from your purchase price. The probability of selecting a slip indicating $5 is $\frac{7}{10}$, and the probability of selecting a slip indicating $10 is $\frac{3}{10}$. If your original purchase before you select the slip of paper is $200, determine

a) the expected dollar amount to be deducted from your purchase. $6.50

b) the expected dollar amount you will pay for your purchase. $193.50

13. Fortune Cookies At the Royal Dragon Chinese restaurant, a slip in the fortune cookies indicates a dollar amount that will be subtracted from your total bill. A bag of 10 fortune cookies is given to you from which you will select one. If seven fortune cookies contain "$1 off," two contain "$2 off," and one contains "$5 off," determine the expectation of a selection. $1.60 off

14. Pick a Card Mike and Dave play the following game. Mike picks a card from a deck of cards. If he selects a club, Dave gives him $4. If not, he gives Dave $2.

a) Determine Mike's expectation. −$0.50

b) Determine Dave's expectation. $0.50

15. Roll a Die Alyssa and Gabriel play the following game. Alyssa rolls a die. If she rolls a 1, 2, or 3, Gabriel gives Alyssa $3. If Alyssa rolls a 4 or 5, Gabriel gives Alyssa $2. However, if Alyssa rolls a 6, she gives Gabriel $14.

a) Determine Alyssa's expectation. ≈ −$0.17

b) Determine Gabriel's expectation. ≈ $0.17

16. Blue Chips and Red Chips A bag contains 4 blue chips and 6 red chips. Chi and Dolly play the following game. Chi selects one chip at random from the bag. If Chi selects

a blue chip, Dolly gives Chi $6. If Chi selects a red chip, Chi gives Dolly $5.

a) Determine Chi's expectation. −$0.60

b) Determine Dolly's expectation. $0.60

17. Multiple-Choice Test A multiple-choice exam has five possible answers for each question. For each correct answer, you are awarded 5 points. For each incorrect answer, 1 point is subtracted from your score. For answers left blank, no points are added or subtracted.

a) If you do not know the correct answer to a particular question, is it to your advantage to guess? Explain.
Yes, because you have a positive expectation of $\frac{1}{5}$

b) If you do not know the correct answer but can eliminate one possible choice, is it to your advantage to guess? Explain. Yes, because you have a positive expectation of $\frac{1}{2}$

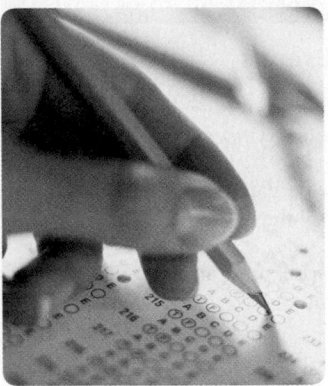

18. Multiple-Choice Test A multiple-choice exam has four possible answers for each question. For each correct answer, you are awarded 5 points. For each incorrect answer, 2 points are subtracted from your score. For answers left blank, no points are added or subtracted.

a) If you do not know the correct answer to a particular question, is it to your advantage to guess? Explain.
No, because you have a negative expectation of $-\frac{1}{4}$

b) If you do not know the correct answer but can eliminate one possible choice, is it to your advantage to guess? Explain. Yes, because you have a positive expectation of $\frac{1}{3}$

19. Fair Price The expected value when you purchase a lottery ticket is −$2.00, and the cost of the ticket is $5.00. Determine the fair price of the lottery ticket. $3.00

20. Fair Price The expected value of a carnival game is −$6.50, and the cost to play the game is $10.00. Determine the fair price to play the game. $3.50

21. Raffle Tickets Five hundred raffle tickets are sold for $3 each. One prize of $500 is to be awarded. Raul Mondesi purchases one ticket.

a) Determine his expected value. −$2.00

b) Determine the fair price of a ticket. $1.00

22. *Raffle Tickets* One thousand raffle tickets are sold for $1 each. One prize of $800 is to be awarded. Rena Condos purchases one ticket.

 a) Determine her expected value. −$0.20

 b) Determine the fair price of a ticket. $0.80

23. *Raffle Tickets* Two thousand raffle tickets are sold for $3 each. Three prizes will be awarded: one for $1000 and two for $500. Assume that the probability that any given ticket is selected for the $1000 prize is $\frac{1}{2000}$ and the probability that any given ticket is selected for the $500 prize is $\frac{2}{2000}$. Jeremy Sharp purchases one of these tickets.

 a) Determine his expected value. −$2.00

 b) Determine the fair price of a ticket. $1.00

24. *Raffle Tickets* Ten thousand raffle tickets are sold for $5 each. Four prizes will be awarded: one for $5000, one for $2500, and two for $1000. Assume that the probability that any given ticket is selected for the $5000 prize is $\frac{1}{10,000}$, the probability that any given ticket is selected for the $2500 prize is $\frac{1}{10,000}$, and the probability that any given ticket is selected for a $1000 prize is $\frac{2}{10,000}$. Sidhardt purchases one of these tickets.

 a) Determine his expected value. −$4.05

 b) Determine the fair price of a ticket. $0.95

Spinners In Exercises 25 and 26, assume that a person spins the pointer and is awarded the amount indicated by the pointer. Determine the person's expectation.

25. $3.00   **26.** $5.25

    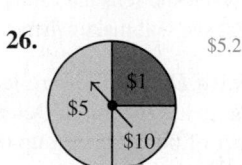

Spinners In Exercises 27 and 28, assume that a person spins the pointer and is awarded the amount indicated if the pointer points to a positive number but must pay the amount indicated if the pointer points to a negative number. Determine the person's expectation if the person plays the game.

27. $−1.25   **28.** $0.50

Selecting an Envelope In Exercises 29–32, a person randomly selects one of the six envelopes shown below. Each envelope contains a check that the person gets to keep. Determine the person's expectation if the checks in the envelopes are as follows.

29. Three envelopes contain a $500 check, and three envelopes contain a $1000 check. $750

30. Four envelopes contain a $1000 check, and two envelopes contain a $5000 check. $2333.33

31. The six envelopes contain checks for $100, $200, $300, $400, $500, and $1000, respectively. $416.67

32. Two envelopes contain a check for $600, two envelopes contain a check for $2000, and two envelopes contain a check for $5000. $2533.33

Spinners In Exercises 33–36, assume that a person spins the pointer and is awarded the amount indicated by the pointer. If it costs $2 to play the game, determine

 a) *the expectation of a person who plays the game.*

 b) *the fair price to play the game.*

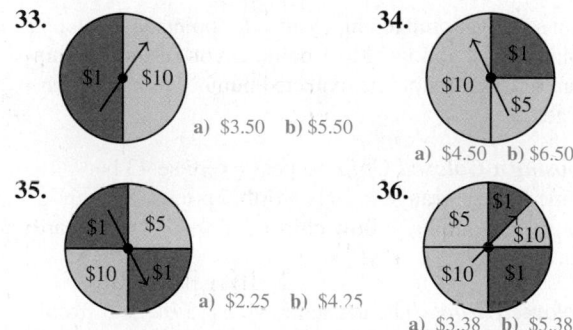

33. a) $3.50 b) $5.50

34. a) $4.50 b) $6.50

35. a) $2.25 b) $4.25

36. a) $3.38 b) $5.38

Selecting an Envelope In Exercises 37–40 on page 706, a person randomly selects one of the four envelopes shown below. Each envelope contains a check that the person gets to keep. However, before the person can select an envelope, he or she must pay $15 to play. For the value of the checks indicated in the exercises, determine the expectation for a person who plays.

37. Two envelopes contain a $10 check, and two envelopes contain a $25 check. $2.50

38. Three envelopes contain a $20 check, and one envelope contains a $0 check. $0

39. The checks in the envelopes are for $0, $2, $5, and $20, respectively. −$8.25

40. The checks in the envelopes are for $2, $2, $100, and $400, respectively. $111.00

41. *Reaching Base Safely*   Based on his past baseball history, Jim Devias has a 17% chance of reaching first base safely, a 10% chance of hitting a double, a 2% chance of hitting a triple, an 8% chance of hitting a home run, and a 63% chance of making an out at his next at bat. Determine Jim's expected number of bases for his next at bat. 0.75 base

42. *Life Insurance*   According to Bristol Mutual Life Insurance's mortality table, the probability that a 20-year-old woman will survive 1 year is 0.994 and the probability that she will die within 1 year is 0.006. If a 20-year-old woman buys a $10,000 1-year policy for $100, what is Bristol Mutual's expected gain or loss? $40.00 gain

43. *Choosing a Colored Chip*   In a box, there are a total of 10 chips. The chips are orange, green, and yellow, as shown below.

If you select an orange chip, you get 4 points, a green chip 3 points, and a yellow chip 1 point. If you select one chip at random, determine the expected number of points you will get. 2.9 points

44. *Choosing a Colored Chip*   Repeat Exercise 43 but assume that an orange chip is worth 5 points, a green chip 2 points, and a yellow chip −3 points (3 points are taken away). 1.9

45. *Employee Hiring*   The academic vice president at Brookdale Community College has requested that new academic programs be added to the college curriculum. If the college's Board of Trustees approves the new programs, the college will hire 75 new employees. If the new programs are not approved, the college will hire only 20 new employees. If the probability that the new programs will be approved is 0.65, what is the expected number of new employees to be hired by Brookdale Community College? Round your answer to the nearest whole number of employees. 56 employees

46. *Completing a Project*   A mechanical contractor is preparing for a construction project. He determines that if he completes the project on schedule, his net profit will be $450,000. If he completes the project between 0 and 3 months late, his net profit decreases to $120,000. If he completes the project more

than 3 months late, his net loss is $275,000. The probability that he completes the project on schedule is 0.6, the probability that he completes the project between 0 and 3 months late is 0.3, and the probability that he completes the project more than 3 months late is 0.1. Determine his expected gain or loss for this project. $278,500

47. *New Store*   Dunkin' Donuts is opening a new store. The company estimates that there is a 75% chance the store will have a profit of $20,000, a 10% chance the store will break even, and a 15% chance the store will lose $3000. Determine the expected gain or loss for this store. $14,550

48. *China Cabinet*   The owner of an antique store estimates that there is a 40% chance she will make $2000 when she sells an antique china cabinet, a 50% chance she will make $750 when she sells the cabinet, and a 10% chance she will break even when she sells the cabinet. Determine the expected amount she will make when she sells the cabinet. $1175

49. *Rolling a Die*   A die is rolled many times, and the points facing up are recorded. Determine the expected (average) number of points facing up over the long run. 3.5

50. *Lawsuit*   Don Vello is considering bringing a lawsuit against the Dummote Chemical Company. His lawyer estimates that there is a 70% chance Don will make $60,000, a 10% chance Don will break even, and a 20% chance they will lose the case and Don will need to pay $30,000 in legal fees. Estimate Don's expected gain or loss if he proceeds with the lawsuit. $36,000

51. *Road Service*   On a clear day in Boston, the Automobile Association of American (AAA) makes an average of 110 service calls for motorist assistance, on a rainy day it makes an average of 160 service calls, and on a snowy day it makes an average of 210 service calls. If the weather in Boston is clear 200 days of the year, rainy 100 days of the year, and snowy 65 days of the year, determine the expected number of service calls made by the AAA in a given day. ≈ 141.51 service calls

52. *Real Estate*   The expenses for Jorge Estrada, a real estate agent, to list, advertise, and attempt to sell a house are $1400. If Jorge succeeds in selling the house, he will receive a commission of 6% of the sales price. If an agent with a different company sells the house, Jorge still receives 3% of the sales price. If the house is unsold after 3 months, Jorge loses the listing and receives nothing. Suppose that the probability that he sells a $150,000 house is 0.2, the probability that another agent sells the house is 0.5, and the probability that the house is unsold after 3 months is 0.3. Determine Jorge's expectation if he accepts this house for listing. Should Jorge list the house? Gain $2650; yes

Dart Board *In Exercises 53 and 54, assume that you are blindfolded and throw a dart at the dart board shown below. Assume that your dart sticks in the dart board, and not on a line.*

a) *Determine the probabilities that the dart lands on $1, $10, $20, and $100, respectively.*

b) *If you win the amount of money indicated by the section of the board where the dart lands, determine your expectation when you throw the dart.*

53.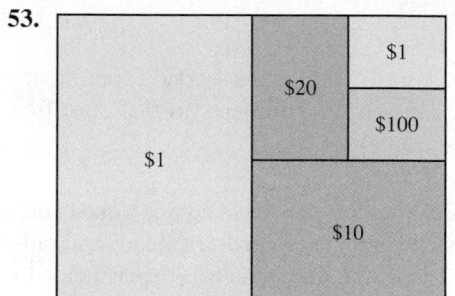
a) $\frac{9}{16}, \frac{1}{4}, \frac{1}{8}, \frac{1}{16}$
b) $11.81

54.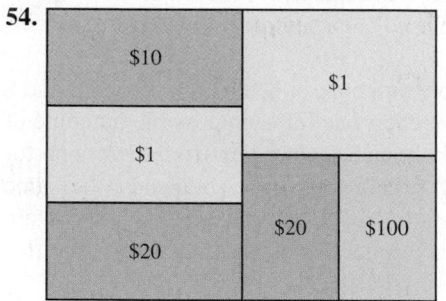
a) $\frac{5}{12}, \frac{1}{6}, \frac{7}{24}, \frac{1}{8}$
b) $20.42

Challenge Problems/Group Activities

55. **Term Life Insurance** An insurance company will pay the face value of a term life insurance policy if the insured person dies during the term of the policy. For how much should an insurance company sell a 10-year term policy with a face value of $40,000 to a 30-year-old man for the company to make a profit? The probability of a 30-year-old man living to age 40 is 0.97. Explain your answer. Remember that the customer pays for the insurance before the policy becomes effective. An amount greater than $1200

56. **Lottery Ticket** Is it possible to determine your expectation when you purchase a lottery ticket? Explain. No, you do not know how many others are selecting the same numbers you are picking.

Roulette *In Exercises 57 and 58, use the roulette wheel illustrated. A roulette wheel typically contains slots with numbers 1–36 and slots marked 0 and 00. A ball is spun on the wheel and comes to rest in one of the 38 slots. Eighteen numbers are colored red, and 18 numbers are colored black. The 0 and 00 are colored green. If you bet on one particular number and the ball lands on that number, the house pays off odds of 35 to 1. If you bet on a red number or black number and win, the house pays 1 to 1 (even money).*

57. Determine the expected value of betting $1 on a particular number. −$0.053 or −5.3¢

58. Determine the expected value of betting $1 on red. −$0.053 or −5.3¢

Recreational Mathematics

59. **Wheel of Fortune** The following is a miniature version of the Wheel of Fortune. When Dave Salem spins the wheel, he is awarded the amount on the wheel indicated by the pointer. If the wheel points to Bankrupt, he loses the total amount he has accumulated and also loses his turn. Assume that the wheel stops on a position at random and that each position is equally likely to occur.

a) Determine Mr. Salem's expectation when he spins the wheel at the start of the game (he has no money to lose if he lands on Bankrupt). $458.33

b) If Mr. Salem presently has a balance of $1800, determine his expectation when he spins the wheel. $308.33

SECTION 12.5   Tree Diagrams

▲ *We can use a tree diagram to illustrate the possible lunch specials at a deli.*

Suppose a deli offers a lunch special consisting of a sandwich, a beverage, and a dessert. The sandwich choices are roast beef, ham, or turkey. The beverage choices are soda, coffee, or tea. The dessert choices are a brownie or a chocolate chip cookie. If a customer purchases a lunch special and makes selections at random, what is the probability the customer selects a roast beef sandwich and a chocolate chip cookie? In this section, we will illustrate how the counting principle and tree diagrams can be used to determine the answers to questions like the one posed above. We will also illustrate how tree diagrams can be used to determine all the possible outcomes of an experiment.

Why *This is Important* Being able to determine the number of possible outcomes in an experiment is essential to solving many probability problems.

Now we will introduce the counting principle. The counting principle will be used again in Section 12.8.

Counting Principle
If a first experiment can be performed in M distinct ways and a second experiment can be performed in N distinct ways, then the two experiments in that specific order can be performed in $M \cdot N$ distinct ways.

If we wanted to find the number of possible outcomes when a coin is tossed and a die is rolled, we could reason that the coin has two possible outcomes, heads and tails. The die has six possible outcomes: 1, 2, 3, 4, 5, and 6. Thus, the two experiments together have $2 \cdot 6$, or 12, possible outcomes.

A list of all the possible outcomes of an experiment is called a *sample space*. Each individual outcome in the sample space is called a *sample point*. *Tree diagrams* are helpful in determining sample spaces.

A tree diagram illustrating all the possible outcomes when a coin is tossed and a die is rolled (see Fig. 12.6) has two initial branches, one for each possible outcome of the coin. Each of these branches will have six branches emerging from them, one for each possible outcome of the die. That will give a total of 12 branches, the same number of possible outcomes found by using the counting principle. We can obtain the sample space by listing all the possible combinations of branches. Note that this sample space consists of 12 sample points.

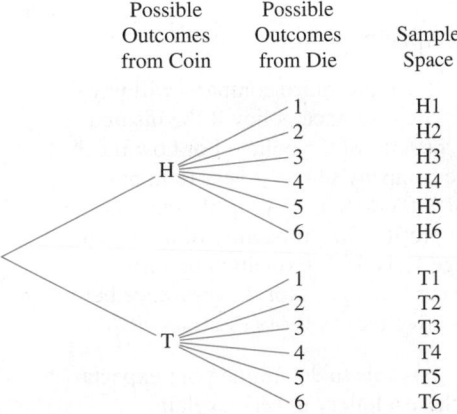

Figure 12.6

Example 1 uses the phrase "without replacement." This phrase tells us that once an item is selected, it cannot be selected again, making it impossible to select the same item twice.

Example 1 Selecting Balls without Replacement

Two balls are to be selected *without replacement* from a bag that contains one red, one blue, one green, and one orange ball (see Fig. 12.7).

a) Use the counting principle to determine the number of points in the sample space.

b) Construct a tree diagram and list the sample space.

c) Determine the probability that one orange ball is selected.

d) Determine the probability that a green ball followed by a red ball is selected.

Solution

a) The first selection may be any one of the four balls. Once the first ball is selected, only three balls remain for the second selection. Thus, there are 4 · 3, or 12, sample points in the sample space.

b) The first ball selected can be red, blue, green, or orange. Since this experiment is done without replacement, the same colored ball cannot be selected twice. For example, if the first ball selected is red, the second ball selected must be either blue, green, or orange. The tree diagram and sample space are shown in Fig. 12.8. The sample space contains 12 points. That result checks with the answer obtained in part (a) using the counting principle.

First Selection	Second Selection	Sample Space
R	B	RB
	G	RG
	O	RO
B	R	BR
	G	BG
	O	BO
G	R	GR
	B	GB
	O	GO
O	R	OR
	B	OB
	G	OG

Figure 12.8

c) If we know the sample space, we can compute probabilities using the formula

$$P(E) = \frac{\text{number of outcomes favorable to } E}{\text{total number of outcomes}}$$

The total number of outcomes will be the number of points in the sample space. From Fig. 12.8, we determine that there are 12 possible outcomes. Six outcomes have one orange ball: RO, BO, GO, OR, OB, and OG.

$$P(\text{one orange ball is selected}) = \frac{6}{12} = \frac{1}{2}$$

d) One possible outcome meets the criteria of a green ball followed by a red ball: GR.

$$P(\text{green followed by red}) = \frac{1}{12}$$

The counting principle can be extended to any number of experiments, as illustrated in Example 2.

Figure 12.7

Example 2 *Lunch Choices*

At Finlay's Restaurant, each lunch special consists of a sandwich, a salad, and a beverage. The sandwich choices are roast beef (R), ham (H), or turkey (T). The salad choices are macaroni (M) or potato (P). The beverage choices are coffee (C) or soda (S).

a) Use the counting principle to determine the number of different lunch specials offered by this restaurant.

b) Construct a tree diagram and list the sample space.

c) If a customer randomly selects one of the lunch specials, determine the probability that a roast beef sandwich and soda are selected.

d) If a customer randomly selects one of the lunch specials, determine the probability that neither macaroni salad nor coffee is selected.

Solution

a) There are 3 choices for a sandwich, 2 choices for a salad, and 2 choices for a beverage. Using the counting principle, we can determine that there are $3 \cdot 2 \cdot 2$, or 12, different lunch specials.

b) The tree diagram illustrating the 12 lunch specials is given in Fig. 12.9.

Sandwich	Salad	Beverage	Sample Space
R	M	C	RMC
		S	RMS
	P	C	RPC
		S	RPS
H	M	C	HMC
		S	HMS
	P	C	HPC
		S	HPS
T	M	C	TMC
		S	TMS
	P	C	TPC
		S	TPS

Figure 12.9

c) Of the 12 lunch specials, 2 contain both a roast beef sandwich and soda (RMS, RPS).

$$P(\text{roast beef sandwich and soda are selected}) = \frac{2}{12} = \frac{1}{6}$$

d) Of the 12 lunch specials, 3 contain neither macaroni salad nor coffee (RPS, HPS, TPS).

$$P(\text{neither macaroni salad nor coffee are selected}) = \frac{3}{12} = \frac{1}{4}$$

Example 3 *Selecting Ticket Winners*

A radio station has two tickets to give away to a Bon Jovi concert. It held a contest and narrowed the possible recipients down to four people: Christine (C), Mike Hammer (MH), Mike Levine (ML), and Phyllis (P). The names of two of these four people will be selected at random from a hat, and the two people selected will be awarded the tickets.

a) Use the counting principle to determine the number of points in the sample space.

b) Construct a tree diagram and list the sample space.

c) Determine the probability that Christine is selected.

d) Determine the probability that neither Mike Hammer nor Mike Levine is selected.

e) Determine the probability that at least one Mike is selected.

▲ *Bon Jovi*

Solution

a) The first selection may be any one of the four people; see Fig. 12.10. Once the first person is selected, only three people remain for the second selection. Thus, there are 4 · 3, or 12, sample points in the sample space.

b)

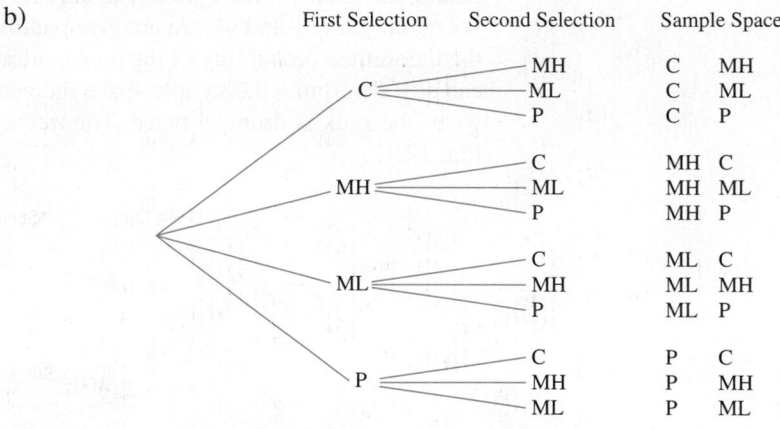

| | First Selection | Second Selection | Sample Space |

Figure 12.10

c) Of the 12 points in the sample space, 6 have Christine. They are C MH, C ML, C P, MH C, ML C, and P C.

$$P(\text{Christine is selected}) = \frac{6}{12} = \frac{1}{2}$$

d) Of the 12 points in the sample space, two have neither Mike. They are C P and P C.

$$P(\text{neither Mike selected}) = \frac{2}{12} = \frac{1}{6}$$

e) At least one Mike means that one or more Mikes are selected. There are 10 points in the sample space with at least one Mike (all those except C P and P C).

$$P(\text{at least one Mike is selected}) = \frac{10}{12} = \frac{5}{6}$$

In Example 3, if you add the probability of no Mike being selected with the probability of at least one Mike being selected, you get $\frac{1}{6} + \frac{5}{6}$, or 1. In any probability problem, if E is a specific event, then either E happens at least one time or it does not happen at all. Thus, $P(E$ happening at least once$) + P(E$ does not happen$) = 1$, which leads to the following rule.

Probability of an Event Happening At Least Once
The probability of an event happening at least once can be determined by the following formula.

$$P(\text{event happening at least once}) = 1 - P(\text{event does not happen})$$

For example, suppose that the probability of not getting any red flowers from the seeds that are planted is $\frac{2}{7}$. Then the probability of getting at least one red flower from the seeds that are planted is $1 - \frac{2}{7} = \frac{5}{7}$. We will use this rule in later sections.

In all the tree diagrams in this section, the outcomes were always equally likely; that is, each outcome had the same probability of occurrence. Consider a rock that has 4 faces such that each face has a different surface area and the rock is not

Figure 12.11

uniform in density (see Fig. 12.11). When the rock is dropped, the probability that the rock lands on face 1 will not be the same as the probability that the rock lands on face 2. In fact, the probabilities that the rock lands on face 1, face 2, face 3, and face 4 may all be different. Therefore, the outcomes of the rock landing on face 1, face 2, face 3, and face 4 are not equally likely outcomes. Because the outcomes are not equally likely and we are not given additional information, we cannot determine the theoretical probability of the rock landing on each individual face. However, we can still determine the sample space indicating the faces that the rock may land on when the rock is dropped twice. The tree diagram and sample space are shown in Fig. 12.12.

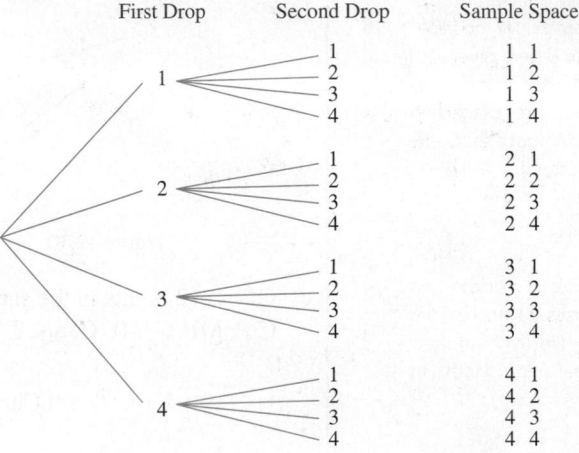

Figure 12.12

Since the outcomes are not equally likely, the probability of each of the 16 sample points in the sample space occurring cannot be determined. If the outcomes were equally likely, then each of the 16 points in the sample space would have a probability of $\frac{1}{16}$. See Exercises 27 and 28, which deal with outcomes that are not equally likely.

SECTION 12.5   *Exercises*

Warm Up Exercises

In Exercises 1–4, fill in the blank with an appropriate word, phrase, or symbol(s).

1. A list of all possible outcomes of an experiment is called a(n) _____ space. Sample

2. Each individual outcome in a sample space is called a sample _____. Point

3. If a first experiment can be performed in two distinct ways and a second experiment can be performed in seven distinct ways, the two experiments together can be performed in _____ distinct ways. 14

4. A helpful method to determine a sample space is to construct a(n) _____ diagram. Tree

Practice the Skills

5. *Selecting States* If two states are selected at random from the 50 U.S. states, use the counting principle to determine the number of possible outcomes if the states are selected

   a) with replacement. 2500

   b) without replacement. 2450

6. *Selecting Dates* If two dates are selected at random from the 365 days of the year, use the counting principle to determine the number of possible outcomes if the dates are selected

   a) with replacement. 133,225

   b) without replacement. 132,860

7. **Selecting Golfballs** A bag contains six golfballs, all the same size and equally likely to be selected. Each golfball is a different brand. If you select three golfballs at random, use the counting principle to determine how many points will be in the sample space if the golfballs are selected

a) with replacement. 216

b) without replacement. 120

8. **Remote Control** Your television remote control has buttons for digits 0–9. If you press two buttons, how many numbers are possible if

a) the same button may be pressed twice. 100

b) the same button may not be pressed twice. 90

Problem Solving

In Exercises 9–26, use the counting principle to determine the answer to part (a). Assume that each event is equally likely to occur.

9. **Coin Toss** Two coins are tossed.

a) Determine the number of points in the sample space. 4

b) Construct a tree diagram and list the sample space.*

Determine the probability that

c) no heads are tossed. $\frac{1}{4}$

d) exactly one head is tossed. $\frac{1}{2}$

e) two heads are tossed. $\frac{1}{4}$

10. **Boys and Girls** A couple plans to have two children.

a) Determine the number of points in the sample space of the possible arrangements of boys and girls. 4

b) Construct a tree diagram and list the sample space.*

Assuming that boys and girls are equally likely, determine the probability that the couple has

c) two girls. $\frac{1}{4}$

d) at least one girl. $\frac{3}{4}$

e) a girl and then a boy. $\frac{1}{4}$

11. **Cards** A box contains three cards. On one card there is a sun, on another card there is a question mark, and on the third card there is an apple.

Two cards are to be selected at random with replacement.

a) Determine the number of points in the sample space. 9

b) Construct a tree diagram and list the sample space.*

Determine the probability that

c) two apples are selected. $\frac{1}{9}$

d) a sun and then a question mark are selected. $\frac{1}{9}$

e) at least one apple is selected. $\frac{5}{9}$

12. **Cards** Repeat Exercise 11 but assume that the cards are drawn without replacement. *

13. **Marble Selection** A hat contains four marbles: 1 yellow, 1 red, 1 blue, and 1 green. Two marbles are to be selected at random without replacement from the hat.

a) Determine the number of points in the sample space. 12

b) Construct a tree diagram and list the sample space.*

Determine the probability of selecting

c) exactly 1 red marble. $\frac{1}{2}$

d) at least 1 marble that is not red. 1

e) no green marbles. $\frac{1}{2}$

14. **Three Coins** Three coins are tossed.

a) Determine the number of points in the sample space. 8

b) Construct a tree diagram and list the sample space.*

Determine the probability that

c) no heads are tossed. $\frac{1}{8}$

d) exactly one head is tossed. $\frac{3}{8}$

e) three heads are tossed. $\frac{1}{8}$

15. **Paint Choices** The Flotterons plan to purchase paint for the walls and paint for the trim in their living room. They will select one color for the walls and one color for the trim from the following colors.

Walls	Trim
Sable	Alabaster
Java	White
Chocolate	Oyster

a) Determine the number of points in the sample space. 9

b) Construct a tree diagram and list the sample space.*

Determine the probability that they select

c) Java. $\frac{1}{3}$

d) Java and Oyster. $\frac{1}{9}$

*See Instructor Answer Appendix

e) paint other than Java. $\frac{2}{3}$

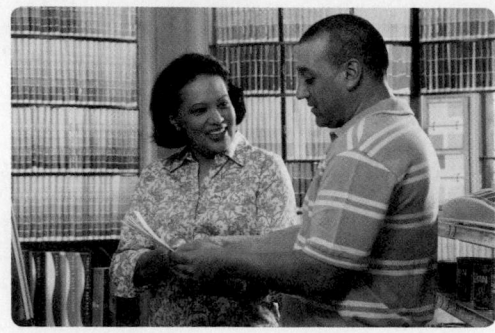

16. *Pet Shop* A pet shop is selling a calico cat, a Siamese cat, a Persian cat, and a Himalayan cat. The Chens are going to select two cats to bring home as pets.

a) Determine the number of points in the sample space. 12

b) Construct a tree diagram and list the sample space.*

Determine the probability that they select

c) the Persian cat. $\frac{1}{2}$

d) the Persian cat and the calico cat. $\frac{1}{6}$

e) cats other than the Persian cat. $\frac{1}{2}$

17. *Rolling Dice* Two dice are rolled.

a) Determine the number of points in the sample space. 36

b) Construct a tree diagram and list the sample space.*

Determine the probability that

c) a double (a 1, 1 or 2, 2, etc.) is rolled. $\frac{1}{6}$

d) a sum of 8 is rolled. $\frac{5}{36}$

e) a sum of 2 is rolled. $\frac{1}{36}$

f) Are you as likely to roll a sum of 2 as you are of rolling a sum of 8? No

18. *Voting* At a homeowners' association meeting, a board member can vote yes, vote no, or abstain on a motion. There are three motions on which a board member must vote.

a) Determine the number of points in the sample space. 27

b) Construct a tree diagram and determine the sample space.*

Determine the probability that a board member votes

c) no, yes, no in that order. $\frac{1}{27}$

d) yes on exactly two of the motions. $\frac{2}{9}$

e) yes on at least one motion. $\frac{19}{27}$

19. *Dinner Specials* At Brio Restaurant, each dinner special consists of an appetizer, a salad, and an entrée. The choices of appetizer, salad, and entrée are listed below.

Appetizer	Salad	Entrée
Bruschetta	Caesar	Ravioli
Antipasto	Greens	Salmon
		Lasagna

a) Determine the number of points in the sample space. 12

b) Construct a tree diagram and determine the sample space.*

If a customer randomly selects one of the dinner specials, determine the probability the customer selects

c) bruschetta for the appetizer. $\frac{1}{2}$

d) greens and lasagna. $\frac{1}{6}$

e) an entrée other than ravioli. $\frac{2}{3}$

20. *Gift Cards* Three different people are to be selected at random, and each will be given one gift card. There is one card from Home Depot, one from Best Buy, and one from Red Lobster. The first person selected gets to choose one of the cards. The second person selected gets to choose between the two remaining cards. The third person selected gets the third card.

a) Determine the number of points in the sample space. 6

b) Construct a tree diagram and determine the sample space.*

Determine the probability that

c) the Best Buy card is selected first. $\frac{1}{3}$

d) the Home Depot card is selected first and the Red Lobster card is selected last. $\frac{1}{6}$

e) The cards are selected in this order: Best Buy, Red Lobster, Home Depot. $\frac{1}{6}$

21. *Apartment Options* Don Cater plans to rent an apartment from Rustic Village Apartments. The following chart displays information regarding the possible number of bedrooms, bathrooms, and other features from which he can choose. For his apartment, Don will select the number of bedrooms, number of bathrooms, and one other feature.

Bedrooms	Bathrooms	Other Features
1	1	Fireplace
2	2	Hardwood floors
3		Balcony

*See Instructor Answer Appendix

a) Determine the number of points in the sample space. 18

b) Construct a tree diagram and determine the sample space.*

Determine the probability that Don selects

c) a two-bedroom apartment. $\frac{1}{3}$

d) a two-bedroom apartment with a fireplace. $\frac{1}{9}$

e) an apartment without a balcony. $\frac{2}{3}$

22. *A New Home Theater System* You visit Best Buy to purchase a new home theater system. You are going to purchase a Blu-ray player, a receiver, and a speaker system from among the following brands.

Blu-ray Player	Receiver	Speaker System
LG	Yamaha	Bose
Toshiba	Onkyo	JBL
Sony	Pioneer	
Insignia		

a) Determine the number of points in the sample space. 24

b) Construct a tree diagram and determine the sample space.*

Determine the probability of selecting

c) a Sony Blu-ray player. $\frac{1}{4}$

d) Bose speakers. $\frac{1}{2}$

e) a Sony Blu-ray player and Bose speakers. $\frac{1}{8}$

23. *Landscaping* Mr. and Mrs. Frank just moved into a new home and need to do some landscaping. They are going to purchase one tree, one shrub, and one lilac bush from the list below.

Trees	Shrubs	Lilac Bushes
Dogwood	Forsythia	Common
Maple	Holly	Sensation
Birch	Juniper	Primrose

a) Determine the number of points in the sample space. 27

b) Construct a tree diagram and determine the sample space.*

Determine the probability that the Franks select

c) a maple tree. $\frac{1}{3}$

d) a dogwood tree and a holly shrub. $\frac{1}{9}$

e) a lilac bush other than Sensation. $\frac{2}{3}$

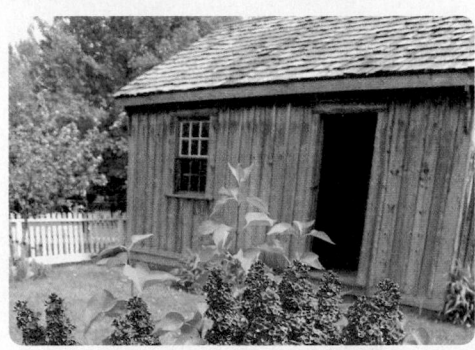

▲ Lilacs

24. *Literature Choices* You decide to take a literature course. A requirement for the course is that you must read one classic book, one nonfiction book, and one science fiction book from the list below.

Classic	Nonfiction	Science Fiction
A Farewell to Arms (*F*)	*John Adams* (*J*)	*Dune* (*D*)
The Grapes of Wrath (*G*)	*Angela's Ashes* (*A*)	*Ender's Game* (*E*)
Tom Sawyer (*T*)		
Moby-Dick (*M*)		

a) Determine the number of points in the sample space. 16

b) Construct a tree diagram and determine the sample space.*

Determine the probability that

c) *John Adams* is selected. $\frac{1}{2}$

d) either *A Farewell to Arms* or *Tom Sawyer* is selected. $\frac{1}{2}$

e) *Moby Dick* is not selected. $\frac{3}{4}$

25. *Personal Characteristics* An individual can be classified as male or female with red, brown, black, or blond hair and with brown, blue, or green eyes.

a) How many different classifications are possible (for example, male, red-headed, blue-eyed)? 24

b) Construct a tree diagram to determine the sample space.*

*See Instructor Answer Appendix

c) If each outcome is equally likely, determine the probability that the individual will be a male with black hair and blue eyes. $\frac{1}{24}$

d) Determine the probability that the individual will be a female with blond hair. $\frac{1}{8}$

26. *Mendel Revisited* A pea plant must have exactly one of each of the following pairs of traits: short (*s*) or tall (*t*); round (*r*) or wrinkled (*w*) seeds; yellow (*y*) or green (*g*) peas; and white (*wh*) or purple (*p*) flowers (for example, short, wrinkled, green pea with white flowers).

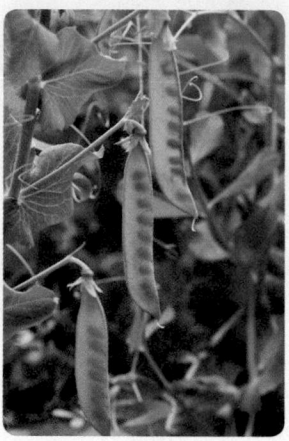

a) How many different classifications of pea plants are possible? 16

b) Use a tree diagram to determine all the classifications possible.*

c) If each characteristic is equally likely, find the probability that the pea plant will have round peas. $\frac{1}{2}$

d) Determine the probability that the pea plant will be short, have wrinkled seeds, have yellow seeds, and have purple flowers. $\frac{1}{16}$

Challenge Problems/Group Activities

27. *Three Chips* Suppose that a bag contains one white chip and two red chips. Two chips are going to be selected at random from the bag *with replacement*.

a) What is the probability of selecting a white chip from the bag on the first selection? $\frac{1}{3}$

b) What is the probability of selecting a red chip from the bag on the first selection? $\frac{2}{3}$

c) Are the outcomes of selecting a white chip and selecting a red chip on the first selection equally likely? Explain.*

d) The sample space when two chips are selected from the bag with replacement is ww, wr, rw, rr. Do you believe that the probability of selecting ww is greater than, equal to, or less than the probability of selecting rr? Explain. Answers will vary.

28. *Thumbtacks* A thumbtack is dropped on a concrete floor. Assume that the thumbtack can land only point up (u) or point down (d), as shown in the figure below.

If two thumbtacks are dropped, one after the other, the tree diagram below can be used to show the possible outcomes.

First Thumbtack — Second Thumbtack — Sample Space

u — u — *u u*
u — d — *u d*
d — u — *d u*
d — d — *d d*

a) Do you believe that the outcomes of the thumbtack landing point up and the thumbtack landing point down are equally likely? Explain. Answers will vary.

b) List the sample points in the sample space of this experiment. uu, ud, du, dd

c) Do you believe that the probability that both thumbtacks land point up (*uu*) is the same as the probability that both thumbtacks land point down (*dd*)? Explain. Answers will vary.

d) Can you compute the theoretical probability of a thumbtack landing point up and the theoretical probability of a thumbtack landing point down? Explain. It is not possible; answers as to why it is not possible will vary.

e) Obtain a box of thumbtacks and drop the thumbtacks out of the box with care. Determine the empirical probability of a thumbtack landing point up when dropped and the empirical probability of a thumbtack landing point down when dropped. Answers will vary.

Recreational Mathematics

29. *Ties* All my ties are red except two. All my ties are blue except two. All my ties are brown except two. How many ties do I have? 3; 1 red, 1 blue, and 1 brown

30. *Rock Faces* An experiment consists of 3 parts: flipping a coin, tossing a rock, and rolling a die. If the sample space consists of 60 sample points, determine the number of faces on the rock. 5 faces

Jumble For Exercises 31–32, refer to the Recreational Math box on page 711. Determine

a) *the number of possible arrangements of the letters given.*

b) *the word when the letters are placed in the proper order.*

31. RAHIC a) 120   b) CHAIR

32. STEABK a) 720   b) BASKET

*See Instructor Answer Appendix

▲ *Selecting items from a restaurant menu often requires an understanding of the words* or *and* and.

Every day we see and interpret the words **or** and **and**. For example, in a court case a judge may sentence a person to five years in prison *and* payment of a $100,000 fine. Or a judge may sentence a person to either 1 night in jail *or* payment of a $100 fine. When you go into a restaurant, the menu may indicate that you should select soup *or* salad, *and* an entrée, *and* a dessert. In this section, we will learn to solve probability problems involving the words *or* and *and*.

Why *This is Important* Many real-life situations involve the words *or* and *and*. For example, what is the probability that a family planning to have 3 children has 3 boys (a boy *and* a boy *and* a boy)?

In Section 12.5, we showed how to work probability problems by constructing sample spaces. Often it is inconvenient or too time consuming to solve a problem by first constructing a sample space. For example, if an experiment consists of selecting two cards with replacement from a deck of 52 cards, there would be 52 · 52 or 2704 points in the sample space. Trying to list all these sample points could take hours. In this section, we learn how to solve *compound probability* problems that contain the words *and* or *or* without constructing a sample space.

Or Problems

The *or probability problem* requires obtaining a "successful" outcome for *at least one* of the given events. For example, suppose that we roll one die and we are interested in finding the probability of rolling an even number *or* a number greater than 4. For this situation, rolling either a 2, 4, or 6 (an even number) or a 5 or 6 (a number greater than 4) would be considered successful. Note that the number 6 satisfies both criteria. Since 4 of the 6 numbers meet the criteria (the 2, 4, 5, and 6), the probability of rolling an even number *or* a number greater than 4 is $\frac{4}{6}$ or $\frac{2}{3}$.

A formula for finding the probability of event A or event B, symbolized $P(A \text{ or } B)$, follows.

> ### Probability of *A* or *B*
> To determine the probability of A or B, use the following formula.
> $$P(A \text{ or } B) = P(A) + P(B) - P(A \text{ and } B)$$

Since we add (and subtract) probabilities to find $P(A \text{ or } B)$, this formula is sometimes referred to as the *addition formula*. We explain the use of the *or* formula in Example 1.

Even and greater than 6

Even

U

A B

2   8   7

4   10

6   9

1, 3, 5

Greater than 6

Figure 12.13

Example 1 *Using the Addition Formula*

Each of the numbers 1, 2, 3, 4, 5, 6, 7, 8, 9, and 10 is written on a separate piece of paper. The 10 pieces of paper are then placed in a hat, and one piece is randomly selected. Determine the probability that the piece of paper selected contains an even number or a number greater than 6.

Solution We are asked to find the probability that the number selected is *even* or is *greater than 6*. Let's use set A to represent the statement "the number is even" and set B to represent the statement "the number is greater than 6." Figure 12.13 is a

Venn diagram, as introduced in Chapter 2, with sets A (even) and B (greater than 6). There are a total of 10 numbers, of which five are even (2, 4, 6, 8, and 10). Thus, the probability of selecting an even number is $\frac{5}{10}$. Four numbers are greater than 6: the 7, 8, 9, and 10. Thus, the probability of selecting a number greater than 6 is $\frac{4}{10}$. Two numbers are both even and greater than 6: the 8 and 10. Thus, the probability of selecting a number that is both even and greater than 6 is $\frac{2}{10}$.

If we substitute the appropriate statements for A and B in the formula, we obtain

$$P(A \text{ or } B) = P(A) + P(B) - P(A \text{ and } B)$$

$$P\left(\begin{array}{c}\text{even or}\\\text{greater than 6}\end{array}\right) = P(\text{even}) + P\left(\begin{array}{c}\text{greater}\\\text{than 6}\end{array}\right) - P\left(\begin{array}{c}\text{even and}\\\text{greater than 6}\end{array}\right)$$

$$= \frac{5}{10} + \frac{4}{10} - \frac{2}{10}$$

$$= \frac{7}{10}$$

Thus, the probability of selecting an even number or a number greater than 6 is $\frac{7}{10}$. The seven numbers that are even or greater than 6 are 2, 4, 6, 7, 8, 9, and 10. ∎

Example 1 illustrates that when finding the probability of A or B, we add the probabilities of events A and B and then subtract the probability of both events occurring simultaneously.

Less than 5 and greater than 8

Figure 12.14

⌐ Example 2 *Using the Addition Formula*

Consider the same sample space, the numbers 1 through 10, as in Example 1. If one piece of paper is selected, determine the probability that it contains a number less than 5 or a number greater than 8.

Solution   Let A represent the statement "the number is less than 5" and B represent the statement "the number is greater than 8." A Venn diagram illustrating these statements is shown in Figure 12.14.

$$P(\text{number is less than 5}) = \frac{4}{10}$$

$$P(\text{number is greater than 8}) = \frac{2}{10}$$

Since there are no numbers that are *both* less than 5 and greater than 8, P(number is less than 5 and greater than 8) = 0. Therefore,

$$P\left(\begin{array}{c}\text{number is}\\\text{less than 5}\\\text{or greater}\\\text{than 8}\end{array}\right) = P\left(\begin{array}{c}\text{number is}\\\text{less than 5}\end{array}\right) + P\left(\begin{array}{c}\text{number is}\\\text{greater than 8}\end{array}\right) - P\left(\begin{array}{c}\text{number is}\\\text{less than 5}\\\text{and greater}\\\text{than 8}\end{array}\right)$$

$$= \frac{4}{10} + \frac{2}{10} - 0 = \frac{6}{10} = \frac{3}{5}$$

Thus, the probability of selecting a number less than 5 or greater than 8 is $\frac{3}{5}$. The six numbers that are less than 5 or greater than 8 are 1, 2, 3, 4, 9, and 10. ∎

In Example 2, it is impossible to select a number that is both less than 5 *and* greater than 8 when only one number is to be selected. Events such as these are said to be *mutually exclusive*.

> **Definition: Mutually Exclusive**
> Two events A and B are **mutually exclusive** if it is impossible for both events to occur simultaneously.

If events A and B are mutually exclusive, then $P(A \text{ and } B) = 0$ and the addition formula simplifies to $P(A \text{ or } B) = P(A) + P(B)$.

Example 3 *Probability of A or B*

One card is selected from a standard deck of playing cards. Determine whether the following pairs of events are mutually exclusive and determine $P(A \text{ or } B)$.

a) A = an ace, B = a 9
b) A = an ace, B = a heart
c) A = a red card, B = a black card
d) A = a picture card, B = a red card

The ace of hearts is both an ace and a heart.

Solution

a) There are four aces and four 9's in a standard deck of 52 cards. It is impossible to select both an ace and a 9 when only one card is selected. Therefore, these events are mutually exclusive.

$$P(\text{ace or }9) = P(\text{ace}) + P(9) = \frac{4}{52} + \frac{4}{52} = \frac{8}{52} = \frac{2}{13}$$

b) There are 4 aces and 13 hearts in a standard deck of 52 cards. One card, the ace of hearts, is both an ace and a heart. Therefore, these events are not mutually exclusive.

$$P(\text{ace}) = \frac{4}{52} \qquad P(\text{heart}) = \frac{13}{52} \qquad P(\text{ace and heart}) = \frac{1}{52}$$

$$P(\text{ace or heart}) = P(\text{ace}) + P(\text{heart}) - P(\text{ace and heart})$$

$$= \frac{4}{52} + \frac{13}{52} - \frac{1}{52}$$

$$= \frac{16}{52} = \frac{4}{13}$$

c) There are 26 red cards and 26 black cards in a standard deck of 52 cards. It is impossible to select one card that is both a red card and a black card. Therefore, the events are mutually exclusive.

$$P(\text{red or black}) = P(\text{red}) + P(\text{black})$$

$$= \frac{26}{52} + \frac{26}{52} = \frac{52}{52} = 1$$

Since $P(\text{red or black}) = 1$, a red card or a black card must be selected.

d) There are 12 picture cards in a standard deck of 52 cards. Six of the 12 picture cards are red (the jacks, queens, and kings of hearts and diamonds). Thus, selecting a picture card and a red card are not mutually exclusive.

$$P\left(\begin{array}{c}\text{picture card}\\\text{or red card}\end{array}\right) = P\left(\begin{array}{c}\text{picture}\\\text{card}\end{array}\right) + P\left(\begin{array}{c}\text{red}\\\text{card}\end{array}\right) - P\left(\begin{array}{c}\text{picture card}\\\text{and red card}\end{array}\right)$$

$$= \frac{12}{52} + \frac{26}{52} - \frac{6}{52}$$

$$= \frac{32}{52} = \frac{8}{13}$$

■

And Problems

A second type of probability problem is the *and probability problem*, which requires obtaining a favorable outcome in *each* of the given events. For example, suppose that *two* cards are to be selected from a deck of cards and we are interested in the probability of selecting two aces (one ace *and* then a second ace). Only if *both* cards selected are aces would this experiment be considered successful. A formula for finding the probability of events A and B, symbolized $P(A$ and $B)$, follows.

Probability of *A* and *B*
To determine the probability of A and B, use the following formula.
$$P(A \text{ and } B) = P(A) \cdot P(B)$$

Since we multiply to find $P(A$ and $B)$, this formula is sometimes referred to as the *multiplication formula*. When using the multiplication formula, we **always assume that event A has occurred when calculating $P(B)$** because we are determining the probability of obtaining a favorable outcome in both of the given events.*

Unless we specify otherwise, $P(A$ and $B)$ indicates that we are determining the probability that event A occurs *and then* event B occurs (in that order). Consider a bag that contains three chips: 1 red chip, 1 blue chip, and 1 green chip. Suppose that two chips are selected from the bag with replacement. The tree diagram and sample space for the experiment are shown in Fig. 12.15. There are nine possible outcomes for the two selections, as indicated in the sample space.

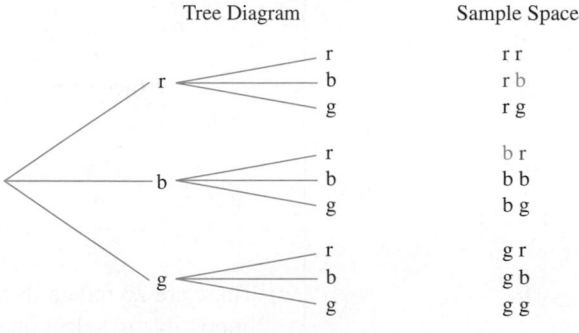

Figure 12.15

Note that the probability of selecting a red chip followed by a blue chip (rb), indicated by P(red and blue), is $\frac{1}{9}$. The probability of selecting a red chip and a blue chip, in any order (rb or br), is $\frac{2}{9}$. In this section, when we ask for $P(A$ and $B)$, it means the probability of event A occurring *and then* event B occurring, in that order.

Example 4 *An Experiment with Replacement*

Two cards are to be selected *with replacement* from a deck of cards. Determine the probability that two spades will be selected.

Solution Since the deck of 52 cards contains thirteen spades, the probability of selecting a spade on the first draw is $\frac{13}{52}$. The card selected is then returned to the deck. Therefore, the probability of selecting a spade on the second draw remains $\frac{13}{52}$.

---

*$P(B)$, assuming that event A has occurred, may be denoted $P(B|A)$, which is read "the probability of B, given A." We will discuss this type of probability (conditional probability) further in section 12.7

If we let A represent the selection of the first spade and B represent the selection of the second spade, the formula may be written as follows.

$$P(A \text{ and } B) = P(A) \cdot P(B)$$
$$P(2 \text{ spades}) = P(\text{spade 1 } and \text{ spade 2}) = P(\text{spade 1}) \cdot P(\text{spade 2})$$
$$= \frac{13}{52} \cdot \frac{13}{52}$$
$$= \frac{1}{4} \cdot \frac{1}{4} = \frac{1}{16}$$

Example 5 *An Experiment without Replacement*

Two cards are to be selected *without replacement* from a deck of cards. Determine the probability that two spades will be selected.

Solution This example is similar to Example 4. However, this time we are doing the experiment without replacing the first card selected to the deck before selecting the second card.

The probability of selecting a spade on the first draw is $\frac{13}{52}$. When calculating the probability of selecting the second spade, we must assume that the first spade has been selected. Once this first spade has been selected, only 51 cards, including 12 spades, remain in the deck. The probability of selecting a spade on the second draw becomes $\frac{12}{51}$. The probability of selecting two spades without replacement is

$$P(2 \text{ spades}) = P(\text{spade 1}) \cdot P(\text{spade 2})$$
$$= \frac{13}{52} \cdot \frac{12}{51}$$
$$= \frac{1}{4} \cdot \frac{4}{17} = \frac{1}{17}$$

Now we introduce *independent events*.

Definition: Independent Events
Event A and event B are **independent events** if the occurrence of either event in no way affects the probability of occurrence of the other event.

Rolling dice and tossing coins are examples of independent events. In Example 4, the events are independent since the first card was returned to the deck. The probability of selecting a spade on the second draw was not affected by the first selection. The events in Example 5 are not independent since the probability of the selection of the second spade was affected by removing the first spade selected from the deck. Such events are called *dependent events*. *Experiments done with replacement will result in independent events, and those done without replacement will result in dependent events.*

Example 6 *Independent or Dependent Events?*

One hundred people attended a charity benefit to raise money for cancer research. Three people in attendance will be selected at random without replacement, and each will be awarded one door prize. Are the events of selecting the three people who will be awarded the door prize independent or dependent events?

Solution The events are dependent since each time one person is selected, it changes the probability of the next person being selected. In the first selection, the probability that a specific individual is selected is $\frac{1}{100}$. If that person is not selected first, the probability that the specific person is selected second changes to $\frac{1}{99}$. In general, in any experiment in which two or more items are selected *without replacement*, the events will be dependent.   ∎

The multiplication formula may be extended to more than two events, as illustrated in Example 7.

Example 7 *Drug Reaction*

A new medicine was given to a sample of 25 of Dr. Cleary's patients with flu symptoms. Of the total, 19 patients reacted favorably, 2 reacted unfavorably, and 4 were unaffected. Three of these patients are selected at random. Determine the probability of each of the following.

a) All three reacted favorably.

b) The first patient reacted favorably, the second patient reacted unfavorably, and the third patient was unaffected.

c) No patient reacted favorably.

d) At least one patient reacted favorably.

Solution Each time a patient is selected, the number of patients remaining decreases by one.

a) The probability that the first patient reacted favorably is $\frac{19}{25}$. If the first patient reacted favorably, of the 24 remaining patients only 18 patients are left who reacted favorably. The probability of selecting a second patient who reacted favorably is $\frac{18}{24}$. If the second patient reacted favorably, only 17 patients are left who reacted favorably. The probability of selecting a third patient who reacted favorably is $\frac{17}{23}$.

$$P\begin{pmatrix} \text{three patients} \\ \text{reacted} \\ \text{favorably} \end{pmatrix} = P\begin{pmatrix} \text{first patient} \\ \text{reacted} \\ \text{favorably} \end{pmatrix} \cdot P\begin{pmatrix} \text{second patient} \\ \text{reacted} \\ \text{favorably} \end{pmatrix} \cdot P\begin{pmatrix} \text{third patient} \\ \text{reacted} \\ \text{favorably} \end{pmatrix}$$

$$= \frac{19}{25} \cdot \frac{18}{24} \cdot \frac{17}{23} = \frac{969}{2300}$$

b) The probability that the first patient reacted favorably is $\frac{19}{25}$. Once a patient is selected, there are only 24 patients remaining. Two of the remaining 24 patients reacted unfavorably. Thus, the probability that the second patient reacted unfavorably is $\frac{2}{24}$. After the second patient is selected, there are 23 remaining patients, of which 4 were unaffected. The probability that the third patient was unaffected is therefore $\frac{4}{23}$.

$$P\begin{pmatrix} \text{first patient reacted favorably, the} \\ \text{second patient reacted unfavorably, and} \\ \text{the third patient was unaffected} \end{pmatrix}$$

$$= P\begin{pmatrix} \text{first patient} \\ \text{reacted} \\ \text{favorably} \end{pmatrix} \cdot P\begin{pmatrix} \text{second patient} \\ \text{reacted} \\ \text{unfavorably} \end{pmatrix} \cdot P\begin{pmatrix} \text{third patient} \\ \text{was} \\ \text{unaffected} \end{pmatrix}$$

$$= \frac{19}{25} \cdot \frac{2}{24} \cdot \frac{4}{23} = \frac{19}{1725}$$

Which formula to use

It is sometimes difficult to determine when to use the *or* formula and when to use the *and* formula. The following information may be helpful in deciding which formula to use.

Or formula

Or problems will almost always contain the word *or* in the statement of the problem. For example, determine the probability of selecting a heart *or* a 6. *Or* problems in this book generally involve only *one* selection. For example, "one card is selected" or "one die is rolled."

And formula

And problems often do *not* use the word *and* in the statement of the problem. For example, "determine the probability that both cards selected are red" or "determine the probability that none of those selected is a banana" are both *and*-type problems. *And* problems in this book will generally involve *more than one* selection. For example, the problem may read "two cards are selected" or "three coins are flipped."

c) If none of the patients reacted favorably, the patients either reacted unfavorably or were unaffected. Six patients did not react favorably (2 reacted unfavorably and 4 were unaffected). The probability that the first patient selected did not react favorably is $\frac{6}{25}$. After the first patient is selected, 5 of the remaining 24 patients did not react favorably. After the second patient is selected, 4 of the remaining 23 patients did not react favorably.

$$P\begin{pmatrix} \text{none} \\ \text{reacted} \\ \text{favorably} \end{pmatrix} = P\begin{pmatrix} \text{first patient} \\ \text{did not react} \\ \text{favorably} \end{pmatrix} \cdot P\begin{pmatrix} \text{second patient} \\ \text{did not react} \\ \text{favorably} \end{pmatrix} \cdot P\begin{pmatrix} \text{third patient} \\ \text{did not react} \\ \text{favorably} \end{pmatrix}$$

$$= \frac{6}{25} \cdot \frac{5}{24} \cdot \frac{4}{23} = \frac{1}{115}$$

d) In Section 12.5, we learned that

$$P(\text{event happening at least once}) = 1 - P(\text{event does not happen})$$

In part (c), we found that the probability of selecting three patients none of whom reacted favorably was $\frac{1}{115}$. Therefore, the probability that at least one of the patients selected reacted favorably can be found as follows.

$$P\begin{pmatrix} \text{at least one of the three} \\ \text{patients reacted favorably} \end{pmatrix} = 1 - P\begin{pmatrix} \text{none of the three} \\ \text{patients reacted favorably} \end{pmatrix}$$

$$= 1 - \frac{1}{115} = \frac{115}{115} - \frac{1}{115} = \frac{114}{115} \qquad \blacksquare$$

Exercises

Warm Up Exercises

In Exercises 1–10, fill in the blank with an appropriate ward, phrase, or symbol(s).

1. Probability problems that contain the words *and* or *or* are considered _____ probability problems. Compound

2. Probability problems that require obtaining a successful outcome for at least one of the given events are _____ probability problems. Or

3. Probability problems that require obtaining a favorable outcome in each of the given events are _____ probability problems. And

4. If it is impossible for two events *A* and *B* to occur simultaneously, then the events are considered to be _____ exclusive. Mutually

5. For two events *A* and *B*, if the occurrence of either event in no way affects the probability of the occurrence of

the other event, then the two events are considered to be _____ events. Independent

6. For two events *A* and *B*, if the occurrence of either event has an effect on the probability of the occurrence of the other event, then the two events are considered to be _____ events. Dependent

7. Experiments done with replacement will result in _____ events. Independent

8. Experiments done without replacement will result in _____ events. Dependent

9. The formula for finding the probability of event *A* or event *B* is $P(A \text{ or } B) = $ _____. $P(A) + P(B) - P(A \text{ and } B)$

10. The formula for finding the probability of event *A* and event *B* is $P(A \text{ and } B) = $ _____. $P(A) \cdot P(B)$

Practice the Skills

In Exercises 11–14, determine the indicated probability.

11. If $P(A) = 0.8$, $P(B) = 0.4$, and $P(A \text{ and } B) = 0.5$, determine $P(A \text{ or } B)$. 0.7

12. If $P(A \text{ or } B) = 0.9$, $P(A) = 0.8$, and $P(B) = 0.3$, determine $P(A \text{ and } B)$. 0.2

13. If $P(A \text{ or } B) = 0.7$, $P(A) = 0.6$, and $P(A \text{ and } B) = 0.3$, determine $P(B)$. 0.4

14. If $P(A \text{ or } B) = 0.6$, $P(B) = 0.3$, and $P(A \text{ and } B) = 0.1$, determine $P(A)$. 0.4

15. *Exam Preparation* Professor Connell is in charge of a program to prepare students for a high school equivalency exam. Records show that the probability that a student in the program needs help in mathematics is 0.7, the probability that a student needs help in English is 0.6, and the probability that a student needs help in both mathematics and English is 0.55. Determine the probability that a student in the program needs help in mathematics or English. 0.75

16. *Car Repair* The manager at Arango Automotive has found that the probability that a car brought into the shop requires an oil change is 0.6, the probability that a car brought into the shop requires brake repair is 0.2, and the probability that a car requires both an oil change and brake repair is 0.1. For a car brought into the shop, determine the probability that the car will require an oil change or brake repair. 0.7

Roll a Die In Exercises 17–20, a single die is rolled one time. Determine the probability of rolling

17. a 2 or 6. $\frac{1}{3}$

18. an odd number or a number greater than 4. $\frac{2}{3}$

19. a number greater than 4 or less than 2. $\frac{1}{2}$

20. a number greater than 3 or less than 5. 1

Select One Card In Exercises 21–26, one card is selected from a deck of playing cards. Determine the probability of selecting

21. an ace or a 4. $\frac{2}{13}$

22. a jack or a club. $\frac{4}{13}$

23. a picture card or a black card. $\frac{8}{13}$

24. a club or a red card. $\frac{3}{4}$

25. a card less than 6 or a club. (*Note:* The ace is considered a low card.) $\frac{7}{13}$

26. a card greater than 9 or a black card. $\frac{17}{26}$

Problem Solving

Select Two Cards In Exercises 27–34, a board game uses the deck of 20 cards shown.

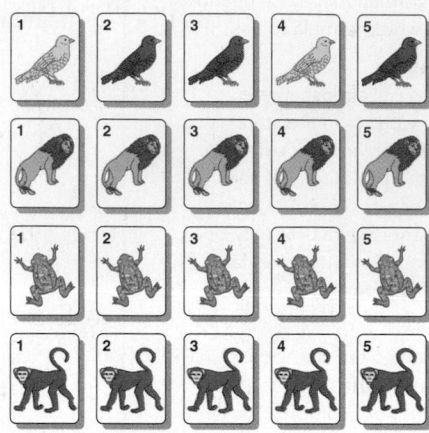

Two cards are selected at random from this deck. Determine the probability of the following

  a) *with replacement.*

  b) *without replacement.*

27. They both show lions. a) $\frac{1}{16}$ b) $\frac{1}{19}$

28. They both show the number 3. a) $\frac{1}{25}$ b) $\frac{3}{95}$

29. The first shows a monkey, and the second shows a bird. a) $\frac{1}{16}$ b) $\frac{5}{76}$

30. The first shows a 2, and the second shows a 4. a) $\frac{1}{25}$ b) $\frac{4}{95}$

31. The first shows a yellow bird, and the second shows a frog. a) $\frac{1}{40}$ b) $\frac{1}{38}$

32. They both show even numbers. a) $\frac{4}{25}$ b) $\frac{14}{95}$

33. Neither shows an even number. a) $\frac{9}{25}$ b) $\frac{33}{95}$

34. The first shows a lion, and the second shows a red bird. a) $\frac{3}{80}$ b) $\frac{3}{76}$

Select One Card In the deck of cards used in Exercises 27–34, if one card is drawn, determine the probability that the card shows

35. a monkey or an even number. $\frac{11}{20}$

36. a yellow bird or a number greater than 3. $\frac{9}{20}$

37. a lion or a 2. $\frac{2}{5}$

38. a red bird or an even number. $\frac{1}{2}$

Two Spins In Exercises 39–48, assume that the pointer cannot land on the line and that each spin is independent. If the pointer in Fig. 12.16 is spun twice, determine the probability that the pointer lands on

39. red on both spins. $\frac{1}{4}$ **40.** red and then yellow. $\frac{1}{4}$

Figure 12.16

Two Spins If the pointer in Fig. 12.17 is spun twice, determine the probability that the pointer lands on

41. green and then red. $\frac{1}{8}$ **42.** red on both spins. $\frac{1}{16}$

Figure 12.17

Two Spins If the pointer in Fig. 12.18 is spun twice, determine the probability that the pointer lands on

43. red on both spins. $\frac{9}{64}$

44. a color other than green on both spins. $\frac{9}{16}$

Figure 12.18

Two Spins In Exercises 45–48, assume that the pointer in Fig. 12.16 is spun and then the pointer in Fig. 12.17 is spun. Determine the probability of the pointers landing on

45. red on both spins. $\frac{1}{8}$

46. yellow on the first spin and red on the second spin. $\frac{1}{8}$

47. a color other than red on both spins. $\frac{3}{8}$

48. yellow on the first spin and a color other than yellow on the second spin. $\frac{3}{8}$

Selecting an Envelope In Exercises 49–56, consider the colored envelopes shown below.

If one of the envelopes is selected at random, determine the probability that

49. a yellow or a blue envelope is selected. $\frac{3}{7}$

50. an envelope other than a red envelope is selected. $\frac{4}{7}$

If two envelopes are selected at random, with replacement, determine the probability that

51. both are red envelopes. $\frac{9}{49}$

52. the first is a blue envelope and the second is a yellow envelope. $\frac{2}{49}$

If three envelopes are selected at random, without replacement, determine the probability that

53. they are all red envelopes. $\frac{1}{35}$

54. none is a red envelope. $\frac{4}{35}$

55. the first is a red envelope, the second is a blue envelope, and the third is a blue envelope. $\frac{1}{35}$

56. the first is a red envelope, the second is a green envelope, and the third is a red envelope. $\frac{1}{35}$

Having a Family In Exercises 57–60, a couple has three children. Assuming independence and that the probability of a boy is $\frac{1}{2}$, determine the probability that

57. all three children are girls. $\frac{1}{8}$

58. all three children are boys. $\frac{1}{8}$

59. the youngest child is a boy and the two older children are girls. $\frac{1}{8}$

60. the youngest child is a girl, the middle child is a boy, and the oldest child is a girl. $\frac{1}{8}$

61. a) *Five Children* The Martinos plan to have five children. Determine the probability that all their children will be boys. (Assume that $P(\text{boy}) = \frac{1}{2}$ and assume independence.) $\frac{1}{32}$

b) If their first four children are boys and Mrs. Martino is expecting another child, what is the probability that the fifth child will be a boy? $\frac{1}{2}$

62. a) *The Probability of a Girl* The Bronsons plan to have eight children. Determine the probability that all their children will be girls. (Assume that $P(\text{girl}) = \frac{1}{2}$ and assume independence.) $\frac{1}{256}$

b) If their first seven children are girls and Mrs. Bronson is expecting another child, what is the probability that the eighth child will be a girl? $\frac{1}{2}$

Books *Angel Sanchez has seven books on a shelf: 4 mysteries, 2 science fiction books, and 1 biography. In Exercises 63–66, two books will be selected at random. Determine the probability of selecting each of the following*

   a) *with replacement.*

   b) *without replacement.*

63. a mystery and then a biography **a)** $\frac{4}{49}$ **b)** $\frac{2}{21}$

64. no science fiction books **a)** $\frac{25}{49}$ **b)** $\frac{10}{21}$

65. at least one science fiction book **a)** $\frac{24}{49}$ **b)** $\frac{11}{21}$

66. two biographies **a)** $\frac{1}{49}$ **b)** 0

Health Insurance *A sample of 75 people yielded the following information about their health insurance.*

Number of People	Type of Insurance
33	Managed care plan
27	Traditional insurance
15	No insurance

Two people who provided information for the table were selected at random, without replacement. Determine the probability that

67. neither had traditional insurance. $\frac{376}{925}$

68. they both had a managed care plan. $\frac{176}{925}$

69. at least one had traditional insurance. $\frac{549}{925}$

70. the first had traditional insurance and the second had a managed care plan. $\frac{297}{1850}$

Hiring An Attorney *A sample of 40 people who recently hired an attorney yielded the following information about their attorneys.*

Number of People	Would You Recommend Your Attorney to a Friend
23	Yes
7	No
10	Not sure

Three people who provided information for the table were selected at random. Determine the probability that

71. they would all recommend their attorneys. $\frac{1771}{9880}$

72. the first would not recommend the attorney, but the second and third would recommend their attorneys. $\frac{1771}{29,640}$

73. the first two would not recommend their attorneys, and the third is not sure if he or she would recommend the attorney. $\frac{7}{988}$

74. the first would recommend the attorney, but the second and third would not recommend their attorneys. $\frac{161}{9880}$

A New Medicine *In Exercises 75–78, a new medicine was given to a sample of 100 hospital patients. Of the total, 70 patients reacted favorably, 10 reacted unfavorably, and 20 were unaffected by the drug. Assume that this sample is representative of the entire population. If this medicine is given to Mr. and Mrs. Rivera and their son Carlos, what is the probability of each of the following? (Assume independence.)*

75. Mrs. Rivera reacts favorably. $\frac{7}{10}$

76. Mr. and Mrs. Rivera react favorably, and Carlos is unaffected. $\frac{49}{500}$

77. All three react favorably. $\frac{343}{1000}$

78. No one reacts favorably. $\frac{27}{1000}$

Multiple-Choice Exam *In Exercises 79–84, each question of a five-question multiple-choice exam has four possible answers. Gurshawn Salk picks an answer at random for each question. Determine the probability that he selects the correct answer on*

79. any one question. $\frac{1}{4}$

80. only the first question. $\frac{81}{1024}$

81. only the third and fourth questions. $\frac{27}{1024}$

82. all five questions. $\frac{1}{1024}$

83. none of the questions. $\frac{243}{1024}$

84. at least one of the questions. $\frac{781}{1024}$

A Slot Machine *In Exercises 85–88, consider a slot machine.*

Most people who play slot machines end up losing money because the machines are designed to favor the casino (the house). There are 22 positions on each reel. Assume that the following is a list of the number of symbols of each type on each of the three reels and each symbol has the same chance of occurring (which is not the case; see the Mathematics Today on page 722).

Pictures on Reels		Reels	
	1	2	3
Cherries 🍒	2	5	4
Oranges 🟠	5	4	5
Plums ●	6	4	4
Bells 🔔	3	4	4
Melons ⬤	3	2	3
Bars BAR	2	2	1
7s 7	1	1	1

For this slot machine, assuming that the wheels are independent, determine the probability of obtaining

85. an orange on the first reel. $\frac{5}{22}$

86. bells on all three reels. $\frac{6}{1331}$

87. no bars. $\frac{1050}{1331}$

88. three 7's. $\frac{1}{10,648}$

Two Wheels *In Exercises 89–92, suppose that you spin the following double wheel.*

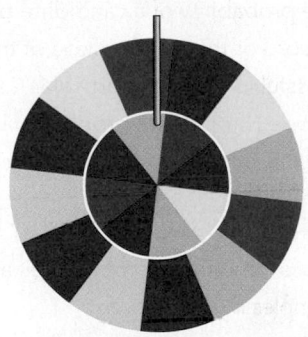

Assuming that the wheels are independent and each outcome is equally likely, determine the probability that you get

89. blue on both wheels. $\frac{1}{24}$

90. red on the outer wheel and blue on the inner wheel. $\frac{1}{12}$

91. red on neither wheel. $\frac{5}{12}$

92. red on at least one wheel. $\frac{7}{12}$

Hitting a Target *In Exercises 93–96, the probability that a heat-seeking torpedo will hit its target is 0.4. If the first torpedo hits its target, the probability that the second torpedo will hit the target increases to 0.9 because of the extra heat generated by the first explosion. If two heat-seeking torpedoes are fired at a target, determine the probability that*

93. neither hits the target. 0.36

94. the first hits the target and the second misses the target. 0.04

95. both hit the target. 0.36

96. the first misses the target and the second hits the target. 0.24

97. *Polygenetic Afflictions* Certain birth defects and syndromes are *polygenetic* in nature. Typically, the chance that an offspring will be born with a polygenetic affliction is small. However, once an offspring is born with the affliction, the probability that future offspring of the same parents will be born with the same affliction increases. Let's assume that the probability of a child being born with affliction *A* is 0.001. If a child is born with this affliction, the probability of a future child being born with the same affliction becomes 0.04.

a) Are the events of the births of two children in the same family with affliction *A* independent? No

b) A couple plans to have one child. Determine the probability that the child will be born with this affliction. 0.001

A couple plans to have two children. Use the information provided to determine the probability that

c) both children will be born with the affliction. 0.00004

d) the first will be born with the affliction and the second will not. 0.00096

e) the first will not be born with the affliction and the second will. 0.000999

f) neither will be born with the affliction. 0.998001

98. *Lottery Ticket* In a bin are an equal number of balls marked with the digits 0, 1, 2, 3, . . . , 9. Three balls are to be selected from the bin, one after the other, at random with replacement to make the winning three-digit lottery number. Ms. Jones has a lottery ticket with a three-digit number in the range 000 to 999. Determine the probability that Ms. Jones's number is the winning number. $\frac{1}{1000}$

Chance of an Audit *In Exercises 99–102, assume that 36 in every 1000 people in the $34,000–$82,400 income bracket are audited yearly. Assuming that the returns to be audited are selected at random and each year's selections are independent of the previous year's selections, determine the probability that a person in this income bracket will be audited*

99. this year. $\frac{9}{250}$

100. the next two years in succession. $\frac{81}{62,500}$

101. this year but not next year. $\frac{2169}{62,500}$

102. neither this year nor next year. $\frac{58,081}{62,500}$

Challenge Problems/Group Activities

103. *Picking Chips* A bag contains five red chips, three blue chips, and two yellow chips. Two chips are selected from the bag without replacement. Determine the probability that two chips of the same color are selected. $\frac{14}{45}$

104. *Peso Coins* Ron has ten coins from Mexico: three 1-peso coins, one 2-peso coin, two 5-peso coins, one 10-peso coin, and three 20-peso coins. He selects two coins at random without replacement. Assuming that each coin is equally likely to be selected, determine the probability that Ron selects at least one 1-peso coin. $\frac{8}{15}$

105. *A Fair Game?* Two playing cards are dealt to you from a well-shuffled standard deck of 52 cards. If either card is a diamond or if both are diamonds, you win; otherwise, you lose. Determine whether this game favors you, is fair, or favors the dealer. Explain your answer. Favors dealer. The probability of at least one diamond is ≈ 0.44, which is less than 0.5

106. *Picture Card Probability* You have three cards: an ace, a king, and a queen. A friend shuffles the cards, selects two of them at random, and discards the third. You ask your friend to show you a picture card, and she turns over the king. What is the probability that she also has the queen? $\frac{1}{2}$

Recreational Mathematics

A Different Die For exercises 107–110, consider a six-sided die that has 1 dot on one side, 2 dots on two sides, and 3 dots on three sides.

If the die is rolled twice, determine the probability of rolling

107. two 2's. $\frac{1}{9}$ 108. two 3's. $\frac{1}{4}$

If the die is rolled only once, determine the probability of rolling

109. an even number or a number less than 3. $\frac{1}{2}$

110. an odd number or a number greater than 1. 1

Internet/Research Activity

111. Girolamo Cardano (1501–1576) wrote *Liber de Ludo Aleae*, which is considered to be the first book on probability. Cardano had a number of different vocations. Do research and write a paper on the life and accomplishments of Girolamo Cardano.

SECTION 12.7   Conditional Probability

▲ *Conditional probability may play a role in a candidate's bid for re-election.*

Often the probability of an event occurring may depend on one or more other events that previously occurred. For example, the probability of a candidate being re-elected may depend on the candidate's voting record or the current state of the economy. Or the probability that a salesperson is successful in selling a particular item may depend on whether the customer is a male or female. Probability problems like these, where the outcome of a previous event affects the probability of a later event, are called conditional probability problems.

Why *This is Important* We consider and use conditional probabilities all the time without realizing it, as you will see from the examples in this section.

In Section 12.6, we learned when two events are *dependent*, the occurrence of the first event, A, affected the probability of the second event, B, occurring. When we calculated $P(A$ and $B)$, when we determined the probability of event B, we assumed that event A occurred. That is, we calculated the probability of event B, given event A. The probability of event B, given event A, is called a *conditional probability*. The definition of conditional probability follows.

Definition: Conditional Probability

In general, the probability of event E_2 occurring, given that an event E_1 has happened (or will happen; the time relationship does not matter), is called a **conditional probability** and is written $P(E_2 | E_1)$.

The symbol $P(E_2 | E_1)$, read "the probability of E_2, given E_1," represents the probability of E_2 occurring, assuming that E_1 has already occurred (or will occur).

MATHEMATICS TODAY

Chance of Showers

At one time or another, you probably have been caught in a downpour on a day the weather forecaster had predicted sunny skies. Short-term (24-hour) weather forecasts are correct nearly 85% of the time, a level of accuracy achieved through the use of conditional probability. Computer models are used to analyze data taken on the ground and in the air and make predictions of atmospheric pressures at some future time, say 10 minutes ahead. Based on these predicted conditions, another forecast is then computed. This process is repeated until a weather map has been generated for the next 12, 24, 36, and 48 hours. Since each new prediction relies on the previous prediction being correct, the margin of error increases as the forecast extends further into the future.

Why *This is Important*
Weather forecasting is one of many real-life applications of conditional probability.

Example **1** *Using Conditional Probability*

A single card is selected from a deck of cards. Determine the probability it is a club, given that it is black.

Solution We are told that the card is black. Thus, only 26 cards are possible, of which 13 are clubs. Therefore,

$$P(\text{club} | \text{black}) \text{ or } P(C | B) = \frac{13}{26} = \frac{1}{2}$$

Example **2** *Girls in a Family*

A family has two children. Assuming that boys and girls are equally likely, determine the probability that the family has

a) two girls.

b) two girls if you know that at least one of the children is a girl.

c) two girls given that the older child is a girl.

Solution

a) To determine the probability that the family has two girls, we can determine the sample space of a family with two children. Then, from the sample space we can determine the probability that both children are girls. The sample space of two children can be determined by a tree diagram (see Fig. 12.19).

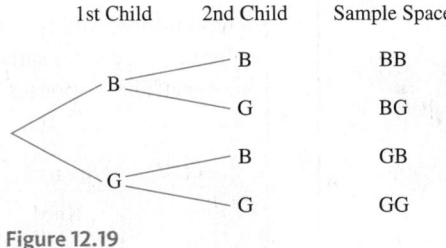

Figure 12.19

There are four possible equally likely outcomes: BB, BG, GB, and GG. Only one of the outcomes has two girls, GG. Thus,

$$P(2 \text{ girls}) = \frac{1}{4}$$

b) We are given that at least one of the children is a girl. Therefore, for this example the sample space is BG, GB, GG. Since there are three possibilities, of which only one has two girls, GG,

$$P(\text{both girls} | \text{at least one is a girl}) = \frac{1}{3}$$

c) If the older child is a girl, the sample space reduces to GB, GG. Thus,

$$P(\text{both girls} | \text{older child is a girl}) = \frac{1}{2}$$

A number of formulas can be used to find conditional probabilities. The one we will use follows on page 730.

Conditional Probability

For any two events, E_1 and E_2, the conditional probability, $P(E_2|E_1)$, is determined as follows.

$$P(E_2|E_1) = \frac{n(E_1 \text{ and } E_2)}{n(E_1)}$$

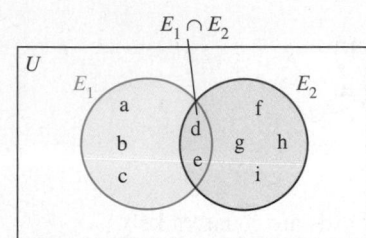

Figure 12.20

In the formula, $n(E_1 \text{ and } E_2)$ represents the number of sample points common to both event 1 and event 2, and $n(E_1)$ is the number of sample points in event E_1, the given event. Since the intersection of E_1 and E_2, symbolized $E_1 \cap E_2$, represents the sample points common to both E_1 and E_2, the formula can also be expressed as

$$P(E_2|E_1) = \frac{n(E_1 \cap E_2)}{n(E_1)}$$

Figure 12.20 is helpful in explaining conditional probability.

Here, the number of elements in E_1 is five, the number of elements in E_2 is six, and the number of elements in both E_1 and E_2, or $E_1 \cap E_2$, is two.

$$P(E_2|E_1) = \frac{n(E_1 \text{ and } E_2)}{n(E_1)} = \frac{2}{5}$$

Thus, for this situation, the probability of selecting an element from E_2, given that the element is in E_1, is $\frac{2}{5}$.

Example 3 Using the Conditional Probability Formula

Two hundred and fifty patients who had knee, hip, or heart surgery were asked whether they were satisfied, dissatisfied, or neutral regarding the results of their surgery. The responses are given in the table below.

Surgery	Satisfied	Dissatisfied	Total
Knee	70	25	95
Hip	90	15	105
Heart	45	5	50
Total	205	45	250

If one person from the 250 patients surveyed is selected at random, determine the probability that the person

a) was satisfied with the results of the surgery.

b) was satisfied with the results of the surgery, given that the person had knee surgery.

c) was dissatisfied with the results of the surgery, given that the person had hip surgery.

d) had heart surgery, given that the person was dissatisfied with the results of the surgery.

Solution

a) The total number of patients is 250, of which 205 were satisfied with the results of the surgery.

$$P(\text{satisfied with the results of the surgery}) = \frac{205}{250} = \frac{41}{50}$$

b) We are given that the person had knee surgery. Thus, we have a conditional probability problem. Let E_1 be the given information "the person had knee surgery." Let E_2 be "the person was satisfied with the results of the surgery." We are being asked to determine $P(E_2|E_1)$. The number of people who had knee surgery, $n(E_1)$, is 95. The number of people who had knee surgery and were satisfied with the results of the surgery, $n(E_1 \text{ and } E_2)$, is 70. Thus,

$$P(E_2|E_1) = \frac{n(E_1 \text{ and } E_2)}{n(E_1)} = \frac{70}{95} = \frac{14}{19}$$

c) We are given that the person had hip surgery. Thus, we have a conditional probability problem. Let E_1 be the given information "the person had hip surgery." Let E_2 be "the person was dissatisfied with the results of the surgery." We are asked to find $P(E_2|E_1)$. The number of people who had hip surgery, $n(E_1)$, is 105. The number of people who had hip surgery and were dissatisfied with the results of the surgery, $n(E_1 \text{ and } E_2)$, is 15. Thus,

$$P(E_2|E_1) = \frac{n(E_1 \text{ and } E_2)}{n(E_1)} = \frac{15}{105} = \frac{1}{7}$$

d) We are given that the person was dissatisfied with the results of the surgery. Thus, we have a conditional probability problem. Let E_1 be the given information "the person was dissatisfied with the results of the surgery." Let E_2 be "the person had heart surgery." We are asked to determine $P(E_2|E_1)$. The number of people who were dissatisfied with the results of the surgery, $n(E_1)$, is 45. The number of people who were dissatisfied with the results of the surgery and had heart surgery, $n(E_1 \text{ and } E_2)$, is 5. Thus,

$$P(E_2|E_1) = \frac{n(E_1 \text{ and } E_2)}{n(E_1)} = \frac{5}{45} = \frac{1}{9}$$ ∎

In many of the examples, we used the words *given that*. Other words may be used instead. For example, in Example 3(b), the question could have been worded "was satisfied with their surgery *if* the person had knee surgery."

SECTION 12.7 *Exercises*

Warm Up Exercises

In Exercises 1–4, fill in the blank with an appropriate word, phrase, or symbol(s).

1. The probability of event E_2 occurring, given that event E_1 has happened, is called a(n) _____ probability. Conditional

2. The notation for the probability of E_2, given E_1, is _____. $P(E_2|E_1)$

3. If $n(E_1 \text{ and } E_2) = 4$ and $n(E_1) = 12$, then $P(E_2|E_1) =$ _____. $\frac{1}{3}$

4. If $n(E_1 \text{ and } E_2) = 5$ and $n(E_1) = 22$, then $P(E_2|E_1) =$ _____. $\frac{5}{22}$

Practice the Skills

Select a Circle In Exercises 5–10, consider the circles shown.

Assume that one circle is selected at random and each circle is equally likely to be selected. Determine the probability of selecting

5. a 3, given that the circle is orange. $\frac{1}{3}$

6. a 5, given that the circle is yellow. 0

7. an even number, given that the circle is not orange. $\frac{2}{3}$

8. a number less than 2, given that the number is less than 5. $\frac{1}{4}$

9. a red number, given that the circle is orange. $\frac{2}{3}$

10. a number greater than 4, given that the circle is yellow. $\frac{1}{2}$

Select a Number *In Exercises 11–16, consider the following figures.*

Assume that one number from 1 to 7 is equally likely to be selected at random. Each number corresponds to one of the seven figures shown. Determine the probability of selecting

11. a triangle, given that an even number is selected. $\frac{2}{3}$

12. a triangle, given that a number greater than or equal to 5 is selected. $\frac{1}{3}$

13. a red figure, given that an even number is selected. $\frac{2}{3}$

14. a red or a blue figure, given that an even number is selected. 1

15. a circle or square, given that a number less than 4 is selected. $\frac{2}{3}$

16. a triangle, given that an odd number is selected. 0

Spin the Wheel *In Exercises 17–24, consider the following wheel.*

If the wheel is spun and each section is equally likely to stop under the pointer, determine the probability that the pointer lands on

17. a two, given that the color is purple. $\frac{1}{5}$

18. an odd number, given that the color is red. $\frac{2}{3}$

19. purple, given that the number is odd. $\frac{1}{3}$

20. a number greater than 6, given that the color is red. $\frac{1}{3}$

21. a number greater than 4, given that the color is purple. $\frac{3}{5}$

22. an even number, given that the color is red or purple. $\frac{1}{2}$

23. gold, given that the number is greater than 5. $\frac{1}{7}$

24. gold, given that the number is greater than 10. 0

Money from a Hat *In Exercises 25–28, assume that a hat contains four bills: a \$1 bill, a \$5 bill, a \$10 bill, and a \$20 bill. Two bills are to be selected at random with replacement. Construct a sample space as was done in Example 2 and determine the probability that*

25. both bills are \$1 bills. $\frac{1}{16}$

26. both bills are \$1 bills if the first selected is a \$1 bill. $\frac{1}{4}$

27. both bills are \$5 bills if at least one of the bills is a \$5 bill. $\frac{1}{7}$

28. both bills have a value greater than a \$5 bill if the second bill is a \$10 bill. $\frac{1}{2}$

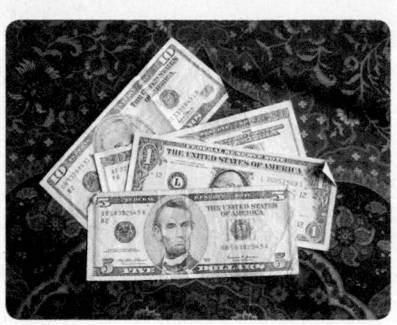

Two Dice *In Exercises 29–34, two dice are rolled one after the other. Construct a sample space and determine the probability that the sum of the dots on the dice total*

29. 7. $\frac{1}{6}$

30. 7 if the first die is a 1. $\frac{1}{6}$

31. 7 if the first die is a 3. $\frac{1}{6}$

32. an even number if the second die is a 2. $\frac{1}{2}$

33. a number greater than 7 if the second die is a 5. $\frac{2}{3}$

34. a 7 or 11 if the first die is a 5. $\frac{1}{3}$

Problem Solving

Costliest Hurricanes *In Exercises 35–40, use the following information concerning the nine costliest hurricanes to strike the U.S. mainland as of January 1, 2010.*

Hurricane	Category	Damage (billions of dollars)
Katrina (2005)	3	81.0
Andrew (1992)	5	35.0
Wilma (2005)	3	20.6
Ike (2008)	2	18.0
Charley (2004)	4	14.0
Ivan (2004)	3	13.0
Rita (2005)	3	10.0
Hugo (1989)	4	9.7
Frances (2004)	2	8.9

Source: *National Oceanic and Atmospheric Administration*

If one hurricane from the list is selected at random, determine the probability that it

35. was a category 4. $\frac{2}{9}$

36. had damages of at least \$16 billion. $\frac{4}{9}$

37. had damages of at least \$20 billion, given that it was a category 3. $\frac{1}{2}$

38. had damages of at least \$15 billion, given that it was a category 2. $\frac{1}{2}$

39. was a category 5, given that it had damages of at least \$25 billion. $\frac{1}{2}$

40. was a category 3, given that it had damages of at least \$10 billion. $\frac{4}{7}$

E-Z Pass *In Exercises 41–46, use the following table, which shows the number of cars and trucks that used the Pennsylvania Turnpike on a particular day. The number of cars and trucks that used, and did not use, the E-Z Pass on that same day was also recorded.*

E-Z Pass	Cars	Trucks	Total
Used	527	316	843
Did not use	935	683	1618
Total	1462	999	2461

If one of these vehicles is selected at random, determine the probability (as a decimal number rounded to four decimal places) that the

41. vehicle was a car. 0.5941

42. vehicle used the E-Z Pass. 0.3425

43. vehicle used the E-Z Pass, given that the vehicle was a car. 0.3605

44. vehicle used the E-Z Pass, given that the vehicle was a truck. 0.3163

45. vehicle was a car, given that the vehicle used the E-Z Pass. 0.6251

46. vehicle was a truck, given that the vehicle used the E-Z Pass. 0.3749

▲ *A sign on the Pennsylvania Turnpike.*

Sales Effectiveness *In Exercises 47–52, use the following information. Sales representatives at a car dealership were split into two groups. One group used an aggressive approach to sell a customer a new automobile. The other group used a passive approach. The following table summarizes the records for 650 customers.*

Approach	Sale	No Sale	Total
Aggressive	100	250	350
Passive	220	80	300
Total	320	330	650

If one of these customers is selected at random, determine the probability

47. that the aggressive approach was used. $\frac{7}{13}$

48. of a sale. $\frac{32}{65}$

49. of no sale, given that the passive approach was used. $\frac{4}{15}$

50. of a sale, given that the aggressive approach was used. $\frac{2}{7}$

51. of a sale, given that the passive approach was used. $\frac{11}{15}$

52. of no sale, given that the aggressive approach was used. $\frac{5}{7}$

New Residence *For Exercises 53–58, use the following information, which shows the educational attainment and the location of their new residence for people who moved in 2008. The data are rounded to the nearest thousand people.*

Educational Attainment	Same County	Different County, Same State	Different State	Abroad	Total
		Location of New Residence			
Not a high school graduate	2247	470	254	98	3069
High school graduate	3842	1074	712	145	5773
Some college	3319	1020	707	112	5158
Bachelor's degree	2072	760	667	182	3681
Graduate degree	913	383	461	118	1875
Total	12,393	3707	2801	655	19,556

Source: *U.S. Census Bureau*

If one of these individuals is selected at random, determine the probability (as a decimal number rounded to four decimal places) that the individual

53. moved within the same county. 0.6337

54. moved within the same county, given the individual has a bachelor's degree. 0.5629

55. moved to a different state, given the individual has a graduate degree. 0.2459

56. has a graduate degree, given the individual moved abroad. 0.1802

57. is a high school graduate, given the individual moved within the same state but different county. 0.2897

58. moved to a different state or abroad, given the individual has a bachelor's degree. 0.2306

Quality Control In Exercises 59–64, Sally Horsefall, a quality control inspector, is checking a sample of lightbulbs for defects. The following table summarizes her findings.

Wattage	Good	Defective	Total
20	80	15	95
50	100	5	105
100	120	10	130
Total	300	30	330

If one of these lightbulbs is selected at random, determine the probability that the lightbulb is

59. good. $\frac{10}{11}$

60. good, given that it is 50 watts. $\frac{20}{21}$

61. defective, given that it is 20 watts. $\frac{3}{19}$

62. good, given that it is 100 watts. $\frac{12}{13}$

63. good, given that it is 50 or 100 watts. $\frac{44}{47}$

64. defective, given that it is not 50 watts. $\frac{1}{9}$

News Survey In Exercises 65–70, 270 individuals are asked which evening news they watch most often. The results are summarized as follows.

Viewers	ABC	NBC	CBS	Other	Total
Men	30	20	40	55	145
Women	50	10	20	45	125
Total	80	30	60	100	270

If one of these individuals is selected at random, determine the probability that the person watches

65. ABC or NBC. $\frac{11}{27}$

66. ABC, given that the individual is a woman. $\frac{2}{5}$

67. ABC or NBC, given that the individual is a man. $\frac{10}{29}$

68. a station other than CBS, given that the individual is a woman. $\frac{21}{25}$

69. a station other than ABC, NBC, or CBS, given that the individual is a man. $\frac{11}{29}$

70. NBC or CBS, given that the individual is a woman. $\frac{6}{25}$

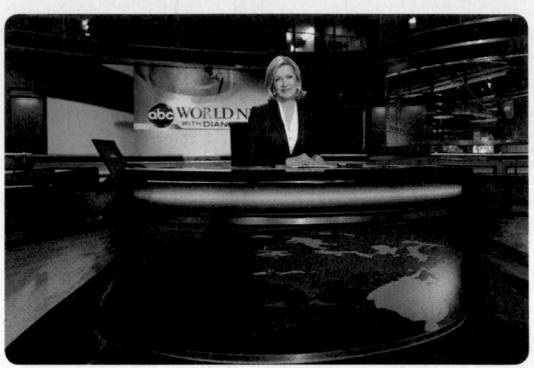

▲ *Diane Sawyer*, ABC Evening News

Challenge Problems/Group Activities

Mutual Fund Holdings Use the following information in Exercises 71–74. Mutual funds often hold many stocks. Each stock may be classified as a value stock, a growth stock, or a blend of the two. The stock may also be categorized by how large the company is. It may be classified as a large company stock, medium company stock, or small company stock. A selected mutual fund contains 200 stocks as illustrated in the following chart.

	Value	Blend	Growth	
	28	23	42	Large
	19	15	18	Medium
	26	12	17	Small

Equity Investment Style

If one stock is selected at random from the mutual fund, determine the probability that it is

71. a large company stock. $\frac{93}{200}$

72. a value stock. $\frac{73}{200}$

73. a blend, given that it is a medium company stock. $\frac{15}{52}$

74. a large company stock, given that it is a blend stock. $\frac{23}{50}$

75. Consider the Venn diagram below. The numbers in the regions of the circle indicate the number of items that belong to that region. For example, 60 items are in set A but not in set B.

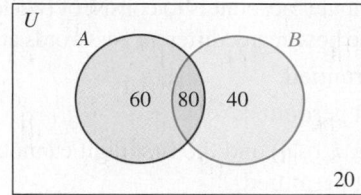

Determine **a)** $n(A)$ **b)** $n(B)$ **c)** $P(A)$ $\frac{7}{10}$ **d)** $P(B)$ $\frac{3}{5}$
140   120

Use the formula on page 730 to determine

e) $P(A\,|\,B)$. $\frac{2}{3}$ **f)** $P(B\,|\,A)$. $\frac{4}{7}$

g) Explain why $P(A\,|\,B) \neq P(A) \cdot P(B)$.
Because A and B are not independent events

76. A formula we gave for conditional probability is

$$P(E_2\,|\,E_1) = \frac{n(E_1 \text{ and } E_2)}{n(E_1)}$$

This formula may be derived from the formula

$$P(E_2\,|\,E_1) = \frac{P(E_1 \text{ and } E_2)}{P(E_1)}$$

Can you explain why? [*Hint:* Consider what happens to the denominators of $P(E_1 \text{ and } E_2)$ and $P(E_1,)$ when they are expressed as fractions and the fractions are divided out.]
The denominators of the probabilities will be the same and thus will divide out.

77. Given that $P(A) = 0.3$, $P(B) = 0.5$, and $P(A \text{ and } B) = 0.15$, use the formula

$$P(E_2\,|\,E_1) = \frac{P(E_1 \text{ and } E_2)}{P(E_1)}$$

to determine

a) $P(A\,|\,B)$. 0.3   **b)** $P(B\,|\,A)$. 0.5

c) Are A and B independent? Explain.
Yes; $P(A\,|\,B) = P(A) \cdot P(B)$

Recreational Mathematics

In Exercises 78–83, suppose that each circle is equally likely to be selected. One circle is selected at random.

Determine the probability indicated.

78. $P(\text{green circle}\,|\,+\text{ obtained})$ $\frac{1}{3}$

79. $P(+\,|\,\text{ orange circle obtained})$ $\frac{1}{2}$

80. $P(\text{yellow circle}\,|\,-\text{ obtained})$ $\frac{1}{3}$

81. $P(\text{green}\,+\,|\,+\text{ obtained})$ $\frac{1}{3}$

82. $P(\text{green or orange circle}\,|\,\text{green}\,+\text{ obtained})$ 1

83. $P(\text{orange circle with green}\,+\,|\,+\text{ obtained})$ $\frac{1}{3}$
*See Instructor Answer Appendix

The Counting Principle and Permutations

▲ *In how many different ways can movie posters be displayed?*

You are the manager of a movie theater and want to display a poster for each of the eight different movies showing at your theater. In how many different ways can you display the eight posters? In this section, we will learn how to determine the number of different ordered arrangements of a set of objects.

Why **This is Important** There are many real-life situations in which we need to determine the number of different ordered arrangements of a set of objects, such as the number of 5-digit zip codes or the number of 7-digit telephone numbers.

The Counting Principle

In Section 12.5, we introduced the counting principle, which is repeated here for your convenience.

> **Definition: Counting Principle**
> If a first experiment can be performed in M distinct ways and a second experiment can be performed in N distinct ways, then the two experiments in that specific order can be performed in $M \cdot N$ distinct ways.

The counting principle is illustrated in Examples 1 and 2.

Example 1 *Counting Principle: Passwords*

A password used to gain access to a computer account is to consist of two lowercase letters followed by four digits. Determine how many different passwords are possible if

a) repetition of letters and digits is permitted.

b) repetition of letters and digits is not permitted.

c) the first letter must be a vowel (*a, e, i, o, u*) and the first digit cannot be a 0, and repetition of letters and digits is not permitted.

Solution There are 26 letters and 10 digits (0–9). We have six positions to fill, as indicated.

$$\underline{L}\ \underline{L}\ \underline{D}\ \underline{D}\ \underline{D}\ \underline{D}$$

a) Since repetition is permitted, there are 26 possible choices for both the first and second positions. There are 10 possible choices for the third, fourth, fifth, and sixth positions.

$$\frac{26}{L}\ \frac{26}{L}\ \frac{10}{D}\ \frac{10}{D}\ \frac{10}{D}\ \frac{10}{D}$$

Since $26 \cdot 26 \cdot 10 \cdot 10 \cdot 10 \cdot 10 = 6,760,000$, there are 6,760,000 different possible arrangements.

b) There are 26 possibilities for the first position. Since repetition of letters is not permitted, there are only 25 possibilities for the second position. The same reasoning is used when determining the number of digits for positions 3 through 6.

$$\frac{26}{L}\ \frac{25}{L}\ \frac{10}{D}\ \frac{9}{D}\ \frac{8}{D}\ \frac{7}{D}$$

Since $26 \cdot 25 \cdot 10 \cdot 9 \cdot 8 \cdot 7 = 3,276,000$, there are 3,276,000 different possible arrangements.

c) Since the first letter must be an *a, e, i, o,* or *u,* there are five possible choices for the first position. The second position can be filled by any of the letters except for the vowel selected for the first position. Therefore, there are 25 possibilities for the second position.

Since the first digit cannot be a 0, there are nine possibilities for the third position. The fourth position can be filled by any digit except the one selected for the third position. Thus, there are nine possibilities for the fourth position. Since the fifth position cannot be filled by any of the two digits previously used, there are eight possibilities for the fifth position. The last position can be filled by any of the seven remaining digits.

$$\frac{5}{L}\ \frac{25}{L}\ \frac{9}{D}\ \frac{9}{D}\ \frac{8}{D}\ \frac{7}{D}$$

Since $5 \cdot 25 \cdot 9 \cdot 9 \cdot 8 \cdot 7 = 567,000$, there are 567,000 different arrangements that meet the conditions specified.   ∎

Example 2 *Counting Principle: T-Shirt Colors*

At Old Navy, a supply of solid-colored T-shirts has just been received. The T-shirts come in the following colors: green, blue, white, yellow, and red. Billy Bragg, the floor manager, decides to display one of each color T-shirt in a row on a shelf.

a) In how many different ways can he display the five different color T-shirts on a shelf?

b) If he wants to place the blue T-shirt in the middle, in how many different ways can he arrange the T-shirts?

c) If Billy wants the white T-shirt to be the first T-shirt and the blue T-shirt to be the last T-shirt, in how many different ways can he arrange the T-shirts?

Solution

a) There are five positions to fill, using the five colors. In the first position, on the left, he can use any one of the five colors. In the second position, he can use any of the four remaining colors. In the third position, he can use any of the three remaining colors, and so on. The number of distinct possible arrangements is

$$\underline{5} \cdot \underline{4} \cdot \underline{3} \cdot \underline{2} \cdot \underline{1} = 120$$

b) We begin by satisfying the specified requirements stated. In this case, the blue T-shirt must be placed in the middle. Therefore, there is only one possibility for the middle position.

$$\underline{} \; \underline{} \; \underline{1} \; \underline{} \; \underline{}$$

For the first position, there are now four possibilities. For the second position, there will be three possibilities. For the fourth position, there will be two possibilities. Finally, in the last position, there is only one possibility.

$$\underline{4} \cdot \underline{3} \cdot \underline{1} \cdot \underline{2} \cdot \underline{1} = 24$$

Thus, under the condition stated, there are 24 different possible arrangements.

c) For the first T-shirt, there is only one possibility, the white T-shirt. For the last T-shirt, there is only one possibility, the blue T-shirt.

$$\underline{1} \; \underline{} \; \underline{} \; \underline{} \; \underline{1}$$

The second position can be filled by any of the three remaining T-shirts. The third position can be filled by any of the two remaining T-shirts. There is only one T-shirt left for the fourth position. Thus, the number of possible arrangements is

$$\underline{1} \cdot \underline{3} \cdot \underline{2} \cdot \underline{1} \cdot \underline{1} = 6$$

There are only six possible arrangements that satisfy the given conditions. ■

Permutations

Now we introduce the definition of a permutation.

> **Definition: Permutations**
> A **permutation** is any *ordered arrangement* of a given set of objects.

"Larry, Shemp, Moe" and "Shemp, Moe, Larry" represent two different ordered arrangements or two different permutations of the same three names. In Example 2(a), there are 120 different ordered arrangements, or permutations, of the five colored T-shirts. In Example 2(b), there are 24 different ordered arrangements, or permutations possible, if the blue T-shirt must be displayed in the middle.

▲ *Shemp   Moe   Larry*

When determining the number of permutations possible, we assume that repetition of an item is not permitted. To help you understand and visualize permutations, we illustrate the various permutations possible when a triangle, rectangle, and circle are to be placed in a line; see Fig. 12.21.

Figure 12.21

For this set of three shapes, six different arrangements, or six permutations, are possible. We can obtain the number of permutations by using the counting principle. For the first position, there are three choices. There are then two choices for the second position, and only one choice is left for the third position.

$$\text{Number of permutations} = 3 \cdot 2 \cdot 1 = 6$$

The product $3 \cdot 2 \cdot 1$ is referred to as 3 factorial, and is written 3!. Thus,

$$3! = 3 \cdot 2 \cdot 1 = 6$$

> ### Number of Permutations
> The number of permutations of n distinct items is n factorial, symbolized $n!$, where
> $$n! = n(n - 1)(n - 2) \cdots (3)(2)(1)$$

It is important to note that 0! is defined to be 1. Many calculators have the ability to determine factorials. Often to determine factorials you need to press the ⎡2nd⎤ or ⎡INV⎤ key. Read your calculator manual to determine how to find factorials on your calculator.

Example 3 *Cell Phones*

In how many different ways can six different cell phones be arranged on top of one another?

Solution Since there are six different cell phones, the number of permutations is 6!.

$$6! = 6 \cdot 5 \cdot 4 \cdot 3 \cdot 2 \cdot 1 = 720$$

The six cell phones can be arranged in 720 different ways.   ∎

Example 4 illustrates how to use the counting principle to determine the number of permutations possible when only a part of the total number of items is to be selected and arranged.

Example 4 *Permutations of Three Out of Five Letters*

Consider the five letters *a, b, c, d, e*. In how many distinct ways can three letters be selected and arranged if repetition is not allowed?

Solution We are asked to select and arrange only three of the five possible letters. Figure 12.22 shows some possibilities. Using the counting principle, we find that there are five possible letters for the first choice, four possible letters for the second choice, and three possible letters for the third choice:

$$5 \cdot 4 \cdot 3 = 60$$

Thus, there are 60 different possible ordered arrangements, or permutations. On the left, we show 5 of the 60 possible permutations.   ∎

Some of the many permutations of 3 of the 5 letters

Figure 12.22

In Example 4, we determined the number of different ways in which we could select and arrange three of the five items. We can indicate that result by using the notation $_5P_3$. The notation $_5P_3$ is read "the number of permutations of five items taken three at a time." The notation $_nP_r$ is read "the number of permutations of n items taken r at a time."

We use the counting principle below to evaluate $_8P_4$, $_9P_3$, and $_{10}P_5$. Note the relationship between the number preceding the P, the number following the P, and the last number in the product.

$$_8P_4 = 8 \cdot 7 \cdot 6 \cdot 5 \qquad \text{One more than } 8 - 4$$

$$_9P_3 = 9 \cdot 8 \cdot 7 \qquad \text{One more than } 9 - 3$$

$$_{10}P_5 = 10 \cdot 9 \cdot 8 \cdot 7 \cdot 6 \qquad \text{One more than } 10 - 5$$

To evaluate $_nP_r$, we begin with n and form a product of r consecutive descending factors. For example, to evaluate $_{10}P_5$, we start with 10 and form a product of five consecutive descending factors (see the preceding illustration).

In general, the number of permutations of n items taken r at a time, $_nP_r$, may be found by the formula

$$_nP_r = n(n-1)(n-2) \cdots (n-r+1) \qquad \text{One more than } n - r$$

Therefore, when evaluating $_{20}P_{15}$, we would find the product of consecutive decreasing integers from 20 to $(20 - 15 + 1)$ or 6, which is written as $20 \cdot 19 \cdot 18 \cdot 17 \cdot \cdots \cdot 6$.

Now let's develop an alternative formula that we can use to find the number of permutations possible when r objects are selected from n objects:

$$_nP_r = n(n-1)(n-2) \cdots (n-r+1)$$

Now multiply the expression on the right side of the equals sign by $\dfrac{(n-r)!}{(n-r)!}$, which is equivalent to multiplying the expression by 1.

$$_nP_r = n(n-1)(n-2) \cdots (n-r+1) \times \frac{(n-r)!}{(n-r)!}$$

For example,

$$_{10}P_5 = 10 \cdot 9 \cdot \cdots \cdot 6 \times \frac{5!}{5!}$$

or

$$_{10}P_5 = \frac{10 \cdot 9 \cdot \cdots \cdot 6 \times 5!}{5!}$$

Since $(n-r)!$ means $(n-r)(n-r-1) \cdots (3)(2)(1)$, the expression for $_nP_r$ can be rewritten as

$$_nP_r = \frac{n(n-1)(n-2) \cdots (n-r+1)\overbrace{(n-r)(n-r-1) \cdots (3)(2)(1)}^{(n-r)!}}{(n-r)!}$$

Since the numerator of this expression is $n!$, we can write

$$_nP_r = \frac{n!}{(n-r)!}$$

For example,

$$_{10}P_5 = \frac{10!}{(10-5)!}$$

> **Permutation Formula**
> The number of permutations possible when r objects are selected from n objects is found by the **permutation formula**
>
> $$_nP_r = \frac{n!}{(n-r)!}$$

In Example 4, we found that when selecting three of five letters, there were 60 permutations. We can obtain the same result using the permutation formula:

$$_5P_3 = \frac{5!}{(5-3)!} = \frac{5!}{2!} = \frac{5 \cdot 4 \cdot 3 \cdot \cancel{2 \cdot 1}}{\cancel{2 \cdot 1}} = 60$$

Example 5 *Using the Permutation Formula*

You are among eight people forming a skiing club. Collectively, you decide to put each person's name in a hat and to randomly select a president, a vice president, and a secretary. How many different arrangements or permutations of officers are possible?

Solution There are eight people, $n = 8$, of which three are to be selected; thus, $r = 3$.

$$_8P_3 = \frac{8!}{(8-3)!} = \frac{8!}{5!} = \frac{8 \cdot 7 \cdot 6 \cdot \cancel{5 \cdot 4 \cdot 3 \cdot 2 \cdot 1}}{\cancel{5 \cdot 4 \cdot 3 \cdot 2 \cdot 1}} = 336$$

Thus, with eight people there can be 336 different arrangements for president, vice president, and secretary. ∎

In Example 5, the fraction

$$\frac{8 \cdot 7 \cdot 6 \cdot \cancel{5 \cdot 4 \cdot 3 \cdot 2 \cdot 1}}{\cancel{5 \cdot 4 \cdot 3 \cdot 2 \cdot 1}} = 336$$

can be also expressed as

$$\frac{8 \cdot 7 \cdot 6 \cdot 5!}{5!} = 336$$

The solution to Example 5, like other permutation problems, can also be obtained using the counting principle.

EXAMPLE 6

The Prince George County bicycle club has 10 different routes members wish to travel exactly once, but they have only 6 specific dates for their trips. In how many ways can the different routes be assigned to the dates scheduled for their trips?

TECHNOLOGY TIP

TECHNOLOGY TIP

Many scientific calculators and all graphing calculators have the ability to evaluate permutations. Read your calculator's instruction manual to determine the procedure to follow to evaluate permutations.

To evaluate $_{10}P_6$ on a TI-83 Plus or a TI-84 Plus calculator, enter the number 10. Then press the MATH key. Use the right arrow key to scroll over to PRB, which stands for probability. Then scroll down to $_nP_r$. Press the ENTER key. You should now see 10 $_nP_r$ on your screen. Next press 6. Press the ENTER key again. The answer will be 151,200, which agrees with our answer in Example 6.

RECREATIONAL MATH

Jumble

Read the material on Permutations of Duplicate Items on this page and the next page before working this Jumble.

In the *Recreational Mathematics* box on page 711 we introduced the JUMBLE puzzles. Sometimes the puzzles contain one or more letters multiple times. For each Jumble below, use the knowledge you have learned in this section to determine
a) the number of possible arrangements of the letters given.
b) the word that results when the letters are placed in their proper order (note that only one word is possible).
1. NOOZE
2. ZBEERE
3. LOCGEEL
The answers are listed upside down below. See Exercises 53–56, 70, 71 for more examples.

Answers:
1. a) 60 b) OZONE
2. a) 120 b) BREEZE
3. a) 1260 b) COLLEGE

Solution There are 10 possible routes but only 6 specific dates scheduled for the trips. Since traveling route A on day 1 and traveling route B on day 2 is different than traveling route B on day 1 and traveling route A on day 2, we have a permutation problem. There are 10 possible routes; thus, $n = 10$. There are 6 routes that are going to be selected and assigned to different days; thus, $r = 6$. Now we calculate the number of different permutations of selecting and arranging the dates for 6 out of 10 possible routes.

$$_{10}P_6 = \frac{10!}{(10 - 6)!} = \frac{10!}{4!} = \frac{10 \cdot 9 \cdot 8 \cdot 7 \cdot 6 \cdot 5 \cdot \cancel{4!}}{\cancel{4!}} = 151{,}200$$

There are 151,200 different ways that 6 routes can be selected and scheduled from the 10 possible routes. ∎

Example 6 could also be worked using the counting principle because we are discussing an *ordered arrangement* (a permutation) that is done *without replacement*. For the first date scheduled, there are 10 possible outcomes. For the second date selected, there are 9 possible outcomes. By continuing this process we would determine that the number of possible outcomes for the 6 different trips is $10 \cdot 9 \cdot 8 \cdot 7 \cdot 6 \cdot 5 = 151{,}200$.

We have worked permutation problems (selecting and arranging, without replacement, r items out of n *distinct* items) by using the counting principle and using the permutation formula. When you are given a permutation problem, unless specified by your instructor, you may use either technique to determine its solution.

Permutations of Duplicate Items

So far, all the examples we have discussed in this section have involved arrangements with distinct items. Now we will consider permutation problems in which some of the items to be arranged are duplicates. For example, the name BOB contains three letters, of which the two Bs are duplicates. How many permutations of the letters in the name BOB are possible? If the two Bs were distinguishable (one red and the other blue), there would be six permutations.

BOB	BBO	OBB
BOB	BBO	OBB

However, if the Bs are not distinguishable (replacing all colored Bs with black print), we see that there are only three permutations.

BOB	BBO	OBB

The number of permutations of the letters in BOB can be computed as

$$\frac{3!}{2!} = \frac{3 \cdot \cancel{2 \cdot 1}}{\cancel{2 \cdot 1}} = 3$$

where 3! represents the number of permutations of three letters, assuming that none are duplicates, and 2! represents the number of ways the two items that are duplicates can be arranged (BB or BB). In general, we have the following rule.

Permutations of Duplicate Items

The number of distinct permutations of n objects where n_1 of the objects are identical, n_2 of the objects are identical, ..., n_r of the objects are identical is found by using

$$\frac{n!}{n_1! n_2! \cdots n_r!}$$

EXAMPLE 7   Duplicate Letters

In how many different ways can the letters of the word "TALLAHASSEE" be arranged?

Solution   Of the 11 letters, three are A's, two are S's, two are L's, and two are E's. The number of possible arrangements is

$$\frac{11!}{3!2!2!2!} = \frac{11 \cdot 10 \cdot 9 \cdot \cancel{8} \cdot 7 \cdot 6 \cdot 5 \cdot 4 \cdot \cancel{3 \cdot 2 \cdot 1}}{\cancel{3 \cdot 2 \cdot 1} \cdot 2 \cdot 1 \cdot 2 \cdot 1 \cdot 2 \cdot 1} = 11 \cdot 10 \cdot 9 \cdot 7 \cdot 6 \cdot 5 \cdot 4 = 831{,}600$$

There are 831,600 different possible arrangements of the letters in the word "TALLAHASSEE." ∎

SECTION 12.8   Exercises

Warm Up Exercises

In Exercises 1–8, fill in the blank with an appropriate word, phrase, or symbol(s).

1. To determine the number of distinct ways two or more experiments can be performed, the _____ principle can be used. Counting

2. Any ordered arrangement of a given set of objects is called a(n) _____. Permutation

3. The symbol for n factorial is _____. $n!$

4. The formula for the number of permutations of n distinct items is $n! =$ _____ $n(n-1)(n-2) \cdots (3)(2)(1)$

5. The formula for the number of permutations when r objects are selected from n objects is ${}_nP_r =$ _____ $\frac{n!}{(n-r)!}$

6. The number of permutations of n objects, where n_1 of the items are identical, n_2 of the items are identical, ..., n_r are identical, is found by _____. $\frac{n!}{n_1! n_2! \cdots n_r!}$

7. The notation used to express the number of permutations of five items taken three at a time is _____. ${}_5P_3$

8. The notation used to express the number of permutations of seven items taken two at a time is _____. ${}_7P_2$

Practice the Skills

In Exercises 9–20, evaluate the expression.

9. $5!$ 120   10. $6!$ 720   11. ${}_4P_2$ 12   12. ${}_5P_2$ 20

13. $0!$ 1   14. ${}_7P_3$ 210   15. ${}_8P_0$ 1   16. ${}_6P_0$ 1

17. ${}_9P_5$ 15,120   18. ${}_3P_3$ 6   19. ${}_8P_3$ 336   20. ${}_{10}P_6$ 151,200

Problem Solving

21. *ATM Codes* To use an automated teller machine, you generally must enter a four-digit code, using the digits 0–9. How many four-digit codes are possible if repetition of digits is permitted? 10,000

22. *Routes* There are three different routes that Cassidy Cole can walk from home to the post office and two different routes that she can walk from the post office to the bank. How many different routes can Cassidy walk from home to the post office and then to the bank? 6

23. *Outfits* Juan Rivera has three ties, four shirts, and two pairs of pants. How many different outfits can he wear if he chooses one tie, one shirt, and one pair of pants for each outfit? 24

24. *Passwords* Assume that a password to log onto a computer account is to consist of any four digits or letters (repetition is permitted). Determine the number of passwords possible if

   a) the letters are not case sensitive (that is, a lowercase letter is treated the same as an uppercase letter). 1,679,616

   b) the letters are case sensitive (that is, an uppercase letter is considered different than the same lowercase letter). 14,776,336

25. Car Door Locks Some doors on cars can be opened by pressing a correct sequence of buttons. A display of the five buttons by the door handle of a car follows.*

The correct sequence of five buttons must be pressed to unlock the door.

a) How many different sequences of five buttons are possible (repetition is permitted)? $5^5 = 3125$

b) If a sequence of five buttons is pressed at random, determine the probability that the sequence unlocks the door. $\frac{1}{3125} = 0.00032$

26. Social Security Numbers A social security number consists of nine digits. How many different social security numbers are possible if repetition of digits is permitted? 1,000,000,000

27. License Plate In Italy, most car and motorcycle license plates consist of 2 letters, followed by 3 digits, followed by 2 letters. (See photo.) Determine the number of license plates possible if

▲ An Italian license plate

a) repetition is permitted (as it is in Italy). 456,976,000

b) repetition is not permitted. 258,336,000

28. Winning the Trifecta The trifecta at most racetracks consists of selecting the first-, second-, and third-place finishers in a particular race in their proper order. If there are seven entries in the trifecta race, how many tickets must you purchase to guarantee a win? 210

29. Choosing Classes Kai Lu plans to enroll in four classes: sociology, chemistry, economics, and humanities. There

are seven sociology classes, four chemistry classes, three economics classes, and four humanities classes that fit his schedule. How many different ways can he select his four classes? 336

30. Geometric Shapes Consider the five figures shown.

In how many different ways can the figures be arranged

a) from left to right? 120

b) from top to bottom if placed one under the other? 120

c) from left to right if the triangle is to be placed on the far right? 24

d) from left to right if the circle is to be placed on the far left and the triangle is to be placed on the far right? 6

31. Arranging Pictures The six pictures shown are to be placed side by side along a wall.

In how many ways can they be arranged from left to right if

a) they can be arranged in any order? 720

b) the bird must be on the far left? 120

c) the bird must be on the far left and the giraffe must be next to the bird? 24

d) a four-legged animal must be on the far right? 600

32. Club Officers If a club consists of 10 members, how many different arrangements of president, vice-president, and secretary are possible? 720

33. Restaurant Positions There are 10 candidates for three positions at Johnny Rockets. One position is for a cook. The second position is for a food server. The third position is for a cashier. If all 10 candidates are equally qualified for the three positions, in how many different ways can the three positions be filled? 720

34. ISBN Codes Each book registered in the Library of Congress must have an ISBN code number. For an ISBN number of the form D-DD-DDDDDD-D, where D represents a digit from 0–9, how many different ISBN numbers are possible if repetition of digits is allowed? (See research activity Exercise 72 on page 746.) 10,000,000,000

*On most cars, although each key lists two numbers, the key acts as a single number. Therefore, if your code is 1, 6, 8, 5, 3, the code 2, 5, 7, 6, 4 will also open the lock.

35. *Wedding Reception* At the reception line of a wedding, the bride, the groom, the best man, the maid of honor, the four ushers, and the four bridesmaids must line up to receive the guests.

   a) If these individuals can line up in any order, how many arrangements are possible? 479,001,600

   b) If the groom must be the last in line and the bride must be next to the groom, and the others can line up in any order, how many arrangements are possible? 3,628,800

   c) If the groom is to be last in line, the bride next to the groom, and males and females are to alternate, how many arrangements are possible? 14,400

36. *DJ* A disc jockey (DJ) has 9 songs to play. Five are slow songs, and 4 are fast songs. Each song is to be played only once. In how many ways can the DJ play the 9 songs if

   a) the songs can be played in any order? 362,880

   b) the first song must be a slow song and the last song must be a slow song? 100,800

   c) the first two songs must be fast songs? 60,480

Identification Codes *In Exercises 37–40, an identification code is to consist of three letters followed by four digits. How many different codes are possible if*

37. repetition is not permitted? 78,624,000

38. repetition is permitted? 175,760,000

39. repetition of letters is permitted, repetition of numbers is not permitted, and the first three entries must all be the same letter? 131,040

40. the first letter must be an *A, B, C,* or *D* and repetition is not permitted? 12,096,000

License Plates *In Exercises 41–44, a license plate is to consist of three digits followed by two uppercase letters. Determine the number of different license plates possible if*

41. repetition of numbers and letters is permitted. 676,000

42. repetition of numbers and letters is not permitted. 468,000

43. the first and second digits must be odd, and repetition is not permitted. 104,000

44. the first digit cannot be zero, and repetition is not permitted. 421,200

45. *Possible Phone Numbers* A telephone number consists of seven digits with the restriction that the first digit cannot be 0 or 1.

   a) How many distinct telephone numbers are possible? 8,000,000

   b) How many distinct telephone numbers are possible with three-digit area codes preceding the seven-digit number, where the first digit of the area code is not 0 or 1? 6,400,000,000

   c) With the increasing use of cell phones and paging systems, our society is beginning to run out of usable phone numbers. Various phone companies are developing phone numbers that use 8 digits instead of 7. How many distinct phone numbers can be made using a three digit area code followed by an eight digit phone number, where the first digit of the area code and the phone number cannot be 0 or 1? 64,000,000,000

46. *Fruit Juice Selection* Mrs. Hernandez and her three children go shopping at a local grocery store. Each of the children will be allowed to select one bottle of fruit juice. On the store's shelf there are 12 bottles of fruit juice, and each bottle contains a different type of juice. In how many ways can the selections be made? 1320

47. *Skiing Event* A skiing event has 16 participants for the slalom. The 5 participants with the fastest speeds will be listed, in the order of their speed, on the leader board. How many different ways are there for the names to be listed? 524,160

48. *History Test* In one question on a history test, a student is asked to match 10 dates with 10 events; each date can only be matched with 1 event. In how many different ways can this question be answered? 3,628,800

49. *Color Permutations* Determine the number of permutations of the colors in the spectrum that follows. 5040

50. *Drive-Through at a Bank* A bank has three drive-through stations. Assuming that each is equally likely to be selected by customers, in how many different ways can the next six drivers select a station? 729

51. Computer Systems At a computer store, a customer is considering 5 different computers, 4 different monitors, 7 different printers, and 2 different scanners. Assuming that each of the components is compatible with one another and that one of each is to be selected, determine the number of different computer systems possible. 280

52. Selecting Furniture The Johnsons just moved into their new home and are selecting furniture for the family room. They are considering 5 different sofas, 2 different chairs, and 6 different tables. They plan to select one item from each category. Determine the number of different ways they can select the furniture. 60

53. Determine the number of permutations of the letters of the word "EDUCATION." 362,880

54. Determine the number of permutations of the letters of the word "EFFECTIVE." 30,240

55. In how many ways can the letters in the word "TENNESSEE" be arranged? 3780

56. In how many ways can the letters in the word "COMMUNICATION" be arranged? 194,594,400

57. In how many ways can the digits in the number 4,568,865 be arranged? 630

58. In how many ways can the digits of the number 2,142,332 be arranged? 420

59. Flag Messages Five different colored flags will be placed on a pole, one beneath another. The arrangement of the colors indicates the message. How many messages are possible if five flags are to be selected from nine different colored flags? 15,120

60. Multiple-Choice Test Keri Kershaw is taking a 12-question multiple-choice exam. Each question has three possible answers, (a), (b), and (c). In how many possible ways can Keri answer the questions? 531,441

61. Batting Order In how many ways can the manager of a National League baseball team arrange his batting order of nine players if

a) the pitcher must bat last? 40,320

b) there are no restrictions? 362,880

62. Painting Exhibit Five Monet paintings are to be displayed in a museum.

a) In how many different ways can they be arranged if they must be next to one another? 120

b) In how many different ways can they be displayed if a specific one is to be in the middle? 24

▲ The Water Lily Pond, Pink Harmony, *1900 by Claude Monet*

Challenge Problems/Group Activities

63. Car Keys Door keys for a certain automobile are made from a blank key on which five cuts are made. Each cut may be one of five different depths.

a) How many different keys can be made? 3125

b) If 400,000 of these automobiles are made such that each of the keys determined in part (a) opens the same number of cars, determine how many cars can be opened by a specific key. 128

c) If one of these cars is selected at random, what is the probability that the key selected at random will unlock the door? 0.00032

64. Voting On a ballot, each committee member is asked to rank three of eight candidates for recommendation for promotion, giving first, second, and third choices (no ties). What is the minimum number of ballots that must be cast to guarantee that at least two ballots are the same? 337

65. Scrabble Nancy Lin, who is playing Scrabble with Dale Grey, has seven different letters. She decides to test each five-letter permutation before her next move. If each permutation takes 5 sec, how long will it take Nancy to check all the permutations? 12,600 sec, or 3.5 hr

66. Scrabble In Exercise 65, assume, of Nancy's seven letters, that three are identical and two are identical. How long will it take Nancy to try all different permutations of her seven letters? 2100 sec, or 35 min

67. Does $_nP_r = {_n}P_{(n-r)}$ for all whole numbers, where $n \geq r$? No

Recreational Mathematics

68. Stations There are eight bus stations from town A to town B. How many different single tickets must be printed so that a passenger may purchase a ticket from any station to any other station? 56

```
o   o   o   o   o   o   o   o
A                           B
```

69. Bus Loop How many tickets with different points of origin and destination can be sold on a bus line that travels a loop with 25 stops? 600

Jumble *Many newspapers contain Jumble puzzles, where the letters of a word are given out of order. In Exercises 70 and 71, read the Recreational Math box on page 741 and determine*

a) *the number of possible arrangements of the letters given.*

b) *the word.*

70. HEICOC a) 360   b) CHOICE

71. ROSEGOC a) 2520   b) SCROOGE

Internet/Research Activity

72. When a book is published, it is assigned a 10-digit code number called the International Standard Book Number (ISBN). Do research and write a report on how this coding system works.

SECTION 12.9   Combinations

▲ *Combinations can be used to determine the number of different arrangements of toppings that can be placed on a hamburger.*

Zebb's Restaurant has 10 different toppings that can be added to a hamburger. Chase Weichman is going to select three of those toppings to add to his hamburger. How many different selections are possible? In this section, we will learn how to determine the number of selections when the order of selection of the items is not important to the final outcome.

Why) This is Important There are many situations in which the order of the selections made is not important to the final outcome. For example, in determining the number of ways a committee can select 3 out of 8 candidates to receive a scholarship, the order in which the 3 are selected is not important.

When the order of the selection of the items is important to the final outcome, the problem is a permutation problem. When the order of the selection of the items is unimportant to the final outcome, the problem is a *combination* problem.

Recall from Section 12.8 that permutations are *ordered* arrangements. For example, *a, b, c* and *b, c, a* are two different permutations because the ordering of the three letters is different. The letters *a, b, c* and *b, c, a* represent the same combination of letters because the *same letters* are used in each set. However, the letters *a, b, c* and *a, b, d* represent two different combinations of letters because the letters contained in each set are different.

Definition: Combination

A **combination** is a distinct group (or set) of objects without regard to their arrangement.

Example 1 *Permutation or Combination*

Determine whether the situation represents a permutation or combination problem.

a) A group of five friends, Arline, Inez, Judy, Dan, and Eunice, are forming a club. The group will elect a president and a treasurer. In how many different ways can the president and treasurer be selected?

b) Of the five individuals named, two will be attending a meeting together. In how many different ways can they do so?

Solution

a) Since the president's position is different from the treasurer's position, we have a permutation problem. Judy as president with Dan as treasurer is different from Dan as president with Judy as treasurer. The order of the selection is important.

b) Since the order in which the two individuals selected to attend the meeting is not important, we have a combination problem. There is no difference if Judy is selected and then Dan is selected, or if Dan is selected and then Judy is selected. ∎

In Section 12.8, you learned that $_nP_r$ represents the number of permutations when r items are selected from n distinct items. *Similarly,* $_nC_r$ *represents the number of combinations when r items are selected from n distinct items.*

Consider the set of elements $\{a, b, c, d, e\}$. The number of permutations of two letters from the set is represented as $_5P_2$, and the number of combinations of two letters from the set is represented as $_5C_2$. Twenty permutations of two letters and 10 combinations of two letters are possible from these five letters. Thus, $_5P_2 = 20$ and $_5C_2 = 10$, as shown.

Permutations	**Combinations**
$\left.\begin{array}{l} ab, ba, ac, ca, ad, da, ae, ea, bc, cb, \\ bd, db, be, eb, cd, dc, ce, ec, de, ed \end{array}\right\} 20$	$\left.\begin{array}{l} ab, ac, ad, ae, bc, \\ bd, be, cd, ce, de \end{array}\right\} 10$

When discussing both combination and permutation problems, we always assume that the experiment is performed without replacement. That is why duplicate letters such as *aa* or *bb* are not included in the preceding example.

Note that from one combination of two letters, two permutations can be formed. For example, the combination *ab* gives the permutations *ab* and *ba*, or twice as many permutations as combinations. Thus, for this example we may write

$$_5P_2 = 2 \cdot (_5C_2)$$

Since $2 = 2!$, we may write

$$_5P_2 = 2!(_5C_2)$$

If we repeated this same process for comparing the number of permutations in $_nP_r$ with the number of combinations in $_nC_r$, we would find that

$$_nP_r = r!(_nC_r)$$

Dividing both sides of the equation by $r!$ gives

$$_nC_r = \frac{_nP_r}{r!}$$

Since $_nP_r = \dfrac{n!}{(n-r)!}$, the combination formula may be expressed as

$$_nC_r = \frac{n!/(n-r)!}{r!} = \frac{n!}{(n-r)!r!}$$

Did You Know?

Poker versus Bridge

A nice bridge hand

In popular card games, there is such a variety of possible combinations of cards that a player rarely gets the same hand twice. The total number of different 5-card poker hands using a standard deck of 52 cards is 2,598,960, and for 13-card bridge hands this number increases to 635,013,559,600.

Combination Formula

The number of combinations possible when r objects are selected from n objects is found by the **combination formula**

$$_nC_r = \frac{n!}{(n-r)!r!}$$

Example 2 *Museum Selection*

While visiting New York City, the Friedmans are interested in visiting 8 museums but have time to visit only 3. In how many ways can the Friedmans select 3 of the 8 museums to visit?

Solution This problem is a combination problem because the order in which the three museums are selected does not matter.

$$_8C_3 = \frac{8!}{(8-3)!3!} = \frac{8!}{5!3!} = \frac{8 \cdot 7 \cdot 6 \cdot 5 \cdot 4 \cdot 3 \cdot 2 \cdot 1}{5 \cdot 4 \cdot 3 \cdot 2 \cdot 1 \cdot 3 \cdot 2 \cdot 1} = 56$$

There are 56 different ways that 3 of the 8 museums can be selected to visit. ∎

Example 3 *Floral Arrangements*

Jan Funkhauser has 10 different cut flowers from which she will choose 6 to use in a floral arrangement. How many different ways can she do so?

Solution This problem is a combination problem because the order in which the 6 flowers are selected is unimportant. There are a total of 10 different flowers, so $n = 10$. Six flowers are to be selected, so $r = 6$.

$$_{10}C_6 = \frac{10!}{(10-6)!6!} = \frac{10!}{4!6!} = \frac{10 \cdot \overset{3}{9} \cdot 8 \cdot 7 \cdot 6 \cdot 5 \cdot 4 \cdot 3 \cdot 2 \cdot 1}{4 \cdot 3 \cdot 2 \cdot 1 \cdot 6 \cdot 5 \cdot 4 \cdot 3 \cdot 2 \cdot 1} = 210$$

Thus, there are 210 different ways Jan can choose 6 cut flowers from a group of 10 cut flowers. ∎

Example 4 *Dinner Combinations*

At the Royal Dynasty Chinese restaurant, dinner for eight people consists of 3 items from column A, 4 items from column B, and 3 items from column C. If columns A, B, and C have 5, 7, and 6 items, respectively, how many different dinner combinations are possible?

Solution For column A, 3 of 5 items must be selected, which can be represented as $_5C_3$. For column B, 4 of 7 items must be selected, which can be represented as $_7C_4$. For column C, 3 of 6 items must be selected, or $_6C_3$.

$$_5C_3 = 10 \quad _7C_4 = 35 \quad \text{and} \quad _6C_3 = 20$$

Using the counting principle, we can determine the total number of dinner combinations by multiplying the number of choices from columns A, B, and C:

$$\text{Total number of dinner choices} = _5C_3 \cdot _7C_4 \cdot _6C_3$$
$$= 10 \cdot 35 \cdot 20 = 7000$$

Therefore, 7000 different combinations are possible under these conditions. ∎

We have presented various counting methods, including the counting principle, permutations, and combinations. You often need to decide which method to use to solve a problem. Table 12.4 may help you in selecting the procedure to use.

Table 12.4 Summary of Counting Methods

Counting Principle: If a first experiment can be performed in M distinct ways and a second experiment can be performed in N distinct ways, then the two experiments in that specific order can be performed in $M \cdot N$ distinct ways. The counting principle may be used with or without repetition of items. It is used when determining the number of different ways that two or more experiments can occur. It is also used when there are specific placement requirements, such as the first digit must be a 0 or 1.	Determining the Number of Ways of Selecting r Items from n Items (Repetition is not Permitted)	
	Permutations	**Combinations**
	Permutations are used when order is important. For example, a, b, c and b, c, a are two different permutations of the same three letters. $$_nP_r = \frac{n!}{(n-r)!}$$ Problems solved with the permutation formula may also be solved by using the counting principle.	Combinations are used when order is not important. For example, a, b, c and b, c, a are the same combination of three letters. But a, b, c, and a, b, d are two different combinations of three letters. $$_nC_r = \frac{n!}{(n-r)!r!}$$

SECTION 12.9 *Exercises*

Warm Up Exercises

In Exercises 1–6, fill in the blank with an appropriate word, phrase, or symbol(s).

1. A distinct group of objects without regard to their arrangement is called a(n) _____. Combination

2. The symbol for the number of combinations when r items are selected from n distinct items is _____. $_nC_r$

3. If we want to select r items from n items, and the order of the arrangement is important, then _____ are used.
   Permutations

4. If we want to select r items from n items, and the order of the arrangement is not important, then _____ are used.
   Combinations

5. The notation used to express the number of combinations of 3 items selected from 7 distinct items is _____. $_7C_3$

6. The notation used to express the number of combinations of 4 items selected from 10 distinct items is _____. $_{10}C_4$

Practice the Skills

In Exercises 7–20, evaluate the expression.

7. $_6C_2$ 15

8. $_9C_3$ 84

9. a) $_8C_4$ 70 b) $_8P_4$ 1680 10. a) $_8C_2$ 28 b) $_8P_2$ 56

11. a) $_8C_0$ 1 b) $_8P_0$ 1 12. a) $_{12}C_8$ 495 b) $_{12}P_8$ 19,958,400

13. a) $_{10}C_3$ 120 b) $_{10}P_3$ 720 14. a) $_5C_5$ 1 b) $_5P_5$ 120

15. $\dfrac{_5C_3}{_5P_3}$ $\frac{1}{6}$

16. $\dfrac{_7C_2}{_7P_2}$ $\frac{1}{2}$

17. $\dfrac{_6C_4}{_6C_3}$ $\frac{3}{4}$

18. $\dfrac{_6C_6}{_8C_0}$ 1

19. $\dfrac{_9P_4}{_{10}C_5}$ 12

20. $\dfrac{_7P_0}{_7C_0}$ 1

Problem Solving

21. *Hiring* There are 12 qualified applicants for 4 nursing positions at a hospital. In how many ways can the positions be filled? 495

22. *Banana Split* An ice-cream parlor has 20 different flavors. Cynthia orders a banana split and has to select 3 different flavors. How many different selections are possible? 1140

23. *Test Essays* Tina Campbell must select and answer four of five essay questions on a test. In how many ways can she do so? 5

24. *Software Packages* During a special promotion at CompUSA, a customer purchasing a computer and a printer is given the choice of 2 free software packages. If there are 9 different software packages from which to select, how many different ways can the 2 packages be selected? 36

25. *Scholarships* A scholarship committee has received 8 applications for a $500 scholarship. The committee has decided to select 3 of the 8 candidates for further consideration. In how many ways can the committee do so? 56

26. *Attending Plays* While visiting New York City, the Nygens want to attend 3 plays out of 10 plays they would like to see. In how many ways can they do so? 120

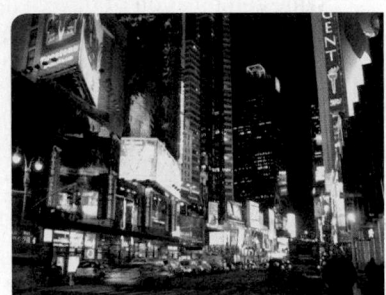

▲ *Theater district, New York City*

27. *Taxi Ride* A group of 7 people wants to use taxis to go to a local restaurant. When the first taxi arrives, the group decides that 4 people should get into the taxi. In how many ways can that be done? 35

28. *Plants* Mary Robinson purchased a package of 24 different plants, but she only needed 20 plants for planting. In how many ways can she select the 20 plants from the package to be planted? 10,626

29. *Entertainers* Ruth Eckerd Hall must select 8 of 12 possible entertainers for its summer schedule. In how many ways can that be done? 495

30. *CD Selection* James Ruiz has 7 CDs and wants to select 4 to play in his car CD player. In how many ways can he select 4 of 7 CDs? 35

31. *Shirts* Matthew Abbott has 10 shirts in his closet and must select 4 to take with him on vacation. In how many ways can Matthew select the shirts? 210

32. *Quinella Bet* A quinella bet consists of selecting the first- and second-place winners, in any order, in a particular event. For example, suppose you select a 2–5 quinella. If 2 wins and 5 finishes second, or if 5 wins and 2 finishes second, you win. Mr. Smith goes to a jai alai match. In the match, 8 jai alai teams compete. How many quinella tickets must Mr. Smith purchase to guarantee a win? 28

33. *Cameras and Lenses* Rowe Photography has nine different digital cameras and six different long-range lenses in stock. The manager wants to place three of the nine cameras and

two of the six lenses on sale. In how many ways can the manager select the items to be listed as sale items? 1260

34. *Test Question* On an English test, Tito Ramirez must write an essay for three of the five questions in Part 1 and four of the six questions in Part 2. How many different combinations of questions can he answer? 150

35. *Plasma and LCD TVs* A television/stereo store has 12 different plasma televisions and 8 different LCD televisions in stock. The store's manager wishes to place 3 plasma televisions and 2 LCD televisions on sale. In how many ways can that be done? 6160

36. *Newsletter* An animal shelter has 15 cats and 12 dogs available for adoption. The shelter wants to select 6 cats and 4 dogs to feature in the adoption newsletter. In how many ways can this be done? 2,477,475

37. *Dinner Party* Sue Less is having a dinner party. She has 10 different bottles of red wine and 8 different bottles of white wine on her wine rack. She wants to select 4 bottles of red wine and 2 bottles of white wine to serve at her party. In how many ways can she do so? 5880

38. *Forming a Committee* The Webster Town Board is forming a committee to explore ways to improve public safety in the town. The committee will consist of 4 representatives from the town board and 3 representatives from a citizens advisory board. If there are 7 town board members and 5 citizens advisory board members from which to choose, how many different ways can the committee be formed? 350

39. *Selecting Soda* Angel Ramirez is sent to the store to get 5 different bottles of regular soda and 3 different bottles of diet soda. If there are 10 different types of regular sodas and 7 different types of diet sodas to choose from, how many different choices does Angel have? 8820

40. *Constructing a Test* A teacher is constructing a mathematics test consisting of 10 questions. She has a pool of 28 questions, which are classified by level of difficulty as follows: 6 difficult questions, 10 average questions, and 12 easy questions. How many different 10-question tests can she construct from the pool of 28 questions if her test is to have 3 difficult, 4 average, and 3 easy questions? 924,000

41. *Selecting Mutual Funds* Joe Chang recently graduated from college and now has a job that provides a retirement investment plan. Joe wants to diversify his investments, so he wants to invest in four stock mutual funds and two bond mutual funds. If he has a choice of eight stock mutual funds and five bond mutual funds, how many different selections of mutual funds does he have? 700

42. Door Prize As part of a door prize, Mary McCarty won three tickets to a baseball game and three tickets to a theater performance. She decided to give all the tickets to friends. For the baseball game she is considering six different friends, and for the theater she is considering eight different friends. In how many ways can she distribute the tickets? 1120

43. New Breakfast Cereals General Mills is testing 4 oat cereals, 5 wheat cereals, and 6 rice cereals. If it plans to market 3 of the oat cereals, 2 of the wheat cereals, and 2 of the rice cereals, how many different combinations are possible? 600

44. Catering Service A catering service is making up trays of hors d'oeuvres. The hors d'oeuvres are categorized as inexpensive, average, and expensive. If the client must select three of the eight inexpensive, five of the nine average, and two of the four expensive hors d'oeuvres, how many different choices are possible? 42,336

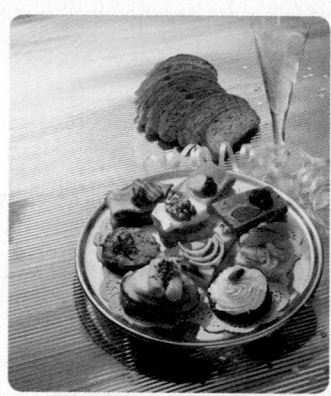

Challenge Problems/Group Activities

45. Test Answers Consider a 10-question test in which each question can be answered either correctly or incorrectly.

a) How many different ways are there to answer the questions so that eight are correct and two are incorrect? 45

b) How many different ways are there to answer the questions so that at least eight are correct? 56

46. a) A Dinner Toast Four people at dinner make a toast. If each person is to tap glasses with each other person one at a time, how many taps will take place? 6

b) Repeat part (a) with five people. 10

c) How many taps will there be if there are n people at the dinner table? $_nC_2$

47. Pascal's Triangle The notation $_nC_2$ may be written $\binom{n}{r}$.

a) Use this notation to evaluate each of the combinations in the following array. Form a triangle of the results,

similar to the one given, by placing the answer to each combination in the same relative position in the triangle. *

$$\binom{0}{0}$$
$$\binom{1}{0} \quad \binom{1}{1}$$
$$\binom{2}{0} \quad \binom{2}{1} \quad \binom{2}{2}$$
$$\binom{3}{0} \quad \binom{3}{1} \quad \binom{3}{2} \quad \binom{3}{3}$$
$$\binom{4}{0} \quad \binom{4}{1} \quad \binom{4}{2} \quad \binom{4}{3} \quad \binom{4}{4}$$

b) Using the number pattern in part (a), find the next row of numbers of the triangle (known as *Pascal's triangle*). *

48. Lottery Combinations Determine the number of combinations possible in a state lottery where you must select

a) 6 of 46 numbers. 9,366,819

b) 6 of 47 numbers. 10,737,573

c) 6 of 48 numbers. 12,271,512

d) 6 of 49 numbers. 13,983,816

e) Does the number of combinations increase by the same amount going from part (a) to part (b) as from part (b) to part (c)? No

49. a) Table Seating Arrangements How many distinct ways can four people be seated in a row? 24

b) How many distinct ways can four people be seated at a circular table? 24

50. Show that $_nC_r = {_nC_{(n-r)}}$. Answers will vary.

51. Forming a Committee A group of 15 people wants to form a committee consisting of a chair, vice chair, and three additional members. How many different committees can be formed? 60,060

Recreational Mathematics

52. a) Combination Lock To open a combination lock, you must know the lock's three-number sequence in its proper order. Repetition of numbers is permitted. Why is this lock more like a permutation lock than a combination lock? Why is it not a true permutation problem? The order is important. Since the numbers may be repeated, it is not a true permutation lock.

b) Assuming that a combination lock has 40 numbers, determine how many different three-number arrangements are possible if repetition of numbers is allowed. 64,000

*See Instructor Answer Appendix

c) Answer the question in part (b) if repetition is not allowed. 59,280

Internet/Research Activity

53. The area of mathematics called combinatorics is the science of counting. Do research and write a paper on combinatorics and its many applications.

<table>
<tr><td>**SECTION 12.10**</td><td># Solving Probability Problems by Using Combinations</td></tr>
</table>

▲ *What is the probability of selecting two picture cards from a standard deck of 52 cards when the two cards are selected without replacement?*

Suppose that we want to find the probability of selecting two picture cards (jacks, queens, or kings) when two cards are selected, without replacement, from a standard deck of cards. In Section 12.6, we used the *and* probability formula to solve this type of probability problem. In this section, we will learn another way to solve this type of probability problem by using combinations.

Why *This is Important* Combinations can be used in a variety of real-world probability applications.

Using the *and* formula for determining the probability of selecting two picture cards from a dark of 52 cards, we could reason as follows:

$$P(\text{2 picture cards}) = P(\text{first picture card}) \cdot P(\text{second picture card})$$

$$= \frac{12}{52} \cdot \frac{11}{51} = \frac{132}{2652} \quad \text{or} \quad \frac{11}{221}$$

Since the order of the two picture cards selected is not important to the final answer, this problem can be considered a combination probability problem.

We can also find the probability of selecting two picture cards, using combinations, by finding the number of possible successful outcomes (selecting two picture cards) and dividing that answer by the total number of possible outcomes (selecting any two cards).

The number of ways in which two picture cards can be selected from the 12 picture cards in a deck is $_{12}C_2$, or

$$_{12}C_2 = \frac{12!}{(12-2)!2!} = \frac{\overset{6}{\cancel{12}} \cdot 11 \cdot \cancel{10!}}{\cancel{10!} \cdot \cancel{2} \cdot 1} = 66$$

The number of ways in which two cards can be selected from a deck of 52 cards is $_{52}C_2$, or

$$_{52}C_2 = \frac{52!}{(52-2)!2!} = \frac{\overset{26}{\cancel{52}} \cdot 51 \cdot \cancel{50!}}{\cancel{50!} \cdot \cancel{2} \cdot 1} = 1326$$

Thus,

$$P(\text{selecting 2 picture cards}) = \frac{_{12}C_2}{_{52}C_2} = \frac{66}{1326} = \frac{11}{221}$$

Note that the same answer is obtained with either method. To give you more exposure to counting techniques, we will work the problems in this section using combinations.

Example 1 *Committee of Three Women*

A club consists of four men and five women. Three members are to be selected at random to form a committee. What is the probability that the committee will consist of three women?

Solution The order in which the three members are selected is not important. Therefore, we may work this problem using combinations.

$$P\left(\begin{array}{c}\text{committee consists}\\\text{of 3 women}\end{array}\right) = \frac{\text{number of possible committees with 3 women}}{\text{total number of possible 3-member committees}}$$

Since there is a total of 5 women, the number of possible committees with three women is $_5C_3 = 10$. Since there is a total of 9 people, the total number of possible three-member committees is $_9C_3 = 84$.

$$P(\text{committee consists of 3 women}) = \frac{10}{84} = \frac{5}{42}$$

The probability of randomly selecting a committee with three women is $\frac{5}{42}$. ∎

Example 2 *A Heart Flush*

A flush in the game of poker is five cards of the same suit (5 hearts, 5 diamonds, 5 clubs, or 5 spades). If you are dealt a five-card hand, determine the probability that you will be dealt a heart flush.

Solution The order in which the five hearts are dealt is not important. Therefore, we may work this problem using combinations.

$$P(\text{heart flush}) = \frac{\text{number of possible 5-card heart flushes}}{\text{total number of possible 5-card hands}}$$

Since there are 13 hearts in a deck of cards, the number of possible five-card heart flush hands is $_{13}C_5 = 1287$. The total number of possible five-card hands in a deck of 52 cards is $_{52}C_5 = 2{,}598{,}960$.

$$P(\text{heart flush}) = \frac{_{13}C_5}{_{52}C_5} = \frac{1287}{2{,}598{,}960} = \frac{33}{66{,}640}$$

The probability of being dealt a heart flush is $\frac{33}{66{,}640}$, or ≈ 0.000495. ∎

Example 3 *Employment Assignments*

A temporary employment agency has six men and five women who wish to be assigned for the day. One employer has requested four employees for security guard positions, and the second employer has requested three employees for moving furniture in an office building. If we assume that each of the potential employees has the same chance of being selected and being assigned at random and that only seven employees will be assigned, find the probability that

a) three men will be selected for moving furniture.

b) three men will be selected for moving furniture and four women will be selected for security guard positions.

Solution

a) $P\left(\begin{array}{c}\text{3 men selected}\\\text{for moving furniture}\end{array}\right) = \dfrac{\left(\begin{array}{c}\text{number of possible combinations}\\\text{of 3 men selected}\end{array}\right)}{\left(\begin{array}{c}\text{total number of possible combinations}\\\text{for selecting 3 people}\end{array}\right)}$

The number of possible combinations with 3 men is $_6C_3$. The total number of possible selections of 3 people is $_{11}C_3$.

$$P\left(\begin{array}{c}\text{3 men selected}\\\text{for moving furniture}\end{array}\right) = \dfrac{_6C_3}{_{11}C_3} = \dfrac{20}{165} = \dfrac{4}{33}$$

Thus, the probability that 3 men are selected is $\frac{4}{33}$.

b) The number of ways of selecting 3 men out of 6 is $_6C_3$, and the number of ways of selecting 4 women out of 5 is $_5C_4$. The total number of possible selections when 7 people are selected from 11 is $_{11}C_7$. Since both the 3 men *and* the 4 women must be selected, the probability is calculated as follows:

$$P\left(\begin{array}{c}\text{3 men and}\\\text{4 women selected}\end{array}\right) = \dfrac{\left(\begin{array}{c}\text{number of combinations}\\\text{of 3 men selected}\end{array}\right) \cdot \left(\begin{array}{c}\text{number of combinations}\\\text{of 4 women selected}\end{array}\right)}{\left(\begin{array}{c}\text{total number of possible combinations}\\\text{for selecting 7 people}\end{array}\right)}$$

$$= \dfrac{_6C_3 \cdot _5C_4}{_{11}C_7} = \dfrac{20 \cdot 5}{330} = \dfrac{100}{330} = \dfrac{10}{33}$$

Thus, the probability is $\frac{10}{33}$. ■

Example 4 *DVD Selection*

Jennifer Alfredo has 4 *Scooby Doo* DVDs, 5 *Magic School Bus* DVDs, and 3 *Bob the Builder* DVDs. If Jennifer randomly selects 4 DVDs for her children to take on a road trip, determine the probability that

a) no *Scooby Doo* DVDs are selected.
b) at least 1 *Scooby Doo* DVD is selected.
c) 2 *Scooby Doo* DVDs and 2 *Magic School Bus* DVDs are selected.

Solution

a) If no *Scooby Doo* DVDs are to be selected, then only *Magic School Bus* and *Bob the Builder* DVDs must be selected. Eight DVDs are either *Magic School Bus* or *Bob the Builder*. Thus, the number of ways that 4 *Magic School Bus* or *Bob the Builder* DVDs may be selected from the possible 8 *Magic School Bus* or *Bob the Builder* DVDs is $_8C_4$. The total number of possible selections is $_{12}C_4$.

$$P(\text{no } Scooby\ Doo \text{ DVDs}) = \dfrac{_8C_4}{_{12}C_4} = \dfrac{70}{495} = \dfrac{14}{99}$$

b) When 4 DVDs are selected, the choice must contain either no *Scooby Doo* DVDs or at least 1 *Scooby Doo* DVD. Since one of these outcomes must occur, the sum of the probabilities must be 1, or

$$P(\text{no } Scooby\ Doo \text{ DVDs}) \ + \ P(\text{at least 1 } Scooby\ Doo \text{ DVD}) = 1$$

Therefore,

$$P(\text{at least 1 } \textit{Scooby Doo} \text{ DVD}) = 1 - P(\text{no } \textit{Scooby Doo} \text{ DVDs})$$

$$= 1 - \frac{14}{99} = \frac{99}{99} - \frac{14}{99} = \frac{85}{99}$$

Note that the probability of selecting no *Scooby Doo* DVDs, $\frac{14}{99}$, was found in part (a).

c) The number of ways of selecting 2 *Scooby Doo* DVDs out of 4 *Scooby Doo* DVDs is $_4C_2$, which equals 6. The number of ways of selecting 2 *Magic School Bus* DVDs out of 5 *Magic School Bus* DVDs is $_5C_2$, which equals 10. The total number of possible selections when 4 DVDs are selected from the 12 choices is $_{12}C_4$, which equals 495. Since both the 2 *Scooby Doo* and 2 *Magic School Bus* DVDs must be selected, the probability is calculated as follows.

$$P(2 \textit{ Scooby Doo} \text{ and 2 } \textit{Magic School Bus}) = \frac{_4C_2 \cdot _5C_2}{_{12}C_4} = \frac{6 \cdot 10}{495} = \frac{60}{495} = \frac{4}{33} \blacksquare$$

Example 5 *Rare Coins*

Conner Shanahan's rare coin collection is made up of 8 silver dollars, 7 quarters, and 5 dimes. Conner plans to sell 8 of his 20 coins to finance part of his college education. If he selects the coins at random, what is the probability that 3 silver dollars, 2 quarters, and 3 dimes are selected?

Solution The number of ways that Conner can select 3 out of 8 silver dollars is $_8C_3$. The number of ways he can select 2 out of 7 quarters is $_7C_2$. The number of ways he can select 3 out of 5 dimes is $_5C_3$. He will select 8 coins from a total of 20 coins. The number of ways he can do so is $_{20}C_8$. The probability that Conner selects 3 silver dollars, 2 quarters, and 3 dimes is calculated as follows.

$$P(3 \text{ silver dollars, 2 quarters, and 3 dimes}) = \frac{_8C_3 \cdot _7C_2 \cdot _5C_3}{_{20}C_8}$$

$$= \frac{56 \cdot 21 \cdot 10}{125,970} = \frac{11,760}{125,970} = \frac{392}{4199} \blacksquare$$

SECTION 12.10 *Exercises*

Practice the Skills

In Exercises 1–8, set up the problem as if it were to be solved, but do not solve. Assume that each problem is to be done without replacement.

1. Ten red balls and four blue balls are in a bag. If four balls from the bag are to be selected at random, determine the probability of selecting four red balls. $\frac{_{10}C_4}{_{14}C_4}$

2. A class consists of 15 girls and 12 boys. If 8 of the students are to be selected at random, determine the probability that they are all girls. $\frac{_{15}C_8}{_{27}C_8}$

3. Three letters are to be selected at random from the English alphabet of 26 letters. Determine the probability that 3 vowels (a, e, i, o, u) are selected. $\frac{_5C_3}{_{26}C_3}$

4. Determine the probability of being dealt 3 aces from a standard deck of 52 cards when 3 cards are dealt. $\frac{_4C_3}{_{52}C_3}$

5. A dog breeder has 15 puppies for sale, of which 8 are yellow Labrador retrievers. If 5 puppies are selected at random, determine the probability they are all yellow Labrador retrievers. $\frac{_8C_5}{_{15}C_5}$

6. Of 80 people attending a dance, 28 have a college degree. If 4 people at the dance are selected at random, determine the probability that each of the 4 has a college degree. $\frac{_{28}C_4}{_{80}C_4}$

7. Of 120 students attending a college orientation session, 23 are criminal justice majors. If 5 students at the orientation are selected at random, determine the probability that each of the 5 is a criminal justice major. $\frac{_{23}C_5}{_{120}C_5}$

8. A class of 16 people contains 4 people whose birthday is in October. If 3 people from the class are selected at random, determine the probability that *none* of those selected has an October birthday. $\frac{_{12}C_3}{_{16}C_3}$

Problem Solving

In Exercises 9–18, the problems are to be done without replacement. Use combinations to determine probabilities.

9. *Selecting Lightbulbs* A box contains 3 defective and 7 good lightbulbs. If two lightbulbs are to be selected at random from the box, determine the probability that both lightbulbs are defective. $\frac{1}{15}$

10. *Green and Red Balls* A bag contains four red balls and five green balls. You plan to select three balls at random. Determine the probability of selecting three green balls. $\frac{5}{42}$

11. *Flu Vaccine* A doctor has five doses of flu protection vaccine left. He has six women and eight men who want the medication. If the names of five of these people are selected at random, determine the probability that five men's names are selected. $\frac{4}{143}$

12. *Bills of Four Denominations* Duc Tran's wallet contains 8 bills of the following denominations: four $5 bills, two $10 bills, one $20 bill, and one $50 bill. If Duc selects two bills at random, determine the probability that he selects two $5 bills. $\frac{3}{14}$

13. *Selecting Digits* Each of the digits 0–9 is written on a slip of paper, and the slips are placed in a hat. If three slips of paper are selected at random, determine the probability that the three numbers selected are greater than 5. $\frac{1}{30}$

14. *Selecting Books* Barnes & Noble has 20 different books listed on its clearance list. Twelve books are listed as mystery, and 8 are listed as romance. If 4 books are selected at random from the list, determine the probability that they are all mystery books. $\frac{33}{323}$

15. *Gift Certificates* The sales department at Atwell Studios consists of three people, the manufacturing department consists of six people, and the accounting department consists of two people. Three people will be selected at random from these people and will be given gift certificates to Sweet Tomatoes, a local restaurant. Determine the probability that two of those selected will be from the manufacturing department and one will be from the accounting department. $\frac{2}{11}$

16. *Faculty-Student Committee* A committee of four is to be randomly selected from a group of seven teachers and eight students. Determine the probability that the committee will consist of two teachers and two students. $\frac{28}{65}$

17. *Winning the Grand Prize* A lottery consists of 46 numbers. You select 6 numbers, and if they match the 6 numbers selected by the lottery commission, you win the grand prize. Determine the probability of winning the grand prize. $\frac{1}{9,366,819}$

18. *Red Cards* You are dealt 5 cards from a standard deck of 52 cards. Determine the probability that you are dealt 5 red cards. $\frac{253}{9996}$

TV Game Show In Exercises 19–22, a television game show has five doors, of which the contestant must pick two. Behind two of the doors are expensive cars, and behind the other three doors are consolation prizes. The contestant gets to keep the items behind the two doors she selects. Determine the probability that the contestant wins

19. no cars. $\frac{3}{10}$

20. both cars. $\frac{1}{10}$

21. at least one car. $\frac{7}{10}$

22. exactly one car. $\frac{3}{5}$

Baseball In Exercises 23–26, assume that a particular professional baseball team has 10 pitchers, 6 infielders, and 9 other players. If 3 players' names are selected at random, determine the probability that

23. all 3 are infielders. $\frac{1}{115}$

24. none of the three is a pitcher. $\frac{91}{460}$

25. 2 are pitchers and 1 is an infielder. $\frac{27}{230}$

26. 1 is a pitcher and 2 are players other than pitchers and infielders. $\frac{18}{115}$

Car Rental In Exercises 27–30, a car rental agency has 10 midsized and 15 compact cars on its lot, from which 6 will be selected. Assuming that each car is equally likely to be selected and the cars are selected at random, determine the probability (as a decimal number rounded to four decimal places) that the cars selected consist of

27. all midsized cars. 0.0012

28. 2 midsized cars and 4 compact cars. 0.3468

29. 3 midsized cars and 3 compact cars. 0.3083

30. at least 1 compact car. 0.9988

New Soup In Exercises 31–34, Campbell's is testing 12 new soups for possible production. They are testing 3 Chunky soups, 4 Healthy Request soups, and 5 Select Harvest soups. If we assume each of the 12 soups has the same chance of being selected and 4 new soups will be produced, determine the probability that the four new soups selected will be as follows

31. 2 are Healthy Request soups and 2 are Chunky soups. $\frac{2}{55}$

32. 3 are Select Harvest soups and 1 is a Healthy Request soup. $\frac{8}{99}$

33. 1 is a Healthy Request soup, 1 is a Select Harvest soup, and 2 are Chunky soups. $\frac{4}{33}$

34. at least one is a Chunky soup. $\frac{41}{55}$

Theater In Exercises 35–38, five men and six women are going to be assigned to a specific row of seats in a theater. If the 11 tickets for the numbered seats are given out at random, determine the probability that

35. five women are given the first five seats next to the center aisle. $\frac{1}{77}$

36. at least one woman is in one of the first five seats. $\frac{461}{462}$

37. exactly one woman is in one of the first five seats. $\frac{5}{77}$

38. three women are seated in the first three seats and two men are seated in the next two seats. $\frac{10}{231}$

39. *Working Overtime* Of 24 employees at Lowe's home improvement store, 10 work as cashiers and 14 stock shelves. If 3 of the 24 employees are selected at random to work overtime, determine the probability that all 3 are cashiers. $\frac{15}{253}$

40. *Poker Probability* A full house in poker consists of three of one kind and two of another kind in a five-card hand. For example, if a hand contains three kings and two 5's, it is a full house. If 5 cards are dealt at random from a standard deck of 52 cards, without replacement,

determine the probability of getting three kings and two 5's. $\frac{1}{108,290}$

41. *A Royal Flush* A royal flush consists of an ace, king, queen, jack, and 10 all in the same suit. If 7 cards are dealt at random from a standard deck of 52 cards, determine the probability of getting a

a) royal flush in spades. $\frac{1}{123,760}$

b) royal flush in any suit. $\frac{1}{30,940}$

42. *Restaurant Staff* The staff of a restaurant consists of 25 people, including 8 waiters, 12 waitresses, and 5 cooks. For Mother's Day, a total of 9 people will need to be selected to work. If the selections are made at random, determine the probability that 3 waiters, 4 waitresses, and 2 cooks will be selected. $\frac{1008}{7429}$

43. *"Dead Man's Hand"* A pair of aces and a pair of 8's is often known as a "dead man's hand." (See the *Did You Know?* on page 753.)

a) Determine the probability of being dealt a dead man's hand (any two aces, any two 8's, and one other card that is not an ace or an 8) when 5 cards are dealt, without replacement, from a standard deck of 52 cards. $\frac{33}{54,145}$

b) The actual cards "Wild Bill" Hickok was holding when he was shot were the aces of spades and clubs, the 8's of spades and clubs, and the 9 of diamonds. If you are dealt five cards without replacement, determine the probability of being dealt this exact hand. $\frac{1}{2,598,960}$

Challenge Problems/Group Activities

44. *Alternate Seating* If three men and three women are to be assigned at random to six seats in a row at a theater, determine the probability that they will alternate by gender. $\frac{1}{10}$

45. *Selecting Officers* A club consists of 15 people including Ali, Kendra, Ted, Alice, Marie, Dan, Linda, and Frank. From the 15 members, a president, vice president, and treasurer will be selected at random. An advisory committee of 5 other individuals will also be selected at random.

a) Determine the probability that Ali is selected president, Kendra is selected vice president, Ted is selected treasurer, and the other 5 individuals named form the advisory committee. $\frac{1}{2,162,160}$

b) Determine the probability that 3 of the 8 individuals named are selected for the three officers' positions and the other 5 are selected for the advisory board. $\frac{1}{6435}$

46. A Marked Deck A number is written with a magic marker on each card of a deck of 52 cards. The number 1 is put on the first card, 2 on the second, and so on. The cards are then shuffled and cut. What is the probability that the top 4 cards will be in ascending order? (For example, the top card is 12, the second 22, the third 41, and the fourth 51.) $\frac{1}{24}$

Recreational Mathematics

47. Hair When the Isle of Flume took its most recent census, the population was 100,002 people. Nobody on the isle has more than 100,001 hairs on his or her head. Determine the probability that at least two people have exactly the same number of hairs on their head. 1; Since there are more hairs than people, two or more people must have the same number of hairs on their head.

SECTION 12.11   Binomial Probability Formula

Suppose that you are a waiter at a restaurant and have learned from past experience that 80% of your customers leave a tip. If you wait on 6 customers, what is the probability that all 6 customers will leave a tip? If you wait on 8 customers, what is the probability that at least 5 of them will leave you a tip? In this section, we will learn how to use the binomial probability formula to answer these and similar questions.

Why *This is Important* Binomial probabilities have many applications in business and industry, as well as in the sciences and the pharmacological industry.

Suppose that a basket contains three identical balls, except for their color. One is red, one is blue, and one is yellow (Fig. 12.23). Suppose further that we are going to select three balls *with replacement* from the basket. We can determine specific probabilities by examining the tree diagram shown in Fig. 12.24. Note that 27 different selections are possible, as indicated in the sample space.

▲ *We can use the binomial formula to determine the probability that selected customers waited on will leave a tip.*

Figure 12.23

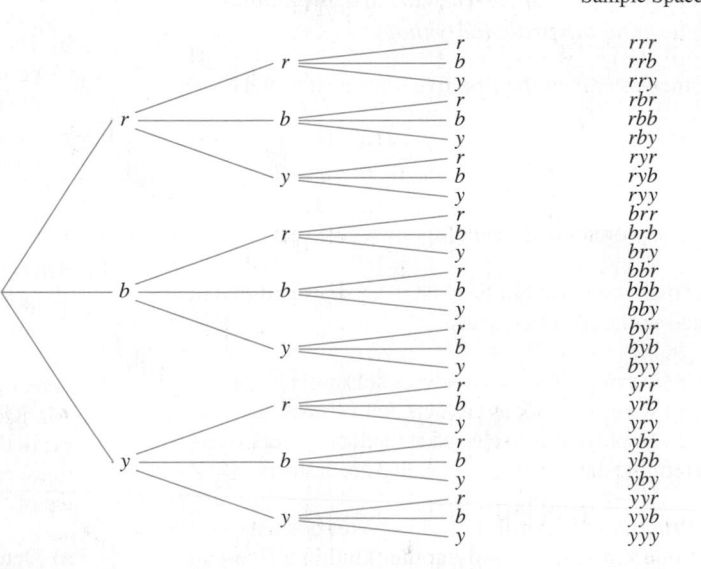

Figure 12.24

Our three selections may yield 0, 1, 2, or 3 red balls. We can determine the probability of selecting exactly 0, 1, 2, or 3 red balls by using the sample space. To determine the probability of selecting 0 red balls, we count those outcomes that do not contain a red ball. There are 8 of them (*bbb, bby, byb, byy, ybb, yby, yyb, yyy*). Thus, the probability of obtaining exactly 0 red balls is 8/27. We determine the probability of selecting exactly 1 red ball by counting the sample points that contain exactly 1 red ball. There are 12 of them. Thus, the probability is $\frac{12}{27}$, or $\frac{4}{9}$.

We can determine the probability of selecting exactly 2 red balls and exactly 3 red balls in a similar manner. The probabilities of selecting exactly 0, 1, 2, and 3 red balls are illustrated in Table 12.5.

Table 12.5 A Probability Distribution for Three Balls Selected with Replacement

Number of Red Balls Selected, (x)	Probability of Selecting the Number of Red Balls, $P(x)$
0	$\frac{8}{27}$
1	$\frac{12}{27}$
2	$\frac{6}{27}$
3	$\frac{1}{27}$
	Sum $= \dfrac{27}{27} = 1$

Note that the sum of the probabilities is 1. This table is an example of a *probability distribution*, which shows the probabilities associated with each specific outcome of an experiment. *In a probability distribution, every possible outcome must be listed and the sum of the probabilities must be 1.*

Let us specifically consider the probability of selecting 1 red ball in 3 selections. We see from Table 12.5 that this probability is $\frac{12}{27}$, or $\frac{4}{9}$. Can we determine this probability without developing a tree diagram? The answer is yes.

Suppose that we consider selecting a red ball success, S, and selecting a non–red ball failure, F. Furthermore, suppose that we let *p* represent the probability of success and *q* the probability of failure on any trial. Then $p = \frac{1}{3}$ and $q = \frac{2}{3}$. We can obtain 1 success in three selections in the following ways:

$$\text{SFF} \qquad \text{FSF} \qquad \text{FFS}$$

We can compute the probabilities of each of these outcomes using the multiplication formula because each of the selections is independent.

$$P(\text{SFF}) = P(\text{S}) \cdot P(\text{F}) \cdot P(\text{F}) = p \cdot q \cdot q = pq^2 = \frac{1}{3}\left(\frac{2}{3}\right)^2 = \frac{4}{27}$$

$$P(\text{FSF}) = P(\text{F}) \cdot P(\text{S}) \cdot P(\text{F}) = q \cdot p \cdot q = pq^2 = \frac{1}{3}\left(\frac{2}{3}\right)^2 = \frac{4}{27}$$

$$P(\text{FFS}) = P(\text{F}) \cdot P(\text{F}) \cdot P(\text{S}) = q \cdot q \cdot p = pq^2 = \frac{1}{3}\left(\frac{2}{3}\right)^2 = \frac{4}{27}$$

$$\text{Sum} = \frac{12}{27} = \frac{4}{9}$$

We obtained an answer of $\frac{4}{9}$, the same answer that was obtained using the tree diagram. Note that each of the 3 sets of outcomes above has 1 success and 2 failures.

Rather than listing all the possibilities containing 1 success and 2 failures, we can use the combination formula to determine the number of possible combinations of 1 success in 3 trials. To do so, evaluate $_3C_1$.

$$_3C_1 = \frac{3!}{(3-1)!1!} = \frac{3 \cdot 2 \cdot 1}{2 \cdot 1 \cdot 1} = 3$$

Number of trials   Number of successes

Thus, we see that there are 3 ways the 1 success could occur in 3 trials. To compute the probability of 1 success in 3 trials, we can multiply the probability of success in any one trial, $p \cdot q^2$, by the number of ways the 1 success can be arranged among the 3 trials, $_3C_1$. Thus, the probability of selecting 1 red ball, $P(1)$, in 3 trials may be found as follows.

$$P(1) = (_3C_1)p^1q^2 = 3\left(\frac{1}{3}\right)\left(\frac{2}{3}\right)^2 = \frac{12}{27} = \frac{4}{9}$$

The binomial probability formula, which we introduce shortly, explains how to obtain expressions like $P(1) = (_3C_1)p^1q^2$ and is very useful in finding certain types of probabilities.

To use the binomial probability formula, the following three conditions must hold.

To Use The Binomial Probability Formula
1. There are n repeated independent trials.
2. Each trial has two possible outcomes, *success* and *failure*.
3. For each trial, the probability of success (and failure) remains the same.

Before going further, let's discuss why we can use the binomial probability formula to find the probability of selecting a specific number of red balls when three balls are selected with replacement. First, since each trial is performed *with replacement*, the three trials are independent of each other. Second, we may consider selecting a red ball as success and selecting any ball of another color as failure. Third, for each selection, the probability of success (selecting a red ball) is $\frac{1}{3}$ and the probability of failure (selecting a ball of another color) is $\frac{2}{3}$. Now let's discuss the binomial probability formula.

Binomial Probability Formula
The probability of obtaining exactly x successes, $P(x)$, in n independent trials is given by the binomial probability formula

$$P(x) = (_nC_x)p^xq^{n-x}$$

where p is the probability of success on a single trial and q is the probability of failure on a single trial.

In the formula, p will be a number between 0 and 1, inclusive, and $q = 1 - p$. Therefore, if $p = 0.2$, then $q = 1 - 0.2 = 0.8$. If $p = \frac{3}{5}$, then $q = 1 - \frac{3}{5} = \frac{2}{5}$. Note that $p + q = 1$ and the values of p and q remain the same for each independent trial. The combination $_nC_x$ is called the *binomial coefficient*.

In Example 1, we use the binomial probability formula to solve the same problem we recently solved by using a tree diagram.

Example 1 *Selecting Colored Balls with Replacement*

A basket contains 3 balls: 1 red, 1 blue, and 1 yellow. Three balls are going to be selected with replacement from the basket. Find the probability that

a) no red balls are selected.

b) exactly 1 red ball is selected.

c) exactly 2 red balls are selected.

d) exactly 3 red balls are selected.

Solution

a) We will consider selecting a red ball a success and selecting a ball of any other color a failure. Since only 1 of the 3 balls is red, the probability of success on any single trial, p, is $\frac{1}{3}$. The probability of failure on any single trial, q, is $1 - \frac{1}{3} = \frac{2}{3}$. We are finding the probability of selecting 0 red balls, or 0 successes. Since x represents the number of successes, we let $x = 0$. There are 3 independent selections (or trials), so $n = 3$. In our calculations, we will need to evaluate $\left(\frac{1}{3}\right)^0$. Note that any nonzero number raised to a power of 0 is 1. Thus, $\left(\frac{1}{3}\right)^0 = 1$. We determine the probability of 0 successes, or $P(0)$, as follows.

$$P(x) = (_nC_x)p^xq^{n-x}$$

$$P(0) = (_3C_0)\left(\frac{1}{3}\right)^0\left(\frac{2}{3}\right)^{3-0}$$

$$= (1)(1)\left(\frac{2}{3}\right)^3$$

$$= \left(\frac{2}{3}\right)^3 = \frac{8}{27}$$

b) We are finding the probability of obtaining exactly 1 red ball or exactly 1 success in 3 independent selections. Thus, $x = 1$ and $n = 3$. We find the probability of exactly 1 success, or $P(1)$, as follows.

$$P(x) = (_nC_x)p^xq^{n-x}$$

$$P(1) = (_3C_1)\left(\frac{1}{3}\right)^1\left(\frac{2}{3}\right)^{3-1}$$

$$= 3\left(\frac{1}{3}\right)\left(\frac{2}{3}\right)^2$$

$$= 3\left(\frac{1}{3}\right)\left(\frac{4}{9}\right) = \frac{4}{9}$$

c) We are finding the probability of selecting exactly 2 red balls in 3 independent trials. Thus, $x = 2$ and $n = 3$. We find $P(2)$ as follows.

$$P(x) = (_nC_x)p^xq^{n-x}$$

$$P(2) = {_3C_2}\left(\frac{1}{3}\right)^2\left(\frac{2}{3}\right)^{3-2}$$

$$= 3\left(\frac{1}{3}\right)^2\left(\frac{2}{3}\right)^1$$

$$= 3\left(\frac{1}{9}\right)\left(\frac{2}{3}\right) = \frac{2}{9}$$

d) We are finding the probability of selecting exactly 3 red balls in 3 independent trials. Thus, $x = 3$ and $n = 3$. We find $P(3)$ as follows.

$$P(x) = (_nC_x)p^x q^{n-x}$$

$$P(3) = (_3C_3)\left(\frac{1}{3}\right)^3\left(\frac{2}{3}\right)^{3-3}$$

$$= 1\left(\frac{1}{3}\right)^3\left(\frac{2}{3}\right)^0$$

$$= 1\left(\frac{1}{27}\right)(1) = \frac{1}{27}$$ ∎

All the probabilities obtained in Example 1 agree with the answers obtained by using the tree diagram. Whenever you obtain a value for $P(x)$, you should obtain a value between 0 and 1, inclusive. If you obtain a value greater than 1, you have made a mistake.

Example 2 *Quality Control for Batteries*

A manufacturer of batteries knows that 0.4% of the batteries produced by the company are defective.

a) Write the binomial probability formula that would be used to determine the probability that exactly x out of n batteries produced are defective.

b) Write the binomial probability formula that would be used to find the probability that exactly 3 batteries of 75 produced will be defective. Do not evaluate.

Solution

a) We want to find the probability that exactly x batteries are defective where selecting a defective battery is considered success. The probability, p, that an individual battery is defective is 0.4%, or 0.004 in decimal form. The probability that a battery is not defective, q, is $1 - 0.004$, or 0.996. The general formula for finding the probability that exactly x out of n batteries produced are defective is

$$P(x) = (_nC_x)p^x q^{n-x}$$

Substituting 0.004 for p and 0.996 for q, we obtain the formula

$$P(x) = (_nC_x)(0.004)^x(0.996)^{n-x}$$

b) We want to determine the probability that exactly 3 batteries out of 75 produced are defective. Thus, $x = 3$ and $n = 75$. Substituting these values into the formula in part (a) gives

$$P(3) = (_{75}C_3)(0.004)^3(0.996)^{75-3}$$

$$= (_{75}C_3)(0.004)^3(0.996)^{72}$$

The answer may be obtained using a scientific calculator.   ∎

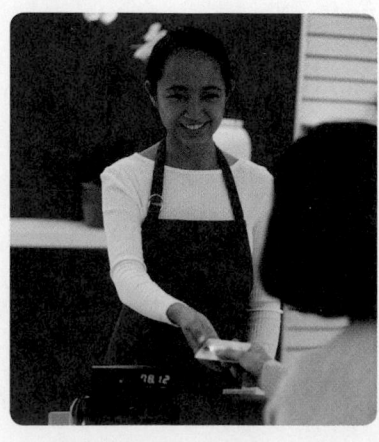

Example 3 *Spring Break*

According to a survey conducted by OnCampus Research, 20% of college students reported they will work during spring break. Determine the probability that

a) exactly 3 of 5 college students selected at random will work during spring break.

b) exactly 4 of 4 college students selected at random will work during spring break.

Solution

a) We want to determine the probability that exactly 3 of 5 college students selected at random will work during spring break. Therefore a college student working during spring break is considered a success. Thus, $x = 3$ and $n = 5$. The probability of success, p, is 20%, or 0.2. The probability of failure, q, is $1 - 0.2$, or 0.8. Substituting these values into the binomial formula yields

$$P(x) = (_nC_x)p^x q^{n-x}$$
$$P(3) = (_5C_3)(0.2)^3(0.8)^{5-3}$$
$$= 10(0.2)^3(0.8)^2$$
$$= 10(0.008)(0.64)$$
$$= 0.0512$$

Thus, the probability that exactly 3 of 5 randomly selected college students will work during spring break is 0.0512.

b) We want to find the probability that 4 of 4 college students selected at random will work during spring break. Thus, $x = 4$ and $n = 4$. We wish to find $P(4)$.

$$P(x) = (_nC_x)p^x q^{n-x}$$
$$P(4) = (_4C_4)(0.2)^4(0.8)^{4-4}$$
$$= 1(0.2)^4(0.8)^0$$
$$= 10(0.0016)(1)$$
$$= 0.016$$

Thus, the probability that exactly 4 of 4 randomly selected college students will work during spring break is 0.016. ∎

Example 4 *Planting Trees*

The probability that a tree planted by a landscaping company will survive is 0.8. Determine the probability that

a) none of four trees planted will survive.

b) at least one of four trees planted will survive.

Solution

a) Success is a tree survives. Thus, $p = 0.8$ and $q = 1 - p = 1 - 0.8 = 0.2$.
   We want to find the probability of 0 successes in 4 trials. Thus, $x = 0$ and $n = 4$. We find the probability of 0 successes, or $P(0)$, as follows.

$$P(x) = (_nC_x)p^x q^{n-x}$$
$$P(0) = (_4C_0)(0.8)^0(0.2)^{4-0}$$
$$= 1(1)(0.2)^4$$
$$= 1(1)(0.0016)$$
$$= 0.0016$$

Thus, the probability that none of the four trees planted will survive is 0.0016.

b) The probability that at least one tree of the four trees planted will survive can be found by subtracting from 1 the probability that none of the four trees survives. We worked problems of this type in earlier sections of the chapter, including Sections 12.6 and 12.10.

In part (a), we determined the probability that none of the four trees planted survives is 0.0016. Thus,

$$P(\text{at least one tree planted will survive}) = 1 - P\left(\begin{array}{c}\text{none of the four trees}\\\text{planted will survive}\end{array}\right)$$
$$= 1 - 0.0016$$
$$= 0.9984$$ ∎

SECTION 12.11   *Exercises*

Warm Up Exercises

In Exercises 1–4, fill in the blank with an appropriate word, phrase, or symbol(s).

1. A distribution that shows the probabilities associated with each specific outcome of an experiment is called a(n) _____ distribution. Probability

2. In a probability distribution, the sum of all the probabilities must be _____. 1

3. In the binomial probability formula, p represents the probability of _____. Success

4. In the binomial probability formula, q represents the probability of _____. Failure

Practice the Skills

In Exercises 5–10, assume that each of the n trials is independent and that p is the probability of success on a given trial. Use the binomial probability formula to find P(x).

5. $n = 4, x = 3, p = 0.1$ 0.0036

6. $n = 5, x = 2, p = 0.6$ 0.2304

7. $n = 5, x = 2, p = 0.4$ 0.3456

8. $n = 3, x = 3, p = 0.8$ 0.512

9. $n = 6, x = 0, p = 0.5$ 0.015625

10. $n = 5, x = 3, p = 0.9$ 0.0729

Problem Solving

11. *A Dozen Eggs* An egg distributor determines that the probability that any individual egg has a crack is 0.14.

    a) Write the binomial probability formula to determine the probability that exactly x eggs of n eggs are cracked. $P(x) = (_nC_x)(0.14)^x(0.86)^{n-x}$

    b) Write the binomial probability formula to determine the probability that exactly 2 eggs in a one-dozen egg carton are cracked. Do not evaluate. $P(2) = (_{12}C_2)(0.14)^2(0.86)^{10}$

12. *Facebook* According to *Social Media Today*, as of April 2010, 41.6% of Americans had a Facebook account.

    a) Write the binomial formula to determine the probability that exactly x out of n randomly selected Americans had a Facebook account. $P(x) = (_nC_x)(0.416)^x(0.584)^{n-x}$

    b) Write the binomial formula to determine the probability that exactly 5 out of 20 randomly selected Americans had a Facebook account. Do not evaluate. $P(5) = (_{20}C_5)(0.416)^5(0.584)^{15}$

In Exercises 13–21, use the binomial probability formula to answer the question. Round answers to five decimal places.

13. *Auto Insurance* An insurance company reported that 60% of all automobile damage claims were made by people under the age of 25. If eight automobile damage claims were selected at random, determine the probability that exactly five of them were made by someone under the age of 25. 0.27869

14. *Leaving a Tip* Thomas Zellner works as a waiter at Outback Steakhouse. He has learned from experience that 80% of customers who dine alone leave a tip. If Thomas waits on 6 customers dining alone, determine the probability that exactly 4 of them leave a tip. 0.24576

15. *Staying Connected* According to a survey conducted by American Express, 77% of adults stated they want access to their cell phones and laptops while on vacation. If ten adults are selected at random, determine the probability that exactly six of them want access to their cell phones and laptops while on vacation. 0.12248

16. *Bank Loans* Records from a specific bank show that 70% of car loan applications are approved. If eight car loan applications from this bank are selected at random, determine the probability that exactly five of the applications are approved. 0.25412

17. *Dolphin Drug Care* When treated with the antibiotic resonocyllin, 92% of all dolphins are cured of a particular bacterial infection. If six dolphins with the particular bacterial infection are treated with resonocyllin, determine the probability that exactly four are cured. 0.06877

18. *Manufacturing Lightbulbs* A quality control engineer at a GE lightbulb plant finds that 1% of its bulbs are defective. Determine the probability that exactly two of the next six bulbs made are defective. 0.00144

19. *Water Heaters* The probability that a specific brand of water heater produces the water temperature it is set to produce is $\frac{4}{5}$. Determine the probability that if five of these water heaters are selected at random, exactly four of them will produce the water temperature they are set to produce. 0.4096

20. *TV Purchases* At a Circuit City store, $\frac{1}{4}$ of those purchasing color televisions purchase a large-screen TV. Determine the probability that

a) none of the next four people who purchase a color television at Circuit City purchases a large-screen TV. 0.31641

b) at least one of the next four people who purchase a color television at Circuit City purchases a large-screen TV. 0.68359

21. *Multiple-Choice Quiz* Edward Dunn has to take a five-question multiple-choice quiz in his sociology class. Each question has four choices for answers, of which only one is correct. Assuming that Edward guesses on all five questions, what is the probability that he will answer

a) all five questions correctly. 0.00098

b) exactly three questions correctly. 0.08789

c) at least three questions correctly. 0.10352

Challenge Problems/Group Activities

22. *Transportation to Work* In a random sample of 80 working mothers in Duluth, Minnesota, the following data indicating how they get to work were obtained.

Mode of Transportation	Number of Mothers
Car	40
Bus	20
Bike	16
Other	4

If this sample is representative of all working mothers in Duluth, determine the probability that exactly three of five working mothers selected at random

a) take a car to work. 0.3125

b) take a bus to work. ≈ 0.08789

23. *Selecting 6 Cards* Six cards are selected from a standard deck of playing cards with replacement. Determine the probability that

a) exactly three picture cards are obtained. ≈ 0.1119

b) exactly two spades are obtained. ≈ 0.2966

24. *Office Visit* The probability that a person visiting Dr. Guillermo Suarez's office is more than 60 years old is 0.7. Determine the probability that

a) exactly three of the next five people visiting the office are more than 60 years old. 0.3087

b) at least three of the next five people visiting the office are more than 60 years old. 0.83692

Recreational Mathematics

25. *Aruba* The island of Aruba is well known for its beaches and predictable warm, sunny weather. In fact, Aruba's weather is so predictable that the daily newspapers don't even bother to print a forecast. Strangely enough, however, on New Year's Eve, as the islanders were counting down the last 10 sec of 2011, it began to rain. What is the probability, from 0 to 1, that 72 hr later the sun will be shining? 0; it will be midnight.

CHAPTER 12 *Summary*

Important Facts And Concepts

Examples and Discussion

Section 12.1

Empirical Probability

$$P(E) = \frac{\text{number of times event } E \text{ has occurred}}{\begin{pmatrix} \text{total number of times the} \\ \text{experiment has been performed} \end{pmatrix}}$$

Examples 1–2, pages 676–677

The Law of Large Numbers

Probability statements apply in practice to a large number of trials, not to a single trial. It is the relative frequency over the long run that is accurately predictable, not individual events or precise totals.

Discussion, pages 678–679

Section 12.2

Theoretical Probability

$$P(E) = \frac{\text{number of outcomes favorable to } E}{\text{total number of possible outcomes}}$$

Examples 1–3, pages 684–687

Probability Facts

The probability of an event that cannot occur is 0. The probability of an event that must occur is 1. Every probability must be a number between 0 and 1 inclusively; that is

$$0 \leq P(E) \leq 1$$

The sum of the probabilities of all possible outcomes of an event is 1.

$$P(A) + P(\text{not } A) = 1$$

Discussion, page 684

Example 3, page 686

Section 12.3

Odds Against an Event

$$\text{Odds against} = \frac{P(\text{event fails to occur})}{P(\text{event occurs})} = \frac{P(\text{failure})}{P(\text{success})}$$

Examples 1–3, pages 691–693

Odds in Favor of an Event

$$\text{Odds in favor} = \frac{P(\text{event occurs})}{P(\text{event fails to occur})} = \frac{P(\text{success})}{P(\text{failure})}$$

Example 3, page 693

Section 12.4

Expected Value

$$E = P_1 A_1 + P_2 A_2 + P_3 A_3 + \cdots + P_n A_n$$

Examples 1–6, pages 699–702

Section 12.5

Counting Principle

If a first experiment can be performed in M distinct ways and a second experiment can be performed in N distinct ways, then the two experiments in that specific order can be performed in $M \cdot N$ distinct ways.

Examples 1–3, pages 709–711

Section 12.6

OR and AND problems

$$P(A \text{ or } B) = P(A) + P(B) - P(A \text{ and } B)$$
$$P(A \text{ and } B) = P(A) \cdot P(B)$$

Examples 1–3, pages 717–719
Examples 4–7, pages 720–723

Section 12.7

Conditional Probability

$$P(E_2 | E_1) = \frac{n(E_1 \text{ and } E_2)}{n(E_1)}$$

Examples 1–3, pages 729–731

Section 12.8

The **number of permutations** of n items is $n!$.

$$n! = n(n-1)(n-2) \cdots (3)(2)(1)$$

Example 3, page 738

Permutation Formula

$$_nP_r = \frac{n!}{(n-r)!}$$

Examples 4–6, pages 738–741

The number of different permutations of n objects where $n_1, n_2, \ldots, n_r$ of the objects are identical is

$$\frac{n!}{n_1! n_2! \cdots n_r!}$$

Example 7, page 742

Section 12.9, 12.10 **Combination Formula**	
$$_nC_r = \dfrac{n!}{(n-r)!\,r!}$$	Examples 2–4, page 748 Examples 1–5, pages 753–755
Section 12.11 **Binomial Probability Formula**	
$$P(x) = (_nC_x)p^x q^{n-x}$$	Examples 1–4, pages 761–763

CHAPTER 12) *Review Exercises*

12.1–12.11

1. In your own words, explain the law of large numbers. Answers will vary.

2. Explain how empirical probability can be used to determine whether a die is "loaded" (not a fair die). Answers will vary.

3. *Cars* Of 45 people who purchase a vehicle at a car dealership, 9 purchased an SUV. Determine the empirical probability that the next person who purchases a vehicle from that car dealership purchases an SUV. $\frac{1}{5}$

4. *Cards* Select a card from a deck of cards 40 times with replacement and compute the empirical probability of selecting a heart. Answers will vary.

5. *Television News* In a small town, 250 people were asked whether they watched ABC, CBS, NBC, Fox, or MSNBC news. The results are indicated below.

Network	Number of People
ABC	80
CBS	35
NBC	60
Fox	35
MSNBC	40

Determine the empirical probability that the next person selected at random from the town watches ABC news. $\frac{8}{25}$

Digits In Exercises 6–9, each of the digits 0, 1, 2, 3, 4, 5, 6, 7, 8, 9 is written on a piece of paper and all the pieces of paper are placed in a hat. One number is selected at random. Determine the probability that the number selected is

6. even. $\frac{1}{2}$

7. odd or greater than 3. $\frac{4}{5}$

8. greater than 2 or less than 6. 1

9. even and greater than 4. $\frac{1}{5}$

Yogurt Preference In Exercises 10–13, a taste test is given to 50 customers at a supermarket. The customers are asked to taste 4 types of yogurt and to list their favorite. The results are summarized below.

Type	Number of People
Strawberry	18
Raspberry	14
Blueberry	11
Banana creme pie	7

If one person who participated in the taste test is selected at random, determine the probability that the person's favorite was

10. strawberry $\frac{9}{25}$

11. blueberry $\frac{11}{50}$

12. either strawberry or raspberry. $\frac{16}{25}$

13. a yogurt other than banana creme pie. $\frac{43}{50}$

14. *Obesity* According to the U.S. Centers for Disease Control and Prevention, 20% of children in the United States,

age 6–11, are obese. If a child age 6–11 was selected at random, determine the odds

a) against the child being obese. 4:1

b) in favor of the child being obese. 1:4

15. *Vegetable Mix-up* Nicholas Delaney, a mischievous little boy, has removed labels on the eight cans of vegetables in the cabinet. Nicholas's father knows that there are three cans of corn, three cans of beans, and two cans of carrots. If the father selects and opens one can at random, determine the odds against his selecting a can of corn. 5:3

16. *Horseracing* The odds against Buttermilk winning the Triple Crown in horse racing are 82:3. Determine the probability that Buttermilk wins the Triple Crown. $\frac{3}{85}$

17. *Dry Cleaner Success* The probability that a new dry cleaner will succeed at a given location is 0.85. Determine the odds in favor of the dry cleaner succeeding. 17:3

18. *Raffle Tickets* One thousand raffle tickets are sold at $2 each. Three prizes of $200 and two prizes of $100 will be awarded. Assume that the probability that any given ticket is selected for a $200 prize is $\frac{3}{1000}$ and the probability that any given ticket is selected for a $100 prize is $\frac{2}{1000}$.

a) Determine the expectation of a person who purchases a ticket. − $1.20

b) Determine the expectation of a person who purchases three tickets. − $3.60

19. *Expectation of a Card* If Cameron selects a picture card from a standard deck of 52 cards, Lindsey will give him $9. If Cameron does not select a picture card, he must give Lindsey $3.

a) Determine Cameron's expectation. − $0.23

b) Determine Lindsey's expectation. $0.23

c) If Cameron plays this game 100 times, how much can he expect to lose or gain? Lose $23.08

20. *Expected Attendance* If the day is sunny, 1000 people will attend the baseball game. If the day is cloudy, only 500 people will attend. If it rains, only 100 people will attend. The local meteorologist states that the probability of a sunny day is 0.4, of a cloudy day is 0.5, and of a rainy day is 0.1. Determine the number of people that are expected to attend. 660 people

21. *Fair Price* At a game of chance, the expected value is found to be − $2.50, and the cost to play the game is $6.50. Determine the fair price to play the game. $4.00

22. *Fair Price* The expected value when you purchase a lottery ticket is − $1.50, and the cost to play the game is $5.00. Determine the fair price of the lottery ticket. $3.50

23. *Club Officers* Tina, Jake, Gina, and Carla form a club. They plan to select a president and a vice president.

a) Construct a tree diagram showing all the possible outcomes.*

b) List the sample space.*

c) Determine the probability that Gina is selected president and Jake is selected vice president. $\frac{1}{12}$

24. *A Coin and a Number* A coin is flipped and then a number from 1 through 4 is selected at random from a bag.

a) Construct a tree diagram showing all the possible outcomes.*

b) List the sample space.*

c) Determine the probability that a head is flipped and an odd number is selected. $\frac{1}{4}$

d) Determine the probability that a head is flipped or an odd number is selected. $\frac{3}{4}$

Spinning Two Wheels   In Exercises 25–30, the outer and inner wheels are spun.

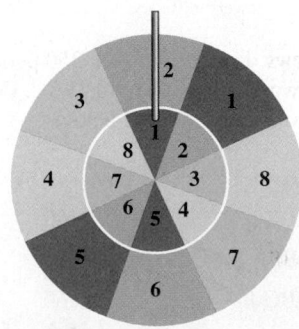

Assuming that the wheels are independent and the outcomes are equally likely, determine the probability of obtaining

25. even numbers on both wheels. $\frac{1}{4}$

26. numbers greater than 5 on both wheels. $\frac{9}{64}$

27. an odd number on the outer wheel and a number less than 6 on the inner wheel. $\frac{5}{16}$

28. an even number or a number less than 6 on the outer wheel. $\frac{7}{8}$

29. an even number or a color other than green on the inner wheel. 1

30. gold on the outer wheel and a color other than gold on the inner wheel. $\frac{3}{16}$

*See Instructor Answer Appendix

Sports Drink Selection *In Exercises 31–34, assume that Skip Bailey is going to purchase three bottles of sports drinks at a convenience store. The store has 12 different bottles of sports drinks, including 5 different bottles made by Gatorade, 4 different bottles made by Powerade, and 3 different bottles made by All Sport. If Skip selects 3 of these 12 bottles at random, determine the probability he selects*

31. 3 bottles of Gatorade. $\frac{1}{22}$

32. no bottles of Powerade. $\frac{14}{55}$

33. at least 1 bottle of Powerade. $\frac{41}{55}$

34. a bottle of Gatorade, a bottle of Gatorade, and a bottle of All Sport, in that order. $\frac{1}{22}$

Spinner Probabilities *In Exercises 35–38, assume that the spinner cannot land on a line.*

If spun once, determine

35. the probability that the spinner lands on yellow. $\frac{1}{4}$

36. the odds against and the odds in favor of the spinner landing on yellow. Against, 3 : 1; in favor, 1 : 3

37. You are awarded $5 if the spinner lands on red, $10 if it lands on yellow, and $20 if it lands on green. Determine your expected value. $13.75

38. If the spinner is spun twice, determine the probability that it lands on red and then green (assume independence). $\frac{1}{8}$

Spinner Probabilities *In Exercises 39–42, assume that the spinner cannot land on a line.*

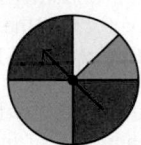

If spun once, determine

39. the probability that the spinner does not land on green. $\frac{5}{8}$

40. the odds in favor of and the odds against the spinner landing on green. In favor, 3 : 5; against, 5 : 3

41. A person wins $10 if the spinner lands on green, wins $5 if the spinner lands on red, and loses $20 if the spinner lands on yellow. Find the expectation of a person who plays this game. $3.75

42. If the spinner is spun three times, determine the probability that at least one spin lands on red. $\frac{7}{8}$

Restaurant Service *In Exercises 43–46, use the results of a survey regarding the service at the Lake View Diner, which is summarized as follows.*

Meal	Service Rated Good	Service Rated Poor	Total
Breakfast	85	10	95
Lunch	65	10	75
Total	150	20	170

If one person who completed the survey is selected at random, determine the probability that the person indicated that the

43. service was rated good. $\frac{15}{17}$

44. service was rated good, given that the meal was breakfast. $\frac{17}{19}$

45. service was rated poor, given that the meal was lunch. $\frac{2}{15}$

46. meal was breakfast, given that the service was rated poor. $\frac{1}{2}$

Neuroscience *In Exercises 47–50, assume that in a neuroscience course the students perform an experiment. Tests are given to determine if people are right brained, are left brained, or have no predominance. It is also recorded whether they are right handed or left handed. The following chart shows the results obtained.*

	Right Brained	Left Brained	No Predominance	Total
Right handed	40	130	60	230
Left handed	120	30	20	170
Total	160	160	80	400

If one person who completed the survey is selected at random, determine the probability the person selected is

47. right handed. $\frac{23}{40}$

48. left brained, given that the person is left handed. $\frac{3}{17}$

49. right handed, given that the person has no predominance. $\frac{3}{4}$

50. right brained, given that the person is left handed. $\frac{12}{17}$

51. *Television Show* Four contestants are on a television show. There are four different-colored rubber balls in a box, and each contestant gets to pick one from the box. Inside each ball is a slip of paper indicating the amount the contestant has won. The amounts are $10,000, $5000, $2000, and $1000.

a) In how many different ways can the contestants select the balls? 24

b) What is the expectation of a contestant? $4500

52. *Spelling Bee* Five finalists remain in a high school spelling bee. Two will receive $50 each, two will receive $100 each, and one will receive $500. How many different arrangements of prizes are possible? 30

53. *Candy Selection* Mrs. Williams takes her 3 children shopping. Each of her children gets to select a different type of candy that only that child will eat. At the store, there are only 10 boxes of candy left and each is a different type. In how many ways can the 3 children select the candy? 720

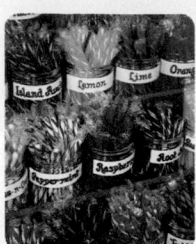

54. *Astronaut Selection* Three of nine astronauts must be selected for a mission. One will be the captain, one will be the navigator, and one will perform scientific experiments. Assuming each of the nine astronauts can perform any of the tasks, in how many ways can a three-person crew be selected so that each person has a different assignment? 504

55. *Vaccine* Dr. Goldberg has three doses of vaccine for influenza type A. Six patients in the office require the vaccine. In how many different ways could Dr. Goldberg dispense the vaccine? 20

56. *Dogsled* Ten huskies are to be selected to pull a dogsled. How many different arrangements of the 10 huskies on a dogsled are possible? 3,628,800

57. *Mega Millions* To play the lottery game Mega Millions, you select 5 numbers from 1 through 56 and 1 Mega Ball number from 1 through 46. If you match all 6 numbers, you win the jackpot!

Select 5 numbers from 1–56

a) What is the probability that you match the first 5 numbers? $\frac{1}{3,819,816}$

b) What is the probability that you match the first 5 numbers and the Mega Ball? $\frac{1}{175,711,536}$

58. *Parent-Teacher Committee* A committee of 7 is to be formed from 10 parents and 12 teachers. If the committee is to consist of 2 parents and 5 teachers, how many different committees are possible? 35,640

59. *Selecting Test Subjects* In a psychology research laboratory, one room contains eight men and another room contains five women. Three men and two women are to be selected at random to be given a psychological test. How many different combinations of these people are possible? 560

60. *Choosing Two Aces* Two cards are selected at random, without replacement, from a standard deck of 52 cards. Determine the probability that two aces are selected (use combinations). $\frac{1}{221}$

Color Chips In Exercises 61–64, a bag contains five red chips, three white chips, and two blue chips. Three chips are to be selected at random, without replacement. Determine the probability that

61. all are red. $\frac{1}{12}$

62. the first two are red and the third is blue. $\frac{1}{18}$

63. the first is red, the second is white, and the third is blue. $\frac{1}{24}$

64. at least one is red. $\frac{11}{12}$

Magazines In Exercises 65–68, on a table in a doctor's office are five Newsweek magazines, six Parenting magazines, and three Sports Illustrated magazines. If Ramona Cleary randomly selects three magazines, determine the probability that

65. three *Newsweek* magazines were selected. $\frac{5}{182}$

66. two *Parenting* magazines and one *Sports Illustrated* magazine were selected. $\frac{45}{364}$

67. no *Parenting* magazine was selected. $\frac{2}{13}$

68. at least one *Parenting* magazine was selected. $\frac{11}{13}$

69. *New Homes* In the community of Spring Hill, 60% of the homes purchased cost more than $160,000.

a) Write the binomial probability formula to determine the probability that exactly *x* of the next *n* homes purchased in Spring Hill cost more than $160,000
$P(x) = (_nC_x)(0.6)^x(0.4)^{n-x}$

b) Write the binomial probability formula to determine the probability that exactly 75 of the next 100 home purchases cost more than $160,000.
$P(75) = (_{100}C_{75})(0.6)^{75}(0.4)^{25}$

70. *Long-Stemmed Roses* At the Floyd's Flower Shop, $\frac{1}{5}$ of people ordering flowers select long-stemmed roses. Determine the probability that exactly 3 of the next 5 customers ordering flowers select long-stemmed roses. 0.0512

71. *Taking a Math Course* During any semester at City College, 60% of the students are taking a mathematics course. Determine the probability that of five students selected at random,

a) none is taking a mathematics course this semester. 0.01024

b) at least one is taking a mathematics course this semester. 0.98976

CHAPTER 12) TEST

1. *Flowers* Of the last 50 people who purchased flowers at Whistlestop Florist, 14 purchased roses. Determine the empirical probability that the next person who purchases flowers at Whistlestop Florist purchases roses. $\frac{7}{25}$

One Sheet of Paper In Exercises 2–4, each of the numbers 1–9 is written on a sheet of paper and the nine sheets of paper are placed in a hat. If one sheet of paper is selected at random from the hat, determine the probability that the number selected is

2. greater than 4. $\frac{5}{9}$

3. even. $\frac{4}{9}$

4. even or greater than 5. $\frac{2}{3}$

Two Sheets of Paper In Exercises 5–7, if two of the same nine sheets of paper mentioned above are selected, without replacement, from the hat, determine the probability that

5. both numbers are greater than 5. $\frac{1}{6}$

6. the first number is odd and the second number is even. $\frac{5}{18}$

7. neither of the numbers is greater than 6. $\frac{5}{12}$

8. One card is selected at random from a standard deck of 52 cards. Determine the probability that the card selected is a red card or a picture card. $\frac{8}{13}$

One Chip and One Die In Exercises 9–13, one colored chip–red, blue, or green–is selected at random and a die is rolled.

9. Use the counting principle to determine the number of sample points in the sample space. 18

10. Construct a tree diagram illustrating all the possible outcomes and list the sample space.*

In Exercises 11–13, by observing the sample space of the chips and die, determine the probability of obtaining

11. the color green and the number 2. $\frac{1}{18}$

12. the color red or the number 1. $\frac{4}{9}$

13. a color other than red or an even number. $\frac{5}{6}$

14. *Passwords* A personal password for an Internet brokerage account is to consist of a letter, followed by two digits, followed by two letters. Determine the number of personal codes possible if the first digit cannot be zero and repetition is permitted. 1,581,840

15. *Puppies* A litter of collie puppies consists of four males and five females. If one of the puppies is selected at random, determine the odds

a) against the puppy being male. 5:4

b) in favor of the puppy being female. 5:4

16. *Pick a Card* You get to select one card at random from a standard deck of 52 cards. If you pick a club, you win $8. If you pick a heart, you win $4. If you pick any other suit, you lose $6. Determine your expectation for this game. $0

17. *Cars and SUVs* The number of cars and the number of SUVs going through the toll gates of two bridges is recorded. The results are shown below.

Bridge	Cars	SUVs	Total
George Washington	120	106	226
Golden Gate	94	136	230
Total	214	242	456

▲ *A toll booth at the Golden Gate Bridge*

If one of these vehicles going over the bridges is selected at random, determine the probability that

a) it is a car. $\frac{107}{228}$

*See Instructor Answer Appendix

b) it is going over the George Washington Bridge. $\frac{113}{228}$

c) it is an SUV, given that it is going over the George Washington Bridge. $\frac{53}{113}$

d) it is going over the Golden Gate Bridge, given that it is a car. $\frac{47}{107}$

18. *Awarding Prizes* Three of six people are to be selected and given small prizes. One will be given a book, one will be given a calculator, and one will be given an iTunes card. In how many different ways can these prizes be awarded? 120

19. *Quality Control* A bin contains a total of 20 batteries, of which 6 are defective. If you select 2 at random, without replacement, determine the probability that

a) none of the batteries is good. $\frac{3}{38}$

b) at least one battery is good. $\frac{35}{38}$

20. *University Admission* The probability that a person is accepted for admission to a specific university is 0.6. Determine the probability that exactly two of the next five people who apply to the university get accepted. 0.2304

GROUP PROJECTS

The Probability Of An Exact Measured Value

1. Your car's speedometer indicates that you are traveling at 65 mph. What is the probability that you are traveling at *exactly* 65 mph? Explain your answer.

Taking An Exam

2. A 10-question multiple-choice exam is given, and each question has five possible answers. Pascal Gonyo takes this exam and guesses at every question. Use the binomial probability formula to determine the probability (to 5 decimal places) that

a) he gets exactly 2 questions correct.

b) he gets no questions correct.

c) he gets at least 1 question correct (use the information from part (b) to answer this part).

d) he gets at least 9 questions correct.

e) Without using the binomial probability formula, determine the probability that he gets exactly 2 questions correct.

f) Compare your answers to parts (a) and (e). If they are not the same, explain why.

Keyless Entry

3. Many cars have keyless entry. To open the lock, you may press a 5-digit code on a set of buttons like that illustrated. The code may include repeated digits like 11433 or 55512.

a) How many different 5-digit codes can be made using the 10 digits if repetition is permitted?

b) How many different ways are there of pressing 5 buttons if repetition is allowed?

c) A burglar is going to press 5 buttons at random, with repetition allowed. What is the probability that the burglar hits the sequence to open the door?

d) Suppose that each button had only one number associated with it as illustrated below. How many different 5-digit codes can be made with the 5 digits if repetition is permitted?

e) Using the buttons labeled 1–5, how many different ways are there to press 5 buttons if repetition is allowed?

f) A burglar is going to press 5 buttons of those labeled 1–5 at random with repetition allowed. Determine the probability that the burglar hits the sequence to open the door.

g) Is a burglar more likely, is he or she less likely, or does he or she have the same likelihood of pressing 5 buttons and opening the car door if the buttons are labeled as in the first illustration or as in the second illustration? Explain your answer.

h) Can you see any advantages in labeling the buttons as in the first illustration? Explain.*

---

*In actuality, in most cars that have key pads like that shown on the bottom left, each key acts as if it contains a single digit. For example, if your code is 7, 9, 5, 1, 3, the code 8, 0, 6, 2, 4 will unlock the door. The extra numbers, in effect, give the owner a false sense of security.

13

Statistics

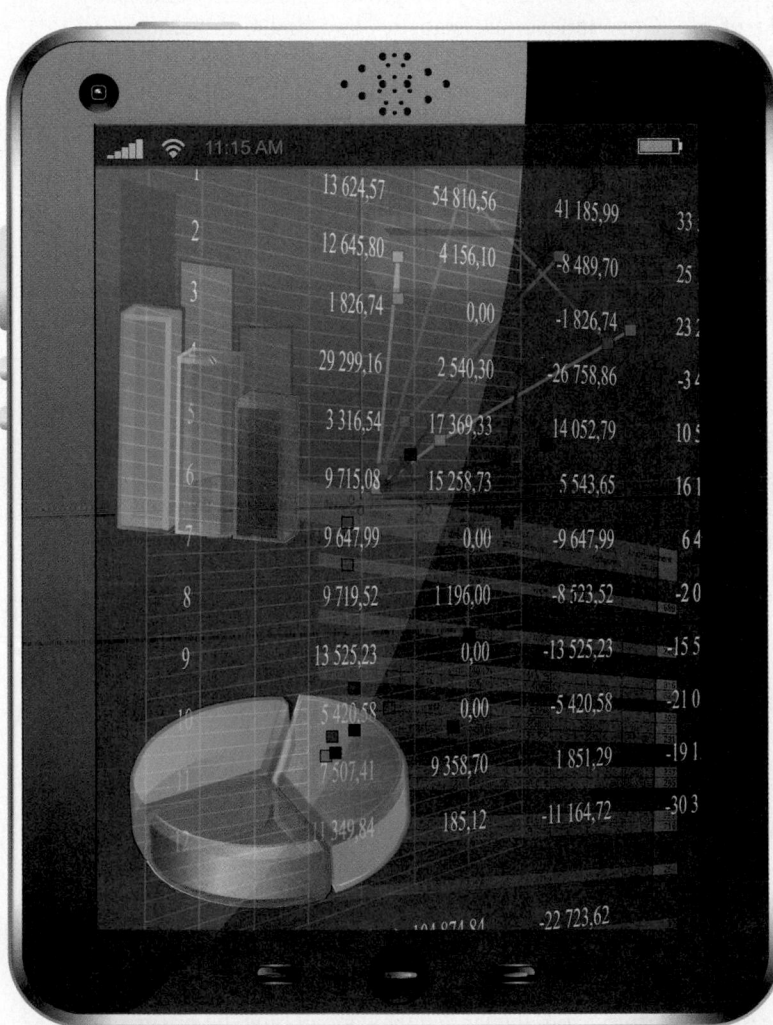

◄ *Numbers are the foundation of all statistical information.*

What You Will Learn

- Sampling techniques
- Misuses of statistics
- Frequency distributions
- Histograms, frequency polygons, stem-and-leaf displays
- Mode, median, mean, and midrange
- Percentiles and quartiles
- Range and standard deviation
- *z*-scores and the normal distribution
- Correlation and regression

Why This is Important

Benjamin Disraeli (1804–1881), once prime minister of the United Kingdom, said that there are three kinds of lies: lies, damned lies, and statistics. Do numbers lie? Numbers are the foundation of all statistical information. The "lie" occurs when, either intentionally or carelessly, a number is used in such a way that leads us to an unjustified or incorrect conclusion. Numbers may not lie, but they can be manipulated and misinterpreted. This chapter will provide information that can help you recognize when statistical information is being manipulated and misinterpreted. It will also help you see the many valuable uses of statistics.

SECTION 13.1   Sampling Techniques

▲ *Statisticians have several different techniques with which they can collect numerical information, such as how many Americans use an e-reader.*

According to Harris Interactive, 20% of Americans use an e-reader, an electronic reading device. It would be very expensive for Harris Interactive to ask every American if he or she uses an e-reader. Instead, to collect this information the polling company may ask a subset of Americans, called a *sample*. If it does not ask every American if he or she uses an e-reader, how do we know that Harris Interactive's results are accurate? In this section, we will discuss different techniques statisticians use to collect numerical information, and how they make accurate conclusions about an entire set of data from the sample collected.

Why This is Important Samples are used to determine a variety of information such as the percentage of college graduates in a city and the average credit card debt of an American family.

The study of statistics was originally used by governments to manage large amounts of numerical information. The use of statistics has grown significantly and today is applied in all walks of life. Governments use statistics to estimate the amount of unemployment and the cost of living. In psychology and education, the statistical theory of tests and measurements has been developed to compare achievements of individuals from diverse places and backgrounds. Newspapers and magazines carry the results of different polls on topics ranging from the president's popularity to the number of cans of soda consumed. Statistics is used in scores of other professions; in fact, it is difficult to find any profession that does not depend on some aspect of statistics.

Before we discuss different techniques used to collect numerical information, we will first introduce a few important definitions. *Statistics* is the art and science of gathering, analyzing, and making inferences (predictions) from numerical information obtained in an experiment. The numerical information so obtained is referred to as *data*. Statistics is divided into two main branches: descriptive and inferential. *Descriptive statistics* is concerned with the collection, organization, and analysis of data. *Inferential statistics* is concerned with making generalizations or predictions from the data collected.

Probability and statistics are closely related. Someone in the field of probability is interested in computing the chance of occurrence of a particular event when all the possible outcomes are known. A statistician's interest lies in drawing conclusions about possible outcomes through observations of only a few particular events.

If a probability expert and a statistician find identical boxes, the probability expert might open the box, observe the contents, replace the cover, and proceed to compute the probability of randomly selecting a specific object from the box. The statistician might select a few items from the box without looking at the contents and make a prediction as to the total contents of the box.

The entire contents of the box constitute the *population*. A population consists of all items or people of interest. The statistician often uses a subset of the population, called a *sample*, to make predictions concerning the population. It is important to understand the difference between a population and a sample. A population includes *all* items of interest. A sample includes *some* of the items in the population.

When a statistician draws a conclusion from a sample, there is always the possibility that the conclusion is incorrect. For example, suppose that a jar contains 90 blue marbles and 10 red marbles, as shown in Fig. 13.1 on page 775. If the statistician selects a random sample of five marbles from the jar and they are all blue, he or she may wrongly conclude that the jar contains all blue marbles. If the statistician takes a larger sample, say, 15 marbles, he or she is likely to select some red marbles. At that

The A. C. Nielsen Company, which has been measuring the viewing population of TV shows for more than 50 years, uses a sample of about 9000 metered households in the United States to draw conclusions about more than 110 million American households that have a television. An electronic measurement system, called the People Meter, is placed on each TV in the sample household. Each household member is assigned a personal viewing button on the People Meter to keep track of which channels he or she watches and for how long. Nielsen then computes the rating of the show, using the data obtained from the sample.

You can learn more about the sampling techniques used by A. C. Nielsen at Nielsenmedia.com. A. C. Nielsen is involved in many other areas of statistical testing and measurement.

Why This is Important Television programs that have a large audience can charge more for commercial advertising. A. C. Nielsen is only one of a large number of companies that use a sample to make a prediction about an entire population.

Figure 13.1

point, the statistician may make a prediction about the contents of the jar based on the sample selected. Of course, the most accurate result would occur if every object in the jar, the entire population, were observed. However, in most statistical experiments, observing the entire population is not practical.

Statisticians use samples instead of the entire population for two reasons: (a) it is often impossible to obtain data on an entire population, and (b) sampling is less expensive because collecting the data takes less time and effort. For example, suppose that you wanted to determine the number of each species of all the fish in a lake. To do so would be almost impossible without using a sample. If you did try to obtain this information from the entire population, the cost would be astronomical. Or suppose that you wanted to test soup cans for spoilage. If every can produced by the company was opened and tested, the company wouldn't have any product left to sell. Instead of testing the entire population of soup cans, a sample is selected. The results obtained from the sample of soup cans selected are used to make conclusions about the entire population of soup cans.

Later in this chapter we will discuss statistical measures such as the *mean* and the *standard deviation*. When statisticians calculate the mean and the standard deviation of the entire population, they use different symbols and formulas than when they calculate the mean and standard deviation of a sample. The following chart shows the symbols used to represent the mean and standard deviation of a sample and of a population. Note that the mean and standard deviation of a population are symbolized by Greek letters.

Measure	Sample	Population
Mean	$\bar{x}$ (read "x bar")	μ (mu)
Standard deviation	s	σ (sigma)

Unless otherwise indicated, in this book we will always assume that we are working with a sample and so we will use $\bar{x}$ and s. If you take a course in statistics, you will use all four symbols and different formulas for a sample and for a population.

Consider the task of determining the political strength of a certain candidate running in a national election. It is not possible for pollsters to ask each of the approximately 213 million eligible voters his or her preference of a candidate. Thus, pollsters must select and use a sample of the population to obtain their information. How large a sample do you think they use to make predictions about an upcoming national election? You might be surprised to learn that pollsters use only about 1600 registered voters in their national sample. How can a pollster using such a small percentage of the population make an accurate prediction?

The answer is that when pollsters select a sample, they use sophisticated statistical techniques to obtain an unbiased sample. An *unbiased sample* is one that is a small replica of the entire population with regard to income, education, gender, race, religion, political affiliation, age, and so on. The procedures statisticians use to obtain unbiased samples are quite complex. The following sampling techniques will give you a brief idea of how statisticians obtain unbiased samples.

Random Sampling

If a sample is drawn in such a way that each time an item is selected each item in the population has an equal chance of being drawn, the sample is said to be a *random sample*. When using a random sample, one combination of a specified number of items has the same probability of being selected as any other combination. When all the items in the population are similar with regard to the specific characteristic we are interested in, a random sample can be expected to produce satisfactory results. For example, consider a large container holding 300 tennis balls that are identical except for color. One-third of the balls are yellow, one-third are white, and one-third are green. If the balls can be thoroughly mixed between each draw of a tennis ball so that each ball has an equally likely chance of being selected, randomness is not difficult to achieve. However, if the objects or items are not all the same size, shape, or texture, it might be impossible to obtain a random sample by reaching into a container and selecting an object.

The best procedure for selecting a random sample is to use a random number generator or a table of random numbers. A random number generator is a device, usually a calculator or computer program, that produces a list of random numbers. A random number table is a collection of random digits in which each digit has an equal chance of appearing. To select a random sample, first assign a number to each element in the population. Numbers are usually assigned in order. Then select the number of random numbers needed, which is determined by the sample size. Each numbered element from the population that corresponds to a selected random number becomes part of the sample.

Systematic Sampling

When a sample is obtained by drawing every *n*th item on a list or production line, the sample is a *systematic sample*. The first item should be determined by using a random number.

It is important that the list from which a systematic sample is chosen includes the entire population being studied. See the *Did You Know?* called "Don't Count Your Votes Until They're Cast" on page 777. Another problem that must be avoided when this method of sampling is used is the constantly recurring characteristic. For example, on an assembly line, every 10th item could be the work of robot X. If only every 10th item is checked for defects, the work of other robots doing the same job may not be checked and may be defective.

Cluster Sampling

A *cluster sample* is sometimes referred to as an *area sample* because it is frequently applied on a geographical basis. Essentially, the sampling consists of a random selection of groups of units. To select a cluster sample, we divide a geographic area into sections. Then we randomly select the sections or clusters. Either each member of the selected cluster is included in the sample or a random sample of the members of each cluster is used. For example, geographically we might randomly select city blocks to use as a sample unit. Then either every member of each selected city block would be used or a random sample from each selected city block would be used. Another example is to select *x* boxes of screws from a whole order, count the number of defective screws in the *x* boxes selected, and use this number to determine the expected number of defective screws in the whole order.

Stratified Sampling

When a population is divided into parts, called strata, for the purpose of drawing a sample, the procedure is known as *stratified sampling*. Stratified sampling involves dividing the population by characteristics called *stratifying factors* such as gender, race, religion, or income. When a population has varied characteristics, it is desirable to separate the population into classes with similar characteristics and then take a random sample from each stratum (or class). For example, we could separate the population of undergraduate college students into strata called freshmen, sophomores, juniors, and seniors.

The use of stratified sampling requires some knowledge of the population. For example, to obtain a cross section of voters in a city, we must know where various groups are located and the approximate number of voters in each location.

Convenience Sampling

A *convenience sample* uses data that are easily or readily obtained. Occasionally, data that are conveniently obtained may be all that is available. In some cases, some information is better than no information at all. Nevertheless, convenience sampling can be extremely biased. For example, suppose that a town wants to raise taxes to build a new elementary school. The local newspaper wants to obtain the opinion of some of the residents and sends a reporter to a senior citizens center. The first 10 people who exit the building are asked if they are in favor of raising taxes to build a new school. This sample could be biased against raising taxes for the new school. Most senior citizens would not have school-age children and may not be interested in paying increased taxes to build a new school. Although a convenience sample may be very easy to select, one must be very cautious when using the results obtained by this method.

Example 1 *Identifying Sampling Techniques*

Identify the sampling technique used to obtain a sample in the following. Explain your answer.

a) Every 20th soup can coming off an assembly line is checked for defects.

b) A $50 gift certificate is given away at the Annual Bankers Convention. Tickets are placed in a bin, and the tickets are mixed up. Then the winning ticket is selected by a blindfolded person.

c) Children in a large city are classified based on the neighborhood school they attend. A random sample of five schools is selected. All the children from each selected school are included in the sample.

d) The first 50 people entering a zoo are asked if they support an increase in taxes to support a zoo expansion.

e) Viewers of the *USA Network* are classified according to age. Random samples from each age group are selected.

Solution

a) Systematic sampling. The sample is obtained by drawing every nth item. In this example, every 20th item on an assembly line is selected.

b) Random sampling. Every ticket has an equal chance of being selected.

c) Cluster sampling. A random sample of geographic areas is selected.

d) Convenience sampling. The sample is selected by picking data that are easily obtained.

e) Stratified sampling. The viewers are divided into strata based on their age. Then random samples are selected from each strata.

SECTION 13.1 *Exercises*

Warm Up Exercises

In Exercises 1–12, fill in the blank with an appropriate word, phrase, or symbol(s).

1. The art and science of gathering, analyzing, and making inferences (predictions) from numerical information obtained in an experiment is called _____. Statistics

2. Making generalizations or predictions from the data collected is called _____ statistics. Inferential

3. The collection, organization, and analysis of data is called _____ statistics. Descriptive

4. All items or people of interest in an experiment is called a(n) _____. Population

5. A subset of a population used by statisticians to make predictions about a population is called a(n) _____.
   Sample

6. When a sample is obtained by drawing every *n*th item, the sample is called a(n) _____ sample. Systematic

7. If a sample is drawn in such a way that each time an item is selected, each item in the population has an equal chance of being drawn, the sample is called a(n) _____ sample. Random

8. When a population is divided into parts, called strata, for the purpose of drawing a sample, the procedure is known as _____ sampling. Stratified

9. A sample that consists of a random selection of groups or units is called a(n) _____ sample. Cluster

10. A sample that uses data that are easily or readily obtained is called a(n) _____ sample. Convenience

11. A sample that is a small replica of the entire population is called a(n) _____ sample. Unbiased

12. An area sample is another name for a(n) _____ sample. Cluster

Practice the Skills

Sampling Techniques *In Exercises 13–22, identify the sampling technique used to obtain a sample. Explain your answer.*

13. All registered vehicles in the state of Georgia are classified according to type: subcompact, compact, mid-size, full-size, SUV, and truck. A random sample of vehicles from each category is selected. Stratified sample

14. Every 10th iPod coming off an assembly line is checked for defects. Systematic sample

▲ *See Exercise 14*

15. A state is divided into counties. A random sample of 12 counties is selected. A random sample from each of the 12 selected counties is selected. Cluster sample

16. A door prize is given away at a home improvement seminar. Tickets are placed in a bin, and the tickets are mixed up. Then a ticket is selected by a blindfolded person. Random sample

17. Every 17th person in line at a grocery store is asked his or her age. Systematic sample

18. The businesses in Iowa City are grouped according to type: medical, service, retail, manufacturing, financial, construction, restaurant, hotel, tourism, and other. A random sample of 10 businesses from each type is selected. Stratified sample

19. The first 25 adults leaving a grocery store are asked how much money they spend per week on entertainment. Convenience sample

20. The Food and Drug Administration randomly selects five stores from each of four randomly selected sections of a large city and checks food items for freshness. These stores are used as a representative sample of the entire city. Cluster sample

21. Bingo balls in a bin are shaken, and then balls are selected from the bin. Random sample

22. The Student Senate at the University of North Carolina is electing a new president. The first 25 people leaving the library are asked for whom they will vote. Convenience sample

Challenge Problems/Group Activities

23. a) ***Random Sampling*** Select and indicate a topic and population of interest to which a random sampling technique can be applied to obtain data. Answers will vary.

   b) Explain how you or your group would obtain a random sample for your population of interest. Answers will vary.

   c) Actually obtain the sample by the procedure stated in part (b). Answers will vary.

24. ***Data from Questionnaire*** Some subscribers of *Consumer Reports* respond to an annual questionnaire regarding their satisfaction with new appliances, cars, and other items. The information obtained from these questionnaires is then used as a sample from which frequency of repairs and other ratings are made by the magazine. Are the data obtained from these returned questionnaires representative of the entire population, or are they biased? Biased

Recreational Mathematics

25. Statistically speaking, what is the most dangerous job in the United States? President; 4 out of 44 U.S. presidents have been assassinated (Lincoln, Garfield, McKinley, Kennedy).

Internet/Research Activity

26. We have briefly introduced sampling techniques. Using statistics books and Internet Web sites as references, select one type of sampling technique (it may be one that we have not discussed in this section) and write a report on how statisticians obtain that type of sample. Also indicate when that type of sampling technique may be preferred. List two examples of when the sampling technique may be used.

SECTION 13.2   # The Misuses of Statistics

Many of us may remember the advertisement stating, "Four out of five dentists recommend sugarless gum for their patients who chew gum." Seeing an advertisement like this one may cause some of us to be a bit skeptical. Should we believe that sugarless chewing gum will not harm our teeth? Or should we investigate a bit further before buying that next pack of chewing gum? In this section, we will learn how to examine statistical statements before accepting them as fact.

Why **This is Important** In order to be an educated consumer, it is important to be able to distinguish between misleading advertisements and actual facts.

▲ *It is important to examine statistical statements about products before accepting the statements as fact.*

Statistics, when used properly, is a valuable tool to society. However, many individuals, businesses, and advertising firms misuse statistics to their own advantage. You should examine statistical statements very carefully before accepting them as fact. You should ask yourself two questions: Was the sample used to gather the statistical data unbiased and of sufficient size? Is the statistical statement ambiguous; that is, can it be interpreted in more than one way?

Let's examine two advertisements. "Four out of five dentists recommend sugarless gum for their patients who chew gum." In this advertisement, we do not know the sample size and the number of times the experiment was performed to obtain the desired results. The advertisement does not mention that possibly only 1 out of 100 dentists recommended gum at all.

In a golf ball commercial, a "type A" ball is hit and a second ball is hit in the same manner. The type A ball travels farther. We are supposed to conclude that the type A is the better ball. The advertisement does not mention the number of times the experiment was previously performed or the results of the earlier experiments. Possible sources of bias include (1) wind speed and direction, (2) that no two swings are identical, and (3) that the ball may land on a rough or smooth surface.

Vague or ambiguous words also lead to statistical misuses or misinterpretations. The word *average* is one such culprit. There are at least four different "averages," some of which are discussed in Section 13.4. Each is calculated differently, and each may have a different value for the same sample. During contract negotiations, it is not uncommon for an employer to state publicly that the average salary of its employees is $45,000, whereas the employees' union states that the average is $40,000. Who is lying? Actually, both sides may be telling the truth. Each side will use the average that best suits its needs to present its case. Advertisers also use the average that most enhances their products. Consumers often misinterpret this average as the one with which they are most familiar.

Another vague word is *largest*. For example, ABC claims that it is the largest department store in the United States. Does that mean largest profit, largest sales, largest building, largest staff, largest acreage, or largest number of outlets?

Still another deceptive technique used in advertising is to state a claim from which the public may draw irrelevant conclusions. For example, a disinfectant manufacturer claims that its product killed 40,760 germs in a laboratory in 5 seconds. "To prevent colds, use disinfectant A." It may well be that the germs killed in the laboratory were not related to any type of cold germ. In another example, company C claims that its paper towels are heavier than its competition's towels. Therefore, they will hold more water. Is weight a measure of absorbency? A rock is heavier than a sponge, yet a sponge is more absorbent.

An insurance advertisement claims that in Duluth, Minnesota, 212 people switched to insurance company Z. One may conclude that this company is offering something special to attract these people. What may have been omitted from the advertisement is that 415 people in Duluth, Minnesota, dropped insurance company Z during the same period.

A foreign car manufacturer claims that 9 of every 10 of a popular-model car it sold in the United States during the previous 10 years were still on the road. From this statement, the public is to conclude that this foreign car is well manufactured and would last for many years. The commercial neglects to state that this model has been selling in the United States for only a few years. The manufacturer could just as well have stated that 9 of every 10 of these cars sold in the United States in the previous 100 years were still on the road.

Charts and graphs can also be misleading or deceptive. In Fig. 13.2, the two graphs show the performance of two stocks over a 6-month period. Based on the graphs, which stock would you purchase? Actually, the two graphs present identical information; the only difference is that the vertical scale of the graph for stock B has been exaggerated.

Figure 13.2

The two graphs in Fig. 13.3 show the same change. However, the graph in part (a) appears to show a greater increase than the graph in part (b), again because of a different scale.

Figure 13.3

Figure 13.4

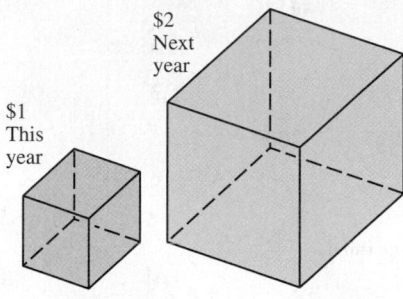

Figure 13.5

Consider a claim that if you invest $1, by next year you will have $2. This type of claim is sometimes misrepresented, as in Fig. 13.4. Actually, your investment has only doubled, but the area of the square on the right is four times that of the square on the left. By expressing the amounts as cubes (Fig. 13.5), you increase the volume eightfold.

Figure 13.6

The graph in Fig. 13.6 is an example of a circle graph. We will discuss circle graphs in Section 13.3. In a circle graph, the total circle represents 100%. Therefore, the sum of the parts should add up to 100%. This graph is misleading since the sum of its parts is 183%. A graph other than a circle graph should have been used to display the top six reasons Americans say they use the Internet.

Despite the examples presented in this section, you should not be left with the impression that statistics is used solely for the purpose of misleading or cheating the consumer. As stated earlier, there are many important and necessary uses of statistics. Most statistical reports are accurate and useful. You should realize, however, the importance of being an aware consumer.

SECTION 13.2   *Exercises*

Practice the Skills

Misinterpretations of Statistics *In Exercises 1–14, discuss the statement and tell what possible misuses or misinterpretations may exist.*

1. *Cold Remedy* In a study of patients with cold symptoms, each patient was found to have improved symptoms after taking honey. Therefore, honey cures the common cold. The patients may have improved on their own without taking honey.

2. In 2011, Liberty Travel received more requests for travel brochures to Hawaii than to Las Vegas. Therefore, in 2012, Liberty Travel sold more travel packages to Hawaii than to Las Vegas. Not all people who request a brochure will purchase a travel package.

3. There are more empty spaces in the parking lot of Mama Mia's Italian restaurant than at Shanghai Chinese restaurant. Therefore, more people prefer Chinese food than Italian food.*

4. Healthy Snacks cookies are fat free. So eat as many as you like and you will not gain weight.*

5. Most accidents occur on Saturday night. That means that people do not drive carefully on Saturday night. More people drive on Saturday evening. Thus, one might expect more accidents.

6. Morgan's is the largest department store in New York. So shop at Morgan's and save money. The fact that Morgan's is the largest department store does not imply that it is inexpensive.

7. Eighty percent of all automobile accidents occur within 10 miles of the driver's home. Therefore, it is safer to take long trips. Most driving is done close to home. Thus, one might expect more accidents close to home.

8. Arizona has the highest death rate for asthma in the United States. Therefore, it is unsafe to go to Arizona if you have asthma. People with asthma may move to Arizona because of its climate. Therefore, more people with asthma may live in Arizona.

▲ *Sedona, Arizona*

*See Instructor Answer Appendix

9. Thirty students said that they would recommend Professor Malone to a friend. Twenty students said that they would recommend Professor Wagner to a friend. Therefore, Professor Malone is a better teacher than Professor Wagner.*

10. A steak is more expensive at Dino's Steak House than at Rick's Prime Rib House. Therefore, the quality of a steak at Dino's Steak House is better than the quality of a steak at Rick's Prime Rib House. The quality of a steak does not necessarily depend on the price of the steak.

11. John Deere lawn tractors cost more than Toro lawn tractors. Therefore, John Deere lawn tractors will last longer than Toro lawn tractors. Just because they are more expensive does not mean that they will last longer.

12. More men than women are involved in automobile accidents. Therefore, women are better drivers. Men may drive more miles than women and men may drive in worse driving conditions (like snow).

13. The average depth of the pond is only 3 ft, so it is safe to go wading. There may be deep sections in the pond, so it may not be safe to go wading.

14. In 2011, more men than women applied for sales positions at Dick's Sporting Goods. Therefore, in 2011, more men than women were hired for sales positions at Dick's Sporting Goods. Not all candidates who apply for a position will be hired.

15. *Population of Honolulu* The following table shows the population, in thousands, in Honolulu, Hawaii, for selected years.

Year	Population
1980	365.0
1990	365.2
2000	371.7
2010	371.7

Source: U.S Census Bureau

Draw a line graph that makes the increase in the population of Honolulu for the years shown appear to be

a) small.*   b) large.*

16. *Officers in the U.S. Marine Corps* The following table shows the number of officers, in thousands, on active duty in the U.S. Marine Corps for the years 2004–2009.

Year	Number of Officers
2004	19.1
2005	19.1
2006	19.2
2007	19.5
2008	20.1
2009	21.0

Draw a line graph that makes the increase in the number of officers on active duty for the U.S. Marine Corps appear to be

a) small.*   b) large.*

First Marriage In Exercises 17 and 18, use the following table.

Median Age at First Marriage

Male		Female	
Year	Age	Year	Age
2002	26.9	2002	25.3
2004	27.1	2004	25.3
2006	27.5	2006	25.5
2008	27.6	2008	25.9

Source: U.S. Census Bureau

17. a) Draw a bar graph that appears to show a small increase in the median age at first marriage for males.*

b) Draw a bar graph that appears to show a large increase in the median age at first marriage for males.*

18. a) Draw a bar graph that appears to show a small increase in the median age at first marriage for females.*

b) Draw a bar graph that appears to show a large increase in the median age at first marriage for females.*

19. *Price of a Movie Ticket* The following graph shows the average price of a movie ticket for the years 2009 and 2010.

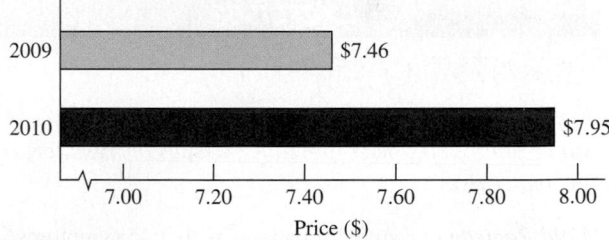

Average Price of a Movie Ticket

a) Draw a bar graph that shows the entire scale from $0 to $8.00.*

b) Does the new graph give a different impression? Explain. Answers will vary.

Concept/Writing Exercises

20. Find five advertisements or commercials that may be statistically misleading. Explain why each may be misleading. Answers will vary.

*See Instructor Answer Appendix

21. The following circle graph shows the percentage of commuters who are frustrated by particular driving situations. Is the graph misleading? Explain.*

**Driving Situations
Frustrating to Commuters**

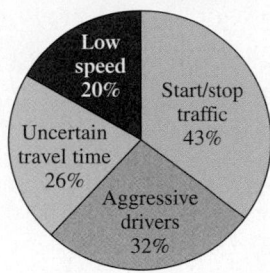

- Low speed 20%
- Start/stop traffic 43%
- Uncertain travel time 26%
- Aggressive drivers 32%

Challenge Problem/Group Activity

22. Consider the following graph, which shows the U.S. population in 2000 and the projected U.S. population in 2050.

America in 2000 and in 2050

Population in 2000
275 million

Projected population in 2050
394 million

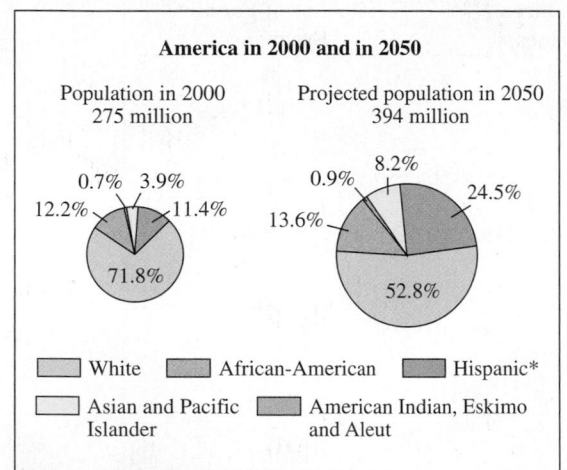

- 0.7% 3.9%
- 12.2%   11.4%
- 71.8%

- 8.2%
- 0.9%   24.5%
- 13.6%
- 52.8%

☐ White   ☐ African-American   ☐ Hispanic*

☐ Asian and Pacific Islander   ☐ American Indian, Eskimo and Aleut

Source: U.S. Census Bureau

a) Compute the projected percent increase in population from 2000 to 2050 by using the formula given on page 603. ≈ 43.3% increase

b) Measure the radius and then compute the area of the circle representing 2000. Use $A = \pi r^2$.
Radius = $\frac{1}{4}$ in., area ≈ 0.196 in.²

c) Repeat part (b) for the circle representing 2050.
Radius = $\frac{3}{8}$ in., area ≈ 0.442 in.²

d) Compute the percent increase in the size of the area of the circle from 2000 to 2050. ≈ 125.5% increase

e) Are the circle graphs misleading? Yes

Recreational Mathematics

23. What mathematical symbol can you place between 1 and 2 to obtain a number greater than 1 but less than 2? A decimal point

Internet/Research Activity

24. Read the book *How to Lie with Statistics* by Darrell Huff and write a book report on it. Select three illustrations from the book that show how people manipulate statistics.

*See Instructor Answer Appendix

SECTION 13.3 Frequency Distributions and Statistical Graphs

Suppose you have a job as a waitress and decide to record the daily amount you make in tips. After keeping a list of your tips each day for several months, you realize that you have a large set of data and want to condense your data into a more manageable form. In this section we will learn a method to organize and summarize data. We will also introduce four types of graphs that can be used to display information in a meaningful way.

Why *This is Important* Organizing and summarizing data and using graphs to display information can make large sets of information more useful.

▲ *Organizing and summarizing data, such as a waitress's daily tips, can make large sets of information more useful.*

It is not uncommon for statisticians and others to have to analyze thousands of pieces of data. A *piece of data* is a single response to an experiment. When the amount of data is large, it is usually advantageous to construct a frequency distribution. A *frequency distribution* is a listing of the observed values and the corresponding frequency of occurrence of each value. Example 1 shows how we construct a frequency distribution.

Example **1** *Frequency Distribution*

The number of children per family is recorded for 64 families surveyed. Construct a frequency distribution of the following data:

$$
\begin{array}{cccccccc}
0 & 1 & 1 & 2 & 2 & 3 & 4 & 5 \\
0 & 1 & 1 & 2 & 2 & 3 & 4 & 5 \\
0 & 1 & 1 & 2 & 2 & 3 & 4 & 6 \\
0 & 1 & 2 & 2 & 2 & 3 & 4 & 6 \\
0 & 1 & 2 & 2 & 2 & 3 & 4 & 7 \\
0 & 1 & 2 & 2 & 3 & 3 & 4 & 8 \\
0 & 1 & 2 & 2 & 3 & 3 & 5 & 8 \\
0 & 1 & 2 & 2 & 3 & 3 & 5 & 9
\end{array}
$$

Solution Listing the number of children (observed values) and the number of families (frequency) gives the following frequency distribution.

Number of Children (Observed Values)	Number of Families (Frequency)
0	8
1	11
2	18
3	11
4	6
5	4
6	2
7	1
8	2
9	1
	64

Eight families had no children, 11 families had one child, 18 families had two children, and so on. Note that the sum of the frequencies is equal to the original number of pieces of data, 64. ■

Often data are grouped in classes to provide information about the distribution that would be difficult to observe if the data were ungrouped. Graphs called *histograms* and *frequency polygons* can be made of grouped data, as will be explained later in this section. These graphs also provide a great deal of useful information.

When data are grouped in classes, certain rules should be followed.

PROCEDURE   **RULES FOR DATA GROUPED BY CLASSES**

1. The classes should be the same "width."
2. The classes should not overlap.
3. Each piece of data should belong to only one class.

In addition, it is often suggested that a frequency distribution should be constructed with 5 to 12 classes. If there are too few or too many classes, the distribution may become difficult to interpret. For example, if you use fewer than 5 classes, you risk losing too much information. If you use more than 12 classes, you may gain more detail but you risk losing clarity. Let the spread of the data be a guide in deciding the number of classes to use.

To understand these rules, let's consider a set of observed values that go from a low of 0 to a high of 26. Let's assume that the first class is arbitrarily selected to go from 0 through 4. Thus, any of the data with values of 0, 1, 2, 3, 4 would belong in this class. We say that the *class width* is 5 since there are five integral values that belong to the class. This first class ended with 4, so the second class must start with 5. If this class is to have a width of 5, at what value must it end? The answer is 9 (5, 6, 7, 8, 9). The second class is 5–9. Continuing in the same manner, we obtain the following set of classes.

Classes

$$
\text{Lower class limits} \left\{ \begin{array}{l} 0-4 \\ 5-9 \\ 10-14 \\ 15-19 \\ 20-24 \\ 25-29 \end{array} \right\} \text{Upper class limits}
$$

We need not go beyond the 25–29 class because the largest value we are considering is 26. The classes meet our three criteria: They have the same width, there is no overlap among the classes, and each of the values from a low of 0 to a high of 26 belongs to one and only one class.

The choice of the first class, 0–4, was arbitrary. If we wanted to have more classes or fewer classes, we would make the class widths smaller or larger, respectively.

The numbers 0, 5, 10, 15, 20, 25 are called the *lower class limits*, and the numbers 4, 9, 14, 19, 24, 29 are called the *upper class limits*. Each class has a width of 5. Note that the class width, 5, can be obtained by subtracting the first lower class limit from the second lower class limit: $5 - 0 = 5$. The difference between any two consecutive lower class or upper class limits is also 5.

Example 2 *A Frequency Distribution of Consumer Magazines*

Table 13.1 on page 786 shows the 2008 circulation for the 46 leading U.S. consumer magazines (excluding *AARP Magazine* and *AARP Bulletin*, which are far ahead of the other magazines). The circulation is rounded to the nearest ten thousand. Construct a frequency distribution of the data, letting the first class be 173–237.

Solution Forty-six pieces of data are given in *descending order* from highest to lowest. We are given that the first class is 173–237. The second class must therefore start at 238. To find the class width, we subtract 173 (the lower class limit of the first class) from 238 (the lower class limit of the second class) to obtain a class width of 65. The upper class limit of the second class is found by adding the class width, 65, to the upper class limit of the first class, 237. Therefore, the upper class limit of the second class is $237 + 65 = 302$. Thus,

$$173-237 \quad \text{first class}$$
$$238-302 \quad \text{second class}$$

The other classes are found using a similar technique. They are 303–367, 368–432, 433–497, 498–562, 563–627, 628–692, 693–757, 758–822. Since the highest value in the data is 817, there is no need to go any further. Note that each two consecutive lower class limits differ by 65, as does each two consecutive upper class limits. There are 23 pieces of data in the 173–237 class. There are 8 pieces of data in the 238–302 class, 6 in the 303–367 class, 5 in the 368–432 class, 1 in the 433–497 class, 1 in the 498–562 class, 0 in the 563–627 class, 0 in the 628–692 class, 0 in the 693–757 class, and 2 in the 758–822 class. The complete frequency distribution of the 10 classes is given on page 786. The number of magazines totals 46, so we have included each piece of data.

Table 13.1

Magazine	Circulation (ten thousands)
Reader's Digest	817
Better Homes and Gardens	766
National Geographic	506
Good Housekeeping	468
Woman's Day	392
Family Circle	391
AAA Westways	384
Ladies' Home Journal	384
People	369
Game Informer	352
Time	336
Prevention	334
TV Guide	326
Sports Illustrated	322
Taste of Home	320
Cosmopolitan	293
Southern Living	283
AAA	281
Newsweek	270
Playboy	262
AAA Going Places	256
Maxim	252
American Legion Magazine	243
O, The Oprah Magazine	237
Glamour	229
Redbook	221
Guideposts	220
AAA World	213
Parenting	213
Parents	206
ESPN The Magazine	206
Seventeen	203
Martha Stewart Living	203
Smithsonian	203
Real Simple	198
Remedy/Remedy MD	196
Money	191
Us Weekly	190
Family Fun	188
Men's Health	186
Entertainment Weekly	180
Endless Vacation	179
Cooking Light	179
Every Day with Rachael Ray	178
InStyle	176
Country Living	173

Source: *Audit Bureau of Circulations*

Circulation	Number of Magazines (ten thousands)
173–237	23
238–302	8
303–367	6
368–432	5
433–497	1
498–562	1
563–627	0
628–692	0
693–757	0
758–822	2
	46

The *modal class* of a frequency distribution is the class with the greatest frequency. In Example 2, the modal class is 173–237. The *midpoint of a class*, also called the *class mark*, is found by adding the lower and upper class limits and dividing the sum by 2. The midpoint of the first class in Example 2 is

$$\frac{173 + 237}{2} = \frac{410}{2} = 205$$

Note that the difference between successive class marks is the class width. The class mark of the second class can therefore be obtained by adding the class width, 65, to the class mark of the first class, 205. The sum is $205 + 65 = 270$. Note that $\frac{238 + 302}{2} = 270$, which checks with the class mark obtained by adding the class width to the first class mark.

Example 3 *A Frequency Distribution of Family Income*

The following set of data represents the family income (in thousands of dollars, rounded to the nearest hundred) of 15 randomly selected families.

46.5	31.8	45.8	44.7	40.9
65.2	52.4	44.6	53.7	48.8
35.5	40.3	39.8	56.3	50.7

Construct a frequency distribution with a first class of 31.5–37.6.

Solution First rearrange the data from lowest to highest so that the data will be easier to categorize.

31.8	40.3	44.7	48.8	53.7
35.5	40.9	45.8	50.7	56.3
39.8	44.6	46.5	52.4	65.2

The first class goes from 31.5 to 37.6. Since the data are in tenths, the class limits will also be given in tenths. The first class ends with 37.6; therefore, the second class must start with 37.7. The class width of the first class is $37.7 - 31.5$, or 6.2. The upper class limit of the second class must therefore be $37.6 + 6.2$, or 43.8. The frequency distribution is given on page 787.

Income ($1000)	Number of Families
31.5–37.6	2
37.7–43.8	3
43.9–50.0	5
50.1–56.2	3
56.3–62.4	1
62.5–68.6	1
	15

Note in Example 3 that the class width is 6.2, the modal class is 43.9–50.0, and the class mark of the first class is $\dfrac{31.5 + 37.6}{2}$, or 34.55.

We have discussed how to organize and summarize data. Now we will introduce graphs that can be used to display information. We will consider four types of graphs: the histogram, the frequency polygon, the stem-and-leaf graph, and the circle graph.

Histograms and Frequency Polygons

Histograms and frequency polygons are statistical graphs used to illustrate frequency distributions. A *histogram* is a graph with observed values on its horizontal scale and frequencies on its vertical scale. A bar is constructed above each observed value (or class when classes are used), indicating the frequency of that value (or class). The horizontal scale need not start at zero, and the calibrations on the horizontal and vertical scales do not have to be the same. The vertical scale must start at zero. To accommodate large frequencies on the vertical scale, it may be necessary to break the scale. Because histograms and other bar graphs are easy to interpret visually, they are used a great deal in newspapers and magazines.

Example 4   *Construct a Histogram*

The frequency distribution developed in Example 1, on page 784, is repeated here. Construct a histogram of this frequency distribution.

Number of Children (Observed Values)	Number of Families (Frequency)
0	8
1	11
2	18
3	11
4	6
5	4
6	2
7	1
8	2
9	1

Solution The vertical scale must extend at least to the number 18 since that is the greatest recorded frequency. The horizontal scale must include the numbers 0–9, the number of children observed. Eight families have no children. We indicate that by constructing a bar above the number 0, centered at 0, on the horizontal scale

TIMELY TIP

When constructing a histogram or frequency polygon, be sure to label both scales of the graph.

extended up to 8 on the vertical scale (Fig. 13.7). Eleven families have one child, so we construct a bar extending to 11 above the number 1, centered at 1, on the horizontal scale. We continue this procedure for each observed value. Both the horizontal and vertical scales should be labeled, the bars should be the same width and centered at the observed value, and the histogram should have a title. In a histogram, the bars should always touch.

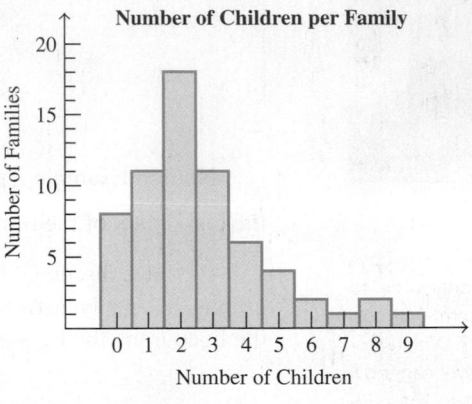

Figure 13.7

Frequency polygons are line graphs with scales the same as those of the histogram; that is, the horizontal scale indicates observed values and the vertical scale indicates frequency. To construct a frequency polygon, place a dot at the corresponding frequency above each of the observed values. Then connect the dots with straight-line segments. When constructing frequency polygons, always put in two additional class marks, one at the lower end and one at the upper end on the horizontal scale (values for these added class marks are not needed on the frequency polygon). Since the frequency at these added class marks is 0, the end points of the frequency polygon will always be on the horizontal scale.

Example 5   Construct a Frequency Polygon

Construct a frequency polygon of the frequency distribution in Example 1 on page 784.

Solution   Since eight families have no children, place a mark above the 0 at 8 on the vertical scale, as shown in Fig. 13.8. Because there are 11 families with one child, place a mark above the 1 on the horizontal scale at the 11 on the vertical scale, and so on. Connect the dots with straight-line segments and bring the end points of the graph down to the horizontal scale, as shown.

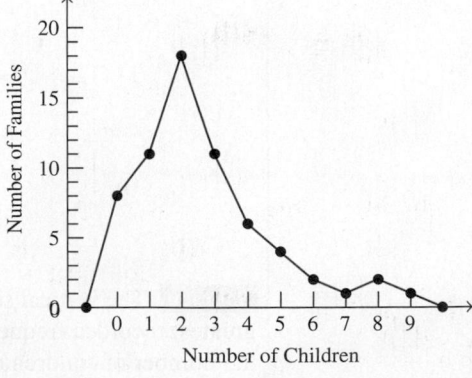

Figure 13.8

Table 13.2

Distance (miles)	Number of Workers
1–7	15
8–14	24
15–21	13
22–28	8
29–35	5
36–42	5

Example 6 *Commuting Distances*

The frequency distribution of the one-way commuting distances for 70 workers is listed in Table 13.2. Construct a histogram and then construct a frequency polygon.

Solution The histogram can be constructed with either class limits or class marks (class midpoints) on the horizontal scale. Frequency polygons are constructed with class marks on the horizontal scale. Since we will construct a frequency polygon on the histogram, we will use class marks. Recall that class marks are found by adding the lower class limit and upper class limit and dividing the sum by 2. For the first class, the class mark is $\frac{1 + 7}{2}$, or 4. Since the class widths are seven units, the class marks will also differ by seven units (see Fig. 13.9).

Figure 13.9

Example 7 *Carry-on Luggage Weights*

The histogram in Fig. 13.10 shows the weights of selected pieces of carry-on luggage at an airport. Construct the frequency distribution from the histogram in Fig. 13.10.

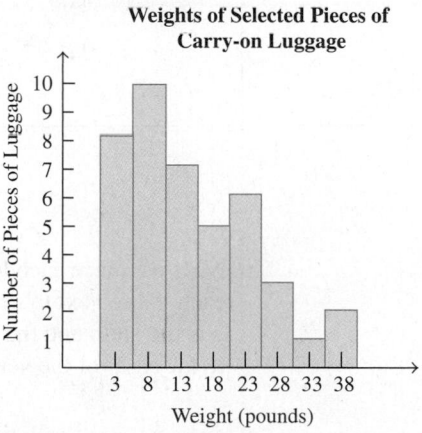

Figure 13.10

Table 13.3

Weight (pounds)	Number of Pieces of Luggage
1–5	8
6–10	10
11–15	7
16–20	5
21–25	6
26–30	3
31–35	1
36–40	2

Solution There are five units between class midpoints, so each class width must also be five units. Since three is the midpoint of the first class, there must be two units below and two units above it. The first class must be 1–5. The second class must therefore be 6–10. The frequency distribution is given in Table 13.3.

Stem-and-Leaf Displays

Frequency distributions and histograms provide very useful tools to organize and summarize data. However, if the data are grouped, we cannot identify specific data values in a frequency distribution and in a histogram. For example, in Example 7, we know that there are eight pieces of luggage in the class of 1 to 5 pounds, but we don't know the specific weights of those eight pieces of luggage.

A *stem-and-leaf display* is a tool that organizes and groups the data while allowing us to see the actual values that make up the data. To construct a stem-and-leaf display each value is represented with two different groups of digits. The left group of digits is called the *stem*. The remaining group of digits on the right is called the *leaf*. There is no rule for the number of digits to be included in the stem. Usually the units digit is the leaf and the remaining digits are the stem. For example, the number 53 would be broken up into 5 and 3. The 5 would be the stem and the 3 would be the leaf. The number 417 would be broken up into 41 and 7. The 41 would be the stem and the 7 would be the leaf. The number 6, which can be represented as 06, would be broken up into 0 and 6. The stem would be the 0 and the leaf would be the 6. With a stem-and-leaf display, the stems are listed, in ascending order, to the left of a vertical line. Then we place each leaf to the right of its corresponding stem, to the right of the vertical line.* Example 8 illustrates this procedure.

▲ *Captain Fairfield Inn Bed and Breakfast*

Example 8 *Stem-and-Leaf Display*

The table below indicates the ages of a sample of 20 guests who stayed at Captain Fairfield Inn Bed and Breakfast. Construct a stem-and-leaf display.

29	31	39	43	56
60	62	59	58	32
47	27	50	28	71
72	44	45	44	68

Solution By quickly glancing at the data, we can see the ages consist of two-digit numbers. Let's use the first digit, the tens digit, as our stem and the second digit, the units digit, as the leaf. For example, for an age of 62, the stem is 6 and the leaf is 2. Our values are numbers in the 20s, 30s, 40s, 50s, 60s, and 70s. Therefore, the stems will be 2, 3, 4, 5, 6, 7 as shown below.

```
2 |
3 |
4 |
5 |
6 |
7 |
```

Next we place each leaf on its stem. We will do so by placing the second digit of each value next to its stem, to the right of the vertical line. Our first value is 29. The 2 is the stem and the 9 is the leaf. Therefore, we place a 9 next to the stem of 2 and to the right of the vertical line.

$$2 \mid 9$$

The next value is 31. We will place a leaf of 1 next to the stem of 3.

```
2 | 9
3 | 1
```

---

*In stem-and-leaf displays, the leaves are sometimes listed from lowest digit to greatest digit, but that is not necessary.

The next value is 39. Therefore, we will place a leaf of 9 after the leaf of 1 that is next to the stem of 3.

$$
\begin{array}{c|cc}
2 & 9 \\
3 & 1 & 9
\end{array}
$$

We continue this process until we have listed all the leaves on the display. The diagram below shows the stem-and-leaf display for the ages of the guests. In our display, we will also include a legend to indicate the values represented by the stems and leaves. For example, 5│6 represents 56.

5│6 represents 56

Stem   Leaves

$$
\begin{array}{c|ccccc}
2 & 9 & 7 & 8 \\
3 & 1 & 9 & 2 \\
4 & 3 & 7 & 4 & 5 & 4 \\
5 & 6 & 9 & 8 & 0 \\
6 & 0 & 2 & 8 \\
7 & 1 & 2
\end{array}
$$

Every piece of the original data can be seen in a stem-and-leaf display. From the above diagram, we can see that five of the guests' ages were in the 40s. Only two guests were older than 70. Note that the stem-and-leaf display gives the same visual impression as a sideways histogram.

Circle Graphs

Circle graphs (also known as pie charts) are often used to compare parts of one or more components of the whole to the whole. The circle graph in Fig. 13.11 shows what moviegoers say is the most annoying distraction during a movie. Since the total circle represents 100%, the sum of the percents of the sectors should be 100%, and it is.

In the next example, we will discuss a circle graph.

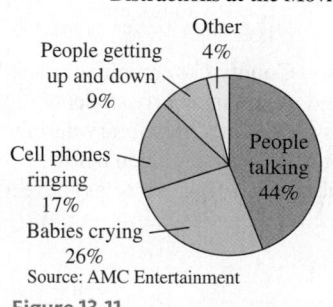

Distractions at the Movies

Other 4%
People getting up and down 9%
Cell phones ringing 17%
Babies crying 26%
People talking 44%

Source: AMC Entertainment

Figure 13.11

Example 9 *Circus Performances*

Eight hundred people who attended a Ringling Bros. and Barnum & Bailey Circus were asked to indicate their favorite performance. The circle graph in Fig. 13.12 shows the percentage of respondents that answered tigers, elephants, acrobats, jugglers, and other. Determine the number of respondents for each category.

Favorite Performance at the Circus

Other 5%
Jugglers 14%
Acrobats 17%
Tigers 38%
Elephants 26%

Figure 13.12

Solution To determine the number of respondents in a category, we multiply the percentage for each category, written as a decimal number, by the total number of people, 800. The table on page 792 indicates the results.

Performance	Percent of Respondents	Percent Written as a Decimal Number	Number of People
Tigers	38%	0.38	$0.38 \times 800 = 304$
Elephants	26%	0.26	$0.26 \times 800 = 208$
Acrobats	17%	0.17	$0.17 \times 800 = 136$
Jugglers	14%	0.14	$0.14 \times 800 = 112$
Other	5%	0.05	$0.05 \times 800 = 40$
Total			800

As we can see from the table, 304 people indicated that the tigers were their favorite performance, 208 indicated elephants, 136 people indicated the acrobats, 112 people indicated the jugglers, and 40 people indicated some other performance. ∎

SECTION 13.3   Exercises

Warm Up Exercises

In Exercises 1–8, fill in the blank with an appropriate word, phrase, or symbol(s).

1. A listing of observed values and the corresponding frequency of occurrence of each value is called a(n) _____ distribution. Frequency

2. In a frequency distribution, the class with the greatest frequency is called the _____ class. Modal

3. In a frequency distribution, another name for the midpoint of a class is the class _____. Mark

4. The class width of a frequency distribution with a first class of 9–16 and a second class of 17–24 is _____. 8

5. A bar graph with observed values on its horizontal scale and frequencies on its vertical scale is called a(n) _____. Histogram

6. A line graph with observed values on its horizontal scale and frequencies on its vertical scale is called a frequency _____. Polygon

7. In a stem-and-leaf display, the group of digits in the left-hand column is called the _____. Stem

8. In a stem-and-leaf display, the group of digits in the right-hand column is called the _____. Leaf

Practice the Skills/Problem Solving

In Exercises 9 and 10, use the frequency distribution to determine

   a) *the total number of observations.*

   b) *the width of each class.*

   c) *the midpoint of the second class.*

   d) *the modal class (or classes).*

   e) *the class limits of the next class if an additional class were to be added.*

9.

Class	Frequency
9–15	4
16–22	7
23–29	1
30–36	0
37–43	3
44–50	5

a) 20   b) 7   c) 19   d) 16–22   e) 51–57

10.

Class	Frequency
40–49	7
50–59	5
60–69	3
70–79	2
80–89	7
90–99	1

a) 25   b) 10   c) 54.5   d) 40–49, 80–89   e) 100–109

11. *Visits to the Library* Johnson County Community College is planning to expand its library. Forty students were asked how many times they visited the library during the previous semester. Their responses are given below. Construct a frequency distribution, letting each class have a width of 1 (as in Example 1 on page 784).*

0	1	1	3	4	5	7	8
0	1	2	3	5	5	7	8
0	1	2	3	5	5	7	9
1	1	2	3	5	6	8	10
1	1	3	4	5	6	8	10

12. *Hot Dog Sales* A hot dog vendor is interested in the number of hot dogs he sells each day at his hot dog cart. The number of hot dogs sold is indicated below for 32 consecutive days. Construct a frequency distribution, letting each class have a width of 1.

15	16	19	20	21	22	24	27
15	18	19	20	21	22	25	27
15	18	19	20	21	23	25	28
16	18	19	21	21	23	26	29

Note that there were no days in which the vendor sold 17 hot dogs. However, it is customary to include a missing value as an observed value and assign to it a frequency of 0.*

*See Instructor Answer Appendix

▲ *See Exercise 12*

Percent of U.S. Residents Living in Poverty in 2008, by State

State	Percent	State	Percent
AK	7.9	MT	12.9
AL	14.4	NC	14.7
AR	14.5	ND	10.5
AZ	16.1	NE	10.3
CA	13.6	NH	6.4
CO	10.4	NJ	9.0
CT	8.5	NM	16.6
DE	9.4	NV	10.3
FL	12.8	NY	14.3
GA	14.6	OH	13.2
HI	8.7	OK	13.5
IA	9.2	OR	11.7
ID	11.1	PA	10.7
IL	11.1	RI	11.1
IN	13.1	SC	14.0
KS	12.2	SD	11.2
KY	16.3	TN	14.9
LA	17.1	TX	16.2
MA	11.2	UT	8.6
MD	8.8	VA	9.5
ME	11.4	VT	9.4
MI	11.9	WA	10.3
MN	9.6	WI	10.4
MO	13.1	WV	14.6
MS	20.4	WY	10.5

Source: *Bureau of the Census*

Magazine Circulation   In Exercises 13–16, use the data given in Table 13.1 on page 786 to construct a frequency distribution with a first class (in ten thousands) of

13. 173–322.*

14. 170–316.*

15. 173–272.*

16. 173–250.*

City Population   In Exercises 17–20, use the following data, which represent the population of the 20 most populous cities in the world in 2010, in millions of people (rounded to the nearest 100,000).

13.8	12.5	10.1	8.8	7.6
13.8	11.2	9.6	8.4	7.3
13.0	10.6	8.9	7.9	7.2
12.6	10.5	8.9	7.8	7.1

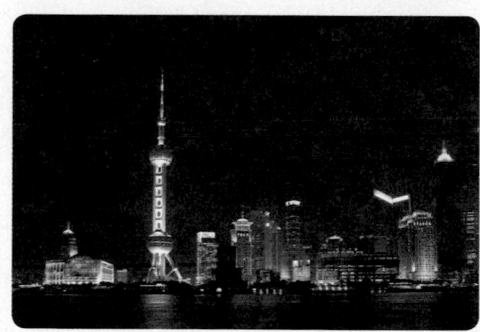

▲ *Shanghai, China, is the world's most populated city.*

Use these data to construct a frequency distribution with a first class of

17. 7.0–7.9.*

18. 6.5–7.4.*

19. 6.5–7.5.*

20. 7.0–7.4.*

Residents in Poverty   In Exercises 21–24, use the data in the table above to the right.

Construct a frequency distribution with a first class of

21. 6.4–8.3.*

22. 6.4–9.0.*

23. 6.4–7.8.*

24. 6.4–8.8.*

25. *Jogging Distances*   Twenty members of a health club who jog were asked how many miles they jog per week. The responses are as follows. Construct a stem-and-leaf display. For single digit data, use a stem of 0.

12	15	4	7	12	25	21
33	18	6	8	27	40	22
19	13	23	34	17	16	

```
1|2 represents 12
0 | 4 6 7 8
1 | 2 2 3 5 6 7 8 9
2 | 1 2 3 5 7
3 | 3 4
4 | 0
```

26. *College Credits* Eighteen students in a geology class were asked how many college credits they had earned. The responses are as follows. Construct a stem-and-leaf display.*

10	15	24	36	48	45
42	53	60	17	24	30
33	45	48	62	54	60

27. *Starting Salaries* Starting salaries (in thousands of dollars) for social workers with a bachelor of science degree and no experience are shown for a random sample of 25 different social workers.

27	28	29	31	33
28	28	29	31	33
28	28	30	32	33
28	29	30	32	34
28	29	30	32	34

a) Construct a frequency distribution. Let each class have a width of one.*

b) Construct a histogram.*

c) Construct a frequency polygon.*

d) Construct a stem-and-leaf display.*

28. *Visiting a Symphony* The ages of a random sample of 40 people attending a symphony are

20	26	31	34	39	45	50	62
20	29	31	35	40	47	51	63
23	30	32	35	40	49	51	66
23	30	33	37	40	49	54	69
26	30	34	38	42	49	57	72

a) Construct a frequency distribution with a first class of 20–30.*

b) Construct a histogram.*

c) Construct a frequency polygon.*

d) Construct a stem-and-leaf display.*

29. *Concert Tours* The following table shows the 25 top-grossing North American concert tours, in millions of dollars, for the years 1985–2008.

Artist	Total Gross ($ millions)
1. The Rolling Stones (2005)	162
2. U2 (2005)	139
3. The Rolling Stones (2006)	139
4. The Police (2007)	133
5. The Rolling Stones (1994)	121
6. Bruce Springsteen & the E Street Band (2003)	116
7. U2 (2001)	110
8. Madonna (2008)	105
9. Pink Floyd (1994)	104
10. Paul McCartney (2002)	103
11. The Rolling Stones (1989)	98
12. Celine Dion (2008)	94
13. Barbra Streisand (2006)	93
14. The Rolling Stones (1997)	89
15. Tim McGraw/Faith Hill (2006)	89
16. The Rolling Stones (2002)	88
17. Prince (2004)	87
18. 'N Sync (2001)	87
19. Madonna (2006)	86
20. Backstreet Boys (2001)	82
21. Cirque de Soleil: Delirium (2006)	82
22. Celine Dion (2005)	81
23. Celine Dion (2003)	81
24. Celine Dion (2004)	80
25. Tina Turner (2000)	80

Source: Pollstar

a) Construct a frequency distribution with a first class of 80–91.*

b) Construct a histogram.*

c) Construct a frequency polygon.*

30. *U.S. Presidents* The ages of the 44 U.S. presidents at their first inauguration (as of 2011) are

57	57	49	52	50	42	54	55	64
61	61	64	56	47	51	51	56	46
57	54	50	46	55	56	60	61	54
57	68	48	54	55	55	62	52	47
58	51	65	49	54	51	43	69	

a) Construct a frequency distribution with a first class of 42–47.*

*See Instructor Answer Appendix

b) Construct a histogram.*

c) Construct a frequency polygon.*

31. *Number of Televisions per Home* Use the histogram below to answer the following questions.

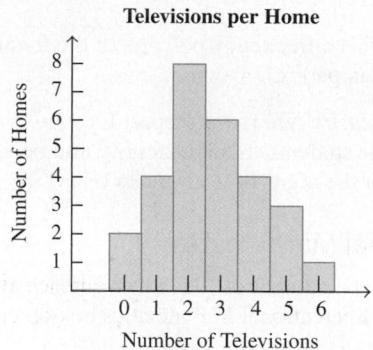

Televisions per Home

a) How many homes were included in the survey? 28

b) In how many homes were four televisions observed? 4

c) What is the modal class? 2

d) How many televisions were observed? 75

e) Construct a frequency distribution from this histogram.*

32. *Car Insurance* Use the histogram below to answer the following questions.

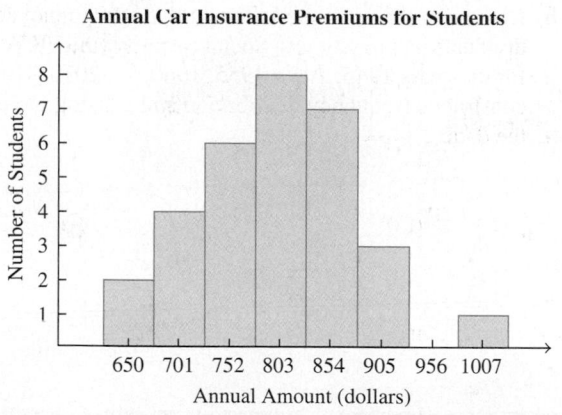

Annual Car Insurance Premiums for Students

a) How many students were surveyed? 31

b) What are the lower and upper class limits of the first and second classes? 625–675, 676–726

c) How many students have an annual car insurance premium in the class with a class mark of $752? 6

d) What is the class mark of the modal class? $803

e) Construct a frequency distribution from this histogram. Use a first class of 625–675.*

33. *E-mail Messages* Use the frequency polygon below to answer the following questions.

Number of E-mail Messages Sent per Day

a) How many people sent five e-mail messages? 7

b) How many people sent six or fewer e-mail messages? 16

c) How many people were included in the survey? 36

d) Construct a frequency distribution from the frequency polygon.*

e) Construct a histogram from the frequency distribution in part (d).*

34. *San Diego Zoo* Use the frequency polygon below to answer the following questions.

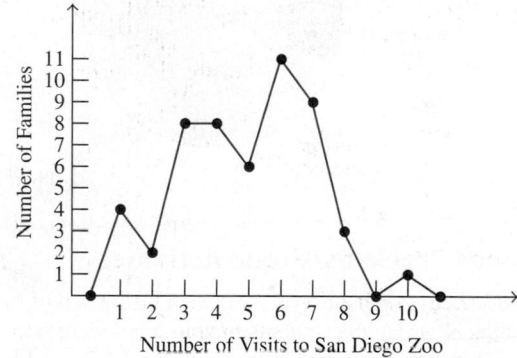

Number of Visits Selected Families Have Made to the San Diego Zoo

a) How many families visited the San Diego Zoo four times? 8

b) How many families visited the San Diego Zoo at least six times? 24

c) How many families were surveyed? 52

d) Construct a frequency distribution from the frequency polygon.*

e) Construct a histogram from the frequency distribution in part (d).*

35. *College Costs* The cost for Florida residents to attend the University of Florida for the 2010–2011 school year was $14,570. The circle graph on page 796 shows the

*See Instructor Answer Appendix

percentage of that cost for tuition/fees, room, board, and computer costs. Determine the cost, in dollars, for each category.*

Cost to Attend the University of Florida for 2010–2011

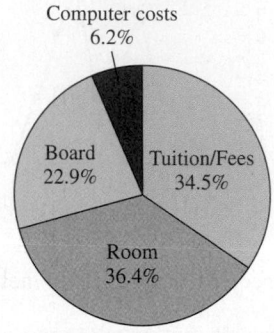

Computer costs 6.2%
Board 22.9%
Tuition/Fees 34.5%
Room 36.4%

36. *Automobile Accessories* A sample of 600 people were asked which one automobile accessory they would most prefer to have on a family road trip. The following circle graph shows the percentage of respondents that answered GPS, DVD player, extra cup holders, roof rack, and other. Determine the number of respondents for each category.*

Automobile Accessories for a Family Road Trip

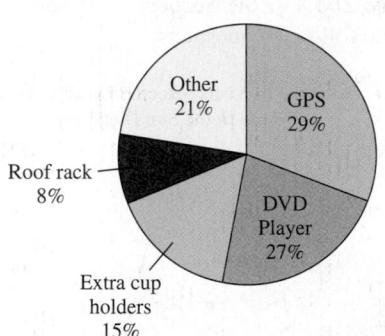

Other 21%
GPS 29%
Roof rack 8%
DVD Player 27%
Extra cup holders 15%

Challenge Problems/Group Activities

37. **a)** *Birthdays* What do you believe a histogram of the months in which the students in your class were born (January is month 1 and December is month 12) would look like? Explain. Answers will vary.

b) By asking, determine the month in which the students in your class were born (include yourself). Answers will vary.

c) Construct a frequency distribution containing 12 classes. Answers will vary.

d) Construct a histogram from the frequency distribution in part (c). Answers will vary.

e) Construct a frequency polygon of the frequency distribution in part (c). Answers will vary.

38. *Social Security Numbers* Repeat Exercise 37 for the last digit of the students' Social Security numbers. Include classes for the digits 0–9. a)–e) Answers will vary.

Recreational Mathematics

39. **a)** Count the number of F's in the sentence at the bottom of the Recreational Mathematics box on page 785. There are 6 F's.
b) Can you explain why so many people count the number of F's incorrectly? Answers will vary.

40. In what month do people take the least number of daily vitamins? February, since it has the fewest number of days

Internet/Research Activity

41. Over the years many changes have been made in the U.S. Social Security System.

a) Do research and determine the number of people receiving Social Security benefits for the years 1945, 1950, 1955, 1960, …, 2010. Then construct a frequency distribution and histogram of the data.

b) Determine the maximum amount that self-employed individuals had to pay into Social Security (the FICA tax) for the years 1945, 1950, 1955, 1960, …, 2010. Then construct a frequency distribution and a histogram of the data.

*See Instructor Answer Appendix

SECTION 13.4 Measures of Central Tendency

▲ *An average is used to describe the fuel efficiency of a car.*

Most people have an intuitive idea of what is meant by an "average." The term is used daily in many familiar ways. "This car averages 19 miles per gallon," "The average test grade was 82," and "The average height of adult males is 5 feet 9 inches" are three examples. In this section, we will introduce four different averages and discuss the circumstances in which each average is used.

Why This is Important An average is one of the most common ways to represent a set of data.

Measures of Central Tendency

An *average* is a number that is representative of a group of data. There are at least four different averages: the mean, the median, the mode, and the midrange. Each is calculated differently and may yield different results for the same set of data. Each will result in a number near the center of the data; for this reason, averages are commonly referred to as *measures of central tendency*.

The *arithmetic mean*, or simply the *mean*, is symbolized either by $\bar{x}$ (read "*x* bar") or by the Greek letter mu, μ. The symbol $\bar{x}$ is used when the mean of a *sample* of the population is calculated. The symbol μ is used when the mean of the *entire population* is calculated. Unless otherwise indicated, we will assume that the data featured in this book represent samples; therefore, we will use $\bar{x}$ for the mean.

The Greek letter sigma, Σ, is used to indicate "summation." The notation Σx, read "the sum of *x*," is used to indicate the sum of all the data. For example, if there are five pieces of data—4, 6, 1, 0, 5—then $\Sigma x = 4 + 6 + 1 + 0 + 5 = 16$.

Now we can discuss the procedure for determining the mean of a set of data.

Definition: Mean

The **mean**, $\bar{x}$, is the sum of the data divided by the number of pieces of data. The formula for calculating the mean is

$$\bar{x} = \frac{\Sigma x}{n}$$

where Σx represents the sum of all the data and *n* represents the number of pieces of data.

The most common use of the word *average* is the mean.

Example 1 *Determine the Mean*

Determine the mean age of a group of patients at a doctor's office if the ages of the individuals are 28, 19, 49, 35, and 49.

Solution

$$\bar{x} = \frac{\Sigma x}{n} = \frac{28 + 19 + 49 + 35 + 49}{5} = \frac{180}{5} = 36$$

Therefore, the mean, $\bar{x}$, is 36 years. ■

The mean represents "the balancing point" of a set of data. For example, if a seesaw were pivoted at the mean and uniform weights were placed at points corresponding to the ages in Example 1, the seesaw would balance. Figure. 13.13 shows the five ages given in Example 1 and the calculated mean.

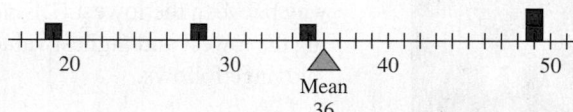

Mean
36

Figure 13.13

A second average is the *median*. To find the median of a set of data, *rank the data from smallest to largest, or largest to smallest, and determine the value in the middle of the set of ranked data*. This value will be the median.

Definition: Median

The **median** is the value in the middle of a set of *ranked data*.

Example 2   *Determine the Median*

Determine the median of the patients' ages in Example 1 on page 797.

Solution   Ranking the data from smallest to largest gives 19, 28, 35, 49, and 49. Since 35 is the value in the middle of this set of ranked data (two pieces of data above it and two pieces below it), 35 years is the median. ∎

When there are an even number of pieces of data, the median is halfway between the two middle pieces. In this case, to find the median, add the two middle pieces and divide this sum by 2.

Example 3   *Determine the Median of an Even Number of Pieces of Data*

Determine the median of the following sets of data.

a) 9, 14, 16, 17, 11, 16, 11, 12   b) 7, 8, 8, 8, 9, 10

Solution

a) Ranking the data gives 9, 11, 11, 12, 14, 16, 16, 17. There are eight pieces of data. Therefore, the median will lie halfway between the two middle pieces, the 12 and the 14. The median is $\frac{12 + 14}{2}$, or $\frac{26}{2}$, or 13.

b) There are six pieces of data, and they are already ranked. Therefore, the median lies halfway between the two middle pieces. Both middle pieces are 8's. The median is $\frac{8 + 8}{2}$, or $\frac{16}{2}$, or 8. ∎

A third average is the *mode*.

Definition: Mode

The **mode** is the piece of data that occurs most frequently.

Example 4   *Determine the Mode*

Determine the mode of the patients' ages in Example 1 on page 797.

Solution   The ages are 28, 19, 49, 35, and 49. The age 49 is the mode because it occurs twice and the other values occur only once. ∎

If each piece of data occurs only once, the set of data has no mode. For example, the set of data 1, 2, 3, 4, 5 has no mode. If two values in a set of data occur more often than all the other data, we consider both these values as modes and say that the data are **bimodal*** (which means two modes). For example, the set of data 1, 1, 2, 3, 3, 5 has two modes, 1 and 3.

The last average we will discuss is the midrange. The *midrange* is the value halfway between the lowest (L) and highest (H) values in a set of data. It is found by adding the lowest and highest values and dividing the sum by 2. A formula for finding the midrange follows.

Midrange

The **midrange** of a set of data can be calculated using the following formula.

$$\text{Midrange} = \frac{\text{lowest value} + \text{highest value}}{2}$$

*Some textbooks say that sets of data such as 1, 1, 2, 3, 3, 5 have no mode.

Example 5   *Determine the Midrange*

Determine the midrange of the patients' ages given in Example 1 on page 797.

Solution   The ages of the patients are 28, 19, 49, 35, and 49. The lowest age is 19, and the highest age is 49.

$$\text{Midrange} = \frac{\text{lowest} + \text{highest}}{2} = \frac{19 + 49}{2} = \frac{68}{2} = 34 \text{ years}$$

The "average" of the ages 28, 19, 49, 35, 49 can be considered any one of the following values: 36 (mean), 35 (median), 49 (mode), or 34 (midrange). Which average do you feel is most representative of the ages? We will discuss this question later in this section.

Example 6   *Measures of Central Tendency*

The salaries of eight selected social workers rounded to the nearest thousand dollars are 40, 25, 28, 35, 42, 60, 60, and 73. For this set of data, determine the (a) mean, (b) median, (c) mode, and (d) midrange. Then (e) list the measures of central tendency from lowest to highest.

Solution

a) $\bar{x} = \dfrac{\Sigma x}{n} = \dfrac{40 + 25 + 28 + 35 + 42 + 60 + 60 + 73}{8} = \dfrac{363}{8} = 45.375$

b) Ranking the data from the smallest to largest gives

$$25, 28, 35, 40, 42, 60, 60, 73$$

Since there are an even number of pieces of data, the median is halfway between 40 and 42. The median $= \dfrac{40 + 42}{2} = \dfrac{82}{2} = 41$.

c) The mode is the piece of data that occurs most frequently. The mode is 60.

d) The midrange $= \dfrac{\text{L} + \text{H}}{2} = \dfrac{25 + 73}{2} = \dfrac{98}{2} = 49$.

e) The averages from lowest to highest are the median, mean, midrange, and mode. Their values are 41, 45.375, 49, and 60, respectively.

At this point, you should be able to calculate the four measures of central tendency: mean, median, mode, and midrange. Now let's examine the circumstances in which each is used.

The mean is used when each piece of data is to be considered and "weighed" equally. It is the most commonly used average. It is the only average that can be affected by *any* change in the set of data; for this reason, it is the most sensitive of all the measures of central tendency (see Exercise 23).

Occasionally, one or more pieces of data may be much greater or much smaller than the rest of the data. When this situation occurs, these "extreme" values have the effect of increasing or decreasing the mean significantly so that the mean will not be representative of the set of data. Under these circumstances, the median should be used instead of the mean. The median is often used in describing average family incomes because a relatively small number of families have extremely large incomes. These few incomes would inflate the mean income, making it nonrepresentative of the millions of families in the population.

Consider a set of exam scores from a mathematics class: 0, 16, 19, 65, 65, 65, 68, 69, 70, 72, 73, 73, 75, 78, 80, 85, 88, 92. Which average would best represent these grades? The mean is 64.06. The median is 71. Since only 3 of the 18 scores fall below the mean, the mean would not be considered a good representative score. The median of 71 probably would be the better average to use.

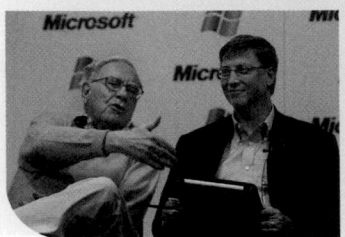
The mode is the piece of data, if any, that occurs most frequently. Builders planning houses are interested in the most common family size. Retailers ordering shirts are interested in the most common shirt size. An individual purchasing a thermometer might choose one, from those on display, whose temperature reading is the most common reading among those on display. These examples illustrate how the mode may be used.

The midrange is sometimes used as the average when the item being studied is constantly fluctuating. Average daily temperature, used to compare temperatures in different areas, is calculated by adding the lowest and highest temperatures for the day and dividing the sum by 2. The midrange is actually the mean of the high value and the low value of a set of data. Occasionally, the midrange is used to estimate the mean since it is much easier to calculate.

Sometimes an average itself is of little value, and care must be taken in interpreting its meaning. For example, Jim is told that the average depth of Willow Pond is only 3 feet. He is not a good swimmer but decides that it is safe to go out a short distance in this shallow pond. After he is rescued, he exclaims, "I thought this pond was only 3 feet deep." Jim didn't realize that an average does not indicate extreme values or the spread of the values. The spread of data is discussed in Section 13.5.

Measures of Position

Measures of position are used to describe the position of a piece of data in relation to the rest of the data. If you took the Scholastic Aptitude Test (SAT) before applying to college, your score was described as a measure of position rather than a measure of central tendency. *Measures of position* are often used to make comparisons, such as comparing the scores of individuals from different populations, and are generally used when the amount of data is large.

Two measures of position are *percentiles* and *quartiles*. There are 99 percentiles dividing a set of data into 100 equal parts; see Fig. 13.14. For example, suppose that you scored 520 on the math portion of the SAT, and the score of 520 was reported to be in the 78th percentile of high school students. This wording *does not* mean that 78% of your answers were correct; it *does* mean that you outperformed about 78% of all those taking the exam. In general, a score in the nth percentile means that you outperformed about n% of the population who took the test and that $(100 - n)$% of the people taking the test performed better than you did.

Percentiles

$$
\begin{array}{ccccccc}
1 & 2 & 3 & 4 & & 100 & \text{— 100 equal parts} \\
P_1 & P_2 & P_3 & P_4 & & P_{99} & \text{— Percentile indicators}
\end{array}
$$

Figure 13.14

Example 7 *English Achievement Test*

Kara Hopkins took an English achievement test to obtain college credit by exam for freshman English. Her score was at the 81st percentile. Explain what that means.

Solution If a score is at the 81st percentile, it means that about 81% of the scores are below that score. Therefore, Kara scored better than about 81% of the students taking the exam. Also, about 19% of all students taking the exam scored higher than she did.   ∎

Quartiles are another measure of position. Quartiles divide data into four equal parts: The first quartile is the value that is higher than about $\frac{1}{4}$, or 25%, of the population. It is the same as the 25th percentile. The second quartile is the value that is higher than about $\frac{1}{2}$ the population and is the same as the 50th percentile, or the median. The third quartile is the value that is higher than about $\frac{3}{4}$ of the population and is the same as the 75th percentile; see Fig. 13.15.

Quartiles

Figure 13.15

PROCEDURE   **TO DETERMINE THE QUARTILES OF A SET OF DATA**

1. List the data from smallest to largest.

2. Determine the median, or the 2nd quartile, of the set of data. If there is an odd number of pieces of data, the median is the middle value. If there is an even number of pieces of data, the median will be halfway between the two middle pieces of data.

3. The first quartile, Q_1, is the median of the lower half of the data; that is, Q_1 is the median of the data less than Q_2.

4. The third quartile, Q_3, is the median of the upper half of the data; that is, Q_3 is the median of the data greater than Q_2.

Example 8 *Finding Quartiles*

Electronics World is concerned about the high turnover of its sales staff. A survey was done to determine how long (in months) the sales staff had been in their current positions. The responses of 27 sales staff follow. Determine Q_1, Q_2, and Q_3.

$$\begin{array}{ccccccccc}
25 & 3 & 7 & 15 & 31 & 36 & 17 & 21 & 2 \\
11 & 42 & 16 & 23 & 19 & 21 & 9 & 20 & 5 \\
8 & 12 & 27 & 14 & 39 & 24 & 18 & 6 & 10
\end{array}$$

Solution   First we list the data from smallest to largest.

$$\begin{array}{ccccccccc}
2 & 3 & 5 & 6 & 7 & 8 & 9 & 10 & 11 \\
12 & 14 & 15 & 16 & 17 & 18 & 19 & 20 & 21 \\
21 & 23 & 24 & 25 & 27 & 31 & 36 & 39 & 42
\end{array}$$

Next we determine the median. Since there are 27 pieces of data, an odd number, the median will be the middle value. The middle value is 17, with 13 pieces of data less than 17 and 13 pieces of data greater than 17. Therefore, the median, Q_2, is 17, shown in red.

    To find Q_1, the median of the lower half of the data, we need to find the median of the 13 pieces of data that are less than Q_2. The middle value of the lower half of the data is 9. There are 6 pieces of data less than 9 and 6 pieces of data greater than 9. Therefore, Q_1 is 9, shown in blue.

    To find Q_3, the median of the upper half of the data, we need to find the median of the 13 pieces of data that are greater than 17, or Q_2. The middle value of the upper half of the data is 24. There are 6 pieces of data greater than 17 but less than 24 and 6 pieces of data greater than 24. Therefore, Q_3 is 24, shown in blue. ∎

TECHNOLOGY TIP

Several computer software programs and calculators can be used to determine the mean of a set of data. These programs and calculators can also provide other types of statistical information that we will discuss in this chapter. In this *Technology Tip* we will provide the instructions for using a software program called Microsoft Excel as well as information on how to use Texas Instruments TI-83 Plus and TI-84 Plus graphing calculators. In the example, we will use the data from Example 1 on page 797, which represent the ages of patients in a doctor's office.

EXCEL

In our discussion, we will use the symbol > to indicate the next item to be selected from the list or menu of items.

Begin by entering the five pieces of data in column A. Press the Enter key after each piece of data is entered. Next select

Insert > Function ... > Statistical > AVERAGE

Then click the ☐ OK ☐ box at the bottom. The program will then generate a gray box, where you need to enter the data. In the area to the right of **Number1,** you need to enter the data for which you want to find the mean. Since you have already entered the data in column A, rows 1 to 5, if A1:A5 is not already listed, you can enter A1:A5 in the area to the right of **Number1.** Then, at the bottom of the gray box, *Formula Results* = 36 is displayed. The 36 is the mean of the set of data. If you then press the ☐ OK ☐ box, the mean will be displayed in the cell where the cursor was located. If you do not want the mean displayed in a cell, press ☐ CANCEL ☐. To find the median or mode you follow a similar procedure, except that instead of selecting AVERAGE you would select MEDIAN or MODE, respectively.

TI-83 PLUS AND TI-84 PLUS GRAPHING CALCULATORS

To enter the data, press ☐ STAT ☐. Then highlight **1: Edit** and press the ☐ ENTER ☐ key. If any data are currently listed in column **L1**, move the cursor to the **L1** and press ☐ CLEAR ☐ and then the ☐ ENTER ☐ key. This step will eliminate all data from column **L1**. Now enter the data in column **L1**. After you enter each piece of data, press the ☐ ENTER ☐ key. After all the data have been entered, press ☐ STAT ☐. Then highlight **CALC.** At this point, **1: 1–Var Stats** should be highlighted. Press the ☐ ENTER ☐ key twice. You will now see $\bar{x}$ = 36. Thus, the mean is 36. Several other descriptive statistics that we will discuss shortly are also shown. If you scroll down, you will eventually see the values of Q_1, the median, and Q_3.

SECTION 13.4   *Exercises*

Warm Up Exercises

In Exercises 1–10, fill in the blank with an appropriate word, phrase, or symbol(s).

1. A number that is representative of a set of data is called a(n) _____. Average

2. Averages are referred to as measures of central _____. Tendency

3. The average that is found by summing the data and then dividing the sum by the number of pieces of data is called the _____. Mean

4. The value in the middle of a set of ranked data is called the _____. Median

5. The piece of data that occurs most frequently is called the _____. Mode

6. The value halfway between the lowest and highest values in a set of data is called the _____. Midrange

7. The measures of position that divide a set of data into four equal parts are called _____. Quartiles

8. Data that are listed from the lowest value to the highest value or from the highest value to the lowest value are called _____ data. Ranked

9. a) The symbol for the sample mean is _____. $\bar{x}$

   b) The symbol for the population mean is _____. μ

10. a) Another name for the 25th percentile is the _____ quartile. First

    b) Another name for the 50th percentile is the _____ quartile. Second

    c) Another name for the 75th percentile is the _____ quartile. Third

Practice the Skills

In Exercises 11–20, determine the mean, median, mode, and midrange of the set of data. Where appropriate, round your answer to the nearest tenth.

11. 8, 9, 9, 11, 13, 13, 13, 24, 26 14, 13, 13, 17

12. 7, 9, 10, 10, 10, 12, 12 10, 10, 10, 9.5

13. 76, 82, 94, 55, 100, 52, 96 79.3, 82, none, 76

14. 4, 6, 10, 12, 10, 9, 365, 40, 37, 8 50.1, 10, 10, 184.5

15. 1, 3, 5, 7, 9, 11, 13, 15 8, 8, none, 8

16. 40, 50, 30, 60, 90, 100, 140 72.9, 60, none, 85

17. 1, 7, 11, 27, 36, 14, 12, 9, 1 13.1, 11, 1, 18.5

18. 1, 1, 1, 1, 4, 4, 4, 4, 6, 8, 10, 12, 15, 21 6.6, 4, 1 and 4, 11

19. 6, 8, 12, 13, 11, 13, 15, 17 11.9, 12.5, 13, 11.5

20. 5, 15, 5, 15, 5, 15 10, 10, 5 and 15, 10

21. *Cholesterol Level* The total cholesterol level of 10 patients of Dr. Novak are 176, 202, 285, 153, 200, 182, 248, 132, 214, and 195. Determine the

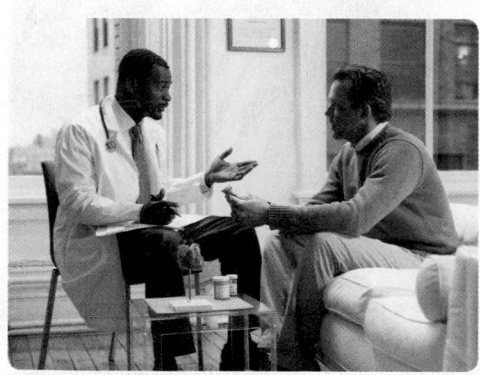

a) mean. 198.7   **b)** median. 197.5

c) mode. None   **d)** midrange. 208.5

22. *Daily Commission* The amount of money Steve Kline collected in sales commission in each of seven days is $48, $67, $51, $25, $102, $61, $80. Determine the mean, median, mode, and midrange. $62, $61, none, $63.50

Problem Solving

23. *Change in the Data* The mean is the "most sensitive" average because it is affected by any change in the data.

a) Determine the mean, median, mode, and midrange for 1, 2, 3, 5, 5, 7, 11. 4.9, 5, 5, 6

b) Change the 7 to a 10 in part (a). Determine the mean, median, mode, and midrange. 5.3, 5, 5, 6

c) Which averages were affected by changing the 7 to a 10? Only the mean

d) Which averages will be affected by changing the 11 to a 10 in part (a)? The mean and the midrange

24. *Life Expectancy* In 2010, the National Center for Health Statistics indicated a record "average life expectancy" of 78.2 years for the total U.S. population. The average life expectancy for men was 75.6 years, and for women it was 80.8 years. Which "average" do you think the National Center for Health is using? *

25. *A Grade of B* To get a grade of B, a student must have a mean average of 80 or greater. Jim Condor has a mean average of 79 for 10 quizzes. He approaches his teacher and asks for a B, reasoning that he missed a B by only one point. What is wrong with Jim's reasoning? *

26. *Employee Salaries* The salaries of 10 employees of a small company follow.

$29,000	$65,000
26,000	25,000
32,000	28,000
27,000	82,000
27,000	30,000

Determine the

a) mean. $37,100   **b)** median. $28,500

c) mode. $27,000   **d)** midrange. $53,500

e) If the employees wanted to demonstrate the need for a raise, which average would they use to show they are being underpaid: the mean or the median? Explain. The median because it is lower

f) If the management did not want to give the employees a raise, which average would they use: the mean or the median? Explain. The mean because it is higher

27. *Ice Cream Consumption* The 10 countries with the highest per person consumption of ice cream in 2008 are listed below.

Country	Consumption (pints per person)
Australia	31.7
USA	26.0
Nauru	25.3
New Zealand	23.4
Canada	22.7
Norway	22.3
Finland	20.9
Sweden	20.4
Iceland	18.5
Italy	18.5

Source: *Euromonitor International*

*See Instructor Answer Appendix

Determine, to the nearest tenth, the

a) mean. 23.0 pints

b) median. 22.5 pints

c) mode. 18.5 pints

d) midrange. 25.1 pints

28. Living Expenses Bob Bennet's monthly living expenses for 1 year are as follows:

$1200	$1050	$1570	$1600
2000	1050	1550	1450
1800	1100	1310	1430

Where appropriate, round your answer to the nearest cent. Determine the

a) mean. $1425.83

b) median. $1440

c) mode. $1050

d) midrange. $1525

29. Internet Retailers The ten U.S. retailers with the highest Internet sales in 2008 are listed below.

Company	Sales ($ billion)
Amazon.com, Inc.	14.8
Staples, Inc.	5.6
Office Depot, Inc.	4.9
Dell, Inc.	4.2
HP Home & Home Office Store	3.4
OfficeMax, Inc.	3.2
Apple, Inc.	2.7
Sears Holding Corp.	2.6
CDW Corp.	2.4
Newegg.com	1.9

Source: *Internet Retailer*

Determine to the nearest tenth the

a) mean. $4.6 billion

b) median. $3.3 billion

c) mode. None

d) midrange. $8.4 billion

30. Exam Average Malcolm Sander's mean average on five exams is 86. Determine the sum of his scores. 430

31. Exam Average Jeremy Urban's mean average on six exams is 92. Determine the sum of his scores. 552

32. Creating a Data Set Construct a set of five pieces of data in which the mode has a lower value than the median and the median has a lower value than the mean. .
One example is 1, 1, 2, 5, 6.

33. Creating a Data Set Construct a set of six pieces of data with a mean, median, and midrange of 75 and where no two pieces of data are the same. One example is 72, 73, 74, 76, 77, 78.

34. Creating a Data Set Construct a set of six pieces of data with a mean of 84 and where no two pieces of data are the same. One example is 81, 82, 83, 85, 86, 87.

35. Water Park For the 2011 season, 27,000 people visited the Blue Lagoon Water Park. The park was open 120 days for water activities. The highest number of visitors on a single day was 500. The lowest number of visitors on a single day was 50. Determine whether it is possible to find the following with the given information.

a) the mean number of visitors per day Yes

b) the median number of visitors per day No

c) the mode number of visitors per day No

d) the midrange number of visitors per day Yes

36. Determine a Necessary Grade A mean average of 80 or greater for five exams is needed for a final grade of B in a course. Jorge Rivera's first four exam grades are 73, 69, 85, and 80. What grade does Jorge need on the fifth exam to get a B in the course? 93 or greater

37. Grading Methods A mean average of 60 on seven exams is needed to pass a course. On her first six exams, Sheryl Ward received grades of 51, 72, 80, 62, 57, and 69.

a) What grade must she receive on her last exam to pass the course? 29 or greater

b) An average of 70 is needed to get a C in the course. Is it possible for Sheryl to get a C? If so, what grade must she receive on the seventh exam? Yes; 99 or greater

c) If her lowest grade of the exams already taken is to be dropped, what grade must she receive on her last exam to pass the course? 20 or greater

d) If her lowest grade of the exams already taken is to be dropped, what grade must she receive on her last exam to get a C in the course? 80 or greater

38. Central Tendencies Which of the measures of central tendency *must* be an actual piece of data in the distribution?
Mode

39. Creating a Data Set Construct a set of six pieces of data such that if only one piece of data is changed, the mean, median, and mode will all change.
One example: 1, 2, 3, 3, 4, 5 changed to 1, 2, 3, 4, 4, 5

40. Changing One Piece of Data Consider the set of data 1, 1, 1, 2, 2, 2. If one 2 is changed to a 3, which of the following will change: mean, median, mode, midrange?
The mean, mode, and midrange will all change.

41. Changing One Piece of Data Is it possible to construct a set of six different pieces of data such that by changing only one piece of data you cause the mean, median, mode, and midrange to change? Explain. No. By changing only one piece of the 6 pieces of data, you cannot alter both the median and the midrange.

42. Grocery Expenses The Taylors have recorded their weekly grocery expenses for the past 12 weeks and determined that the mean weekly expense was $85.20. Later Mrs. Taylor discovered that 1 week's expense of $74 was incorrectly recorded as $47. What is the correct mean? $87.45

43. Percentiles For any set of data, what must be done to the data before percentiles can be determined?
The data must be ranked.

44. Percentiles Josie Waverly scored in the 73rd percentile on the verbal part of her College Board test. What does that mean? She scored above approximately 73 percent of all the students who took the test.

45. Percentiles When a national sample of heights of kindergarten children was taken, Kevin Geis was told that he was in the 35th percentile. Explain what that means.
He is taller than approximately 35 percent of all kindergarten children.

46. Quartiles A union leader is told that, when all workers' salaries are considered, the first quartile is $22,750. Explain what that means. About 25% of the workers earn $22,750 or less.

47. Quartiles The prices of a gallon of the 21 top-rated interior paints, as rated in the March 2010 issue of *Consumer Reports*, are as follows:

$18 $19 $19 $19 $20 $20 $21
$21 $22 $22 $23 $23 $25 $27
$30 $33 $35 $35 $35 $58 $61

Determine

a) Q_2. $23 **b)** Q_1. $20 **c)** Q_3. $34

48. Quartiles The prices of the 20 top-rated 16-inch laptops, as rated in the June 2010 issue of *Consumer Reports*, are as follows:

$450 $460 $500 $530 $550
$550 $650 $650 $680 $700
$720 $730 $800 $850 $900
$1000 $1200 $1350 $1700 $1900

Determine

a) Q_2. $710 **b)** Q_1. $550 **c)** Q_3. $950

49. The 50th Percentile Give the names of two other statistics that have the same value as the 50th percentile.
Second quartile, median

50. College Admissions Jonathan Burd took an admission test for the University of California and scored in the 85th percentile. The following year, Jonathan's sister Kendra took a similar admission test for the University of California and scored in the 90th percentile.

a) Is it possible to determine which of the two answered the higher percent of questions correctly on their respective exams? No

b) Is it possible to determine which of the two was in a better relative position with regard to their respective populations? Explain. Yes, Kendra was in better relative position.

51. Employee Salaries The following statistics represent weekly salaries at the Midtown Construction Company:

Mean	$600	First quartile	$560
Median	$590	Third quartile	$625
Mode	$580	83rd percentile	$665

a) What is the most common salary? $580

b) What salary did half the employees' salaries surpass? $590

c) About what percent of employees' salaries surpassed $625? 25%

d) About what percent of employees' salaries were less than $560? 25%

e) About what percent of employees' salaries surpassed $665? 17%

f) If the company has 100 employees, what is the total weekly salary of all employees? $60,000

Challenge Problems/Group Activities

52. The Mean of the Means Consider the following five sets of values.

i) 5 6 7 7 8 9 14

ii) 3 6 8 9

iii) 1 1 1 2 5

iv) 6 8 9 12 15

v) 50 51 55 60 80 100

a) Compute the mean of each of the five sets of data.
8, 6.5, 2, 10, 66

b) Compute the mean of the five means in part (a). 18.5

c) Find the mean of the 27 pieces of data. ≈ 19.926

d) Compare your answer in part (b) to your answer in part (c). Are the values the same? Does your answer make sense? No, the values are not the same.

53. *Ruth Versus Mantle* The tables below compare the batting performances for selected years for two well-known former baseball players, Babe Ruth and Mickey Mantle.

Babe Ruth
Boston Red Sox 1914–1919
New York Yankees 1920–1934

Year	At Bats	Hits	Pct.
1925	359	104	
1930	518	186	
1933	459	138	
1916	136	37	
1922	406	128	
Total	1878	593	

Mickey Mantle
New York Yankees 1951–1968

Year	At Bats	Hits	Pct.
1954	543	163	
1957	474	173	
1958	519	158	
1960	527	145	
1962	377	121	
Total	2440	760	

a) For each player, compute the batting average percent (pct.) for each year by dividing the number of hits by the number of at bats. Round to the nearest thousandth. Place the answers in the pct. column.*

b) Going across each of the five horizontal lines (for example Ruth, 1925, vs. Mantle, 1954), compare the percents (pct.) and determine which is greater in each case. Mantle's is greater in every case.

c) For each player, compute the mean batting average percent for the 5 given years by dividing the total hits by the total at bats. Which is greater, Ruth's or Mantle's? Ruth: 0.316; Mantle: 0.311; Ruth's is greater.

d) Based on your answer in part (b), does your answer in part (c) make sense? Explain. Answers will vary.

e) Find the mean percent for each player by adding the five pcts. and dividing by 5. Which is greater, Ruth's or Mantle's? Ruth: 0.307; Mantle: 0.313; Mantle's is greater.

f) Why do the answers obtained in parts (c) and (e) differ? Explain. Answers will vary.

g) Who would you say has the better batting average percent for the 5 years selected? Explain. Answers will vary.

54. *Employee Salaries* The following table gives the annual salary distribution for employees at Kulzer's Home Improvement.

Annual Salary	Number Receiving Salary
$100,000	1
85,000	2
24,000	6
21,000	4
18,000	5
17,000	7

Using the information provided in the table, determine the

a) mean annual salary. $28,280

b) median annual salary. $21,000

c) mode annual salary. $17,000

d) midrange annual salary. $58,500

e) Which is the best measure of central tendency for this set of data? Explain your answer. Answers will vary.

Weighted Average Sometimes when we wish to find an average, we may wish to assign more importance, or weight, to some of the pieces of data. To calculate a *weighted average*, we use the formula: weighted average $= \dfrac{\Sigma xw}{\Sigma w}$, where w is the weight of the piece of data, x; Σxw is the sum of the products of each piece of data multiplied by its weight; and Σw is the sum of the weights. For example, suppose that students in a class need to submit a report

*See Instructor Answer Appendix

that counts for 20% of their grade, they need to take a midterm exam that counts for 30% of their grade, and they need to take a final exam that counts for 50% of their grade. Suppose that a student got a 72 on the report, an 85 on the midterm exam, and a 93 on the final exam. To determine this student's weighted average, first find Σxw:

$\Sigma xw = 72(0.20) + 85(0.30) + 93(0.50) = 86.4.$
Next find Σw, the sum of the weights: $\Sigma w = 0.20 + 0.30 + 0.50 = 1.00.$ *Now determine the weighted average as follows.*

$$\text{Weighted average} = \frac{\Sigma xw}{\Sigma w} = \frac{86.4}{1.00} = 86.4$$

Thus, the weighted average is 86.4. Note that Σw does not always have to be 1.00. In Exercises 55 and 56, use the weighted average formula.

55. *Course Average* Suppose that your final grade for a course is determined by a midterm exam and a final exam. The midterm exam is worth 40% of your grade, and the final exam is worth 60%. If your midterm exam grade is 84 and your final exam grade is 94, calculate your final average. 90

56. *Grade Point Average* In a four-point grade system, an A corresponds to 4.0 points, a B corresponds to 3.0 points, a C corresponds to 2.0 points, and a D corresponds to 1.0 points. No points are awarded for an F. Last semester, Tanya Reeves received a B in a four-credit hour course, an A in a three-credit hour course, a C in a three-credit hour course, and an A in another three-credit hour course. Grade point average (GPA) is calculated as a weighted average using the credit hours as weights and the number of points corresponding to the grade as pieces of data. Calculate Tanya's GPA for the previous semester. (Round your answer to the nearest hundredth.) 3.23

Recreational Mathematics

57. *Your Exam Average* **a)** Calculate the mean, median, mode, and midrange of your exam grades in your mathematics course. Answers will vary.

 b) Which measure of central tendency best represents your average grade? Answers will vary.

 c) Which measure of central tendency would you rather use as your average grade? Answers will vary.

58. *Purchases* Matthew Riveria purchased some items at Staples each day for five days. The mode of the number of items Matthew purchased is higher than the median of the number of items he purchased. The median of the number of items Matthew purchased is higher than the mean of the number of items he purchased. He purchased at least two items but no more than seven items each day.

 a) How many items did Matthew purchase each day? (*Note:* There is more than one correct answer.) Answers will vary. One example is 2, 3, 5, 7, 7.

 b) Determine the mean, median, and mode for your answer to part (a). Answers will vary.

Internet/Research Activity

59. Two other measures of location that we did not mention in this section are *stanines* and *deciles*. Use statistics books, books on educational testing and measurements, and Internet Web sites to write a report on what stanines and deciles are and when percentiles, quartiles, stanines, and deciles are used.

Measures of Dispersion

▲ *The average life span of a tablet PC battery may not be enough information to make a sound purchasing decision.*

Measures of central tendency by themselves do not always give sufficient information to analyze a situation and make decisions. For example, suppose Apple Computer is considering two companies to produce batteries for its iPads. Testing shows that Company A batteries have a mean life of 10 hours. Company B batteries have a mean life of 9.5 hours. If both manufacturers' batteries cost the same, which one should be purchased? The average battery life may not be the most important factor. If half of Company A batteries last only 5 hours, while half last 15 hours, there is a large variability in the life of the batteries. If all of Company B batteries last between 9.0 and 10.0 hours, the batteries are more consistent and reliable. This example illustrates the importance of knowing something about the *spread*, or *variability*, of the data. In this section we will discuss two measures of variability or dispersion.

Why **This is Important** Knowing the spread, or variability of a set of data helps us make accurate conclusions about the set of data.

Measures of dispersion are used to measure the variability of the data, including the *spread of the data,* and how the data varies about the mean. The range and standard deviation* are the measures of dispersion that will be discussed in this section.

Range and Standard Deviation

The *range* is the difference between the highest and lowest values; it indicates the total spread of the data.

> **Range**
>
> The range of a set of data can be calculated using the following formula.
>
> $$\textbf{Range} = \text{highest value} - \text{lowest value}$$

Example 1 *Determine the Range*

The amount of caffeine, in milligrams, of 10 different soft drinks is given below. Determine the range of these data.

$$38, 43, 26, 80, 55, 34, 40, 30, 35, 43$$

Solution Range = highest value − lowest value = 80 − 26 = 54. The range of the amounts of caffeine is 54 milligrams. ∎

The second measure of dispersion we discuss in this section, the *standard deviation*, measures how much the data *differ from the mean.* It is symbolized either by the letter s or by the Greek letter sigma, σ.[†] The s is used when the standard deviation of a *sample* is calculated. The σ is used when the standard deviation of the entire *population* is calculated. *Since we are assuming that all data presented in this section are for samples, we use s to represent the standard deviation* (note, however, that on the height and weight charts on page 814, σ is used).

The larger the variability of the data about the mean, the larger the standard deviation is. Consider the following two sets of data.

$$5, 8, 9, 10, 12, 13 \qquad 8, 9, 9, 10, 10, 11$$

Figure 13.16

Both have a mean of 9.5. Which set of values on the whole do you believe differs less from the mean of 9.5? Figure 13.16 may make the answer more apparent. The scores in the second set of data are closer to the mean and therefore have a smaller standard deviation. You will soon be able to verify such relationships yourself.

Sometimes only a very small standard deviation is desirable or acceptable. Consider a cereal box that is to contain 8 oz of cereal. If the amount of cereal put into the boxes varies too much—sometimes underfilling, sometimes overfilling—the manufacturer will soon be in trouble with consumer groups and government agencies.

At other times, a larger spread of data is desirable or expected. For example, intelligence quotients (IQs) are expected to exhibit a considerable spread about the

---

*Variance, another measure of dispersion, is the square of the standard deviation.

[†]Our alphabet uses both uppercase and lowercase letters, for example, A and a. The Greek alphabet also uses both uppercase and lowercase letters. The symbol Σ is the capital Greek letter sigma, and σ is the lowercase Greek letter sigma.

mean because everyone is different. The following procedure explains how we determine the standard deviation of a set of data.

PROCEDURE **TO DETERMINE THE STANDARD DEVIATION OF A SET OF DATA**

1. Determine the mean of the set of data.
2. Make a chart having three columns:
   Data   Data − Mean   (Data − Mean)^2
3. List the data vertically under the column marked Data.
4. Subtract the mean from each piece of data and place the difference in the Data − Mean column.
5. Square the values obtained in the Data − Mean column and record these values in the (Data − Mean)^2 column.
6. Determine the sum of the values in the (Data − Mean)^2 column.
7. Divide the sum obtained in Step 6 by $n - 1$, where n is the number of pieces of data.[*]
8. Determine the square root of the number obtained in Step 7. This number is the standard deviation of the set of data.

Example 2 illustrates the procedure to follow to determine the standard deviation of a set of data.

Example 2 *Determine the Standard Deviation*

A veterinarian in an animal hospital recorded the following life spans of selected Labrador retrievers (to the nearest year):

$$7, 9, 11, 15, 18, 12$$

Determine the standard deviation of the life spans.

Solution First determine the mean:

$$\bar{x} = \frac{\Sigma x}{n} = \frac{7 + 9 + 11 + 15 + 18 + 12}{6} = \frac{72}{6} = 12$$

Next construct a table with three columns, as illustrated in Table 13.4 on page 810, and list the data in the first column (it is often helpful to list the data in ascending or descending order). Complete the second column by subtracting the mean, 12 in this case, from each piece of data in the first column.

The sum of the values in the Data − Mean column should always be zero; if not, you have made an error. (If a rounded value of $\bar{x}$ is used, the sum of the values in the Data − Mean column will not always be exactly zero; however, the sum will be very close to zero.)

---

[*]To determine the standard deviation of a sample, divide the sum of (Data − Mean)^2 column by $n - 1$. To find the standard deviation of a population, divide the sum by n. In this book, we assume that the set of data represents a sample and divide by $n - 1$. The quotient obtained in Step 7 represents a measure of dispersion called the *variance*.

Table 13.4

Data	Data − Mean	(Data − Mean)²
7	7 − 12 = −5	
9	9 − 12 = −3	
11	11 − 12 = −1	
12	12 − 12 = 0	
15	15 − 12 = 3	
18	18 − 12 = 6	
	0	

Next square the values in the second column and place the squares in the third column (Table 13.5).

Table 13.5

Data	Data − Mean	(Data − Mean)²
7	−5	$(-5)^2 = (-5)(-5) = 25$
9	−3	$(-3)^2 = (-3)(-3) = 9$
11	−1	$(-1)^2 = (-1)(-1) = 1$
12	0	$(0)^2 = (0)(0) = 0$
15	3	$(3)^2 = (3)(3) = 9$
18	6	$(6)^2 = (6)(6) = 36$
	0	80

Add the squares in the third column. In this case, the sum is 80. Divide this sum by one less than the number of pieces of data $(n - 1)$. In this case, the number of pieces of data is 6. Therefore, we divide by 5 and get

$$\frac{80}{5} = 16*$$

Finally, take the square root of this number. Since $\sqrt{16} = 4$, the standard deviation, symbolized s, is 4. ∎

Now we will develop a formula for determining the standard deviation of a set of data. If we call the individual data x and the mean $\bar{x}$, we could write the three column heads Data, Data − Mean, and (Data − Mean)² in Table 13.4 as

$$x \qquad x - \bar{x} \qquad (x - \bar{x})^2$$

Let's follow the procedure we used to obtain the standard deviation in Example 2. We found the sum of the (Data − Mean)² column, which is the same as the sum of the $(x - \bar{x})^2$ column. We can represent the sum of the $(x - \bar{x})^2$ column by using the summation notation, $\Sigma(x - \bar{x})^2$. Thus, in Table 13.5, $\Sigma(x - \bar{x})^2 = 80$. We then divided this number by 1 less than the number of pieces of data, $n - 1$. Thus, we have

$$\frac{\Sigma(x - \bar{x})^2}{n - 1}$$

*16 is the variance, symbolized s^2, of this set of data.

Finally, we took the square root of this value to obtain the standard deviation.

Standard Deviation

The standard deviation, *s*, of a set of data can be calculated using the following formula.

$$s = \sqrt{\frac{\Sigma (x - \bar{x})^2}{n - 1}}$$

Example 3 *Determine the Standard Deviation of Stock Prices*

The following are the prices of nine stocks on the New York Stock Exchange. Determine the standard deviation of the prices.

$17, $28, $32, $36, $50, $52, $66, $74, $104

Solution The mean, $\bar{x}$, is

$$\bar{x} = \frac{\Sigma x}{n} = \frac{17 + 28 + 32 + 36 + 50 + 52 + 66 + 74 + 104}{9} = \frac{459}{9} = 51$$

The mean is $51.

Table 13.6

x	$x - \bar{x}$	$(x - \bar{x})^2$
17	−34	1156
28	−23	529
32	−19	361
36	−15	225
50	−1	1
52	1	1
66	15	225
74	23	529
104	53	2809
	0	5836

Table 13.6 shows us that $\Sigma(x - \bar{x})^2 = 5836$. Since there are nine pieces of data, $n - 1 = 9 - 1$, or 8.

$$s = \sqrt{\frac{\Sigma (x - \bar{x})^2}{n - 1}} = \sqrt{\frac{5836}{8}} = \sqrt{729.5} \approx 27.01$$

The standard deviation, to the nearest tenth, is $27.01. ∎

Standard deviation will be used in Section 13.6 to find the percent of data between any two values in a normal curve. Standard deviations are also often used in determining norms for a population (see Exercise 29).

TECHNOLOGY TIP

In this *Technology Tip*, we will explain how to find the standard deviation using Excel as well as with the TI-83 Plus and TI-84 Plus graphing calculators. In our illustration, we will use the data from Example 3 on page 811, which represent the prices of nine stocks on the New York Stock Exchange.

EXCEL

The instructions used to determine the standard deviation are very similar to those used to determine the mean in the *Technology Tip* on page 802 in Section 13.4. Please read that material now. Then enter the nine piece of data in columns A1–A9 and press the Enter key. Now select the following:

$$\text{Insert} > \text{Function} \dots > \text{Statistical} > \text{STDEV}$$

Then click the $\boxed{\text{OK}}$ box. The program will then generate a gray box where you need to enter the data. In the area to the right of **Number1** you need to enter the data for which you want to find the standard deviation. Since you have already entered the data in column A, rows 1 to 9, if A1:A9 is not already listed, you can enter A1:A9 in the area to the right of **Number1.** At the bottom of the gray box, *Formula Results* = 27.00925767, which is the standard deviation, is displayed. If you click OK, Excel will place the standard deviation in cell A10.

TI-83 PLUS AND TI-84 PLUS GRAPHING CALCULATORS

To find the standard deviation on Texas Instruments graphing calculators, follow the instructions for finding the mean in the *Technology Tip* on page 802 in Section 13.4. As explained there, press $\boxed{\text{STAT}}$ $\boxed{>}$ $\boxed{\text{EDIT}}$ $\boxed{>}$ $\boxed{\text{ENTER}}$. Remove existing data by highlighting **L1** and then pressing $\boxed{\text{CLEAR}}$ $\boxed{>}$ $\boxed{\text{ENTER}}$. Then enter the nine pieces of data, pressing the Enter key after each entry. Then press $\boxed{\text{STAT}}$ $\boxed{>}$ $\boxed{\text{CALC}}$ $\boxed{>}$ $\boxed{\text{ENTER}}$ $\boxed{>}$ $\boxed{\text{ENTER}}$. The fourth statistic down is $S_x = 27.00925767$. This value is the standard deviation.

SECTION 13.5 *Exercises*

Warm Up Exercises

In Exercises 1–6, fill in the blank with an appropriate word, phrase, or symbol(s).

1. Measures of dispersion are used to indicate the spread or _____ of the data. Variability

2. The difference between the highest and lowest values in a set of data is called the _____. Range

3. The measure of dispersion that measures how much the data differ from the mean is called the _____. Standard deviation

4. The symbol, σ, is used to indicate the standard deviation of a(n) _____. Population

5. The symbol, s, is used to indicate the standard deviation of a(n) _____. Sample

6. The standard deviation of a set of data in which all the data values are the same is _____. 0

Practice the Skills

In Exercises 7–14, determine the range and standard deviation of the set of data. When appropriate, round standard deviations to the nearest hundredth.

7. 11, 9, 6, 12, 17 11, $\sqrt{16.5} \approx 4.06$

8. 15, 15, 19, 21, 13, 13 8, $\sqrt{10.8} \approx 3.29$

9. 130, 131, 132, 133, 134, 135, 136 6, $\sqrt{4.67} \approx 2.16$

10. 3, 7, 8, 12, 0, 9, 11, 12, 6, 2 12, $\sqrt{18} \approx 4.24$

11. 4, 8, 9, 11, 13, 15 11, $\sqrt{15.2} \approx 3.90$

12. 9, 9, 9, 9, 9, 9, 9, 9 0, 0

13. 7, 9, 7, 9, 9, 10, 12 5, $\sqrt{3} \approx 1.73$

14. 60, 58, 62, 67, 48, 51, 72, 70 24, $\sqrt{74} \approx 8.60$

Problem Solving

15. *Digital Cameras* Determine the range and standard deviation of the following prices of selected digital cameras: $158, $95, $175, $180, $95, $129, $228, $300.
$205, $\sqrt{4780.57} \approx \$69.14$

16. *Years Until Retirement* Seven employees at a large company were asked the number of additional years they planned to work before retirement. Their responses were 10, 23, 28, 4, 1, 6, 12. Determine the range and standard deviation of the number of years. 27, $\sqrt{100.33} \approx 10.02$

17. *Camping Tents* Determine the range and standard deviation of the following prices of selected camping tents: $109, $60, $80, $60, $210, $250, $60, $100, $115.
$190, $\sqrt{4725.25} \approx \$68.74$

18. *Prescription Prices* The amount of money seven people spent on prescription medication in a year are as follows: $600, $100, $850, $350, $250, $140, $300. Determine the range and standard deviation of the amounts.
$750, $\sqrt{71,466.67} \approx \$267.33$

19. Can you think of any situations in which a large standard deviation may be desirable? Answers will vary.

20. Can you think of any situations in which a small standard deviation may be desirable? Answers will vary.

21. Without actually doing the calculations, decide which, if either, of the following two sets of data will have the greater standard deviation. Explain why. The first set will have the greater standard deviation because the scores have a greater spread about the mean.

  10, 13, 14, 15, 17, 21   16, 17, 17, 18, 18, 19

22. Without actually doing the calculations, decide which, if either, of the following two sets of data will have the greater standard deviation. Explain why. They would be the same since the spread of data about each mean is the same.

  2, 4, 6, 8, 10   102, 104, 106, 108, 110

23. By studying the standard deviation formula, explain why the standard deviation of a set of data will always be greater than or equal to 0. The sum of the values in the (Data − Mean)² column will always be greater than or equal to 0.

24. Patricia Wolff teaches two statistics classes, one in the morning and the other in the evening. On the midterm exam, the morning class had a mean of 75.2 and a standard deviation of 5.7. The evening class had a mean of 75.2 and a standard deviation of 12.5.

a) How do the means compare? The mean is the same for both classes.

b) If we compare the set of scores from the first class with those in the second class, how will the distributions of the two sets of scores compare? *

25. *Count Your Money* Six people were asked to determine the amount of money they were carrying, to the nearest dollar. The results were

  $32, $60, $14, $25, $5, $68

a) Determine the range and standard deviation of the amounts. $63, $\sqrt{631.6} \approx \$25.13$

b) Add $10 to each of the six amounts. How do you expect the range and standard deviation of the new set of data to change? Answers will vary.

c) Determine the range and standard deviation of the new set of data. Do the results agree with your answer to part (b)? If not, explain why. Answers remain the same, range: $63, standard deviation ≈ $25.13.

26. a) *Adding to or Subtracting from Each Number* Pick any five numbers. Compute the mean and the standard deviation of this distribution. Answers will vary.

b) Add 20 to each of the numbers in your original distribution and compute the mean and the standard deviation of this new distribution. Answers will vary.

c) Subtract 5 from each number in your original distribution and compute the mean and standard deviation of this new distribution. Answers will vary.

d) What conclusions can you draw about changes in the mean and the standard deviation when the same number is added to or subtracted from each piece of data in a distribution? If each piece of data is increased, or decreased, by n, the mean is increased, or decreased, by n. The standard deviation remains the same.

e) How will the mean and standard deviation of the numbers 8, 9, 10, 11, 12, 13, 14 differ from the mean and standard deviation of the numbers 648, 649, 650, 651, 652, 653, 654? Determine the mean and standard deviation of both sets of numbers. Mean of first set is 11; mean of second set is 651. The standard deviation of both sets is ≈2.16.

27. a) *Multiplying Each Number* Pick any five numbers. Compute the mean and standard deviation of this distribution. Answers will vary.

b) Multiply each number in your distribution by 3 and compute the mean and the standard deviation of this new distribution. Answers will vary.

c) Multiply each number in your original distribution by 9 and compute the mean and the standard deviation of this new distribution. Answers will vary.

d) What conclusions can you draw about changes in the mean and the standard deviation when each value in a distribution is multiplied by the same number?*

e) The mean and standard deviation of the distribution 1, 3, 4, 4, 5, 7 are 4 and 2, respectively. Use the conclusion drawn in part (d) to determine the mean and standard deviation of the distribution 20, 10

5, 15, 20, 20, 25, 35

28. *Waiting in Line* Consider the following illustrations of two bank-customer waiting systems.

a) How would you expect the mean waiting time in Bank A to compare with the mean waiting time in Bank B? Answers will vary.

b) How would you expect the standard deviation of waiting times in Bank A to compare with the standard deviation of waiting times in Bank B? Answers will vary.

29. *Height and Weight Distribution* The chart shown on the right uses the symbol σ to represent the standard deviation. Note that 2σ represents the value that is two standard deviations above the mean; -2σ represents the value that is two standard deviations below the mean. The unshaded areas, from two standard deviations below the mean to two standard deviations above the mean, are considered the

normal range. For example, the average (mean) 8-year-old boy has a height of about 50 inches, but any heights between approximately 45 inches and 55 inches are considered normal for 8-year-old boys. Refer to the chart below to answer the following questions.

*Supine length to 6 years, standing height from 6 to 18 years

a) What happens to the standard deviation for weights of boys as the age of boys increases? What is the significance of this fact? The standard deviation increases. There is a greater spread from the mean as they get older.

b) At age 16, what is the mean weight, in pounds, of boys? ≈ 133 lb

c) What is the approximate standard deviation of boys' weights at age 16? ≈ 21 lb

d) Determine the mean weight and normal range for boys at age 13. Mean: ≈ 100 lb; normal range: ≈ 60 to 140 lb

e) Determine the mean height and normal range for boys at age 13. Mean: ≈ 62 in.; normal range: ≈ 53 to 68 in.

f) Assuming that this chart was constructed so that approximately 95% of all boys are always in the normal range, determine what percentage of boys are not in the normal range. 5%

Challenge Problems/Group Activities

30. *Athletes' Salaries* The tables on page 815 list the 10 highest-paid athletes in Major League Baseball and in the National Football League.

*See Instructor Answer Appendix

Major League Baseball (2010 Season)

Player	Salary (millions of dollars)
1. Alex Rodriguez	33.0
2. C. C. Sabathia	24.3
3. Derek Jeter	22.6
4. Mark Teixeira	20.6
5. Johan Santana	20.1
6. Miguel Cabrera	20.0
7. Carlos Beltran	19.4
8. Ryan Howard	19.0
9. Carlos Lee	19.0
10. Alfonso Soriano	19.0

Source: Major League Baseball Players Association

National Football League (2009–2010 season)

Player	Salary (millions of dollars)
1. Philip Rivers	25.6
2. Jay Cutler	22.0
3. Eli Manning	20.5
4. Kurt Warner	19.0
5. Kelvin Hayden	17.5
6. Matt Schaub	17.0
7. Julius Peppers	16.7
8. Chris Long	16.6
9. Greg Jennings	16.3
10. Antonio Smith	15.5

Source: National Football League Players Association

a) Without doing any calculations, which do you believe is greater, the mean salary of the 10 baseball players or the mean salary of the 10 football players? Answers will vary.

b) Without doing any calculations, which do you believe is greater, the standard deviation of the salary of the 10 baseball players or the standard deviation of the salary of the 10 football players? Answers will vary.

c) Compute the mean salary of the 10 baseball players and the mean salary of the 10 football players and determine whether your answer in part (a) was correct. Baseball: $21.70 million; NFL: $18.67 million

d) Compute the standard deviation of the salary of the 10 baseball players and the standard deviation of the salary of the 10 football players and determine whether your answer in part (b) is correct. Round each mean to the nearest tenth to determine the standard deviation. Baseball: ≈ $4.33 million; NFL: ≈ $3.17 million

31. *Oil Change* Jiffy Lube has franchises in two different parts of a city. The number of oil changes made daily, for 25 days, is given below.

East Store					West Store				
33	59	27	30	42	38	46	38	38	30
19	42	25	22	32	38	38	37	39	31
43	27	57	37	52	39	36	40	37	47
40	67	38	44	43	30	34	42	45	29
15	31	49	41	35	31	46	28	45	48

a) Construct a frequency distribution for each store with a first class of 15–20.*

b) Draw a histogram for each store.*

c) Using the histogram, determine which store appears to have a greater mean, or do the means appear about the same? Explain. They appear to have about the same mean since they are both centered around 38.

d) Using the histogram, determine which store appears to have the greater standard deviation. Explain. The distribution for East is more spread out. Therefore, East has a greater standard deviation.

e) Calculate the mean for each store and determine whether your answer in part (c) was correct. East: 38, West: 38

f) Calculate the standard deviation for each store and determine whether your answer in part (d) was correct. East: ≈ 12.64, West: ≈ 5.98

Recreational Mathematics

32. Calculate the range and standard deviation of your exam grades in this mathematics course. Round the mean to the nearest tenth to calculate the standard deviation. Answers will vary.

33. Construct a set of five pieces of data with a mean, median, mode, and midrange of 6 and a standard deviation of 0. 6, 6, 6, 6, 6

Internet/Research Activity

34. Use a calculator with statistical function keys to find the mean and standard deviation of the salaries of the 10 Major League Baseball players and the 10 National Football League players in Exercise 30.

*See Instructor Answer Appendix

▲ *Some sets of data, such as exam grades, may form a bell-shaped distribution.*

Suppose your mathematics teacher states that exam scores for the previous exam followed a bell-shaped distribution and that your score was 1.5 standard deviations above the mean. How does your exam grade compare with the exam grades of your classmates? What percentage of students in your class had exam grades below your exam grade? In this section, we will discuss sets of data that form bell-shaped distributions and learn how to determine the percentage of data that fall below a particular piece of data in the set of data.

Why *This is Important*   There are many real-life applications, such as IQ scores, heights and weights of males, heights and weights of females, and wearout mileage of automobile tires, that have a bell-shaped distribution.

When examining data using a histogram, we can refer to the overall appearance of the histogram as the *shape* of the distribution of the data. Certain shapes of distributions of data are more common than others. In this section, we will illustrate and discuss a few of the more common ones. In each case, the vertical scale is the frequency and the horizontal scale is the observed values.

In a *rectangular distribution* (Fig. 13.17), all the observed values occur with the same frequency. If a die is rolled many times, we would expect the numbers 1–6 to occur with about the same frequency. The distribution representing the outcomes of the die is rectangular.

Figure 13.17

In *J-shaped distributions*, the frequency is either constantly increasing (Fig. 13.18(a)) or constantly decreasing (Fig. 13.18(b)). The number of hours studied per week by students may have a distribution like that in Fig. 13.18(b). The bars might represent (from left to right) 0–5 hours, 6–10 hours, 11–15 hours, and so on.

J-shaped Distributions

(a)   (b)

Figure 13.18

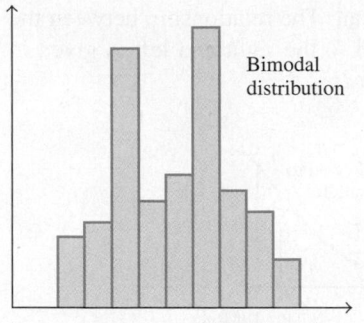

Figure 13.19

A *bimodal distribution* (Fig. 13.19) is one in which two nonadjacent values occur more frequently than any other values in a set of data. For example, if an equal number of men and women were weighed, the distribution of their weights would probably be bimodal, with one mode for the women's weights and the second for the men's weights. For a distribution to be considered bimodal, both modes need not have the same frequency but they must both have a frequency greater than the frequency of each of the other values in the distribution.

The life expectancy of lightbulbs has a bimodal distribution: a small peak very near 0 hours of life, resulting from the bulbs that burned out very quickly because of a manufacturing defect, and a much higher peak representing the nondefective bulbs. A bimodal frequency distribution generally means that you are dealing with two distinct populations, in this case, defective and nondefective lightbulbs.

Another distribution, called a *skewed distribution*, has more of a "tail" on one side than the other. A skewed distribution with a tail on the right (Fig. 13.20(a)) is said to be skewed to the right. If the tail is on the left (Fig. 13.20(b)), the distribution is referred to as skewed to the left.

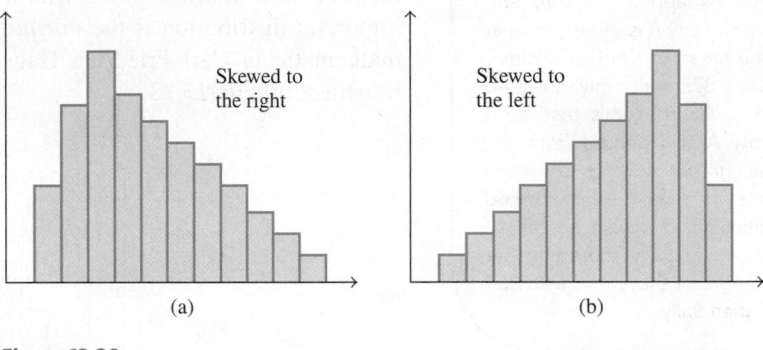

Figure 13.20

The number of children per family might be a distribution skewed to the right. Some families have no children, more families may have one child, the greatest percentage may have two children, fewer may have three children, still fewer may have four children, and so on.

Since few families have high incomes, distributions of family incomes might be skewed to the right.

Smoothing the histograms of the skewed distributions shown in Fig. 13.20 to form curves gives the curves illustrated in Fig. 13.21.

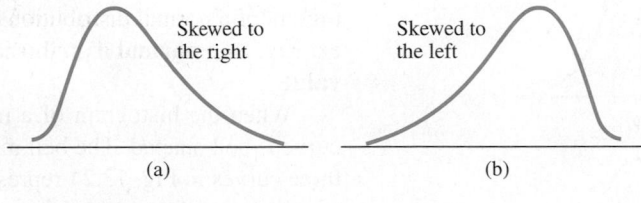

Figure 13.21

In Fig. 13.21(a), the greatest frequency appears on the left side of the curve and the frequency decreases from left to right. Since the mode is the value with the greatest frequency, the mode would appear on the left side of the curve.

Every value in the set of data is considered in determining the mean. The values on the far right side of the curve in Fig. 13.21(a) would tend to increase the value of the mean. Thus, the value of the mean would be farther to the right than the mode.

The median would be between the mode and the mean. The relationship between the mean, median, and mode for curves that are skewed to the right and left is given in Fig. 13.22.

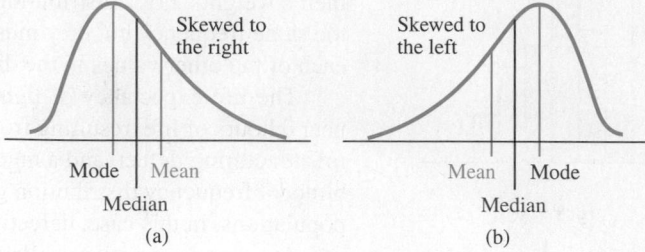

Figure 13.22

Normal Distributions

Each of these distributions is useful in describing sets of data. However, the most important distribution is the *normal* or *Gaussian distribution*, named for German mathematician Carl Friedrich Gauss. The histogram of a normal distribution is illustrated in Fig. 13.23.

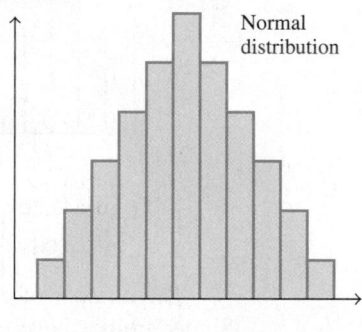

Figure 13.23

The normal distribution is important because many sets of data are normally distributed or closely resemble a normal distribution. Such distributions include intelligence quotients, heights and weights of males, heights and weights of females, lengths of full-grown boa constrictors, weights of watermelons, wearout mileage of automobile brakes, and life spans of refrigerators, to name just a few.

The normal distribution is symmetric about the mean. If you were to fold the histogram of a normal distribution down the middle, the left side would fit the right side exactly. **In a normal distribution, the mean, median, and mode all have the same value.**

When the histogram of a normal distribution is smoothed to form a curve, the curve is bell-shaped. The bell may be high and narrow or short and wide. Each of the three curves in Fig. 13.24 represents a normal curve. Curve 13.24(a) has the smallest standard deviation (spread from the mean); curve 13.24(c) has the largest.

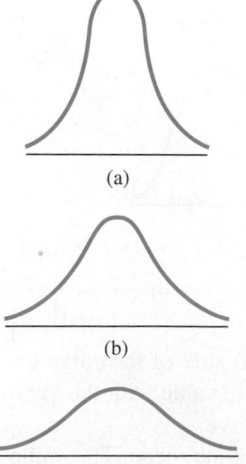

Figure 13.24

Properties of a Normal Distribution
- The graph of a normal distribution is called a normal curve.
- The normal curve is bell-shaped and symmetric about the mean.
- The mean, median, and mode of a normal distribution all have the same value and all occur at the center of the distribution.

Since the curve representing the normal distribution is symmetric, 50% of the data always falls above (to the right of) the mean and 50% of the data falls below (to the left of) the mean. In addition, every normal distribution has approximately 68% of the data between the value that is one standard deviation below the mean, and the value that is one standard deviation above the mean, see Fig. 13.25. Approximately 95% of the data falls between the value that is two standard deviations below the mean and the value that is two standard deviations above the mean. Approximately 99.7% of the data falls between the value that is three standard deviations below the mean, and the value that is three standard deviations above the mean. These three percentages, 68%, 95%, and 99.7%, are used in what is referred to as the *empirical rule*.

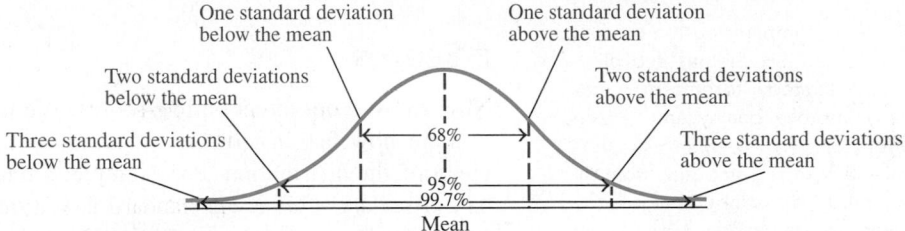

Figure 13.25

Thus, if a normal distribution has a mean of 100 and a standard deviation of 10, then approximately 68% of all the data falls between $100 - 10$ and $100 + 10$, or between 90 and 110. Approximately 95% of the data falls between $100 - 20$ and $100 + 20$, or between 80 and 120, and approximately 99.7% of the data falls between $100 - 30$, and $100 + 30$, or between 70 and 130.

The empirical rule is summarized as follows.

Empirical Rule

In any normal distribution.
- Approximately 68% of all the data lies within one standard deviation of the mean (in both directions).
- Approximately 95% of all the data lies within two standard deviations of the mean (in both directions).
- Approximately 99.7% of all the data lies within three standard deviations of the mean (in both directions).

Example 1 *Applying the Empirical Rule*

The cholesterol levels for females are normally distributed. In a random sample of 500 females, determine the approximate number of females in the sample who are expected to have a cholesterol level

a) within one standard deviation of the mean.

b) within two standard deviations of the mean.

Solution

a) By the empirical rule, about 68% of females have a cholesterol level within one standard deviation of the mean. Since there are 500 females in the sample, the number of females expected to have a cholesterol level within one standard deviation of the mean is

$$68\% \times 500 = 0.68 \times 500 = 340$$

Therefore, about 340 females are expected to have a cholesterol level within one standard deviation of the mean.

b) By the empirical rule, about 95% of females have a cholesterol level within two standard deviations the mean. Since there are 500 females in the sample, the number of females expected to have a cholesterol level within two standard deviations of the mean is

$$95\% \times 500 = 0.95 \times 500 = 475$$

Therefore, about 475 females are expected to have a cholesterol level within two standard deviations of the mean. ∎

z-Scores

Now we turn our attention to z-scores. We use *z-scores* (or *standard scores*) to determine how far, in terms of standard deviations, a given data value is from the mean of the distribution. For example, a data value that has a z-score of 1.5 indicates the data value is 1.5 standard deviations above the mean. The standard score or z-score is calculated as follows.

z-Scores or Standard Scores
The formula for finding **z-scores** or standard scores is

$$z = \frac{\text{value of the piece of data } - \text{ mean}}{\text{standard deviation}}$$

In this book, the notation z_x represents the z-score, or standard score, of the value x. For example, if a normal distribution has a mean of 86 with a standard deviation of 12, a score of 110 has a standard score or z-score of

$$z_{110} = \frac{110 - 86}{12} = \frac{24}{12} = 2$$

Therefore, a value of 110 in this distribution has a z-score of 2 and is two standard deviations above the mean.

Data below the mean will always have negative z-scores; data above the mean will always have positive z-scores. The mean will always have a z-score of 0.

Example 2 *Finding z-Scores*

A normal distribution has a mean of 80 and a standard deviation of 10. Determine z-scores for the following values.

a) 90   b) 95   c) 80   d) 64

Solution

a)
$$z = \frac{\text{value } - \text{ mean}}{\text{standard deviation}}$$

$$z_{90} = \frac{90 - 80}{10} = \frac{10}{10} = 1$$

A value of 90 has a z-score of 1. Therefore, a value of 90 is one standard deviation above the mean.

b)
$$z_{95} = \frac{95 - 80}{10} = \frac{15}{10} = 1.5$$

A value of 95 has a z-score of 1.5, and is 1.5 standard deviations above the mean.

c)
$$z_{80} = \frac{80 - 80}{10} = \frac{0}{10} = 0$$

The mean always has a z-score of 0.

d)
$$z_{64} = \frac{64 - 80}{10} = \frac{-16}{10} = -1.6$$

A value of 64 has a z-score of −1.6, and is 1.6 standard deviations below the mean. ∎

If we are given any normal distribution with a known mean and standard deviation, it is possible through the use of Table 13.7 on pages 822 and 823 (the z-table) to determine the percent of data between any two given values. The total area under any normal curve is 1.00. Table 13.7 will be used to determine the cumulative area under the normal curve that lies to the *left of a specified z-score*. We will use Table 13.7(a) when we wish to determine area to the left of a *negative z-score*, and we will use Table 13.7(b) when we wish to determine area to the left of a *positive z-score*.

Example 3 illustrates the procedure to follow when using Table 13.7 to determine the area under the normal curve. When you are determining the area under the normal curve, it is often helpful to draw a picture and shade the area to be determined.

Example 3 *Determining the Area Under the Normal Curve*

Determine the area under the normal curve
a) to the left of $z = -1.00$.
b) to the left of $z = 1.19$.
c) to the right of $z = 1.19$.
d) between $z = -1.62$ and $z = 2.57$.

Solution

a) To determine the area under the normal curve to the left of $z = -1.00$, as illustrated in Fig. 13.26, we use Table 13.7(a) since we are looking for an area to the left of a negative z-score. In the upper-left corner of the table, we see the letter z. The column under z gives the units and the tenths value for z. To locate the hundredths value of z, we use the column headings to the right of z. In this case, the hundredths value of $z = -1.00$ is 0, so we use the first column labeled .00. To determine the area to the left of $z = -1.00$, we use the row labeled −1.0 and move to the column labeled .00. The table entry, .1587, is circled in blue. Therefore, the total area to the left of $z = -1.00$ is 0.1587

b) To determine the area under the normal curve to the left of $z = 1.19$ (Fig. 13.27), we use Table 13.7(b) since we are looking for an area to the left of a positive z-score. We first look for 1.1 in the column under z. Since the hundredths value

Figure 13.26

Figure 13.27

Continued on p.824

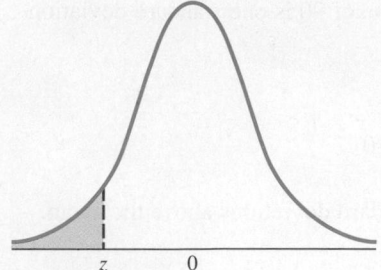

Table entry for z is the area to the left of z.

Table 13.7 Areas of a Standard Normal Distribution

(a) Table of Areas to the Left of z When z is Negative

z	.00	.01	.02	.03	.04	.05	.06	.07	.08	.09
−3.4	.0003	.0003	.0003	.0003	.0003	.0003	.0003	.0003	.0003	.0002
−3.3	.0005	.0005	.0005	.0004	.0004	.0004	.0004	.0004	.0004	.0003
−3.2	.0007	.0007	.0006	.0006	.0006	.0006	.0006	.0005	.0005	.0005
−3.1	.0010	.0009	.0009	.0009	.0008	.0008	.0008	.0008	.0007	.0007
−3.0	.0013	.0013	.0013	.0012	.0012	.0011	.0011	.0011	.0010	.0010
−2.9	.0019	.0018	.0018	.0017	.0016	.0016	.0015	.0015	.0014	.0014
−2.8	.0026	.0025	.0024	.0023	.0023	.0022	.0021	.0021	.0020	.0019
−2.7	.0035	.0034	.0033	.0032	.0031	.0030	.0029	.0028	.0027	.0026
−2.6	.0047	.0045	.0044	.0043	.0041	.0040	.0039	.0038	.0037	.0036
−2.5	.0062	.0060	.0059	.0057	.0055	.0054	.0052	.0051	.0049	.0048
−2.4	.0082	.0080	.0078	.0075	.0073	.0071	.0069	.0068	.0066	.0064
−2.3	.0107	.0104	.0102	.0099	.0096	.0094	.0091	.0089	.0087	.0084
−2.2	.0139	.0136	.0132	.0129	.0125	.0122	.0119	.0116	.0113	.0110
−2.1	.0179	.0174	.0170	.0166	.0162	.0158	.0154	.0150	.0146	.0143
−2.0	.0228	.0222	.0217	.0212	.0207	.0202	.0197	.0192	.0188	.0183
−1.9	.0287	.0281	.0274	.0268	.0262	.0256	.0250	.0244	.0239	.0233
−1.8	.0359	.0351	.0344	.0336	.0329	.0322	.0314	.0307	.0301	.0294
−1.7	.0446	.0436	.0427	.0418	.0409	.0401	.0392	.0384	.0375	.0367
−1.6	.0548	.0537	.0526	.0516	.0505	.0495	.0485	.0475	.0465	.0455
−1.5	.0668	.0655	.0643	.0630	.0618	.0606	.0594	.0582	.0571	.0559
−1.4	.0808	.0793	.0778	.0764	.0749	.0735	.0721	.0708	.0694	.0681
−1.3	.0968	.0951	.0934	.0918	.0901	.0885	.0869	.0853	.0838	.0823
−1.2	.1151	.1131	.1112	.1093	.1075	.1056	.1038	.1020	.1003	.0985
−1.1	.1357	.1335	.1314	.1292	.1271	.1251	.1230	.1210	.1190	(.1170)
−1.0	(.1587)	.1562	.1539	.1515	.1492	.1469	.1446	.1423	.1401	.1379
−0.9	.1841	.1814	.1788	.1762	.1736	.1711	.1685	.1660	.1635	.1611
−0.8	.2119	.2090	.2061	.2033	.2005	.1977	.1949	.1922	.1894	.1867
−0.7	.2420	.2389	.2358	.2327	.2296	.2266	.2236	.2206	.2177	.2148
−0.6	.2743	.2709	.2676	.2643	.2611	.2578	.2546	.2514	.2483	.2451
−0.5	.3085	.3050	.3015	.2981	.2947	.2912	.2877	.2843	.2810	.2776
−0.4	.3446	.3409	.3372	.3336	.3300	.3264	.3228	.3192	.3156	.3121
−0.3	.3821	.3783	.3745	.3707	.3669	.3632	.3594	.3557	.3520	.3483
−0.2	.4207	.4168	.4129	.4090	.4052	.4013	.3974	.3936	.3897	.3859
−0.1	.4602	.4562	.4522	.4483	.4443	.4404	.4364	.4325	.4286	.4247
−0.0	.5000	.4960	.4920	.4880	.4840	.4801	.4761	.4721	.4681	.4641

For z-scores less than −3.49, use 0.000 to approximate the area.

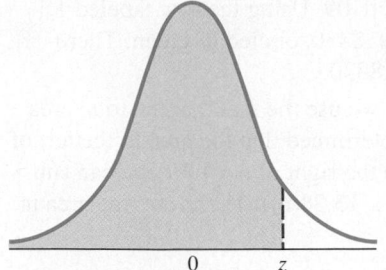

Table entry for z is the area to the left of z.

Table 13.7 Areas of a Standard Normal Distribution *(continued)*

(b) Table of Areas to the Left of z When z is Positive

z	.00	.01	.02	.03	.04	.05	.06	.07	.08	.09
0.0	.5000	.5040	.5080	.5120	.5160	.5199	.5239	.5279	.5319	.5359
0.1	.5398	.5438	.5478	.5517	.5557	.5596	.5636	.5675	.5714	.5753
0.2	.5793	.5832	.5871	.5910	.5948	.5987	.6026	.6064	.6103	.6141
0.3	.6179	.6217	.6255	.6293	.6331	.6368	.6406	.6443	.6480	.6517
0.4	.6554	.6591	.6628	.6664	.6700	.6736	.6772	.6808	.6844	.6879
0.5	.6915	.6950	.6985	.7019	.7054	.7088	.7123	.7157	.7190	.7224
0.6	.7257	.7291	.7324	.7357	.7389	.7422	.7454	.7486	.7517	.7549
0.7	.7580	.7611	.7642	.7673	.7704	.7734	.7764	.7794	.7823	.7852
0.8	.7881	.7910	.7939	.7967	.7995	.8023	.8051	.8078	.8106	.8133
0.9	.8159	.8186	.8212	.8238	.8264	.8289	.8315	.8340	.8365	.8389
1.0	.8413	.8438	.8461	.8485	.8508	.8531	.8554	.8577	.8599	.8621
1.1	.8643	.8665	.8686	.8708	.8729	.8749	.8770	.8790	.8810	.8830
1.2	.8849	.8869	.8888	.8907	.8925	.8944	.8962	.8980	.8997	.9015
1.3	.9032	.9049	.9066	.9082	.9099	.9115	.9131	.9147	.9162	.9177
1.4	.9192	.9207	.9222	.9236	.9251	.9265	.9279	.9292	.9306	.9319
1.5	.9332	.9345	.9357	.9370	.9382	.9394	.9406	.9418	.9429	.9441
1.6	.9452	.9463	.9474	.9484	.9495	.9505	.9515	.9525	.9535	.9545
1.7	.9554	.9564	.9573	.9582	.9591	.9599	.9608	.9616	.9625	.9633
1.8	.9641	.9649	.9656	.9664	.9671	.9678	.9686	.9693	.9699	.9706
1.9	.9713	.9719	.9726	.9732	.9738	.9744	.9750	.9756	.9761	.9767
2.0	.9772	.9778	.9783	.9788	.9793	.9798	.9803	.9808	.9812	.9817
2.1	.9821	.9826	.9830	.9834	.9838	.9842	.9846	.9850	.9854	.9857
2.2	.9861	.9864	.9868	.9871	.9875	.9878	.9881	.9884	.9887	.9890
2.3	.9893	.9896	.9898	.9901	.9904	.9906	.9909	.9911	.9913	.9916
2.4	.9918	.9920	.9922	.9925	.9927	.9929	.9931	.9932	.9934	.9936
2.5	.9938	.9940	.9941	.9943	.9945	.9946	.9948	.9949	.9951	.9952
2.6	.9953	.9955	.9956	.9957	.9959	.9960	.9961	.9962	.9963	.9964
2.7	.9965	.9966	.9967	.9968	.9969	.9970	.9971	.9972	.9973	.9974
2.8	.9974	.9975	.9976	.9977	.9977	.9978	.9979	.9979	.9980	.9981
2.9	.9981	.9982	.9982	.9983	.9984	.9984	.9985	.9985	.9986	.9986
3.0	.9987	.9987	.9987	.9988	.9988	.9989	.9989	.9989	.9990	.9990
3.1	.9990	.9991	.9991	.9991	.9992	.9992	.9992	.9992	.9993	.9993
3.2	.9993	.9993	.9994	.9994	.9994	.9994	.9994	.9995	.9995	.9995
3.3	.9995	.9995	.9995	.9996	.9996	.9996	.9996	.9996	.9996	.9997
3.4	.9997	.9997	.9997	.9997	.9997	.9997	.9997	.9997	.9997	.9998

For z-scores greater than 3.49, use 1.000 to approximate the area.

of $z = 1.19$ is 9, we move to the column labeled .09. Using the row labeled 1.1 and the column labeled 0.09, the table entry is .8830, circled in green. Therefore, the total area to the left of $z = 1.19$ is 0.8830.

c) To determine the area to the right of $z = 1.19$, we use the fact that the total area under the normal curve is 1. In part (b), we determined that the area to the left of $z = 1.19$ was 0.8830. To determine the area to the right of $z = 1.19$, we can subtract the area to the left of $z = 1.19$ from 1 (Fig. 13.28(a)). Therefore, the area to the right of $z = 1.19$ is $1 - 0.8830$, or 0.1170.

Figure 13.28

Another way to determine the area to the right of $z = 1.19$ is to use the fact that the normal curve is symmetric about the mean. Thus, the area to the left of a negative z-score is equal to the area to the right of a positive z-score. Therefore, the area to the left of $z = -1.19$ is equal to the area to the right of $z = 1.19$ (Fig. 13.28(b)). Using Table 13.7(a), we see that the area to the left of $z = -1.19$ is .1170. This value is circled in red in the table. Therefore, the area to the right of $z = 1.19$ is also .1170. This answer agrees with our answer obtained by subtracting the area to the left of $z = 1.19$ from 1.

d) To determine the area between two z-scores, we subtract the smaller area from the larger area (Fig. 13.29). Using Table 13.7(b), we see that the area to the left of $z = 2.57$ is .9949 (Fig. 13.29(a)). Using Table 13.7(a), we see that the area to the left of $z = -1.62$ is .0526 (Fig. 13.29(b)). Thus, the area between $z = -1.62$ and $z = 2.57$ is $0.9949 - 0.0526$, or 0.9423 (Fig. 13.29(c)).

Figure 13.29 ■

To change the area under the normal curve to a percent, multiply the area by 100%. In Example 3(a), we determined the area to the left of $z = -1.00$ to be 0.1587. To change this area to a percent, multiply 0.1587 by 100%.

$$0.1587 = 0.1587 \times 100\% = 15.87\%$$

Therefore 15.87% of the normal curve is less than a score that is one standard deviation below the mean.

Below, we summarize the procedure to determine the percent of data for any interval under the normal curve.

> **PROCEDURE** **TO DETERMINE THE PERCENT OF DATA BETWEEN ANY TWO VALUES IN A NORMAL DISTRIBUTION**
>
> 1. Draw a diagram of the normal curve, indicating the area or percent to be determined.
>
> 2. Use the formula $z = \dfrac{\text{value of the piece of data} - \text{mean}}{\text{standard deviation}}$ to convert the given values to z-scores. Indicate these z-scores on the diagram.
>
> 3. Look up the areas that correspond to the specified z-scores in Table 13.7.
>   a) When determining the area to the left of a negative z-score, use Table 13.7(a).
>
>
>
>   b) When determining the area to the left of a positive z-score, use Table 13.7(b).
>
>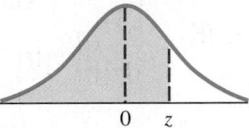
>
>   c) When determining the area to the right of a z-score, subtract the percent of data to the left of the specified z-score from 100%.
>
>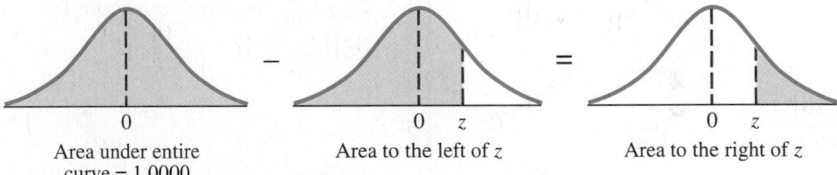
>
> | Area under entire curve = 1.0000 | Area to the left of z | Area to the right of z |
>
>   Or, use the symmetry of a normal distribution.
>
>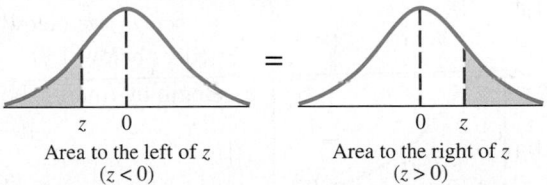
>
>   Area to the left of z Area to the right of z
> $(z < 0)$ $(z > 0)$
>
>   d) When determining the area between two z-scores, subtract the smaller area from the larger area.
>
>   In the figure below, we let z_1 represent the smaller z-score and z_2 represent the larger z-score.
>
>
>
>   Area to the left of z_2 Area to the left of z_1 Area between z_1 and z_2
>
> 4. Change the areas you determined in Step 3 to percents as explained on page 824.

Example 4 *IQ Scores*

Intelligence quotients (IQ scores) are normally distributed with a mean of 100 and a standard deviation of 15. Determine the percent of individuals with IQ scores
a) below 115.
b) below 130.
c) below 70.
d) between 70 and 115.
e) between 115 and 130.
f) above 122.5.

Solution

a) We want to determine the area under the normal curve below the value of 115, as illustrated in Fig. 13.30(a). Converting 115 to a z-score yields a z-score of 1.00.

$$z_{115} = \frac{115 - 100}{15} = \frac{15}{15} = 1.00$$

Figure 13.30

The percent of individuals with IQ scores below 115 is the same as the percent of data below a z-score of 1.00 (Fig. 13.30(b)). Since our z-score is positive, we use Table 13.7(b). From Table 13.7(b), we determine that the area to the left of a z-score of 1.00 is .8413. Therefore, 84.13% of all the IQ scores are below a z-score of 1.00. Thus, 84.13% of individuals have IQ scores below 115.

b) Begin by finding the z-score for 130.

$$z_{130} = \frac{130 - 100}{15} = \frac{30}{15} = 2.00$$

The percent of data below a z-score of 130 is the same as the percent of data below a z-score of 2.00 (Fig. 13.31). Using Table 13.7(b), we determine that the area to the left of a z-score of 2.00 is .9772. Therefore, 97.72% of the IQ scores are below a z-score of 2.00. Thus, 97.72% of all individuals have IQ scores below 130.

c) Begin by finding the z-score for 70.

$$z_{70} = \frac{70 - 100}{15} = \frac{-30}{15} = -2.00$$

The percent of data below a score of 70 is the same as the percent of data below a z-score of −2.00 (Fig. 13.32). Since our z-score is negative, we use Table 13.7(a). Using the table, we determine that the area to the left of $z = -2.00$ is .0228. Therefore, 2.28% of the data is below a z-score of −2.00. Thus, 2.28% of all individuals have IQ scores below 70.

d) In part (a), we determined that $z_{115} = 1.00$, and in part (c), we determined that $z_{70} = -2.00$. The percent of data below a z-score of 1.00 is 84.13% (Fig. 13.33(a) on page 827). The percent of data below a z-score of −2.00 is 2.28% (Fig. 13.33(b)). Since we want to find the percent of data between two z-scores, we subtract the smaller percent from the larger percent: 84.13% − 2.28% = 81.85% (Fig. 13.33(c)). Thus, 81.85% of all individuals have IQ scores between 70 and 115.

Figure 13.31

Figure 13.32

Figure 13.33

e) In part (a), we determined that $z_{115} = 1.00$, and in part (b), we determined $z_{130} = 2.00$. The percent of data below a z-score of 1.00 is 84.13%. The percent of data below a z-score of 2.00 is 97.72%. Since we want to find the percent of data between two z-scores, we subtract the smaller percent from the larger percent: 97.72% − 84.13% = 13.59% (Fig. 13.34). Thus, 13.59% of all individuals have IQ scores between 115 and 130.

f) Begin by determining a z-score for 122.5.

$$z_{122.5} = \frac{122.5 - 100}{15} = \frac{22.5}{15} = 1.50$$

The percent of IQ scores above 122.5 is the same as the percent of data above $z = 1.50$ (Fig. 13.35). To determine the percent of data above $z = 1.50$, we can determine the percent of data below $z = 1.50$ and subtract this percent from 100%. In Table 13.7(b), we see that the area to the left of $z = 1.50$ is .9332. Therefore, 93.32% of the IQ scores are below $z = 1.50$. The percent of IQ scores above $z = 1.50$ are 100% − 93.32%, or 6.68%. Thus, 6.68% of all IQ scores are greater than 122.5.

Figure 13.34

Figure 13.35

Example 5 *Horseback Rides*

Assume that the length of time for a horseback ride on the trail at Triple R Ranch is normally distributed with a mean of 3.2 hours and a standard deviation of 0.4 hour.

a) What percent of horseback rides last at least 3.2 hours?

b) What percent of horseback rides last less than 2.8 hours?

c) What percent of horseback rides are at least 3.7 hours?

d) What percent of horseback rides are between 2.8 hours and 4.0 hours?

e) In a random sample of 500 horseback rides at Triple R Ranch, how many are at least 3.7 hours?

Solution

a) In a normal distribution, half the data are always above the mean. Since 3.2 hours is the mean, half, or 50%, of the horseback rides last at least 3.2 hours.

b) Convert 2.8 hours to a z-score.

$$z_{2.8} = \frac{2.8 - 3.2}{0.4} = -1.00$$

Use Table 13.7(a) to find the area of the normal curve that lies below a z-score of −1.00. The area to the left of $z = -1.00$ is 0.1587. Therefore, the percent of horseback rides that last less than 2.8 hours is 15.87% (Fig. 13.36).

Figure 13.36

Figure 13.37

> **TIMELY TIP**
> Following is a summary of some important items presented in this section.
> - The normal curve is symmetric about the mean.
> - The area under the normal curve cannot be negative.
> - A negative z-score indicates that the corresponding value in the original distribution is less than the mean.
> - A positive z-score indicates that the corresponding value in the original distribution is greater than the mean.
> - A z-score of 0 indicates that the corresponding value in the original distribution is the mean.
> - Table 13.7 provides the area to the left of a specified z-score.
> - When using Table 13.7 to determine the area to the left of a specified z-score, locate the units value and tenths value of your specified z-score under the column labeled z. Then move to the column containing the hundredths value of your specified z-score to obtain the area.

c) At least 3.7 hours means greater than or equal to 3.7 hours. Therefore, we are seeking to find the percent of data to the right of 3.7 hours. Convert 3.7 hours to a z-score.

$$z_{3.7} = \frac{3.7 - 3.2}{0.4} = 1.25$$

From Table 13.7(b), we determine that the area to the left of $z = 1.25$ is .8944. Therefore, 89.44% of the data are below $z = 1.25$. The percent of data above $z = 1.25$ (or to the right of $z = 1.25$) is $100\% - 89.44\%$, or 10.56% (Fig. 13.37). Thus, 10.56% of horseback rides last at least 3.7 hours.

d) Convert 4.0 to a z-score.

$$z_{4.0} = \frac{4.0 - 3.2}{0.4} = 2.00$$

From Table 13.7(b), we determine that the area to the left of $z = 2.00$ is .9772 (Fig.13.38(a)). Therefore the percent of data below a z-score of 2.00 is 97.72%. From part (b), we determined that $z_{28} = -1.00$ and that the percent of data below a z-score of -1.00 is 15.87% (Fig. 13.38(b)). To find the percent of data between a z-score of -1.00 and a z-score of 2.00, we subtract the smaller percent from the larger percent. Thus, the percent of horseback rides that last between 2.8 hours and 4.0 hours is $97.72\% - 15.87\%$, or 81.85% (Fig. 13.38(c)).

Figure 13.38

e) In part (c), we determined that 10.56% of all horseback rides last at least 3.7 hours. We now multiply 0.1056 times the number in the random sample, 500, to determine the number of horseback rides that last at least 3.7 hours. There are $0.1056 \times 500 = 52.8$, or approximately 53, horseback rides that last at least 3.7 hours.   ∎

SECTION 13.6   *Exercises*

Warm Up Exercises

In Exercises 1–12, fill in the blank with an appropriate word, phrase, or symbol(s).

1. A distribution in which all the values have the same frequency is called a(n) _____ distribution. Rectangular

2. A distribution in which the frequency is either constantly increasing or constantly decreasing is called a(n) _____ distribution. J-shaped

3. A distribution that has a "tail" on its right is skewed to the _____. Right

4. A distribution that has a "tail" on its left is skewed to the _____. Left

5. A distribution in which two nonadjacent values occur more frequently than any other values in a set of data is called a(n) _____ distribution. Bimodal

6. A normal distribution is a(n) _____ shaped distribution. Bell

7. A measure of how far, in terms of standard deviations, a given data value is from the mean is called a z-score or a(n) _____ score. Standard

8. The mean of a set of data will always have a z-score of _____. 0

9. A piece of data that has a negative z-score is _____ the mean. Below

10. A piece of data that has a positive z-score is _____ the mean. Above

11. According to the empirical rule, in a normal distribution,

    a) approximately _____ % of the data lie within plus or minus 1 standard deviation of the mean, 68%

    b) approximately _____ % of the data lie within plus or minus 2 standard deviations of the mean, and 95%

    c) approximately _____ % of the data lie within plus or minus 3 standard deviations of the mean. 99.7%

12. In a normal distribution, the mean, median, and mode all have the same _____. Value

In Exercises 13–16, give an example of the type of distribution.

13. Rectangular
    Answers will vary.

14. Skewed
    Answers will vary.

15. J-shaped
    Answers will vary.

16. Bimodal
    Answers will vary.

For the distributions in Exercises 17–20, state whether you think the distribution would be normal, J-shaped, bimodal, rectangular, skewed left, or skewed right.

17. The wearout mileage of automobile tires Normal

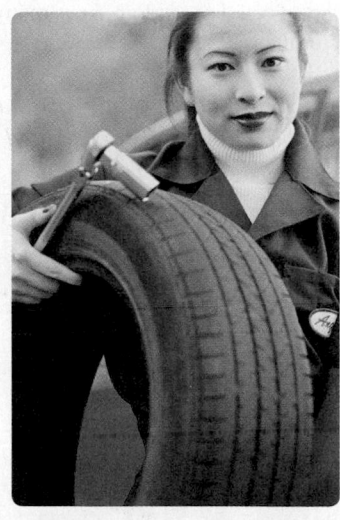

18. The numbers resulting from tossing a die many times
    Rectangular

19. The number of people per household in the United States
    Skewed right

20. The heights of a sample of high school seniors, where there are an equal number of males and females Bimodal

Practice the Skills

In Exercises 21–32, use Table 13.7 on pages 822 and 823 to find the specified area.

21. Above the mean 0.5000

22. Below the mean 0.5000

23. Between two standard deviations below the mean and one standard deviation above the mean 0.8185

24. Between 1.10 and 1.60 standard deviations above the mean 0.0809

25. To the right of $z = 1.53$
    0.0630

26. To the left of $z = 1.62$
    0.9474

27. To the left of $z = -1.78$
    0.0375

28. To the right of $z = -1.78$
    0.9625

29. Between $z = -1.32$ and $z = -1.64$ 0.0429

30. To the left of $z = 1.84$ 0.9671

31. To the left of $z = -2.13$ 0.0166

32. To the left of $z = -0.92$ 0.1788

In Exercises 33–42, use Table 13.7 on pages 822 and 823 to determine the percent of data specified.

33. Less than $z = 0.71$
    76.11%

34. Less than $z = -0.82$
    20.61%

35. Between $z = -1.34$ and $z = 2.24$ 89.74%

36. Between $z = -2.18$ and $z = -1.90$ 1.41%

37. Greater than $z = -1.90$ 97.13%

38. Greater than $z = 2.66$ 0.39%

39. Less than $z = 1.96$ 97.50%

40. Between $z = -1.53$ and $z = -1.82$ 2.86%

41. Between $z = 0.72$ and $z = 2.14$ 21.96%

42. Between $z = -2.15$ and $z = 3.31$ 98.37%

Problem Solving

Heights of Girls In Exercises 43 and 44, assume that the heights of 7-year-old girls are normally distributed. The heights of 8 girls are given in z-scores below.

Emily 0.9	Jenny 0.0	Heather −1.3	Shenice 0.0
Sarah 1.7	Sadaf −0.2	Carol 0.8	Kim −1.2

43. a) Which of these girls are taller than the mean?
       Emily, Sarah, Carol

    b) Which of these girls are at the mean? Jenny, Shenice

    c) Which of these girls are shorter than the mean?
       Sadaf, Heather, Kim

44. a) Which girl is the tallest? Sarah

    b) Which girl is the shortest? Heather

Police Officer's Salaries *In Exercises 45–48, assume the annual salaries of police officers are normally distributed with a mean of $50,000 and a standard deviation of $7000.*

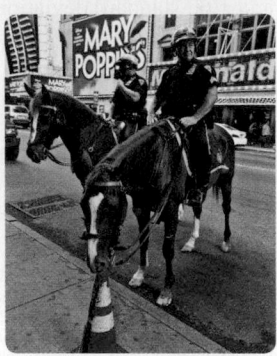

45. Determine the percent of police officers with an annual salary of at least $50,000. 50%

46. Determine the percent of police officers with an annual salary between $43,000 and $64,000. 81.85%

47. Determine the percent of police officers with an annual salary of at least $58,750. 10.56%

48. In a random sample of 500 police officers, how many have an annual salary of at least $58,750. ≈ 53 officers

SAT Scores *In Exercises 49–54, assume that the mathematics scores on the SAT are normally distributed with a mean of 500 and a standard deviation of 100.*

49. What percent of students who took the test have a mathematics score below 550? 69.15%

50. What percent of students who took the test have a mathematics score above 650? 6.68%

51. What percent of students who took the test have a mathematics score between 550 and 650? 24.17%

52. What percent of students who took the test have a mathematics score below 300? 2.28%

53. What percent of students who took the test have a mathematics score between 400 and 525? 44.00%

54. What percent of students who took the test have a mathematics score above 380? 88.49%

Vending Machine *In Exercises 55–58, a vending machine is designed to dispense a mean of 7.6 oz of coffee into an 8-oz cup. If the standard deviation of the amount of coffee dispensed is 0.4 oz and the amount is normally distributed, find the percent of times the machine will*

55. dispense from 7.4 oz to 7.7 oz. 29.02%

56. dispense less than 7.0 oz. 6.68%

57. dispense less than 7.7 oz. 59.87%

58. result in the cup overflowing (therefore dispense more than 8 oz). 15.87%

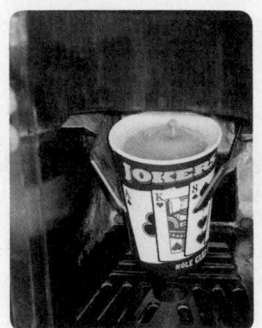

▲ *See Exercises 55–58*

Automobile Speed *In Exercises 59–64, assume that the speed of automobiles on an expressway during rush hour is normally distributed with a mean of 62 mph and a standard deviation of 5 mph.*

59. What percent of cars are traveling faster than 62 mph? 50.00%

60. What percent of cars are traveling between 58 mph and 66 mph? 57.62%

61. What percent of cars are traveling slower than 56 mph? 11.51%

62. What percent of cars are traveling faster than 70 mph? 5.48%

63. If 200 cars are selected at random, how many will be traveling slower than 56 mph? ≈ 23 cars

64. If 200 cars are selected at random, how many will be traveling faster than 70 mph? ≈ 11 cars

Corn Flakes *In Exercises 65–68, assume that the amount of corn flakes in a box is normally distributed with a mean of 16 oz and a standard deviation of 0.1 oz.*

65. Determine the percent of boxes that will contain between 15.83 oz and 16.32 oz of corn flakes. 95.47%

66. Determine the percent of boxes that will contain more than 16.16 oz of corn flakes. 5.48%

67. If the manufacturer produces 300,000 boxes, how many of them will contain less than 15.83 oz of corn flakes? 13,380 boxes

68. If the manufacturer produces 300,000 boxes, how many of them will contain more than 16.16 oz of corn flakes? 16,440 boxes

Cost of Day Care In Exercises 69–74, assume the annual day care cost per child is normally distributed with a mean of $8000 and a standard deviation of $1500.

69. What percent of day care costs are more than $7250 annually? 69.15%

70. What percent of day care costs are between $6500 and $8750 annually? 53.28%

71. What percent of day care costs are more than $11,750 annually? 0.62%

72. What percent of day care costs are less than $11,750 annually? 99.38%

73. In a random sample of 120 families, how many pay more than $7250 annually for day care per child? ≈ 83 families

74. In a random sample of 120 families, how many pay between $6500 and $8750 annually for day care per child? ≈ 64 families

75. *Weight Loss* A weight-loss clinic guarantees that its new customers will lose at least 5 lb by the end of their first month of participation or their money will be refunded. If the weight loss of customers at the end of their first month is normally distributed, with a mean of 6.7 lb and a standard deviation of 0.81 lb, determine the percent of customers who will be able to claim a refund. 1.79%

76. *Battery Warranty* The warranty on a car battery is 36 months. If the breakdown times of this battery are normally distributed with a mean of 46 months and a standard deviation of 8 months, determine the percent of batteries that can be expected to require repair or replacement under warranty. 10.56%

77. *Coffee Machine* A vending machine that dispenses coffee does not appear to be working correctly. The machine rarely gives the proper amount of coffee. Some of the time the cup is underfilled, and some of the time the cup overflows. Does this variation indicate that the mean number of ounces dispensed has to be adjusted, or does it indicate that the standard deviation of the amount of coffee dispensed by the machine is too large? The standard deviation is too large.

78. *Grading on a Normal Curve* Mr. Sanderson marks his class on a normal curve. Those with *z*-scores above 1.8 will receive an A, those between 1.8 and 1.1 will receive a B, those between 1.1 and −1.2 will receive a C, those between −1.2 and −1.9 will receive a D, and those under −1.9 will receive an F. Determine the percent of grades that will be A, B, C, D, and F. A: 3.59%, B: 9.98%, C: 74.92%, D: 8.64%, F: 2.87%

79. Consider the following normal curve, representing a normal distribution, with points *A*, *B*, and *C*. One of these points corresponds to the mean, one point corresponds to the mean plus one standard deviation and one point corresponds to the mean minus two standard deviations.

a) Which point corresponds to the mean? B

b) Which point corresponds to the mean plus one standard deviation? C

c) Which point corresponds to the mean minus two standard deviations? A

80. Consider the following two normal curves.

a) Do these distributions have the same mean? If so, what is the mean? Yes, 36

b) One of these curves corresponds to a normal distribution with a standard deviation of 1. The other curve corresponds to a normal distribution with a standard deviation of 3. Which curve, *A* or *B*, has a standard deviation of 3? B; since curve B is more spread out it has the higher standard deviation.

Concept/Writing Exercises

81. In a distribution that is skewed to the right, which has the greatest value: the mean, median, or mode? Which has the smallest value? Explain. The mean is the greatest value. The median is lower than the mean. The mode is the lowest value.

82. In a distribution skewed to the left, which has the greatest value: the mean, median, or mode? Which has the smallest value? Explain. The mode is the highest value. The median is lower than the mode. The mean is the lowest value.

83. List three populations other than those given in the text that may be normally distributed. Answers will vary.

84. List three populations other than those given in the text that may not be normally distributed. Answers will vary.

Challenge Problems/Group Activities

85. *Salesperson Promotion* The owner at Kim's Home Interiors is reviewing the sales records of two managers who are up for promotion, Katie and Stella, who work in different stores. At Katie's store, the mean sales have been $23,200 per month, with a standard deviation of $2170. At Stella's store, the mean sales have been $25,600 per month, with a standard deviation of $2300. Last month, Katie's store

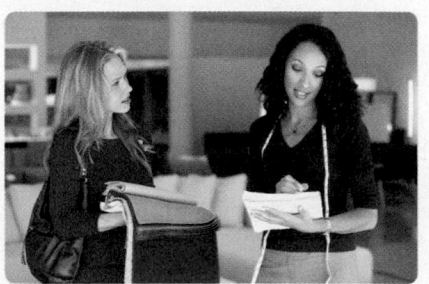

sales were \$28,408 and Stella's store sales were \$29,510. At both stores, the distribution of monthly sales is normal.

a) Convert last month's sales for Katie's store and for Stella's store to z-scores. Katie: $z = 2.4$; Stella: $z = 1.7$

b) If one of the two were to be promoted based solely on the increase in sales last month, who should be promoted? Explain. Katie. Her z-score is higher than Stella's z-score, which means her sales are further above the mean than Stella's sales.

86. *Chebyshev's Theorem* How can you determine whether a distribution is approximately normal? A statistical theorem called *Chebyshev's theorem* states that the *minimum percent* of data between plus and minus K standard deviations from the mean $(K > 1)$ in *any distribution* can be found by the formula

$$\text{Minimum percent} = 1 - \frac{1}{K^2}$$

Thus, for example, between ± 2 standard deviations from the mean there will always be a minimum of 75% of data. This minimum percent applies to any distribution. For $K = 2$,

$$\text{Minimum percent} = 1 - \frac{1}{2^2}$$

$$= 1 - \frac{1}{4} = \frac{3}{4}, \quad \text{or} \quad 75\%$$

Likewise, between ± 3 standard deviations from the mean there will always be a minimum of 89% of the data. For $K = 3$,

$$\text{Minimum percent} = 1 - \frac{1}{3^2}$$

$$= 1 - \frac{1}{9} = \frac{8}{9}, \quad \text{or} \quad 89\%$$

The following table lists the minimum percent of data in *any distribution* and the actual percent of data in *the normal distribution* between ± 1.1, ± 1.5, ± 2.0, and ± 2.5 standard deviations from the mean. The minimum percents of data in any distribution were calculated by using Chebyshev's theorem. The actual percents of data for the normal distribution were calculated by using the area given in the standard normal, or z, table.

	$K = 1.1$	$K = 1.5$	$K = 2$	$K = 2.5$
Minimum (for any distribution)	17.4%	55.6%	75%	84%
Normal distribution	72.9%	86.6%	95.4%	98.8%
Given distribution				

The third row of the chart has been left blank for you to fill in the percents when you reach part (e).

Consider the following 30 pieces of data obtained from a quiz.

1, 1, 1, 1, 2, 2, 2, 2, 3, 3, 4, 4, 4, 5, 6,

6, 6, 7, 7, 7, 7, 8, 8, 8, 8, 9, 9, 9, 10, 10

a) Determine the mean of the set of scores. ≈ 5.33

b) Determine the standard deviation of the set of scores. $\sqrt{8.99} \approx 3.00$

c) Determine the values that correspond to 1.1, 1.5, 2, and 2.5 standard deviations above the mean.
   Then determine the values that correspond to 1.1, 1.5, 2, and 2.5 standard deviations below the mean. 8.63, 9.83, 11.33, 12.83; 2.03, 0.83, −0.67, −2.17, respectively

d) By observing the 30 pieces of data, determine the actual percent of quiz scores between

   ± 1.1 standard deviations from the mean.

   ± 1.5 standard deviations from the mean.

   ± 2 standard deviations from the mean.

   ± 2.5 standard deviations from the mean. $\approx 56\%$, $\approx 93.3\%$, 100%, 100%

e) Place the percents found in part (d) in the third row of the chart. ≈ 56.7, $\approx 93.3\%$, 100%, 100%

f) Compare the percents in the third row of the chart with the minimum percents in the first row and the normal percents in the second row, and then make a judgment as to whether this set of 30 scores is approximately normally distributed. No

87. *Test Scores* Obtain a set of test scores from your instructor.

a) Determine the mean, median, mode, and midrange of the test scores. Answers will vary.

b) Determine the range and standard deviation of the set of scores. (You may round the mean to the nearest tenth when finding the standard deviation.) Answers will vary.

c) Construct a frequency distribution of the set of scores. Select your first class so that there will be between 5 and 12 classes. Answers will vary.

d) Construct a histogram and frequency polygon of the frequency distribution in part (c). Answers will vary.

e) Does the histogram in part (d) appear to represent a normal distribution? Explain. Answers will vary.

f) Use the procedure explained in Exercise 86 to determine whether the set of scores approximates a normal distribution. Explain. Answers will vary.

88. Determine a value of z such that $z \geq 0$ and 47.5% of the standard normal curve lies between 0 and the z-value. 1.96

89. Determine a value of z such that $z \leq 0$ and 38.1% of the standard normal curve lies between 0 and the z-value. −1.18

Recreational Mathematics

90. Ask your instructor for the class mean and class standard deviation for one of the exams taken by your class. For that exam, calculate the z-score for your exam grade. How many standard deviations is your exam grade away from the mean? Answers will vary.

91. If the mean score on a math quiz is 12.0 and 77% of the students in your class scored between 9.6 and 14.4, determine the standard deviation of the quiz scores. 2

Internet/Research Activity

92. In this project, you actually become the statistician.

a) Select a project of interest to you in which data must be collected.

b) Write a proposal and submit it to your instructor for approval. In the proposal, discuss the aims of your project and how you plan to gather the data to make your sample unbiased.

c) After your proposal has been approved, gather 50 pieces of data by the method you proposed.

d) Rank the data from smallest to largest.

e) Compute the mean, median, mode, and midrange.

f) Determine the range and standard deviation of the data. You may round the mean to the nearest tenth when computing the standard deviation.

g) Construct a frequency distribution, histogram, frequency polygon, and stem-and-leaf display of your data. Select your first class so that there will be between 5 and 12 classes. Be sure to label your histogram and frequency polygon.

h) Does your distribution appear to be normal? Explain your answer. Does it appear to be another type of distribution discussed? Explain.

i) Determine whether your distribution is approximately normal by using the technique discussed in Exercise 86.

SECTION 13.7 Linear Correlation and Regression

▲ *You can predict the value of a car based on the age of the car.*

Do you believe that there is a relationship between the time a person studies for an exam and the exam grade the person receives? Is there a relationship between the age of a car and the value of the car? Can we predict the value of a car based on the age of the car? In this section, we will learn how to determine whether there is a relationship between two quantities and, if so, how strong that relationship is. We will also learn how to determine the equation of the line that best describes the relationship between two quantities.

Why **This is Important** There are many real-life applications in which a relationship exists between two variables, such as the amount of time spent studying for an exam and the exam score.

In this section, we discuss two important statistical topics: correlation and regression. *Correlation* is used to determine whether there is a relationship between two quantities and, if so, how strong the relationship is. *Regression* is used to determine the equation that relates the two quantities. Although there are other types of correlation and regression, in this section we discuss only linear correlation and linear regression. We begin by discussing linear correlation.

Linear Correlation

The *linear correlation coefficient*, r, is a unitless measure that describes the strength of the linear relationship between two variables. A positive value of r, or a positive correlation, means that as one variable increases, the other variable also increases. A negative value of r, or a negative correlation, means that as one variable increases, the other variable decreases. The correlation coefficient, r, will always be a value between -1 and 1 inclusive. A value of 1 indicates the strongest possible positive correlation, a value of -1 indicates the strongest possible negative correlation, and a value of 0 indicates no correlation (Fig. 13.39).

Figure 13.39

A visual aid used with correlation is the *scatter diagram*, a plot of data points. To help understand how to construct a scatter diagram, consider the following data from Egan Electronics. During a 6-day period, Egan Electronics kept daily records of the number of assembly line workers absent and the number of defective parts produced. The information is provided in the following chart.

Day	1	2	3	4	5	6
Number of workers absent	3	5	0	1	2	6
Number of defective parts	15	22	7	12	20	30

For each of the 6 days, two pieces of data are provided: number of workers absent and number of defective parts. We call the set of data *bivariate data*. Often when we have a set of bivariate data, we can control one of the quantities. We generally denote the quantity that can be controlled, the *independent variable*, x. The other variable, the *dependent variable*, is denoted as y. In this problem, we will assume that the number of defective parts produced is affected by the number of workers absent. Therefore, we will call the number of workers absent x and the number of defective parts produced y. When we plot bivariate data, the independent variable is marked on the horizontal axis and the dependent variable is marked on the vertical axis. Therefore, for this problem, number of workers absent is marked on the horizontal axis and number of defective parts is marked on the vertical axis. If we plot the six pieces of bivariate data in the Cartesian coordinate system, we get a scatter diagram, as shown in Fig. 13.40.

Figure 13.40

The figure shows that, generally, the more workers that are absent, the more defective parts are produced.

In Fig. 13.41, we show some scatter diagrams and indicate the corresponding strength of correlation between the quantities on the horizontal and vertical axes.

Earlier, we mentioned that r will always be a value between -1 and 1 inclusive. A value of $r = 1$ is obtained only when every point of the bivariate data on a scatter diagram lies in a straight line and the line is increasing from left to right (Fig. 13.41(a)). In other words, the line has a positive slope, as discussed in Section 6.7.

A value of $r = -1$ will be obtained only when every point of the bivariate data on a scatter diagram lies in a straight line and the line is decreasing from left to right. (Fig. 13.41(e)). In other words, the line has a negative slope.

The value of r is a measure of how far a set of points varies from a straight line. The greater the spread, the weaker the correlation and the closer the value of r is to 0. Figure 13.41 shows that the more the points diverge from a straight line, the weaker the correlation becomes.

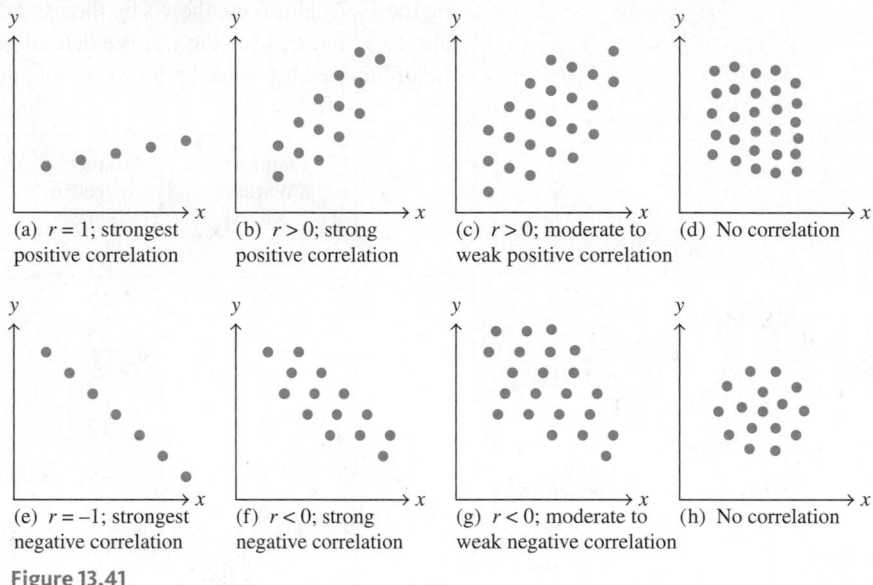

(a) $r = 1$; strongest positive correlation
(b) $r > 0$; strong positive correlation
(c) $r > 0$; moderate to weak positive correlation
(d) No correlation

(e) $r = -1$; strongest negative correlation
(f) $r < 0$; strong negative correlation
(g) $r < 0$; moderate to weak negative correlation
(h) No correlation

Figure 13.41

The following formula is used to calculate r.

Linear Correlation Coefficient

The formula to calculate the **correlation coefficient, r,** is as follows.

$$r = \frac{n(\Sigma xy) - (\Sigma x)(\Sigma y)}{\sqrt{n(\Sigma x^2) - (\Sigma x)^2}\,\sqrt{n(\Sigma y^2) - (\Sigma y)^2}}$$

To determine the correlation coefficient, r, and the equation of the line of best fit (to be discussed shortly), a statistical calculator may be used. On the statistical calculator, you enter the ordered pairs, (x, y) and press the appropriate keys. At the end of this section, we indicate the procedure to follow to use the computer software spreadsheet program, Microsoft Excel, and the TI-83 Plus or the TI-84 Plus calculators to determine the correlation coefficient.

In Example 1, we show how to determine r for a set of bivariate data without the use of a statistical calculator. We will use the same set of bivariate data given on page 834 that was used to make the scatter diagram in Fig. 13.40.

Example 1   *Number of Absences Versus Number of Defective Parts*

Egan Electronics provided the following daily records about the number of assembly line workers absent and the number of defective parts produced for 6 days. Determine the correlation coefficient between the number of workers absent and the number of defective parts produced.

Day	1	2	3	4	5	6
Number of workers absent	3	5	0	1	2	6
Number of defective parts	15	22	7	12	20	30

Solution We plotted this set of data on the scatter diagram in Fig. 13.40 on page 834. We will call the number of workers absent x. We will call the number of defective parts produced y. We list the values of x and y and calculate the necessary sums: $\Sigma x, \Sigma y, \Sigma xy, \Sigma x^2, \Sigma y^2$. We determine the values in the column labeled x^2 by squaring the x's (multiplying the x's by themselves). We determine the values in the column labeled y^2 by squaring the y's. We determine the values in the column labeled xy by multiplying each x-value by its corresponding y-value.

Number of Workers Absent	Number of Defective Parts			
x	y	x^2	y^2	xy
3	15	9	225	45
5	22	25	484	110
0	7	0	49	0
1	12	1	144	12
2	20	4	400	40
6	30	36	900	180
17	106	75	2202	387

Thus, $\Sigma x = 17$, $\Sigma y = 106$, $\Sigma x^2 = 75$, $\Sigma y^2 = 2202$, and $\Sigma xy = 387$. In the formula for r, we use both $(\Sigma x)^2$ and Σx^2. Note that $(\Sigma x)^2 = (17)^2 = 289$ and that $\Sigma x^2 = 75$. Similarly, $(\Sigma y)^2 = (106)^2 = 11{,}236$ and $\Sigma y^2 = 2202$.

The n in the formula represents the number of pieces of bivariate data. Here $n = 6$. Now let's determine r.

$$r = \frac{n(\Sigma xy) - (\Sigma x)(\Sigma y)}{\sqrt{n(\Sigma x^2) - (\Sigma x)^2}\ \sqrt{n(\Sigma y^2) - (\Sigma y)^2}}$$

$$= \frac{6(387) - (17)(106)}{\sqrt{6(75) - (17)^2}\ \sqrt{6(2202) - (106)^2}}$$

$$= \frac{2322 - 1802}{\sqrt{6(75) - 289}\sqrt{6(2202) - 11{,}236}}$$

$$= \frac{520}{\sqrt{450 - 289}\sqrt{13{,}212 - 11{,}236}}$$

$$= \frac{520}{\sqrt{161}\sqrt{1976}} \approx 0.922$$

Since the maximum possible value for r is 1.00, a correlation coefficient of 0.922 is a strong, positive correlation. This result implies that, generally, the more assembly line workers absent, the more defective parts produced.   ∎

In Example 1, had we found r to be a value greater than 1 or less than -1, it would have indicated that we had made an error. Also, from the scatter diagram, we should realize that r should be a positive value and not negative.

Table 13.8 Correlation
Coefficient, r

n	$\alpha = 0.05$	$\alpha = 0.01$
4	0.950	0.990
5	0.878	0.959
6	0.811	0.917
7	0.754	0.875
8	0.707	0.834
9	0.666	0.798
10	0.632	0.765
11	0.602	0.735
12	0.576	0.708
13	0.553	0.684
14	0.532	0.661
15	0.514	0.641
16	0.497	0.623
17	0.482	0.606
18	0.468	0.590
19	0.456	0.575
20	0.444	0.561
22	0.423	0.537
27	0.381	0.487
32	0.349	0.449
37	0.325	0.418
42	0.304	0.393
47	0.288	0.372
52	0.273	0.354
62	0.250	0.325
72	0.232	0.302
82	0.217	0.283
92	0.205	0.267
102	0.195	0.254

The derivation of this table is beyond the scope of this text. It shows the critical values of the Pearson correlation coefficient.

In Example 1, there appears to be a cause–effect relationship. That is, the more assembly line workers who are absent, the more defective parts are produced. *However, a correlation does not necessarily indicate a cause–effect relationship.* For example, there is a positive correlation between police officers' salaries and the cost of medical insurance over the past 10 years (both have increased), but that does not mean that the increase in police officers' salaries caused the increase in the cost of medical insurance.

Suppose in Example 1 that r had been 0.53. Would this value have indicated a correlation? What is the minimum value of r needed to assume that a correlation exists between the variables? To answer this question, we introduce the term *level of significance*. The *level of significance*, denoted α (alpha), is used to identify the cutoff between results attributed to chance and results attributed to an actual relationship between the two variables. Table 13.8 gives *critical values** (or cutoff values) that are sometimes used for determining whether two variables are related. The table indicates two different levels of significance: $\alpha = 0.05$ and $\alpha = 0.01$. A level of significance of 5%, written $\alpha = 0.05$, means that there is a 5% chance that, when you say the variables are related, they actually are *not* related. Similarly, a level of significance of 1%, or $\alpha = 0.01$, means that there is a 1% chance that, when you say the variables are related, they actually are *not* related. More complete critical value tables are available in statistics books.

To explain the use of the table, we use *absolute value*, symbolized $|\ \ |$. The absolute value of a nonzero number is the positive value of the number, and the absolute value of 0 is 0. Therefore,

$$|3| = 3, \quad |-3| = 3, \quad |5| = 5, \quad |-5| = 5, \quad \text{and} \quad |0| = 0$$

If the absolute value of r, written $|r|$, is *greater than* the value given in the table under the specified α and appropriate sample size n, we assume that a correlation does exist between the variables. If $|r|$ is less than the table value, we assume that no correlation exists.

Returning to Example 1, if we want to determine whether there is a correlation at a 5% level of significance, we find the critical value (or cutoff value) that corresponds to $n = 6$ (there are 6 pieces of bivariate data) and $\alpha = 0.05$. The value to the right of $n = 6$ and under the $\alpha = 0.05$ column is the critical value 0.811. From the formula, we had obtained $r = 0.922$. Since $|0.922| > 0.811$, or $0.922 > 0.811$, we assume that a correlation between the variables exists.

Note in Table 13.8 that the larger the sample size, the smaller is the value of r needed for a significant correlation.

Example 2   *Amount of Drug Remaining in the Bloodstream*

To test the length of time that an infection-fighting drug stays in a person's bloodstream, a doctor gives 300 milligrams of the drug to 10 patients, labeled 1–10 in the table below. Once each hour, for 10 hours, one of the 10 patients is selected at random and that person's blood is tested to determine the amount of the drug remaining in the bloodstream. The results are as follows.

Patient	1	2	3	4	5	6	7	8	9	10
Time (hr)	1	2	3	4	5	6	7	8	9	10
Drug remaining (mg)	250	230	200	210	140	120	210	100	90	85

---

*This table of values may be used only under certain conditions. If you take a statistics course, you will learn more about which critical values to use to determine whether a linear correlation exists.

Determine at a level of significance of 5% whether a correlation exists between the time elapsed and the amount of drug remaining.

Solution   Let time be represented by x and the amount of drug remaining by y. We first draw a scatter diagram (Fig. 13.42).

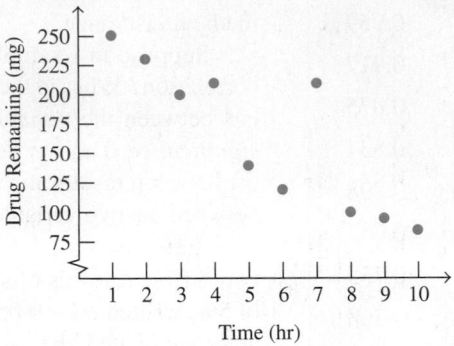

Figure 13.42

The scatter diagram suggests that, if a correlation exists, it will be negative. We now construct a table of values and calculate r.

x	y	x^2	y^2	xy
1	250	1	62,500	250
2	230	4	52,900	460
3	200	9	40,000	600
4	210	16	44,100	840
5	140	25	19,600	700
6	120	36	14,400	720
7	210	49	44,100	1470
8	100	64	10,000	800
9	90	81	8100	810
10	85	100	7225	850
55	1635	385	302,925	7500

$$r = \frac{n(\Sigma xy) - (\Sigma x)(\Sigma y)}{\sqrt{n(\Sigma x^2) - (\Sigma x)^2}\sqrt{n(\Sigma y^2) - (\Sigma y)^2}}$$

$$= \frac{10(7500) - (55)(1635)}{\sqrt{10(385) - (55)^2}\sqrt{10(302,925) - (1635)^2}}$$

$$= \frac{-14,925}{\sqrt{825}\sqrt{356,025}} \approx \frac{-14,925}{17,138.28} \approx -0.871$$

From Table 13.8, for $n = 10$ and $\alpha = 0.05$, we get 0.632. Since $|-0.871| = 0.871$ and $0.871 > 0.632$, a correlation exists. The correlation is negative, which indicates that the longer the time period, the smaller is the amount of drug remaining. ∎

Figure 13.43

Linear Regression

Let's now turn to regression. *Linear regression* is the process of determining the linear relationship between two variables. Recall from Section 6.7 that the slope–intercept form of a straight line is $y = mx + b$, where m is the slope and b is the y-intercept.

Using the set of bivariate data, we will determine the equation of *the line of best fit*. The line of best fit is also called *the regression line*, or *the least squares line*. The *line of best fit* is the line such that the sum of the squares of the vertical distances from the line to the data points (on the scatter diagram) is a minimum, as shown in Fig. 13.43. In Fig. 13.43, the line of best fit minimizes the sum of d_1 through d_8. To determine the equation of the line of best fit, $y = mx + b$,* we must find m and then b. The formulas for finding m and b are as follows.*

The Line of Best Fit
The equation of the line of best fit is

$$y = mx + b,$$

where $m = \dfrac{n(\Sigma xy) - (\Sigma x)(\Sigma y)}{n(\Sigma x^2) - (\Sigma x)^2}$ and $b = \dfrac{\Sigma y - m(\Sigma x)}{n}$

Note that the numerator of the fraction used to find m is identical to the numerator used to find r. Therefore, if you have previously found r, you do not need to repeat this calculation. Also, the denominator of the fraction used to find m is identical to the radicand of the first square root in the denominator of the fraction used to find r.

Example 3 *The Line of Best Fit*

a) Use the data in Example 1 on pages 835–836 to find the equation of the line of best fit that relates the number of workers absent on an assembly line and the number of defective parts produced.

b) Graph the equation of the line of best fit on a scatter diagram that illustrates the set of bivariate points.

Solution

a) In Example 1, we found $n(\Sigma xy) - (\Sigma x)(\Sigma y) = 520$ and $n(\Sigma x^2) - (\Sigma x)^2 = 161$. Thus,

$$m = \frac{n(\Sigma xy) - (\Sigma x)(\Sigma y)}{n(\Sigma x^2) - (\Sigma x)^2} = \frac{520}{161} \approx 3.23$$

Now we find the y-intercept, b. In Example 1, we found $n = 6$, $\Sigma x = 17$, and $\Sigma y = 106$.

$$b = \frac{\Sigma y - m(\Sigma x)}{n}$$

$$\approx \frac{106 - 3.23(17)}{6} \approx \frac{51.09}{6} \approx 8.52$$

---

*Some statistics books use $y = ax + b$, $y = b_0 + b_1 x$, or something similar, for the equation of the line of best fit. In any case, the letter next to the variable x represents the slope of the line of best fit, and the other letter represents the y-intercept of the graph.

Therefore, the equation of the line of best fit is

$$y = mx + b$$
$$y = 3.23x + 8.52$$

where x represents the number of workers absent and y represents the predicted number of defective parts produced.

b) To graph $y = 3.23x + 8.52$, we need to plot at least two points. We will plot three points and then draw the graph.

	$y = 3.23x + 8.52$		x	y
$x = 2$	$y = 3.23(2) + 8.52 = 14.98$		2	14.98
$x = 4$	$y = 3.23(4) + 8.52 = 21.44$		4	21.44
$x = 6$	$y = 3.23(6) + 8.52 = 27.90$		6	27.90

These three calculations indicate that if 2 assembly line workers are absent on the assembly line, the predicted number of defective parts produced is about 15. If 4 assembly line workers are absent, the predicted number of defective parts produced is about 21, and if 6 assembly line workers are absent, the predicted number of defective parts produced is about 28. Plot the three points (the three black points in Fig. 13.44) and then draw a straight line through the three points. The scatter diagram and graph of the equation of the line of best fit are plotted in Fig. 13.44.

Figure 13.44

In Example 3, the line of best fit intersects the y-axis at 8.52, the value we determined for the y-intercept, b, in part (a).

Example 4   *Line of Best Fit for Example 2*

a) Determine the equation of the line of best fit between the time elapsed and the amount of drug remaining in a person's bloodstream in Example 2 on pages 837–838.

b) If the average person is given 300 mg of the drug, how much will remain in the person's bloodstream after 5 hr?

Solution

a) From the scatter diagram on page 838, we see that the slope of the line of best fit, m, will be negative. In Example 2, we found that $n(\Sigma xy) - (\Sigma x)(\Sigma y) = -14{,}925$ and that $n(\Sigma x^2) - (\Sigma x)^2 = 825$. Thus,

$$m = \frac{n(\Sigma xy) - (\Sigma x)(\Sigma y)}{n(\Sigma x^2) - (\Sigma x)^2}$$

$$= \frac{-14{,}925}{825}$$

$$\approx -18.09$$

From Example 2, $n = 10$, $\Sigma x = 55$, and $\Sigma y = 1635$.

$$b = \frac{\Sigma y - m\Sigma x}{n}$$

$$= \frac{1635 - (-18.09)(55)}{10}$$

$$\approx 263.00$$

Thus, the equation of the line of best fit is

$$y = mx + b$$
$$y = -18.09x + 263.00$$

where x is the elapsed time and y is the amount of drug remaining.

b) We evaluate $y = -18.09x + 263.00$ at $x = 5$.

$$y = -18.09x + 263.00$$
$$y = -18.09(5) + 263.00 = 172.55$$

Thus, after 5 hr, about 173 mg of the drug remains in the average person's bloodstream. ∎

TECHNOLOGY TIP

We can use EXCEL and both the TI-83 Plus and the TI-84 Plus graphing calculators to determine the correlation coefficient, r, and the equation of the line of best fit. Below we use the data from Example 1 on page 835–836, where x represents the number of workers absent and y represents the number of defective parts for 6 selected days.

Excel

Begin by reading the *Technology Tip* on page 802. The instructions for determining the correlation coefficient and equation of the line of best fit are similar to the instructions given on page 802. In column A, rows 1 through 6, enter the 6 values representing the number of workers absent. In column B, rows 1 through 6, enter the 6 values that represent the number of defective parts. In general, the items listed on the horizontal axis in the scatter diagram (the independent variable if there is one) are placed in column A and the items listed on the vertical axis are placed in column B. Then select the following:

Insert > Function ... > Statistical

Then to determine the value of the correlation coefficient, select **CORREL** and click $\boxed{\text{OK}}$. Excel will then generate a gray box and ask you for information about your data. In the box to the right of **Array1**, type in A1:A6, and in the box to the right of **Array2**, type in B1:B6. Then at the bottom of the box you will see *Formula results = .921927852*, which is the correlation coefficient. If you then wish to find the equation of the line of best fit, press $\boxed{\text{CANCEL}}$ on the bottom of the gray box. Then select

Insert > Function ... > Statistical > SLOPE > OK

Excel will then generate a gray box. In the box to the right of **Known_y's**, type in B1:B6. In the box to the right of **Known_x's**, type in A1:A6. At that point, at the bottom of the box you will see *Formula results = 3.229813665*, which is the slope of the equation of the line of best fit. To find the y-intercept, press cancel to remove the gray box. Then select

Insert > Function ... > Statistical ... > INTERCEPT > OK

Excel will then generate a gray box. In the box to the right of **Known_y's**, type in B1:B6. In the box to the right of **Known_x's**, type in A1:A6. At that point, at the bottom of the box you will see *Formula results* = 8.51552795, which is the *y*-intercept of the equation of the line of best fit.

TI-83 Plus And TI-84 Plus Graphing Calculators
To determine the correlation coefficient and the equation of the line of best fit on a graphing calculator, press $\boxed{\text{STAT}}$. Then select Edit. If you have any data in **L1** or **L2**, delete the data by going to **L1** and pressing $\boxed{\text{CLEAR}}$ and then $\boxed{\text{ENTER}}$. Follow a similar procedure to clear column **L2**. Now enter the 6 pieces of data representing the number of workers absent in column **L1** and enter the 6 pieces of data representing the number of defective parts in **L2**. Then press $\boxed{\text{STAT}}$ and highlight **CALC**. At this point, **1: 1 – Var Stats** should be highlighted. Scroll down to highlight **4: LinReg (ax+b)**. Then press the Enter key twice. You will get *r* = .921927852, which represents the correlation coefficient. On the screen, you will also see values for *a* and *b*. Note that *a* represents the slope and *b* represents the *y*-intercept of the equation of the line of best fit. Thus, the slope is 3.229813665 and the *y*-intercept is 8.51552795.

SECTION 13.7   *Exercises*

Warm Up Exercises

In Exercises 1–10, fill in the blank with an appropriate word, phrase, or symbol(s).

1. A unitless measure that describes the strength of the linear relationship between two variables is called the linear correlation _____. Coefficient

2. The process of determining the linear relationship between two variables is called linear _____. Regression

3. The value of *r*, the linear correlation coefficient, that represents the strongest positive correlation is _____. 1

4. The value of *r*, the linear correlation coefficient, that represents the strongest negative correlation is _____. −1

5. The value of *r*, the linear correlation coefficient, that represents no correlation between two variables is _____. 0

6. If one quantity increases as the other quantity decreases, the two variables are said to have a(n) _____ correlation. Negative

7. If one quantity increases as the other quantity increases, the two variables are said to have a(n) _____ correlation. Positive

8. A plot of data points is called a(n) _____ diagram. Scatter

9. The line such that the sum of the squares of the vertical distances between the data points in the scatter diagram and the line is a minimum is called the line of best _____. Fit

10. The cutoff between results attributed to chance and results attributed to an actual relationship between two variables is called the level of _____. Significance

In Exercises 11–14, indicate if you believe that a correlation exists between the quantities on the horizontal and vertical axis. If so, indicate if you believe that the correlation is a strong positive correlation, a strong negative correla- tion, a weak positive correlation, a weak negative correlation, or no correlation. Explain your answer.

11.
No correlation

12.
Weak negative correlation

13.
Strong positive correlation

14.
Strong negative correlation

Practice the Skills

In Exercises 15–22, assume that a sample of bivariate data yields the correlation coefficient, r, indicated. Use Table 13.8 on page 837 for the specified sample size and level of significance to determine whether a linear correlation exists.

15. *r* = 0.87 when *n* = 10 at *α* = 0.01 Yes

16. *r* = 0.43 when *n* = 27 at *α* = 0.01 No

17. *r* = −0.92 when *n* = 6 at *α* = 0.05 Yes

18. *r* = −0.49 when *n* = 11 at *α* = 0.05 No

19. *r* = −0.23 when *n* = 102 at *α* = 0.01 No

20. *r* = −0.49 when *n* = 18 at *α* = 0.01 No

21. *r* = 0.75 when *n* = 6 at *α* = 0.01 No

22. *r* = 0.96 when *n* = 5 at *α* = 0.01 Yes

In Exercises 23–30, (a) draw a scatter diagram; (b) determine the value of r, rounded to the nearest thousandth;(c) determine whether a correlation exists at α = 0.05; and (d) determine whether a correlation exists at α = 0.01.

23.

x	y
5	8
6	10
7	12
8	12
11	16

24.

x	y
7	14
9	12
12	10
15	11
18	8

25.

x	y
23	29
35	37
31	26
43	20
49	39

26.

x	y
90	3
80	4
60	6
60	5
40	5
20	7

27.

x	y
5.3	10.3
4.7	9.6
8.4	12.5
12.7	16.2
4.9	9.8

28.

x	y
12	15
16	19
13	45
24	30
100	60
50	28

29.

x	y
100	2
80	3
60	5
60	6
40	6
20	8

30.

x	y
90	90
70	70
65	65
60	60
50	50
40	40
15	15

In Exercises 31–38, determine the equation of the line of best fit from the data in the exercise indicated. Round both the slope and the y-intercept to the nearest hundredth.

31. Exercise 23
$y = 1.26x + 2.25$

32. Exercise 24
$y = -0.46x + 16.57$

33. Exercise 25
$y = 0.18x + 23.82$

34. Exercise 26
$y = -0.05x + 7.84$

35. Exercise 27
$y = 0.81x + 5.84$

36. Exercise 28
$y = 0.36x + 19.99$

37. Exercise 29
$y = -0.08x + 9.50$

38. Exercise 30
$y = 1.00x$

Problem Solving

In Exercises 39–49, round both the slope and y-intercept to the nearest hundredth.

39. *Fitness* Six students provided the following data about the number of sit-ups completed and the number of push-ups completed during a fitness test in their physical education class.

Sit-ups	50	53	60	35	43	62
Push-ups	40	42	45	25	34	45

a) Determine the correlation coefficient between the number of sit-ups completed and the number of push-ups completed. 0.974

b) Determine whether a correlation exists at α = 0.05. Yes

c) Determine the equation of the line of best fit for the number of sit-ups completed and the number of push-ups completed. $y = 0.74x + 1.26$

40. *Amount of Fat in Chicken Nuggets* The June 2010 issue of *Consumer Reports* provided the following information regarding the number of calories and the number of grams of fat per 3-ounce serving of chicken nuggets for the 6 top-rated chicken nuggets.

Calories	210	310	240	210	160	130
Fat (grams)	10	21	16	13	8	4

a) Determine the correlation coefficient between the number of calories and the number of grams of fat. 0.980

b) Determine whether a correlation exists at α = 0.05. Yes

c) Determine the equation of the line of best fit for the number of calories and the number of grams of fat. $y = 0.09x - 7.73$

41. *Time Spent Studying* Six students provided the following data on page 844 about the lengths of time they studied for a psychology exam and the grades they received on the exam.

*See Instructor Answer Appendix

Time studied (minutes)	20	40	50	60	80	100
Grade received (percent)	40	45	70	76	92	95

a) Determine the correlation coefficient between the length of time studied and the grade received. 0.950

b) Determine whether a correlation exists at $\alpha = 0.01$. Yes

c) Find the equation of the line of best fit for the length of time studied and the grade received $y = 0.77x + 24.86$

42. **Price of a Home**   The following table shows the listing price and the selling price, in thousands of dollars, for eight houses listed and sold.

List price (thousands $)	139	165	210	287	189	115	125	95
Sale price (thousands $)	120	165	208	275	160	100	118	90

a) Determine the correlation coefficient between the listing price and the selling price of a house. 0.988

b) Determine whether a correlation exists at $\alpha = 0.01$. Yes

c) Determine the equation of the line of best fit for the listing price and selling price of a house. $y = 0.99x - 9.17$

d) Use the equation in part (c) to estimate the selling price of a house listed for $130,000. ≈$120,000

43. **Blood Pressure**   The following table shows the systolic blood pressure and diastolic blood pressure readings for six adults.

Systolic	110	153	120	143	100	112
Diastolic	70	110	80	98	70	75

a) Determine the correlation coefficient between the systolic blood pressure and the diastolic blood pressure readings. 0.984

b) Determine whether a correlation exists at $\alpha = 0.05$. Yes

c) Determine the equation of the line of best fit for the systolic blood pressure and the diastolic blood pressure readings. $y = 0.79x - 12.98$

d) Use the equation in part (c) to estimate the diastolic blood pressure for an adult with a systolic blood pressure reading of 115. ≈78

44. **Selling Popcorn at the Movies**   The number of movie tickets sold and the number of units of popcorn sold at AMC Cinema for 8 days is shown below.

Ticket sales	89	110	125	92	100	95	108	97
Units of popcorn	22	28	30	26	22	21	28	25

a) Determine the correlation coefficient between ticket sales and units of popcorn sold. 0.800

b) Determine whether a correlation exists at $\alpha = 0.05$. Yes

c) Determine the equation of the line of best fit for tickets sold and units of popcorn sold. $y = 0.23x + 2.26$

d) Use the equation in part (c) to estimate the units of popcorn sold if 115 tickets are sold. ≈29 units

45. **Fuel Efficiency of Cars**   The following table shows the weights, in hundreds of pounds, for six selected cars. Also shown is the corresponding fuel efficiency, in miles per gallon (mpg), for the car in city driving.

Weight (hundreds of pounds)	27	31	35	32	30	30
Fuel efficiency (mpg)	23	22	20	21	24	22

a) Determine the correlation coefficient between the weight of a car and the fuel efficiency. −0.804

b) Determine whether a correlation exists at $\alpha = 0.01$. No

c) Determine the equation of the line of best fit for the weight of a car and the fuel efficiency of a car.
$y = -0.43x + 35.28$

d) Use the equation in part (c) to estimate the fuel efficiency of a car that weighs 33 hundred pounds. 21.1 mpg

46. **City Muggings**   In a certain section of a city, muggings have been a problem. The number of police officers patrolling that section of the city has varied. The following chart shows the number of police officers and the number of muggings for 8 successive days.

Police officers	20	12	18	15	22	10	20	12
Muggings	8	10	12	9	6	15	7	18

a) Determine the correlation coefficient for number of police officers and number of muggings. −0.782

b) Determine whether a correlation exists at $\alpha = 0.05$. Yes

c) Find the equation of the line of best fit for number of police officers and number of muggings. $y = -0.72x + 22.26$

d) Use the equation in part (c) to estimate the average number of muggings when 14 police officers are patrolling that section of the city. 12.2 muggings

47. *Chlorine in a Swimming Pool* A gallon of chlorine is put into a swimming pool. Each hour later for the following 6 hours the percent of chlorine that remains in the pool is measured. The following information is obtained.

Time	1	2	3	4	5	6
Chlorine remaining (percent)	80.0	76.2	68.7	50.1	30.2	20.8

a) Determine the correlation coefficient for time and percent of chlorine remaining. −0.977

b) Determine whether a correlation exists at $\alpha = 0.01$. Yes

c) Determine the equation of the line of best fit for time and amount of chlorine remaining. $y = -12.93x + 99.59$

d) Use the equation in part (c) to estimate the average amount of chlorine remaining after 4.5 hr. 41.4%

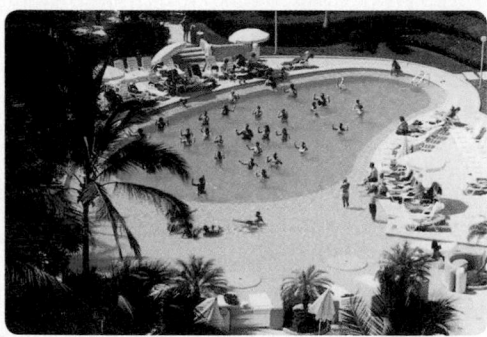

48. *Social Security Numbers* **a)** Match the first 9 digits of your phone number (including area code) with the 9 digits in your Social Security number. To do so, match the first digit in your phone number with the first digit in your Social Security number to get one ordered pair. Match the second digits to get a second ordered pair. Continue this process until you get a total of nine ordered pairs. Answers will vary.

b) Do you believe that this set of bivariate data has a positive correlation, a negative correlation, or no correlation? Explain your answer. Answers will vary.

c) Construct a scatter diagram for the nine ordered pairs. Answers will vary.

d) Calculate the correlation coefficient, *r*. Answers will vary.

e) Is there a correlation at $\alpha = 0.05$? Explain. Answers will vary.

f) Calculate the equation of the line of best fit. Answers will vary.

g) Use the equation in part (f) to estimate the digit in a social Security number that corresponds with a 7 in a telephone number. Answers will vary.

49. *Hitting the Brakes* **a)** Examine the art below. Do you believe that there is a positive correlation, a negative correlation, or no correlation between speed of a car and stopping distance when the brakes are applied? Answers will vary.

b) Do you believe that there is a stronger correlation between speed of a car and stopping distance on wet or dry roads? Answers will vary.

c) Use the figure to construct two scatter diagrams, one for dry pavement and the other for wet pavement. Place the speed of the car on the horizontal axis.*

d) Compute the correlation coefficient for speed of the car and stopping distance for dry pavement. 0.999

e) Repeat part (d) for wet pavement. 0.990

f) Were your answers to parts (a) and (b) correct? Explain. Answers will vary.

g) Determine the equation of the line of best fit for dry pavement. $y = 5.36x - 183.40$

h) Repeat part (g) for wet pavement. $y = 16.22x - 669.80$

i) Use the equations in parts (g) and (h) to estimate the stopping distance of a car going 77 mph on both dry and wet pavements. Dry, 229.3 ft; wet, 579.1 ft

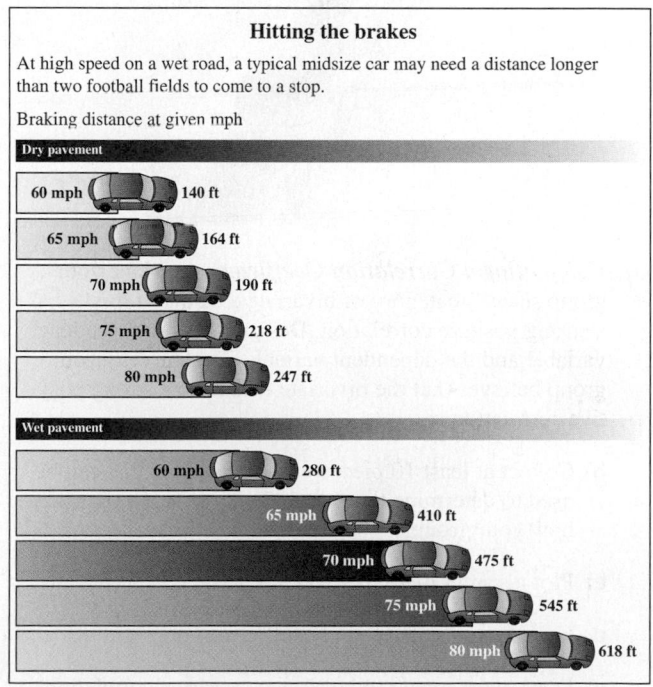

Hitting the brakes

At high speed on a wet road, a typical midsize car may need a distance longer than two football fields to come to a stop.

Braking distance at given mph

Dry pavement

60 mph	140 ft
65 mph	164 ft
70 mph	190 ft
75 mph	218 ft
80 mph	247 ft

Wet pavement

60 mph	280 ft
65 mph	410 ft
70 mph	475 ft
75 mph	545 ft
80 mph	618 ft

Source: *Car and Driver*, American Automobile Association

*See Instructor Answer Appendix

Challenge Problems/Group Activities

50. *Interchanging Variables* **a)** Assume that a set of bivariate data yields a specific correlation coefficient. If the x- and y-values are interchanged and the correlation coefficient is recalculated, will the correlation coefficient change? Correlation will not change.

b) Make up a table of five pieces of bivariate data and determine r using the data. Then switch the values of the x's and y's and recompute the correlation coefficient. Has the value of r changed? Answers will vary.

51. *Height vs. Length* **a)** Do you believe that a correlation exists between a person's height and the length of a person's arm? Answers will vary.

b) Select 10 people from your class and measure (in inches) their heights and the lengths of their arms. Answers will vary.

c) Plot the 10 ordered pairs on a scatter diagram. Answers will vary.

d) Calculate the correlation coefficient, r. Answers will vary.

e) Determine the equation of the line of best fit. Answers will vary.

f) Estimate the length of the arm of a person who is 58 in. tall. Answers will vary.

52. *Calculating a Correlation Coefficient* **a)** Have your group select a category of bivariate data that it thinks has a strong positive correlation. Designate the independent variable and the dependent variable. Explain why your group believes that the bivariate data have a strong positive correlation. Answers will vary.

b) Collect at least 10 pieces of bivariate data that can be used to determine the correlation coefficient. Explain how your group chose these data. Answers will vary.

c) Plot a scatter diagram. Answers will vary.

d) Calculate the correlation coefficient. Answers will vary.

e) Does there appear to be a strong positive correlation? Explain your answer. Answers will vary.

f) Calculate the equation of the line of best fit. Answers will vary.

g) Explain how the equation in part (f) may be used. Answers will vary.

53. *CPI* Use the following table. CPI represents consumer price index.

Year	2005	2006	2007	2008	2009	2010
CPI	195.3	201.6	207.3	215.3	214.5	218.1

a) Calculate r. 0.963

b) If 2005 is subtracted from each year, the table obtained becomes:

Year	0	1	2	3	4	5
CPI	195.3	201.6	207.3	215.3	214.5	218.1

If r is calculated from these values, how will it compare with the r determined in part (a)? Explain. Should be the same

c) Calculate r from the values in part (b) and compare the results with the value of r found in part (a). Are they the same? If not, explain why. 0.963; the values are the same.

54. a) There are equivalent formulas that can be used to find the correlation coefficient and the equation of the line of best fit. A formula used in some statistics books to find the correlation coefficient is

$$r = \frac{SS(xy)}{\sqrt{SS(x)SS(y)}}$$

where

$$SS(x) = \Sigma x^2 - \frac{(\Sigma x)^2}{n}$$

$$SS(y) = \Sigma y^2 - \frac{(\Sigma y)^2}{n}$$

$$SS(xy) = \Sigma xy - \frac{(\Sigma x)(\Sigma y)}{n}$$

Use this formula to find the correlation coefficient of the set of bivariate data given in Example 1 on page 835–836. ≈ 0.922

b) Compare your answer with the answer obtained in Example 1. Should be the same.

Internet/Research Activity

55. a) Obtain a set of bivariate data from a newspaper or magazine.

b) Plot the information on a scatter diagram.

c) Indicate whether you believe that the data show a positive correlation, a negative correlation, or no correlation. Explain your answer.

d) Calculate r and determine whether your answer to part (c) was correct.

e) Determine the equation of the line of best fit for the bivariate data.

56. Find a scatter diagram in a newspaper or magazine and write a paper on what the diagram indicates. Indicate whether you believe that the bivariate data show a positive correlation, a negative correlation, or no correlation and explain why.

CHAPTER 13 *Summary*

Important Facts and Concepts

Examples and Discussion

Important Facts and Concepts	Examples and Discussion
Section 13.1 *Sampling Techniques* Random sampling Systematic sampling Cluster sampling Stratified sampling Convenience sampling	Example 1, page 777
Section 13.2 Misuses of statistics	Discussion pages 779–781
Section 13.3 Frequency Distribution	Examples 1–2, pages 784–786
Rules for Data Grouped by Classes 1. The classes should be the same width. 2. The classes should not overlap. 3. Each piece of data should belong to only one class.	Discussion, page 784; Examples 1–3, pages 784–787
Statistical Graphs Histogram Frequency polygon Stem-and-leaf display Circle graph	Examples 4, 6, 7, pages 787–789 Examples 5–6, pages 788–789 Examples 8, pages 790–791 Examples 9, pages 791–792
Section 13.4 *Measures of Central Tendency* The **mean** is the sum of the data divided by the number of pieces of data: $\bar{x} = \dfrac{\Sigma x}{n}$.	Example 1, page 797
The **median** is the value in the middle of a set of ranked data.	Examples 2–3, 6, pages 798–799
The **mode** is the piece of data that occurs most frequently (if there is one).	Examples 4, 6, pages 798–799
The **midrange** is the value halfway between the lowest and highest values: midrange $= \dfrac{L + H}{2}$.	Examples 5, 6, page 799
Percentiles and **Quartiles** are measures of position.	Examples 7–8, pages 800–801

Section 13.5
Measures of Dispersion

The **range** is the difference between the highest value and lowest value in a set of data.

The **standard deviation,** s, is a measure of the spread of a set of data about the mean: $s = \sqrt{\dfrac{\Sigma(x - \bar{x})^2}{n - 1}}$.

Discussion pages 808–812; Example 1, page 808

Examples 2–3, pages 809–811

Section 13.6
z–SCORES

$$z = \frac{\text{value of the piece of data} - \text{mean}}{\text{standard deviation}}$$

Discussion pages 820–828; Examples 2–5, pages 820–828

Section 13.7
Linear Correlation And Regression

Linear correlation coefficient, r, is

$$r = \frac{n(\Sigma xy) - (\Sigma x)(\Sigma y)}{\sqrt{n(\Sigma x^2) - (\Sigma x)^2}\ \sqrt{n(\Sigma y^2) - (\Sigma y)^2}}$$

Discussion pages 833–835; Examples 1–2, pages 835–838

Equation of the Line of the Best Fit

$y = mx + b$, where

$$m = \frac{n(\Sigma xy) - (\Sigma x)(\Sigma y)}{n(\Sigma x^2) - (\Sigma x)^2}$$

$$b = \frac{\Sigma y - m(\Sigma x)}{n}$$

Discussion pages 839–840; Examples 3–4, pages 839–841

CHAPTER 13) Review Exercises

13.1

1. a) **What is a population?** A population consists of all items or people of interest.
   b) **What is a sample?** A sample is a subset of the population.

2. **What is a random sample?** A random sample is one where every item in the population has the same chance of being selected.

13.2

In Exercises 3 and 4, tell what possible misuses or misinterpretations may exist in the statements.

3. The Stay Healthy Candy Bar indicates on its label that it has no cholesterol. Therefore, it is safe to eat as many of these candy bars as you want. The candy bars may have lots of calories, or fat, or sodium. Therefore, it may not be healthy to eat them.

4. More copies of *Time* magazine are sold than are copies of *Money* magazine. Therefore, *Time* is a more profitable magazine than *Money*. Sales may not necessarily be a good indicator of profit. Expenses must also be considered.

5. *U.S. Households with Cable Television* In 2008, 99.7 million households in the United States subscribed to cable

television. In 2009, 103.0 million households in the United States subscribed to cable television. Draw a graph that appears to show a

a) small increase in the number of households subscribing to cable television from 2008 to 2009.*

b) large increase in the number of households subscribing to cable television from 2008 to 2009.*

13.3

6. Consider the following set of data.

35	37	38	41	43
36	37	38	41	43
36	37	39	41	43
36	37	39	41	44
37	37	39	42	45

a) Construct a frequency distribution letting each class have a width of 1.*

*See Instructor Answer Appendix

b) Construct a histogram.*

c) Construct a frequency polygon.*

7. Average Monthly High Temperature Consider the following average monthly high temperature in July for 40 selected U.S. cities.

71	79	58	73	80	75	84	77
82	72	80	70	75	66	73	72
80	66	74	68	81	84	75	67
91	76	82	79	63	69	68	79
71	76	80	83	73	87	82	71

a) Construct a frequency distribution. Let the first class be 58–62.*

b) Construct a histogram of the frequency distribution.*

c) Construct a frequency polygon of the frequency distribution.*

d) Construct a stem-and-leaf display.*

13.4, 13.5

In Exercises 8–13, for the following test scores 67, 74, 79, 83, 84, 93, determine the

8. mean. 80

9. median. 81

10. mode. None

11. midrange. 80

12. range. 26

13. standard deviation.
$\sqrt{80} \approx 8.94$

In Exercises 14–19, for the set of data 4, 5, 12, 14, 19, 7, 12, 23, 7, 17, 15, 21, determine the

14. mean. 13

15. median. 13

16. mode. 7 and 12

17. midrange. 13.5

18. range. 19

19. standard deviation.
$\sqrt{40} \approx 6.32$

13.6

Police Response Time In Exercises 20–24, assume that police response time to emergency calls is normally distributed with a mean of 9 minutes and a standard deviation of 2 minutes. Determine the percent of emergency calls with a police response time

20. between 7 and 11 minutes. 68.26%

21. between 5 and 13 minutes. 95.44%

22. less than 12.2 minutes. 94.52%

23. more than 12.2 minutes. 5.48%

24. more than 7.8 minutes. 72.57%

Pizza Delivery In Exercises 25–28, assume that the amount of time to prepare and deliver a pizza from Pepe's Pizza

is normally distributed with a mean of 20 minutes and standard deviation of 5 minutes. Determine the percent of pizzas that were prepared and delivered

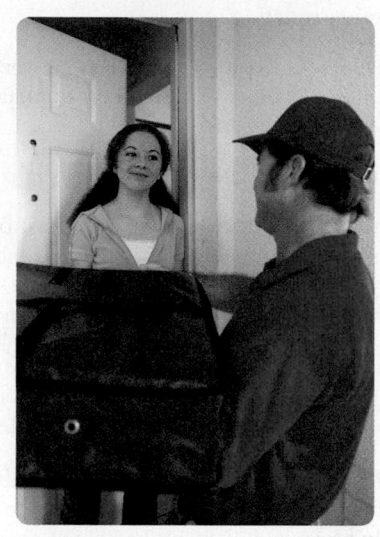

25. between 20 and 25 minutes. 34.1%

26. in less than 18 minutes. 34.5%

27. between 22 and 28 minutes. 29.0%

28. If Pepe's Pizza advertises that the pizza is free if it takes more than 30 min to deliver, what percent of the pizza will be free? 2.3%

13.7

29. Hiking The following table shows the number of hiking permits issued for a specific trail at Yellowstone National Park for selected years and the corresponding number of bears sighted by the hikers on that trail.

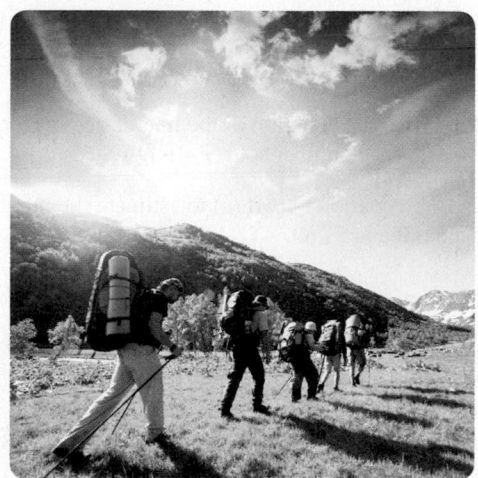

Hiking permits	765	926	1145	842	1485	1702
Bears	119	127	150	119	153	156

a) Construct a scatter diagram with hiking permits on the horizontal axis.*

*See Instructor Answer Appendix

b) Use the scatter diagram in part (a) to determine whether you believe that a correlation exists between the number of hiking permits issued and the number of bears sighted by hikers. If so, is it a positive or negative correlation? Yes; positive

c) Calculate the correlation coefficient between the number of hiking permits issued and the number of bears sighted by hikers. 0.925

d) Determine whether a correlation exists at $\alpha = 0.05$. Yes

e) Determine the equation of the line of best fit between the number of hiking permits issued and the number of bears sighted by hikers. Round both the slope and y-intercept to the nearest hundredth. $y = 0.04x + 88.17$

f) Assuming that this trend continues, use the equation of the line of best fit to estimate the number of bears sighted if 1500 hiking permits were issued. ≈ 148 bears

30. **Daily Sales** Ace Hardware recorded the number of a particular item sold per week for 6 weeks and the corresponding weekly price, in dollars, of the item as shown in the table below.

Price ($)	0.75	1.00	1.25	1.50	1.75	2.00
Number sold	200	160	140	120	110	95

a) Construct a scatter diagram with price on the horizontal axis.*

b) Use the scatter diagram in part (a) to determine whether you believe that a correlation exists between the price of the item and number sold. If so, it is a positive or a negative correlation? Yes; negative

c) Determine the correlation coefficient between the price and the number sold. -0.973

d) Determine whether a correlation exists at $\alpha = 0.05$. Yes

e) Determine the equation of the line of best fit for the price and the number sold. $y = -79.4x + 246.7$

f) Use the equation in part (e) to estimate the number sold if the price is $1.60. ≈ 120 sold

13.4–13.6

Men's Weight In Exercises 31–38, use the following data obtained from a study of the weights of adult men.

Mean	192 lb	First quartile	178 lb
Median	185 lb	Third quartile	232 lb
Mode	180 lb	86th percentile	239 lb
Standard deviation	23 lb		

31. What is the most common weight? 180 lb

32. What weight did half of those surveyed exceed? 185 lb

33. About what percent of those surveyed weighed more than 232 lb? 25%

34. About what percent of those surveyed weighed less than 178 lb? 25%

35. About what percent of those surveyed weighed more than 239 lb? 14%

36. If 100 men were surveyed, what is the total weight of all men? 19,200 lb

37. What weight represents two standard deviations above the mean? 238 lb

38. What weight represents 1.8 standard deviations below the mean? 150.6 lb

13.2–13.6

Presidential Children The following list shows the names of the 43 U.S. presidents and the number of children in their families.

Washington	0	B. Harrison	3
J. Adams	5	McKinley	2
Jefferson	6	T. Roosevelt	6
Madison	0	Taft	3
Monroe	2	Wilson	3
J. Q. Adams	4	Harding	0
Jackson	0	Coolidge	2
Van Buren	4	Hoover	2
W. H. Harrison	10	F. D. Roosevelt	6
Tyler	14	Truman	1
Polk	0	Eisenhower	2
Taylor	6	Kennedy	3
Fillmore	2	L. B. Johnson	2
Pierce	3	Nixon	2
Buchanan	0	Ford	4
Lincoln	4	Carter	4
A. Johnson	5	Reagan	4
Grant	4	G. Bush	6
Hayes	8	Clinton	1
Garfield	7	G. W. Bush	2
Arthur	3	Obama	2
Cleveland	5		

In Exercises 39–50, use the data to determine the following.

39. Mean ≈ 3.53 40. Mode 2

41. Median 3   42. Midrange 7

*See Instructor Answer Appendix

43. Range 14

44. Standard deviation (round the mean to the nearest tenth)
$\sqrt{7.97} \approx 2.82$

45. Construct a frequency distribution; let the first class be 0–1.*

46. Construct a histogram of the frequency distribution.*

47. Construct a frequency polygon of the frequency distribution.*

48. Does this distribution appear to be normal? Explain.
No, it is skewed to the right.

49. Do you think the number of children per family in the United States is a normal distribution? Explain. Answers will vary.

50. Is this set of data representative of the U.S. population? Explain. Answers will vary.

CHAPTER 13) *Test*

In Exercises 1–6, for the set of data 27, 43, 43, 45, 52, determine the

1. mean. 42

2. median. 43

3. mode. 43

4. midrange. 39.5

5. range. 25

6. standard deviation.
$\sqrt{84} \approx 9.17$

In Exercises 7–9, use the set of data

26	28	35	46	49	56
26	30	36	46	49	58
26	32	40	47	50	58
26	32	44	47	52	62
27	35	46	47	54	66

to construct the following.

7. a frequency distribution; let the first class be 25–30*

8. a histogram of the frequency distribution*

9. a frequency polygon of the frequency distribution*

Statistics on Salaries *In Exercises 10–16, use the following data on weekly salaries at Donovan's Construction Company.*

Mean	$740	First quartile	$690
Median	$710	Third quartile	$745
Mode	$735	79th percentile	$752
Standard deviation	$40		

10. What is the most common salary? $735

11. What salary did half the employees exceed? $710

12. About what percent of employees' salaries exceeded $690? 75%

13. About what percent of employees' salaries was less than $752? 79%

14. If the company has 100 employees, what is the total weekly salary of all employees? $74,000

15. What salary represents one standard deviation above the mean? $780

Anthropology *In Exercises 16–19, assume that anthropologists have determined that the akidolestes, a small primitive mammal believed to have lived with the dinosaurs, had a head circumference that was normally distributed with a mean of 42 cm and a standard deviation of 5 cm.*

16. What percent of head circumferences were between 36 and 53 cm? 87.10%

17. What percent of head circumferences were greater than 35.75 cm? 89.44%

18. What percent of head circumferences were greater than 48.25 cm? 10.56%

19. What percent of head circumferences were less than 50 cm? 94.52%

20. ***Minimum Wage*** The following table shows the hourly minimum wage in the U.S. for the years 2006–2010, where the column labeled Year refers to the number of years since 2006.

Year	Minimum Wage
0	$5.15
1	$5.85
2	$6.55
3	$7.25
4	$7.25

Source: *Bureau of Labor Statistics*

a) Construct a scatter diagram placing the year on the horizontal axis.*

b) Use the scatter diagram in part (a) to determine whether you believe a correlation exists between the year and the minimum wage. Yes

*See Instructor Answer Appendix

c) Determine the correlation coefficient between the year and the minimum wage. 0.970

d) Determine whether a correlation exists at $\alpha = 0.05$.
Yes

e) Determine the equation of the line of best fit between the year and the minimum wage. Round

both the slope and y-intercept to the nearest hundredth. $y = 0.56x + 5.29$

f) Use the equation in part (e) to predict the minimum wage in 2014. $9.77

GROUP PROJECTS

Watching TV

1. Do you think that men or women, aged 17–20, watch more hours of TV weekly, or do you think that they watch the same number of hours?

a) Write a procedure to use to determine the answer to that question. In your procedure, use a sample of 30 men and 30 women. State how you will obtain an unbiased sample.

b) Collect 30 pieces of data from men aged 17–20 and 30 pieces of data from women aged 17–20. Round answers to the nearest 0.5 hr. Follow the procedure developed in part (a) to obtain your unbiased sample.

c) Compute the mean for your two groups of data to the nearest tenth.

d) Using the means obtained in part (c), answer the question asked at the beginning of the problem.

e) Is it possible that your conclusion in part (d) is wrong? Explain.

f) Compute the standard deviation for each group to the nearest tenth. How do the standard deviations compare?

g) Do you believe that the distribution of data from either or both groups resembles a normal distribution? Explain.

h) Add the two groups of data to get one group of 60 pieces of data. If these 60 pieces of data are added and

divided by 60, will you obtain the same mean as when you add the two means from part (c) and divide the sum by 2? Explain.

i) Compute the mean of the 60 pieces of data by using both methods mentioned in part (h). Are they the same? If so, why? If not, why not?

j) Do you believe that this group of 60 pieces of data represents a normal distribution? Explain.

Bivariate Data Experiment

2. a) Have your group select a category of bivariate data that it thinks has a strong negative correlation. Indicate the variable that you will designate as the independent variable and the variable that you will designate as the dependent variable. Explain why your group believes that the bivariate data have a strong negative correlation.

b) Collect at least 10 pieces of bivariate data that can be used to determine the correlation coefficient. Explain how your group chose these data.

c) Plot a scatter diagram.

d) Calculate the correlation coefficient.

e) Is there a negative correlation at $\alpha = 0.05$? Explain your answer.

f) Calculate the equation of the line of best fit.

g) Explain how the equation in part (f) may be used.

14

Graph Theory

Why This is Important

In our everyday lives, we often face problems that require us to carry out several tasks to reach a desired solution. *Graph theory* is an important branch of mathematics used to represent and find solutions to such problems. Businesses, governments, and other organizations make use of graph theory to determine the most cost-effective means of solving problems and providing products and services.

Graph theory can also be used in our everyday lives to help make decisions when traveling to multiple locations. For example, if you wish to visit several theme parks on your vacation, graph theory can be used to find the shortest driving route to all of the parks.

◄ *Graph theory can be used to help you plan your vacation.*

SECTION 14.1   Graphs, Paths, and Circuits

▲ *What is the shortest route to deliver Girl Scout cookies to 15 different homes?*

Suppose that you are a Girl Scout leader and you must deliver cookies to 15 different homes. You will use your car to drive from home to home to deliver all the cookies. You realize that you have many possible routes to accomplish the task, but how can you determine the shortest route? In this section, we will introduce a type of diagram that can help you analyze such problems.

Why *This is Important* Graphs can be used to help solve problems from a wide variety of applications that relate to our everyday lives.

The study of graph theory can be traced back to the eighteenth century when people of the East Prussian town of Königsberg sought the solution to a popular problem. Königsberg was situated on both banks and two islands of the Prigel River. From Fig. 14.1, we see that the sections of town were connected with a series of seven bridges. The townspeople wondered if one could walk through town and cross all seven bridges without crossing any of the bridges twice. This question was presented to Swiss mathematician Leonhard Euler (pronounced "oiler," 1707–1783). To study this problem, Euler reduced the problem to one that could be represented with a series of dots and lines. This problem came to be known as the Königsberg bridge problem.

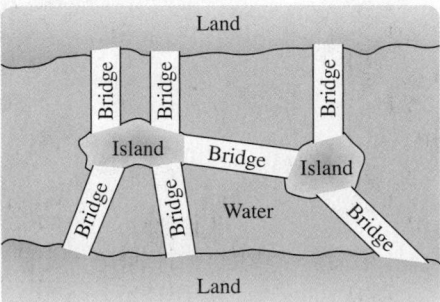

Figure 14.1

We will revisit the Königsberg bridge problem several times in this section and in Section 14.2. Our main focuses in this section are to introduce definitions of graph theory and to explain how these definitions can help represent problems from the physical world. In the next section, we will introduce some basic graph theory used to solve these problems.

Graphs

A *graph* is a finite set of points called *vertices* (singular form is *vertex*) connected by line segments (not necessarily straight) called *edges*. An edge that connects a vertex to itself is called a *loop*. Vertices, edges, and a loop are displayed in the graph in Fig. 14.2. We generally refer to vertices with capitalized letters. The edge between two vertices will be referred to using the two vertices. For example, in Fig. 14.2, the edge that connects vertex *A* to vertex *B* is referred to

Figure 14.2

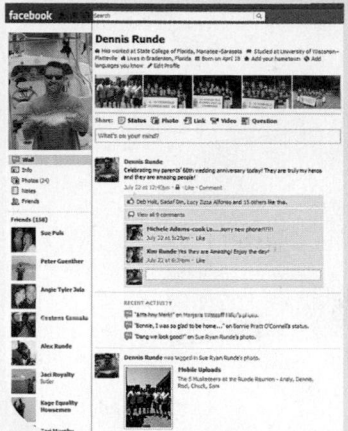
as edge *AB* or as edge *BA*. The loop in Fig. 14.2 is referred to as edge *BB* or loop *BB*. Not every place where two edges cross is a vertex. A dot must be present to represent a vertex. For instance, in Fig. 14.2, even though edges *AD* and *BC* cross, since no dot is indicated, the place where these lines cross is not a vertex.

With these basic definitions, we can begin using graphs to represent physical settings.

Example 1 *Representing the Königsberg Bridge Problem*

Using the definitions of vertex and edge, represent the Königsberg bridge problem with a graph.

Solution   Note that each bridge in Fig. 14.1 on page 854 connects two pieces of land in a manner similar to an edge connecting two vertices. To begin representing the Königsberg bridge problem as a graph, we will label each piece of land with a capital letter, as shown in Fig. 14.3.

Figure 14.3

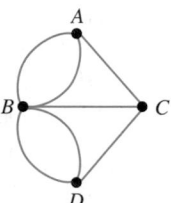

Figure 14.4

Next, we draw edges to represent the bridges. Notice that there are two bridges connecting land *A* to land *B* in Fig. 14.3. Therefore, we need two edges to connect vertex *A* to vertex *B* in our graph (see Fig. 14.4). Notice that there is one bridge connecting land *A* to land *C* in Fig. 14.3. Therefore, we need one edge to connect vertex *A* to vertex *C* in our graph. We continue to let edges represent bridges, and the resulting graph is given in Fig. 14.4.

Although the picture and the graph do not look very similar, the graph represents the key aspects of the problem: The land is represented with vertices, and the bridges are represented with edges.   ■

Graphs are powerful tools in problem solving because they allow us to focus on the key aspects of problems without getting distracted with unnecessary details. Our next three examples show other ways that graphs can be used to represent settings from the physical world.

Example 2 *Navy Region Southwest*

The Navy Region Southwest (NRS) is a division of the United States Navy. NRS includes all Navy facilities in the states shown in Fig. 14.5 on page 856. Construct a graph to show the states that share a common border. States whose borders touch only at a single corner point will not be considered to share a common border.

Figure 14.5

Figure 14.6

Solution   In our graph, each vertex will represent one of the six states shown in Fig. 14.5. We begin by placing six vertices in the same relative positions as the six states on the map and then labeling each vertex with the corresponding two-letter abbreviation (Fig. 14.6). The exact placement of the vertices is not critical.

Next, if two states share a common border, connect the respective vertices with an edge. For example, Nevada shares a common border with Utah, Arizona, and California so there will be edges that connect vertex *NV* to vertices *UT, AZ*, and *CA*, as shown in Fig. 14.7.

NV   UT   CO
●─────────●─────────●
│   ╱│   │
│   ╱ │   │
│   ╱   │   │
●─────────●─────────●
CA   AZ   NM

Figure 14.7

Next, note that Utah shares a common border with Nevada, Arizona, and Colorado. Therefore, the graph in Fig. 14.7 will have edges that connect *UT* to *NV, AZ*, and *CO*, respectively. Note that Utah and New Mexico have borders that touch only at a corner point and thus are not considered to share a common border. Therefore, in the graph shown in Fig. 14.7, no edge connects *UT* to *NM*. Likewise, Arizona and Colorado are not considered to share a common border; thus, no edge connects *AZ* to *CO*. To finish the graph, we continue adding edges until, for every two states in Fig. 14.5 that share a common border, there is an edge between their respective vertices in Fig. 14.7.   ■

NM
●
│╲
│ ╲
CO● ╲AZ   ●CA
    ╲ ●───────│
     ╲│   ╱│
      │   ╱ │
      ●────────●
     UT   NV

Figure 14.8

In Example 2, the graph shown in Fig. 14.7 is only one possible arrangement of vertices and edges that can show which states share a common border. Many other graphs that display the same relationship are equally valid. Figure 14.8 shows one such graph. Although the vertices in the graph in Fig. 14.8 do not resemble the respective locations of the states they represent, the relationship between the vertices is the same as in Fig. 14.7.

Graph Theory Representations

Graphs consisting of points called vertices and lines called edges can represent numerous applications used in many professions. Chemists use graphs to sketch atoms in a molecule. Engineers use graphs in schematic drawings of electrical networks. Genealogists use graphs to represent family trees. Transportation officials use graphs to show airline, railway, and ground transportation routes. Industrial scientists use graphs to represent human and machine interaction times in factories. All these applications can be represented and studied with the branch of mathematics called graph theory, the origins of which can be traced back to Leonhard Euler (1707–1783). The subway map shown at left for the city and surrounding area of Boston, Massachusetts, is a graph of vertices and edges.

Why *This is Important*   Graph theory is an important tool that uses simple diagrams for representing key aspects of many problems.

Outside

Mrs. Robert's Classroom	Restroom *A*	Ms. Starr's Classroom

Hallway

Mrs. Kozak's Classroom	Restroom *B*	Mr. Cannata's Classroom

Figure 14.9

Example 3   *Representing a Floor Plan*

Figure 14.9 shows the floor plan of the kindergarten building at the Pullen Academy. Use a graph to represent the floor plan.

Solution   To create a graph, we start by letting vertices represent each of the six rooms, the hallway, and the outside of the building. To label the vertices, we will use the first letter of the teacher's last names along with *H* for hallway, *A* for restroom *A*, *B* for restroom *B*, and *O* for the outside of the building. Next, connect the vertices with edges. To determine placement of the edges within the graph, visualize walking through the various doorways in the building. For instance, since a person can walk from Mrs. Kozak's room directly into the hallway or into restroom *B*, there is an edge between *K* and *H* and an edge between *K* and *B*. The resulting graph is shown in Fig. 14.10. Notice that since the hallway has two separate doorways that lead to the outside of the building, there are two separate edges that connect vertices *H* and *O*.   ∎

In Example 3, we placed the vertex *O*, for outside, near the top of the graph. However, vertex *O* could have been placed in another location either above, below, or on either side of the vertices that represent the floor plan. If vertex *O* had been placed elsewhere, the graph would look different, but the graph would still represent the floor plan shown in Fig. 14.9.

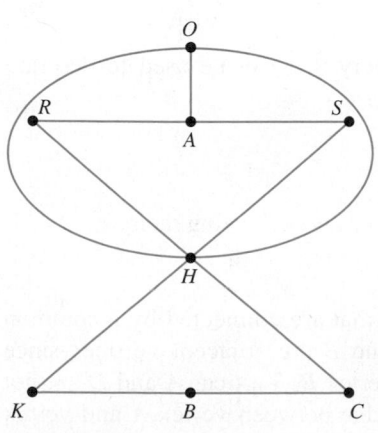

Figure 14.10

Example 4   *Representing a Neighborhood*

Figure 14.11 on page 858 shows a sketch of the Country Oaks subdivision of homes. Use a graph to represent the streets of this neighborhood.

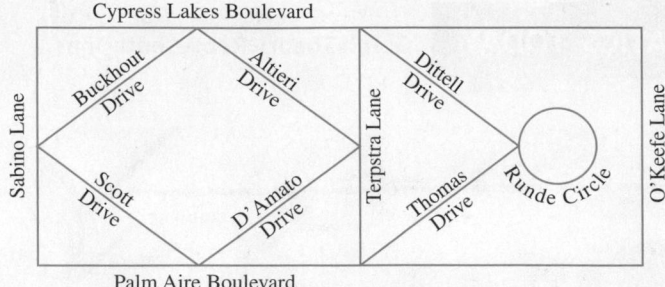

Figure 14.11

Solution   In this problem, the vertices will represent the street intersections and the edges will represent the street blocks. We will use the letters $A, B, C, \ldots, K$ to name the vertices. The resulting graph is shown in Fig. 14.12.

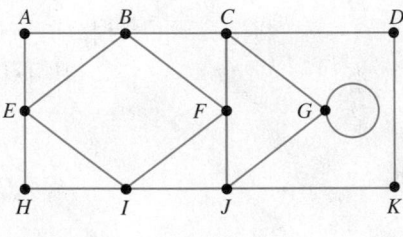

Figure 14.12

Now that we have some experience using graphs to represent real-life settings, we will introduce some additional vocabulary used in graph theory. We will begin with a method of classifying vertices. The *degree* of a vertex is the number of edges that connect to that vertex. For instance, in Fig. 14.13, vertex A has two edges connected to it. Therefore, the degree of vertex A is two. We also see from Fig. 14.13 that vertex B has three edges connected to it, as does vertex C. Therefore, vertices B and C each have degree three. Vertex D has a loop connected to it. A question arises: Should loop DD count as one edge or two edges when determining the degree of vertex D? We will agree to count each end of a loop when determining the degree of a vertex. Thus, vertex D from Fig. 14.13 will have degree four. A vertex with an even number of edges connected to it is an *even vertex*, and a vertex with an odd number of edges connected to it is an *odd vertex*. In Fig. 14.13, vertices A and D are even and vertices B and C are odd.

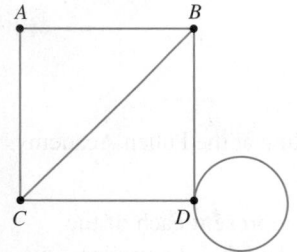

Figure 14.13

Paths, Circuits, and Bridges

We next introduce some definitions of graph theory that can be used to describe "movement."

Definition: Path

A **path** is a sequence of adjacent vertices and the edges connecting them.

By adjacent vertices, we mean two vertices that are connected by a common edge. For example, in Fig. 14.13, vertices A and B are adjacent vertices since there is a common edge between vertex A and vertex B. Vertices A and D are not adjacent vertices since there is not a common edge between vertex A and vertex D. An example of a path is given in Fig. 14.14. It is important to recognize the difference between a graph and a path. The *graph* is the set of black vertices and the blue edges connecting them. The *path*, shown in red, can be thought of as movement from vertex C to vertex D to vertex A to vertex B. For convenience, and to help in explanations, paths will be referred to with the sequence of vertices separated by commas. For example, the path in Fig. 14.14 will be referred to as path C, D, A, B.

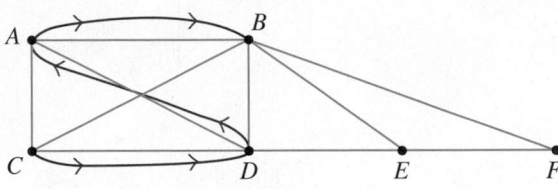

Figure 14.14

A path does not need to include every edge and every vertex of a graph. In addition, a path could include the same vertices and the same edges several times. For example, in Fig. 14.15, we see a graph with four vertices. The path A, B, C, D, A, B, C, D, A, B, C, D, A, B, C starts at vertex A, "circles" the graph three times, and then goes through vertex B to vertex C.

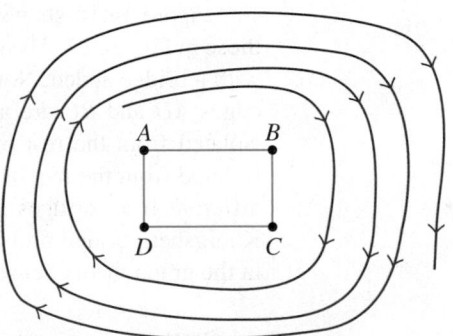

Figure 14.15

We now will discuss a special kind of path called a *circuit*.

Definition: Circuit

A **circuit** is a path that begins and ends at the same vertex.

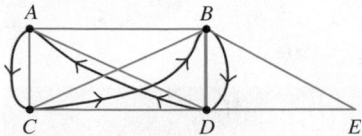

Figure 14.16

Examine Fig. 14.16. The path given by A, C, B, D, A forms a circuit. The path given by B, D, E, B forms another circuit.

Note that every circuit is, by definition, a path; however, not every path is a circuit. A circuit needs to begin and end at the same vertex. For example, in Fig. 14.16, the path given by A, C, B, D is not a circuit, since it does not begin and end at the same vertex. In Sections 14.2 and 14.3, we will discuss paths and circuits in more depth.

Our next definitions classify graphs themselves. A graph is *connected* if, for any two vertices in the graph, there is a path that connects them. All the graphs we have studied thus far have been connected because a path existed between each pair of vertices in each graph. If a graph is not connected, it is *disconnected*.

Figure 14.17 shows three examples of disconnected graphs. In Fig. 14.17(c), although edge *AD* and edge *BC* cross, the graph is not connected because there is no vertex indicated where the edges cross.

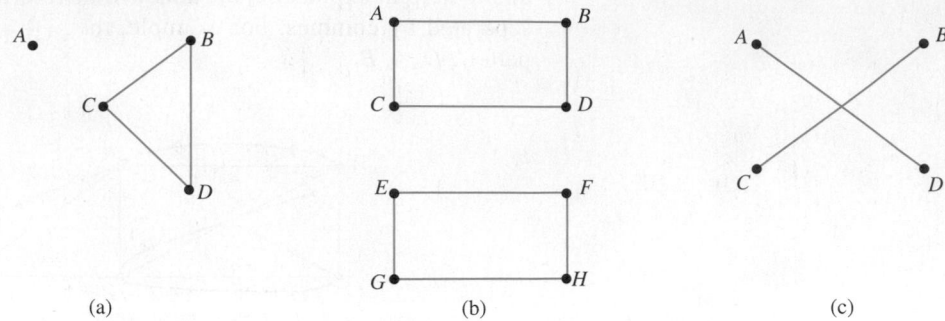

(a)   (b)   (c)

Figure 14.17

We next discuss an important type of edge called a *bridge*.

> ### Definition: Bridge
> A **bridge** is an edge that, if removed from a connected graph, would create a disconnected graph.

Figure 14.18 shows graphs with bridges indicated. Compare these graphs with those in Fig. 14.17. The graphs in Fig. 14.18 are the same graphs as those in Fig. 14.17 with a bridge added. Note in Fig. 14.18(c) that, in addition to edge *AB* that we added, edges *AD* and *BC* are also bridges. If edge *AD* were removed, vertex *D* would be isolated from the rest of the graph. If edge *BC* were removed, vertex *C* would be isolated from the rest of the graph. Note that our graph theory definition of *bridge* is different from bridges as they are used in the Königsberg bridge problem. In the Königsberg bridge problem, none of the edges that represent real bridges is a bridge in the graph theory sense.

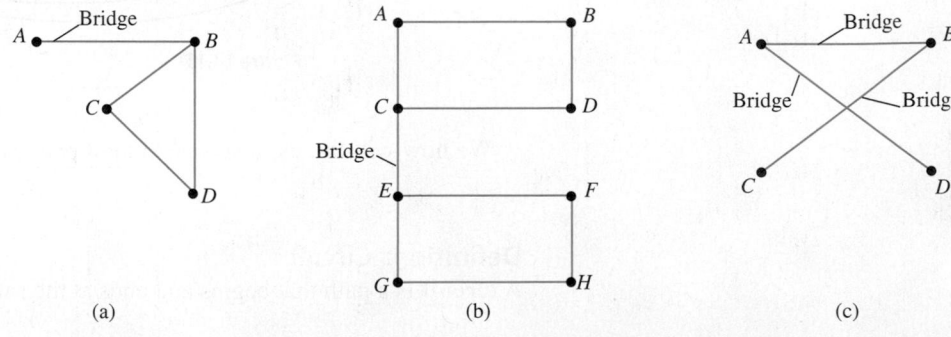

(a)   (b)   (c)

Figure 14.18

SECTION 14.1
Exercises

Warm Up Exercises

In Exercises 1–8, fill in the blanks with an appropriate word, phrase, or symbol(s).

1. A finite set of points connected by line segments is called a(n) _____. Graph

2. A point in a graph is called a(n) _____. Vertex

3. A line segment in a graph is called a(n) _____. Edge

4. An edge that connects a vertex to itself is called a(n) _____. Loop

5. A sequence of adjacent vertices and the edges connecting them is called a(n) _____. Path

6. A path that begins and ends with the same vertex is called a(n) _____. Circuit

7. The number of edges that connect to a vertex is called the _____ of the vertex. Degree

8. A bridge is an edge that, if removed from a connected graph, would create a(n) _____ graph. Disconnected

Practice the Skills

In Exercises 9–14, create a graph with the given properties. There are many possible answers for each problem.

9. Four even vertices*   **10.** Four odd vertices*

11. Two even and two odd vertices*

12. Four odd vertices and one even vertex*

13. Seven vertices and one bridge*

14. Seven vertices and two bridges*

In Exercises 15–20, use the graph below to answer the following questions.

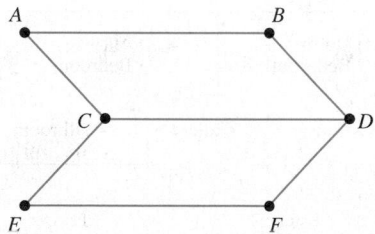

15. Is *A*, *B*, *C*, *D*, *F*, *E* a path? Explain.
No. There is no edge connecting vertices *B* and *C*.

16. Which edge(s) shown on the graph are not included in the following path: *A*, *B*, *D*, *F*, *E*, *C*?
Edge *AC* (or *CA*) and edge *CD* (or *DC*)

17. On the graph, is it possible to determine a path that begins with vertex *A*, contains all the edges exactly once, and ends with vertex *B*? If so, determine one such path. No

18. On the graph, is it possible to determine a circuit that includes only four distinct vertices? If so, determine one such circuit. Yes. One example is *A, B, D, C, A.*

19. On the graph, can you determine a path that includes all the edges without using any edge twice? If so, determine one such path. Yes. One example is *C, A, B, D, F, E, C, D.*

20. On the graph, can you determine a circuit that includes all the vertices without using any vertex (other than the beginning and ending vertex) twice? If so, determine one such circuit. Yes. One example is *A, B, D, F, E, C, A.*

Problem Solving

Modified Königsberg Bridge Problems In Exercises 21 and 22, suppose that the people of Königsberg decide to add several bridges to their city. Two such possibilities are shown. Create graphs that would represent the Königsberg bridge problem with these new bridges.

21.

22.

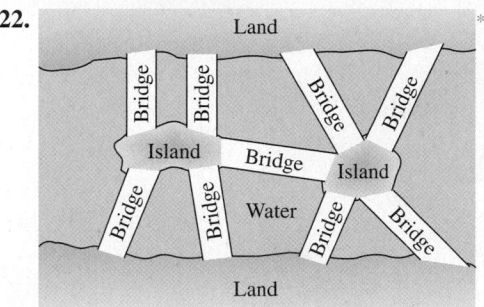

Other Navy Regions In Exercises 23 and 24, the maps of states that are in other Navy regions (see Example 2 on page 855) are shown. Represent each map as a graph where each vertex represents a state and each edge represents a common border between the states. Use the state abbreviations to label the vertices of the graph.

23. Navy Region Northwest*

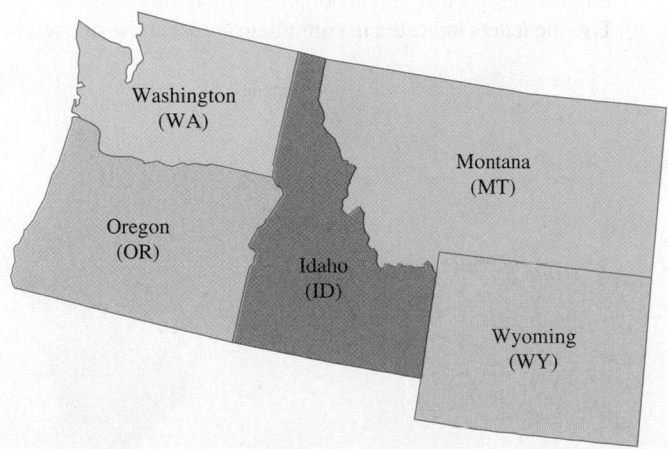

*See Instructor Answer Appendix

24. Navy Region Southeast*

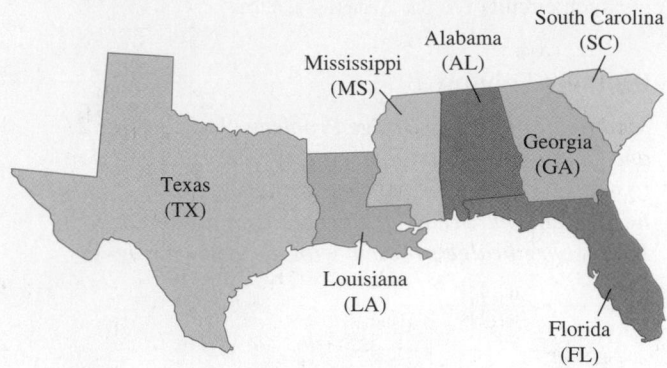

25. *Central America* The map below shows the countries of Belize (*B*), Costa Rica (*C*), El Salvador (*E*), Guatemala (*G*), Honduras (*H*), Nicaragua (*N*), and Panama (*P*). Represent the map as a graph where each vertex represents a country and each edge represents a common border between the countries. Use the letters indicated in parentheses to label the vertices.*

26. *Northern Africa* The map below shows the countries of Algeria (*A*), Egypt (*E*), Libya (*L*), Morocco (*M*), Sudan (*S*), Tunisia (*T*), and Western Sahara (*W*). Represent the map as a graph where each vertex represents a country and each edge represents a common border between the countries. Use the letters indicated in parentheses to label the vertices.*

For Exercises 27–30, use a graph to represent the floor plan shown. In each graph, use the letter O to represent the outside of the building. See Example 3, page 857.

27. *Floor Plan* The drawing below shows the first-floor plan of the Aloha model home offered by the Kim Ghiselin Family Construction Company of Woonsocket, Rhode Island. Place vertex *O* near the top of the graph.*

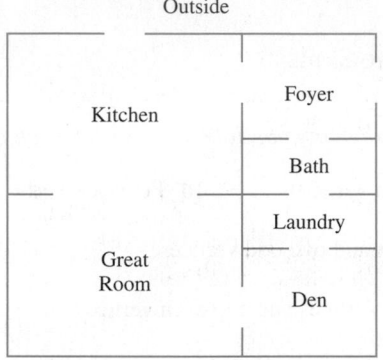

28. *Floor Plan* The drawing below shows the floor plan of the Sun Valley model home offered by Wubben Builders of Pocatello, Idaho. Place vertex *O* near the bottom of the graph.*

29. *Floor Plan* The drawing below shows the floor plan of the first floor of the Oleander model home offered by Nisely Builders of Albuquerque, New Mexico. Place vertex *O* near the bottom of the graph.*

*See Instructor Answer Appendix

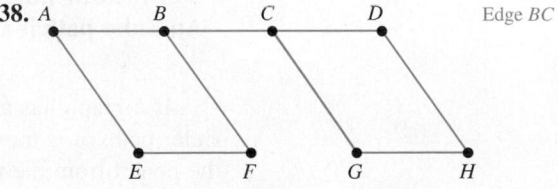

30. *Floor Plan* The drawing below shows the floor plan of the Bougainvillea model home offered by Alstrom Builders of Waco, Texas. Place vertex *O* near the bottom of the graph.*

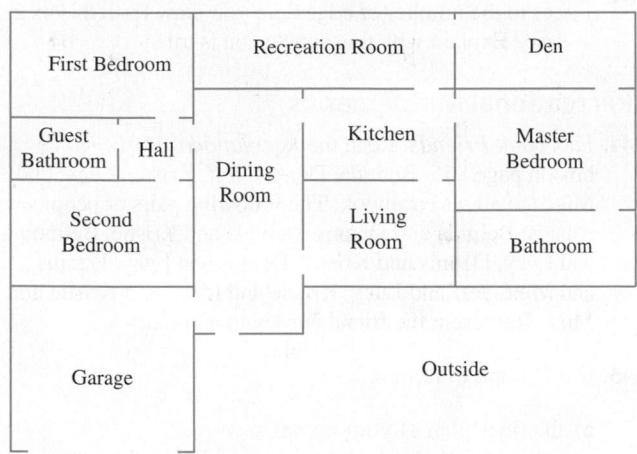

31. *Representing a Neighborhood* The map of the Tree Tops subdivision in Prince George County, Virginia, is shown below. Use a graph to represent the streets in this subdivision. Use letters to label the vertices.*

32. *Representing a Neighborhood* The map of the Crescent Lakes subdivision in Essex County, Maryland, is shown below. Use a graph to represent the streets in this subdivision. Use letters to label the vertices.*

In Exercises 33–36, determine whether the graph shown is connected or disconnected.

33. Disconnected

34. Connected

35. Connected

36. Disconnected

In Exercises 37–40, a connected graph is shown. Identify any bridges in each graph.

37. Edge *AC*

38. Edge *BC*

*See Instructor Answer Appendix

39.

B Edge *EF*

40.

Edge *FK* and edge *HL*

Challenge Problems/Group Activities

41. Poll your entire class to determine which students knew each other prior to taking this course. Draw a graph that shows this relationship. Answers will vary.

42. Attempt to draw a graph that has an odd number of odd vertices. What conclusion can you draw from this exercise? It is impossible to have a graph with an odd number of odd vertices.

43. Draw four different graphs and then for each graph:

a) determine the degree of each vertex. Answers will vary.

b) determine the sum of the degrees from all vertices from this same graph. Answers will vary.

c) determine the number of edges on this same graph. Answers will vary.

d) What conclusion relating the sum of the degrees of vertices to the number of edges can you draw from this exercise? Explain why this conclusion is true.*

Recreational Mathematics

44. *Facebook Friends* Read the *Recreational Mathematics* box on page 855. Belinda, Dennis, Jeff, Kristie, Lucy, and Mike are all on Facebook. The following pairs of people are friends: Belinda and Dennis, Belinda and Kristie, Belinda and Lucy, Dennis and Kristie, Dennis and Lucy, Dennis and Mike, Jeff and Lucy, Kristie and Lucy, and Kristie and Mike. Represent the friendships with a graph.*

45. Use a graph to represent

a) the floor plan of your home. Answers will vary.

b) the streets in your neighborhood within $\frac{1}{2}$ mile from your home in all directions. Answers will vary.

Internet/Research Activity

46. Choose a continent other than North America or Australia and create a graph showing the common boundaries between countries. Be sure to use a current map.

*See Instructor Answer Appendix

Euler Paths and Euler Circuits

▲ *Graph theory can be used to determine the best route for a snowplow to travel.*

A snowplow driver must plow every road in the township. To minimize the time and cost involved, the driver would like to establish a route that would allow the plow to travel over each road exactly one time. In this section, we will study paths and circuits that can be used to determine the best route for the snowplow driver.

Why **This is Important** Graphs, paths, and circuits can be used to solve many real-world problems.

Section 14.1 provided us with some of the basic definitions of graph theory. Although we were able to represent physical settings with graphs, we have not yet discussed solving problems related to these settings. In this section, we will provide more details of graph theory, which allows us to reach solutions to the Königsberg bridge problem and other real-world problems. Before we do so, we need to give two more definitions.

Definition: Euler Path
An **Euler path** is a path that passes through each edge of a graph exactly one time.

If a graph has an Euler path, we say the graph is *traversable*. If a graph has an Euler path, or is traversable, it is possible to trace the entire graph without removing the pencil from the paper and without tracing an edge more than once. For our next definition, recall that a circuit is a path that begins and ends at the same vertex.

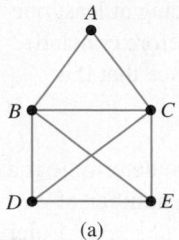

An Euler path
D, E, B, C, A, B, D, C, E

(b)

An Euler circuit *D, E, B, C, A, B, D,*
C, E, F, D

Figure 14.19

Definition: Euler Circuit

An **Euler circuit** is a circuit that passes through each edge of a graph exactly one time.

The difference between an Euler path and an Euler circuit is that an Euler circuit must start and end at the same vertex. An alternate definition for an Euler circuit is that it is an Euler path that begins and ends at the same vertex. To become familiar with Euler paths and Euler circuits, examine the graphs in Fig. 14.19(a) and (b). As we discuss each graph, trace each path or circuit with a pencil or with your finger, or draw the path or circuit on a separate sheet of paper.

In Fig. 14.19(a), the path *D, E, B, C, A, B, D, C, E* is an Euler path since each edge was traced only one time. However, since the path begins at vertex *D* and ends at a different vertex, *E*, the path is not a circuit and therefore is not an Euler circuit. In Fig. 14.19(b), the path *D, E, B, C, A, B, D, C, E, F, D* is an Euler path since each edge was traced only one time. Furthermore, since the path begins and ends with the same vertex, *D*, it is also an Euler circuit. Note that every Euler circuit is an Euler path, but not every Euler path is an Euler circuit.

Our next task is to determine whether a given graph has an Euler path, an Euler circuit, neither, or both. In the next example, we will use trial and error to find Euler paths and Euler circuits. Our discussion will help us introduce *Euler's theorem*, which will be used to solve the Königsberg bridge problem and other problems involving graph theory.

Example 1 *Euler Paths and Circuits*

For the graphs shown in Fig. 14.20, determine if an Euler path, an Euler circuit, neither, or both exist.

(a)

(b)

(c)

Figure 14.20

Solution

a) The graph in Fig. 14.20(a) has many Euler circuits, each of which is also an Euler path. One Euler circuit is *A, B, D, E, B, C, E, F, C, A*. Trace this circuit now. Notice that you traced each edge exactly one time and that you started and finished with vertex *A*. Notice that this graph has no odd vertices (and therefore has all even vertices). This graph has both Euler paths and Euler circuits.

b) Using trial and error, we can see that the graph in Fig. 14.20(b) has an Euler path but it does not have an Euler circuit. One Euler path is *C, A, B, D, C, E, F, D*. Another Euler path is *D, B, A, C, D, F, E, C*. There are actually several Euler paths for this graph, but each one must begin at either vertex *C* or vertex *D*. If the Euler path begins at vertex *C*, it must end at vertex *D*, and vice versa (you should try to find a few more to confirm this observation). Notice that there are exactly two odd vertices, vertex *C* and vertex *D*.

c) Our attempts to trace the graph in Fig. 14.20(c) lead to either tracing at least one edge twice or to omitting at least one of the edges. We must therefore conclude that this graph has neither an Euler path nor an Euler circuit. Notice that this graph has more than two odd vertices.   ∎

We are now ready to introduce Euler's theorem, which is used to determine if a graph contains Euler paths and Euler circuits. As you will see, the number of *odd* vertices of a graph determines whether the graph has Euler paths and Euler circuits.

Euler's Theorem

For a connected graph, the following statements are true.

1. A graph with *no odd vertices* (all even vertices) has at least one Euler path, which is also an Euler circuit. An Euler circuit can be started at any vertex, and it will end at the same vertex.

2. A graph with *exactly two odd vertices* has at least one Euler path but no Euler circuits. Each Euler path must begin at one of the two odd vertices, and it will end at the other odd vertex.

3. A graph with *more than two odd vertices* has neither an Euler path nor an Euler circuit.

The proof of this theorem is beyond the scope of this book. In Example 2, we will reexamine the graphs used in Example 1. However, this time we will use Euler's theorem to determine whether the graph has Euler paths and Euler circuits.

Example 2   *Using Euler's Theorem*

Use Euler's theorem to determine whether an Euler path or an Euler circuit exists in Fig. 14.20(a), (b), and (c) on page 865.

Solution

a) The graph in Fig. 14.20(a) has no odd vertices (all the vertices are even). According to item 1 in Euler's theorem, at least one Euler circuit exists. An Euler circuit can be determined starting at any vertex. The Euler circuit will end at the vertex from which it started. Recall that each Euler circuit is also an Euler path.

b) We see that the graph in Fig. 14.20(b) has four even vertices (A, B, E, and F) and two odd vertices (C and D). Based on item 2 in Euler's theorem, we conclude that since there are exactly two odd vertices, at least one Euler path exists but no Euler circuit exists. Each Euler path must begin at one of the odd vertices and end at the other odd vertex.

c) The graph in Fig. 14.20(c) has four odd vertices (A, B, D, and E) and one even vertex (C). According to item 3 in Euler's theorem, since this graph has more than two odd vertices, the graph has neither an Euler path nor an Euler circuit.   ∎

The results found in Example 2 using Euler's theorem are the same as the results found in Example 1 using trial and error. Although both methods led to the same result, Euler's theorem is superior to trial and error because it gives us a tool to examine more complicated graphs.

Next, we will use Euler's theorem to solve questions regarding the Königsberg bridge problem as well as problems relating to the graphs we developed in Section 14.1.

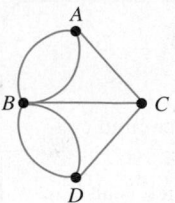

Figure 14.21

Example 3 *Solving the Königsberg Bridge Problem*

In Section 14.1, Example 1 on page 855, we discussed the Königsberg bridge problem and drew a graph to represent the situation. The graph is repeated in Fig. 14.21. Could a walk be taken through Königsberg during which each bridge is crossed exactly one time?

Solution The vertices of the graph given in Fig. 14.21 represent the land areas, and the edges of the graph represent the bridges in the Königsberg bridge problem. The original problem posed by the townspeople of Königsberg, in graph theory terms, was whether or not an Euler path exists for the graph in Fig. 14.21. From the figure, we see that the graph has four odd vertices (*A*, *B*, *C*, and *D*). Thus, according to item 3 of Euler's theorem, no Euler path exists. Therefore, no walk could be taken through Königsberg in which each bridge was crossed exactly one time. ■

Example 4 *Navy Region Southwest*

In Section 14.1, Example 2 on page 855, we discussed the states in the Navy Region Southwest. We drew a graph showing the states that share a common border. The graph is repeated in Fig. 14.22.

Figure 14.22

Secretary of the Navy, Ray Mabus wishes to visit each of these states. He wishes to travel between these states and cross each common state border (or use each edge) exactly one time.

a) Is it possible for him to travel among these six states and cross each common state border (or use each edge) exactly one time?

b) If yes, determine a path that he could take to travel between these states and cross each common state border exactly one time.

Solution

a) Since Secretary Mabus must use each edge (or common border) exactly one time, he is seeking an Euler path for the graph in Fig. 14.22. Notice that this graph has exactly two odd vertices, *NV* and *UT*. According to item 2 of Euler's theorem, at least one Euler path, but no Euler circuit, exists. Therefore, it *is* possible for him to travel among these states and cross each common state border exactly one time. However, since there is no Euler circuit, he must start his travel and end his travel in different states.

b) Many Euler paths exist, but each one must either start with *NV* and end with *UT* or start with *UT* and end with *NV*. One such path is *NV, UT, CO, NM, AZ, CA, NV, AZ, UT*. There are many other Euler paths on this graph. You should try to find at least two now. ■

Euler's theorem can be used to determine whether a graph has an Euler path or an Euler circuit. If an Euler path or Euler circuit exists, how can we determine it? We can always attempt to determine Euler paths and Euler circuits using trial and error. This strategy might work well for simpler graphs. However, we would like to attempt this task with a more systematic approach. Our final topic in this section, Fleury's algorithm, will give us such an approach. An *algorithm* is a procedure for accomplishing some task.

PROCEDURE **FLEURY'S ALGORITHM**

To determine an Euler path or an Euler circuit:

1. Use Euler's theorem to determine whether an Euler path or an Euler circuit exists. If one exists, proceed with Steps 2–5.

2. If the graph has no odd vertices (therefore has an Euler circuit, which is also an Euler path), choose any vertex as the starting point. If the graph has exactly two odd vertices (therefore has only an Euler path), choose one of the two odd vertices as the starting point.

3. Begin to trace edges as you move through the graph. Number the edges as you trace them. Since you can't trace any edges twice in Euler paths and Euler circuits, once an edge is traced consider it "invisible."

4. When faced with a choice of edges to trace, if possible, choose an edge that is not a bridge (i.e., don't create a disconnected graph with your choice of edges).

5. Continue until each edge of the entire graph has been traced once.

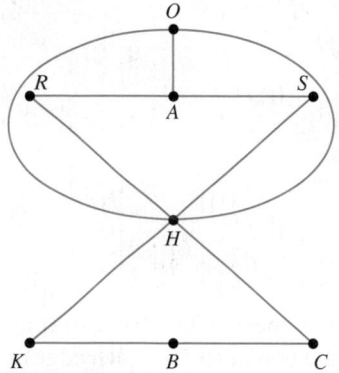

Figure 14.23

Example 5 *Locking a Kindergarten Building*

In Section 14.1, Example 3 on page 857, we introduced the kindergarten building at Pullen Academy and drew the graph that represented its floor plan. The graph is repeated in Fig. 14.23. Joe Mays, the school's custodian, is responsible for locking all the doors at the end of the day. Joe wishes to determine a way to move through the building using each doorway exactly once.

a) Is it possible for Joe to move through the building using each doorway of the building exactly one time? (In other words, does an Euler path exist in the graph in Fig. 14.23?)

b) If so, determine one such Euler path.

Solution

a) To determine if there is an Euler path, we will use Euler's theorem. The graph in Fig. 14.23 contains exactly two odd vertices, O and A. By item 2 of Euler's theorem, the graph has at least one Euler path (but no Euler circuit). By Euler's theorem, the Euler path would have to begin at one of the two odd vertices, either O or A, and end at the other odd vertex. Therefore, Joe could move through the building and use each doorway of the building exactly one time by starting at the outside (vertex O) or at restroom A (vertex A).

b) In part (a), we determined that an Euler path exists. Now we use Fleury's algorithm to determine one such path. We can start at either odd vertex, O or A. Let us choose to start at vertex O (see Fig. 14.23). As a matter of convention, once we trace an edge, we will redraw it using a dashed, instead of solid, edge. The dashes will indicate that the edge has already been traced and so it cannot be traced again. At vertex O, there are three choices of edges: the left-side edge OH, the right-side edge OH, or edge OA. None of these edges is a bridge. Thus, if we were to remove any one of these edges, we would not create a disconnected graph. Since none of these edges is a bridge, we can choose to trace any one of these edges. Let us choose the left-side edge OH as our first edge and number it 1 (see Fig. 14.24).

Now closely examine our position at vertex H. We now must make a choice among the following edges: HR, HS, HK, HC, and the right-side edge HO. None of these edges is a bridge. Thus, if we were to remove any of these edges, we would not create a disconnected graph. Since none of these edges is a bridge, we can choose to trace any one of these edges. Let us choose edge HK and label it edge 2 as shown in Fig. 14.24.

Figure 14.24

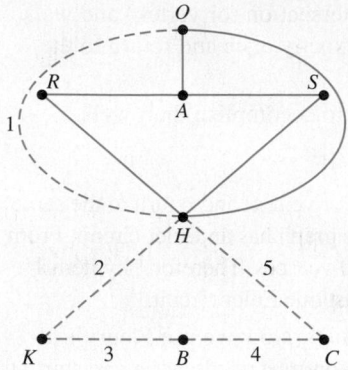

Figure 14.25

Now we are at vertex K. At vertex K, we have no choice but to select edge KB, followed by edge BC, followed by edge CH. We will choose these edges and label them edges 3, 4, and 5, respectively, as in Fig. 14.25. We are now back at vertex H.

Examine our position at vertex H in Fig. 14.25. There are three choices of edges: HR, HS, and right-side edge HO. None of these edges is a bridge, so we may choose to trace any one of these edges. Let us choose edge HR and label it 6. That will put us at vertex R, where our only choice is to trace edge RA and label it 7. We are now at vertex A. At vertex A, there is a choice between edges AO and AS. Because neither edge is a bridge, we may choose either one of these edges. Let us choose edge AS and label it 8. Our choices up to this point are shown in Fig. 14.26.

We are now at vertex S, where our only choice is to trace edge SH followed by edge HO, followed by edge OA. These edges are labeled 9, 10, and 11, respectively, and the completed Euler path is given in Fig. 14.27.

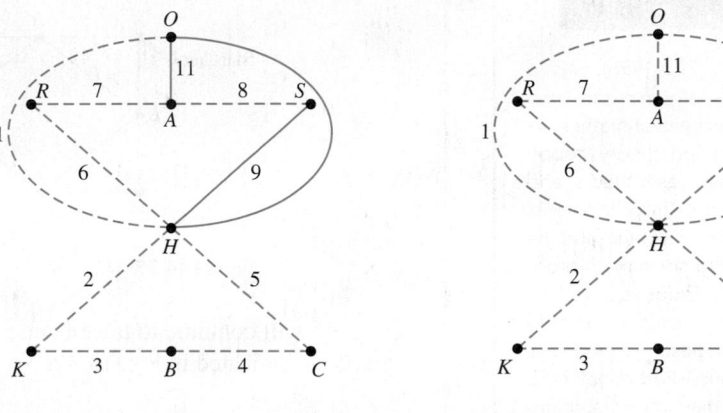

Figure 14.26   **Figure 14.27**

Notice that we started at one odd vertex, O, and ended at the other odd vertex, A. Therefore, if Joe followed the path $O, H, K, B, C, H, R, A, S, H, O, A$, he would travel through each doorway exactly one time. Many other Euler paths also exist for this problem. You will be asked to find another one in Exercise 50. ∎

Example 6 *Crime Stoppers Problem*

In Section 14.1, Example 4 on page 857, we introduced the Country Oaks subdivision of homes and drew a graph to represent it. The graph is repeated in Fig. 14.28 below. The Country Oaks Neighborhood Association is planning to organize a crime stopper group in which residents take turns walking through the neighborhood with cell phones to report any suspicious activity to the police.

Figure 14.28

a) Can the residents of Country Oaks start at one intersection (or vertex) and walk each street block (or edge) in the neighborhood exactly once and return to the intersection where they started?

b) If yes, determine a circuit that could be followed to accomplish their walk.

Solution

a) Since the residents wish to start at one intersection (or vertex) and return to the same intersection (or vertex), we need to determine if this graph has an Euler circuit. From Fig. 14.28 on page 869, we see that there are no odd vertices. Therefore, by item 1 of Euler's theorem, we determine that there is at least one Euler circuit.

b) In part (a), we determined that an Euler circuit exists. Now we use Fleury's algorithm to determine one such circuit. Euler's theorem states that we can start at any vertex to determine an Euler circuit. Let us choose to begin at vertex *A*. We face a choice of tracing edge *AB* or edge *AE*. Since neither edge *AB* nor edge *AE* is a bridge, we can choose either edge. Let us choose edge *AB*. Our first choice is indicated in Fig. 14.29.

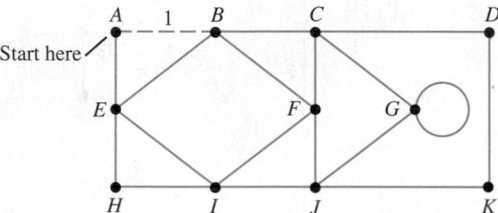

Figure 14.29

We will continue to trace from vertex to vertex around the outside of the graph, as indicated in Fig. 14.30. Notice that no edge chosen is a bridge.

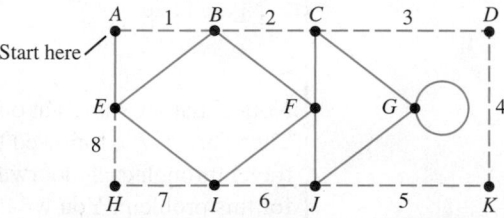

Figure 14.30

We are now at vertex *E*. Our choices are edge *EA*, edge *EB*, or edge *EI*. Edge *EA* is a bridge because removing edge *EA* would leave vertex *A* disconnected from the rest of the untraced graph. Therefore, we need to choose either edge *EB* or edge *EI*. Let us choose edge *EB*. Now we are at vertex *B* and must choose edge *BF*. Our choices so far are shown in Fig. 14.31.

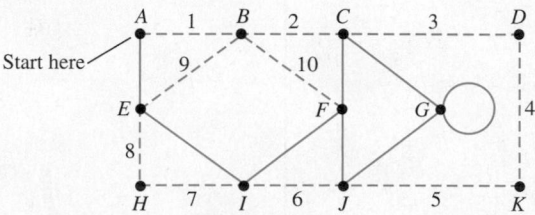

Figure 14.31

We are now at vertex *F* with choices of edge *FC*, edge *FJ*, or edge *FI*. Notice that edge *FI* is a bridge (it connects vertices *A*, *E*, and *I* to the rest of the untraced graph). We can therefore choose either edge *FC* or edge *FJ*. Let us choose edge *FC*, which will put us at vertex *C* (see Fig. 14.32). At vertex *C*, our only choice is edge *CG*.

Figure 14.32

We are now at vertex *G* and have to choose between edge *GJ* and edge *GG* (which is a loop): see Fig. 14.32. Since *GJ* is a bridge, we choose the edge *GG*. We then are back at vertex *G*. Here and throughout the rest of our circuit we only have one choice at each of the remaining vertices. We trace each of these remaining edges to get the result given in Fig. 14.33.

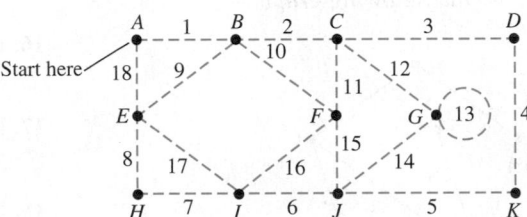

Figure 14.33

The circuit given in Fig. 14.33 gives one possible Euler circuit that would provide the residents of Country Oaks with one way to cover each street block exactly one time starting and ending at vertex *A*. Fleury's algorithm could be used to find many alternative circuits. You will be asked to find several such alternative circuits in Exercises 51 through 54. ∎

In our first two sections on graph theory, we introduced key concepts and theory that allowed us to represent physical settings as graphs and to solve some problems relating to these settings. We solved problems dealing with the bridges of Königsberg, the states in the Navy Region Southwest, the doorways of a kindergarten building, and the street blocks involved in a neighborhood crime stopper program. Although these problems are very different, they are all related because in each case a graph is used to represent a physical setting.

There are many other examples of how Euler paths and Euler circuits can be applied to real-life problems, including problems that deal with the most efficient route for a snowplow or a street sweeper. Another example of a path problem is found in the classic arcade games Pac-Man and Ms. Pac–Man (Fig. 14.34). In both these games, the ideal path (disregarding the ghosts) is an Euler path.

Figure 14.34 The game Pac-Man

SECTION 14.2
Exercises

Warm Up Exercises

In Exercises 1–6, fill in the blanks with an appropriate word, phrase, or symbol(s).

1. A path that passes through each edge of a graph exactly one time is called a(n) _____ path. Euler

2. A circuit that passes through each edge of a graph exactly one time is called a(n) _____ circuit. Euler

3. A connected graph has at least one Euler path that is also an Euler circuit, if the graph has _____ odd vertices. No

4. A connected graph has at least one Euler path, but no Euler circuits, if the graph has exactly _____ odd vertices. Two

5. A connected graph has neither an Euler path nor an Euler circuit, if the graph has more than two _____ vertices. Odd

6. If a connected graph has exactly two odd vertices, *A* and *B*, then each Euler path must begin at vertex *A* and end at vertex _____, or begin at vertex *B* and end at vertex *A*. *B*

Practice the Skills

For Exercises 7–10, use the following graph.

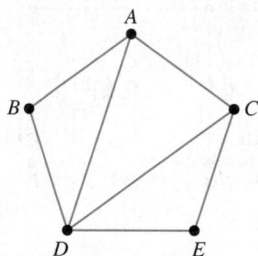

7. Determine an Euler path that begins with vertex *A*.
   A, B, D, E, C, A, D, C

8. Determine an Euler path that begins with vertex *C*.
   C, E, D, B, A, C, D, A

9. Is it possible to determine an Euler path that begins with vertex *B*? Explain. No. This graph has exactly two odd vertices. Each Euler path must begin with an odd vertex. *B* is an even vertex.

10. Is it possible to determine an Euler circuit for this graph? Explain. No. A graph with exactly two odd vertices has no Euler circuits.

For Exercises 11–14, use the following graph.

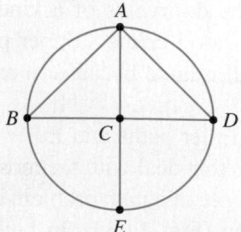

11. Determine an Euler path that begins with vertex *A*.
    A, B, A, C, B, E, C, D, A, D, E

12. Determine an Euler path that begins with vertex *E*.
    E, D, A, B, E, C, D, A, B, C, A

13. Is it possible to determine an Euler circuit for this graph? Explain. No. A graph with exactly two odd vertices has no Euler circuits.

14. Is it possible to determine an Euler path that begins with vertex *C*? Explain. No. This graph has exactly two odd vertices. Each Euler path must begin with an odd vertex. *C* is an even vertex.

For Exercises 15–20, use the following graph.

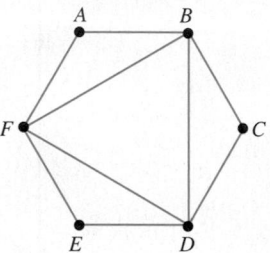

15. Determine an Euler circuit that begins and ends with vertex *A*. *A, B, C, D, E, F, B, D, F, A*

16. Determine an Euler circuit that begins and ends with vertex *B*. *B, C, D, E, F, A, B, D, F, B*

17. Determine an Euler circuit that begins and ends with vertex *C*. *C, D, E, F, A, B, D, F, B, C*

18. Determine an Euler circuit that begins and ends with vertex *D*. *D, E, F, A, B, C, D, F, B, D*

19. Determine an Euler circuit that begins and ends with vertex *E*. *E, F, A, B, C, D, F, B, D, E*

20. Determine an Euler circuit that begins and ends with vertex *F*. *F, A, B, F, D, B, C, D, E, F*

21. Imagine a very large connected graph that has 400 even vertices and no odd vertices.

    a) Does an Euler path exist for this graph? Explain.
       Yes. There are no odd vertices.
    b) Does an Euler circuit exist for this graph? Explain.
       Yes. There are no odd vertices.

22. Imagine a very large connected graph that has two odd vertices and 398 even vertices.

    a) Does an Euler path exist for this graph? Explain.
       Yes. There are exactly two odd vertices.
    b) Does an Euler circuit exist for this graph? Explain.
       No. There is at least one odd vertex.

23. Imagine a very large connected graph that has 400 odd vertices and no even vertices.

    a) Does an Euler path exist for this graph? Explain.
       No. There are more than two odd vertices.
    b) Does an Euler circuit exist for this graph? Explain.
       No. There is at least one odd vertex.

24. Imagine a very large connected graph that has 200 odd vertices and 200 even vertices.

a) Does an Euler path exist for this graph? Explain.
No. There are more than two odd vertices.

b) Does an Euler circuit exist for this graph? Explain.
No. There is at least one odd vertex.

Problem Solving

Revisiting the Königsberg Bridge Problem In Exercises 25 and 26, suppose that the people of Königsberg decide to add several bridges to their city. Two such possibilities are shown.

a) *Would the townspeople be able to walk across all the bridges without crossing the same bridge twice?*

b) *If so, where should they begin and where would they end?*

25.

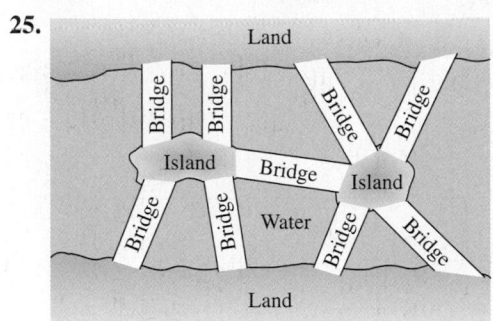

a) Yes
b) They could start on either island and finish at the other.

26.

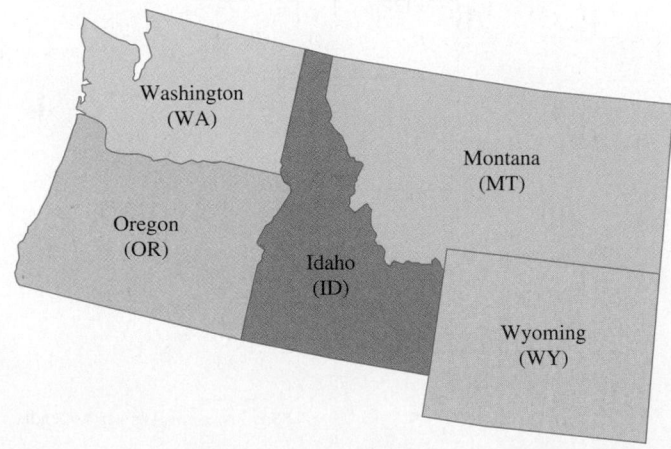

a) Yes
b) They could start either on the land at the top of the artwork or on the island on the left. If they started on the island, they would end on the land at the top, and vice versa.

Other Navy Regions In Exercises 27 and 28, the maps of states that are in other Navy regions (see Example 4 on page 867) are shown. Use these graphs to answer the questions.

27. Navy Region Northwest

a) *Represent the map as a graph. Use the state abbreviations to label the vertices of the graph.* *

b) *Determine (state yes or no) whether the graph in part (a) has an Euler circuit. If yes, give one such Euler circuit.* Yes; WA, ID, MT, WY, ID, OR, WA

28. Navy Region Southeast

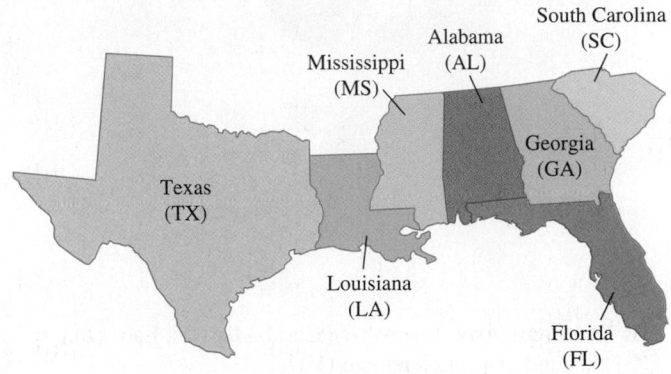

a) *Represent the map as a graph. Use the state abbreviations to label the vertices of the graph.* *

b) *Determine (state yes or no) whether the graph in part (a) has an Euler path or an Euler circuit. If yes, give one such Euler path or circuit.* No

Areas of the World In Exercises 29–32 use each map shown.

a) *Represent the map as a graph. Use the letter indicated in parentheses to label vertices of the graph.*

b) *Determine (state yes or no) whether the graph in part (a) has an Euler path. If yes, give one such Euler path.*

c) *Determine (state yes or no) whether the graph in part (a) has an Euler circuit. If yes, give one such Euler circuit.*

29. *Southwest Asia* Afghanistan (A), Iran (N), Iraq (Q), Jordan (J), Pakistan (P), and Turkey (T)
a)* b) Yes; J, Q, T, N, A, P, N, Q c) No

*See Instructor Answer Appendix

30. *Central Europe* Austria (*A*), Czech Republic (*C*), Germany (*G*), Italy (*I*), Poland (*P*), and Switzerland (*S*)
a) *   b) Yes; *S, I, A, S, G, A, C, G P C*   c) No

31. *Southeast Asia* Burma (*B*), Cambodia (*C*), Laos (*L*), Thailand (*T*), and Vietnam (*V*)
a) *   b) Yes; *T, B, L, V, C, L, T, C*   c) No

32. *South America* Argentina (*A*), Bolivia (*B*), Brazil (*Z*), Chile (*C*), Paraguay (*P*), and Uruguay (*U*)
a) *   b) Yes; *P, B, Z, P, A, B, C, A, U, Z, A*   c) No

Locking Doors *Joe Mays, the custodian at the Pullen Academy (see Example 5 on page 868), is also responsible for locking the doors of four other buildings. The floor plans for these buildings are shown in Exercises 33–36.*

a) *Represent each floor plan as a graph. Use the letters shown to label the vertices of the graph and use the letter O to label the vertex that represents the outside of the building. Place vertex O near where the word Outside is placed in the diagram.*

b) *Determine (state yes or no) whether it is possible for Joe to move through the building using each doorway of the building exactly one time. (In other words, does an Euler path exist in the graph?)*

c) *If your answer to part (b) is yes, determine one such Euler path.*

33. Administration Building

a) *   b) Yes   c) *O, A, B, C, D, F, C, E, O, A*

34. Library

a) *   b) Yes   c) *O, E, C, B, A, D, O* (which is also an Euler circuit)

35. Computer Center

a) *   b) No

36. Fitness Center

a) *   b) Yes   c) *D, C, A, B, D, E, B, O, E*

Crime Stopper Routes *The Country Oaks crime stopper organization (see Example 6 on page 869) was so successful that the residents shared their strategies with friends living in the subdivisions of Crescent Lakes and Tree Tops. In Exercises 37 and 38, the respective maps of these communities are given.*

a) *Determine whether the residents in each subdivision will be able to establish a path through their communities so that each street block is walked exactly one time.*

b) *If yes, where would the residents need to start their walk?*

37. Tree Tops a) Yes b) The residents would need to start at the intersection of Maple Cir., Walnut St., and Willow St. or at the intersection of Walnut St. and Oak St.

38. Crescent Lakes

a) Yes b) The residents would need to start at the intersection of Spring Blvd. and Lake St. or at the rightmost intersection of Stream Cir. and Ocean Blvd.

In Exercises 39–42, use Fleury's algorithm to determine an Euler path.

39.

B, A, C, E, D, B, C

40.

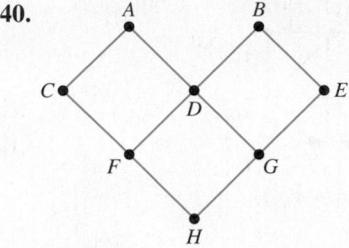

F, C, A, D, B, E, G, H, F, D, G

41.

H, I, F, C, B, D, G, H, E, D, A, B, E, F

42.

D, A, B, E, I, H, D, C, G, K, L, H, M, I, N, O, J, F, E

In Exercises 43–48, use Fleury's algorithm to determine an Euler circuit.

43.

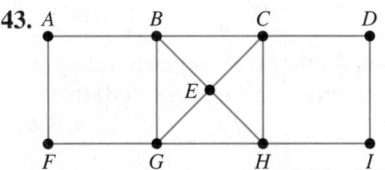

A, B, C, D, I, H, G, B, E, H, C, E, G, F, A

44.

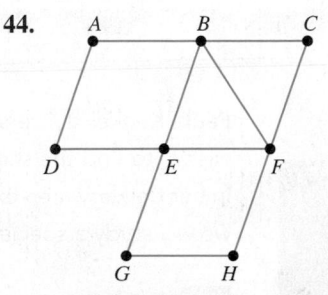

A, B, C, F, H, G, E, B, F, E, D, A

45.

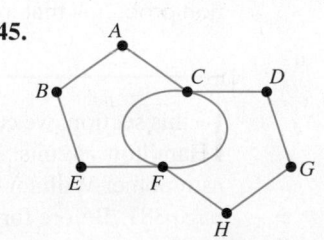

A, C, D, G, H, F, C, F, E, B, A

46.

A, B, C, D, F, C, B, E, F, H, G, E, A

47.

A, B, C, E, B, D, E, F, I, E, H, D, G, H, I, J, F, C, A

48.

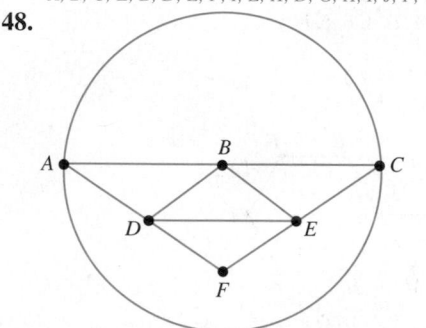

A, B, C, E, B, D, E, F, D, A, C, A

49. Determine an Euler path through the states in the Navy Region Southwest (see Example 4 on page 867) that begins with the state of Utah. *UT, CO, NM, AZ, CA, NV, UT, AZ, NV*

50. Determine an Euler path for the kindergarten building at the Pullen Academy (see Example 5 on page 868) that begins in restroom (vertex) *A*. *A, O, H, C, B, K, H, R, A, S, H, O*

51. Determine an Euler circuit for the Country Oaks crime stopper group (see Example 6 on page 869) that begins with vertex *B* followed by vertex *A*.
B, A, E, H, I, J, K, D, C, G, G, J, F, C, B, F, I, E, B

52. Determine an Euler circuit for the Country Oaks crime stopper group (see Example 6 on page 869) that begins with vertex *B* followed by vertex *E*.
B, E, I, F, B, C, F, J, G, G, C, D, K, J, I, H, E, A, B

53. Determine an Euler circuit for the Country Oaks crime stopper group that begins with vertex *J* followed by vertex *G*.
J, G, G, C, F, J, K, D, C, B, F, I, E, B, A, E, H, I, J

54. Determine an Euler circuit for the Country Oaks crime stopper group that begins with vertex *J* followed by vertex *F*.
J, F, C, B, F, I, E, B, A, E, H, I, J, G, G, C, D, K, J

Challenge Problems/Group Activities

55. Consider a map of the contiguous United States. Imagine a graph with 48 vertices in which each vertex represents one of the contiguous states. Each edge would represent a common border between states.

   a) Would this graph have an Euler path? No

   b) Explain why or why not.*

56. Attempt to draw a graph with an Euler circuit that has a bridge. What conclusion can you develop from this exercise?
It is not possible to draw a graph with an Euler circuit that has a bridge. Therefore, a graph with an Euler circuit has no bridge.

57. a) Draw a graph with one vertex that has both an Euler path and an Euler circuit.*

   b) Draw a graph with two vertices that has an Euler path but no Euler circuit.*

   c) Draw a graph with two vertices that has both an Euler path and an Euler circuit.*

Internet/Research Activity

58. Write a paper on the history and development of the branch of mathematics known as graph theory.

*See Instructor Answer Appendix

SECTION 14.3   Hamilton Paths and Hamilton Circuits

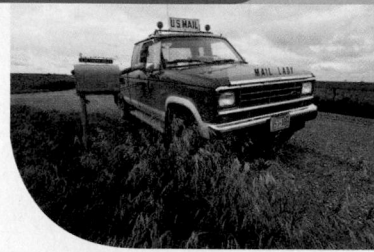

▲ *Graph theory can be used to determine the shortest route for a mail carrier.*

Paula Kunkel delivers mail in a rural area for the United States Postal Service. Paula wishes to find the shortest route that begins at the post office, goes to each mailbox in her delivery area exactly one time, and ends back at the post office. In this section, we will study a special type of problem like the one facing Paula.

Why **This is Important** Graph theory can be used to represent and solve transportation problems that involve finding the most efficient route to complete tasks.

I n this section, we continue our study of graph theory by studying Hamilton paths and Hamilton circuits. These paths and circuits are named for Irish mathematician and astronomer William Rowan Hamilton (1805–1865); see the *Profile in Mathematics* on page 881. Before formally defining Hamilton paths and Hamilton circuits, we will introduce an example that will be examined at several points throughout this section.

┌─ **Example 1** *A Transportation Problem*

Julienne Ward has just been promoted to Southeast District Sales Director for the Addison Wesley Publishing Company. She lives in Orlando, Florida, and oversees regional sales offices in Orlando; Atlanta, Georgia; Memphis, Tennessee; and New Orleans, Louisiana. She frequently needs to fly to each regional office for sales meetings. She would like to determine the least expensive route to visit each city one time and then return to Orlando. To help analyze this problem, Julienne used the Internet to find the least expensive one-way fares offered between each of the four cities (see Table 14.1).

Table 14.1

	Orlando	Atlanta	Memphis	New Orleans
Orlando (O)	*	$67	$95	$69
Atlanta (A)	$67	*	$57	$68
Memphis (M)	$95	$57	*	$99
New Orleans (N)	$69	$68	$99	*

Use this table to create a graph. Let the vertices represent the cities, then connect each pair of cities with an edge. List the airfare between each two cities on the respective edges.

Solution First we note that the cost of a one-way flight between two given cities in the table is the same regardless from which city Julienne starts. For example, the one-way fare from New Orleans to Atlanta is $68 and the one-way fare from Atlanta to New Orleans is also $68. This information will allow us to list the flight cost along an edge with a single number. Next we draw a graph with four vertices that represent the four cities and six edges that represent the flights between each city. We also include the price of one-way flights along the appropriate edge. Two such graphs are shown in Fig. 14.35. Many other graphs could also display this information. ∎

(a)

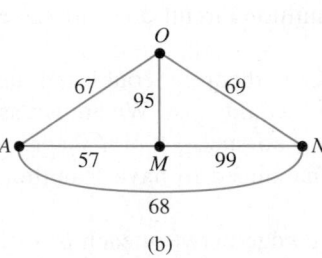

(b)

Figure 14.35

Problems like the one in Example 1 are called *traveling salesman problems*. There are usually variations to the situation, but these problems generally involve seeking the least expensive or shortest way to travel among several locations. To help analyze traveling salesman problems, the costs or distances to travel between locations are indicated along each edge of a graph. Such a graph, as in Fig. 14.35(a) or (b), is called a *weighted graph*. We will use weighted graphs to solve traveling salesman problems, but first we need to introduce Hamilton paths and Hamilton circuits.

Hamilton Paths, Hamilton Circuits, and Complete Graphs

Now we introduce another important definition of graph theory.

Definition: Hamilton Path
A **Hamilton path** is a path that contains each *vertex* of a graph exactly one time.

(a)

(b)

Figure 14.36

(a)

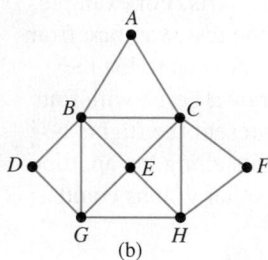

(b)

Figure 14.37

The graph in Fig. 14.36(a) has Hamilton path A, B, C, E, D. The graph in Fig. 14.36(a) also has Hamilton path C, B, A, D, E. The graph in Fig. 14.36(b) has a Hamilton path A, B, C, F, H, E, G, D. The graph in Fig. 14.36(b) also has Hamilton path G, D, E, H, F, C, B, A. Both of the graphs in Fig. 14.36 have other Hamilton paths. Can you find some of them?

Notice that, unlike Euler paths, not every edge needs to be traced in a Hamilton path. To help distinguish between Euler paths and Hamilton paths, remember that *Euler paths are concerned with visiting all the edges, whereas Hamilton paths are concerned with visiting all the vertices.*

Now we introduce Hamilton circuits.

Definition: Hamilton Circuit

A **Hamilton circuit** is a path that begins and ends at the same vertex and passes through all other vertices of a graph exactly one time.

An alternate definition for a Hamilton circuit is that a Hamilton circuit is a Hamilton path that starts and ends at the same vertex. For example, the graph in Fig. 14.37(a) has Hamilton circuit A, B, C, E, D, A. The graph in Fig. 14.37(a) also has Hamilton circuit B, A, D, E, C, B. The graph in Fig. 14.37(b) has Hamilton circuit A, B, D, G, E, H, F, C, A. The graph in Fig. 14.37(b) also has Hamilton circuit E, G, D, B, A, C, F, H, E. Note that in an **_Euler_ circuit**, the path followed must include every edge and must begin and end at the same vertex. In a **_Hamilton_ circuit**, the path followed must include every vertex and must begin and end at the same vertex. Unlike the Euler circuit, however, a Hamilton circuit does not have to include every edge.

In Section 14.2, we were fortunate that Euler's theorem could tell us under what conditions an Euler path or an Euler circuit would exist. We are not as fortunate with Hamilton paths and Hamilton circuits; no such general theorem exists. We now shift our focus to graphs that are guaranteed to have Hamilton circuits.

A *complete graph* is a graph that has exactly one edge between each pair of its vertices. Figure 14.38 shows complete graphs with three, four, and five vertices, respectively.

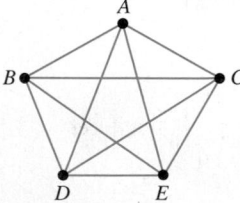

Figure 14.38

Complete graphs are important because *every complete graph has a Hamilton circuit* (but not necessarily an Euler circuit), and traveling salesman problems can be represented by complete graphs. Since each pair of vertices on a complete graph is connected by an edge, we can create a Hamilton circuit by simply starting at any vertex and moving from vertex to vertex until we have passed through each vertex exactly one time. Then to complete the circuit we simply move back to the vertex from which we started. Notice in Fig. 14.38 that although all the graphs have Hamilton circuits, only the first and third graphs have Euler circuits.

Example 2 *Finding Hamilton Circuits*

Determine a Hamilton circuit for the complete graph shown in Fig. 14.39.

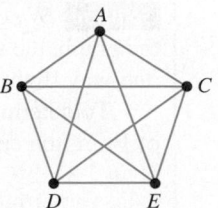

Figure 14.39

Solution We can determine many Hamilton circuits in this complete graph. For example, one is A, B, C, D, E, A. Another is B, A, D, C, E, B. Another is E, B, C, D, A, E. To build a Hamilton circuit from this complete graph, we can list all five vertices in any order and then return to the first vertex. ∎

A question that naturally arises from Example 2 is, "How many different Hamilton circuits are there in a complete graph?" Before we can give a formula that answers this question, we need to discuss *factorials*, which were presented in Section 12.8. We will review that material here. The symbol 5! is read "five factorial" and means to multiply 5 by each natural number less than 5. So $5! = 5 \cdot 4 \cdot 3 \cdot 2 \cdot 1 = 120$. Also $3! = 3 \cdot 2 \cdot 1 = 6$ and $7! = 7 \cdot 6 \cdot 5 \cdot 4 \cdot 3 \cdot 2 \cdot 1 = 5040$. Note that 0! is defined to be 1.

Number of Unique Hamilton Circuits in a Complete Graph

The number of unique Hamilton circuits in a complete graph with n vertices is $(n - 1)!$, where

$$(n - 1)! = (n - 1)(n - 2)(n - 3) \cdots (3)(2)(1)$$

Example 3 *Number of Hamilton Circuits*

How many unique Hamilton circuits are in a complete graph with the following number of vertices?

a) Four   b) Seven   c) Nine   d) Twelve

Solution

a) According to the formula, a complete graph with four vertices has
   $(4 - 1)! = 3! = 3 \cdot 2 \cdot 1 = 6$ unique Hamilton circuits.

b) A complete graph with seven vertices has
   $(7 - 1)! = 6! = 6 \cdot 5 \cdot 4 \cdot 3 \cdot 2 \cdot 1 = 720$ unique Hamilton circuits.

c) A complete graph with nine vertices has
   $(9 - 1)! = 8! = 8 \cdot 7 \cdot 6 \cdot 5 \cdot 4 \cdot 3 \cdot 2 \cdot 1 = 40{,}320$ unique Hamilton circuits.

d) A complete graph with twelve vertices has $(12 - 1)! = 11!$
   $= 11 \cdot 10 \cdot 9 \cdot 8 \cdot 7 \cdot 6 \cdot 5 \cdot 4 \cdot 3 \cdot 2 \cdot 1 = 39{,}916{,}800$ unique Hamilton circuits. ∎

Example 4 *American Idol Travel*

▲ *Steven Tyler, Jennifer Lopez, and Randy Jackson*

Steven Tyler, Jennifer Lopez, and Randy Jackson, the judges for the television show *American Idol*, are in Hollywood (H). They need to travel to the following cities to judge contestants' auditions: San Antonio (SA), East Rutherford (ER),

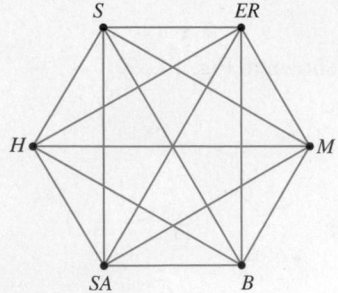

Figure 14.40

Birmingham (B), Memphis (M), and Seattle (S). In how many different ways can Steven, Jennifer, and Randy, traveling together, visit each of these cities and return to Hollywood?

Solution   We can represent this problem with the complete graph in Fig. 14.40. In the graph, the six vertices represent the six locations and the edges represent the one-way flights between these locations.

To determine the number of possible routes, we need to determine the number of Hamilton circuits within this graph. We know that there are $(6 - 1)! = 5! = 5 \cdot 4 \cdot 3 \cdot 2 \cdot 1 = 120$ different Hamilton circuits within this graph. So the judges have 120 different ways to start in Hollywood, visit each of these five cities, and return to Hollywood.   ■

Now that we have been introduced to Hamilton circuits, we will apply this knowledge to solving traveling salesman problems.

Traveling Salesman Problems

In Examples 1 and 4, we saw how complete graphs can represent cities and the process of traveling between these cities. Our goal in a traveling salesman problem is to find the least expensive or shortest way to visit each city once and return home. In terms of graph theory, our goal is to find the Hamilton circuit with the lowest associated cost or distance. The Hamilton circuit with the lowest associated cost (or shortest distance, etc.) is called the *optimal solution*. We will discuss two methods, the *brute force method* and the *nearest neighbor method*, for determining the optimal solution. In both methods, we will use the term *complete, weighted graph*. A *complete, weighted graph* is a complete graph with the weights (or numbers) listed on the edges, as illustrated in Fig. 14.41. We now introduce the brute force method.

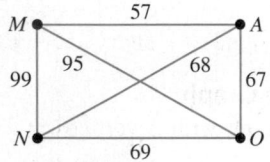

Figure 14.41

PROCEDURE   **THE BRUTE FORCE METHOD OF SOLVING TRAVELING SALESMAN PROBLEMS**

To determine the optimal solution:

1. Represent the problem with a complete, weighted graph.

2. List all possible Hamilton circuits for this graph.

3. Determine the cost (or distance) associated with each of these Hamilton circuits.

4. The Hamilton circuit with the lowest cost (or shortest distance) is the optimal solution.

Example 5   *Using the Brute Force Method*

In Example 1 on page 877, we introduced Julienne Ward, the Southeast District Sales Director for Addison Wesley. We now want to use the brute force method to determine the optimal solution for Julienne to visit her regional sales offices. She will start in Orlando (O); visit offices in Atlanta (A), Memphis (M), and New Orleans (N); and then return to Orlando.

Solution   We illustrated two complete, weighted graphs for the example in Fig. 14.35 on page 877. The graph in Fig. 14.35(a) is repeated in Fig. 14.41. The numbers shown represent the one-way fares, in dollars, between the two cities.

We know that since there are 4 cities that must be visited, there are $(4 - 1)! = 3! = 6$ possible unique Hamilton circuits we need to examine for cost. These Hamilton circuits are listed in the first column of Table 14.2 on page 881.

Table 14.2

Hamilton Circuit	First Leg/Cost	Second Leg/Cost	Third Leg/Cost	Fourth Leg/Cost	Total Cost
O, A, M, N, O	O to A $67	A to M $57	M to N $99	N to O $69	$292
O, A, N, M, O	O to A $67	A to N $68	N to M $99	M to O $95	$329
O, M, A, N, O	O to M $95	M to A $57	A to N $68	N to O $69	($289)
O, M, N, A, O	O to M $95	M to N $99	N to A $68	A to O $67	$329
O, N, A, M, O	O to N $69	N to A $68	A to M $57	M to O $95	($289)
O, N, M, A, O	O to N $69	N to M $99	M to A $57	A to O $67	$292

The Hamilton circuits are listed in the column on the far left. In the next four columns, we place the cost associated with each leg of the given circuit. In the last column, we place the total cost of travel using the given circuit. From this last column, we see that two circuits have the lowest cost of $289 (circled). Julienne has two choices for an optimal solution. She can either fly from Orlando to Memphis to Atlanta to New Orleans then back to Orlando, or she can fly from Orlando to New Orleans to Atlanta to Memphis then back to Orlando. These two Hamilton circuits are shown on the maps in Fig. 14.42. Notice that the second circuit involves visiting the cities in the exact reverse order of the first circuit. Although these are different circuits, the cost is the same regardless of the direction flown. Either circuit provides Julienne with the least expensive way to visit each of her regional sales offices.

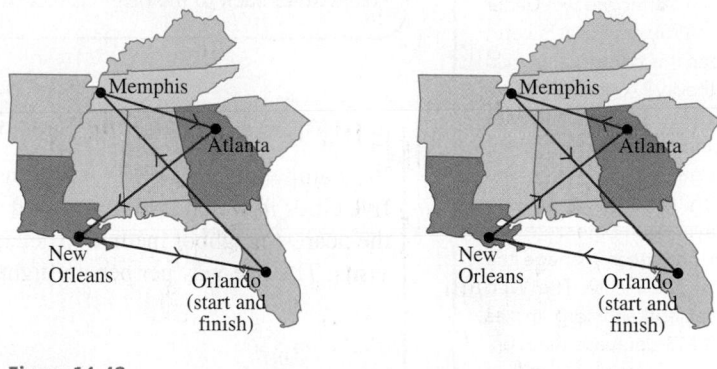

Figure 14.42

Although we used the brute force method in Example 5, it becomes impractical as the number of vertices increases. In fact, with more complex problems, the brute force method is impractical on even the world's fastest supercomputers. For example, suppose that a presidential candidate wished to visit each of the 31 largest cities in the United States. The candidate would have 30! or about 3×10^{32} choices to accomplish this trip. To understand the magnitude of this number, consider that it would take the world's fastest supercomputer (as of January 2011) about 13,000,000,000 (13 *billion*) *years* to perform the brute force method to find the optimal solution. Computer scientists and mathematicians have developed much more efficient algorithms for approximating the optimal solution to traveling salesman problems.

Now we introduce a method for finding an *approximate solution* to a traveling salesman problem. Approximate solutions can be used in cases where determining the optimal solution is not reasonable. One method for finding an approximate solution is the *nearest neighbor method*. In this method, the salesperson begins at a given location. If the salesperson wishes to minimize the distance traveled, the salesperson first visits the city (or location) closest to his or her starting location. Then the salesperson visits the next city (or location) closest to his or her present location. This process continues until all the cities (or locations) are visited. Thus, the salesperson moves to the *nearest neighbor*. Sometimes the salesperson wishes to minimize the cost of travel, such as airfare. In this case, from the starting location the salesperson first visits the city (or location) in which the cost of travel is a minimum. Then from the present location, the salesperson visits the city (or location) where the cost of travel is a minimum. This process continues until all the cities (or locations) are visited. Approximate solutions will always be Hamilton circuits.

PROCEDURE   **NEAREST NEIGHBOR METHOD OF DETERMINING AN APPROXIMATE SOLUTION TO A TRAVELING SALESMAN PROBLEM**

To approximate the optimal solution:

1. Represent the problem with a complete, weighted graph.

2. Identify the starting vertex.

3. Of all the edges attached to the starting vertex, choose the edge that has the smallest weight. This edge is generally either the shortest distance or the lowest cost. Travel along this edge to the second vertex.

4. At the second vertex, choose the edge that has the smallest weight that does not lead to a vertex already visited. Travel along this edge to the third vertex.

5. Continue this process, each time moving along the edge with the smallest weight until all vertices are visited.

6. Travel back to the original vertex.

Example 6   *Using the Nearest Neighbor Method*

In Example 4 on page 879, we discussed the *American Idol* judges' plan to visit five cities in which auditions would take place and then return to Hollywood. Use the nearest neighbor method to determine an approximate solution for the judges' visits. The one-way per person flight prices between cities are given in Table 14.3.

Table 14.3

	Birmingham	East Rutherford	Hollywood	Memphis	San Antonio	Seattle
Birmingham (*B*)	*	$258	$114	$324	$274	$155
East Rutherford (*ER*)	$258	*	$134	$104	$355	$154
Hollywood (*H*)	$114	$134	*	$144	$129	$108
Memphis (*M*)	$324	$104	$144	*	$634	$299
San Antonio (*SA*)	$274	$355	$129	$634	*	$119
Seattle (*S*)	$155	$154	$108	$299	$119	*

Solution We will use the nearest neighbor method to determine the least expensive per person cost for the judges to complete the trip. We begin by modifying the graph from Example 4 by putting the one-way per person prices into place, making it a weighted graph (see Fig. 14.43). The judges start in Hollywood and choose the least expensive flight, which is to Seattle ($108). In Seattle, the judges choose the least expensive flight to a location they have not already visited, San Antonio ($119). Next, in San Antonio, they choose the least expensive flight to a location they have not already visited, Birmingham ($274). In Birmingham, they choose the least expensive flight to a location they have not already visited, East Rutherford ($258). Once in East Rutherford, the judges have no choice but to fly to the only location not yet visited, Memphis ($104). Since they began in Hollywood, are now in Memphis, and have visited all five audition cities, the judges now return to Hollywood ($144) to complete their trip. The nearest neighbor method would produce a Hamilton circuit, of *H, S, SA, B, ER, M, H*. The cost per person is $108 + $119 + $274 + $258 + $104 + $144 = $1007. The total cost for all three judges is $1007 × 3, or $3021.

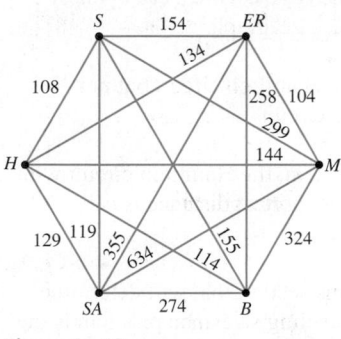

Figure 14.43

For the sake of comparison, let us look at four other randomly chosen Hamilton circuits from Example 6 and the per person costs associated with them (see Table 14.4).

Table 14.4

Randomly Chosen Hamilton Circuit	Cost Calculation	Per Person Cost
H, SA, ER, B, M, S, H	$129 + $355 + $258 + $324 + $299 + $108	$1473
H, M, S, B, ER, SA, H	$144 + $299 + $155 + $258 + $355 + $129	$1340
H, ER, S, M, SA, B, H	$134 + $154 + $299 + $634 + $274 + $114	$1609
H, ER, M, B, S, SA, H	$134 + $104 + $324 + $155 + $119 + $129	$ 965

From Table 14.4, we see that the Hamilton circuit *H, ER, M, B, S, SA, H* results in a per person cost of $965, which is less than the $1007 we obtained in Example 6. Thus, we see that the nearest neighbor method does not always produce the optimal solution. Without using the brute force method, we cannot determine if the Hamilton circuit *H, ER, M, B, S, SA, H* is the optimal solution. The nearest neighbor method produces an *approximation* for the optimal solution. Note also that the nearest neighbor method did produce a Hamilton circuit that was less expensive than three of the four randomly chosen Hamilton circuits.

Warm Up Exercises

In Exercises 1–8, fill in the blanks with an appropriate word, phrase, or symbol(s).

1. Problems that generally involve seeking the least expensive or shortest way to travel among several locations are called traveling _____ problems. Salesman

2. A graph that has numbers along the edges to indicate cost or distance is called a(n) _____ graph. Weighted

3. A path that begins and ends at the same vertex and passes through all other vertices of a graph exactly one time is called a(n) _____ circuit. Hamilton

4. A graph that has exactly one edge between each pair of vertices is called a(n) _____ graph. Complete

5. Every complete graph has a Hamilton circuit but not necessarily a(n) _____ circuit. Euler

6. In a traveling salesman problem, the Hamilton circuit with the lowest associated cost or shortest distance is called the _____ solution. Optimal

7. The method discussed in this section that will determine the optimal solution to a traveling salesman problem is the brute _____ method. Force

8. The method discussed in this section that will determine an approximate solution to a traveling salesman problem is the nearest _____ method. Neighbor

Practice the Skills

In Exercises 9–14, determine two different Hamilton paths in each of the following graphs.

9.
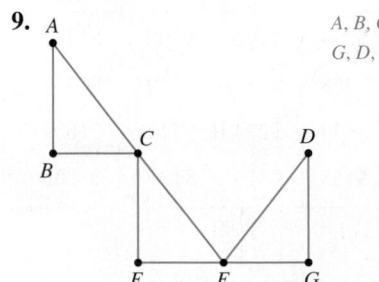
A, B, C, E, F, G, D and
G, D, F, E, C, A, B

10.
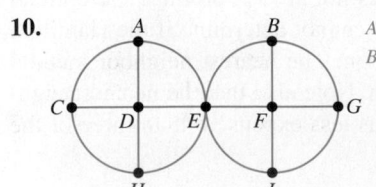
A, C, D, H, E, F, B, G, I and
B, G, I, F, E, A, D, H, C

11.

A, B, C, D, G, F, E, H and
E, H, F, G, D, C, A, B

12.
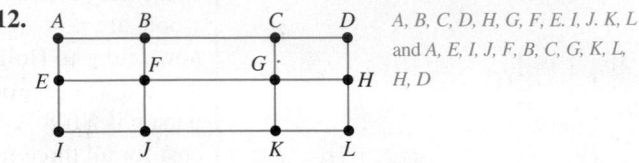
A, B, C, D, H, G, F, E. I, J, K, L
and A, E, I, J, F, B, C, G, K, L,
H, D

13.
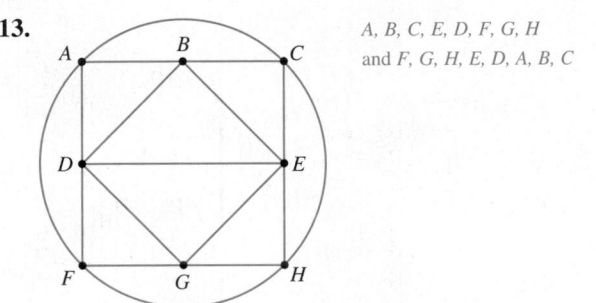
A, B, C, E, D, F, G, H
and F, G, H, E, D, A, B, C

14.

A, D, F, G, H, E, B, C, I
and I, C, B, A, D, E, F, H, G

In Exercises 15–18, determine two different Hamilton circuits in each of the following graphs.

15.
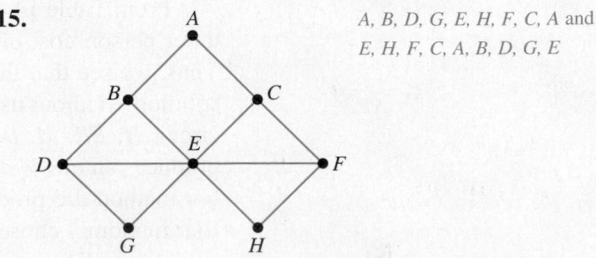
A, B, D, G, E, H, F, C, A and
E, H, F, C, A, B, D, G, E

16.

A, B, C, D, H, L, K, G, F, J, I, E, A and
A, E, I, J, K, L, H, D, C, G, F, B, A

17.

A, B, C, F, I, E, H, G, D, A and
A, E, B, C, F, I, H, G, D, A

18.

D, H, G, F, C, E, B, A, D and A, B, C, E, F, G, H, D, A

19. Draw a complete graph with four vertices.*

20. Draw a complete graph with five vertices.*

Problem Solving

21. *College Visits* Alex Runde is a high school student who lives in Bradenton, FL, and he wishes to visit colleges in the following cities: St. Cloud, MN; Valparaiso, IN; Lindonville, VT; Asheville, NC; and Norman, OK. In how many different ways can Alex visit each of these cities and return home to Bradenton? 5! = 120 ways

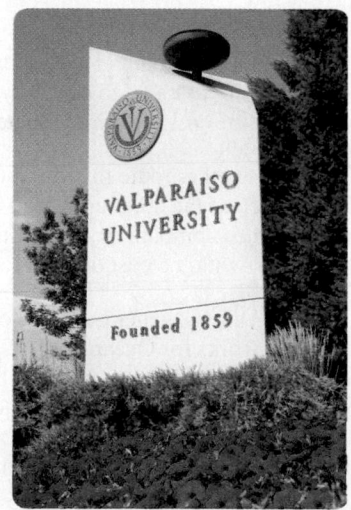
▲ *Valparaiso University*

22. *Culver's Restaurants* Craig Culver, founder of Culver's Restaurants, is at his home in Prairie du Sac, WI, and wishes to investigate locations for a new restaurant in the following cities: Robinson, IL; Erie, PA; Memphis, TN; Little Rock, AR; Tulsa, OK; Topeka, KS; and Dickinson, ND. In how many ways can Craig visit each of these cities and return to his home in Prairie du Sac? 7! = 5040 ways

23. *Inspecting Weigh Stations* Sally Ivan lives in Nashville, Tennessee, and works for the Department of Transportation. She wishes to inspect weigh stations in the following Tennessee cities: Caruthersville, Clarksville, Cleveland, Dyersburg, Jackson, Johnson City, Kingsport, Knoxville, Memphis, Murfreesboro, Oak Ridge, and Pulaski. In how many ways can she visit each of these cities and return to her home in Nashville? 12! = 479,001,600 ways

24. *A Milk Truck Route* Dale Klitzke is a milk truck driver for Swiss Valley Farms Cooperative in eastern Iowa. Dale has to start at the processing plant and pick up milk on 10 different farms. In how many ways can Dale visit each farm and return to the processing plant? 10! = 3,628,800 ways

25. *A Vacationing Family* John and Robyn Pearse promised their three sons that they will each get to pick one spot within 500 miles from their home in Chicago to visit on their vacation. Scott chooses to visit St. Louis so that he can go up in the Gateway Arch. Jacob chooses to visit Green Bay so that he can visit the National Railroad Museum. Jevon chooses to visit Ottawa, Illinois, so that he can visit his grandparents. The approximate distances between these cities are as follows: Chicago to St. Louis is 300 miles, Chicago to Green Bay is 205 miles, Chicago to Ottawa is 80 miles, St. Louis to Green Bay is 500 miles, St. Louis to Ottawa is 245 miles, and Green Bay to Ottawa is 280 miles.

▲ *The Gateway Arch in St. Louis, Missouri*

a) Represent this traveling salesman problem with a complete, weighted graph showing the distances on the appropriate edges. *

b) Use the brute force method to determine the shortest route for the Pearses to complete their vacation.
C, G, S, O, C or C, G, O, S, C or C, S, O, G, C, or C, O, S, G, C

c) What is the minimum distance the Pearses can travel? 1030 miles

26. *Job Interviews* Christina Dwyer is searching for a new job. She lives in Shreveport, Louisiana, and has interviews in Barrow, Alaska; Tucson, Arizona; and Rochester, New York. The costs of the one-way flights between these four cities are as follows: Shreveport to Barrow costs $855, Shreveport to Tucson costs $803, Shreveport to Rochester

*See Instructor Answer Appendix

costs $113, Barrow to Tucson costs $393, Barrow to Rochester costs $337, and Tucson to Rochester costs $841.

a) Represent this traveling salesman problem with a complete, weighted graph showing the prices of the flights on the appropriate edges.*

b) Use the brute force method to determine the least expensive route for Christina to travel to each city and return home to Shreveport. *S, T, B, R, S* or *S, R, B, T, S*

c) What is the minimum cost she can pay? $1646

27. *Picking up Children* Kristin Greenhalgh has to pick up her children, who all attend different schools. She is at home (*H*) and needs to go to Children First Preschool (*C*), Braden River Elementary School (*B*), and Stephens Middle School (*S*). Kristin estimates the distance among these locations as follows: *H* to *C* is 7 miles, *H* to *B* is 5 miles, *H* to *S* is 13 miles, *C* to *B* is 11 miles, *C* to *S* is 18 miles, and *B* to *S* is 9 miles.

a) Represent this traveling salesman problem with a complete, weighted graph showing the distances on the appropriate edges.*

b) Use the brute force method to determine the shortest route for Kristin to start from home, pick up her children, and return to home. *H, C, S, B, H* or *H, B, S, C, H*

c) What is the minimum distance Kristin can travel? 39 miles

28. *Running Errands on Campus* Mary Mahan needs to run errands on the campus of Clarke College. She is in her office and needs to go to the duplicating center, student center, and library. She estimates the walking distances as follows: From her office to the duplicating center is 150 feet, from her office to the student center is 100 feet, from her office to the library is 400 feet, from the duplicating center to the student center is 125 feet, from the duplicating center to the library is 450 feet, and from the student center to the library is 250 feet.

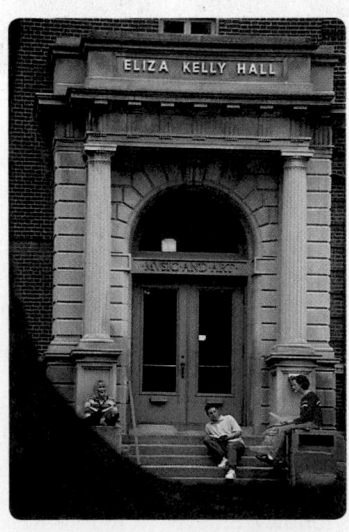

▲ *Clarke College in Dubuque, Iowa*

a) Represent this traveling salesman problem with a complete, weighted graph showing the distances on the appropriate edges.*

b) Use the brute force method to determine the shortest route for Mary to accomplish her errands and then return back to her office. *O, D, S, L, O* or *O, L, S, D, O*

c) What is the minimum distance Mary can walk? 925 feet

29. *Bass Pro Shops* Jim Hagale, the chief executive officer of Bass Pro Shops, is at his office in Springfield, Missouri, and is considering adding new stores in the following locations: Bismarck, North Dakota; Carson City, Nevada; Helena, Montana; and Knoxville, Tennessee. He wishes to visit each of these locations and return to his office in Springfield. The one-way flight prices are given in the following table.

	Bismarck	Carson City	Helena	Knoxville	Springfield
Bismarck	*	$431	$483	$476	$378
Carson City	$431	*	$144	$159	$505
Helena	$483	$144	*	$542	$492
Knoxville	$476	$159	$542	*	$459
Springfield	$378	$505	$492	$459	*

a) Represent this traveling salesman problem with a complete, weighted graph showing the prices of flights on the appropriate edges.*

b) Use the nearest neighbor method to approximate the optimal route for Jim to travel to each city and return to Springfield. Give the cost of the route determined. *S, B, C, H, K, S* for $1954

c) Randomly select another route for Jim to travel from Springfield to each of the other cities and return to Springfield and then compute the cost of this route. Compare this cost with the cost determined in part (b). Answers will vary.

30. *Cranberry Plants* Altay Özgener lives in Boston, Massachusetts, and works for Ocean Spray Cranberries, Inc. Altay wishes to visit cranberry farms in the following locations: Madison, Wisconsin; Princeton, New Jersey; Salem, Oregon; and Walla Walla, Washington. The one-way flight prices are given in the following table.

	Boston	Madison	Princeton	Salem	Walla Walla
Boston	*	$131	$ 256	$298	$ 576
Madison	$131	*	$ 154	$356	$ 970
Princeton	$256	$154	*	$353	$1164
Salem	$298	$356	$ 353	*	$ 179
Walla Walla	$576	$970	$1164	$179	*

*See Instructor Answer Appendix

a) Represent this traveling salesman problem with a complete, weighted graph showing the prices of flights on the appropriate edges.*

b) Use the nearest neighbor method to approximate the optimal route for Altay to travel to each city and return to Boston. Give the cost of the route determined.
   B, M, P, S, W, B for $1393

c) Randomly select another route for Altay to travel from Boston to each of the other cities and return to Boston and then compute the cost of this route. Compare this cost with the cost found in part (b). Answers will vary.

31. **National Laboratories** Steven Chu, the Secretary of Energy, is at his office in Washington, DC (*W*) and needs to schedule visits to the following national research laboratories: Argonne (*A*), Brookhaven (*B*), Livermore (*L*), and Oak Ridge (*O*). He wishes to visit each laboratory and return to his office in Washington. The one-way flight prices to nearby airports are given in the following table.

	Washington	Argonne	Brookhaven	Livermore	Oak Ridge
Washington	*	$101	$ 55	$109	$555
Argonne	$101	*	$129	$135	$346
Brookhaven	$ 55	$129	*	$119	$326
Livermore	$109	$135	$119	*	$318
Oak Ridge	$555	$346	$326	$318	*

a) Represent this traveling salesman problem with a complete, weighted graph showing the prices of the flights on the appropriate edges.*

b) Use the nearest neighbor method to approximate the optimal route for Secretary Chu to travel to each laboratory and return to Washington. Give the cost of the route determined. W, B, L, A, O, W for $1210

c) Randomly select another route for Secretary Chu to travel to each laboratory and return to Washington and then compute the cost of this route. Compare this cost with the cost determined in part (b). Answers will vary.

32. **Locations for a New Factory** Darren Magot works for US Paper Products in New York City. His company is investigating locations for a new factory that will produce a line of disposable clothing. The cities Darren needs to visit are Atlanta, Dallas, Philadelphia, and Washington, DC. The one-way flight prices between these cities are given in the table below.

	Atlanta	Dallas	New York	Philadelphia	Washington
Atlanta	*	$182	$197	$159	$180
Dallas	$182	*	$115	$115	$110
New York	$197	$115	*	$ 55	$156
Philadelphia	$159	$115	$ 55	*	$205
Washington	$180	$110	$156	$205	*

a) Represent this traveling salesman problem with a complete, weighted graph showing the prices of the flights on the appropriate edges.*

b) Use the nearest neighbor method to approximate the optimal route for Darren to travel to each city and return to New York City. Give the cost of the route determined. N, P, D, W, A, N for $657

c) Randomly select another route for Darren to travel from New York City to the other cities and return to New York City and then compute the cost of this route. Compare this cost with the cost determined in part (b). Answers will vary.

Challenge Problems/Group Activities

33. **Visiting Five Cities** Come up with a list of five cities you would like to visit. Use the Internet to search for airline prices between these five cities (make sure to include the city with the airport nearest your home from which you would start and end your trip).

a) Draw a complete, weighted graph that represents these cities and the costs associated with flying between each pair of cities. Answers will vary.

b) Use the brute force method to determine the optimal solution to visiting each city and returning home. Answers will vary.

c) Use the nearest neighbor method to approximate the optimal solution. Answers will vary.

d) How much money does the optimal solution, obtained in part (b), save you over the approximation obtained in part (c)? Answers will vary.

34. **Number of Circuits** The following tasks are intended to help you understand the formula for finding the number of unique Hamilton circuits in a complete graph.

a) Draw a complete graph with three vertices labeled *A*, *B*, and *C*. Assume that you are starting at vertex *A* and wish to move to another vertex. How many choices do you have for moving to the second vertex? Once you choose the second vertex, how many choices do you have for moving to a third vertex? Multiply the number of choices you had from vertex *A* by the number of choices you had from the second vertex. Compare the number you obtained with the number of Hamilton circuits found by using $(n - 1)!$.*

b) Draw a complete graph with four vertices labeled *A*, *B*, *C*, and *D*. Assume that you are starting at vertex *A* and wish to move to a second vertex. How many choices do you have for moving to this second vertex? Once you choose the second vertex, how many choices do you have for moving to the third vertex? Once you choose the third vertex, how many choices do you have for the fourth vertex? Multiply the number of choices you had from each vertex together. Compare the number you obtained with the number of Hamilton circuits found by using $(n - 1)!$.
   3, 2, 1; 3 · 2 · 1 = 6. This result is the same as the number of Hamilton circuits in a complete graph with four vertices.

*See Instructor Answer Appendix

c) Repeat this process for complete graphs with five and six vertices.*

d) Explain why $(n - 1)!$ gives the number of Hamilton circuits in a complete graph with n vertices.*

Recreational Mathematics

35. ***The Icosian Game*** In 1857, William Rowan Hamilton invented the game called the Icosian Game. The game consisted of a round board with 20 holes and 20 numbered pegs. On the surface of the board was a pattern similar to the graphs we have studied in this chapter (see photo and artwork below).

In essence, the object of the game was to use the pegs to form a Hamilton circuit on the graph. The graph below is taken from the Icosian Game. Determine a Hamilton circuit on this graph. A, E, D, N, O, F, G, Q, P, T, M, L, C, B, J, K, S, R, I, H, A

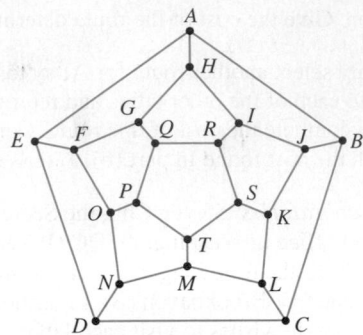

Internet/Research Activity

36. Write a paper on traveling salesman problems. Include a brief history of the problems. Also include advances made toward reducing the computational time of determining the optimal solution as well as advances made toward determining better approximate solutions.

*See Instructor Answer Appendix

SECTION 14.4   Trees

▲ *Graph theory can be used to determine the irrigation system with the lowest cost.*

Ruth Collins wishes to install an irrigation system to water the five flower gardens in her backyard. How can Ruth determine the irrigation system that reaches each of her five gardens and has the lowest cost? In this section, we will introduce a type of graph that can help solve the problem facing Ruth.

Why **This is Important** Certain graphs that we will discuss can be used to provide cost-efficient solutions to a variety of real-life problems.

Introduction

In this chapter, we have introduced graphs as a means to represent problems from everyday life (Section 14.1). We used graph theory to solve a variety of problems by finding Euler paths and Euler circuits (Section 14.2). We also used graph theory to find the optimal and approximate solutions to traveling salesman problems using Hamilton circuits (Section 14.3). We now turn our attention to another type of graph, called a *tree*, which is also frequently used to represent problems from everyday life. Before we define a tree, let's look at Example 1, in which we create a family tree.

Example 1   *A Family Tree*

Wendy has three children: Adan, Konnor, and Norah. Adan has two children: Justine and Seth. Konnor has no children. Norah has three children: Miya, Brianna, and Reuben. Use a graph to represent this family.

Solution   We will construct this graph with three layers, one for each generation. The vertices represent the people, and the edges represent the parent–child relationships. Start with Wendy and make edges to each of her three children, Adan, Konnor, and Norah. Then, make edges from Adan to his two children and from Norah to her three children. Since Konnor has no children, there are no edges below his name.

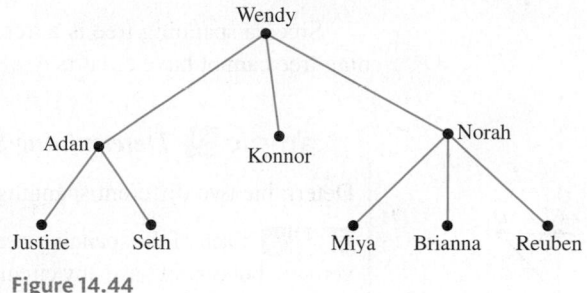

Figure 14.44

The graph shown in Fig. 14.44 is an example of a tree.

Definition: Tree

A **tree** is a connected graph in which each edge is a bridge.

Recall from Section 14.1 that a bridge is an edge that if removed from a connected graph would create a disconnected graph. Thus, if you remove *any edge* in a tree, it creates a disconnected graph. Since each edge would create a disconnected graph if removed, a tree cannot have any Euler circuits or Hamilton circuits. Can you explain why? Figure 14.45(a) gives four examples of graphs that are trees, and Fig. 14.45(b) gives four examples of graphs that are not trees.

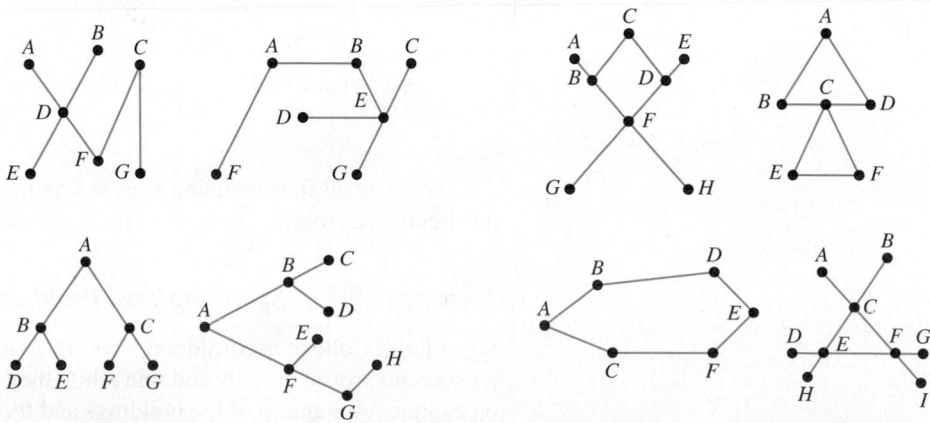

(a) *Graphs that are trees*   (b) *Graphs that are not trees*

Figure 14.45

Spanning Trees

Some applications, like the family tree in Example 1, can be represented with a graph that is a tree. In other applications, the problem may initially be represented with a graph that is not a tree. In this section, to solve certain problems, we will need to remove edges from a graph that is not a tree to form a tree known as a *spanning tree*. We now define spanning tree.

> ### Definition: Spanning Tree
> A **spanning tree** is a tree that is created from another graph by removing edges while still maintaining a path to each vertex.

Since a spanning tree is a tree, and since a tree cannot have any circuits, a spanning tree cannot have circuits.

Example 2 *Determining Spanning Trees*

Determine two different spanning trees for each graph shown in Fig. 14.46.

Solution Each of the spanning trees we create will need to have a path connecting all vertices, but cannot have any circuits. To create a spanning tree from a graph, we remove edges one at a time while leaving all the vertices in place. When we remove an edge, we must make sure the edge is not a bridge. Removing a bridge would create a disconnected graph. We need to reduce our original graph to one that is still connected. Keeping these guidelines in mind, we continue removing edges until the remaining graph is a tree. Two spanning trees formed from each graph in Fig. 14.46(a) and (b) are given in Fig. 14.47(a) and (b), respectively. Other spanning trees are possible in each case.

(a)

(b)

Figure 14.46

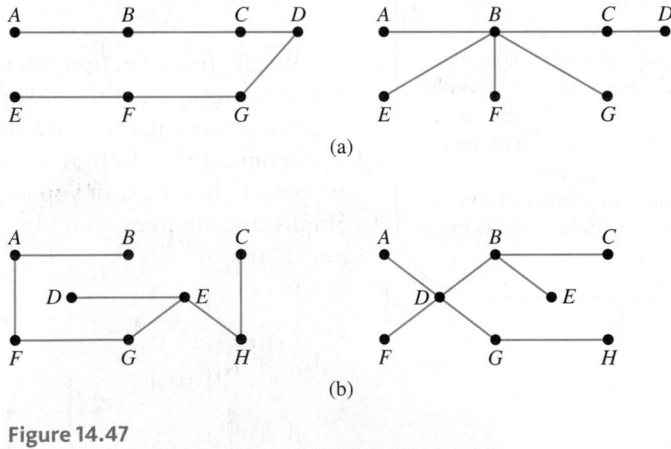

Figure 14.47

Notice in all four spanning trees in Example 2 that each edge is a bridge and that no circuits are present. Our next example provides an application of spanning trees.

Example 3 *A Spanning Tree Problem*

Schoolcraft College is considering adding awnings above its sidewalks to help shelter students from the snow and rain while they walk between some of the buildings on campus. A diagram of the buildings and the connecting sidewalks where the awnings are to be added is given in Fig. 14.48 on page 891.

Originally, the president of the college wished to have awnings placed over all the sidewalks shown in Fig. 14.48, but that was found to be too costly. Instead,

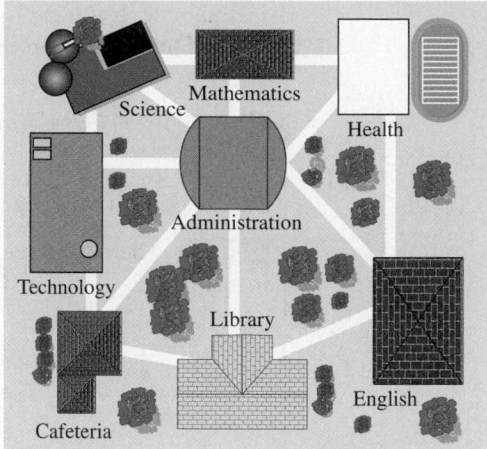

Figure 14.48

the president has proposed to place just enough awnings over a select number of sidewalks so that, by moving from building to building, students would still be able to reach any location shown without being exposed to the elements.

a) Represent all the buildings and sidewalks shown with a graph.

b) Create three different spanning trees from this graph that would satisfy the president's proposal.

Solution

a) Using letters to represent the building names, vertices to represent the buildings, and edges to represent the sidewalks between buildings, we generate the graph in Fig. 14.49.

b) To create a spanning tree we remove nonbridge edges until a tree is created. Three possible spanning trees are given in Fig. 14.50; however, many others are possible.

Figure 14.50

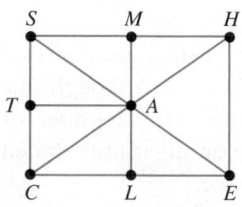

Figure 14.49

Example 3 shows us how spanning trees can be used to represent a real-life problem. However, the administrators at Schoolcraft College still have a problem: Which sidewalks should be chosen to cover with awnings (or which spanning tree should be selected)? Problems like the one faced by Schoolcraft College usually have additional considerations that need to be included in the decision-making process. The most common consideration is the cost of the project. To help analyze these problems, weighted graphs—graphs with costs or distances associated with each edge—and minimum-cost spanning trees are used.

Definition: Minimum-Cost Spanning Tree

A **minimum-cost spanning tree** is the least expensive spanning tree of all spanning trees under consideration.

Figure 14.51

Example 4 will explain how we determine a minimum-cost spanning tree for a weighted graph with three edges.

Example 4 *Finding a Minimum-Cost Spanning Tree*

Examine the weighted graph in Fig. 14.51. This graph shows the costs, in dollars, associated with each edge. Determine the minimum-cost spanning tree for this graph.

Solution There are three spanning trees associated with this graph; they are shown in Fig. 14.52.

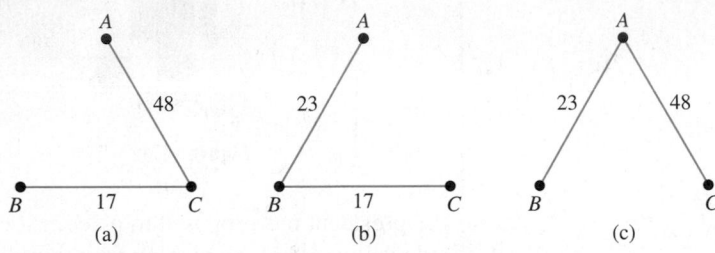

Figure 14.52

The spanning tree in Fig. 14.52(a) has a cost of $\$48 + \$17 = \$65$. The spanning tree in Fig. 14.52(b) has a cost of $\$23 + \$17 = \$40$. The spanning tree in Fig. 14.52(c) has a cost of $\$23 + \$48 = \$71$. Therefore, the minimum-cost spanning tree is shown in Fig. 14.52(b). It has a cost of $40. ■

The process used in Example 4 is similar to the brute force method used to find the optimal solution to traveling salesman problems in Section 14.3. Although this process is easy to carry out for a small graph, such a process would be impossible for graphs with a large number of vertices. Fortunately, we have an algorithm, called *Kruskal's algorithm*, to determine the minimum-cost spanning tree.

PROCEDURE   KRUSKAL'S ALGORITHM

To construct the minimum-cost spanning tree from a weighted graph:

1. Select the lowest-cost edge on the graph.
2. Select the next lowest-cost edge that does not form a circuit with the first edge.
3. Select the next lowest-cost edge that does not form a circuit with previously selected edges.
4. Continue selecting the lowest-cost edges that do not form circuits with the previously selected edges.
5. When a spanning tree is complete, you have the minimum-cost spanning tree.

Figure 14.53

Example 5 *Using Kruskal's Algorithm*

Use Kruskal's algorithm to determine the minimum-cost spanning tree for the weighted graph shown in Fig. 14.53. The numbers along the edges in Fig. 14.53 represent dollars.

Solution We begin by selecting the lowest-cost edge of the graph, edge AG, which is $11 (see Fig. 14.54). Next we select the next lowest-cost edge that does not form

Figure 14.54

Figure 14.55

Figure 14.56

a circuit, edge *GE*, which is $23. Once again, looking for the lowest-cost edge that does not form a circuit, we select edge *CE*, which is $31. The result of our first three selections is shown in Fig. 14.54 on page 892.

Looking at the original weighted graph in Fig. 14.53, we see that the next lowest-cost edge is edge *AC*, which is $38. However, selecting edge *AC* would create a circuit among vertices *A*, *C*, *E*, and *G*, so we must not select edge *AC*. Instead, we select edge *GH*, which is $47, since it is the next lowest-cost edge and its selection does not lead to a circuit; see Fig. 14.55. Next, we select edge *FH*, which is $48.

The next lowest-cost edge not yet selected is edge *EF*, which is $50. However, this edge would create a circuit among vertices *E*, *F*, *H*, and *G*. Instead, we select edge *CD*, which is $53, followed by selecting edge *BD*, which is $57. The result of our selections thus far is shown in Fig. 14.56.

Notice that the graph in Fig. 14.56 is a spanning tree. According to Kruskal's algorithm, the tree in Fig. 14.56 is the minimum-cost spanning tree for the original weighted graph. ∎

Note that in Example 5, all the edges selected were connected to edges we had already selected. However, that will not always be the case. When we select the edges in Example 6, some will be disconnected at the time we select them.

We now will apply our knowledge of minimum-cost spanning trees. Note that in examples and exercises, the graphs need not be drawn to scale.

Example 6 *An Application Using Kruskal's Algorithm*

Recall from Example 3 on page 890 that Schoolcraft College is considering the construction of awnings over a select number of sidewalks on campus. The distances, in feet, between buildings are shown in the weighted graph in Fig. 14.57.

a) Determine the shortest series of sidewalks to cover so that students would be able to move between any buildings shown without being exposed to the elements.

b) The cost of the awnings is $23 per foot regardless of where they are placed on campus. What will it cost to cover the sidewalks found in part (a)?

Figure 14.57

Figure 14.58

Figure 14.59

Solution

a) Schoolcraft College is seeking a minimum-cost spanning tree for the weighted graph shown in Fig. 14.57. To determine the minimum-cost spanning tree, we use Kruskal's algorithm. First, we select the edge *MH* since it has the shortest distance and therefore has the lowest cost. We next select the edge *TC* since it has the second shortest distance and it doesn't form a circuit with our previously selected edge (see Fig. 14.58). Our third and fourth choices will be edge *ST* and edge *MA*, respectively, since these edges have the next shortest distances and they do not form a circuit with previously selected edges. The result of our first four selections is shown in Fig. 14.58.

The next lowest-cost edge is edge *AH*. However, selection of edge *AH* would form a circuit with vertices *A*, *H*, and *M*. Instead, we choose the next lowest-cost edge—edge *SM*—since it does not form a circuit with the previously selected edges (see Fig. 14.59). Our next lowest-cost edge will be edge *CL*. Note that edge *CL* does not form a circuit with the previously selected edges. The result of all our selections so far is shown in Fig. 14.59.

We note that the next lowest-cost edge is edge *TA*, but selecting this edge would create a circuit with vertices *S*, *M*, *A*, and *T*. So we select edge *AE*. The

Figure 14.60

result of our selections so far is shown in Fig. 14.60.

From Fig. 14.60, we can see that we have formed a spanning tree. According to Kruskal's algorithm, this graph is the minimum-cost spanning tree. Therefore, Fig. 14.60 shows which sidewalks should be covered with the awnings. Covering these sidewalks will provide protection to students at the lowest cost to Schoolcraft College.

b) From Fig. 14.60, we see that there are $148 + 42 + 68 + 86 + 54 + 217 + 201 = 816$ feet of sidewalks that need to be covered. At $23 per foot, the cost to cover these sidewalks is $23 \times 816 = \$18,768$.

Example 7

Schools in Budville, Fairplay, Happy Corners, Kieler, Louisburg, and Sinsinawa, Wisconsin, all wish to establish a fiber-optic computer network to share information and to obtain Internet access. The most efficient method of establishing such a network would be to install fiber-optic cable along roadsides. The weighted graph in Fig. 14.61 shows the distance in miles between schools along existing roads.

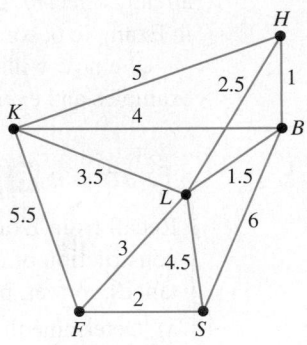

Figure 14.61

a) Determine the shortest distance to link these six schools.

b) The cost to install fiber-optic cable is $1257 per mile. What is the minimum cost to install the fiber-optic cable along the roadsides determined in part (a)?

Solution

a) We are seeking a minimum-cost spanning tree. We will carry out Kruskal's algorithm to find it. The first three edges selected will be edge *HB* (1 mile), edge *BL* (1.5 miles), and edge *FS* (2 miles). Note that these are the three lowest-cost edges, and their selection does not lead to a circuit. The result of our first three selections is shown in Fig. 14.62.

Figure 14.62

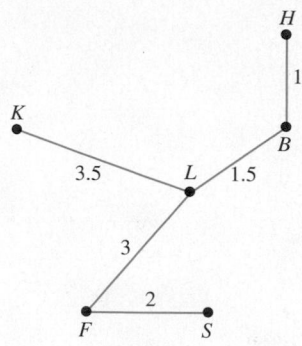

Figure 14.63

The next lowest-cost edge is edge *HL* (2.5 miles), but selecting this edge would lead to a circuit between vertices *H*, *B*, and *L*. Instead, we select the next lowest-cost edge, edge *LF* (3 miles). This edge is followed by the next lowest-cost edge, edge *KL* (3.5 miles). The result of all our selections so far is shown in Fig. 14.63. We now have a spanning tree.

According to Kruskal's algorithm, Fig. 14.63 shows the minimum-cost spanning tree. Therefore, Fig. 14.63 gives the paths along which fiber-optic cable should be placed to connect the schools for the minimum cost.

b) From Fig. 14.63, we can see that there are $1 + 1.5 + 3.5 + 3 + 2 = 11$ miles of fiber-optic cable needed for this network. At \$1257 per mile, the cost to install this fiber-optic network is $\$1257 \times 11 = \$13,827$. ∎

SECTION 14.4   *Exercises*

Warm Up Exercises

In Exercises 1–6, fill in the blanks with an appropriate word, phrase, or symbol(s).

1. A connected graph in which each edge is a bridge is called a(n) _____. Tree

2. If you remove any edge in a tree, it creates a(n) _____ graph. Disconnected

3. A tree does not have any Euler or Hamilton _____. Circuits

4. A tree that is created from another graph by removing edges while still maintaining a path to each vertex is called a(n) _____ tree. Spanning

5. The least expensive spanning tree of all spanning trees under consideration is called the _____ spanning tree. Minimum-cost

6. To determine the minimum-cost spanning tree for a graph, we can use _____ algorithm. Kruskal's

Practice the Skills

7. *A Family Tree* Use a tree to show the parent–child relationships in the following family. Angela has two sons, Eli and Connor. Eli has four children: Jason, Max, Gabriella, and Tony. Connor has three children: Austin, Caleb, and Sandi.*

8. *A Family Tree* Use a tree to show the parent–child relationships in the following family. Joe has two children: Allan and Rosemary. Allan has three children: Christopher, Donetta, and AJ. Rosemary has three children: Peter, Paula, and Martin.*

9. *Corporate Structure* Use a tree to show the following employee relationships at DTX Industries. Kroger is president and has three vice presidents: Dorfman, Blutarsky, and Hoover. Dorfman has three managers: Stratton, Day, and Stork. Blutarsky has three managers: Schoenstein, De Pasto, and Liebowitz. Hoover has two managers: Jennings and Wormer.*

10. *Employment Structure* Use a tree to show the employee relationships at Stephens College. President Pullen has three division directors working for her: Anderson, Wolcott, and Lisk. Anderson has two department heads working for her: Pomeroy and Thomas. Wolcott has three department heads working for her: Hoey, Jones, and Kent. Lisk has four department heads working for him: Teske, Watts, Groell, and Tuff.*

In Exercises 11–18, determine two different spanning trees for the given graph. There are many possible answers.

11.

12.

13.

14.

15.

16.

17.

18.

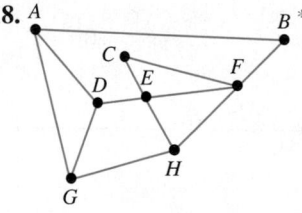

In Exercises 19–26, determine the minimum-cost spanning trees for the given graph.

19.

20.

21.

22.

23.

24.

25.

26.

*See Instructor Answer Appendix

Problem Solving

27. *An Irrigation System* Ruth Collins wishes to install an irrigation system to water her five flower gardens. The distances in feet between her gardens are shown in the figure below.

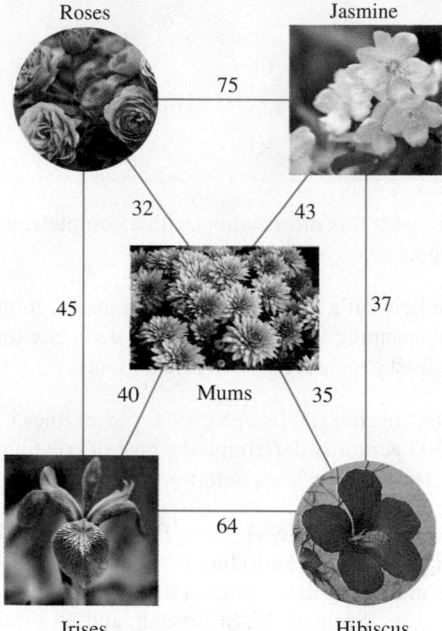

a) Represent this information with a weighted graph.*

b) Use Kruskal's algorithm to determine the minimum-cost spanning tree.*

c) If the cost of installing irrigation pipe is $25 per foot, determine the minimum cost of installing the irrigation system from part (b). $3600

28. *Art Sculpture* Joe Loccisano is creating a modern art sculpture that needs to have electricity available at five different sites. The figure below shows the items included in the sculpture. The distances shown are in inches.

a) Represent this sculpture with a weighted graph.*

b) Use Kruskal's algorithm to determine the minimum-cost spanning tree that would provide electricity to each site on the sculpture.*

c) If the cost of installing wiring on the sculpture is $0.75 per inch, determine the minimum cost for wiring this sculpture. $54.75

29. *Commuter Train System* Several communities in eastern Pennsylvania wish to establish a commuter rail train system between the cities shown in the map below (distances are in miles).

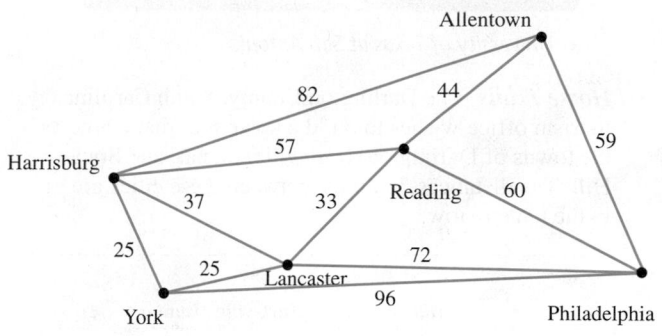

a) Use Kruskal's algorithm to determine the minimum-cost spanning tree that would link the cities using the shortest distance.*

b) If it costs $6800 per mile of railroad track, how much does the commuter rail system determined in part (a) cost? $1,264,800

30. *Linking Campuses* Five of the campuses in the University of Texas system would like to establish a high-speed telephone and data network. The campuses are located in the following cities: Brownsville, Dallas, El Paso, San Antonio, and Tyler. The map below gives the approximate distances in miles between these five campuses.

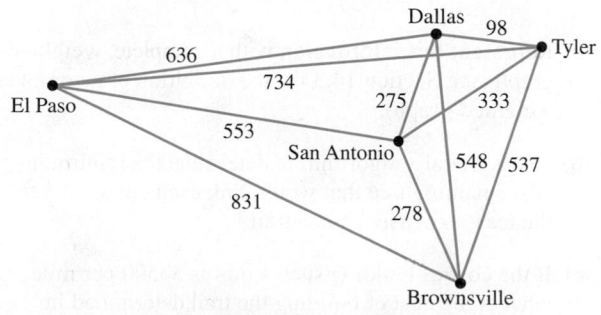

a) Use Kruskal's algorithm to determine the minimum-cost spanning tree that would link each university to create the telephone and data network with the shortest distance.*

*See Instructor Answer Appendix

b) If it costs $1700 per mile to install the network, how much will it cost to produce the network determined in part (a)? $2,046,800

▲ *University of Texas at San Antonia*

31. *Horse Trails* The Darlington County, South Carolina, tourism office wishes to build a horse trail that connects the towns of Darlington, Hartsville, Lamar, and Society Hill. The distances, in miles, between these cities are given in the table below.

	Darlington	Hartsville	Lamar	Society Hill
Darlington	*	12	14	15
Hartsville	12	*	13	16
Lamar	14	13	*	26
Society Hill	15	16	26	*

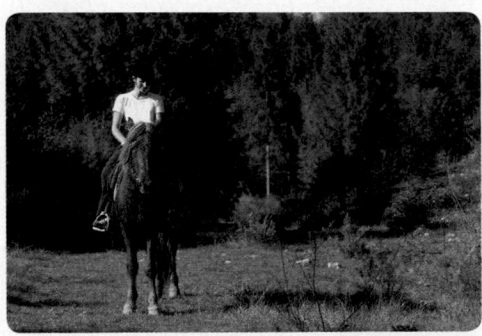

a) Represent this information with a complete, weighted graph (see Section 14.3 for the definition of a complete, weighted graph).*

b) Use Kruskal's algorithm to determine the minimum-cost spanning tree that would link each city to create the least expensive horse trail.*

c) If the cost of building such a trail is $3500 per mile, what is the cost of building the trail determined in part (b)? $140,000

32. *Electrical Power Lines* The Eastern Ohio Electric Cooperative wishes to connect cities within its district with new, higher-quality electrical power lines. The cities include Akron, Canton, Cleveland, Columbus, and Youngstown.

The distances in miles between the cities involved are given in the table below.

	Akron	Canton	Cleveland	Columbus	Youngstown
Akron	*	23	45	127	48
Canton	23	*	68	125	53
Cleveland	45	68	*	146	75
Columbus	127	125	146	*	178
Youngstown	48	53	75	178	*

a) Represent this information with a complete, weighted graph.*

b) Use Kruskal's algorithm to determine the minimum-cost spanning tree that would link each city to create the least expensive power line network.*

c) If the cost to establish electrical power lines is $2300 per mile, determine the cost of creating the electrical power lines determined in part (b). $554,300

33. *Recreation Trail* The Missouri Park and Recreation Association would like to build a recreation trail for biking and hiking that connects the cities of Jefferson City, Kansas City, Springfield, St. Joseph, and St. Louis. The distances in miles between these cities are given in the following table.

	Jefferson City	Kansas City	Springfield	St. Joseph	St. Louis
Jefferson City	*	158	138	215	134
Kansas City	158	*	191	56	249
Springfield	138	191	*	227	218
St. Joseph	215	56	227	*	307
St. Louis	134	249	218	307	*

a) Represent this information with a complete, weighted graph.*

b) Use Kruskal's algorithm to determine the minimum-cost spanning tree that would link each city to create the least expensive recreation trail.*

c) If the cost of building such a trail is $3700 per mile, what is the cost of building the trail determined in part (b)? $1,798,200

34. *Light-rail Transit System* The state of Illinois is applying for a grant to connect several metropolitan areas of the state with a light-rail transport system. The cities involved are Champaign, Chicago, Peoria, Rockford, and Springfield. The distances in miles between these cities are given in the table on page 899.

*See Instructor Answer Appendix

	Champaign	Chicago	Peoria	Rock-ford	Spring-field
Champaign	*	135	89	181	86
Chicago	135	*	170	85	202
Peoria	89	170	*	129	74
Rockford	181	85	129	*	193
Springfield	86	202	74	193	*

a) Represent this information with a complete, weighted graph.*

b) Use Kruskal's algorithm to determine the minimum-cost spanning tree that would link each city using the shortest distance.*

c) What would be the total distance of the light-rail transportation system determined in part (b)? 374 miles

Challenge Problems/Group Activities

35. *Computer Network* Create a minimum-cost spanning tree that would serve as the least expensive way to create a computer network among the five largest cities in your state. Consult maps, atlases, almanacs, or the Internet for distances. Assume that the cost per mile is the same regardless of the path taken. Answers will vary.

36. *College Structure* Create a tree that shows the administrative structure at your college or university. Start with the highest-ranking officer (that is, president, chancellor, provost, headmaster) and work down to the department chair level. Answers will vary.

37. *Sidewalk Covers* Create a minimum-cost spanning tree that would serve as the least expensive way to provide sheltered sidewalks between major buildings on your college campus (see Example 6 on page 893). Assume that the cost per foot is the same regardless of the path taken. Answers will vary.

Internet/Research Activity

38. Write a research paper on the life and work of Joseph Kruskal, who developed Kruskal's algorithm.

*See Instructor Answer Appendix

CHAPTER 14   *Summary*

Important Facts and Concepts

Examples and Discussion

Section 14.1

Paths and Circuits

A **path** is a sequence of adjacent vertices and the edges connecting them.

A **circuit** is a path that begins and ends at the same vertex.

Discussion, pages 858–860.

Section 14.2

Paths and Circuits

An **Euler path** is a path that passes through each *edge* of a graph exactly one time.

An **Euler circuit** is a circuit that passes through each *edge* of a graph exactly one time.

Discussion, pages 864–865, Example 1, page 865.

Euler's Theorem

For a connected graph, the following statements are true:

1. A graph with *no odd vertices* (all even vertices) has at least one Euler path, which is also an Euler circuit. An Euler circuit can be started at any vertex, and it will end at the same vertex.

2. A graph with *exactly two odd vertices* has at least one Euler path but no Euler circuits. Each Euler path must begin at one of the two odd vertices and end at the other odd vertex.

3. A graph with *more than two odd vertices* has no Euler paths or Euler circuits.

Examples 2–6, pages 866–869.

Fleury's Algorithm

To determine an Euler path or an Euler circuit:

1. Use Euler's theorem to determine whether an Euler path or an Euler circuit exists. If one exists, proceed with Steps 2–5.

2. If the graph has no odd vertices (therefore has an Euler circuit that is also an Euler path), choose any vertex as the starting point. If the graph has exactly two odd vertices (therefore has only an Euler path), choose one of the two odd vertices as the starting point.

3. Begin to trace edges as you move through the graph. Number the edges as you trace them. Since you can't trace any edges twice in Euler paths and Euler circuits, once an edge is traced consider it "invisible."

4. When faced with a choice of edges to trace, if possible, choose an edge that is not a bridge (i.e., don't create a disconnected graph with your choice of edges).

5. Continue until each edge of the entire graph has been traced once.

Examples 5–6, pages 868–869.

Section 14.3
Paths and Circuits

A **Hamilton path** is a path that contains each *vertex* of a graph exactly once.

A **Hamilton circuit** is a path that begins and ends at the same vertex and passes through all *vertices* exactly one time.

Discussion, pages 877–878, Example 2, page 879.

Number of Unique Hamilton Circuits in a Complete Graph

The number of unique Hamilton circuits in a complete graph with n vertices is $(n - 1)!$, where

$$(n - 1)! = (n - 1)(n - 2)(n - 3) \cdots (3)(2)(1)$$

Examples 3–5, pages 879–880.

The Brute Force Method of Solving Traveling Salesman Problems

To determine the optimal solution:

1. Represent the problem with a complete, weighted graph.

2. List all possible Hamilton circuits in this graph.

3. Determine the cost associated with each of these Hamilton circuits.

4. The Hamilton circuit with the lowest cost is the optimal solution.

Discussion, page 880, Example 5, page 880

The Nearest Neighbor Method for Determining an Approximate Solution to a Traveling Salesman Problem

To approximate the optimal solution:

1. Represent the problem with a complete, weighted graph.

2. Identify the starting vertex.

3. Of all the edges attached to the starting vertex, choose the edge that has the smallest weight. This edge is the shortest distance or the lowest cost. Travel along this edge to the second vertex.

4. At the second vertex, choose the edge that has the smallest weight that does not lead to a vertex already visited. Travel along this edge to the third vertex.

5. Continue this process, each time moving along the edge with the smallest weight until all vertices are visited.

6. Travel back to the original vertex.

Discussion, page 882, Example 6, page 882.

Section 14.4
Kruskal's Algorithm

To construct the minimum-cost spanning tree from a weighted graph:
1. Select the lowest-cost edge on the graph.
2. Select the next lowest-cost edge that does not form a circuit with the first edge.
3. Select the next lowest-cost edge that does not form a circuit with previously selected edges.
4. Continue selecting the lowest-cost edges that do not form circuits with the previously selected edges.
5. When a spanning tree is complete, you have the minimum-cost spanning tree.

Examples 5–7, pages 892–894.

CHAPTER 14) *Review Exercises*

14.1

In Exercises 1 and 2, create a graph with the given properties.

1. Create a graph with two even vertices, two odd vertices, and a bridge.*

2. Create a graph with four even vertices and two loops.*

In Exercises 3 and 4, use the following graph.

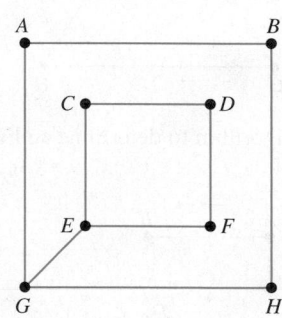

3. Determine a path that passes through each edge exactly one time. *E, C, D, F, E, G, A, B, H, G*

4. Is it possible to have a path that begins at vertex *A*, includes all edges exactly once, and ends at vertex *B*? No. A path that includes each edge exactly one time would start at vertex *E* and end at vertex *G*, or vice versa.

5. *Western States* Represent the map as a graph where each vertex represents a state and each edge represents a common border between the states.*

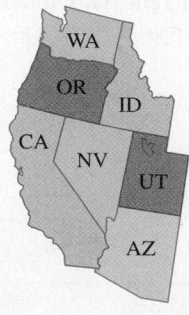

6. *School Floor Plan* The drawing below shows the first-floor plan of Raintree Montessori School. Construct a graph to represent the school using the letters shown to label the vertices. Use the letter *O* to label the vertex that represents the outside of the school. Place vertex *O* near the bottom of the graph.*

A	*B*	*C*
D	*E*	*F*

Outside

In Exercises 7 and 8, determine whether the graph shown is connected or disconnected.

7.   Connected

8. 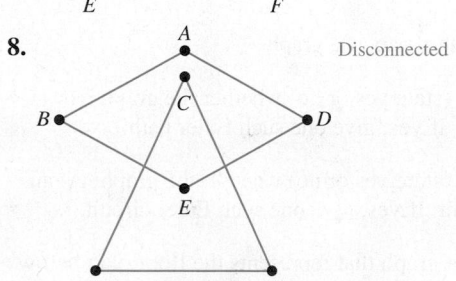   Disconnected

9. Identify all bridges in the graph below. Edge *CD*

*See Instructor Answer Appendix

14.2

Use the following graph for Exercises 10 and 11.

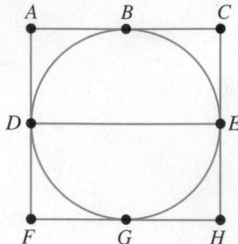

10. Determine an Euler path that begins with vertex *D*.

D, A, B, C, E, H, G, F, D, B, E, G, D, E; other answers are possible.

11. Determine an Euler path that begins with vertex *E*.

E, D, B, E, G, D, A, B, C, E, H, G, F, D; other answers are possible.

Use the following graph for Exercises 12 and 13.

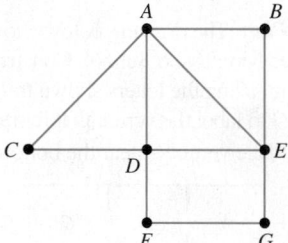

12. Determine an Euler circuit that begins with vertex *A*.

A, B, E, G, F, D, C, A, D, E, A

13. Determine an Euler circuit that begins with vertex *E*.

E, D, C, A, E, B, A, D, F, G, E

14. Consider the following map.

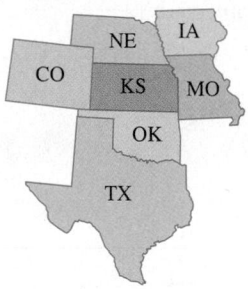

a) Represent the map as a graph.*

b) Determine (state yes or no) whether the graph has an Euler path. If yes, give one such Euler path.*

c) Determine (state yes or no) whether the graph has an Euler circuit. If yes, give one such Euler circuit. No

15. a) Construct a graph that represents the floor plan below.*

b) Is it possible for a person to walk through each doorway in the house whose floor plan is shown below (at the bottom of the first column) without using any of the doorways twice? Explain. Yes

c) If so, where can the person start and where will the person finish? Explain. The person may start in any room or outside and will finish in the location from which he or she started.

16. a) Can a police officer walk each street shown in the figure below without walking any street more than once? Explain. Yes

b) If yes, where would the police officer have to start the walk? The officer would have to start at either the intersection of Dayne St., Gibson Pl., and Alvarez Ave. or at the intersection of Chambers St., Fletcher Ct., and Alvarez Ave.

17. Use Fleury's algorithm to determine an Euler path in the following graph. *A, B, F, E, H, G, D, C, A, D, E, B; other answers are possible.*

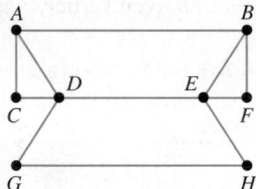

18. Use Fleury's algorithm to determine an Euler circuit in the following graph. *A, B, D, E, I, J, O, N, L, K, G, H, L, M, I, H, D, C, G, F, A; other answers are possible.*

14.3

19. Determine two different Hamilton paths in the following graph. *A,C,B,F,E,D,G and A,C,D,G,F,B,E; other answers are possible.*

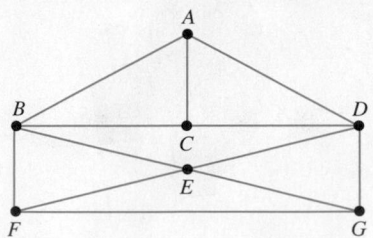

*See Instructor Answer Appendix

20. Determine two different Hamilton circuits in the following graph. *A, B, E, F, J, I, L, K, H, G, C, D, A* and *I, J, F, E, B, A, D, C, G, H, K, L, I*; other answers are possible.

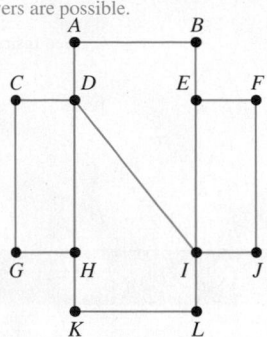

21. Draw a complete graph with five vertices.*

22. *Baseball* The American League Eastern Division has the following teams: Baltimore Orioles, Boston Red Sox, New York Yankees, Tampa Bay Rays, and Toronto Blue Jays. How many different possible ways could a Boston Red Sox fan visit each team in the American League Eastern Division one time and return home to Boston? 4! = 24 ways

23. *Job Interviews* Lance Lopez is searching for a new job. He lives in Portland, Oregon, and has interviews in Des Moines, Iowa; Charleston, West Virginia; and Montgomery, Alabama. The costs of the one-way flights between these four cities are as follows: Portland to Des Moines is $428, Portland to Charleston is $787, Portland to Montgomery is $902, Des Moines to Charleston is $449, Des Moines to Montgomery is $458, and Charleston to Montgomery is $415.

   a) Represent this traveling salesman problem with a complete, weighted graph showing the prices of the flights on the appropriate edges.*

   b) Use the brute force method to determine the least expensive route for Lance Lopez to travel to each city and return home to Portland. *P, D, M, C, P* or *P, C, M, D, P*

   c) What is the total cost of airfare for Lance's trip in part (b)? $2088

24. *Visiting Sales Offices* Jennifer Adams is the sales manager for AT&T for the state of Missouri. There are major sales offices in Columbia, Kansas City, St. Joseph, St. Louis, and Springfield. The distances in miles between these cities are given in the following table.

	Columbia	Kansas City	St. Joseph	St. Louis	Springfield
Columbia	*	130	177	127	168
Kansas City	130	*	54	256	192
St. Joseph	177	54	*	304	224
St. Louis	127	256	304	*	210
Springfield	168	192	224	210	*

   a) Represent this traveling salesman problem with a complete, weighted graph showing the prices of the flights on the appropriate edges.*

   b) Use the nearest neighbor method to approximate the optimal route for Jennifer to begin in St. Joseph, visit each city once, and return to St. Joseph. *SJ, KC, C, SL, Sp, SJ* traveling a total of 745 miles

   c) Suppose that Jennifer starts in Springfield. Use the nearest neighbor method to approximate the optimal route for Jennifer to visit each city once and return to Springfield. *Sp, C, SL, KC, SJ, Sp* traveling a total of 829 miles

14.4

25. *Employee Relationships* Use a tree to show the employees' relationships in the Hulka Consulting Corporation. Hulka is president. Winger and Ziskey are vice presidents who work for Hulka. Markowicz, Oxburger, and Soyer are district managers who work for Winger. Elmo, Hector, and Jenesky are district managers who work for Ziskey.*

26. Determine two different spanning trees for the following graph.*

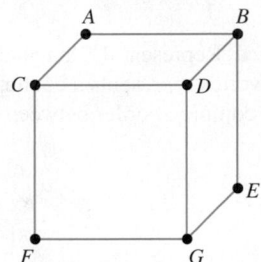

27. Determine the minimum-cost spanning tree for the following graph.*

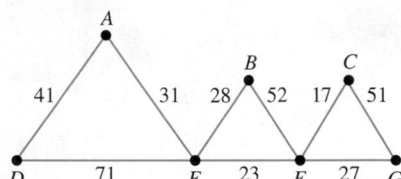

28. *An Irrigation System* Lucille Groenke wants to install an irrigation system to water all six of her flowerbeds in her backyard. The drawing shows the location of each flowerbed and the distance between them in feet.

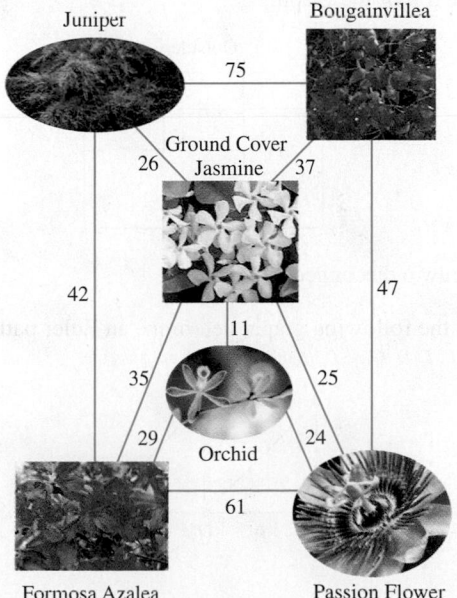

   a) Represent this information with a weighted graph.*

*See Instructor Answer Appendix

b) Use Kruskal's algorithm to determine the minimum-cost spanning tree*

c) The irrigation materials cost $2.50 per foot. Determine the cost of installing the irrigation system found in part (b). $317.50

*See Instructor Answer Appendix

CHAPTER 14) *Test*

1. Create a graph with six vertices, a bridge, and two loops.*

2. *Part of Africa* Represent the map below as a graph where each vertex represents a country and each edge represents a common border between the countries.*

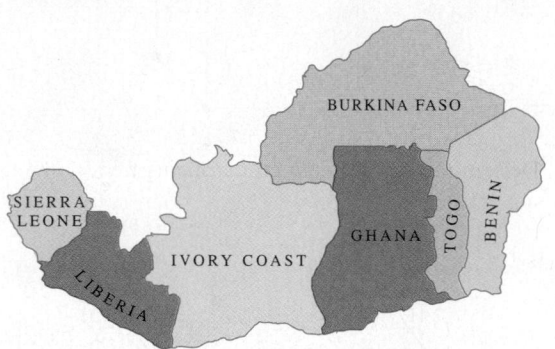

3. *Photography Studio* The drawing below shows the floor plan of Carol Ann's Photography Studio. Construct a graph to represent the studio using the letters shown to label the vertices. Use the letter *O* to label the vertex that represents the outside of the studio. Place vertex *O* near the top of the graph.*

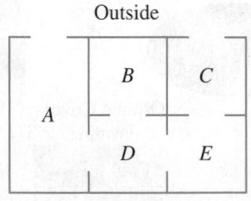

4. Draw a disconnected graph.*

5. In the following graph, determine an Euler path.
A, B, E, D, C, A, D, B; other answers are possible.

6. In the following graph, determine an Euler circuit.
A, B, C, F, H, G, E, F, B, E, D, A; other answers are possible.

7. Is it possible for a person to walk through each doorway in the house, whose floor plan is below, without using any of the doorways twice? If so, indicate in which room the person may start and where he or she will end.
Yes. The person may start in room *A* and end at room *B*, or vice versa.

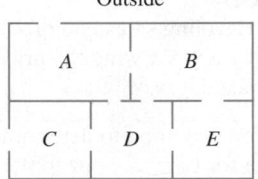

8. Use Fleury's algorithm to determine an Euler circuit in the following graph. *A, D, E, A, F, E, H, F, I, G, F, B, G, C, B, A*; other answers are possible.

9. In the following graph, determine a Hamilton path.
B, A, D, E, F, C, G; other answers are possible.

*See Instructor Answer Appendix

10. In the following graph, determine a Hamilton circuit.

A, B, C, G, E, D, H, I, K, J, F, A; other answers are possible.

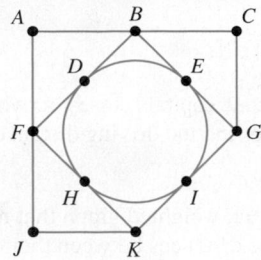

11. Draw a complete graph with four vertices.*

12. *Conference Sites* Rachel Goodwin, president of the English Teachers Association (ETA), is trying to determine the site of the next ETA conference. Rachel lives in Concord, Ohio, and wishes to travel to the following cities: Washington, DC; Las Vegas, Nevada; Boston, Massachusetts; and Austin, Texas. How many different ways can Rachel visit each city and return to her home in Concord? 4! = 24

Business Travel *In Exercises 13–15, use the following information.*

Doug Hauck is a purchasing agent for Champs Sports *(C)*. For his job, he must travel to meet with representatives from the following sports companies: Nike *(N)*, Reebok *(R)*, and Under Armour *(U)*. The prices of one-way flights between these companies are as follows: Champs to Nike is $253, Champs to Reebok is $114, Champs to Under Armour is $122, Nike to Reebok is $199, Nike to Under Armour is $183, and Reebok to Under Armour is $89.

13. Represent this traveling salesman problem with a complete weighted graph showing the prices of flights on the appropriate edges.*

14. Use the brute force method to determine the least expensive route for Doug to visit each company and return to Champs Sports. What is the cost of this route?
C, R, N, U, C or *C, U, N, R, C* for $618

15. Use the nearest neighbor method to approximate the optimal route for Doug to visit each company and return to Champs Sports. What is the cost of this route?
C, R, U, N, C for $639

16. *Family Tree* Use a tree to show the parent–child relationships in the following family. Beth has three children: Kevin, Darrell, and Teri. Kevin has one child, Chris. Darrell has two children: Michelle and April. Teri has one child, Lucy.*

17. Determine a spanning tree for the graph shown below.*

18. Determine the minimum-cost spanning tree for the following weighted graph.*

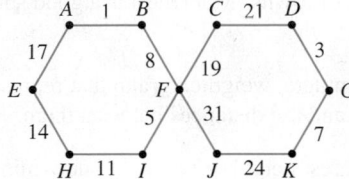

Irrigation System *In exercises 19 and 20, use the following information.*

Daniel Kimborowicz is planning a new irrigation system for his yard. His current system has valves already in place as shown in the figure below. The numbers shown are in feet.

19. Determine the minimum-cost spanning tree that reaches each valve.*

20. If the new irrigation materials cost $1.25 per foot, what is the cost of installing the system determined in part (a)?
$183.75

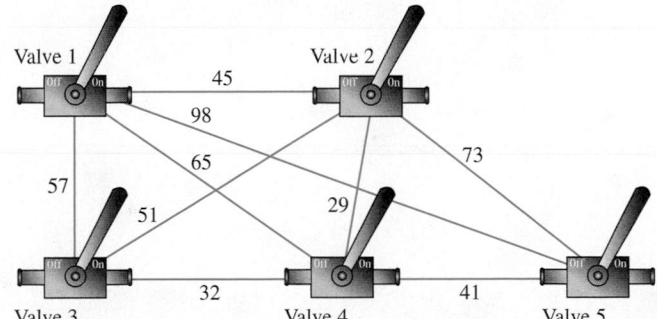

*See Instructor Answer Appendix

GROUP PROJECTS

1. Street Sweeper Route

Make a map of all streets or roads within 2 miles of your college campus. Now add roads as needed so that a street sweeper would be able to sweep all streets on this map, starting at the school and returning to the school without sweeping any street twice.

2. Hometown Road Trip

Select five students in your class so that no two have the same hometown. Use the Internet to find the distances between each pair of towns (MapQuest is a good source to check).

a) Draw a complete, weighted graph that represents the five towns and the distances between them.

b) Use the nearest neighbor method to determine an approximation for the optimal solution when starting at your college, visiting each hometown, and then returning to your college.

c) Use Kruskal's algorithm to determine the minimum cost spanning tree for the complete, weighted graph in part (a).

d) Determine the total distance one would travel along the minimum-cost spanning tree found in part (c).

3. State Capital Tour

Identify the five state capitals closest to where you live. Use the Internet to find the driving distances between these five capitals.

a) Draw a complete, weighted graph that represents the capitals and the distances between them.

b) Use the nearest neighbor method to determine an approximation for the optimal solution of starting at your state capital, visiting the other four capitals, and then returning to your state capital.

c) Use Kruskal's algorithm to determine the minimum-cost spanning tree for the complete, weighted graph determined in part (a).

d) Determine the total distance a person would travel along the minimum-cost spanning tree found in part (c).

4. Computer Network On Campus

Measure the distance between the five busiest buildings on your campus. Create a weighted graph showing the buildings and the distances between buildings. Determine the minimum-cost spanning tree that could be used to install a new computer/telephone network on your campus. Assume that the cost per foot is the same regardless of the path used.

15

Voting and Apportionment

Why This Is Important

We are frequently told that it is our civic duty to vote in an election. We may often wonder if our vote really matters. Can one person's vote make a difference? How are voting decisions made? Could a candidate for student government president receive a majority of votes and still lose the election? Depending on the voting method used, determining the winner of an election can sometimes lead to different results. In this chapter, we will discuss different voting methods and some flaws of these methods. We will also discuss apportionment problems, such as how to determine the number of representatives each state has in the U.S. House of Representatives, and some flaws that can occur with apportionment methods.

◄ Registering to vote and then voting in elections are part of our civic duties as citizens.

SECTION 15.1   Voting Methods

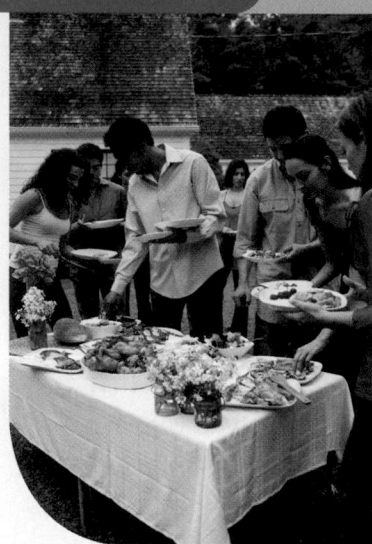

▲ *There is more than one voting method that can be used to determine what meal you should serve at a party.*

Suppose that you are hosting a party and you ask your 11 guests to vote on whether they would like you to serve pizza, hot dogs, or hamburgers at the party. How would you determine the winner of this election? Is there more than one way to determine the winner? In this section, we will discuss four of the most popular voting methods. We will also discover that the voting method chosen can greatly affect the results of an election.

Why *This is Important* Voting methods are used in a variety of real-world problems.

In a constitutional democracy, one of the most fundamental rights and responsibilities of its citizens is the right to vote. Voting gives us a voice in decisions that affect our lives. Conducting a fair election to select representatives lies at the heart of a democratic form of government. In general, elections for public officials seem to be a simple proposition: You vote for the person you wish to represent you, and the candidate who obtains the most votes is elected. However, when more than one choice is involved in the election or when voters are asked to rank their choices, the selection is not as simple. The outcome of the election is greatly influenced by the voting method used, as will be discussed in this section. Consider the following example.

The Ridgemoor Homeowners Association board of directors needs to choose one type of flower to plant at the main entrance to the housing development. The choices available are begonia, impatiens, marigold, or periwinkle. Each of the five directors is asked to rank the flowers according to preference. The results of this election are given in Table 15.1.

Table 15.1 Ridgemoor Board of Directors Flower Choices

Choice	Charlie	Denise	Edwardo	Gerry	Joe
First	Impatiens	Impatiens	Impatiens	Marigold	Marigold
Second	Marigold	Marigold	Marigold	Begonia	Begonia
Third	Periwinkle	Periwinkle	Periwinkle	Periwinkle	Periwinkle
Fourth	Begonia	Begonia	Begonia	Impatiens	Impatiens

If we were to run a simple election in which we only considered each director's first choice, impatiens would be chosen. It also can be said that impatiens received a *majority* of first-place votes. A majority simply refers to receiving more than 50% of the votes. However, looking at the table, it appears that marigolds might be a better choice since all the directors have marigolds listed either as their first or second choice.

In this first section, we will describe four of the most popular voting methods and explain how they are implemented. In the next section, we will discuss the weaknesses and flaws of each method. We will discuss the following methods:

1. Plurality method
2. Borda count method
3. Plurality with elimination method
4. Pairwise comparison method

Before we discuss any of these voting methods, though, we will illustrate how the results of an election might be indicated in a table called a *preference table*. A preference table summarizes the results of an election and shows how often each particular outcome was selected, as illustrated in Example 1.

Example 1 *Balloting by Committee Members*

The planning committee of Erie, Pennsylvania, is voting on a mascot for an upcoming winter festival. The choices are a snowman (S), a polar bear (P), and a husky (H).There are 15 planning committee members (labeled CM1, CM2, CM3, ..., CM15). Their ballots are shown in Fig. 15.1.

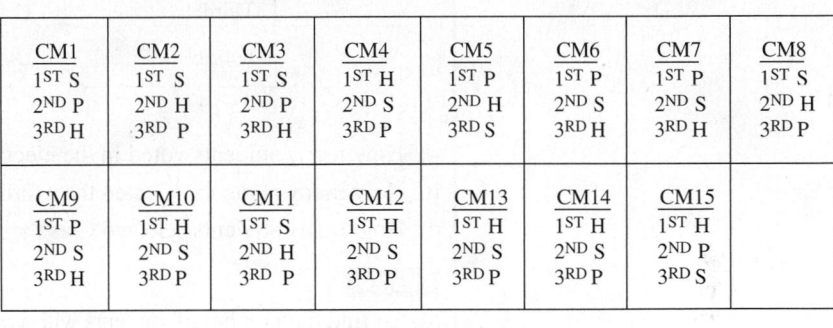

CM1	CM2	CM3	CM4	CM5	CM6	CM7	CM8
1ST S	1ST S	1ST S	1ST H	1ST P	1ST P	1ST P	1ST S
2ND P	2ND H	2ND P	2ND S	2ND H	2ND S	2ND S	2ND H
3RD H	3RD P	3RD H	3RD P	3RD S	3RD H	3RD H	3RD P

CM9	CM10	CM11	CM12	CM13	CM14	CM15	
1ST P	1ST H	1ST S	1ST H	1ST H	1ST H	1ST H	
2ND S	2ND S	2ND H	2ND S	2ND S	2ND S	2ND P	
3RD H	3RD P	3RD P	3RD P	3RD P	3RD P	3RD S	

Figure 15.1

Construct a preference table to illustrate the results of the election.

Solution Notice that committee member 1 (CM1) listed S, P, H as his or her choice. Also, notice that committee member 3 (CM3) also listed S, P, H, in that order. None of the other committee members listed this order of selection. Therefore, there are two committee members who listed S, P, H in that order. This information is indicated in boldface in column one of Table 15.2. Next look at CM2. He or she listed S, H, P. Two other committee members, CM8 and CM11, listed S, H, P in that order. Therefore, three committee members list the order S, H, P. This information is indicated in column two of Table 15.2. Continue this process to obtain the preference table.

Table 15.2 Winter Festival Mascot Preference Table

Number of Votes	2	3	5	1	3	1
First	S	S	H	P	P	H
Second	P	H	S	H	S	P
Third	H	P	P	S	H	S

Notice that the total number of votes indicated in the preference table is 15, which checks with the individual number of votes given. ∎

When an election has many voters, a preference table is an efficient way to report the results.

The initial purpose of Example 1 was to introduce the preference table. We will revisit the winter festival mascot election several times in this section. Example 2 introduces another election that will be used frequently in this section.

Example **2** *Voting for the Honor Society President*

Four students are running for president of the Honor Society: Antoine (A), Betty (B), Camille (C), and Don (D). The club members were asked to rank all candidates. The resulting preference table for this election is given in Table 15.3.

Table 15.3 Honor Society Preference Table

Number of Votes	19	15	11	7	2
First	B	C	D	A	C
Second	A	A	C	D	D
Third	C	D	A	C	A
Fourth	D	B	B	B	B

a) How many students voted in the election?
b) How many students selected the candidates in this order: C, A, D, B?
c) How many students selected C as their first choice?

Solution

a) To find the number of students who voted, we add the numbers in the row labeled Number of Votes.

$$19 + 15 + 11 + 7 + 2 = 54$$

Therefore, 54 students voted in the election.

b) Fifteen students voted in the given order (the second column of letters).

c) To determine the number who voted for C as their first choice, read across the row that says First. When you see a C in the row, record the number above it. Then find the sum of the numbers. Thus,

$$15 + 2 = 17 \text{ students selected C as their first choice.} \quad \blacksquare$$

Now we will begin to examine the results of the elections in Examples 1 and 2. Each election will be analyzed using each of the four different voting methods discussed in this section: plurality method, Borda count method, plurality with elimination method, and pairwise comparison method.

Plurality Method

When electing a candidate using the *plurality method*, each voter votes for only one candidate. The candidate receiving the most votes is declared the winner. With the plurality method, a preference table does not have to be used since the candidates are not ranked. In this section, we will often use a preference table since the data may often be given in that form from a previous example. The plurality method is the most commonly used method, and it is the easiest method to use when there are more than two candidates.

PROCEDURE **PLURALITY METHOD**

1. Each voter votes for one candidate.
2. The candidate receiving the most votes is declared the winner.

If a candidate has a majority of votes, he or she will win an election using the plurality method. However, it is possible for a candidate to win an election using the plurality method without the candidate having a majority of votes, as we will see in the next example.

Example 3 *Selecting a Mascot Using the Plurality Method*

Consider the winter festival mascot election given in Example 1. Which mascot is selected using the plurality method?

Solution Using the plurality method, the candidate with the most votes is selected as mascot. In Example 1, the planning committee members ranked the candidates. We will assume that each planning committee member would vote for his or her first choice as listed in Table 15.2 on page 909. From Table 15.2, we see that the snowman received $2 + 3 = 5$ votes, the polar bear received $1 + 3 = 4$ votes, and the husky received $5 + 1 = 6$ votes. These results indicate that by using the plurality method, the husky is chosen as the mascot for the winter festival. Note that the husky received only $\frac{6}{15}$, or 40%, of the first-place votes, which is less than a majority. ∎

Example 4 *Electing the Honor Society President by the Plurality Method*

Consider the Honor Society election given in Example 2. Who is elected president using the plurality method?

Solution We will assume that each member would vote for the person he or she listed in first place in Table 15.3 on page 910. From Table 15.3, we can see that Antoine received 7 votes, Betty received 19 votes, Camille received $15 + 2 = 17$ votes, and Don received 11 votes. Therefore, using the plurality method, Betty received the most votes and is elected president of the Honor Society. Note that Betty received only $\frac{19}{54}$, or about 35%, of the first-place votes, which is less than a majority. ∎

As simple as the plurality method is, this voting method ignores voters' second and subsequent choices. The rest of the voting methods we will discuss take all voters' choices into consideration.

Borda Count Method

The *Borda count* method, developed by Jean-Charles de Borda, requires that voters rank candidates in order from most favorable to least favorable. The Borda count method then quantifies this ranking to determine a winner.

> **PROCEDURE** **BORDA COUNT METHOD**
>
> 1. Voters rank the candidates from the most favorable to the least favorable.
> 2. Each last-place vote is awarded one point, each next-to-last-place vote is awarded two points, each third-from-last-place vote is awarded three points, and so forth.
> 3. The candidate receiving the most points is the winner of the election.

The primary advantage of the Borda count method is that voters are able to provide more information than in the plurality method. Many well-known ranking

Profile In Mathematics

Jean-Charles de Borda

J ean-Charles de Borda (1733–1799), a French calvary officer and naval captain for whom the Borda count method is named, wrote on a variety of subjects, including mathematics, physics, design of scientific experiments, and voting theory.

systems use variations of the Borda count method. The Heisman trophy, given annually to the best college football player, is awarded by having the voters (sportswriters and former Heisman trophy winners) rank their first, second, and third choices out of possibly thousands of college football players. A player receives 3 points for each first-place vote, 2 points for each second-place vote, and 1 point for each third-place vote.

Example 5 Selecting the Winter Festival Mascot Using the Borda Count Method

Let's reexamine the Erie, Pennsylvania, election for a winter festival mascot. For convenience, the preference table is reproduced in Table 15.4. Recall that S represents snowman, P represents polar bear, and H represents husky. Which mascot is selected using the Borda count method?

Table 15.4 Winter Festival Mascot Preference Table

Number of Votes	2	3	5	1	3	1
First	S	S	H	P	P	H
Second	P	H	S	H	S	P
Third	H	P	P	S	H	S

Solution   In this problem, there are three candidates, so a first-place vote is worth 3 points, a second-place vote is worth 2 points, and a third-place vote is worth 1 point. To award points, we examine each candidate starting with the snowman.

From Table 15.4, we see that the **snowman receives**

$2 + 3 =$ **5** first-place votes producing **5** $\times$ 3 = 15 points,

$5 + 3 =$ **8** second-place votes producing **8** $\times$ 2 = 16 points, and

$1 + 1 =$ **2** third-place votes producing **2** $\times$ 1 = 2 points

Therefore, the snowman receives 15 + 16 + 2 = 33 points.

Next we see that the **husky receives**

$5 + 1 =$ **6** first-place votes producing **6** $\times$ 3 = 18 points,

$3 + 1 =$ **4** second-place votes producing **4** $\times$ 2 = 8 points, and

$2 + 3 =$ **5** third-place votes producing **5** $\times$ 1 = 5 points

Therefore, the husky receives 18 + 8 + 5 = 31 points.

Finally, we see that the **polar bear receives**

$1 + 3 =$ **4** first-place votes producing **4** $\times$ 3 = 12 points,

$2 + 1 =$ **3** second-place votes producing **3** $\times$ 2 = 6 points, and

$3 + 5 =$ **8** third-place votes producing **8** $\times$ 1 = 8 points

Therefore, the polar bear receives 12 + 6 + 8 = 26 points.

The snowman receives 33 points, the husky receives 31 points, and the polar bear receives 26 points. By using the Borda count method, the snowman is chosen as the winter festival mascot.   ∎

We will now reexamine the election for president of the Honor Society by using the Borda count method.

Example **6** *Electing the Honor Society President Using the Borda Count Method*

Use the Borda count method to determine the winner of the election for president of the Honor Society discussed in Example 2. Recall that the candidates are Antoine (A), Betty (B), Camille (C), and Don (D). For convenience, the preference table is reproduced below in Table 15.5.

Table 15.5 Honor Society Preference Table

Number of Votes	19	15	11	7	2
First	B	C	D	A	C
Second	A	A	C	D	D
Third	C	D	A	C	A
Fourth	D	B	B	B	B

Solution In this problem, there are four candidates, so a first-place vote is worth 4 points, a second-place vote is worth 3 points, a third-place vote is worth 2 points, and a fourth-place vote is worth 1 point.

Using Table 15.5, we see that:

Antoine receives

7 first-place votes producing **7** $\times$ 4 = 28 points,

19 + 15 = **34** second-place votes producing **34** $\times$ 3 = 102 points, and

11 + 2 = **13** third-place votes producing **13** $\times$ 2 = 26 points

Antoine has no fourth-place votes. Therefore, Antoine receives 28 + 102 + 26 = 156 points.

Betty receives

19 first-place votes producing **19** $\times$ 4 = 76 points, and

15 + 11 + 7 + 2 = **35** fourth-place votes producing **35** $\times$ 1 = 35 points

Betty has no second- or third-place votes. Therefore, Betty receives 76 + 35 = 111 points.

Camille receives

15 + 2 = **17** first-place votes producing **17** $\times$ 4 = 68 points,

11 second-place votes producing **11** $\times$ 3 = 33 points, and

19 + 7 = **26** third-place votes producing **26** $\times$ 2 = 52 points

Camille has no fourth-place votes. Therefore, Camille receives 68 + 33 + 52 = 153 points.

Don receives

11 first-place votes producing **11** $\times$ 4 = 44 points,

7 + 2 = **9** second-place votes producing **9** $\times$ 3 = 27 points,

15 third-place votes producing **15** $\times$ 2 = 30 points, and

19 fourth-place votes producing **19** $\times$ 1 = 19 points

Therefore, Don receives 44 + 27 + 30 + 19 = 120 points.

Antoine, with 156 points, receives the most points using the Borda count method and is declared the winner. ∎

Even though Antoine received the fewest number of first-place votes, he is declared the winner under the Borda count method.

Notice that with both the winter festival mascot election (Examples 3 and 5) and the Honor Society president election (Examples 4 and 6), the plurality method and the Borda count method produced different winners. This result indicates the importance of choosing a voting method *prior to the election*. This will become even more evident when we examine the remaining voting methods. Next we will examine the plurality with elimination method, which also takes voters' second and subsequent preferences into account.

Plurality with Elimination

The next method we will discuss, *plurality with elimination*, may involve a series of elections. When using the plurality with elimination method each voter votes for only one candidate. If a candidate initially receives a majority of votes, that candidate is declared the winner. If no candidate receives a majority of votes, the candidate with the fewest number of votes is eliminated and a second election is held. This process continues until a candidate receives a majority of votes.

PROCEDURE **PLURALITY WITH ELIMINATION METHOD**

1. Each voter votes for one candidate.

2. If a candidate receives a majority of votes, that candidate is declared the winner.

3. If no candidate receives a majority, eliminate the candidate with the fewest votes and hold another election. (If there is a tie for the fewest votes, eliminate all candidates tied for the fewest votes.)

4. Repeat this process until a candidate receives a majority.

One of the immediate disadvantages of the plurality with elimination method is the possible need for two or more elections, depending on the number of candidates. One way to limit the number of elections held is to begin with a *runoff election* in which voters choose among a field of candidates. In the second election, the voters only select among the top two candidates from the runoff election. Another way to avoid multiple elections entirely is to have voters rank candidates from most to least favorable just as we did with the Borda count method. We assume that in the first round, the voters would have selected their first choice. We must also assume that after a candidate is eliminated, the order of preference is not changed. For instance, let's say that a voter's original ranking order was E, G, B, D, F. Suppose that B is eliminated. This voter's ranking order now becomes E, G, D, F. *In this book, when working the examples and exercises, we will assume that the order preference remains the same in the second election as it was in the first election.* The next two examples will demonstrate the elimination process when used with the plurality with elimination method.

Example 7 *Selecting the Winter Festival Mascot Using the Plurality with Elimination Method*

Once again, we will consider the winter festival mascot election in Erie, Pennsylvania. Recall that S represents snowman, P represents polar bear, and H represents husky. Which mascot is selected using the plurality with elimination method?

Solution Reexamine the preference table shown in Table 15.6.

Table 15.6 Winter Festival Mascot Preference Table

Number of Votes	2	3	5	1	3	1
First	S	S	H	P	P	H
Second	P	H	S	H	S	P
Third	H	P	P	S	H	S

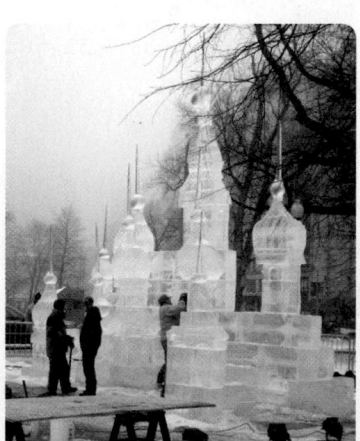

▲ *A winter festival*

We first count the number of first-place votes for each mascot:

Snowman: 2 + 3 = 5   Husky: 5 + 1 = 6   Polar bear: 1 + 3 = 4

To receive a majority, a candidate must have more than half of the votes. Since there are 15 people voting, 8 or more votes are needed to receive a majority. In this election, no candidate received a majority. Since the polar bear received the fewest number of first-place votes, it is eliminated in the first round. Next, we assume that all preference orders remain the same. For example, the three committee members who had their preference order of P, S, and H will now have a preference order of S and H. Table 15.7 shows the new preference table after the polar bear is eliminated.

Table 15.7 Winter Festival Mascot Preference Table After the Polar Bear Is Eliminated

Number of Votes	2	3	5	1	3	1
First	S	S	H	H	S	H
Second	H	H	S	S	H	S

We see now that the snowman has 2 + 3 + 3 = 8 first-place votes and the husky has 5 + 1 + 1 = 7 first-place votes. The snowman has eight of 15 first-place votes, a majority. Using the plurality with elimination method, the snowman is chosen as the winter festival mascot. ∎

Example 8 *Electing the Honor Society President Using the Plurality with Elimination Method*

Use the plurality with elimination method to determine the winner of the election for president of the Honor Society from Example 2. The preference table is shown again in Table 15.8. Recall that A represents Antoine, B represents Betty, C represents Camille, and D represents Don.

Table 15.8 Honor Society Preference Table

Number of Votes	19	15	11	7	2
First	B	C	D	A	C
Second	A	A	C	D	D
Third	C	D	A	C	A
Fourth	D	B	B	B	B

Solution First we count the number of first-place votes for each candidate:

Antoine: 7   Betty: 19   Camille: 17   Don: 11

Since 54 votes were cast, a candidate must have at least 28 first-place votes to receive a majority. In this election, no candidate received a majority. Antoine has the fewest number of first-place votes, so he is eliminated. From column one of Table 15.8, we see that 19 voters ranked their preference as B, A, C, D. With A eliminated, we assume that those same 19 voters would now rank their preference as B, C, D. From column two in Table 15.8, 15 voters ranked their preference as C, A, D, B. With A eliminated, we assume that those same 15 voters would now rank their preference as C, D, B. We eliminate A from the other columns of the table in a similar manner.

The new preference table with A eliminated is given in Table 15.9.

Table 15.9 Honor Society Preference Table After Antoine Is Eliminated

Number of Votes	19	15	11	7	2
First	B	C	D	D	C
Second	C	D	C	C	D
Third	D	B	B	B	B

The number of first-place votes is now

Betty: 19   Camille: 17   Don: 18

Still, no candidate received a majority. Camille now has the fewest number of first-place votes, so she is eliminated. With Camille eliminated, the new preference table is given in Table 15.10.

Table 15.10 Honor Society Preference Table After Camille Is Eliminated

Number of Votes	19	15	11	7	2
First	B	D	D	D	D
Second	D	B	B	B	B

The number of first-place votes is now

Betty: 19   Don: 35

Don has a majority of first-place votes and is declared the winner using the plurality with elimination method. ∎

The Honor Society elections in the previous examples are quite interesting. When the plurality method was used, Betty was declared the winner. When the Borda count method was used, Antoine was declared the winner. When the plurality with elimination method was used, Don was declared the winner. This dilemma, once again, underscores the importance of publicly stating the voting method to be used *before* the election takes place.

The selection of the city to host the Olympic Games occurs by using a type of plurality with elimination. The election process for the Academy Awards involves several stages. One stage involves a variation of the plurality with elimination method in which the motion picture nominee with the fewest number of first-place votes is eliminated.

Now we will discuss our next voting method, the pairwise comparison method.

Pairwise Comparison Method

To use the pairwise comparison method, each voter first ranks all the candidates. Then each candidate is compared with each of the other candidates using the rankings. It is treated like a round-robin tournament. For instance, if the candidates for an election were Bert, Ernie, and Louis, the following comparisons would be made: Bert versus Ernie, Bert versus Louis, and Ernie versus Louis. The winner of each individual comparison is awarded one point. If there is a tie, each candidate receives $\frac{1}{2}$ point. The candidate who obtains the most points in the one-to-one comparisons is declared the winner.

PROCEDURE **PAIRWISE COMPARISON METHOD**

1. Voters rank the candidates.
2. A series of comparisons in which each candidate is compared with each of the other candidates follows.
3. If candidate A is preferred to candidate B, A receives 1 point. If candidate B is preferred to candidate A, B receives 1 point. If the candidates tie, each receives $\frac{1}{2}$ point.
4. After making all comparisons among the candidates, the candidate receiving the most points is declared the winner.

Example 9 *Selecting the Winter Festival Mascot Using the Pairwise Comparison Method*

We will again examine the Erie, Pennsylvania, winter festival mascot election. Which mascot is selected if the pairwise comparison method is used?

Solution The preference table is shown again in Table 15.11. Recall that S stands for snowman, P stands for polar bear, and H stands for husky.

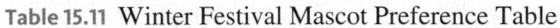

Table 15.11 Winter Festival Mascot Preference Table

Number of Votes	2	3	5	1	3	1
First	S	S	H	P	P	H
Second	P	H	S	H	S	P
Third	H	P	P	S	H	S

To determine the winner, it is necessary to make comparisons between the snowman and the polar bear, between the snowman and the husky, and between the polar bear and the husky.

We will begin by comparing the snowman and the polar bear. We see from Table 15.11 that the 2 voters in the first column, the 3 voters in the second column, and the 5 voters in the third column all prefer the snowman to the polar bear. We also see that the 1 voter in the fourth column, the 3 voters in the fifth column, and the 1 voter in the sixth column all prefer the polar bear to the snowman.

The pairwise comparison of the **snowman versus the polar bear** is

Snowman: $2 + 3 + 5 = 10$ votes   Polar bear: $1 + 3 + 1 = 5$ votes

Thus, the snowman wins the pairwise comparison between the snowman and the polar bear and is awarded 1 point.

The pairwise comparison of the **snowman versus the husky** is

Snowman: $2 + 3 + 3 = 8$ votes   Husky: $5 + 1 + 1 = 7$ votes

The snowman wins the pairwise comparison between the snowman and the husky and is awarded another point.

The pairwise comparison of the **polar bear versus the husky** is

Polar bear: $2 + 1 + 3 = 6$ votes   Husky: $3 + 5 + 1 = 9$ votes

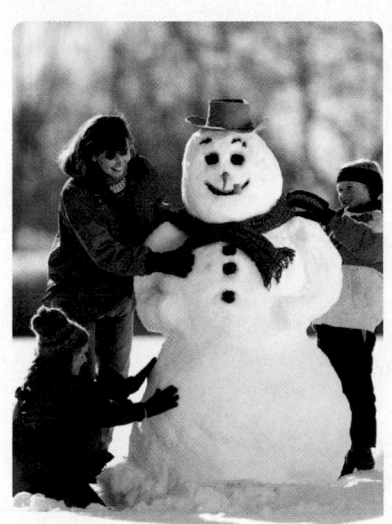

TIMELY TIP

When we compared the snowman and the polar bear in Example 9, we found the sum of the snowman's votes to be 10. Then we found the sum of the polar bear's votes to be 5. Notice that $10 + 5 = 15$, the number of votes in the preference table. If the snowman had 10 votes, the polar bear must have $15 - 10$ or 5 votes. When we use the pairwise comparison method, if you determine the number of votes of one member in the comparison, the number of votes of the second member can be found by subtracting the first number of votes found from the total number of votes.

The husky wins the pairwise comparison between the polar bear and the husky and is awarded 1 point. Since the snowman received 2 points, the husky received 1 point, and the polar bear received 0 points, using the pairwise comparison method the snowman is declared the winter festival mascot.   ■

Let's look at how we arrived at the comparisons. Each candidate was compared one-to-one with all the other candidates. In Example 9, we started with the snowman. Since the snowman had to be compared with each of the other candidates, we compared the snowman with the polar bear and then we compared the snowman with the husky. Next, we chose the polar bear. Since the polar bear had already been compared with the snowman, we only needed to compare the polar bear with the husky. The last candidate was the husky. Since the husky was already compared with each of the other candidates, we have made all the necessary comparisons. This process is used regardless of the number of candidates.

In Example 9, there were 3 candidates and we made 3 comparisons. The formula to determine the number of comparisons that are needed when n candidates are being considered follows.

Number of Comparisons

The number of comparisons, c, needed when using the pairwise comparison method when there are n candidates is

$$c = \frac{n(n-1)}{2}$$

For example, when there are 5 candidates, $n = 5$ and the number of comparisons is

$$c = \frac{n(n-1)}{2} = \frac{5(4)}{2} = \frac{20}{2} = 10$$

In this book, we will not work with more than 5 candidates.

Example 10 *Electing the Honor Society President Using the Pairwise Comparison Method*

Use the pairwise comparison method to determine the winner of the election for president of the Honor Society that was originally discussed in Example 2 on page 910.

Solution The preference table is shown again in Table 15.12. Recall that A represents Antoine, B represents Betty, C represents Camille, and D represents Don.

Table 15.12 Honor Society Preference Table

Number of Votes	19	15	11	7	2
First	B	C	D	A	C
Second	A	A	C	D	D
Third	C	D	A	C	A
Fourth	D	B	B	B	B

Since we have 4 candidates, $n = 4$ and the number of comparisons needed is

$$c = \frac{n(n-1)}{2} = \frac{4(3)}{2} = 6$$

Since the United States was founded in 1776, Americans and their elected representatives have had many disputes regarding election procedures. As you read through this chapter, you will see various voting methods that were used to try to make the voting procedures as fair as possible. You will also learn that there is no ideal voting method, that is, one that has no flaws. Although there may be flaws in the voting procedures, the American election procedure is still a model to democracies all around the world. One current debate is whether we should continue using our present electoral system or change to use the popular vote to decide presidential elections. As of this writing, four presidents were elected even though they lost the popular vote: John Quincy Adams (1824), Rutherford B. Hayes (1876), Benjamin Harrison (1888), and George W. Bush (2000).

The 6 comparisons we will make are A versus B, A versus C, A versus D, B versus C, B versus D, and C versus D.

1. The pairwise comparison of **Antoine versus Betty** is

$$\text{Antoine: } 15 + 11 + 7 + 2 = 35 \text{ votes} \qquad \text{Betty: } 19 \text{ votes}$$

Antoine wins this comparison and is awarded 1 point.

2. The pairwise comparison of **Antoine versus Camille** is

$$\text{Antoine: } 19 + 7 = 26 \text{ votes} \qquad \text{Camille: } 15 + 11 + 2 = 28 \text{ votes}$$

Camille wins this comparison and is awarded 1 point.

3. The pairwise comparison of **Antoine versus Don** is

$$\text{Antoine: } 19 + 15 + 7 = 41 \text{ votes} \qquad \text{Don: } 11 + 2 = 13 \text{ votes}$$

Antoine wins this comparison and is awarded a second point.

4. The pairwise comparison of **Betty versus Camille** is

$$\text{Betty: } 19 \text{ votes} \qquad \text{Camille: } 15 + 11 + 7 + 2 = 35 \text{ votes}$$

Camille wins this comparison and is awarded a second point.

5. The pairwise comparison of **Betty versus Don** is

$$\text{Betty: } 19 \text{ votes} \qquad \text{Don: } 15 + 11 + 7 + 2 = 35 \text{ votes}$$

Don wins this comparison and is awarded 1 point.

6. The pairwise comparison of **Camille versus Don** is

$$\text{Camille: } 19 + 15 + 2 = 36 \text{ votes} \qquad \text{Don: } 11 + 7 = 18 \text{ votes}$$

Camille wins this comparison and is awarded a third point.

We have made all possible one-to-one comparisons. Antoine received 2 points, Betty received 0 points, Camille received 3 points, and Don received 1 point. Since Camille received 3 points, the most points from the pairwise comparison method, Camille wins the election. ∎

As we have illustrated, using four different voting methods resulted in four different winners for the president of the Honor Society. Each candidate could claim that he or she should be declared the winner. Thus, the voting method we choose to use could greatly affect the election results and therefore should be chosen prior to an election.

Tie Breaking

Just as the four methods we have examined can produce four different winners, each method could also produce a tie between two or more candidates. In each of the previous examples, the voting method used led to one winner, but that is not always the case. With each method described—plurality method, Borda count method, plurality with elimination method, and pairwise comparison method—the possibility of the method producing a tie is very real. A tie could be achieved simply by having only two candidates each with the same number of supporters.

Breaking a tie can be achieved by either making an arbitrary choice, such as flipping a coin, or by bringing in an additional voter. For example, under Robert's Rules of Order, the president of any group votes only when there is a tie or to create a tie. There are other ways of breaking a tie that are less arbitrary than flipping a coin. If a tie results from using the Borda count method, it could be broken by choosing the candidate with the most first-place votes. If a tie results from the pairwise comparison method, it could be broken by choosing the winner of the one-to-one comparison between the candidates involved in the tie. Different tie-breaking methods could produce different winners. Therefore, to remain fair, the tie-breaking method should be decided upon in advance, as is done in the next example.

Example 11 *Choosing a Commencement Speaker*

The University of Pennsylvania Student Government Association (SGA) is trying to decide whom to invite as the keynote speaker for commencement exercises. The choices are Katie Couric (C), Tom Hanks (H), and Denzel Washington (W). To make this difficult decision, the SGA decides to hold an election among graduating seniors. It also decides that the plurality method will be used to determine the winner and that the Borda count method will decide the winner in the event that the plurality method leads to a tie. The results of the election are represented in Table 15.13. Who will be asked to speak at the commencement ceremony?

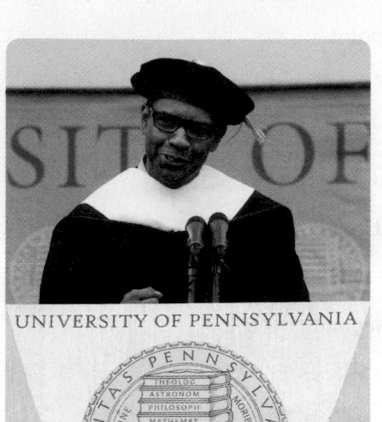

▲ *Denzel Washington giving commencement address*

Table 15.13 University of Pennsylvania Commencement Speaker Election

Number of Votes	400	250	150
First	W	C	C
Second	H	H	W
Third	C	W	H

Solution Katie Couric and Denzel Washington each receive 400 first-place votes; therefore, the plurality method leads to a tie. Thus, the Borda count method is used to break the tie between Couric and Washington. From Table 15.13, we award the following points:

Denzel Washington: $400(3) + 150(2) + 250(1) = 1750$
Katie Couric: $400(3) + 0(2) + 400(1) = 1600$

Since the Borda count method breaks the tie, Denzel Washington is asked to present the commencement address. ■

Table 15.14 summarizes the voting methods we discussed in this section.

Table 15.14 Summary of Voting Methods

Voting Method	Description
Plurality method	Each voter votes for one candidate. The candidate receiving the most votes is declared the winner.
Borda count method	Voters rank candidates from the most favorable to the least favorable. Each last-place vote is awarded 1 point, each next-to-last-place vote is awarded 2 points, each third-from-last-place vote is awarded 3 points, and so forth. The candidate receiving the most points is the winner.
Plurality with elimination method	Each voter votes for one candidate. If a candidate receives a majority of first-place votes, that candidate is declared the winner. If no candidate receives a majority of first-place votes, eliminate the candidate with the fewest number of first-place votes and hold another election. (If there is a tie for the fewest number of first-place votes, eliminate all candidates tied for the fewest number of first-place votes.) Repeat this process until a candidate receives a majority of first-place votes.
Pairwise comparison method	Voters rank the candidates. A series of comparisons in which each candidate is compared with each of the other candidates follows. If candidate A is preferred to candidate B, A receives 1 point. If candidate B is preferred to candidate A, B receives 1 point. If the candidates tie, each receives $\frac{1}{2}$ point. The candidate receiving the most points is declared the winner.

Exercises

Warm Up Exercises

In Exercises 1–8, fill in the blank with an appropriate word, phrase, or symbol(s).

1. A candidate who receives more than 50% of the votes in an election is said to have a _____ of votes. Majority

2. A table that summarizes the results of an election is called a(n) _____ table. Preference

3. When using the pairwise comparison method, the number of comparisons, c, needed when there are n candidates is determined by the formula $c =$ _____ . $\frac{n(n-1)}{2}$

4. When there are four candidates, the number of comparisons needed with the pairwise comparison method is _____ . 6

5. The voting method in which each voter votes for one candidate and the candidate receiving the most votes is declared the winner is called the _____ method. Plurality

6. The voting method in which voters rank candidates from most favorable to least favorable is called the _____ method. Borda count

7. The voting method in which each candidate is compared with each of the other candidates is called the _____ method. Pairwise comparison

8. The voting method that may involve a series of elections until a candidate receives a majority of the votes is called the _____ with elimination method. Plurality

Practice the Skills

9. *Plurality* Three candidates are running for mayor of Tucson. They receive the following votes:

    Wade   101,253   Alvarez   75,296

    Jackson   93,451

a) Determine the winner using the plurality method. Wade

b) Did this candidate receive a majority of votes? No

10. *Plurality Method* Five candidates are running for president of the Student Senate. They receive the following votes:

Michael   2192   Gerry   2562   Karen   1671
Felicia   2863   Stephen   1959

a) Determine the winner using the plurality method. Felicia

b) Did this candidate receive a majority of votes? No

11. *Preference Table for Spaghetti Sauce* Nine voters are asked to rank three brands of spaghetti sauce: Ragu (R),

Prego (P), and Newman's Own (N). The nine voters turn in the following ballots showing their preferences in order:

    R   N   R   P   P   P   R   N   P
    N   R   N   R   R   N   N   P   N
    P   P   P   N   N   R   P   R   R

Make a preference table for these ballots. *

12. *Preference Table for Yogurt* Eight voters are asked to rank three brands of yogurt: Dannon (D), Breyers (B), and Columbo (C). The eight voters turn in the following ballots showing their preferences in order:

    D   C   C   B   C   B   C   D
    B   D   D   D   B   D   D   B
    C   B   B   C   D   C   B   C

Make a preference table for these ballots. *

Problem Solving

Logo Choice In Exercises 13–18, employees at the Bloomfield Fire Department are choosing a new department logo. The choices are a hydrant (H), a fireman (F), and a fire truck (T). Each employee ranks the three choices from first to third. The preference table below shows the results of the ballots.

Number of Votes	10	5	4	2
First	H	F	F	T
Second	F	H	T	F
Third	T	T	H	H

13. How many employees voted? 21

14. Is there a majority winner? No

15. Determine the winner using the plurality method. Hydrant

16. Determine the winner using the Borda count method. Fireman

17. Determine the winner using the plurality with elimination method. Fireman

18. Determine the winner using the pairwise comparison method. Fireman

*See Instructor Answer Appendix

Choosing a Vacation Destination In Exercises 19–22, the Zellner family is trying to decide whether to go to Yellowstone National Park (Y), Rocky Mountain National Park (R), or Great Smoky Mountains National Park (S) on their summer vacation. The two parents, five children, and two grandparents rank their three choices according to the following preference table.

Number of Votes	3	2	1	2	1
First	Y	S	Y	R	S
Second	R	Y	S	S	R
Third	S	R	R	Y	Y

▲ Yellowstone National Park

19. Determine the winner using the Borda count method.
Yellowstone National Park

20. Determine the winner using the plurality method.
Yellowstone National Park

21. Determine the winner using the pairwise comparison method. Three-way tie, no winner

22. Determine the winner using the plurality with elimination method. Great Smoky Mountains National Park

NFL Expansion In Exercises 23–26, the National Football League (NFL) is considering four cities for expansion: San Antonio (S), Los Angeles (L), Honolulu (H), and Toronto (T). The 32 current owners rank the four candidates according to the following preference table.

Number of Votes	8	6	3	4	3	3	2	1	2
First	L	S	S	H	L	H	L	T	H
Second	S	H	L	S	S	S	H	H	L
Third	H	T	H	T	T	L	S	L	S
Fourth	T	L	T	L	H	T	T	S	T

23. Determine the winner using the plurality method.
Los Angeles

24. Determine the winner using the Borda count method.
San Antonio

25. Determine the winner using the plurality with elimination method. No winner, a tie between Honolulu and Los Angeles

26. Determine the winner using the pairwise comparison method. San Antonio

▲ Los Angeles, CA

Board of Trustees Election In Exercises 27–31, 12 members of the executive committee of the Student Senate must vote for a student representative for the college board of trustees from among three candidates: Greenburg (G), Haskins (H), and Vazquez (V). The preference table follows.

Number of Votes	4	1	3	2
First	G	H	V	V
Second	H	V	G	H
Third	V	G	H	G

27. Determine the winner using the Borda count method.
A tie between Greenburg and Vazquez

28. Determine the winner using the plurality method. Vazquez

29. Determine the winner using the pairwise comparison method. Vazquez

30. Determine the winner using the plurality with elimination method. Vazquez

31. Another way to determine the winner if the plurality with elimination method is used is to eliminate the candidate with the most *last*-place votes at each step. Using the preference table given above, determine the winner if the plurality with elimination method is used and the candidate with the most *last*-place votes is eliminated at each step. Greenburg

Post Office Sites In Exercises 32–36, the 11 members of the Henrietta Town Board must decide where to build a new post office. Their three choices are Lehigh Road (L), Erie Road (E), and Ontario Road (O). The preference table follows.

Number of Votes	5	2	4
First	L	E	O
Second	E	O	E
Third	O	L	L

32. Determine the winner using the plurality method. Lehigh

33. Determine the winner using the Borda count method. Erie

34. Determine the winner using the plurality with elimination method. Ontario

35. Determine the winner using the pairwise comparison method. Erie

36. Determine the winner using the plurality with elimination method if the candidate with the most *last*-place votes is eliminated at each step. Erie

37. *Choosing a Contractor* The board of directors of Birds Eye Foods is holding an election to decide which company should be awarded the contract to build an expansion to its corporate headquarters. The 15 members of Birds Eye's board of directors are considering a proposal from each of the following companies: Becker (B), DiMarco (D), LaChase (L), and Merendez (M). The members rank the four choices according to the preference table below.

Number of Votes	6	4	3	2
First	B	B	L	D
Second	L	D	B	B
Third	M	L	M	L
Fourth	D	M	D	M

a) Determine which company is selected using the plurality method. Becker

b) Determine which company is selected using the Borda count method. Becker

c) Determine which company is selected using the plurality with elimination method. Becker

d) Determine which company is selected using the pairwise comparison method. Becker

38. *Prime-Time Programming* The programmers at the Retro-Vision cable television station are deciding which classic TV show should lead their prime-time programming. Their choices are *Friends* (F), *Seinfeld* (S), *Everyone Loves Raymond* (E), and *The Cosby Show* (C). The 17 programmers rank their choices according to the following table.

Number of Votes	8	4	3	2
First	E	F	S	C
Second	C	C	C	S
Third	S	S	F	F
Fourth	F	E	E	E

▲ *The cast of Seinfeld*

a) Determine which TV show is selected using the plurality method. *Everyone Loves Raymond*

b) Determine which TV show is selected using the Borda count method. *The Cosby Show*

c) Determine which TV show is selected using the plurality with elimination method. *Seinfeld*

d) Determine which TV show is selected using the pairwise comparison method. *The Cosby Show*

39. *Flowers in a Garden* The flowers in a garden at a resort need to be replaced. The choices for the flowers are Geraniums (G), Impatiens (I), Petunias (P), and Zinnias (Z). The head gardener holds an election in which all employees get to vote. The results of the election are given in the table below.

Number of Votes	8	11	3	4	3
First	G	P	P	Z	I
Second	P	Z	I	I	G
Third	I	I	Z	G	P
Fourth	Z	G	G	P	Z

a) Determine which flowers are selected using the Borda count method. Petunias

b) Determine which flowers are selected using the plurality method. Petunias

c) Determine which flowers are selected using the plurality with elimination method. Geraniums

d) Determine which flowers are selected using the pairwise comparison method. Tie between petunias and zinnias

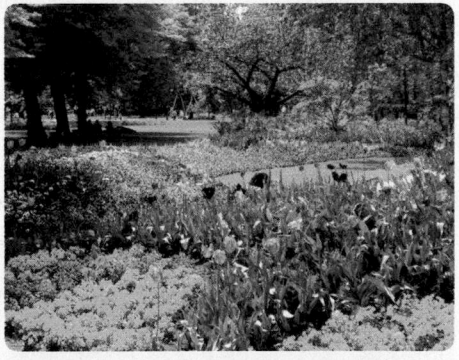

40. *Choosing a Computer* The Wizards Computer Club is ordering five new computers. To obtain a discount price, the club has decided that all five should be the same brand. The choices they are considering are Mac (M), Hewlett-Packard (H), Dell (D), and Gateway (G). The 142 members' choices are reflected below.

Number of Votes	43	30	29	26	14
First	G	M	H	D	D
Second	M	D	D	H	H
Third	H	H	M	G	M
Fourth	D	G	G	M	G

a) Determine which brand of computer is selected using the pairwise comparison method. Mac

b) Determine which brand of computer is selected using the plurality with elimination method. Dell

c) Determine which brand of computer is selected using the Borda count method. Hewlett-Packard

d) Determine which brand of computer is selected using the plurality method. Gateway

e) What does this example display about the need for choosing a voting method prior to the election? You must choose the voting method to use before the election takes place.

Concept/Writing Exercises

41. Describe a benefit of the Borda count method over the plurality method. Voters are able to provide more information, such as ranking choices, with the Borda count method.

42. Describe one way other than flipping a coin to settle a tied election. One way to settle a tie in an election is to bring in an additional voter. Other answers are possible.

Challenge Problems/Group Activities

43. *A Lost Preference Table* A ski club is having an election for president. There are three candidates and 15 voters. Each voter casts a ballot listing his or her preferences for the candidates. Right before the winner is to be announced, the previous president announces that the preference table has been lost. The only information he can remember from the preference table is that there were only *two* columns in the table.

a) Explain why there must be a majority winner.*

b) Explain why there must always be a majority winner, regardless of the number of candidates, when all voters vote, when there are an odd number of voters and only two columns in the preference table.*

44. *Cat Competition* Friskies Cat Food is looking for a new cat for the cover of their 2012 calendar. Four cats are finalists: A, B, C, and D. They are ranked first, second, third, and fourth in each of the following four categories: looks, eye color, size, and attitude. The preference table is shown below.

| | Categories | | | |
Cat	Looks	Eyes	Size	Attitude
A	4	3	2	3
B	2	4	1	2
C	1	1	4	4
D	3	2	3	1

a) Which cat wins if a Borda count method is used that awards 4 points, 3 points, 2 points, and 1 point for first, second, third, and fourth place, respectively, in each category? Tie between B and D

b) Which cat wins if a modified Borda count method is used where 5, 3, 1, and 0 points are awarded for first, second, third, and fourth place, respectively, in each category? B

45. *Ranking the Swim Teams* The results of a swim meet between the Comets (C), Rams (R), Warriors (W), and Tigers (T) are shown in the preference table below. Notice, for example, that in the sprint competition, the Comets (C) took both first and fourth place.

	Sprint	Distance	Relay	Medley
First	C	R	R	T
Second	W	T	W	R
Third	T	W	T	W
Fourth	C	W	W	C

a) Assume that the finishing positions are scored 4, 3, 2, 1 for first, second, third, and fourth place, respectively. How do the teams rank if the Borda count method is used? Warriors, Rams and Tigers tied, Comets

b) Assume that the finishing positions are scored 5, 3, 1, 0 points for first, second, third, and fourth place, respectively. How do the teams rank if we modify the Borda count method to use these values? Rams, Tigers, Warriors, Comets

46. *Using the Borda Count Method* Suppose that 20 voters rank three candidates.

a) What is the total number of points awarded to the candidates using the Borda count method? 120

b) Suppose that, using the Borda count method, candidate A receives 55 points and candidate C receives 25 points. How many points does candidate B receive? 40

c) Given the information from part (b), is it possible for candidate B to win an election if the Borda count method is used to determine the winner? Explain. No. Candidate A has more points than candidate B.

47. Suppose that 15 voters rank four candidates.

a) What is the total number of points awarded to candidates using the Borda count method? 150

b) Suppose that using the Borda count method, A receives 35 points, B receives 40 points, and C receives 25 points. How many points does D receive? 50

c) Is it possible for D to win? Explain. Yes

48. *Using Approval Voting* In many corporations and professional societies, the members of the board of directors are elected by a method called *approval voting*. With

*See Instructor Answer Appendix

approval voting, a voter does not cast a ranked ballot. Instead, the voter votes for as many candidates as he or she would support. If a voter does not approve of a candidate, he or she simply does not cast a vote for that candidate. The candidate(s) with the most votes wins.

The board of directors of CSC Computers is using approval voting to fill two vacancies on their executive committee. Twenty-one ballots are cast as follows for candidates A, B, C, and D.

	1	2	3	4	5	6	7	8	9	10	11	12	13	14	15	16	17	18	19	20	21
A	X	X		X					X		X	X			X	X				X	X
B			X	X	X			X		X							X	X			
C		X			X							X	X				X				
D		X		X	X						X	X			X	X	X			X	

Which two candidates will win seats on the executive committee? A, D

Recreational Mathematics

49. Construct a preference table showing 12 votes for 3 candidates, A, B, and C, where candidates A and B both have 5 first-place votes. Many answers are possible. *

Internet/Research Activity

50. *Awards' Methods* Research and write a report on how voting is conducted on one of the following events:

a) Academy Awards   **b)** Grammy Awards

c) Heisman Trophy Award   **d)** Nobel Prizes

e) Pulitzer Prize

Include in your report how nominees are picked, who votes, how the voting takes place, and who tabulates the results.

▲ *Natalie Portman*   *See Instructor Answer Appendix

SECTION 15.2   Flaws of Voting

▲ *It is possible that the Borda count method could produce a winning candidate that does not have a majority of votes.*

Recall the situation from Section 15.1 in which you are hosting a party and ask your 11 guests to vote on whether they would like you to serve pizza, hot dogs, or hamburgers at the party. Each guest is asked to complete a ballot by ranking the three choices from most favorable to least favorable. You decide to use the Borda count method to determine the winner and announce that pizza wins. After reviewing the ballots, one of your friends quickly points out that hot dogs should win because a majority of voters ranked hot dogs as their first choice. This scenario indicates that there is a flaw with the Borda count method. In this section, we will discuss flaws with each of the voting methods introduced in Section 15.1.

Why This is Important Understanding the flaws of different voting methods can help to determine which method to use for an election.

In Section 15.1, we discussed four voting methods: the plurality method, the Borda count method, the plurality with elimination method, and the pairwise comparison method. We discovered that the voting method chosen can be as important to the outcome as the preferences in the voting. Sometimes all four methods will result in the same winner. At other times, the four methods may produce four different winners. Although each of these methods seems to provide a reasonable means for determining a winner, we soon shall see that there are certain flaws with each method.

In this section, we will examine four criteria, known as the *fairness criteria*, that mathematicians and political scientists have agreed that a voting method should meet to be considered fair. The fairness criteria include the *majority criterion*, the *head-to-head criterion*, the *monotonicity criterion*, and the *irrelevant alternatives criterion*. The first fairness criterion we will discuss is the majority criterion.

Majority Criterion

If a single candidate is the first choice of a majority (more than 50%) of voters, most voters would agree that that candidate should be declared the winner. If that does not happen with a voting method, that voting method violates the majority criterion.

> ### Majority Criterion
>
> If a candidate receives a majority (more than 50%) of first-place votes, that candidate should be declared the winner.

Table 15.15 Lawn Maintenance Company Selection Preference Table

Number of Votes	5	3	1
First	A	B	B
Second	B	M	A
Third	M	A	M

Example 1 *Lawn Maintenance Company Selection*

The members of the Mumford Town Board are holding an election to select a company to maintain the lawn located at the town's community center. The choices are Allen Lawn Maintenance (A), B & N Lawn Maintenance (B), and Mayzon Lawn Maintenance (M). The 9 board members rank the three choices and then use the Borda count method to make their selection. The preference table is shown in Table 15.15.

a) Which company is chosen using the Borda count method?

b) Does the winner from part (a) have a majority of first place votes?

Solution

a) Using the Borda count method, B & N Lawn Maintenance is chosen. Verify this outcome yourself.

b) B & N has 4 out of 9 first-place votes, which is less than 50%. So the winner of the election, B & N, does not have a majority of first place votes. In fact, a majority of the town board members, 5 out of 9, chose Allen Lawn Maintenance. ∎

In Example 1, although a majority of town board members preferred one choice, Allen Lawn Maintenance, the Borda count method yielded a different choice, B & N Lawn Maintenance. This example demonstrates that **the Borda count method has the potential to violate the majority criterion.**

Table 15.16

Number of Votes	15	10	3
First	A	B	C
Second	B	C	B
Third	C	A	A

Example 2 *Applying the Majority Criterion*

Preference Table 15.16 shows the outcomes of 28 votes.

Decide which candidate would be chosen with each of the following voting methods. Also discuss whether or not the method violates the majority criterion.

a) The plurality method

b) The Borda count method

c) The plurality with elimination method

d) The pairwise comparison method

Solution

a) The plurality method awards the election to A. Notice that A also has a majority—15 out of 28—of first-place votes. The plurality method does not violate the majority criterion. In general, a candidate who holds a majority of first-place votes also holds a plurality of first-place votes. Therefore, **the plurality method never violates the majority criterion.** However, that does not mean that the plurality method always produces a winner that has a majority of the votes. It does mean that if a candidate has a majority of first-place votes, that candidate will also have a plurality of votes and will be selected with the plurality method.

b) The Borda count method awards the election to candidate B. Since candidate A holds a majority of first-place votes, this method violates the majority criterion. This example is the second example in which the Borda count method violates the majority criterion. The Borda count method does not always violate the majority criterion; however, from our examples, we can conclude that **the Borda count method has the potential for violating the majority criterion.**

c) The plurality with elimination method awards the election to candidate A. Therefore, the majority criterion is not violated. In general, a candidate who holds a majority of first-place votes is awarded the election without having to hold a second election, or without having to consider eliminating a candidate and then realigning voters' choices. Therefore, **the plurality with elimination method never violates the majority criterion.**

d) The pairwise comparison method awards the election to candidate A. In general, if a candidate holds a majority of first-place votes, this candidate always wins every pairwise comparison, thereby granting this candidate the victory. Thus, **the pairwise comparison method never violates the majority criterion.** ∎

Of the four methods we discussed, only the Borda count method can violate the majority criterion. Therefore, the Borda count method has a flaw that none of the other voting methods has. An advantage of the Borda count method is that it takes into account voters' preferences by having all candidates ranked. However, a candidate with a majority of first-place votes can lose an election with the Borda count method. Next we will introduce a second fairness criterion and use it to uncover flaws in other voting methods.

Head-to-Head Criterion

Suppose that it is found that one candidate is preferred over each of the other candidates using head-to-head comparisons. It would seem reasonable that this candidate should be chosen as the winner. That, however, is not always the case, and the head-to-head criterion will be used to uncover the next voting method flaw.

Head-to-Head Criterion
If a candidate is favored when compared head-to-head with every other candidate, that candidate should be declared the winner.

The head-to-head criterion is also known as the *Condorcet criterion*. This criterion is named after the Marquis de Condorcet; see the *Profile in Mathematics* on page 928.

Example 3 Applying the Head-to-Head Criterion

Suppose that four candidates are running for mayor of Springwater: Alvarez (A), Buchannon (B), Czechanski (C), and Davis (D). The election involves voters ranking the candidates with the results shown in Table 15.17.

Table 15.17 Springwater Mayor Preference Table

Number of Votes	129	90	87	78	42
First	D	A	B	C	C
Second	A	C	C	B	B
Third	B	B	A	D	A
Fourth	C	D	D	A	D

a) Is there one candidate who is favored over all others using a head-to-head comparison?

b) Who wins this election if the plurality method is used? Does that result violate the head-to-head criterion?

c) Who wins this election if the Borda count method is used? Does that result violate the head-to-head criterion?

d) Who wins this election if the plurality with elimination method is used? Does that result violate the head-to-head criterion?

e) Who wins this election if the pairwise comparison method is used? Does that result violate the head-to-head criterion?

Solution

a) Using Table 15.17 on page 927, we can determine that Alvarez is favored, using head-to-head comparison, over Buchannon. Alvarez is favored over Buchannon in columns 1 and 2, giving Alvarez $129 + 90$ or 219 votes. Buchannon is favored over Alvarez in columns 3, 4, and 5, giving Buchannon $87 + 78 + 42$ or 207 votes. Alvarez is favored over Buchannon by a margin of 219 votes to 207 votes. Using this procedure, we can determine that Alvarez is also favored over Czechanski by a margin of 219 votes to 207 votes and Alvarez is also favored over Davis by a margin of 219 votes to 207 (you should verify these numbers). Therefore, Alvarez is favored over all the candidates, and according to the head-to-head criterion, Alvarez should be declared the winner.

b) Using the plurality method, Davis is elected by virtue of the 129 first-place votes. Therefore, this result violates the head-to-head criterion. This example demonstrates that **the plurality method has the potential to violate the head-to-head criterion.**

c) Using the Borda count method, Buchannon receives 1146 points, Czechanski receives 1140 points, Alvarez receives 1083 points, and Davis receives 891 points (you should verify these tallies). Therefore, Buchannon is elected using the Borda count method. Therefore, this result violates the head-to-head criterion. This example also demonstrates that **the Borda count method has the potential to violate the head-to-head criterion.**

d) Using plurality with elimination, we see that Buchannon is eliminated in the first round, Alvarez is eliminated in the second round, and in the third round Czechanski defeats Davis by a count of 297 to 129 (you should verify these results). Therefore, Czechanski is elected using the plurality with elimination method. Therefore, this result violates the head-to-head criterion. This example demonstrates that **the plurality with elimination method has the potential to violate the head-to-head criterion.**

e) Using the pairwise comparison method, we see that Alvarez is favored over Buchannon, Czechanski, and Davis, thereby giving Alvarez 3 points. Buchannon is favored using head-to-head comparison over Czechanski and Davis, thereby giving Buchannon 2 points. Czechanski is favored over Davis, thereby giving Czechanski 1 point. Davis is not favored over any of the other candidates, thereby giving Davis 0 points. (You should verify these results.) Therefore, Alvarez is elected using the pairwise comparison method. It should be clear that if a certain candidate were favored to all other candidates, then this candidate would be elected using the pairwise comparison method. Therefore, **the pairwise comparison method never violates the head-to-head criterion.** ■

By looking at Example 3, we can conclude that the **only voting method that does not have the potential to violate the head-to-head criterion is the pairwise comparison method.**

At this point in our discussion, we should note the differences between the *head-to-head fairness criterion* and the *pairwise comparison voting method*. The head-to-head criterion is one of the fairness criteria used to determine the fairness of a voting method and therefore is not used to determine the winner of an election. The pairwise comparison method is a voting method and is used to determine the winner of an election. When applying the head-to head criterion, we are trying to determine if there is one candidate who is favored when compared head-to-head with every other candidate. If there is such a candidate, this candidate, according to the head-to-head criterion, should win an election, regardless of which voting method is used to determine the winner. As we have seen in Example 3, it is possible for a candidate to be favored when compared head-to-head with every other candidate yet lose an election. When a candidate is favored when compared with all other candidates and does not win the election, as in Example 3, we say that the voting method used violated the head-to-head criterion.

Example 3 highlighted how the head-to-head criterion uncovered flaws in the plurality method, Borda count method, and the plurality with elimination method. Now, we will introduce a third criterion for fair elections, the monotonicity criterion, and use it to uncover an additional flaw in the plurality with elimination method.

Monotonicity Criterion

The third criterion for fair elections is only relevant when an election is repeated. A repeated election refers to the same number of voters choosing among the same candidates. One example of a repeated election is a *straw vote* followed by another vote. Frequently, preceding an election, voters discuss the candidates' strengths and weaknesses. Prior to holding an official election, voters may take a straw vote to gain a preliminary measure of the candidates' strength. After discussions, some voters may decide to change their preferences. If a candidate gains votes at the expense of the other candidates, this candidate's chances of winning should increase. If that candidate was already leading, this candidate should still win with additional votes in his or her favor. The repeated election leads us to our next criterion, the monotonicity criterion. The monotonicity criterion uncovers a strange flaw in the plurality with elimination voting method. As we soon shall see, it is possible for the winner of the first election to gain additional support before the second election and then lose the second election!

Monotonicity Criterion

A candidate who wins a first election and then gains additional support without losing any of the original support should also win a second election.

Our next example demonstrates this unusual occurrence.

Example 4 *Choosing a Television Show*

The members of a Web site blog team are trying to decide which television show to feature on its Web site. The choices under consideration are *Modern Family* (M), *Glee* (G), and *The Office* (O). To obtain an initial measure of the intentions of the committee, a straw vote is taken. The results of this first election, the straw vote, are given in Table 15.18.

Table 15.18 Television Show Committee Preference Table: First Election

Number of Votes	8	9	5	11
First	M	G	M	O
Second	G	O	O	M
Third	O	M	G	G

▲ The cast of Glee

After several hours of debate and discussion, a second vote is taken. In the second election, only five people change their initial vote. The five people who previously voted M, O, G now vote O, M, G. That is, they moved *The Office* into first place ahead of *Modern Family*. This change has the effect of eliminating the M, O, G column of Table 15.18 and increasing the number voting O, M, G from 11 to 16. The results of the second election are given in Table 15.19.

Table 15.19 Television Show Committee Preference Table: Second Election

Number of Votes	8	9	16
First	M	G	O
Second	G	O	M
Third	O	M	G

a) Using the plurality with elimination method, which show wins the first election?
b) Using the plurality with elimination method, which show wins the second election?
c) Does this result violate the monotonicity criterion?

Solution

a) Refer to Table 15.18 on page 929. Using the plurality with elimination method, the first election (the straw vote) results in *Glee* being eliminated and in *The Office* gaining a majority over *Modern Family* by a vote of 20 to 13. Thus, *The Office* would be chosen as the television show to feature.

b) Refer to Table 15.19 above. Using the plurality with elimination method, the second election results in *Modern Family* being eliminated and in *Glee* gaining a majority over *The Office* by a vote of 17 to 16. Thus, *Glee* would be chosen as the television show to feature.

c) Although the five voters who changed their ballots did so in a way to add support to *The Office*, *The Office*'s victory was not repeated in the second election. Therefore, this result violates the monotonicity criterion. This occurrence shows that **the plurality with elimination method has the potential to violate the monotonicity criterion.**   ■

In Example 4, we showed that the plurality with elimination method has the potential to violate the monotonicity criterion. **Note that the Borda count method and the pairwise comparison method also have the potential to violate the monotonicity criterion.**

We have thus far shown how the majority criterion, the head-to-head criterion, and the monotonicity criterion have all uncovered flaws in our voting methods. You may have noticed that we have yet to find a flaw in the pairwise comparison method. Our next criterion, the irrelevant alternatives criterion, uncovers a flaw in the pairwise comparison method.

Irrelevant Alternatives Criterion

The last criterion we will discuss, the irrelevant alternatives criterion, will address the result of removing a candidate from an election who has no chance of winning. Suppose that four candidates, A, B, C, and D, are involved in an election. The voting takes place and it is found that candidate B is the winner. However, it is discovered that just prior to the election, candidate C had dropped out of the election. Since candidate C had no chance of winning, we might conclude that this action should not have any effect on the outcome of the election. We shall soon see that such action can negatively affect the winner. We now have our fourth fairness criterion.

Irrelevant Alternatives Criterion

If a candidate is the winner of an election and in a second election one or more of the other candidates is removed, the previous winner should still be the winner.

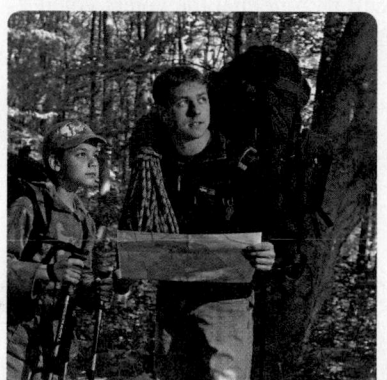

Example 5 *Selecting a Hiking Club President*

The members of the Richmond Hiking Club are holding an election to select a club president. The choices are Anderson (A), Bacari (B), Mendolson (M), Sanchez (S), and Tompkins (T). The election results are shown in Table 15.20.

Table 15.20 Richmond Hiking Club President Preference Table

Number of Votes	24	16	16	16	8	4	4
First	B	B	T	A	S	M	M
Second	S	S	S	M	T	B	T
Third	M	T	A	T	M	S	S
Fourth	T	A	M	B	B	T	B
Fifth	A	M	B	S	A	A	A

Prior to the announcement of the election results, it is discovered that Mendolson had dropped out of the election. The election officials then decide to eliminate Mendolson's name from the election results.

a) Using the pairwise comparison method, which candidate wins this election if Mendolson is included?

b) Using the pairwise comparison method, which candidate wins the election if Mendolson is eliminated from the preference table?

c) Does this result violate the irrelevant alternatives criterion?

Solution

a) Using the pairwise comparison method, since we have five candidates, $n = 5$ and the number of comparisons needed is

$$c = \frac{n(n-1)}{2} = \frac{5(4)}{2} = 10$$

We will do the comparisons in the following order: Anderson versus Bacari, Anderson versus Mendolson, Anderson versus Sanchez, Anderson versus Tompkins, Bacari versus Mendolson, Bacari versus Sanchez, Bacari versus Tompkins, Mendolson versus Sanchez, Mendolson versus Tompkins, Sanchez versus Tompkins. These are the 10 possible comparisons. The following results can be verified from Table 15.20.

1. Bacari defeats Anderson (56 to 32), so Bacari gets 1 point.
2. Anderson defeats Mendolson (48 to 40), so Anderson gets 1 point.
3. Sanchez defeats Anderson (72 to 16), so Sanchez gets 1 point.
4. Tompkins defeats Anderson (72 to 16), so Tompkins gets 1 point.
5. Mendolson defeats Bacari (48 to 40), so Mendolson gets 1 point.
6. Bacari defeats Sanchez (60 to 28), so Bacari gets 1 point.
7. Bacari ties Tompkins (44 to 44), so Bacari gets $\frac{1}{2}$ point and Tompkins gets $\frac{1}{2}$ point.
8. Sanchez defeats Mendolson (64 to 24), so Sanchez gets 1 point.

9. Mendolson defeats Tompkins (48 to 40), so Mendolson gets 1 point.

10. Sanchez defeats Tompkins (52 to 36), so Sanchez gets 1 point.

We have made all possible one-to-one comparisons. Sanchez has 3 points, Bacari has $2\frac{1}{2}$ points, Mendolson has 2 points, Tompkins has $1\frac{1}{2}$ points, and Anderson has 1 point. Therefore, Sanchez is the winner when Mendolson is included.

b) Once Mendolson is eliminated from consideration, there is a new election and a new preference table. In the new election we will assume that the voters voted in the same order as in the first election. The new preference table is obtained by eliminating Mendolson from Table 15.20 and keeping the remaining candidates in the same order. See Table 15.21. Since we now have four candidates, $n = 4$ and the number of comparisons needed is

$$c = \frac{n(n-1)}{2} = \frac{4(3)}{2} = 6$$

Table 15.21   Richmond Hiking Club President Preference Table

Number of Votes	24	16	16	16	8	4	4
First	B	B	T	A	S	B	T
Second	S	S	S	T	T	S	S
Third	T	T	A	B	B	T	B
Fourth	A	A	B	S	A	A	A

The pairwise comparison method, using Table 15.21, produces the following 6 results:

1. Bacari defeats Anderson (56 to 32), so Bacari gets 1 point.

2. Sanchez defeats Anderson (72 to 16), so Sanchez gets 1 point.

3. Tompkins defeats Anderson (72 to 16), so Tompkins gets 1 point.

4. Bacari defeats Sanchez (60 to 28), so Bacari gets 1 point.

5. Bacari ties Tompkins (44 to 44), so Bacari gets $\frac{1}{2}$ point and Tompkins gets $\frac{1}{2}$ point.

6. Sanchez defeats Tompkins (52 to 36), so Sanchez gets 1 point.

We have made all 6 possible one-to-one comparisons. Now Bacari has $2\frac{1}{2}$ points, Sanchez has 2 points, Tompkins has $1\frac{1}{2}$ points, and Anderson has 0 points. Thus, Bacari is selected.

c) The first election produced Sanchez as the winner. Then, even though Mendolson was not the winning candidate, Mendolson's removal from the election produced Bacari as the winner. Therefore, this result violates the irrelevant alternatives criterion. This example demonstrates that the **pairwise comparison method has the potential for violating the irrelevant alternatives criterion.**   ■

In Example 5, we showed that the pairwise comparison method has the potential to violate the irrelevant alternatives criterion. **Note that each voting method we have discussed—the plurality method, the Borda count method, the plurality with elimination method, and the pairwise comparison method—has the potential to violate the irrelevant alternatives criterion.**

Table 15.22

Number of Votes	14	6	4
First	A	B	C
Second	B	C	B
Third	C	A	A

Example 6 *Satisfying the Four Fairness Criteria*

Suppose that the plurality method is used to determine the winner of an election. The results of the election are given in Table 15.22. Does this method satisfy the four fairness criteria, that is, the majority criterion, the head-to-head criterion, the monotonicity criterion, and the irrelevant alternatives criterion?

Profile In Mathematics

Kenneth Arrow

Kenneth Arrow (1921–), an economist, was interested in the theory of corporations and how corporations make decisions when their leaders have different opinions. His particular interest in stockholders led to his discovery that majority voting can be flawed. While working at the RAND Corporation, he studied how mathematical concepts, game theory in particular, apply to decision making in the military and in diplomatic affairs. As a result, he developed a set of properties for any fair and reasonable voting method. After experimenting for days, he realized that there was no voting method that would satisfy all reasonable conditions. This conclusion is called the Arrow impossibility theorem, which he proved in 1951. In 1972, Arrow received the Nobel Prize in Economics for his exceptional work in the theory of general economic equilibrium.

Solution   By the plurality method, A is the winner with 14 votes. Since a total of 14 votes is also a majority of the 24 votes cast (58%), the majority criterion is satisfied. Examining pairwise comparison matchups, we see that A is favored to B (14 to 10) and that A is also favored to C (14 to 10). Therefore, the head-to-head criterion is satisfied. Since A holds a majority of first-place votes, the monotonicity criterion is satisfied when a second election is held in which A picks up additional votes; A still wins by plurality. Last, if B or C drops out, A still wins by plurality and the irrelevant alternatives criterion is satisfied. Therefore, this election satisfies all four fairness criteria.   ∎

We saw in Example 6 that in a particular election, it is possible that all of the fairness criteria are satisfied. However, in a different election, with a different preference table, it is quite possible for the same voting method to violate one or more of the fairness criteria.

Table 15.23 summarizes the four fairness criteria, and Table 15.24 summarizes which voting methods always satisfy the criteria.

Table 15.23 Summary of Fairness Criteria

Majority criterion	If a candidate receives a majority of first-place votes, that candidate should be declared the winner.
Head-to-head criterion	If a candidate is favored when compared individually with every other candidate, that candidate should be declared the winner.
Monotonicity criterion	A candidate who wins a first election and then gains additional support without losing any of the original support should also win a second election.
Irrelevant alternatives criterion	If a candidate is the winner of an election and in a second election one or more of the other candidates is removed, the previous winner should still be the winner.

Table 15.24 Summary of the Voting Methods and Whether They Satisfy the Fairness Criteria

	Plurality Method	Borda Count Method	Plurality with Elimination Method	Pairwise Comparison Method
Majority criterion	Always satisfies	May not satisfy	Always satisfies	Always satisfies
Head-to-head criterion	May not satisfy	May not satisfy	May not satisfy	Always satisfies
Monotonicity criterion	Always satisfies	May not satisfy	May not satisfy	May not satisfy
Irrelevant alternatives criterion	May not satisfy	May not satisfy	May not satisfy	May not satisfy

As we have shown, each of the voting methods introduced in Section 15.1 has the potential to violate at least one of the fairness criteria. Is there another method that does satisfy all four criteria? Mathematicians and political scientists struggled with this question for two centuries. Finally, in 1951, an economist, Kenneth Arrow, (see *Profile in Mathematics* on page 933) proved mathematically that there is no voting method that can satisfy all four fairness criteria. This result is called *Arrow's impossibility theorem*. See the *Profile in Mathematics* on page 933.

Arrow's Impossibility Theorem

It is mathematically impossible for any democratic voting method to simultaneously satisfy each of the following fairness criteria:

The majority criterion
The head-to-head criterion
The monotonicity criterion
The irrelevant alternatives criterion

SECTION 15.2   *Exercises*

Warm Up Exercises

In Exercises 1–8, fill in the blank with an appropriate word, phrase, or symbol(s).

1. If a candidate receives a majority of first-place votes in an election, that candidate should be declared the winner. This criterion is called the _____ criterion. Majority

2. If a candidate is favored when compared head-to-head with every other candidate in an election, that candidate should be declared the winner. This criterion is called the _____ criterion. Head-to-head

3. A candidate who wins a first election then gains additional support without losing any of the original support should also win a second election. This criterion is called the _____ criterion. Monotonicity

4. If a candidate is the winner of an election and in a second election one or more of the other candidates is removed, the previous winner should still be the winner. This criterion is called the _____ criterion. Irrelevant alternatives

5. A voting method that may not satisfy any of the fairness criteria is the _____ method. Borda count

6. A voting method that always satisfies the majority criterion but may not satisfy any other criterion is the _____ method. Plurality with elimination

7. A voting method that always satisfies the majority criterion and head-to-head criterion, but may not satisfy any other criterion, is the _____ method. Pairwise comparison

8. A voting method that always satisfies the majority criterion and the monotonicity criterion, but may not satisfy any other criterion, is the _____ method. Plurality

Practice the Skills/Problem Solving

9. *Annual Meeting* Members of the board of directors of the American Nursing Association are voting to select a city to host the association's annual meeting. The board is considering the following cities: Las Vegas (L), New Orleans (N), and Boston (B). The preference table for the 17 members of the board of directors is shown below. Show that the Borda count method violates the majority criterion. Boston wins with the Borda count method, but New Orleans has a majority of first-place votes.

Number of Votes	9	6	2
First	N	B	B
Second	B	L	N
Third	L	N	L

▲ *New Orleans*

10. *Restructuring a Company* The board of directors at The Limited is considering three different administrative restructuring plans, A, B, and C. The 11 members of the board of directors rank the plans according to the preference table below.

a) Which restructuring plan is preferred to all the others in a head-to-head comparison? Plan A is preferred.

b) Suppose that the plurality method is used to determine the winner. Is the head-to-head criterion satisfied? Explain. No. C wins by the plurality method, but A is preferred to B and to C.

Number of Votes	2	4	2	3
First	B	A	C	C
Second	A	B	A	B
Third	C	C	B	A

11. Hiring a New Director Irvine Valley College is hiring a new director of counseling and advisement. The hiring committee ranks the four candidates, Alvarez (A), Brown (B), Singleton (S), and Yu (Y), according to the preference table below. Suppose that the Borda count method is used to determine the winner. Is the majority criterion satisfied? Explain. No. Brown is the Borda count winner, but Alvarez has a majority of first-place votes.

Number of Votes	4	3	1	1
First	A	B	B	A
Second	B	S	Y	B
Third	S	Y	S	Y
Fourth	Y	A	A	S

12. Party Theme The children in Ms. Cohn's seventh-grade class are voting on a theme for their class party. Their choices are beach (B), western (W), superheroes (S), or rock and roll (R). The results are shown in the preference table below.

a) Which theme is preferred to all the other themes in a head-to-head comparison? Beach is preferred.

b) Suppose that the plurality method is used to determine the winner. Is the head-to-head criterion satisfied? Explain. Yes. Beach is the winner by the plurality method.

Number of Votes	12	6	4	3
First	B	S	R	W
Second	W	B	S	R
Third	S	W	B	B
Fourth	R	R	W	S

13. Residence Hall Improvements The administration at St. Cloud State University is considering three possible areas of improvement to the school's residence halls: parking (P), security (S), and lounge areas (L). The nine members of the executive committee of the Student Senate rank the choices according to the preference table shown below. Suppose that the Borda count method is used to determine the winner. Is the head-to-head criterion satisfied? Explain. No. Lounge areas wins by the Borda count method, but Parking is preferred to Security and to Lounge areas.

Number of Votes	4	1	1	1	2
First	P	L	S	S	L
Second	L	P	L	P	S
Third	S	S	P	L	P

14. Design of a Technology Building The planning committee of Tulsa Community College is considering three proposals, A, B, and C, for the design of a new technology building for the college. The eleven members of the planning committee rank the proposals according to the preference table shown below. Suppose that the Borda count method is used to determine the winner. Is the head-to-head criterion satisfied? Explain.

Number of Votes	6	3	2
First	C	A	B
Second	A	B	A
Third	B	C	C

No. A is the winner by the Borda count method, but C is preferred to A and B.

15. Preference for Grape Jelly Twenty-one people are asked to taste test and rank three different brands of grape jelly. The preference table below shows the rankings of the 21 voters. Suppose that the plurality with elimination method is used to determine the winner. Is the head-to-head criterion satisfied? Explain.*

Number of Votes	8	7	6
First	B	C	A
Second	A	A	C
Third	C	B	B

16. A Taste Test Twenty-seven people are surveyed in the Mall of America and asked to taste and rank four different brands of vanilla ice cream. The preference table below shows the rankings of the 27 voters. Suppose that the plurality with elimination method is used to determine the winner. Is the head-to-head criterion satisfied? Explain. No. C wins by plurality with elimination, but B wins the head-to-head comparisons.

Number of Votes	11	3	5	8
First	A	B	D	C
Second	B	C	B	B
Third	D	A	C	A
Fourth	C	D	A	D

▲ The Mall of America, Minneapolis, MN

*See Instructor Answer Appendix

17. *Plurality: Irrelevant Alternatives Criterion* Suppose that the plurality method is used on the following preference table. If B drops out, is the irrelevant alternatives criterion satisfied? Explain. No. A wins the first election by plurality. If B drops out, C wins by plurality.

Number of Votes	12	9	4
First	A	C	B
Second	C	B	C
Third	B	A	A

18. *Plurality: Irrelevant Alternatives Criterion* Suppose that the plurality method is used on the following preference table. If C drops out, is the irrelevant alternatives criterion satisfied? Explain. No. B wins by the plurality method. If C drops out, A wins by the plurality method.

Number of Votes	6	5	3
First	B	C	A
Second	C	A	C
Third	A	B	B

19. *Borda Count: Irrelevant Alternatives Criterion* Suppose that the Borda count method is used on the following preference table. If C drops out, is the irrelevant alternatives criterion satisfied? Explain.
Yes. B wins by the Borda count method. If C drops out, B still wins.

Number of Votes	10	9	8
First	B	C	A
Second	A	B	C
Third	C	A	B

20. *Borda Count: Irrelevant Alternatives Criterion* Suppose that the Borda count method is used on the following preference table. If B drops out, is the irrelevant alternatives criterion satisfied? Explain. No. A wins by the Borda count method. If B drops out, C wins by the Borda count method.

Number of Votes	7	6	5
First	A	C	B
Second	B	A	C
Third	C	B	A

21. *Plurality with Elimination: Monotonicity Criterion* Suppose that the plurality with elimination method is used on the following preference table. If the four voters who voted A, C, B, in that order, change their vote to C, A, B, is the monotonicity criterion satisfied? Explain.*

Number of Votes	7	8	4	10
First	A	B	A	C
Second	B	C	C	A
Third	C	A	B	B

22. *Plurality with Elimination: Monotonicity Criterion* Suppose that the plurality with elimination method is used on the following preference table. If the three voters who voted C, B, A, in that order, change their vote to B, C, A, is the monotonicity criterion satisfied? Explain.*

Number of Votes	5	6	3	7
First	C	A	C	B
Second	A	B	B	C
Third	B	C	A	A

23. *Pairwise Comparison Method: Monotonicity Criterion* Suppose that the pairwise comparison method is used on the following preference table. If the five voters who voted C, D, A, B, in that order, change their votes to D, B, C, A, is the monotonicity criterion satisfied? Explain.*

Number of Votes	8	7	6	5
First	D	B	B	C
Second	C	A	A	D
Third	A	C	D	A
Fourth	B	D	C	B

24. *Borda Count: Monotonicity Criterion* Suppose that the Borda count method is used on the following preference table. If the five voters who voted D, A, C, B, in that order, change their votes to A, B, D, C and the three voters who voted C, A, D, B, in that order, change their votes to A, B, C, D, is the monotonicity criterion satisfied? Explain.*

Number of Votes	8	7	5	3
First	A	B	D	C
Second	B	D	A	A
Third	C	C	C	D
Fourth	D	A	B	B

25. *Pairwise Comparison: Irrelevant Alternatives Criterion* Suppose that the pairwise comparison method is used on the following preference table. If A, C, and E drop out, is the irrelevant alternatives criterion satisfied? Explain.*

Number of Votes	1	1	1	1	1
First	B	B	A	C	E
Second	A	C	D	D	D
Third	C	E	B	B	B
Fourth	E	A	C	E	A
Fifth	D	D	E	A	C

*See Instructor Answer Appendix

26. *Pairwise Comparison: Irrelevant Alternatives Criterion*
Suppose that the pairwise comparison method is used on the
following preference table. If A, B, and E drop out, is the
irrelevant alternatives criterion satisfied? Explain.
No. C wins by pairwise comparison. If A, B, and E drop out, D wins by
pairwise comparison.

Number of Votes	2	1	1	1	1	1
First	C	C	D	A	E	B
Second	E	B	C	D	A	E
Third	A	A	B	C	D	D
Fourth	B	E	A	B	C	C
Fifth	D	D	E	E	B	A

27. *Borda Count: Majority Criterion* Suppose that the Borda
count method is used on the following preference table. Is
the majority criterion satisfied?
No. B wins by the Borda count method, but A has a majority of first-place votes.

Number of Votes	5	3	1
First	A	B	C
Second	B	C	B
Third	C	A	A

28. *Borda Count: Majority Criterion* Suppose that the Borda
count method is used on the following preference table. Is
the majority criterion satisfied? No. C wins by the Borda count
method, but B has a majority of first-place votes.

Number of Votes	5	1	4	1
First	B	B	C	A
Second	C	A	A	C
Third	A	C	B	B

29. *Spring Trip* The History Club of St. Louis is voting on
which city to visit for its spring trip. The choices are New
York City (N), Washington, D.C. (W), Philadelphia (P),
and Boston (B). The preference table for the 23 members'
choices is given below.

▲ Boston, MA

Number of Votes	12	8	3
First	W	P	B
Second	N	N	W
Third	P	B	P
Fourth	B	W	N

a) Which city, if any, holds a majority of first-place votes?
Washington, D.C.

b) Which city is selected using the plurality method?
Washington, D.C.

c) Which city is selected using the Borda count method?
Washington, D.C.

d) Which city is selected using the plurality with elimination method? Washington, D.C.

e) Which city is selected using the pairwise comparison
method? Washington, D.C.

f) For this preference table, which voting method(s), if
any, violate the majority criterion? None of them

30. *Investment Choices* The Motley Crew Investing Club
wishes to purchase stock in a pharmaceutical company.
The choices are American Pharmacy (A), Burrows-
Welcome (B), Chicago Labs (C), Dow Chemical (D), and
Emerging Medicines (E). The choice rankings are shown
in the following preference table.

Number of Votes	12	8	8	8	4	2	2
First	B	B	E	A	D	C	C
Second	D	D	D	C	E	B	E
Third	C	E	A	E	C	D	D
Fourth	E	A	C	B	B	E	B
Fifth	A	C	B	D	A	A	A

Before calculating the results of this election, the club
learns that Chicago Labs has filed for bankruptcy.

a) Using the pairwise comparison method, which company
is chosen if Chicago Labs is included? Dow Chemical

b) Using the pairwise comparison method, which company is chosen if Chicago Labs is eliminated from the
preference table? Burrows-Welcome

c) Does this second result violate the irrelevant alternatives criterion? Yes

31. *Selecting a Spokesperson* The Campbell Soup Company
is selecting a new spokesperson for its advertisements. The
choices are Sandra Bullock (B), Will Smith (S), and Albert
Pujols (P). At the annual meeting of its managers, a straw
vote is taken to gauge the managers' initial reaction to the
candidates. The results of this straw vote are given in the
following preference table.

Number of Votes	28	24	20	10
First	P	S	B	B
Second	B	P	S	P
Third	S	B	P	S

▲ *Sandra Bullock*

After discussion about the candidates, eight people who had supported Sandra Bullock over Albert Pujols now switch their preferences to Albert Pujols over Sandra Bullock. This switch leads to the following preference table.

Number of Votes	36	24	20	2
First	P	S	B	B
Second	B	P	S	P
Third	S	B	P	S

a) Using the plurality with elimination method, which person is selected from the first (or straw) vote? Albert Pujols

b) Using the plurality with elimination method, which person is selected from the second vote? Will Smith

c) Does this second result violate the monotonicity criterion? Yes

32. *Electing a Parks Director* The City of Birmingham is electing a new parks director. The choices for the position are Diane Allen (A), Brac Brady (B), Faye Conrad (C), Stacy Davis (D), and Bill Evers (E). The election is conducted, and the preference table is shown below.

Number of Votes	80	50	50	50	30	20	20
First	B	B	E	A	D	C	C
Second	D	D	D	C	E	B	E
Third	C	E	A	E	C	D	D
Fourth	E	A	C	B	B	E	B
Fifth	A	C	B	D	A	A	A

Before calculating the results of this election, it is learned that Faye Conrad has dropped out of the race for personal reasons.

a) Using the pairwise comparison method, which candidate is chosen if Faye Conrad is included? Stacy Davis

b) Using the pairwise comparison method, which candidate is chosen if Faye Conrad is eliminated from the preference table? Brac Brady

c) Does this second result violate the irrelevant alternatives criterion? Yes

Challenge Problems/Group Activities

33. Explain why the plurality method always satisfies the monotonicity criterion. A candidate who holds a plurality only gains strength and holds an even larger lead if more favorable votes are added.

34. Construct a preference table with four candidates and four rankings of the candidates, similar to the preference table in Exercise 11 on page 935, such that the plurality method violates the head-to-head criterion. Have the total number of votes be 25. Answers will vary.

35. Construct a preference table with three candidates and three rankings of the candidates, similar to the preference table in Exercise 9 on page 934, such that the Borda count method violates the majority criterion. Have the total number of votes be 19. Answers will vary.

36. Construct a preference table with three candidates and four rankings of the candidates, similar to the preference table in Exercise 10 on page 934, such that the plurality with elimination method violates the monotonicity criterion. Have the total number of votes be 21. Answers will vary.

37. Construct a preference table with four candidates and three rankings of the candidates, similar to the preference table in Exercise 29 on page 937, such that the pairwise comparison method violates the irrelevant alternatives criterion. Have the total number of votes be 6. Answers will vary.

Not voting according to a voter's true preference, called insincere voting, is frequently practiced to affect the outcome of an election. Insincere voting is used in Exercise 38.

38. *Voting Strategy* Consider the preference table below. Assume that a majority is needed to win the election. Since no candidate has a majority but C has the most first-place votes, a runoff election is held between A and B. The winner of the runoff election will run against C.

Number of Votes	5	4	2
First	C	A	B
Second	A	C	A
Third	B	B	C

a) Using the plurality method, which candidate will win the runoff election, A or B? A

b) Will the candidate determined in part (a) win the election against candidate C? Yes, A

c) Suppose that the voters who support candidate C, the candidate with the most first-place votes, find out prior to the vote that C will not win if B is eliminated and C runs against A. How can the voters who support C vote insincerely to enable C to win? The five voters who favor C should vote C, B, A instead of C, A, B.

Internet/Research Activities

39. Choose a country other than the United States and write a research paper on how the president or prime minister is chosen. Describe in detail the voting method used. Include the strengths and weaknesses of the method used.

40. Write a research paper on the history of voting methods. Include how the flaws in the voting methods discussed in this section were uncovered.

SECTION 15.3 | Apportionment Methods

▲ Apportionment methods can be used to distribute e-readers to libraries.

Suppose a college receives a grant to purchase 50 electronic readers (e-readers) to be distributed to four different libraries on campus. Since the libraries do not all serve the same number of students, the director of libraries decides to apportion the e-readers based on the number of students served at each library. In this section, we will discuss some apportionment methods the college can use to distribute the e-readers to the four libraries.

Why *This is Important* Apportionment methods are used in many applications that relate to our everyday lives.

When the delegates for the original 13 states met in 1787 to draft a constitution, their most important discussion concerned the representation of the states in the legislature. Some states, particularly the small states, preferred that each state have the same number of representatives. The large states wanted a proportional representation based on population. The delegates resolved this issue by creating a Senate, in which each state received two Senators, and a House of Representatives, in which each state received a number of representatives based on its population. Article 1, Section 2, of the Constitution of the United States includes the statement "Representatives ... shall be apportioned among the several states ... according to their respective numbers." What the constitution did not say is how the apportionments are determined. In this section, we will discuss four different apportionment methods.

The goal of *apportionment* is to determine a method to allocate the total number of items to be apportioned in a fair manner. One of the most important examples of apportionment is in determining the representation of governing bodies. However, apportionment problems occur in many other places, from determining how many police officers should be assigned to each precinct in a city to determining how many nurses should be assigned to each shift at a hospital.

In this section, we will discuss four different apportionment methods:

1. Hamilton's method
2. Jefferson's method
3. Webster's method
4. Adams's method

Apportionment Problems

Let's begin by considering a problem facing the Shanahan Law Firm. The firm needs to apportion 60 new fax machines to be distributed among the firm's five offices. Since the offices do not all have the same number of employees, the firm's managing partner decides to apportion the fax machines based on the number of employees at each office. Table 15.25 shows the number of employees at each office.

Table 15.25 Shanahan Law Firm Employees

Office	A	B	C	D	E	Total
Employees	246	201	196	211	226	1080

If the firm wants to distribute the fax machines based on the number of employees at each office, it would take each office's number of employees and divide it by the total number of employees. For example, office A would be entitled to $\frac{246}{1080}$, or $22\frac{7}{9}\%$, of the fax machines. Similarly, office B would be entitled to $\frac{201}{1080}$, or $18\frac{11}{18}\%$, of the fax machines. Dividing the number of employees in each office by the total number of employees leaves each office with a fractional part of a fax machine. Since an office cannot receive a fraction of a fax machine, the law firm has a problem. How can it apportion the fax machines so that each office receives its fair allotment?

Before we discuss how to apply apportionment methods, we will introduce some important terms used in this section, *standard divisor* and *standard quota*. The *standard divisor* is found by dividing the total population under consideration by the number of items to be allocated.

Standard Divisor

To obtain the standard divisor when determining apportionment, use the following formula.

$$\text{Standard divisor} = \frac{\text{total population}}{\text{number of items to be allocated}}$$

For our fax machine problem, the standard divisor is found as follows:

$$\text{Standard divisor} = \frac{\text{total number of employees}}{\text{number of fax machines to be allocated}} = \frac{1080}{60} = 18$$

The *standard quota* for a particular group is found by dividing the population of the group by the standard divisor.

Standard Quota

To obtain the standard quota when determining apportionment, use the following formula.

$$\text{Standard quota} = \frac{\text{population for the particular group}}{\text{standard divisor}}$$

For our fax machine problem, the standard quota for office A is found as follows:

$$\text{Standard quota for office A} = \frac{\text{number of employees at office A}}{\text{standard divisor}} = \frac{246}{18} \approx 13.67$$

We will round all standard divisors and standard quotas to the nearest hundredth.

Example 1 *Determining Standard Quotas*

Determine the standard quotas for offices B, C, D, and E of the Shanahan Law Firm and complete Table 15.26. Use 18 as the standard divisor, as was determined above.

Table 15.26 Shanahan Law Firm Employees

Office	A	B	C	D	E	Total
Employees	246	201	196	211	226	1080
Standard quota	13.67					

Solution The standard quota for office B is $\frac{201}{18} = 11.17$, rounded to the nearest hundredth. The other standard quotas are found in a similar manner. Table 15.27 shows the completed table.

Table 15.27 Shanahan Law Firm Employees

Office	A	B	C	D	E	Total
Employees	246	201	196	211	226	1080
Standard quota	13.67	11.17	10.89	11.72	12.56	60.01

The standard quota represents the exact number of fax machines each office would receive if we were able to divide the fax machines into fractional parts. Notice that the sum of the standard quotas is slightly above 60, the total number of fax machines, due to rounding. ■

Now we introduce two more important definitions, the *lower quota* and the *upper quota*. The *lower quota* is the standard quota rounded down to the nearest integer. The *upper quota* is the standard quota rounded up to the nearest integer. For example, office A has a lower quota of 13 and an upper quota of 14, office B has a lower quota of 11 and an upper quota of 12, and so on.

How should we round the standard quotas so that each office receives its fair share? If we were to use conventional rounding and round each office's standard quota to the nearest whole number, office A would receive 14 fax machines and office B would receive 11 fax machines. Offices C, D, and E would receive 11, 12, and 13 fax machines, respectively. The total number of fax machines needed would be 61. Since there are only 60 fax machines to distribute, conventional rounding of standard quotas can be problematic. We need a more sophisticated apportionment method to avoid the problems that can occur with rounding standard quotas. We will now discuss the first of our four apportionment methods, Hamilton's method.

Hamilton's Method

Mathematically, Hamilton's method is the easiest to apply.

PROCEDURE   **HAMILTON'S METHOD**

To use Hamilton's method for apportionment, do the following.

1. Calculate the standard divisor for the set of data.

2. Calculate each group's* standard quota.

3. Round each standard quota **down** to the nearest integer (the lower quota). Initially, each group receives its lower quota.

4. Distribute any leftover items to the groups with the largest fractional parts until all items are distributed.

---

*We use the word *group* in Steps 1, 2, and 3 as a general term. However, *group* could refer to a state, a school, or even an individual.

Example 2 *Using Hamilton's Method for Apportioning Fax Machines*

Use Hamilton's method to distribute the 60 fax machines for the Shanahan Law Firm discussed in Example 1 on page 940.

Solution Table 15.28 includes the standard quotas (row 2) calculated from Example 1, along with the lower quotas (row 3) and the apportionment using Hamilton's method (row 4).

Table 15.28 Shanahan Law Firm Employees

Office	A	B	C	D	E	Total
Employees	246	201	196	211	226	1080
Standard quota	13.67	11.17	10.89	11.72	12.56	60.01
Lower quota	13	11	10	11	12	57
Hamilton's apportionment	14	11	11	12	12	60

The sum of the lower quotas is 57, leaving three additional fax machines to distribute. Since offices C, D, and A, in this order, have the three highest fractional parts (0.89, 0.72, and 0.67, respectively) in the standard quota, each receives one of the additional fax machines using Hamilton's method. Note that with Hamilton's method, each office receives either its lower quota or its upper quota of laser printers. Also note that the total number of fax machines apportioned by Hamilton's method is 60, which is what we expected. ∎

Let's look at another example using Hamilton's method.

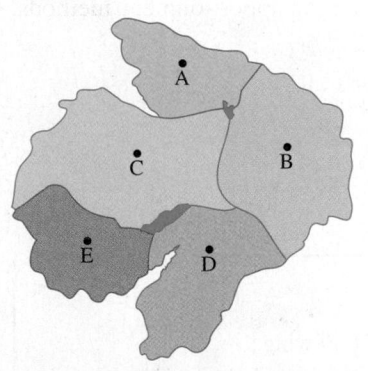

Republic of Geranium
population 8,800,000

Example 3 *Using Hamilton's Method for Apportioning Legislative Seats*

The Republic of Geranium needs to apportion 250 seats in the legislature. Suppose that the population is 8,800,000 and that there are five states, A, B, C, D, and E. The 250 seats are to be divided among the five states according to their respective populations, given in Table 15.29.

Table 15.29 Republic of Geranium Population

State	A	B	C	D	E	Total
Population	1,003,200	1,228,600	4,990,700	813,000	764,500	8,800,000

Use Hamilton's method to apportion the seats.

Solution The standard divisor is determined by dividing the total population by the number of seats in the legislature.

$$\text{Standard divisor} = \frac{8,800,000}{250} = 35,200$$

The standard quotas are determined by dividing the population of each state by the standard divisor. Recall we will round the standard quotas to the nearest hundredth. The results are shown in the second row in Table 15.30 on page 943.

Table 15.30 Republic of Geranium Population

State	A	B	C	D	E	Total
Population	1,003,200	1,228,600	4,990,700	813,000	764,500	8,800,000
Standard quota	28.50	34.90	141.78	23.10	21.72	
Lower quota	28	34	141	23	21	247
Hamilton's apportionment	28	35	142	23	22	250

The sum of the lower quotas is 247, leaving three additional seats to distribute. Since states B, C, and E, in this order, have the three highest fractional parts in the standard quota (0.90, 0.78, and 0.72, respectively), they each receive the additional seats using Hamilton's method. ■

As we can see from both examples, an advantage of Hamilton's method is that every apportionment is either the lower quota or the upper quota. If an apportionment method assigns either the lower or upper quota to every group under consideration, it is said to satisfy the *quota rule*.

The Quota Rule
An apportionment for every group under consideration should always be either the upper quota or the lower quota.

We have just discussed Alexander Hamilton's method for apportionment. In this section, we will also discuss Thomas Jefferson's method for apportionment, Daniel Webster's method for apportionment, and John Quincy Adams's method for apportionment. Here is a brief history of the use of these different methods to apportion members of the U.S. House of Representatives. Although Hamilton's method for apportionment was the first method approved by Congress after the 1790 census, it was not used until 1852. Shortly after Congress approved Hamilton's method, President George Washington vetoed it. Congress then adopted a method developed by Thomas Jefferson. As there were apportionment problems with Jefferson's method in 1822 and 1832, Webster's method replaced Jefferson's method in 1842. Webster's method had similar flaws as Jefferson's method and was replaced in 1852 by Hamilton's method, the first apportionment method proposed. When it was discovered in the late 1800s that there were also flaws with Hamilton's method, Webster's method was once again used to apportion the number of representatives for each state. Webster's method was used from 1900 until it was replaced by the current method in 1941, the Hill–Huntington method (see Exercise 51). Adams's method, although considered, was never actually used by Congress to apportion members.

Jefferson's Method

To determine the standard quota with Hamilton's method, the population of each group was divided by the standard divisor. Then each lower quota was used. Any leftover items were distributed to the groups with the highest fractional part. As we saw with Examples 2 and 3, each group received either its lower quota or its upper quota. A weakness that can occur with Hamilton's method is that the groups that received their upper quota gained an advantage over the groups that received their lower quota. Is there a way to modify the quotas to overcome this weakness in Hamilton's method? Jefferson's method uses a divisor other than the standard divisor, called the *modified divisor*, to obtain quotas. A modified divisor is a divisor that approximates the standard divisor. We will explain how to determine modified divisors shortly. **A modified**

divisor is used in Jefferson's method, Webster's method, and Adams's method, each of which will be discussed shortly.

In each case, a modified divisor is used to obtain *modified quotas*. Modified quotas are obtained by dividing a group's population by a modified divisor. **The differences in Jefferson's method, Webster's method, and Adams's method are in the modified divisor used to obtain the modified quotas and in the rounding process used to apportion the items. Hamilton's method is the only method that uses the standard quota rather than a modified quota in determining apportionments.**

Now we will discuss Jefferson's method.

PROCEDURE   **JEFFERSON'S METHOD**

To use Jefferson's method for apportionment, do the following.

1. Determine a modified divisor, *d*, such that when each group's modified quota is *rounded **down** to the nearest integer*, the total of the integers is the exact number of items to be apportioned. We will refer to the modified quotas that are rounded down as **modified lower quotas.**

2. Apportion to each group its modified lower quota.

With Jefferson's method, we use a modified divisor that is *less than* the standard divisor. This results in the modified quotas being slightly greater than the standard quotas. When using Hamilton's method, the standard quotas are *rounded down* and then leftover items are distributed. With Jefferson's method, the modified quotas are also *rounded down*. The modified divisor used with Jefferson's method must result in all items being distributed, with no items left over, when the modified quotas are rounded down. We will explain Jefferson's method in Example 4.

┌─ **EXAMPLE 4** *Using Jefferson's Method for Apportioning Legislative Seats*

Consider the Republic of Geranium from Example 3. Use Jefferson's method to apportion the 250 legislature seats among the five states. Use the population from Table 15.31.

Table 15.31   Republic of Geranium Population

State	A	B	C	D	E	Total
Population	1,003,200	1,228,600	4,990,700	813,000	764,500	8,800,000

Solution   In Example 3, the standard divisor was calculated to be 35,200. With Jefferson's method, the modified quota for each group needs to be slightly greater than the standard quota. To accomplish this we use a *modified divisor, which is slightly less than the standard divisor*. When you divide a quantity by a smaller number, the quotient becomes greater. There is no formula to determine this new modified divisor, and usually more than one divisor will work. We will use trial and error until we find a divisor that apportions exactly 250 legislative seats using modified lower quotas.

Suppose that we try 35,000 as our modified divisor, *d*. To determine each modified quota, we will divide each state's population by 35,000. For example, the modified quota for state A is

$$\frac{1,003,200}{35,000} \approx 28.66$$

We will round modified quotas to the nearest hundredth as we did with standard quotas. Since the modified quota for state A is 28.66, the modified *lower* quota for state A is 28. This result is indicated in column 1, row 4, of Table 15.32.

Table 15.32 shows the results for all the states. In the table, we give the standard quotas as references, but they are not used in obtaining the apportionment using Jefferson's method.

Table 15.32 Republic of Geranium Population Using a Modified Divisor, $d = 35,000$

State	A	B	C	D	E	Total
Population	1,003,200	1,228,600	4,990,700	813,000	764,500	8,800,000
Standard quota	28.50	34.90	141.78	23.10	21.72	
Modified quota	28.66	35.10	142.59	23.23	21.84	
Modified lower quota	28	35	142	23	21	249

The sum of the modified lower quotas, 249, is less than the number of available seats, 250. If the sum of the modified lower quotas is too low (as it is in this case), use a lower modified divisor. If the sum of the modified lower quotas is too high, use a higher modified divisor. Since our sum is too low, we will try a lower modified divisor. Let's see what happens if we use 34,900 as our modified divisor. This modified divisor is a little lower than the modified divisor of 35,000 previously used.

Using 34,900 as the modified divisor, the modified quota for state A is

$$\frac{1,003,200}{34,900} \approx 28.74$$

Table 15.33 shows the modified quotas for all the states.

Table 15.33 Republic of Geranium Population Using a Modified Divisor, $d = 34,900$

State	A	B	C	D	E	Total
Population	1,003,200	1,228,600	4,990,700	813,000	764,500	8,800,000
Standard quota	28.50	34.90	141.78	23.10	21.72	
Modified quota	28.74	35.20	143.00	23.30	21.91	
Modified lower quota	28	35	143	23	21	250

The sum of the modified lower quotas is now 250, our desired sum. Each state is awarded the number of legislative seats listed in Table 15.33 under the category of modified lower quota. ■

In Example 4, we used a modified divisor of 34,900 to obtain the desired sum of 250. There are an infinite number of modified divisors (in a small range) that could be used to obtain the modified lower quotas that we obtained. In fact, any modified divisor from about 34,751 to about 34,901 would result in the modified lower quotas we obtained in Table 15.33. If you selected a modified divisor lower than about 34,751, you would obtain modified lower quotas for which the sum of the seats is too high. For example, if you selected a modified divisor of 34,750, you would obtain modified lower quotas of 28, 35, 143, 23, and 22. The sum of these seats is 251, which is above the number of seats to be allocated. If you selected a modified divisor greater than about 34,901, you would obtain modified lower quotas for which the sum of the seats is too low. For example, if you selected a modified divisor of 34,902, you would obtain modified lower quotas of 28, 35, 142, 23, and 21. The sum of these seats is 249, which is below the number of seats to be allocated.

With Jefferson's method, we will always use a modified divisor that is less than the standard divisor used with Hamilton's method.

Recall from the discussion of Hamilton's method that if an apportionment method assigns either the lower or upper quota, it is said to satisfy the quota rule. Hamilton's method satisfies the quota rule since it uses either the lower quota or upper quota of the standard quota. Notice that the standard quota for state C from Example 3 is 141.78. According to the quota rule, state C should receive either 141 or 142 seats. Using Jefferson's method, state C received 143 seats (see Table 15.33 on page 945). Therefore, Jefferson's method violates the quota rule.

The first case in the House of Representatives in which Jefferson's method led to a violation of the quota rule occurred in 1832. New York had a standard quota of 38.59 but was awarded 40 seats using Jefferson's method. Daniel Webster argued that this result was unconstitutional and suggested a compromise between Hamilton's method and Jefferson's method, leading to Webster's method. Let's discuss how Webster proposed to apportion the seats in the House of Representatives.

Webster's Method

Hamilton's method rounded **standard** *quotas* **down** to the nearest integer. Jefferson's method rounded **modified** *quotas* **down** to the nearest integer. With Webster's method, we round **modified** *quotas* **to** the nearest integer such that the rounding gives the exact sum to be apportioned.

PROCEDURE **WEBSTER'S METHOD**

To use Webster's method for apportionment, do the following.

1. Determine a modified divisor, *d*, such that when each group's modified quota is *rounded to the nearest integer*, the total of the integers is the exact number of items to be apportioned. We will refer to modified quotas that are rounded to the nearest integer as **modified rounded quotas**.

2. Apportion to each group its modified rounded quota.

With Webster's method, we use a modified divisor that may be *less than, equal to,* or *greater than* the standard divisor and we use *modified rounded quotas*. With Webster's method, as with Jefferson's method, the modified divisor used must result in all the items being distributed, with no items left over. We will use Webster's method in Example 5.

Example 5 *Using Webster's Method for Apportioning Legislative Seats*

Once again, let's consider the Republic of Geranium and apportion the 250 seats among the five states using Webster's method. Use the population from Table 15.34.

Table 15.34 Republic of Geranium Population

State	A	B	C	D	E	Total
Population	1,003,200	1,228,600	4,990,700	813,000	764,500	8,800,000

Solution   Our first task is to determine the modified divisor, d. We could choose a number either less than, greater than, or equal to the standard divisor. As with Jefferson's method, there is no formula to determine this new divisor and usually there is more than one divisor that works. Again, we must use trial and error until we find a divisor that apportions the 250 legislative seats.

Let's use the results from Example 3 on pages 942–943 as a guide. If we round the standard quotas from Table 15.30 on page 943 to the nearest integer, the sum is $29 + 35 + 142 + 23 + 22$, or 251. This number is too high since we want a sum of 250. If the sum is too high, as it is in this case, we need to use a larger divisor. If the sum is too low, we need to use a smaller divisor. In Example 3, we used the standard divisor of 35,200. Let's try using 35,250 as our modified divisor, d. Using 35,250 as the modified divisor, the modified quota for state A is

$$\frac{1{,}003{,}200}{35{,}250} \approx 28.46$$

Table 15.35 shows the results using $d = 35{,}250$.

Table 15.35 Republic of Geranium Population Using a Modified Divisor, $d = 35{,}250$

State	A	B	C	D	E	Total
Population	1,003,200	1,228,600	4,990,700	813,000	764,500	8,800,000
Standard quota	28.50	34.90	141.78	23.10	21.72	
Modified quota	28.46	34.85	141.58	23.06	21.69	
Modified rounded quota	28	35	142	23	22	250

Now round each modified quota to the nearest integer to get the modified rounded quotas, as shown in Table 15.35. Our sum of the modified rounded quotas is 250, as desired.

Therefore, each state is awarded the number of legislative seats listed in Table 15.35 under the category of modified rounded quota.   ∎

In Example 5, we used a modified divisor of 35,250 to obtain the desired sum of 250. There are an infinite number of modified divisors (in a small range) that could be used to obtain the modified rounded quotas. In fact, any modified divisor from about 35,202 to about 35,271 would result in the modified rounded quotas we obtained in Table 15.35. If you selected a modified divisor lower than about 35,202, you would obtain modified rounded quotas for which the sum of the seats is too high. If you selected a modified divisor greater than about 35,271, you would obtain modified rounded quotas for which the sum of the seats is too low.

Occasionally, the results of Webster's method agree with the results from Hamilton's method. With Webster's method, we can use a modified divisor that is less than, greater than, or equal to the standard divisor used with Hamilton's method.

Webster's method is similar to Jefferson's method since they both make use of a modified divisor. Webster's method, however, is a little more difficult in practice to apply than Jefferson's method since the modified divisor could be less than, equal to, or greater than the standard divisor. Webster's method may seem the most reasonable since the modified quotas are rounded in the conventional way. Webster's method, however, does have a flaw in that it can violate the quota rule.

Even though Example 5 did not uncover this flaw, there are examples in which Webster's method violates the quota rule. This violation happens more in theory than in practice. As a result, many experts consider Webster's method the best overall apportionment method.

Let's discuss one more apportionment method that was proposed (but never used by the House of Representatives) by John Quincy Adams around the same time that Webster proposed his method.

Adams's Method

When Jefferson's method was discovered to be problematic because it violated the quota rule, John Quincy Adams proposed a method that is exactly the opposite of Jefferson's method. Instead of using modified lower quotas as Jefferson proposed, Adams suggested using modified upper quotas.

> **PROCEDURE   ADAMS'S METHOD**
>
> To use Adams's method for apportionment, do the following.
>
> 1. Determine a modified divisor, d, such that when each group's modified quota is *rounded **up** to the nearest integer* the total of the integers is the exact number of items to be apportioned. We will refer to the modified quotas that are rounded up as **modified upper quotas.**
>
> 2. Apportion to each group its modified upper quota.

With Adams's method, we use a modified divisor that is *greater than* the standard divisor and we use quotas that are *rounded up*, or *modified upper quotas*. As with Jefferson's and Webster's methods, the modified divisor used must result in all items being distributed, with no items left over.

Let's see what happens when we apply Adams's method to the Republic of Geranium.

Example 6 *Using Adams's Method for Apportioning Legislative Seats*

Once again, consider the Republic of Geranium. Apportion the 250 seats among the five states using Adams's method. Use the population from Table 15.36.

Table 15.36 Republic of Geranium Population

State	A	B	C	D	E	Total
Population	1,003,200	1,228,600	4,990,700	813,000	764,500	8,800,000

Solution With Adams's method, the modified quota for each group needs to be slightly smaller than the standard quota. To accomplish that, we use a modified divisor that is slightly greater than the standard divisor. When you divide a quantity by a larger number, the quotient becomes smaller. Since the standard divisor is 35,200, let's try letting $d = 35,400$. Using 35,400 as the modified divisor, the modified quota for state A is

$$\frac{1,003,200}{35,400} \approx 28.34$$

Table 15.37 on page 949 shows the results.

Table 15.37 Republic of Geranium Population Using a Modified Divisor, $d = 35,400$

State	A	B	C	D	E	Total
Population	1,003,200	1,228,600	4,990,700	813,000	764,500	8,800,000
Standard quota	28.50	34.90	141.78	23.10	21.72	
Modified quota	28.34	34.71	140.98	22.97	21.60	
Modified upper quota	29	35	141	23	22	250

Using $d = 35,400$ and rounding up to the modified quotas, we have a sum of 250 seats, as desired. Therefore, each state will be awarded the number of legislative seats listed in Table 15.37 under the category of modified upper quota. ■

In Example 6, we used a modified divisor of 35,400 to obtain the desired sum of 250 seats. There are an infinite number of modified divisors (in a small range) that could be used to obtain the modified upper quotas that we obtained. In fact, any modified divisor from about 35,394 to, about 35,646 would result in the modified upper quotas we obtained in Table 15.37. If you selected a modified divisor lower than about 35,394, you would obtain modified upper quotas for which the sum of the seats is too high. If you selected a modified divisor greater than about 35,646, you would obtain modified upper quotas for which the sum of the seats is too low.

With Adams's method, we will always use a modified divisor that is greater than the standard divisor used with Hamilton's method.

In some cases, the range of numbers that can be used as a modified divisor is very narrow and you may need to use a decimal. For example, 34 may be too small for a modified divisor and 35 may be too large for a modified divisor. In that case, you will need to use a decimal number between 34 and 35 as the modified divisor.

Looking at the results from Example 6, we may want to conclude that Adams's method is the best since the quota rule was not violated in this example. Unfortunately, that is not always the case. We have seen that Jefferson's method can result in a state receiving more than its upper quota of seats. Adams's method can lead to just the opposite: a state receiving fewer than its lower quota of seats. Although the Jefferson method favors large states, such as his state of Virginia, Adams's method favors small states, such as those in his area of New England.

Example 7 *Comparing Apportionment Methods*

Suppose that the Panda Republic is a small country with a population of 10,400,000 that consists of four states A, B, C, and D. There are 260 seats in the legislature that need to be apportioned among the four states. The population of each state is shown in Table 15.38.

Table 15.38

State	A	B	C	D	Total
Population	3,350,000	1,850,000	2,365,000	2,835,000	10,400,000

a) Find each state's apportionment using Hamilton's method.
b) Find each state's apportionment using Jefferson's method.
c) Find each state's apportionment using Adams's method.
d) Find each state's apportionment using Webster's method.

Solution

a) First we must find the standard divisor. The standard divisor is found by dividing the total population by the number of seats to be apportioned. The standard divisor is

$$\frac{10,400,000}{260} = 40,000$$

Next we find the standard quotas by dividing each state's population by the standard divisor, 40,000. Recall that we round standard quotas to the nearest hundredth. With Hamilton's method, we round each standard quota down to obtain the lower quota. Then we distribute any leftover seats to the states with the largest fractional parts until all seats are distributed. Table 15.39 shows the apportionment using Hamilton's method.

Table 15.39 Hamilton's Method, Standard Divisor of 40,000

State	A	B	C	D	Total
Population	3,350,000	1,850,000	2,365,000	2,835,000	10,400,000
Standard quota	83.75	46.25	59.13	70.88	
Lower quota	83	46	59	70	258
Hamilton's apportionment	84	46	59	71	260

Since states D and A, in that order, had the highest fractional parts (0.88 and 0.75, respectively), each receives one additional seat.

b) With Jefferson's method, we use a modified divisor that is *less than* the standard divisor and use modified *lower quotas*. Table 15.40 shows the results using a modified divisor of 39,700.

Table 15.40 Jefferson's Method, Modified Divisor, $d = 39,700$

State	A	B	C	D	Total
Population	3,350,000	1,850,000	2,365,000	2,835,000	10,400,000
Modified quota	84.38	46.60	59.57	71.41	
Modified lower quota	84	46	59	71	260

Using $d = 39,700$, we have a sum of 260 seats, as desired. Therefore, each state receives the number of seats listed under the modified lower quotas in Table 15.40.

c) With Adams's method, we use a modified divisor that is *greater than* the standard divisor and use modified *upper quotas*. Table 15.41 shows the results using a modified divisor of 40,300.

Table 15.41 Adams's Method, Modified Divisor, $d = 40,300$

State	A	B	C	D	Total
Population	3,350,000	1,850,000	2,365,000	2,835,000	10,400,000
Modified quota	83.13	45.91	58.68	70.35	
Modified upper quota	84	46	59	71	260

Using $d = 40,300$, we have a sum of 260 seats, as desired. Therefore, each state receives the number of seats listed under the modified upper quotas in Table 15.41.

d) With Webster's method, we need to find a modified divisor such that when each state's modified quota is rounded to the nearest integer, the total of the integers is 260. The modified divisor may be *less than, equal to,* or *greater than* the standard divisor. If we round the standard quotas from part (a) to the nearest integer, the sum of the rounded quotas is 260. Therefore, we will use the standard divisor as our modified divisor. Table 15.42 shows the results when we round the modified quotas to the nearest integer.

Table 15.42 Webster's Method, Modified Divisor, $d = 40,000$

State	A	B	C	D	Total
Population	3,350,000	1,850,000	2,365,000	2,835,000	10,400,000
Standard quota	83.75	46.25	59.13	70.88	
Modified quota	83.75	46.25	59.13	70.88	
Modified rounded quota	84	46	59	71	260

Each state receives the number of seats listed under the modified rounded quotas in Table 15.42. Note that in this example, all four methods led to the same apportionment. However, that is not always the case. ∎

Of the four methods we have discussed in this section, *Hamilton's method uses standard quotas. Jefferson's method, Webster's method, and Adams's method all make use of a modified quota and can all lead to violations of the quota rule.* As we will see in the next section, Hamilton's method can also be problematic by producing paradoxes. Table 15.43 summarizes the four apportionment methods.

Table 15.43 Summary of Apportionment Methods

Method	Divisor	Apportionment
Hamilton's	$$\text{Standard divisor} = \frac{\text{total population}}{\text{number of items to be allocated}}$$	Round each standard quota down. Distribute any leftover items to the groups with the largest fractional parts until all items are distributed. **Favors large states**.
Jefferson's	The modified divisor is *less than* the standard divisor.	Each group's modified quota is *rounded **down** to the nearest integer.* Apportion to each group its modified lower quota. **Favors large states**.
Webster's	The modified divisor is *less than, greater than,* or *equal to,* the standard divisor.	Each group's modified quota is *rounded **to the nearest** integer.* Apportion to each group its modified rounded quota. **Favors small states**.
Adams's	The modified divisor is *greater than* the standard divisor.	Each group's modified quota is *rounded **up** to the nearest integer.* Apportion to each group its modified upper quota. **Favors small states**.

Warm Up Exercises

In Exercises 1–10, fill in the blank with an appropriate word, phrase, or symbol(s).

1. The total population under consideration divided by the number of items to be allocated is called the standard _____. Divisor

2. When each group's population is divided by the standard divisor, a standard _____ is obtained. Quota

3. A standard quota rounded down to the nearest whole number is called a(n) _____ quota. Lower

4. A standard quota rounded up to the nearest whole number is called a(n) _____ quota. Upper

5. The rule stating that an apportionment should always be either the upper quota or the lower quota is called the _____ rule. Quota

6. The apportionment method that requires rounding the *standard quota down* to the lower quota is called _____ method. Hamilton's

7. Jefferson's method, Webster's method, and Adams's method require using a(n) _____ quota. Modified

8. a) The apportionment method that uses a modified divisor that is less than the standard divisor is _____ method. Jefferson's
   b) The apportionment method that uses a modified divisor that is greater than the standard divisor is _____ method. Adams's
   c) The apportionment method that uses a modified divisor that could be less than, greater than, or equal to the standard divisor is _____ method. Webster's

9. a) The apportionment method that uses a *modified quota* that is always rounded to the nearest integer is _____ method. Webster's
   b) The apportionment method that uses a *modified quota* that is always rounded up to the nearest integer is _____ method. Adams's
   c) The apportionment method that uses a *modified quota* that is always rounded down to the nearest integer is _____ method. Jefferson's

10. Jefferson's method, Webster's method, and Adams's method all make use of a modified quota and can all lead to violations of the _____ rule. Quota

Practice the Skills/Problem Solving

In Exercises 11–49, round quotas to the nearest hundredth.

Legislative Seats *In Exercises 11–18, suppose that Turtlestan is a small country with a population of 7,500,000* that consists of four states, A, B, C, and D. There are 150 seats in the legislature that need to be apportioned among the four states. The population of each state is shown in the table.

State	A	B	C	D	Total
Population	1,220,000	2,730,000	857,000	2,693,000	7,500,000

11. a) Determine the standard divisor. 50,000

    b) Determine each state's standard quota. 24.40, 54.60, 17.14, 53.86

12. Determine each state's apportionment using Hamilton's method. 24, 55, 17, 54

13. a) Determine each state's modified quota using the divisor 49,300. 24.75, 55.38, 17.38, 54.62

    b) Determine each state's apportionment using Jefferson's method. 24, 55, 17, 54

14. a) Determine each state's modified quota using the divisor 49,250. 24.77, 55.43, 17.40, 54.68

    b) Determine each state's apportionment using Jefferson's method. 24, 55, 17, 54

15. a) Determine each state's modified quota using the divisor 50,700. 24.06, 53.85, 16.90, 53.11

    b) Determine each state's apportionment using Adams's method. 25, 54, 17, 54

16. a) Determine each state's modified quota using the divisor 50,600. 24.11, 53.95, 16.94, 53.22

    b) Determine each state's apportionment using Adams's method. 25, 54, 17, 54

17. Determine each state's apportionment using Webster's method using the standard divisor. 24, 55, 17, 54

18. a) Determine each state's modified quota using the divisor 49,900. 24.45, 54.71, 17.17, 53.97

    b) Determine each state's apportionment using Webster's method. 24, 55, 17, 54

Hotel Staff *In Exercises 19–26, a large hotel chain needs to apportion 25 new staff members among three hotels based on the numbers of rooms in each hotel as shown below.*

Hotel	A	B	C	Total
Number of rooms	306	214	155	675

19. a) Determine the standard divisor. 27

b) Determine each hotel's standard quota. 11.33, 7.93, 5.74

20. Determine each hotel's apportionment using Hamilton's method. 11, 8, 6

21. a) Determine each hotel's modified quota using the divisor 25.8. 11.86, 8.29, 6.01

b) Determine each hotel's apportionment using Jefferson's method. 11, 8, 6

22. a) Determine each hotel's modified quota using the divisor 25.7. 11.91, 8.33, 6.03

b) Determine each hotel's apportionment using Jefferson's method. 11, 8, 6

23. a) Determine each hotel's modified quota using the divisor 29. 10.55, 7.38, 5.34

b) Determine each hotel's apportionment using Adams's method. 11, 8, 6

24. a) Determine each hotel's modified quota using the divisor 28. 10.93, 7.64, 5.54

b) Determine each hotel's apportionment using Adams's method. 11, 8, 6

25. Determine each hotel's apportionment using Webster's method using the standard divisor. 11, 8, 6

26. a) Determine each hotel's modified quota using the divisor 28.1. 10.89, 7.62, 5.52

b) Determine each hotel's apportionment using Webster's method. 11, 8, 6

Umbrellas In Exercises 27–30, Sandy Shores Resorts operates four beach resorts in the Caribbean islands. Sandy Shores Resorts plans to apportion 50 new beach umbrellas among the four resorts based on the number of rooms in each resort as shown below.

Resort	A	B	C	D	Total
Number of rooms	98	114	143	245	600

27. a) Determine the standard divisor. 12

b) Determine each resort's standard quota. 8.17, 9.50, 11.92, 20.42

c) Determine each resort's apportionment using Hamilton's method. 8, 10, 12, 20

28. Determine each resort's apportionment using Jefferson's method. (*Hint:* Some divisors between 11 and 12 will work.) 8, 9, 12, 21

29. Determine each resort's apportionment using Adams's method. (*Hint:* Some divisors between 12 and 13 will work.) 8, 10, 12, 20

30. Determine each resort's apportionment using Webster's method. (*Hint:* Some divisors between 11.5 and 12.5 will work.) 8, 10, 12, 20

New Computers In Exercises 31–34, a university is made up of five schools: Liberal Arts, Sciences, Engineering, Business, and Humanities. There are 250 new computers to be apportioned among the five schools based on their enrollment shown below. The total enrollment is 13,000.

School	Liberal Arts	Sciences	Engi- neering	Business	Human- ities
Enrollment	1746	7095	2131	937	1091

▲ Princeton University

31. a) Determine the standard divisor. 52

b) Determine each school's standard quota.
33.58, 136.44, 40.98, 18.02, 20.98

c) Determine each school's apportionment using Hamilton's method. 34, 136, 41, 18, 21

32. Determine each school's apportionment using Adams's method. (*Hint:* Some divisors between 52 and 53 will work.) 34, 136, 41, 18, 21

33. Determine each school's apportionment using Jefferson's method. (*Hint:* Some divisors between 51 and 52 will work.) 33, 137, 41, 18, 21

34. Determine each school's apportionment using Webster's method. 34, 136, 41, 18, 21

New Cars In Exercises 35–38, a car manufacturer has 150 cars of a new model to be apportioned to four dealerships. The manufacturer decides to apportion the cars based on the number of cars each dealership sold in the previous year. The number of cars sold by each dealership is shown below.

Dealership	A	B	C	D	Total
Annual Sales	4800	3608	2990	2102	13,500

35. a) Determine the standard divisor. 90

b) Determine each dealership's standard quota.
53.33, 40.09, 33.22, 23.36

c) Determine each dealership's apportionment using Hamilton's method. 53, 40, 33, 24

36. Determine each dealership's apportionment using Jefferson's method. (*Hint:* Some divisors between 88 and 89 will work.) 54, 40, 33, 23

37. Determine each dealership's apportionment using Webster's method. (*Hint:* Some divisors between 89 and 90 will work.) 54, 40, 33, 23

38. Determine each dealership's apportionment using Adams's method. 53, 40, 33, 24

New Buses In Exercises 39–42, the Transit Department in the city of Houston has 100 new buses to be apportioned among six routes. The department decides to apportion the buses based on the average number of daily passengers per route, as shown in the table below.

Route	A	B	C	D	E	F	Total
Passengers	9070	15,275	12,810	5720	25,250	6875	75,000

39. a) Determine the standard divisor. 750

b) Determine each route's standard quota.
12.09, 20.37, 17.08, 7.63, 33.67, 9.17

c) Determine each route's apportionment using Hamilton's method. 12, 20, 17, 8, 34, 9

40. Determine each route's apportionment using Jefferson's method. 12, 21, 17, 7, 34, 9

41. Determine each route's apportionment using Adams's method. 12, 20, 17, 8, 34, 9

42. Determine each route's apportionment using Webster's method. 12, 20, 17, 8, 34, 9

Nursing Shifts In Exercises 43–46, a hospital has 200 nurses to be apportioned among four shifts: Shifts A, B, C, and D. The hospital decides to apportion the nurses based on the average number of room calls reported during each shift. Room calls are shown in the table below.

Shift	A	B	C	D	Total
Room calls	751	980	503	166	2400

43. a) Determine the standard divisor. 12

b) Determine each shift's standard quota.
62.58, 81.67, 41.92, 13.83

c) Determine each shift's apportionment using Hamilton's method. 62, 82, 42, 14

44. Determine each shift's apportionment using Adams's method. (*Note:* Divisors do not have to be whole numbers.) 63, 81, 42, 14

45. Determine each shift's apportionment using Jefferson's method. (*Note:* Divisors do not have to be whole numbers.) 63, 82, 42, 13

46. Determine each shift's apportionment using Webster's method. (*Hint:* Some divisors between 12 and 12.05 will work.) 62, 82, 42, 14

Challenge Problems/Group Activities

47. *The First Census* The first census taken in the United States after the adoption of the U.S. Constitution was in 1790. The following table shows the results of this census.

State	Population
Connecticut	236,841
Delaware	55,540
Georgia	70,835
Kentucky	68,705
Maryland	278,514
Massachusetts	475,327
New Hampshire	141,822
New Jersey	179,570
New York	331,589
North Carolina	353,523
Pennsylvania	432,879
Rhode Island	68,446
South Carolina	206,236
Vermont	85,533
Virginia	630,560
Total	3,615,920

a) Determine the apportionment that would have resulted if Hamilton's method had been used as the method originally approved by Congress. One hundred five seats were to be distributed. 7, 2, 2, 2, 8, 14, 4, 5, 10, 10, 13, 2, 6, 2, 18

b) Determine the apportionment that was used with Jefferson's method. 7, 1, 2, 2, 8, 14, 4, 5, 10, 10, 13, 2, 6, 2, 19

c) Compare the apportionments from parts (a) and (b). Which state(s) benefited from Jefferson's method? Which state(s) were at a disadvantage from Jefferson's method? Benefited: Virginia; Disadvantage: Delaware

48. *Legislative Seats* Suppose that a country with a population of 10,000,000 has 250 legislative seats to be apportioned among four states, where each state has a different population. Determine a population for each state in which Hamilton's method, Jefferson's method, Webster's method, and Adams's method all lead to the same apportionment of the 250 legislative seats. Many answers are possible.*

49. *Police Officers* Suppose that a police department has 210 new officers to apportion among six precincts. The department plans to apportion the officers based on the number of crimes committed during the previous year in each precinct. Suppose that the number of crimes committed in each precinct is different and that the total number of crimes committed in all six precincts was 2940. Determine the number of crimes committed in each precinct such that Hamilton's method, Jefferson's method, Webster's method, and Adams's method all lead to the same apportionment of the 210 new officers. Many answers are possible. Answers will vary. One possible answer is A: 743, B: 367, C: 432, D: 491, E: 519, F: 388.

Internet/Research Activities

50. Do research and write a report on the apportionment method used in the House of Representatives in 1872. Include in your report a description of the method used.

51. Do research and write a report on the Huntington–Hill method, the current method used to apportion the representatives in the House of Representatives. Include historical background and describe how the method works.

*See Instructor Answer Appendix

SECTION 15.4   Flaws of the Apportionment Methods

▲ *It is possible for a library to receive fewer e-readers when 51 e-readers are to be apportioned than when 50 e-readers are to be apportioned.*

Recall from Section 15.3 the situation in which a college receives a grant to purchase 50 e-readers that will be placed in four different libraries on campus. Suppose that before the e-readers are purchased the price of the e-readers decreases enough so that 51 e-readers can now be purchased and apportioned to the four libraries. Because of a flaw in the apportionment method to be used, it is possible that one of the libraries would receive fewer e-readers with 51 e-readers being apportioned than with 50 e-readers being apportioned. In this section, we will discuss this flaw and other flaws with apportionment methods.

Why **This is Important** With each new census taken, the number of representatives allocated to various states may change. How these representatives are assigned can make an important difference in the laws and bills that are passed.

Just as we have discovered that voting methods can have flaws, apportionment methods can also have flaws. In this section, as we did in Section 15.2 with voting methods, we will consider several reasonable properties that an apportionment method should have. Then we will see examples in which these properties are violated. Problems with apportionment can occur in a variety of ways. Population changes, changes in the number of items to be distributed, and the addition of one or more groups can lead to problems with apportionment.

Recall from Section 15.3 that the quota rule states that an apportionment for every group under consideration should always be either the upper quota or the lower quota. Hamilton's method, which satisfies the quota rule, would appear to be a reasonable and fair apportionment method. As we will discuss in this section, though, Hamilton's method can result in some serious flaws. In this section, we will discuss three flaws of Hamilton's method: the *Alabama paradox*, the *population paradox*, and the *new-states paradox*. **These flaws apply only to Hamilton's method and not to Jefferson's method, Webster's method, or Adams's method.**

The Alabama Paradox

The first, and perhaps most serious, flaw of Hamilton's method occurs when an increase in the total number of items to be apportioned results in a loss of an item for one of the groups. This flaw first occurred in the apportionment of the House of Representatives in 1880 when a discussion occurred on whether to have 299 or 300 members in the House. Using Hamilton's method with 299 members, Alabama would receive eight seats. But if the total number of representatives were increased to 300, Alabama would only receive seven seats. As a result, this situation became known as the *Alabama paradox*.

> **Alabama Paradox**
> The **Alabama paradox** occurs when an increase in the total number of items to be apportioned results in a loss of an item for a group.

Example 1 illustrates the Alabama paradox.

Example 1   *Demonstrating the Alabama Paradox*

Consider Stanhope, a small country with a population of 16,500 people and three states A, B, and C (Table 15.44). There are 150 seats in the legislature that must be apportioned among the three states, according to their population. Show that the Alabama paradox occurs if the number of seats is increased to 151.

Round standard divisors and standard quotas to the nearest hundredth.

Table 15.44

State	A	B	C	Total
Population	814	7403	8283	16,500

Solution With 150 seats in the legislature, the standard divisor is

$$\frac{16,500}{150} = 110$$

The standard quotas for each state and the apportionment for each state are shown in Table 15.45.

Table 15.45

State	A	B	C	Total
Population	814	7403	8283	16,500
Standard quota	7.40	67.30	75.30	
Lower quota	7	67	75	149
Hamilton's apportionment	8	67	75	150

With 151 seats in the legislature, the standard divisor is

$$\frac{16,500}{151} \approx 109.27$$

The standard quotas for each state and the apportionment for each state with 151 total seats are shown in Table 15.46.

Table 15.46

State	A	B	C	Total
Population	814	7403	8283	16,500
Standard quota	7.45	67.75	75.80	
Lower quota	7	67	75	149
Hamilton's apportionment	7	68	76	151

When the number of seats increased from 150 to 151, state A's apportionment actually decreased, from 8 to 7. This example illustrates the Alabama paradox. ■

When the total number of items increases, each group's standard quota increases, but not by the same amount. Therefore, it is possible that the order of assignment of the items can change. As a result, some groups can lose items they already had. When the total number of items increases, usually the larger groups benefit at the expense of the smaller groups.

The next paradox we will discuss is the population paradox.

Population Paradox

Another paradox that can occur with Hamilton's method may occur when the population of one or more states changes. It was discovered in the early 1900s that under Hamilton's method, one state could lose a seat to another state even though its population is growing at a faster rate. At the time, Virginia lost a seat in the House of Representatives while Maine gained a seat, although Virginia's population was growing at a much faster rate than Maine's population. Thus, this paradox became known as the *population paradox*.

Population Paradox

The **population paradox** occurs when group A loses items to group B even though group A's population grew at a faster rate than group B's.

Example 2 illustrates the population paradox.

Example 2 *Demonstrating the Population Paradox*

Consider Alexandria, a small country with a population of 100,000 and three states A, B, and C. There are 100 seats in the legislature that must be apportioned among the three states. Using Hamilton's method, the apportionment is shown in Table 15.47.

Table 15.47

State	A	B	C	Total
Population	23,527	5548	70,925	100,000
Standard quota	23.53	5.55	70.93	
Lower quota	23	5	70	98
Hamilton's apportionment	23	6	71	100

Suppose that the population increases according to Table 15.48 and that the 100 seats are reapportioned. Show that the population paradox occurs when Hamilton's method is used.

Table 15.48

State	A	B	C	Total
Population	23,926	5648	71,110	100,684

Solution To calculate the percent increase, we use the procedure discussed in Section 11.1. State A has an increase of 399 people. Therefore, state A has a percent increase of

$$\frac{399}{23,527} \approx 0.01696 \approx 1.696\%$$

State B has an increase of 100 people. Therefore, state B has a percent increase of

$$\frac{100}{5548} \approx 0.01802 \approx 1.802\%$$

State C has an increase of 185 people. Therefore, state C has a percent increase of

$$\frac{185}{70,925} \approx 0.00261 \approx 0.261\%$$

All three states had an increase in their population, but state B is increasing at a faster rate than state A and state C.

The standard divisor using the new population is

$$\frac{100,684}{100} = 1006.84$$

Table 15.49 shows the reapportionment, using Hamilton's method using the standard divisor 1006.84.

Table 15.49

State	A	B	C	Total
Population	23,926	5648	71,110	100,684
Standard quota	23.76	5.61	70.63	
Lower quota	23	5	70	98
Hamilton's apportionment	24	5	71	100

State B has lost a seat to state A even though state B's population grew at a faster rate than state A's. As a result, we have an example of the population paradox. ∎

The next and final paradox we will discuss is the new-states paradox.

The New-States Paradox

The new-states paradox was discovered in 1907 when Oklahoma was added as a state. When a new state is added, new seats must be added to the legislature. How do we determine the number of new seats to add? A reasonable answer would be to add the number of seats the new state would be entitled to based on its population. When reapportioning the House of Representatives with the additional five seats Oklahoma was entitled to, Maine's apportionment increased from three to four seats and

TIMELY TIP

In Example 2, the population paradox occurred because state B lost a seat to state A even though state B's population grew at a faster rate than state A's population. When checking for the population paradox, it is possible for a state to lose a seat to another state without the population paradox occurring. *Remember that for the population paradox to occur, the state that loses the seat must be growing at a faster rate than the state that gains the seat.*

New York's apportionment decreased from 38 to 37. By adding a new state and its fair share of seats, New York was required to give a seat to Maine. This paradox became known as the *new-states paradox*.

New-States Paradox

The **new-states paradox** occurs when the addition of a new group, and additional items to be apportioned, reduces the previous apportionment of another group.

Example 3 *Demonstrating the New-States Paradox*

The Oklahoma Public Library System has received a grant to purchase 100 laptop computers to be distributed between two libraries A and B. The 100 laptops will be apportioned based on the population served by each library. The apportionment using Hamilton's method is shown in Table 15.50. The standard divisor is

$$\frac{10,000}{100} = 100$$

Table 15.50

Library	A	B	Total
Population	2145	7855	10,000
Standard quota	21.45	78.55	
Lower quota	21	78	99
Hamilton's apportionment	21	79	100

Suppose that an anonymous donor decides to donate money to purchase six more laptops provided that a third library, *C*, that serves a population of 625, is included in the apportionment. Show that the new-states paradox occurs when the laptops are reapportioned.

Solution The total population is now $10,000 + 625$ or 10,625 and the total number of laptops to be apportioned is now $100 + 6$ or 106. Therefore, when the third library is added, the new standard divisor is

$$\frac{10,625}{106} = 100.24$$

The new standard quotas and Hamilton's apportionment are shown in Table 15.51.

Table 15.51 Using a New Standard Divisor of 100.24

Library	A	B	C	Total
Population	2145	7855	625	10,625
Standard quota	21.40	78.36	6.24	
Lower quota	21	78	6	105
Hamilton's apportionment	22	78	6	106

Before library C was added, library B would receive 79 laptops. By adding a new library and increasing the total number of laptops to be apportioned, library B ended up losing a laptop to library A. Thus, we have a case of the new-states paradox. ∎

When a new group is added to the apportionment, we must determine how many additional items should be added to the total to be apportioned. In Example 3, we were told that six additional laptops were to be added to the total apportioned when a new library was included in the apportionment. If we are given the new group's population but are not given the number of additional items to be added to the total to be apportioned, we calculate the number of items to be apportioned to the new group as follows. First determine the new group's standard quota. The number of additional items would be the new group's standard quota *rounded down* to the nearest integer. For example, in Example 3, the new library, library C, served a population of 625. The standard quota for library C would be

$$\frac{625}{100} = 6.25$$

Rounding 6.25 down to the nearest integer gives us six laptops to be added to the total to be apportioned, or 106 laptops.

As we have discovered in Section 15.3, Hamilton's method appears to be a fair and reasonable apportionment method since it satisfies the quota rule. In this section, however, we discovered that Hamilton's method can produce paradoxes. Jefferson's, Adams's, and Webster's methods can all violate the quota rule but do not produce paradoxes. Hamilton's and Jefferson's methods can favor large states, whereas Adams's and Webster's methods can favor small states. Is there a perfect apportionment method that satisfies the quota rule, does not produce any paradoxes, and favors neither large nor small states? In 1980, mathematicians Michel Balinski and H. Payton Young proved that there is no apportionment method that satisfies the quota rule while also avoiding any paradoxes. Their theorem is called Balinski and Young's impossibility theorem.

Balinski and Young's Impossibility Theorem

There is no perfect apportionment method that satisfies the quota rule and avoids any paradoxes.

Table 15.52 summarizes the four apportionment methods we have discussed in this chapter and indicates which methods may violate the quota rule and which methods may produce the paradoxes we have discussed.

Table 15.52 Comparison of Apportionment Methods

	Apportionment Method			
	Hamilton	Jefferson	Adams	Webster
May violate the quota rule (apportionment should always be either upper or lower quota)	No	Yes	Yes	Yes
May produce the Alabama paradox (an increase in the total number of items results in a loss of an item for a group)	Yes	No	No	No
May produce the population paradox (group A loses an item to group B although group A's population grew faster than group B's population)	Yes	No	No	No
May produce the new-states paradox (the addition of a new group reduces the apportionment of another group)	Yes	No	No	No
Apportionment method favors	Large states	Large states	Small states	Small states

Just as there is no perfect voting method, there is also no perfect apportionment method.

SECTION 15.4 *Exercises*

Warm Up Exercises

In Exercises 1–6, fill in the blank with an appropriate word, phrase, or symbol(s).

1. When group A loses an item or items to group B even though group A's population grew at a faster rate than group B's, the _____ paradox occurs. Population

2. When the addition of a new group and additional items to be apportioned reduces the prior apportionment of another group, the _____ paradox occurs. New-states

3. When an increase in the total number of items to be apportioned results in a loss of an item for a group, the _____ paradox occurs. Alabama

4. Hamilton's method and Jefferson's method favor _____ states. Large

5. Adams's method and Webster's method favor _____ states. Small

6. The apportionment method that satisfies the quota rule but may produce a paradox is called _____ method. Hamilton's

Practice the Skills/Problem Solving

In Exercises 7–18, round quotas to the nearest hundredth.

7. **Fax Machines** Consider the apportionment of 60 fax machines for Shanahan Law Firm given in Example 2 on page 942 of Section 15.3. The apportionment using Hamilton's method is shown in the table below.

Office	A	B	C	D	E	Total
Employees	246	201	196	211	226	1080
Standard quota	13.67	11.17	10.89	11.72	12.56	60.01
Lower quota	13	11	10	11	12	57
Hamilton's apportionment	14	11	11	12	12	60

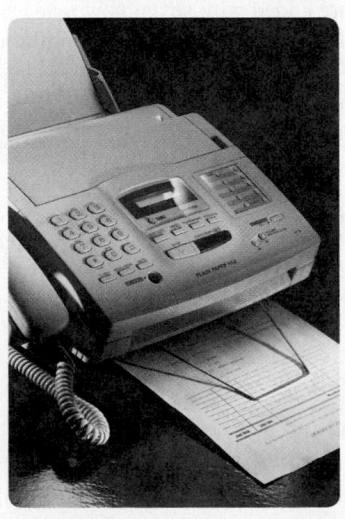

Does the Alabama paradox occur using Hamilton's method if the number of fax machines is increased from 60 to 61? Explain your answer. No. The new apportionment is 14, 11, 11, 12, 13. No office suffers a loss, so the Alabama paradox doesn't occur.

8. **Ergonomic Chairs** A large company with offices in four cities must distribute 148 new ergonomic chairs to the four offices. The chairs will be apportioned based on the number of employees in each office as shown in the table below.

Office	A	B	C	D	Total
Employees	757	295	636	976	2664

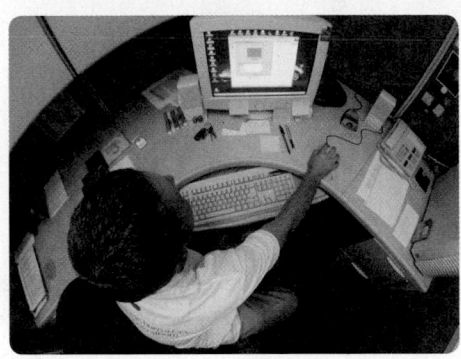

a) Apportion the chairs using Hamilton's method. 42, 17, 35, 54

b) Does the Alabama paradox occur using Hamilton's method if the number of new chairs is increased from 148 to 149? Explain your answer.*

9. **Legislative Seats** A country with three states has 30 seats in the legislature. The population of each state is shown in the table below.

State	A	B	C	Total
Population	161	250	489	900

a) Apportion the seats using Hamilton's method. 6, 8, 16

b) Does the Alabama paradox occur using Hamilton's method if the number of seats is increased from 30 to 31? Explain your answer. Yes. When the number of seats increases, states B and C gain a seat and state A loses a seat.

10. **Legislative Seats** A country with three states has 200 seats in the legislature. The population of each state is shown in the table below.

State	A	B	C	Total
Population	247,100	481,900	271,000	1,000,000

a) Apportion the seats using Hamilton's method. 50, 96, 54

b) Does the Alabama paradox occur using Hamilton's method if the number of seats is increased from 200 to 201? Explain your answer. No

*See Instructor Answer Appendix

In Exercises 11–14, assume that the number of items to be apportioned does not change.

11. *Apportioning Promotions* Apple Inc. has 30,000 employees in three cities as shown in the table below. It wishes to give promotions to 200 employees.

Cities	A	B	C	Total
Employees	9130	6030	14,840	30,000

a) Apportion the promotions using Hamilton's method.
61, 40, 99

b) Suppose that in 10 years the cities have the following number of employees and the company wishes to again give promotions to 200 employees. Does the population paradox occur using Hamilton's method? No

Cities	A	B	C	Total
Employees	9150	6030	14,945	30,125

12. *Apportioning Doctors* First Physicians Group has 30 doctors to apportion among 3 clinics. The doctors are to be apportioned based on the weekly average number of patients at each clinic as shown below.

Clinic	A	B	C	Total
Patients	217	436	337	990

a) Apportion the doctors using Hamilton's method. 7, 13, 10

b) Suppose that 1 year later the clinics have the following weekly average number of patients. If the 30 doctors are reapportioned to the clinics, does the population paradox occur using Hamilton's method? No

Clinic	A	B	C	Total
Patients	230	450	362	1042

13. *College Internships* A college with five divisions has funds for 54 internships. The student population for each division is shown in the table below.

Division	A	B	C	D	E	Total
Population	733	1538	933	1133	1063	5400

a) Apportion the internships using Hamilton's method.
7, 16, 9, 11, 11

b) Suppose that 1 year later the divisions have the following populations. If the college wishes to apportion 54 internships, does the population paradox occur using Hamilton's method?*

Division	A	B	C	D	E	Total
Population	733	1539	933	1133	1116	5454

14. *Legislative Seats* A country with three states has 250 seats in the legislature. The population of each state is shown in the table below.

State	A	B	C	Total
Population	459	10,551	18,990	30,000

a) Apportion the seats using Hamilton's method. 4, 88, 158

b) Suppose that in 10 years the states have the following population. If the country reapportions 250 seats in the legislature, does the population paradox occur using Hamilton's method? No

State	A	B	C	Total
Population	464	10,551	19,100	30,115

15. *Additional Employees* Cynergy Telecommunications has employees in Europe, labeled A, and in the United States, labeled B. The number of employees in each group is shown in the table below. There are 48 managers to be apportioned between the two groups.

Cynergy Telecommunications	A	B	Total
Employees	844	3956	4800

a) Apportion the managers using Hamilton's method. 8, 40

b) Suppose that additional employees in Asia, labeled C, with the number of employees shown in the table below, are added with seven new managers. Does the new-states paradox occur using Hamilton's method?*

Cynergy Telecommunications	A	B	C	Total
Employees	844	3956	724	5524

16. *Adding a Park* The town of Manlius purchased 25 new picnic tables to be apportioned between two parks. The picnic tables are to be apportioned based on the annual number of visitors to each park as shown below.

Park	A	B	Total
Visitors	3750	6250	10,000

a) Apportion the picnic tables using Hamilton's method. 9, 16

*See Instructor Answer Appendix

b) Suppose that the town decides to purchase five additional picnic tables and include a third park with an annual number of visitors as shown in the table below. The town will now apportion 30 picnic tables among the three parks. Does the new-states paradox occur using Hamilton's method?

No. The apportionment is 9, 16, 5.

Park	A	B	C	Total
Visitors	3750	6250	2100	12,100

17. *Adding a State* A country with three states has 60 seats in the legislature. The population of each state is shown in the table below.

State	A	B	C	Total
Population	62,700	230,700	606,600	900,000

a) Apportion the seats using Hamilton's method. 4, 15, 41

b) Suppose that a fourth state with the population shown in the table below is added, with five additional seats. Does the new-states paradox occur using Hamilton's method?
Yes. The apportionment is now 4, 16, 40, 5, and state C loses a seat.

State	A	B	C	D	Total
Population	62,700	230,700	606,600	78,000	978,000

18. *Adding a State* A country with two states has 33 seats in the legislature. The population of each state is shown in the table below.

State	A	B	Total
Population	744	2556	3300

a) Apportion the states using Hamilton's method. 7, 26

b) Suppose that a third state with the population shown in the table below is added, with seven additional seats. Does the new-states paradox occur using Hamilton's method? No. The apportionment is 7, 26, 7.

State	A	B	C	Total
Population	744	2556	710	4010

Internet/Research Activity

19. Write a paper on which apportionment method you think is the best. Include reasons to support your choice including the advantages and disadvantages of the method you have selected.

CHAPTER 15) *Summary*

Important Facts and Concepts	**Examples and Discussion**
Section 15.1 *Voting Methods*	
Plurality	Examples 3–4, page 911
Borda count method	Examples 5–6, pages 912–913
Plurality with elimination method	Examples 7–8, pages 914–915
Pairwise comparison method	Examples 9–10, pages 917–918, Discussion, pages 916–919
Section 15.2 *Flaws of Voting Methods*	
Majority criterion	Examples 1–2, 6, pages 926, 932
Head-to-head criterion	Examples 3, 6, pages 927, 932
Monotonicity criterion	Examples 4, 6, pages 929, 932
Irrelevant alternatives criterion	Examples 5, 6, pages 931, 932, Discussion, pages 930–934
Section 15.3 Standard quota *Apportionment Methods*	Example 1, page 940
Hamilton's method	Examples 2–3, 7, pages 942, 949
Jefferson's method	Examples 4, 7, pages 944, 949
Webster's method	Examples 5, 7, pages 946, 949
Adams's method	Examples 6–7, pages 943–949, Discussion, pages 948–951

Section 15.4	
Flaws of Apportionment Methods	
Alabama paradox	Example 1, page 956
Population paradox	Example 2, page 957
New-states paradox	Example 3, page 959, Discussion, pages 958–960

CHAPTER 15   *Review Exercises*

15.1

1. *Electing the Club President* The town of Bakersfield's chess club is holding an election to choose a club president. The 36 votes were cast as follows: Robert Rivera, 16 votes; Charlotte Kaiser, 12 votes; and Rhonda Timmerman, 8 votes.

  a) Using the plurality method, which candidate is elected president? Robert Rivera

  b) Did this candidate receive a majority of the votes? No

2. *Electing a Chairperson* Suffolk Community College is holding an election to appoint a chairperson of the board of trustees. The 413 faculty members vote as follows: Michelle MacDougal, 231 votes; Jeffrey Stuart, 155 votes; and Donald Campbell, 27 votes.

  a) Using the plurality method, who is elected?
  Michelle MacDougal
  b) Did this candidate receive a majority of votes? Yes

3. *Ranking Candidates* Ten voters are asked to rank four candidates. The 10 voters turn in the following ballots showing their preferences in order:

```
B  A  D  B  A  C  B  C  D  C
A  C  C  A  C  B  A  B  A  B
C  D  A  C  D  A  C  A  B  A
D  B  B  D  B  D  D  D  C  D
```

Make a preference table for these ballots.*

4. *Ranking Candidates* Seven voters are asked to rank three candidates. The seven voters turn in the following ballots showing their preferences in order:

```
C  C  A  C  A  B  B
A  A  C  B  C  A  A
B  B  B  A  B  C  C
```

Make a preference table for these ballots.*

In Exercises 5–10, the members of the Student Council at Hillsborough Community College must decide which item to use in a raffle to raise money for the Salvation Army. Their choices are an iPod (I), a portable DVD player (D), a digital camera (C), or a Blu-ray player (B). The members rank their choices according to the following preference table.

Number of Votes	9	6	5	3	1
First	D	C	I	C	B
Second	I	I	B	B	D
Third	C	B	C	D	I
Fourth	B	D	D	I	C

5. How many members voted? 24

6. Using the plurality method, which item is chosen?
A tie between the portable DVD player and the digital camera

7. Using the Borda count method, which item is chosen? iPod

8. Using the plurality with elimination method, which item is chosen? Digital camera

9. Using the pairwise comparison method, which item is chosen?
Tie between iPod and digital camera

10. Which item is selected if the plurality with elimination method is used and the item with the most *last*-place votes is eliminated at each step? iPod

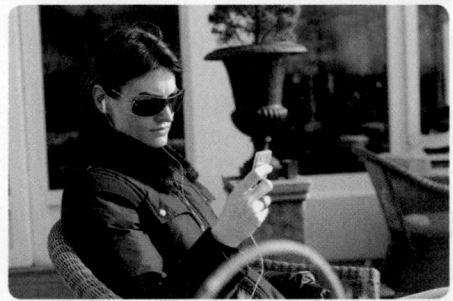

Sports Preferences In Exercises 11–16, the employees at Delphi Engineering must decide whether to play baseball (B), soccer (S), or volleyball (V) at their year-end picnic. The preference table follows.

Number of Votes	38	30	25	7	10
First	S	V	B	B	V
Second	B	S	V	S	B
Third	V	B	S	V	S

*See Instructor Answer Appendix

11. How many employees voted? 110

12. Determine the winner using the plurality method. Volleyball

13. Determine the winner using the Borda count method. Soccer

14. Determine the winner using the plurality with elimination method. Volleyball

15. Determine the winner using the pairwise comparison method. None, a three-way tie

16. Determine the winner if the plurality with elimination method is used and the candidate with the most *last*-place votes is eliminated at each step. Soccer

17. *Choosing a License Plate Style* Park Forest retirement community in Tennessee is purchasing a van to be used by the residents. The 372 residents are unable to agree on a style of license plate for the van and decide to hold an election in which the residents rank their choices from among the following: American Association of Retired Persons (A), standard issue Tennessee license plate (T), Wildlife Federation (W), and State Parks (S). The results of this election are given in the preference table below.

Number of Votes	161	134	65	12
First	A	A	T	W
Second	S	W	A	S
Third	T	S	W	T
Fourth	W	T	S	A

a) Does any plate receive a majority of first-place votes? If so, which plate received a majority?
Yes, American Association of Retired Persons

b) Using the plurality method, which plate is selected?
American Association of Retired Persons

c) Using the Borda count method, which plate is selected?
American Association of Retired Persons

d) Using the plurality with elimination method, which plate is selected? American Association of Retired Persons

e) Using the pairwise comparison method, which plate is selected? American Association of Retired Persons

18. *Accountants Convention* The National Association of Accountants held an election among its delegates to decide on the 2018 conference site. The 200 delegates ranked their choices among Chicago (C), Seattle (S), Dallas (D), and Las Vegas (L). The preference table giving the results of the election is shown below.

Number of Votes	60	55	45	30	10
First	S	L	D	C	S
Second	L	D	C	L	D
Third	C	C	L	D	L
Fourth	D	S	S	S	C

▲ *Dallas, Texas*

a) Does any city receive a majority of first-place votes? If so, which city received a majority? No

b) Using the plurality method, which city is selected? Seattle

c) Using the Borda count method, which city is selected? Las Vegas

d) Using the plurality with elimination method, which city is selected? Las Vegas

e) Using the pairwise comparison method, which city is selected? Las Vegas

19. *Selecting an Encyclopedia* Park Street Library is planning to invest in a set of encyclopedias for the library, but the staff members differ regarding which set to buy. To settle the debate, the 16 staff members decide to rank the following choices: *Encyclopedia Britannica* (E), *Funk and Wagnall's* (F), *Grolier* (G), and *World Book* (W). Aware that sentiments seem to be evenly divided, the staff members agree to use the plurality with elimination method, with the Borda count method used in case of a tie. The results of this election are given in the following preference table.

Number of Votes	6	4	3	1	1	1
First	W	E	E	F	F	W
Second	G	G	W	W	E	F
Third	E	W	F	G	W	E
Fourth	F	F	G	E	G	G

a) Which encyclopedia is selected if the plurality with elimination method is used?
A tie between *Encyclopedia Britannica* and *World Book*

b) According to the rules described above, which encyclopedia is chosen? *World Book*

c) If the staff members had agreed to break a tie using the pairwise comparison method, which encyclopedia is chosen? A tie between *Encyclopedia Britannica* and *World Book*

15.2

Hiring a New Paralegal In Exercises 20 and 21, a law firm is hiring one new paralegal from among four candidates, A, B, C, and D. The search committee decides to use the Borda count method to determine the winner. The preference table follows.

Number of Votes	9	6	2
First	A	C	B
Second	B	B	D
Third	C	D	C
Fourth	D	A	A

20. Is the majority criterion satisfied?
No. A has a majority, but B wins by the Borda count method.

21. Is the head-to-head criterion satisfied?*

22. *Plurality with Elimination* Consider the following preference table.

Number of Votes	12	16	8	14
First	B	C	B	A
Second	A	B	C	C
Third	C	A	A	B

a) Who wins the election if the plurality with elimination method is used? C wins the election by plurality with elimination.

b) Assume that in a second election the eight voters who voted for B, C, A, in that order, all change their preference to C, B, A, in that order. If the plurality with elimination method is used, is the monotonicity criterion satisfied? When the order is changed A wins. Therefore, the monotonicity criterion is not satisfied.

c) Using the preference table from part (a), assume that B drops out. Does the plurality with elimination method satisfy the irrelevant alternatives criterion?*

23. *A Taste Test* In a taste test, 114 people are asked to taste and rank four different brands of hot dogs. The choices are Ball Park (B), Oscar Mayer (O), Nathan's (N), and Hebrew National (H). The preference table is shown below.

Number of Votes	34	24	23	21	12
First	O	B	N	H	H
Second	B	H	H	N	N
Third	N	N	B	O	B
Fourth	H	O	O	B	O

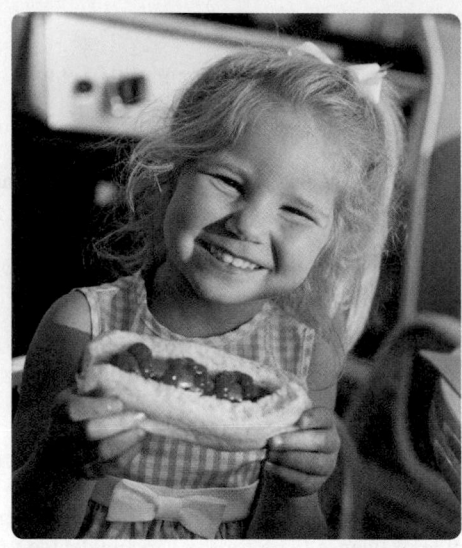

a) Which brand is favored over all others in a head-to-head comparison? Ball Park

b) Which brand wins if the plurality method is used? Oscar Mayer

c) Which brand wins if the Borda count method is used? Tie between Nathan's and Hebrew National

d) Which brand wins if the plurality with elimination method is used? Hebrew National

e) Which brand wins if the pairwise comparison method is used? Ball Park

f) Which voting method(s) in parts (b) through (e) violate the head-to-head criterion?*

24. *Selecting a Band* The Southwestern High School Class of 1979 is organizing its 35-year class reunion and is trying to pick out a band to play at the reunion. The choices are REO Speedwagon (R), Boston (B), Journey (J), and Fleetwood Mac (F). The class members have ranked their choices as indicated in the following preference table.

Number of Votes	34	25	15	9	4
First	B	F	R	J	J
Second	F	J	J	R	R
Third	R	R	F	B	F
Fourth	J	B	B	F	B

▲ *Journey*

*See Instructor Answer Appendix

a) Is one band favored over all others in a head-to-head comparison? Fleetwood Mac

b) Which band is chosen if the plurality method is used? Boston

c) Which band is chosen if the Borda count method is used? Fleetwood Mac

d) Which band is chosen if the plurality with elimination method is used? REO Speedwagon

e) Which band is chosen if the pairwise comparison method is used? Fleetwood Mac

f) Which voting methods in parts (a) through (e) violate the head-to-head criterion?
The plurality method and the plurality with elimination method

25. *Violating the Majority Criterion* Which voting method(s) violate the majority criterion in the following election data? The Borda count method

Number of Votes	36	20	8	6
First	A	B	C	D
Second	B	C	B	B
Third	D	A	D	A
Fourth	C	D	A	C

26. *Violating the Monotonicity Criterion* Using the following tables, determine which voting method(s) violate the monotonicity criterion.

First Election

Number of Votes	28	24	20	10
First	A	B	C	C
Second	C	A	B	A
Third	B	C	A	B

Second Election

Number of Votes	36	24	20	2
First	A	B	C	C
Second	C	A	B	A
Third	B	C	A	B

The plurality with elimination method

27. *Violating the Irrelevant Alternatives Criterion* Using the following table, determine which voting method(s) violates the irrelevant alternatives criterion. Assume that candidate D drops out prior to the conclusion of the election.

Number of Votes	24	16	16	16	8	4	5
First	B	B	E	C	A	D	D
Second	A	A	A	D	E	B	E
Third	D	E	C	E	D	A	A
Fourth	E	C	D	B	B	E	B
Fifth	C	D	B	A	C	C	C

The pairwise comparison method and the Borda count method

15.3, 15.4

Postal Service Apportionment In Exercises 28–32, a post office in the city of Riverside has three regions in which to distribute the mail and 10 mail trucks. The trucks are to be apportioned based on the number of houses in each region, as shown in the table below.

Region	A	B	C	Total
Number of houses	2592	1428	1980	6000

28. Determine each region's apportionment using Hamilton's method. 4, 3, 3

29. Determine each region's apportionment using Jefferson's method. 5, 2, 3

30. Determine each region's apportionment using Adams's method. 4, 3, 3

31. Determine each region's apportionment using Webster's method. 5, 2, 3

32. Suppose that the post office purchases one new truck. Using Hamilton's method, does the Alabama paradox occur if the number of trucks is increased from 10 to 11?
Yes. The apportionment is 5, 2, 4. Region B loses one truck.

Apportioning Sociology Sections In Exercises 33–37, Miami Dade College plans to offer 29 sections of three different sociology courses: Introduction to Sociology (A), Advanced Sociology (B), and Social Problems (C). The sections will be apportioned based on preregistration as shown in the table below.

Course	A	B	C	Total
Number of students	371	279	220	870

▲ *Miami Dade College*

33. Determine the apportionment for each course using Hamilton's method. 13, 9, 7

34. Determine the apportionment for each course using Jefferson's method. 13, 9, 7

35. Determine the apportionment for each course using Adams's method. 12, 9, 8

36. Determine the apportionment for each course using Webster's method. 13, 9, 7

37. Suppose that the following table shows the final registration for each course. If the sections are reapportioned using Hamilton's method, does the population paradox occur? No. The apportionment with the additional population is still 13, 9, 7.

Course	A	B	C	Total
Number of students	376	279	222	877

Apportioning Seats *In Exercises 38–42, a country has two states, A and B, and 50 seats in the legislature. The population of each state is shown in the table below.*

State	A	B	Total
Population	4420	45,580	50,000

38. Determine each state's apportionment using Hamilton's method. 4, 46

39. Determine each state's apportionment using Jefferson's method. 4, 46

40. Determine each state's apportionment using Adams's method. 5, 45

41. Determine each state's apportionment using Webster's method. 4, 46

42. Suppose that a third state, C, with the population shown in the table below, is added along with five new seats. Does the new-states paradox occur using Hamilton's method?

State	A	B	C	Total
Population	4420	45,580	5400	55,400

Yes. The new apportionment is 5, 45, 5. State B loses a seat.

CHAPTER 15 *Test*

Lunch Choices *In Exercises 1–6, the employees of an accounting firm are planning to have lunch delivered to a meeting. Their choices are tacos (T), pizza (P), and burgers (B). The preference table follows.*

Number of Votes	7	6	6	5
First	T	P	B	P
Second	P	B	T	T
Third	B	T	P	B

1. How many members voted? 24

2. Does any choice have a majority of votes? No

3. Determine the winner using the plurality method. Pizza

4. Determine the winner using the Borda count method. Pizza

5. Determine the winner using the plurality with elimination method. Tacos

6. Determine the winner using the pairwise comparison method. Tacos

Favorite Animal *In Exercises 7–11, the children of Happy Faces Preschool are voting on their favorite classroom animal. The choices are hamster (H), iguana (I), lemming (L), and salamander (S). The results of the election are given in the following preference table.*

Number of Votes	43	30	29	26	14
First	S	L	I	H	H
Second	L	H	H	I	I
Third	I	I	L	S	L
Fourth	H	S	S	L	S

7. How many children voted? 142

8. Which animal wins this election if the plurality method is used? Salamander

9. Which animal wins this election if the Borda count method is used? Iguana

10. Which animal wins this election if the plurality with elimination method is used? Hamster

11. Which animal wins this election if the pairwise comparison method is used? Lemming

12. *Violating the Head-to-Head Criterion* Which voting method(s)—plurality, Borda count, plurality with elimination, or pairwise comparison—violate the head-to-head criterion using the following election data? Plurality method, Borda count method, and plurality with elimination method

Number of Votes	86	60	58	52	28
First	W	Y	Z	X	X
Second	Y	X	X	Z	Z
Third	Z	Z	Y	W	Y
Fourth	X	W	W	Y	W

13. *Voting for a Logo Design* The park rangers in Yosemite National Park are holding a contest to choose a new logo design. The four logo choices for their stationery are El Capitan (E), a sequoia tree (S), a mule deer (M), and a waterfall (W). The 35 rangers rank their choices according to the following preference table.

Number of Votes	18	10	4	3
First	E	M	W	S
Second	M	W	M	M
Third	S	E	S	E
Fourth	W	S	E	W

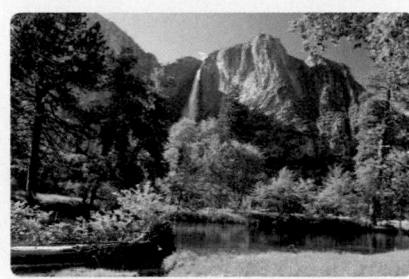

▲ *Yosemite National Park, California*

Using the data provided, does the Borda count method violate the majority criterion?

Yes, El Capitan has a majority of first-place votes but mule deer wins.

Apportioning Legislative Seats In Exercises 14–20, a country has three states and 30 seats in the legislature. The population of each state is shown below.

State	A	B	C	Total
Population	6933	9533	16,534	33,000

14. Determine each state's apportionment using Hamilton's method. 6, 9, 15

15. Determine each state's apportionment using Jefferson's method. 6, 9, 15

16. Determine each state's apportionment using Adams's method. 6, 9, 15

17. Determine each state's apportionment using Webster's method. 6, 9, 15

18. If the number of seats in the legislature increases to 31, does the Alabama paradox occur using Hamilton's method? No. The apportionment is 6, 9, 16.

19. Suppose that in 10 years the states have the following population and 30 seats are apportioned. If the seats are reapportioned, does the population paradox occur using Hamilton's method? No. The apportionment is 6, 9, 15.

State	A	B	C	Total
Population	7072	9724	17,030	33,826

20. Suppose that a fourth state with the population shown in the table below is added, with five additional seats for a total of 35 seats. Does the new-states paradox occur using Hamilton's method? No. The apportionment is 6, 9, 15, 5.

State	A	B	C	D	Total
Population	6933	9533	16,534	5100	38,100

GROUP PROJECT

1. *Voting Project* In this project, each group will select a topic of their choice that students in your class can vote on. Have each student in the class cast a ballot where they rank the candidates or items on which they are voting.

a) After the ballots are cast, construct a preference table.

b) Determine the winner of the election using each of the four voting methods discussed in Section 15.1.

c) Check to see if any of the fairness criteria are violated as described in Section 15.2.

d) After you complete your project, write a final report of how the entire process was conducted and the results obtained and submit it to your instructor.

Answers

Chapter 1

RECREATIONAL MATH. PAGE 24

The farmer crosses with the goat first. Then he can take the herbs across the river. But he must return the goat temporarily so that the goat doesn't eat the herbs. He then takes the wolf across the river. Then he returns for the goat. He will make seven crossings—four forward and three back.

The answer to the St. Ives riddle is 1.

SECTION 1.1, PAGE 5

15. **16.** **17.** **18.**

31. c) No, 72 is between 8^2 and 9^2, so it is not a square number.

32. b) To obtain the 7th triangular number, add 7 to the 6th triangular number. To obtain the 8th triangular number, add 8 to the 7th triangular number, and so on.

37.   38.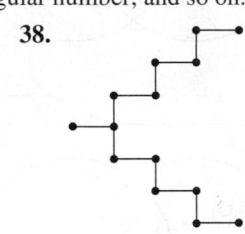

41. d) $n, n + 1, \dfrac{n + (n + 1) + 9}{2} = \dfrac{2n + 10}{2} = n + 5,$

$n + 5 - n = 5$

42. d) $n, n + 10, \dfrac{n + 10}{5}, 5\left(\dfrac{n + 10}{5}\right) = n + 10,$

$n + 10 - 10 = n, n - n = 0$

SECTION 1.3, PAGE 28

33. d) Differences exist in water/milk because the amount for 4 servings is not twice that for 2 servings. Differences also exist in Cream of Wheat because $\frac{1}{2}$ cup is not twice 3 tbsp.

34.

	a)	b)	c)	d)
r:	2 cups	2 cups	2 cups	2 cups
w:	$5\frac{1}{3}$ cups	$4\frac{1}{2}$ cups	$4\frac{2}{3}$ cups	$3\frac{3}{4}$ cups
s:	1 tsp	1 tsp	1 tsp	1 tsp
b:	4 tsp	4 tsp	4 tsp	4 tsp

48. a) Place the object, 1 g, and 3 g on one side and 9 g on the other side.

   b) Place the object, 9 g, and 3 g on one side and 27 g and 1 g on the other side.

49.

51.

8	6	16
18	10	2
4	14	12

52.

10	5	6
3	7	11
8	9	4

59.

	7	
3	1	4
5	8	6
	2	

Other answers are possible, but 1 and 8 must appear in the center.

60. The number of times each part is used is shown below.

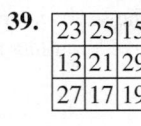

61.

1	2	3	4	5
2	3	4	5	1
3	4	5	1	2
4	5	1	2	3
5	1	2	3	4

Other answers are possible.

67. Thomas would have opened the box labeled grapes and cherries. Because all the boxes are labeled incorrectly, whichever fruit he pulls from the grapes and cherries box will be the only fruit in that box. If he pulls a grape from the box, the box must be labeled grapes; if he pulls a cherry from the box, the box must be labeled cherries. That leaves two boxes whose original labels were incorrect. Because all labels must be changed, there will be only one way for Thomas to assign the two remaining labels.

REVIEW EXERCISES, PAGE 35

7.   8.

38.

21	7	8	18
10	16	15	13
14	12	11	17
9	19	20	6

39.

23	25	15
13	21	29
27	17	19

42. $\begin{array}{ll}\$ 25 & \text{Room} \\ \$ \ \ 3 & \text{Friends} \\ \$ \ \ 2 & \text{Clerk} \\ \hline \$ 30 \end{array}$

44. Yes; 3 quarters and 4 dimes, or 1 half dollar, 1 quarter and 4 dimes, or 1 quarter and 9 dimes. Other answers are possible.

46. Place six coins in each pan with one coin off to the side. If it balances, the heavier coin is the one on the side. If the pan does not balance, take the six coins on the heavier side and split them into two groups of three. Select the three heavier coins and weigh two coins. If the pan balances, it is the third coin. If the pan does not balance, you can identify the heavier coin.

50. The fifth figure will be an octagon with sides of equal length. Inside the octagon will be a seven-sided figure with each side of equal length. The figure will have one antenna.

52. Some possible answers are shown. Others are possible.

CHAPTER TEST, PAGE 38

14.

40	15	20
5	25	45
30	35	10

Chapter 2

SECTION 2.1, PAGE 47

35. { Louvre Museum, British Museum, National Gallery of Art, Tate Modern, Metropolitan Museum of Art}

36. { Musee d'Art Moderne Prado, Museum of Modern Art }

37. { Musee d'Orsay, Musee d'Art Moderne Prado, Museum of Modern Art }

38. { National Gallery of Art, Tate Modern, Metropolitan Museum of Art, Vatican Museums, National Gallery }

86. **a)** Set A is the set of natural numbers greater than 2 and less than or equal to 5. Set *B* is the set of numbers greater than 2 and less than or equal to 5.

92. Answers will vary. Here are some examples: The set of elephants that can fly. The set of dogs that can talk. The set of books that have no pages.

94. Answers will vary. Here are some examples.

   a) The set of men. The set of actors. The set of people over 12 years old. The set of people with two legs. The set of people who have been in a movie.

SECTION 2.2, PAGE 55

39. **a)** { }, {a}, {b}, {c}, {d}, {a, b}, {a, c}, {a, d}, {b, c}, {b, d}, {c, d}, {a, b, c}, {a, b, d}, {a, c, d}, {b, c, d}, {a, b, c, d}

60. **b)** YYYY, YYYN, YYNY, YNYY, NYYY, YYNN, YNYN, YNNY, NYNY, NNYY, NYYN, YNNN, NYNN, NNYN, NNNY, NNNN

SECTION 2.3, PAGE 63

9.

10.

11.

12.

13.

17.

18.

19.

20.
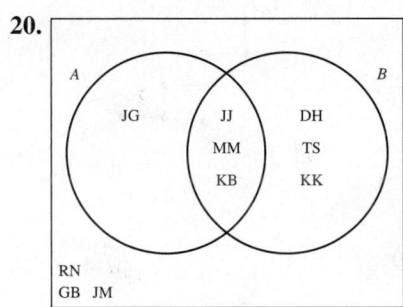

SECTION 2.4, PAGE 72

8.

9.

10.

11.

12.

13.

14.

77.

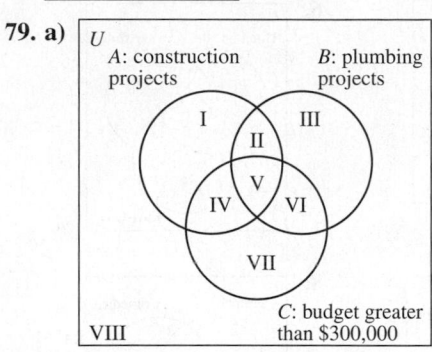

79. a)

$$\begin{array}{l} U \\ A\text{: construction projects} \quad B\text{: plumbing projects} \end{array}$$

I, II, III, IV, V, VI, VII

C: budget greater than $300,000

VIII

80. $n(A \cup B \cup C) = n(A) + n(B) + n(C)$

$\quad - 2n(A \cap B \cap C)$

$\quad - n(A \cap B \cap C')$

$\quad - n(A \cap B' \cap C)$

$\quad - n(A' \cap B \cap C)$

81. a)

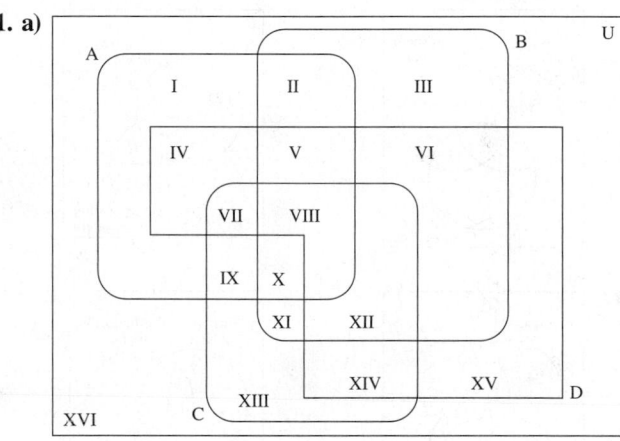

b)

Region	Set	Region	Set
I	$A \cap B' \cap C' \cap D'$	IX	$A \cap B' \cap C \cap D'$
II	$A \cap B \cap C' \cap D'$	X	$A \cap B \cap C \cap D'$
III	$A' \cap B \cap C' \cap D'$	XI	$A' \cap B \cap C \cap D'$
IV	$A \cap B' \cap C' \cap D$	XII	$A' \cap B \cap C \cap D$
V	$A \cap B \cap C' \cap D$	XIII	$A' \cap B' \cap C \cap D'$
VI	$A' \cap B \cap C' \cap D$	XIV	$A' \cap B' \cap C \cap D$
VII	$A \cap B' \cap C \cap D$	XV	$A' \cap B' \cap C' \cap D$
VIII	$A \cap B \cap C \cap D$	XVI	$A' \cap B' \cap C' \cap D'$

SECTION 2.5, PAGE 79

1.

2.

3.

U
Family room   Deck

17 30 12

24

4.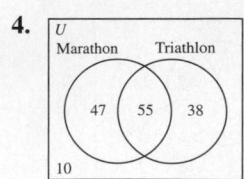

U
Marathon   Triathlon

47 55 38

10

5.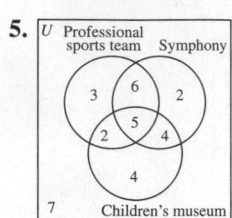

U
Professional
sports team   Symphony

3 6 2
2 5 4
4

7   Children's museum

6.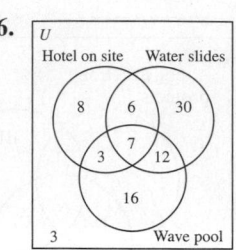

U
Hotel on site   Water slides

8 6 30
3 7 12
16

3   Wave pool

7.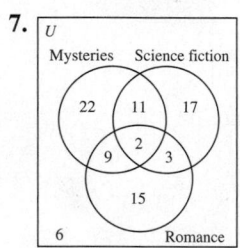

U
Mysteries   Science fiction

22 11 17
9 2 3
15

6   Romance

8.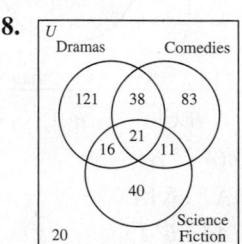

U
Dramas   Comedies

121 38 83
16 21 11
40

20   Science Fiction

9.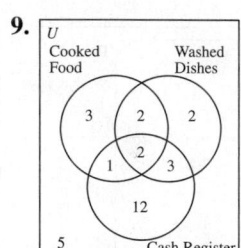

U
Cooked
Food   Washed
Dishes

3 2 2
1 2 3
12

5   Cash Register

10.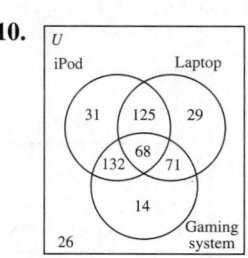

U
iPod   Laptop

31 125 29
132 68 71
14

26   Gaming system

11.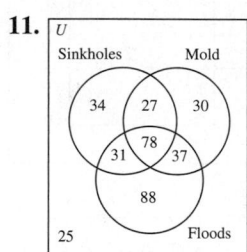

U
Sinkholes   Mold

34 27 30
31 78 37
88

25   Floods

12.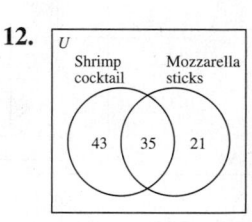

U
Shrimp
cocktail   Mozzarella
sticks

43 35 21

14.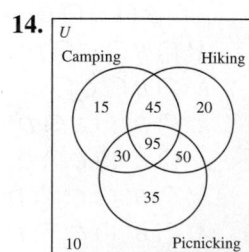

U
Camping   Hiking

15 45 20
30 95 50
35

10   Picnicking

15.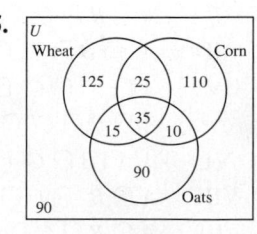

U
Wheat   Corn

125 25 110
15 35 10
90

90   Oats

SECTION 2.6, PAGE 86

3. $\{3, 4, 5, 6, 7, \ldots, n + 2, \ldots\}$
$\downarrow \downarrow \downarrow \downarrow \downarrow \quad\quad \downarrow$
$\{4, 5, 6, 7, 8, \ldots, n + 3, \ldots\}$

4. $\{30, 31, 32, 33, 34, \ldots, n + 29, \ldots\}$
$\downarrow \downarrow \downarrow \downarrow \downarrow \quad\quad \downarrow$
$\{31, 32, 33, 34, 35, \ldots, n + 30, \ldots\}$

5. $\{3, 5, 7, 9, 11, \ldots, 2n + 1, \ldots\}$
$\downarrow \downarrow \downarrow \downarrow \downarrow \quad\quad \downarrow$
$\{5, 7, 9, 11, 13, \ldots, 2n + 3, \ldots\}$

6. $\{20, 22, 24, 26, 28, \ldots, 2n + 18, \ldots\}$
$\downarrow \downarrow \downarrow \downarrow \downarrow \quad\quad \downarrow$
$\{22, 24, 26, 28, 30, \ldots, 2n + 20, \ldots\}$

7. $\{5, 9, 13, 17, 21, \ldots, 4n + 1, \ldots\}$
$\downarrow \downarrow \downarrow \downarrow \downarrow \quad\quad \downarrow$
$\{9, 13, 17, 21, 25, \ldots, 4n + 5, \ldots\}$

8. $\{6, 11, 16, 21, 26, \ldots, 5n + 1, \ldots\}$
$\downarrow \downarrow \downarrow \downarrow \downarrow \quad\quad \downarrow$
$\{11, 16, 21, 26, 31, \ldots, 5n + 6, \ldots\}$

9. $\left\{\dfrac{1}{2}, \dfrac{1}{4}, \dfrac{1}{6}, \dfrac{1}{8}, \dfrac{1}{10}, \ldots, \dfrac{1}{2n}, \ldots\right\}$
$\downarrow \downarrow \downarrow \downarrow \downarrow \quad\quad \downarrow$
$\left\{\dfrac{1}{4}, \dfrac{1}{6}, \dfrac{1}{8}, \dfrac{1}{10}, \dfrac{1}{12}, \ldots, \dfrac{1}{2n + 2}, \ldots\right\}$

10. $\left\{1, \dfrac{1}{2}, \dfrac{1}{3}, \dfrac{1}{4}, \dfrac{1}{5}, \ldots, \dfrac{1}{n}, \ldots\right\}$
$\downarrow \downarrow \downarrow \downarrow \downarrow \quad\quad \downarrow$
$\left\{\dfrac{1}{2}, \dfrac{1}{3}, \dfrac{1}{4}, \dfrac{1}{5}, \dfrac{1}{6}, \ldots, \dfrac{1}{n + 1}, \ldots\right\}$

11. $\left\{\dfrac{4}{11}, \dfrac{5}{11}, \dfrac{6}{11}, \dfrac{7}{11}, \dfrac{8}{11}, \ldots, \dfrac{n + 3}{11}, \ldots\right\}$
$\downarrow \downarrow \downarrow \downarrow \downarrow \quad\quad \downarrow$
$\left\{\dfrac{5}{11}, \dfrac{6}{11}, \dfrac{7}{11}, \dfrac{8}{11}, \dfrac{9}{11}, \ldots, \dfrac{n + 4}{11}, \ldots\right\}$

12. $\left\{\dfrac{6}{13}, \dfrac{7}{13}, \dfrac{8}{13}, \dfrac{9}{13}, \dfrac{10}{13}, \ldots, \dfrac{n + 5}{13}, \ldots\right\}$
$\downarrow \downarrow \downarrow \downarrow \downarrow \quad\quad \downarrow$
$\left\{\dfrac{7}{13}, \dfrac{8}{13}, \dfrac{9}{13}, \dfrac{10}{13}, \dfrac{11}{13}, \ldots, \dfrac{n + 6}{13}, \ldots\right\}$

13. $\{1, 2, 3, 4, 5, \ldots, n, \ldots\}$
$\downarrow \downarrow \downarrow \downarrow \downarrow \quad\quad \downarrow$
$\{3, 6, 9, 12, 15, \ldots, 3n, \ldots\}$

14. $\{1, 2, 3, 4, 5, \ldots, n, \ldots\}$
$\downarrow \downarrow \downarrow \downarrow \downarrow \quad\quad \downarrow$
$\{40, 41, 42, 43, 44, \ldots, n + 39, \ldots\}$

15. $\{1, 2, 3, 4, 5, \ldots, n, \ldots\}$
$\downarrow \downarrow \downarrow \downarrow \downarrow \quad\quad \downarrow$
$\{4, 6, 8, 10, 12, \ldots, 2n + 2, \ldots\}$

16. $\{1, 2, 3, 4, 5, \ldots, n, \ldots\}$
$\downarrow \downarrow \downarrow \downarrow \downarrow \quad\quad \downarrow$
$\{0, 2, 4, 6, 8, \ldots, 2n - 2, \ldots\}$

17. $\{1, 2, 3, 4, 5, \ldots, \quad n, \ldots\}$
$\quad\downarrow\downarrow\downarrow\downarrow\downarrow\qquad\downarrow$
$\quad\{2, 5, 8, 11, 14, \ldots, 3n - 1, \ldots\}$

18. $\{1, 2, 3, 4, 5, \ldots, \quad n, \ldots\}$
$\quad\downarrow\downarrow\downarrow\downarrow\downarrow\qquad\downarrow$
$\quad\{7, 11, 15, 19, 23, \ldots, 4n + 3, \ldots\}$

19. $\{1, 2, 3, 4, 5, \ldots, \quad n, \ldots\}$
$\quad\downarrow\downarrow\downarrow\downarrow\downarrow\qquad\downarrow$
$\quad\left\{\dfrac{1}{3}, \dfrac{1}{6}, \dfrac{1}{9}, \dfrac{1}{12}, \dfrac{1}{15}, \ldots, \dfrac{1}{3n}, \ldots\right\}$

20. $\{1, 2, 3, 4, 5, \ldots, \quad n, \ldots\}$
$\quad\downarrow\downarrow\downarrow\downarrow\downarrow\qquad\downarrow$
$\quad\left\{\dfrac{1}{2}, \dfrac{1}{4}, \dfrac{1}{6}, \dfrac{1}{8}, \dfrac{1}{10}, \ldots, \dfrac{1}{2n}, \ldots\right\}$

21. $\{1, 2, 3, 4, 5, \ldots, \quad n, \ldots\}$
$\quad\downarrow\downarrow\downarrow\downarrow\downarrow\qquad\downarrow$
$\quad\left\{\dfrac{1}{3}, \dfrac{1}{4}, \dfrac{1}{5}, \dfrac{1}{6}, \dfrac{1}{7}, \ldots, \dfrac{1}{n + 2}, \ldots\right\}$

22. $\{1, 2, 3, 4, 5, \ldots, \quad n, \ldots\}$
$\quad\downarrow\downarrow\downarrow\downarrow\downarrow\qquad\downarrow$
$\quad\left\{\dfrac{1}{2}, \dfrac{2}{3}, \dfrac{3}{4}, \dfrac{4}{5}, \dfrac{5}{6}, \ldots, \dfrac{n}{n + 1}, \ldots\right\}$

23. $\{1, 2, 3, 4, 5, \ldots, n, \ldots\}$
$\quad\downarrow\downarrow\downarrow\downarrow\downarrow\qquad\downarrow$
$\quad\{1, 4, 9, 16, 25, \ldots, n^2, \ldots\}$

24. $\{1, 2, 3, 4, 5, \ldots, n, \ldots\}$
$\quad\downarrow\downarrow\downarrow\downarrow\downarrow\qquad\downarrow$
$\quad\{2, 4, 8, 16, 32, \ldots, 2^n, \ldots\}$

25. $\{1, 2, 3, 4, 5, \ldots, \quad n, \ldots\}$
$\quad\downarrow\downarrow\downarrow\downarrow\downarrow\qquad\downarrow$
$\quad\{3, 9, 27, 81, 243, \ldots, 3^n, \ldots\}$

26. $\{1, 2, 3, 4, 5, \ldots, \quad n, \ldots\}$
$\quad\downarrow\downarrow\downarrow\downarrow\downarrow\qquad\downarrow$
$\quad\left\{\dfrac{1}{3}, \dfrac{1}{6}, \dfrac{1}{12}, \dfrac{1}{24}, \dfrac{1}{48}, \ldots, \dfrac{1}{3 \times 2^{n-1}}, \ldots\right\}$

REVIEW EXERCISES, PAGE 88

37.

54.

55.
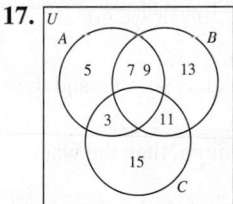

56. $\{2, 4, 6, 8, 10, \ldots, \quad 2n, \ldots\}$
$\quad\downarrow\downarrow\downarrow\downarrow\downarrow\qquad\downarrow$
$\quad\{4, 6, 8, 10, 12, \ldots, 2n + 2, \ldots\}$

57. $\{3, 5, 7, 9, 11, \ldots, 2n + 1, \ldots\}$
$\quad\downarrow\downarrow\downarrow\downarrow\downarrow\qquad\downarrow$
$\quad\{5, 7, 9, 11, 13, \ldots, 2n + 3, \ldots\}$

58. $\{1, 2, 3, 4, 5, \ldots, \quad n, \ldots\}$
$\quad\downarrow\downarrow\downarrow\downarrow\downarrow\qquad\downarrow$
$\quad\{5, 8, 11, 14, 17, \ldots, 3n + 2, \ldots\}$

59. $\{1, 2, 3, 4, 5, \ldots, \quad n, \ldots\}$
$\quad\downarrow\downarrow\downarrow\downarrow\downarrow\qquad\downarrow$
$\quad\{4, 9, 14, 19, 24, \ldots, 5n - 1, \ldots\}$

CHAPTER TEST, PAGE 91

16. $\{(3, 3), (3, 11), (3, 15), (5, 3), (5, 11), (5, 15), (7, 3),$
$(7, 11), (7, 15), (9, 3), (9, 11), (9, 15)\}$

17.
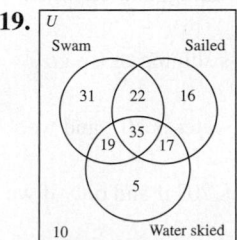

19.

20. $\{7, 8, 9, 10, 11, \ldots, n + 6, \ldots\}$
$\quad\downarrow\downarrow\downarrow\downarrow\downarrow\qquad\downarrow$
$\quad\{8, 9, 10, 11, 12, \ldots, n + 7, \ldots\}$

Chapter 3

Answer to Recreational Math on page 97

7	1	9	4	8	2	5	6	3
5	4	6	7	3	9	8	1	2
2	3	8	6	5	1	4	9	7
8	2	4	3	9	5	1	7	6
6	7	5	1	2	4	3	8	9
1	9	3	8	6	7	2	4	5
9	6	1	5	4	3	7	2	8
3	8	7	2	1	6	9	5	4
4	5	2	9	7	8	6	3	1

86.

6	4	8	7	5	3	2	1	9
3	9	2	8	6	1	7	5	4
7	5	1	9	4	2	8	6	3
9	1	6	3	2	5	4	8	7
5	7	3	4	8	6	9	2	1
8	2	4	1	9	7	5	3	6
4	3	5	6	7	8	1	9	2
2	6	9	5	1	4	3	7	8
1	8	7	2	3	9	6	4	5

SECTION 3.1, PAGE 101

41. Brie does not have a MacBook.

42. Joe does not have an iPad.

43. Joe has an iPad and Brie has a MacBook.

44. Brie has a MacBook or Joe has an iPad.

45. If Joe does not have an iPad then Brie has a MacBook.

46. Joe does not have an iPad if and only if Brie does not have a Macbook.

47. Joe does not have an iPad or Brie does not have a MacBook.

48. It is false that Brie has a MacBook or Joe has an iPad.

49. It is false that Joe has an iPad and Brie has a MacBook.

50. Joe does not have an iPad and Brie does not have a MacBook.

61. The water is 70° or the sun is shining, and we do not go swimming.

62. The water is 70° and the sun is shining, or we go swimming.

63. The water is not 70°, and the sun is shining or we go swimming.

64. If the sun is shining then the water is 70°, or we go swimming.

65. If we do not go swimming, then the sun is shining and the water is 70°.

66. If the sun is shining and we go swimming, then the water is 70°.

67. If the sun is shining then we go swimming, and the water is 70°.

68. If the water is not 70°, then the sun is shining or we go swimming.

69. The sun is shining if and only if the water is 70°, and we go swimming.

70. If the sun is shining, then the water is 70° if and only if we go swimming.

73. Not permissible, you cannot have both potatoes and pasta. The *or* used on menus is the *exclusive or*.

74. Not permissible, you cannot have both pasta and potatoes. The *or* used on the menu is the *exclusive or*.

SECTION 3.2, PAGE 115

7.	8.	9.
T	F	F
F	T	T
T	F	T
T	F	T

10.	11.	12.	13.	14.
F	T	T	T	T
F	F	T	F	F
T	T	T	T	T
F	T	F	T	F
			F	F
			F	F
			T	T
			T	F

15.	16.	17.	18.
T	F	F	F
F	F	F	F
T	F	T	F
T	F	F	F
T	T	F	T
F	F	F	T
T	F	T	T
F	F	T	F

19. $p \wedge q$	20. $p \wedge \sim q$	21. $p \wedge \sim q$
T	F	F
F	T	T
F	F	F
F	F	F

22. $\sim(p \vee q)$	23. $\sim(p \wedge q)$	24. $(p \wedge q) \wedge r$
F	F	T
F	T	F
F	T	F
T	T	F
		F
		F
		F
		F

25. $p \lor (q \lor r)$

T
T
T
T
T
T
T
F

26. $p \land (q \land r)$

T
F
F
F
F
F
F
F

53. $p \land \sim q$

F
T
F
F
True in case 2.

54. $\sim p \land q$

F
F
T
F
True in case 3.

55. $p \lor \sim q$

T
T
F
T
True in cases 1, 2, and 4.

56. $\sim p \lor \sim q$

F
T
T
T
True in cases 2, 3, and 4.

57. $(r \lor q) \land p$

T
T
T
F
F
F
F
F
True in cases 1, 2, and 3.

58. $(p \land q) \lor r$

T
T
T
F
T
F
T
F
True in cases 1, 2, 3, 5, and 7.

59. $q \lor (p \land \sim r)$

T
T
F
T
T
T
F
F
True in cases 1, 2, 4, 5, and 6.

60. $\sim p \land (\sim r \land q)$

F
F
F
F
F
T
F
F
True in cases 6.

61. a) Mr. Duncan and Mrs. Tuttle qualify.

b) Mrs. Rusinek does not qualify, since their combined income is less than $46,000.

62. a) Mr. Argento qualifies.

b) Ms. McVey does not qualify, since she is single and her income is less than $30,000. Mr. Siewert does not qualify since their assets are less than $10,000.

63. b) Gina Vela is returning on April 3. Kara Sharo is returning on a Monday. Christos Supernaw is not staying over on a Saturday. Alex Chang is returning on a Monday.

64.
F
T
T
T
F
F
F

65.
T
T
T
T
F
T

66. b)

p	q	r	s
T	T	T	T
T	T	T	F
T	T	F	T
T	T	F	F
T	F	T	T
T	F	T	F
T	F	F	T
T	F	F	F
F	T	T	T
F	T	T	F
F	T	F	T
F	T	F	F
F	F	T	T
F	F	T	F
F	F	F	T
F	F	F	F

c)
T
T
T
F
F
T
F
F
F
T
F
F
F
T
F
F

d)
F
F
T
F
F
F
F
F
F
T
F
F
F
F
T

SECTION 3.3, PAGE 124

7. T
T
T
F

8. T
T
F
T

9. T
F
F
F

10. T
F
F
T

11. F
T
T
F

12. T
T
T
F

13. T
T
F
T

14. T
T
T
T

15. F
T
T
T

16. T
F
F
T

17. T
T
T
T
F
F
F

18. T
T
F
T
T
T
T

19. F
F
T
F
T
T
F
T

20.	21.	22.	23.	24.
T	T	F	T	F
T	T	T	T	T
T	T	T	T	T
T	T	T	F	T
T	T	T	T	T
T	F	F	T	T
T	F	T	F	T
T	F	F	T	F

25. $p \rightarrow (q \wedge r)$

T
F
F
F
T
T
T

26. $(p \leftrightarrow q) \vee \sim r$

T
T
F
T
F
T
T

27. $(p \leftrightarrow q) \vee r$

T
T
T
F
T
F
T

28. $(p \rightarrow q) \leftrightarrow \sim r$

F
T
T
F
F
T
F
T

29. $(\sim p \rightarrow q) \vee r$

T
T
T
T
T
T
T
F

30. $\sim [p \rightarrow (\sim q \wedge r)]$

T
T
F
T
F
F
F
F

73. No, the statement only states what will occur if your sister gets straight A's. If your sister does not get straight A's, your parents may still get her a computer.

74. No, the statement only states what will occur if the interview goes well. If the interview does not go well, you may or may not be offered the job.

75. F
F
T
T
T
F
F
F

76. T
T
T
F
T
T
T
T

77. It is a tautology. The statement may be expressed as $(p \rightarrow q) \vee (\sim p \rightarrow q)$, where p: It is a head and q: I win. This statement is a tautology.

79. Allen was born in January. Booker was born in February. Chris was born in March. Dennis was born in April.

80.

Tiger	Boots	Sam	Sue
Blue	Yellow	Red	Green
Nine Lives	Whiskas	Friskies	Meow Mix

SECTION 3.4, PAGE 136

Answer to Recreational Math on page 134

34. If Phil Murphy buys us dinner, then it is false that we will go to the top of the CN Tower or we will not be able to walk to the Red Bistro Restaurant.

49. *Converse:* If she needs extra yarn, then Nanette Berry teaches macramé.

Inverse: If Nanette Berry does not teach macramé, then she does not need extra yarn.

Contrapositive: If she does not need extra yarn, then Nanette Berry does not teach macramé.

50. *Converse:* If Linus is getting a drink, then the water is running.

Inverse: If the water is not running, then Linus is not getting a drink.

Contrapositive: If Linus is not getting a drink, then the water is not running.

51. *Converse:* If I buy silver jewelry, then I go to Mexico.

Inverse: If I do not go to Mexico, then I do not buy silver jewelry.

Contrapositive: If I do not buy silver jewelry, then I do not go to Mexico.

52. Converse: If Bob Dylan goes on tour, then he recorded a new CD.

Inverse: If Bob Dylan did not record a new CD, then he will not go on tour.

Contrapositive: If Bob Dylan did not go on tour, then he did not record a new CD.

53. *Converse:* If I scream, then that annoying paper clip shows up on my computer screen.

Inverse: If that annoying paper clip does not show up on my computer screen, then I will not scream.

Contrapositive: If I do not scream, then that annoying paper clip does not show up on my screen.

54. *Converse:* If we go down to the marina and take out the sailboat, then the sun is shining.

Inverse: If the sun is not shining, then we will not go down to the marina or we will not take out the sailboat.

Contrapositive: If we do not go down to the marina or we will not take out the sailboat, then the sun is not shining.

75. True. If $p \rightarrow q$ is false, it must be of the form T → F. Therefore, the converse must be of the form F → T, which is true.

76. True. If $p \rightarrow q$ is false, it must be of the form T → F. Therefore, the inverse must be to the form F → T, which is true.

83.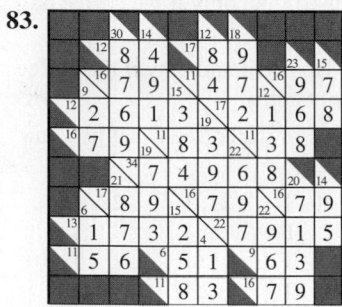

SECTION 3.5, PAGE 147

33. a) $p \rightarrow q$ **b)** Valid
$$\frac{\sim q}{\therefore \sim p}$$

34. a) $p \rightarrow q$ **b)** Invalid
$$\frac{q}{\therefore p}$$

35. a) $p \rightarrow q$ **b)** Valid
$$\frac{p}{\therefore q}$$

36. a) $p \rightarrow q$ **b)** Valid
$$\frac{q \rightarrow r}{\therefore p \rightarrow r}$$

37. a) $p \rightarrow q$ **b)** Valid
$$\frac{\sim q}{\therefore \sim p}$$

38. a) $p \vee q$ **b)** Valid
$$\frac{\sim q}{\therefore p}$$

39. a) $p \rightarrow q$ **b)** Invalid
$$\frac{q}{\therefore p}$$

40. a) $p \rightarrow q$ **b)** Valid
$$\frac{p}{\therefore q}$$

41. a) $p \vee q$ **b)** Valid
$$\frac{\sim p}{\therefore q}$$

42. a) $p \rightarrow q$ **b)** Valid
$$\frac{\sim q}{\therefore \sim p}$$

43. a) $p \rightarrow q$ **b)** Valid
$$\frac{q \rightarrow r}{\therefore p \rightarrow r}$$

44. a) $f \rightarrow w$ **b)** Invalid
$$\frac{w \wedge \sim t}{\therefore w \rightarrow \sim f}$$

45. a) $p \wedge q$ **b)** Valid
$$\frac{q \rightarrow r}{\therefore r \rightarrow p}$$

46. a) $p \vee q$ **b)** Invalid
$$\frac{q \rightarrow r}{\therefore p \wedge r}$$

47. a) $s \wedge g$ **b)** Valid
$$\frac{g \rightarrow c}{\therefore s \rightarrow c}$$

48. a) $g \vee f$ **b)** Valid
$$\frac{\sim f \rightarrow g}{\therefore f \vee g}$$

49. a) $p \rightarrow q$ **b)** Valid
$$\frac{\sim q}{\therefore \sim p}$$

50. a) $p \vee \sim q$ **b)** Valid
$$\frac{q}{\therefore p}$$

51. a) $p \vee q$ **b)** Valid
$$\frac{\sim p}{\therefore q}$$

52. a) $c \rightarrow m$ **b)** Valid
$$\frac{\sim m}{\therefore \sim c}$$

53. a) $t \wedge g$ **b)** Valid
$$\frac{\sim t \vee \sim g}{\therefore \sim t}$$

54. a) $b \rightarrow p$ **b)** Valid
$$\frac{\sim p}{\therefore \sim b}$$

55. a) $c \wedge \sim h$ **b)** Invalid
$$\frac{h \rightarrow c}{\therefore h}$$

56. a) $n \rightarrow a$ **b)** Valid
$$\frac{\sim n \wedge a}{\therefore \sim n}$$

57. a) $p \rightarrow q$ **b)** Invalid
$$\frac{q \rightarrow \sim r}{\therefore p \rightarrow r}$$

58. a) $e \wedge c$ **b)** Invalid
$$\frac{c \rightarrow a}{\therefore e \wedge \sim a}$$

65. Yes, if the conclusion does not necessarily follow from the premises, the argument is invalid, even if the conclusion is true.

66. Yes, if the conclusion necessarily follows from the premises, the argument is valid, even if the conclusion is false.

67. Yes, if the conclusion does not necessarily follow from the premises, the argument is invalid, even if the premises are true.

68. Yes, if the conclusion necessarily follows from the premises, the argument is valid, even if the premises are false.

70. No. The conditional statement will always be true, and therefore the statement will be a tautology, and the argument will be valid.

SECTION 3.7, PAGE 161

5. a) $p \vee q$

 b) The lightbulb will be on when either p or q are closed.

6. a) $(p \wedge q) \vee \sim q$

 b) The lightbulb will be on in all cases except when p is open and q is closed.

7. a) $(p \vee q) \wedge \sim q$

 b) The lightbulb will be on when p is closed and q is open.

8. a) $(p \wedge q) \vee (\sim p \wedge q)$

 b) The lightbulb will be on when p is closed and q is closed, or when p is open and q is closed.

9. a) $(p \wedge q) \wedge [(p \wedge \sim q) \vee r]$

 b) The lightbulb will be on when p, q, and r are all closed.

10. a) $[(p \wedge r) \vee \sim q] \wedge (p \vee q)$

 b) The lightbulb will be on when p, q, and r are all closed; when p and r are closed and q is open; or when p is closed and q and r are open.

11. a) $p \lor q \lor (r \land \sim p)$

　　b) The lightbulb will be on in all cases except when p, q, and r are all open.

12. a) $[(p \land \sim q) \lor (\sim p \land q)] \lor (p \land q)$

　　b) The lightbulb will be on in all cases except when p and q are both open.

13.

14.

15.

16.

17.

18.

19.

20.

27. It is a series circuit; therefore, both switches must be closed for current to flow and the lightbulb to go on. When the p switch is closed, the $\overline{p}$ switch is open and no current will flow through the circuit. When the $\overline{p}$ switch is closed, the p switch is open and no current will flow through the circuit.

28. It is a parallel circuit; therefore, only one of the switches must be closed for current to flow and the lightbulb to go on. Since the p switch and the $\overline{p}$ switch cannot both be open at the same time, current will always flow through one or the other branch of the parallel circuit to make the lightbulb go on.

29. a)　　　　　**b)**

REVIEW EXERCISES, PAGE 164

5. The coffee is Maxwell House or the coffee is hot.

6. The coffee is not hot and the coffee is strong.

7. If the coffee is hot, then the coffee is strong and the coffee is not Maxwell House.

8. The coffee is Maxwell House if and only if the coffee is not strong.

9. The coffee is not Maxwell House, if and only if the coffee is strong and the coffee is not hot.

10. The coffee is Maxwell House or the coffee is not hot, and the coffee is not strong.

17.	**18.**	**19.**	**20.**	**21.**	**22.**
F	T	T	T	F	F
F	F	T	F	T	T
T	F	T	T	F	T
F	F	T	T	F	T
		T	F	T	T
		F	F	T	T
		F	F	T	T
		T	F	T	T

40. a) If you know Jay Stu, then you listen to Jim Rome.

　　b) If you do not listen to Jim Rome, then you do not know Jay Stu.

　　c) If you do not know Jay Stu, then you do not listen to Jim Rome.

41. a) If we will learn the table's value, then we take the table to *Antiques Roadshow*.

　　b) If we do not take the table to *Antiques Roadshow*, then we will not learn the table's value.

　　c) If we will not learn the table's value, then we do not take the table to *Antiques Roadshow*.

42. a) If you do not sell more doughnuts, then you do not advertise.

　　b) If you advertise, then you sell more doughnuts.

　　c) If you sell more doughnuts, then you advertise.

43. a) If we will not buy a desk at Miller's Furniture, then the desk is made by Winner's Only and the desk is in the Rose catalog.

　　b) If the desk is not made by Winner's Only or the desk is not in the Rose catalog, then we will buy a desk at Miller's Furniture.

　　c) If we will buy a desk at Miller's Furniture, then the desk is not made by Winner's Only or the desk is not in the Rose catalog.

44. a) If I let you attend the prom, then you will get straight A's on your report card.

　　b) If you do not get straight A's on your report card, then I will not let you attend the prom.

　　c) If I will not let you attend the prom, then you did not get straight A's on your report card.

58.

CHAPTER TEST, PAGE 167

4. Phobos is not a moon of Mars and Rosalind is a moon of Uranus, if and only if Callisto is not a moon of Jupiter.

5. If Phobos is a moon of Mars or Callisto is not a moon of Jupiter, then Rosalind is a moon of Uranus.

6.	7.	15.
F	T	$s \rightarrow f$
T	T	$f \rightarrow p$
F	T	$\therefore s \rightarrow p$
F	T	Valid
F	F	
F	T	
F	T	
F	F	

19. *Converse:* If today is Saturday, then the garbage truck comes.

Inverse: If the garbage truck does not come, then today is not Saturday.

Contrapositive: If today is not Saturday, then the garbage truck does not come.

20.

Chapter 4

SECTION 4.1, PAGE 176

19. ∽ꟿꟿꟿꟿ𓏺𓏺𓏺9999999999∩∩∩∩ⅠⅠⅠⅠⅠ

20. ✻✻✻∽∽ꟿꟿ𓏺𓏺𓏺𓏺9999999∩ⅠⅠⅠⅠ

53. 五十三   54. 一百七十八   55. 三百七十八   56. 二千零一   57. 四千二百六十   58. 六千九百零五

59. 七千零五十六   60. 三千零九   73. 1021, MXXI, —, ˏακα, 一千零二十一

74. 1936, 𓏺999999999∩∩∩ⅠⅠⅠⅠⅠⅠ, ˏαϠλϛ, 一千九百三十六

75. 527, 999999∩∩ⅠⅠⅠⅠⅠⅠⅠ,   76. 422, 9999∩∩Ⅱ, CDXXII, 四百二十二
DXXVII, φκζ

SECTION 4.2, PAGE 183

18. $(3 \times 1000) + (7 \times 100) + (6 \times 10) + (9 \times 1)$

---

20. $(2 \times 10{,}000) + (3 \times 1000) + (4 \times 100) + (6 \times 10) + (8 \times 1)$

21. $(1 \times 10{,}000) + (6 \times 1000) + (4 \times 100) + (0 \times 10) + (2 \times 1)$

22. $(1 \times 100{,}000) + (2 \times 10{,}000) + (5 \times 1000) + (6 \times 100) + (7 \times 10) + (8 \times 1)$

23. $(3 \times 100{,}000) + (4 \times 10{,}000) + (6 \times 1000) + (8 \times 100) + (6 \times 10) + (1 \times 1)$

24. $(3 \times 1{,}000{,}000) + (7 \times 100{,}000) + (6 \times 10{,}000) + (5 \times 1000) + (9 \times 100) + (3 \times 10) + (4 \times 1)$

31. ⟨⟨⟨⟨Ⅰ   32. ⅠⅠ ⟨ⅠⅠⅠ

33. ⟨ⅠⅠⅠⅠ ⟨⟨⟨⟨⟨Ⅰ   34. ⟨ⅠⅠⅠ ⟨⟨⟨ⅠⅠ

35. Ⅰ   ⅠⅠⅠⅠⅠ   36. ⅠⅠⅠ ⟨⟨⟨ⅠⅠⅠⅠ ⟨ⅠⅠⅠⅠⅠ

43. ≡̇   44. ⹀̇   45. ≡̈   46. •   47. ⸱   48. ∷
    ≡   ⹀   ≡   •   ⊙   •
                •   ⸫   •
                    •

49. 1944, ⟨⟨⟨ⅠⅠ ⟨⟨ⅠⅠⅠⅠ   50. 33, •
    ≡

51. $\left(\triangle \times \bigcirc^{2}\right) + \left(\square \times \bigcirc\right) + \left(\lozenge \times 1\right)$

52. $\left(\varobslash \times \bigcirc^{3}\right) + \left(\triangle \times \bigcirc^{2}\right) + \left(\lozenge \times \bigcirc\right) + \left(\square \times 1\right)$

54. **a)** There may be confusion because numerals could be interpreted in different ways. For example, Ⅰ could be interpreted to be either 1 or 60.

b) ⅠⅠ ⟨ⅠⅠⅠ for both numerals.

55. **a)** •   **b)** ⅠⅠⅠⅠ ⟨⟨⟨⟨ⅠⅠⅠⅠ ⟨⟨⟨⟨ⅠⅠⅠⅠⅠⅠ ⟨⟨⟨⟨ⅠⅠ
    •••

    ⹀
    •••
    ∷

56. ⅠⅠ ⟨⟨⟨⟨⟨ⅠⅠⅠⅠⅠ   57. ⅠⅠⅠ Ⅰ   58. ≡   59. ⹀
                                    ∷   •••
                                    •••

SECTION 4.3, PAGE 190

49. ⊖◐₅   50. ◐⊖₅
51. ◐◐◐₅   52. ⊖◐◐₅
57. ⦾●●₄   58. ●●₄
59. ●●●₄   60. ●●●₄

67. **a)** $1_3, 2_3, 10_3, 11_3, 12_3, 20_3, 21_3, 22_3, 100_3, 101_3, 102_3, 110_3, 111_3, 112_3, 120_3, 121_3, 122_3, 200_3, 201_3, 202_3$

71. **b)** ●●●●₄

SECTION 4.4, PAGE 198

55. ⊖⊖₅   56. ⊖◐₅
57. ◐⊖₅   58. ⊖⊖◐₅

59. ●● ₄   **60.** ●●● ₄

61. ●●● ₄   **62.** ●●●● ₄

63. ●● ₄   **64.** ● ● ₄

65. ●●● ₄   **66.** ●●● ₄

71. ● = 0,   ● = 1,   ● = 2,   ● = 3

SECTION 4.5, PAGE 203

33. ꝯꝯ∩∩∩∩∩∩∩ⅢⅢ

REVIEW EXERCISES, PAGE 205

5. 𐎛𐎛𐎛𐎛ꝯꝯꝯ‖   **6.** ꝯ|ꝯꝯ   **7.** ⌐⌐𐎛𐎛𐎛𐎛ꝯꝯꝯ∩∩|

8. 𐎛𐎛𐎛𐎛∩∩∩‖   **21.** 二十三   **22.** 五十四   **23.** 四百九十二

24. 二千六百五十二

37. ▮▮▮ ▮   **38.** ▮ ▮ ⟨⟨▮̄▮   **39.** ▮▮ ▮ ⟨⟨

40. ⟨ ▮▮▮ ▮▮▮▮   **45.** ⋯ ⋯⋯   **46.** ⋅⋅ ⋯⋯   **47.** ⋯⋅ ⋅ ⋅   **48.** ⋅⋅ ⋯⋯ ⋯ ⋯

CHAPTER TEST, PAGE 207

7. 𐎛𐎛ꝯ∩∩‖‖   **8.** ꞗ𝜐𝑜𝑓

9. ⋯ ⋅⋅ ⋯⋯   **10.** ⟨⟨▮▮▮▮▮▮ ⟨⟨⟨▮▮▮▮▮▮

Chapter 5

SECTION 5.1, PAGE 217

13. The prime numbers between 1 and 100 are 2, 3, 5, 7, 11, 13, 17, 19, 23, 29, 31, 37, 41, 43, 47, 53, 59, 61, 67, 71, 73, 79, 83, 89, and 97.

14. The prime numbers between 1 and 150 are 2, 3, 5, 7, 11, 13, 17, 19, 23, 29, 31, 37, 41, 43, 47, 53, 59, 61, 67, 71, 73, 79, 83, 89, 97, 101, 103, 107, 109, 113, 127, 131, 137, 139, and 149.

58. No. Any other two consecutive natural numbers will include one number that is divisible by 2 and is therefore composite.

62. $4 = 2 + 2, 6 = 3 + 3, 8 = 3 + 5, 10 = 3 + 7$, $12 = 5 + 7, 14 = 7 + 7, 16 = 3 + 13, 18 = 5 + 13$, $20 = 3 + 17$

65. $2 \times 60, 3 \times 40, 4 \times 30, 5 \times 24, 6 \times 20, 8 \times 15$, $10 \times 12, 12 \times 10, 15 \times 8, 20 \times 6, 24 \times 5, 30 \times 4$, $40 \times 3, 60 \times 2$

86. No, not every number divisible by both 2 and 4 is divisible by 8, for example, 20. If two *prime* numbers divide a number, then their product will divide the number.

87. For any three consecutive natural numbers, one of the numbers is divisible by 2 and another number is divisible by 3. Therefore, the product of the three numbers would be divisible by 6.

91. $8 = 2 + 3 + 3, 9 = 3 + 3 + 3, 10 = 2 + 3 + 5$, $11 = 2 + 2 + 7, 12 = 2 + 5 + 5, 13 = 3 + 3 + 7$, $14 = 2 + 5 + 7, 15 = 3 + 5 + 7, 16 = 2 + 7 + 7$, $17 = 5 + 5 + 7, 18 = 2 + 5 + 11, 19 = 3 + 5 + 11$, $20 = 2 + 7 + 11$

SECTION 5.2, PAGE 227

Answer to *Recreational Mathematics* box on page 225

$$0 = 4 + 4 - 4 - 4$$

$$1 = \frac{4 + 4}{4 + 4}$$

$$2 = \frac{4 \cdot 4}{4 + 4}$$

$$3 = \frac{4 + 4 + 4}{4}$$

$$4 = \frac{4 - 4}{4} + 4$$

$$5 = \frac{4 \cdot 4 + 4}{4}$$

$$6 = \frac{4 + 4}{4} + 4$$

$$7 = 4 + 4 - \frac{4}{4}$$

$$8 = 4 + 4 + 4 - 4$$

$$9 = 4 + 4 + \frac{4}{4}$$

Other answers are possible.

52. False; the difference of a positive integer and a negative integer will always be positive. For example, $5 - (-4) = 9$.

80. b) From the diagram, notice that the third pentagonal number is $3^2 + 2 + 1 = 12$; the fourth pentagonal number is $4^2 + 3 + 2 + 1 = 22$. The next five pentagonal numbers then are

$5^2 + 4 + 3 + 2 + 1 = 35$,
$6^2 + 5 + 4 + 3 + 2 + 1 = 51$,
$7^2 + 6 + 5 + 4 + 3 + 2 + 1 = 70$,
$8^2 + 7 + 6 + 5 + 4 + 3 + 2 + 1 = 92$, and
$9^2 + 8 + 7 + 6 + 5 + 4 + 3 + 2 + 1 = 117$.

82. a) $4\left(4 - \dfrac{4}{4}\right) = 12, 4 \cdot 4 - \dfrac{4}{4} = 15, \dfrac{4 \cdot 4 \cdot 4}{4} = 16,$

$4 \cdot 4 + \dfrac{4}{4} = 17, 4\left(4 + \dfrac{4}{4}\right) = 20$ **b)** $\dfrac{44 - 4}{4} = 10$

SECTION 5.4, PAGE 249

69. Between 3 and 3.5; $\sqrt{11} \approx 3.32$.

70. Between 8 and 8.5; $\sqrt{67} \approx 8.19$.

71. Between 10 and 10.5; $\sqrt{107} \approx 10.34$.

72. Between 11.5 and 12; $\sqrt{135} \approx 11.62$.

73. Between 13 and 13.5; $\sqrt{170} \approx 13.04$.

74. Between 14 and 14.5; $\sqrt{200} \approx 14.14$.

75. False. $\sqrt{c}$ may be a rational number or an irrational number for a composite number c. (For example, $\sqrt{25}$ is rational number; $\sqrt{8}$ is an irrational number.)

79. False. The product of a rational number and an irrational number may be a rational number or an irrational number.

95. b) Irrational $\sqrt{0.7} = 0.8366600265 \ldots$. Since the decimal number is not a terminating or a repeating decimal number, this number is an irrational number

SECTION 5.5, PAGE 256

Answer to *Recreational Mathematics* box on page 254

8× 4	2	4+ 3	1
10+ 3	4	4× 1	2
1 1	3	2	11+ 4
3+ 2	1	4	3

29. Commutative property of addition. The only difference between the expressions on both sides of the equal sign is the order of 5 and x.

30. Associative property of addition. On the left side of the equal sign, the x and 5 are in parentheses. On the right side of the equal sign, the 5 and 6 are in parentheses.

84.

2 2	2− 3	2+ 1	24× 4
3− 4	1	2	3
1	7+ 4	3	2
1− 3	2	5+ 4	1

SECTION 5.7, PAGE 275

58. $a_n = -16 \cdot \left(\dfrac{1}{2}\right)^{n-1}$ **59.** $a_n = 2 \cdot \left(\dfrac{1}{2}\right)^{n-1}$

60. $a_n = -3(-2)^{n-1}$ **61.** $a_n = 9 \cdot \left(\dfrac{1}{3}\right)^{n-1}$

62. $a_n = -4 \cdot \left(\dfrac{2}{3}\right)^{n-1}$

90. e) It is risky because it is likely that you won't have enough money to continue doubling your previous bet if you lose several times in a row. (Also, there may be a maximum amount you can bet in a game of chance.)

SECTION 5.8, PAGE 282

10. Each number in the Fibonacci sequence is either a prime number or is relatively prime with the number preceding or succeeding it in sequence. Therefore, the GCF of any two consecutive Fibonacci numbers is 1.

29. The first and second terms are 1. Each term thereafter is the sum of the previous two terms.

33. $\dfrac{1}{1} = 1, \dfrac{2}{1} = 2, \dfrac{3}{2} = 1.5, \dfrac{5}{3} \approx 1.667, \dfrac{8}{5} = 1.6, \dfrac{13}{8} = 1.625,$ $\dfrac{21}{13} \approx 1.615, \dfrac{34}{21} \approx 1.619, \dfrac{55}{34} \approx 1.6176, \dfrac{89}{55} \approx 1.6182.$ The consecutive ratios alternate, increasing and decreasing about the golden ratio.

35. a) $-10, 4, -6, -2, -8, -10, -18, -28, -46, -74$

   b) $-10, 5, -5, 0, -5, -5, -10, -15, -25, -40$

   c) $-10, 6, -4, 2, -2, 0, -2, -2, -4, -6$

   d) $-10, 7, -3, 4, 1, 5, 6, 11, 17, 28$

   e) $-10, 8, -2, 6, 4, 10, 14, 24, 38, 62$

Chapter 6

SECTION 6.1, PAGE 295

46. $(-1)^n = 1$ for any even number n since an even number of factors of (-1) when multiplied will always be 1.

SECTION 6.3, PAGE 312

35. $y = \dfrac{5x - 14}{4}$ or $y = \dfrac{5}{4}x - \dfrac{7}{2}$

36. $y = \dfrac{7x - 23}{3}$ or $y = \dfrac{7}{3}x - \dfrac{23}{3}$

37. $y = \dfrac{-8x + 21}{7}$ or $y = -\dfrac{8}{7}x + 3$

38. $y = \dfrac{9x + 11}{4}$ or $y = \dfrac{9}{4}x + \dfrac{11}{4}$

39. $y = \dfrac{2x + 6}{3}$ or $y = \dfrac{2}{3}x + 2$

41. $y = \dfrac{2x - z + 15}{3}$ or $y = \dfrac{2}{3}x - \dfrac{1}{3}z + 5$

42. $y = \dfrac{-5x + 2z + 22}{3}$ or $y = -\dfrac{5}{3}x + \dfrac{2}{3}z + \dfrac{22}{3}$

43. $y = \dfrac{9x + 4z - 7}{8}$ or $y = \dfrac{9}{8}x + \dfrac{1}{2}z - \dfrac{7}{8}$

44. $y = \dfrac{2x + 5z}{3}$ or $y = \dfrac{2}{3}x + \dfrac{5}{3}z$

58. $w_1 = \dfrac{w_2(f_2 - f)}{f - f_1}$ **60.** $V_2 = \dfrac{P_1 V_1 T_2}{T_1 P_2}$

SECTION 6.4, PAGE 317

51. $x + (x + 1) + (x + 2) = 3(x + 2) - 3$

$3x + 3 = 3x + 6 - 3$

$3x + 3 = 3x + 3$

SECTION 6.6, PAGE 333

9. [number line: closed dot at 5, shaded right]
5

10. [number line: open dot at 3, shaded left]
3

11. [number line: closed dot at −5, shaded right]
−5

12. [number line: open dot at −1, shaded right]
−1

13. [number line: closed dots at −6 and 0, shaded between]
−6   0

14. [number line: open dots at −3 and 0, shaded between]
−3   0

15. [number line: open dot at 18, shaded left]
18

16. [number line: open dot at 10, shaded right]
10

17. [number line: closed dots, shaded left to −9]
−9

18. [number line: closed dot at 8, shaded right]
8

19. [number line: closed dots at 0 and 4, shaded right]
0   4

20. [number line: open dots at −1 and 0, shaded right]
−1 0

21. No solution
0

22. [number line: closed dot at 0, shaded]
0

23. [number line: closed dots at −1 and 3, shaded between]
−1   3

24. [number line: open dot at −4, closed dot at 1, shaded between]
−4   1

25. [number line: open dots at 6 and 10, shaded between]
6   10

26. [number line: open dot at −3, closed dot at 4, shaded between]
−3   4

27. [number line dots] −1 0 1 2 3 4 5 6 ···

28. [number line dots] −5 −4 −3 −2 −1 0 1 2 ···

29. [number line dots] −11 −10 −9 −8 −7 −6 −5 −4 ···

30. [number line dots] 5 6 7 8 9 10 11 12 ···

31. ··· [number line dots] −5 −4 −3 −2 −1 0 1 2

32. [number line dots] −5 −4 −3 −2 −1 0 1 2 ···

33. ··· [number line dots] −9 −8 −7 −6 −5 −4 −3 −2

34. [number line dots] −15 −14 −13 −12 −11 −10 −9 −8 ···

35. ··· [number line dots] −11 −10 −9 −8 −7 −6

36. ··· [number line dots] 0 1 2 3 4 5 6 7

37. ··· [number line dots] −2 −1 0 1 2 3 4 5

38. [number line dots] −9 −8 −7 −6 −5 −4 −3 −2 ···

39. ··· [number line dots] −6 −5 −4 −3 −2 −1 0 1

40. [number line dots] 0 1 2 3 4 5 6 7 ···

41. ··· [number line dots] −5 −4 −3 −2 −1 0 1 2

42. [number line dots] −2 −1 0 1 2 3 4 5 6

43. [number line dots] −1 0 1 2 3 4 5 6

44. [number line dots] −4 −3 −2 −1 0 1 2 3

45. [number line dots] −3 −2 −1 0 1 2 3 4

46. [number line dots] −2 −1 0 1 2 3 4 5 6

SECTION 6.7, PAGE 345

For Exercises 9–16, see the following figure.

For Exercises 17–24, see the following figure.

43.

Slope: undefined

44.

Slope: undefined

45.

Slope is 0.

46.

Slope is 0.

47.

48.

49.

50.

61.

62.

51.

52.

63.

64.

53.

54.

65.

66.

55.

56.

77.

78.

57.

58.

79.

80.

59.

60.

81.

82.

83.

84.

85.

86.

99. a)

100. a)

101. a)

102. a)

107. a) Solve the equations for y to put them in slope-intercept form. Then compare the slopes and y-intercepts. If the slopes are equal but the y-intercepts are different, then the lines are parallel.

SECTION 6.8, PAGE 351

5.

6.

7.

8.

9.

10.

11.

12.

13.

14.

15.

16.

17.

18.

19.

20.

21.

22.

23.

24.

25.

26.

27. b)

28. b)

29. b)

SECTION 6.10, PAGE 373

47.

48.

49.

50.

51.

52.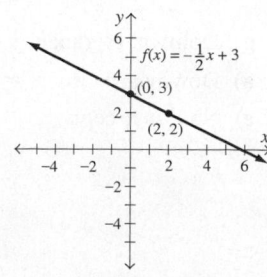

53. a) Upward **b)** $x = 0$ **c)** $(0, -1)$ **d)** $(0, -1)$
e) $(1, 0)$, $(-1, 0)$

f)

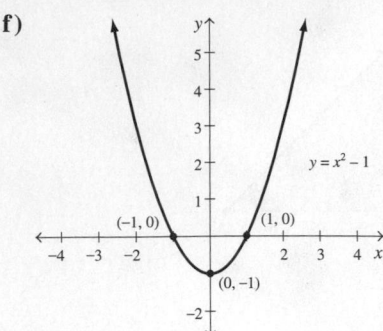

g) Domain: $\mathbb{R}$; range: $y \geq -1$

54. a) Upward **b)** $x = 0$ **c)** $(0, -9)$ **d)** $(0, -9)$
e) $(3, 0)$, $(-3, 0)$

f)

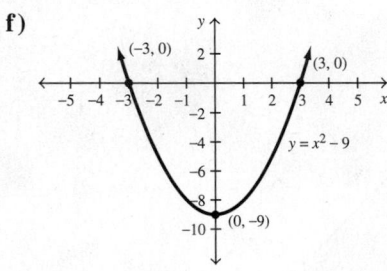

g) Domain: $\mathbb{R}$; range: $y \geq -9$

55. a) Downward **b)** $x = 0$ **c)** $(0, 4)$ **d)** $(0, 4)$
e) $(-2, 0)$, $(2, 0)$

f)

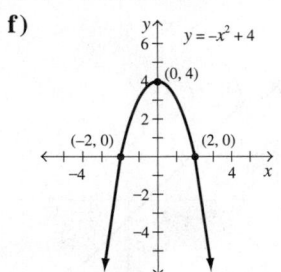

g) Domain: $\mathbb{R}$; range: $y \leq 4$

56. a) Downward **b)** $x = 0$ **c)** $(0, 16)$ **d)** $(0, 16)$
e) $(-4, 0)$, $(4, 0)$

f)

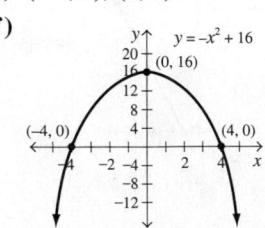

g) Domain: $\mathbb{R}$; range: $y \leq 16$

57. a) Downward **b)** $x = 0$ **c)** $(0, -8)$ **d)** $(0, -8)$
e) No x-intercepts

f)

g) Domain: $\mathbb{R}$; range: $y \leq -8$

58. a) Downward **b)** $x = 0$ **c)** $(0, -4)$ **d)** $(0, -4)$
e) No x-intercepts

f)

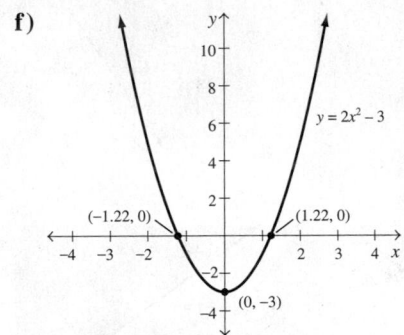

g) Domain: $\mathbb{R}$; range: $y \leq -4$

59. a) Upward **b)** $x = 0$ **c)** $(0, -3)$ **d)** $(0, -3)$
e) $(-1.22, 0)$, $(1.22, 0)$

f)

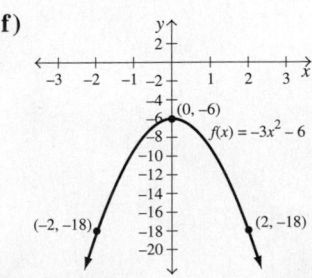

g) Domain: $\mathbb{R}$; range: $y \geq -3$

60. a) Downward **b)** $x = 0$ **c)** $(0, -6)$ **d)** $(0, -6)$
e) No x-intercepts

f)

g) Domain: $\mathbb{R}$; range: $y \leq -6$

61. a) Upward **b)** $x = -2$ **c)** $(-2, -8)$ **d)** $(0, -4)$
e) $(-4.83, 0)$, $(0.83, 0)$

f)

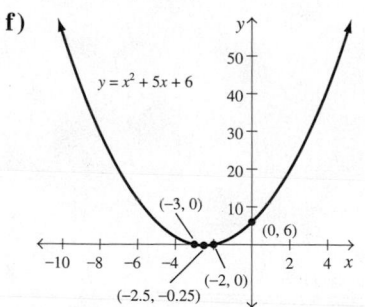

g) Domain: $\mathbb{R}$; range: $y \geq -8$

62. a) Upward   **b)** $x = 4$ **c)** $(4, -15)$ **d)** $(0, 1)$
   e) $(7.87, 0), (0.13, 0)$
   f)

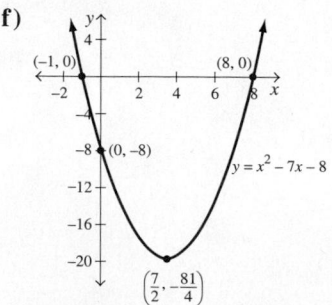

g) Domain: $\mathbb{R}$; range: $y \geq -15$

63. a) Upward   **b)** $x = -\frac{5}{2}$ **c)** $(-2.5, -0.25)$ **d)** $(0, 6)$
   e) $(-3, 0), (-2, 0)$
   f)

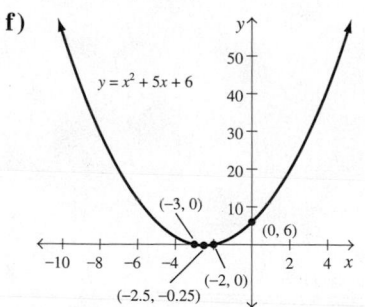

g) Domain: $\mathbb{R}$; range: $y \geq -0.25$

64. a) Upward   **b)** $x = \frac{7}{2}$ **c)** $(\frac{7}{2}, -\frac{81}{4})$ **d)** $(0, -8)$
   e) $(-1, 0), (8, 0)$
   f)

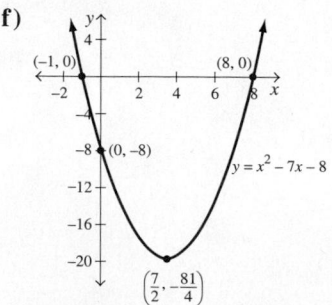

g) Domain: $\mathbb{R}$; range: $y \geq -\frac{81}{4}$

65. a) Downward   **b)** $x = 2$ **c)** $(2, -2)$ **d)** $(0, -6)$
   e) No x-intercepts
   f)

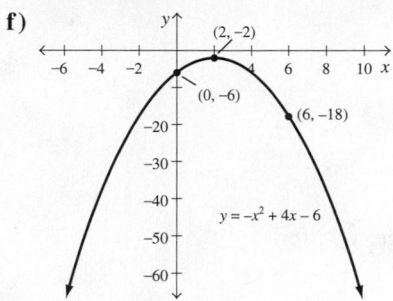

g) Domain: $\mathbb{R}$; range: $y \leq -2$

66. a) Downward   **b)** $x = 4$ **c)** $(4, 8)$ **d)** $(0, -8)$
   e) $(1.17, 0), (6.83, 0)$
   f)

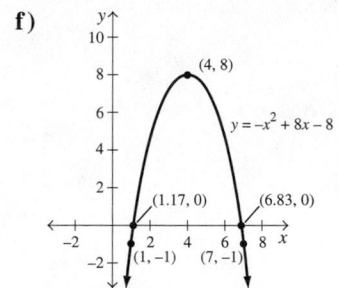

g) Domain: $\mathbb{R}$; range: $y \leq 8$

67. a) Downward   **b)** $x = \frac{3}{4}$ **c)** $(\frac{3}{4}, -\frac{7}{8})$ **d)** $(0, -2)$
   e) No x-intercepts
   f)

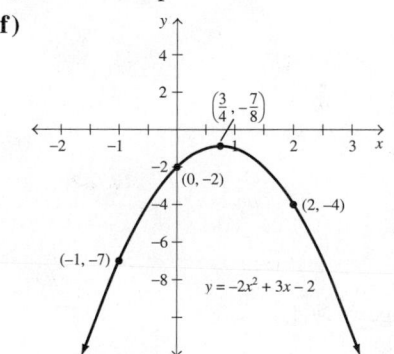

g) Domain: $\mathbb{R}$; range: $y \leq -\frac{7}{8}$

68. a) Downward   **b)** $x = -\frac{3}{4}$ **c)** $(-\frac{3}{4}, 6\frac{1}{4})$ **d)** $(0, 4)$
   e) $(-2, 0), (\frac{1}{2}, 0)$
   f)

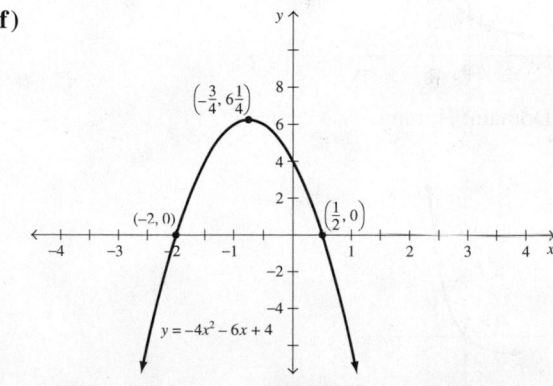

g) Domain: $\mathbb{R}$; range: $y \leq 6\frac{1}{4}$

69. Domain: $\mathbb{R}$; range: $y > 0$

70. Domain: $\mathbb{R}$; range: $y > 0$

71. Domain: $\mathbb{R}$; range: $y > 0$

72. Domain: $\mathbb{R}$; range: $y > 0$

73. Domain: $\mathbb{R}$; range: $y > 1$

74. Domain: $\mathbb{R}$; range: $y > -1$

75. Domain: $\mathbb{R}$; range: $y > 1$

76. Domain: $\mathbb{R}$; range: $y > -1$

77. Domain: $\mathbb{R}$; range: $y > 0$

78. Domain: $\mathbb{R}$; range: $y > 0$

79. Domain: $\mathbb{R}$; range: $y > 0$

80. Domain: $\mathbb{R}$; range: $y > 0$

REVIEW EXERCISES, PAGE 380

18. $y = \dfrac{-2x + 17}{9}$ or $y = -\dfrac{2}{9}x + \dfrac{17}{9}$

43.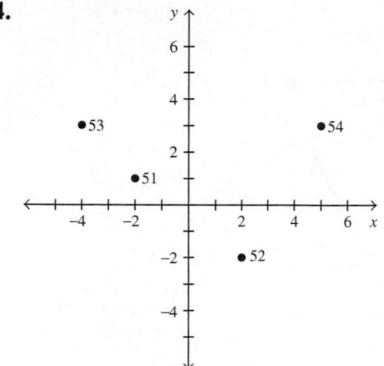

44.

45.

46.

47.

48.

49.

50.

51.–54.

57.

58.

59.

60.

65.

66.

69. a)

70. a)

71.

72.

73.

74.

95. a) Downward   **b)** $x = -2$ **c)** $(-2, 25)$ **d)** $(0, 21)$
  e) $(-7, 0), (3, 0)$
  f)

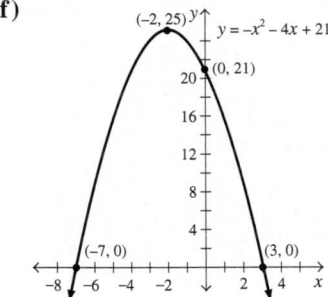

  g) Domain: $\mathbb{R}$; range: $y \le 25$

96. a) Upward   **b)** $x = -2$ **c)** $(-2, -2)$ **d)** $(0, 6)$
  e) $(-3, 0), (-1, 0)$
  f)

  g) Domain: $\mathbb{R}$; range: $y \ge -2$

97. Domain: $\mathbb{R}$; range: $y > 0$

98. Domain: $\mathbb{R}$; range: $y > 0$

CHAPTER TEST, PAGE 383

10.

12.

13.

14.

20. f)

Chapter 7

SECTION 7.1, PAGE 393

13.

14.

15.

16.

17.

18.

19.

20.

21.

22.

23.

24.

25.

26.

27.

Dependent

28.

Inconsistent

29.

Dependent

30.

Inconsistent

31.

32.

51. a) Cost for U-Haul: $C = 0.79x + 30$
Cost for Discount Rentals: $C = 0.85x + 24$

b)

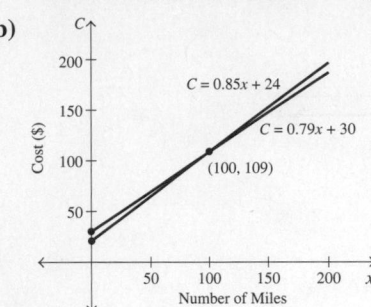

52. a) Tom's Tree and Landscape: $C = 60h + 200$
Lawn Perfect: $C = 25h + 305$

b)

53. b)

54. a) Mark Demo Agency: $C = 0.08s + 40$
Andy Harris and Associates: $C = 0.18s + 15$

b)

55. b)

56. Solve each equation for y to determine the slope and y-intercept for each. If the slopes are not the same, the system is consistent. If the slopes and the y-intercepts are the same, the system is dependent. If the slopes are the same and the y-intercepts are not the same, the system is inconsistent.

57. b)

58. b)

59. e) To determine the number of points of intersection for *n* lines, add $n - 1$ to the number of points of intersection for $n - 1$ lines. For example, for 5 lines there were 10 points of intersection. Therefore, for 6 lines ($n = 6$) there are $10 + (6 - 1) = 15$ points of intersection.

60.

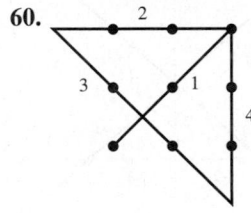

SECTION 7.2, PAGE 403

11. An infinite number of solutions; dependent system

32. An infinite number of solutions; dependent system

37. $s = 0.15p + 12,000$
$s = 0.05p + 27,000$
$150,000 annual profit

38. $x + y = 25,000$
$0.045x + 0.06y = 1380$
$8000 at 4.5%, $17,000 at 6%

39. $l + n = 55$
$34.08l + 41.90n = 2109$
25 shares of LG Electronics, 30 shares of Nintendo Company

40. $x + y = 45$
$2x + 3y = 101$
34 2-pointers, 11 3-pointers

41. $x + y = 15$
$0.40x + 0.10y = 0.25(15)$
$7.5l$ of 40%, $7.5l$ of 10%

42. $x + y = 100$
$30x + 40y = 3200$
80 sets at \$30 per set, 20 sets at \$40 per set

43. $y = 0.02x + 18$
$y = 0.015x + 24$
1200 copies

45. $x + y = 20$
$3x + y = 30$
Mix 5 lb of nuts with 15 lb of pretzels.

46. $0.10A + 0.20B = 20$
$0.06A + 0.02B = 6$
80 g of mix A, 60 g of mix B

47. $x + y = 4600$
$27x + 14y = 104,700$
3100 amphitheatre tickets and 1500 lawn tickets

56. When solving a system of equations, if you obtain a true statement such as $0 = 0$, the system is dependent and has an infinite number of solutions. Therefore the student's answer is not correct. The correct answer is all real numbers.

SECTION 7.3, PAGE 412

9. $\begin{bmatrix} 1 & 0 \\ 0 & 1 \end{bmatrix}$

10. $\begin{bmatrix} 1 & 0 & 0 \\ 0 & 1 & 0 \\ 0 & 0 & 1 \end{bmatrix}$

12. $\begin{bmatrix} 6 & 4 & 4 \\ 7 & -6 & 6 \end{bmatrix}$

14. $\begin{bmatrix} 1 & 9 & 4 \\ 6 & -8 & 5 \\ 5 & 3 & 13 \end{bmatrix}$

18. $\begin{bmatrix} 1 & 0 & -7 \\ 9 & 8 & -7 \\ 6 & 1 & -9 \end{bmatrix}$

29. $\begin{bmatrix} 4 & 7 & 6 \\ -2 & 3 & 1 \\ 5 & 1 & 2 \end{bmatrix}$

31. $A + B = \begin{bmatrix} 8 & 1 & 3 \\ 4 & 3 & 0 \end{bmatrix}$; cannot be multiplied

33. Cannot be added; $A \times B = \begin{bmatrix} 24 & 34 \\ 24 & 34 \end{bmatrix}$

34. $A + B = \begin{bmatrix} 12 & 10 \\ 8 & 6 \\ 4 & 2 \end{bmatrix}$; cannot be multiplied

36. $A + B = \begin{bmatrix} -1 & 6 \\ 9 & 3 \end{bmatrix}$; $A \times B = \begin{bmatrix} 7 & -18 \\ 27 & -10 \end{bmatrix}$

37. $A + B = B + A = \begin{bmatrix} 6 & 0 \\ 13 & 8 \end{bmatrix}$

38. $A + B = B + A = \begin{bmatrix} 11 & 4 \\ 0 & 13 \end{bmatrix}$

39. $A + B = B + A = \begin{bmatrix} 8 & 0 \\ 6 & -8 \end{bmatrix}$

41. $(A + B) + C = A + (B + C) = \begin{bmatrix} 7 & 13 \\ 2 & 10 \end{bmatrix}$

42. $(A + B) + C = A + (B + C) = \begin{bmatrix} -11 & -1 \\ 2 & 15 \end{bmatrix}$

43. $(A + B) + C = A + (B + C) = \begin{bmatrix} 5 & 5 \\ 7 & -37 \end{bmatrix}$

51. $(A \times B) \times C = A \times (B \times C) = \begin{bmatrix} 41 & 13 \\ 56 & 16 \end{bmatrix}$

52. $(A \times B) \times C = A \times (B \times C) = \begin{bmatrix} -27 & 79 \\ -4 & 148 \end{bmatrix}$

53. $(A \times B) \times C = A \times (B \times C) = \begin{bmatrix} 16 & -10 \\ -24 & 2 \end{bmatrix}$

54. $(A \times B) \times C = A \times (B \times C) = \begin{bmatrix} 0 & 0 \\ 0 & 0 \end{bmatrix}$

55. $(A \times B) \times C = A \times (B \times C) = \begin{bmatrix} 17 & 0 \\ -7 & 0 \end{bmatrix}$

57.

	Students	Adult	Senior citizen	
	158	280	95	Matinee
	215	362	94	Evening

58.

	Male	Female	
	17	9	Small
	21	7	Medium
	22	7	Large
	19	12	Extra large

59. Total cost

$\begin{bmatrix} 53 \\ 55 \end{bmatrix}$ Java's Coffee Shop / Spot Coffee Shop

60. Meat Vegetable Salad Dessert

[4158 805 655 1023] Total cost

61.

	Large	Small	
	38	50	Sugar
	56	72	Flour
	17	26	Milk
	10	14	Eggs

64.

	Cost	Revenue
Hot dogs	39.35	97.75
Soft drinks	34.15	84.50
Candy bars	45.00	111.45

71. c) $\begin{bmatrix} 28.7 & 24.6 \\ 41.3 & 35.7 \\ 69.3 & 60.1 \end{bmatrix}$

72. Yes. Answers will vary. One example is
$A = \begin{bmatrix} 1 & 3 \\ 0 & 6 \\ 3 & 1 \end{bmatrix}$, $B = \begin{bmatrix} 5 & 0 \\ -1 & 2 \\ 6 & 8 \end{bmatrix}$.

73. Yes. Answers will vary. One example is
$A = \begin{bmatrix} 2 & 7 & 6 \\ -3 & 0 & 8 \end{bmatrix}$, $B = \begin{bmatrix} 1 & 2 \\ 3 & 4 \\ 5 & 6 \end{bmatrix}$.

74. Answers will vary.

SECTION 7.4, PAGE 421

10. An infinite number of solutions; dependent system

SECTION 7.5, PAGE 425

5.

(0, 3)
2 (1, 2)
(0, 0)

−4 −2   2   x

y > −x + 3
y > 2x

6.

(−1, 4) 4

y > −4x
y ≤ −2x + 2

(0, 0) (1, 0)

−4 −2   2   4   x

17.

4 (0, 4)
2
(0, 1)   (2, 0)

−4 −2   2   4   x
−2
(−1, 0)
−4

4x + 2y > 8
x ≥ y − 1

7.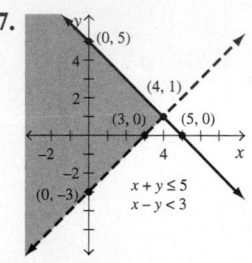

(0, 5)
4
(4, 1)
2
(3, 0)   (5, 0)

−2   4   x
−2
(0, −3)

x + y ≤ 5
x − y < 3

8.

6
(0, 4)
(0, 3)
2
(4, 0)
−4 −2 (2, 0) 4   x
−2

−4 x + y < 4
3x + 2y ≥ 6

18.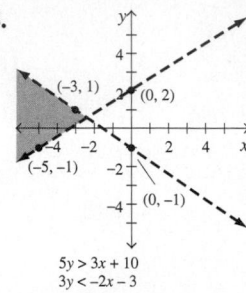

4

(−3, 1) 2 (0, 2)

−4 −2   2   4   x
(−5, −1) −2
−4 (0, −1)

5y > 3x + 10
3y < −2x − 3

9.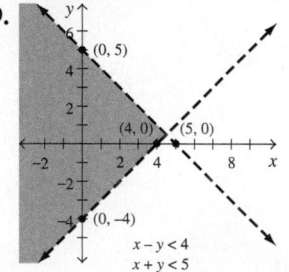

6
(0, 5)
4
2
(4, 0) (5, 0)
−2   2   4   8   x
−2
−4 (0, −4)

x − y < 4
x + y < 5

10.

2
(2, 0)
−6 −4 −2   2   4 −6 x
−2
−4 (0, −4)
(4, 0)
−6 (0, −6)

3x − y ≤ 6
x − y > 4

19.

4

2

(2, 0)   (3, 0)
−4 −2   2   4   x
−2
(0, −3) 3x ≥ 2y + 6
x ≤ y + 3

11.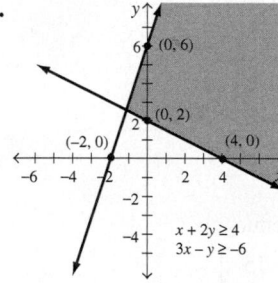

6 (0, 6)

(0, 2)
2
(−2, 0)   (4, 0)
−6 −4 −2   2   4   x
−2

−4 x + 2y ≥ 4
3x − y ≥ −6

12.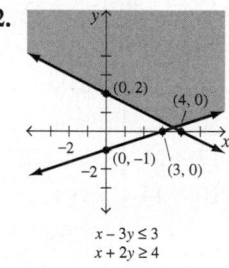

y

(0, 2)
(4, 0)
−2   2   x
−2 (0, −1) (3, 0)

x − 3y ≤ 3
x + 2y ≥ 4

20.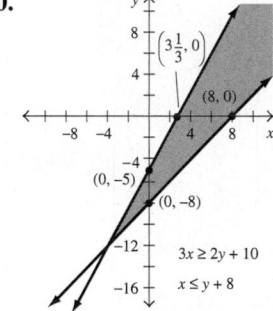

8 (3⅓, 0)
4
(8, 0)
−8 −4   4   8   x
−4
(0, −5)
(0, −8)
−12 3x ≥ 2y + 10
x ≤ y + 8
−16

13.

4
(1, 3)
2
(3, 1)
−4 −2   2   4   6   x
(0, 0)
−4 y ≤ 3x
x ≥ 3y

14.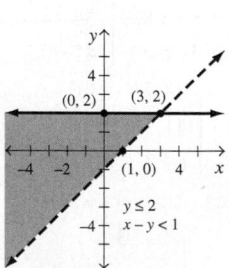

4
(0, 2)   (3, 2)

−4 −2   (1, 0) 4   x

−4 y ≤ 2
x − y < 1

21. b)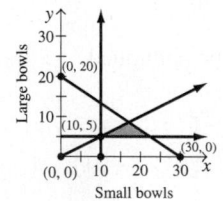

30
(0, 20)
20
Large bowls
10
(10, 5)
(30, 0)
(0, 0) 10 20 30 x
Small bowls

15.

4

2 (1, 1)

−2   2   4   x
−2

−4

x ≥ 1
y ≤ 1

16.

6
4
2 (0, 0)
−6 −4 −2   2   4   6   x
−2
x ≤ 0
−4 y ≤ 0
−6

22. b)

(0, 500)
500
400
Rice (calories) 300
200
100 (150, 150)
(500, 0)
100 200 300 400 500   x
Chicken (calories)

24. b) One example: $x + y > 4$
$$x + y < 1$$

SECTION 7.6, PAGE 430

11. a)

b) Maximum is 18 at (3, 2); minimum is 0 at (0, 0).

12. a)

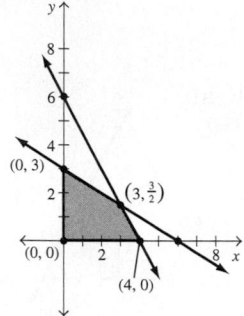

b) Maximum is 18 at (0, 3); minimum is 0 at (0, 0).

13. a)

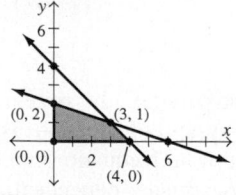

b) Maximum is 28 at (4, 0); minimum is 0 at (0, 0).

14. a)

b) Maximum is 1400 at (30, 20); minimum is 0 at (0, 0).

15. a)

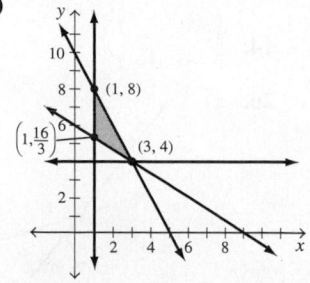

b) Maximum is 15.4 at (1, 8); minimum is 11 at $\left(1, \frac{16}{3}\right)$.

16. a)

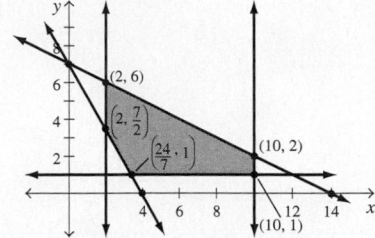

b) Maximum is 170 at (10, 2); minimum is 61.22 at $\left(\frac{24}{7}, 1\right)$.

17. c)

18. c)

19. c)

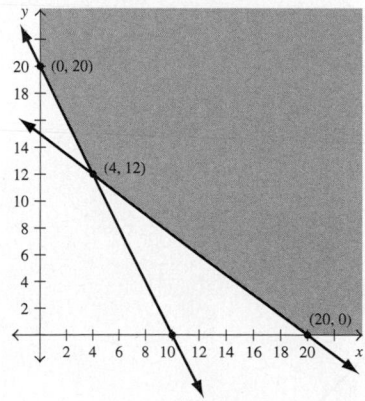

20. $x + \frac{1}{2}y \leq 200$

$\frac{1}{2}y \leq 150$

$x \geq 0$

$y \geq 0$

$P = 0.40x + 0.30y$

Maximum profit occurs at (50, 300). Thus, the manufacturer should make 50 lb of the all-beef hot dogs and 300 lb of the regular hot dogs for a profit of $110.

22. c)

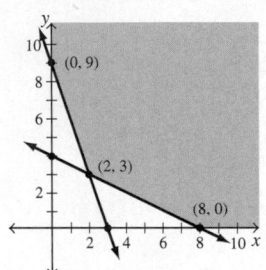

REVIEW EXERCISES, PAGE 433

1.

2.

3.

4.

36.

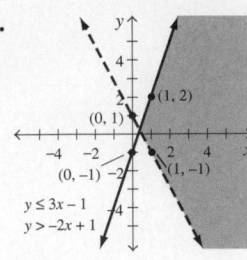

$y \leq 3x - 1$
$y > -2x + 1$

37.

$2x + y < 8$
$y \geq 2x - 1$

38.

$x + 3y \leq 6$
$2x - 7y \geq 14$

39.

$x - y > 5$
$6x + 5y \leq 30$

40. a)

CHAPTER TEST, PAGE 434

1. If the lines do not intersect (are parallel), the system of equations is inconsistent. The system of equations is consistent if the lines intersect. If both equations represent the same line, the system of equations is dependent.

2.

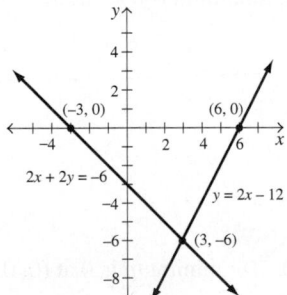

13. $\begin{bmatrix} 1 & -8 \\ 6 & 5 \end{bmatrix}$

14. $\begin{bmatrix} 4 & 1 \\ -9 & -1 \end{bmatrix}$

17.

$y < -2x + 2$
$y > 3x + 2$

20. a)

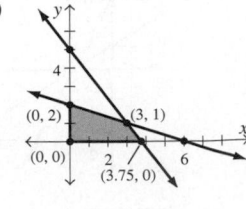

Chapter 9

SECTION 9.1, PAGE 486

75. Angles 3, 4, and 7 each measure 125°; angles 1, 2, 5, and 6 each measure 55°.

76. Angles 2, 4, and 5 each measure 120°; angles 1, 3, 6, and 7 each measure 60°.

77. Angles 1, 4, and 7 each measure 30°; angles 2, 3, 5, and 6 each measure 150°.

78. Angles 2, 5, and 6 each measure 25°; angles 1, 3, 4, and 7 each measure 155°.

95. b) First, Euclid introduced undefined terms. Second, he introduced certain definitions. Third, he stated primitive propositions called postulates about the undefined terms and definitions. Fourth, he proved, using deductive reasoning, other propositions called theorems.

96. An axiom is a statement that is accepted as being true on the basis of its "obviousness" and its relation to the physical world. A theorem is a statement that has been proven using undefined terms, definitions, and axioms.

102. Sometimes true. A triangle must always contain at least two acute angles. Some triangles contain three acute angles.

104. Sometimes true. Alternate exterior angles are only supplementary when each is equal to 90°.

105. Sometimes true. Alternate interior angles are only complementary when each is equal to 45°.

110.

112. a)

Other answers are possible.

SECTION 9.2, PAGE 496

33. $m\angle 1 = 90°, m\angle 2 = 50°, m\angle 3 = 130°, m\angle 4 = 50°,$
$m\angle 5 = 50°, m\angle 6 = 40°, m\angle 7 = 90°, m\angle 8 = 130°,$
$m\angle 9 = 140°, m\angle 10 = 40°, m\angle 11 = 140°, m\angle 12 = 40°$

34. $m\angle 1 = 51°, m\angle 2 = 59°, m\angle 3 = 70°, m\angle 4 = 70°,$
$m\angle 5 = 51°, m\angle 6 - 110°, m\angle 7 = 51°, m\angle 8 = 129°,$
$m\angle 9 = 70°, m\angle 10 = 110°, m\angle 11 = 129°, m\angle 12 = 51°$

77. The different types of triangles are acute, obtuse, right, isosceles, equilateral, and scalene. Descriptions will vary.

78. The different types of quadrilaterals are trapezoid, parallelogram, rhombus, rectangle, and square. Descriptions will vary.

81. a) $m\angle HMF = m\angle TMB, m\angle HFM = m\angle TBM,$
$m\angle MHF = m\angle MTB$

82. a) $m\angle CED = m\angle ABC, m\angle ACB = m\angle DCE,$
$m\angle BAC = m\angle CDE$

SECTION 9.4, PAGE 520

59. f) If we double the length of each edge of a cube, the new volume will be eight times the original volume.

60. f) If we double the radius of a sphere, the new volume will be eight times the original volume.

61. b) $V_1 = a^3; V_2 = a^2b; V_3 = a^2b; V_4 = ab^2;$
$V_5 = a^2b; V_6 = ab^2; V_7 = b^3$

SECTION 9.5, PAGE 537

This figure contains the answers to Exercises 15 and 16.

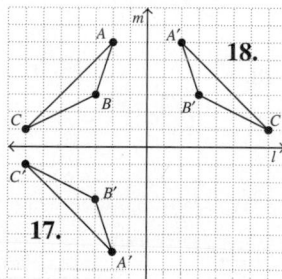

This figure contains the answers to Exercises 17 and 18.

This figure contains the answers to Exercises 19 and 20.

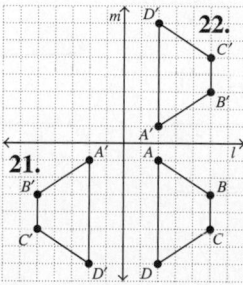

This figure contains the answers to Exercises 21 and 22.

This figure contains the answers to Exercises 23 and 24.

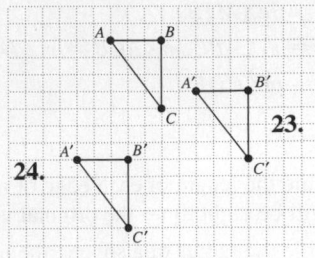

This figure contains the answers to Exercises 25 and 26.

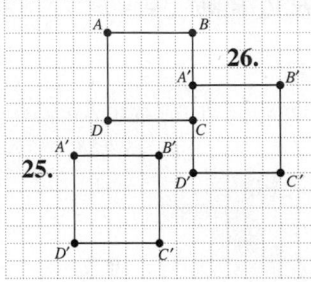

This figure contains the answers to Exercises 27 and 28.

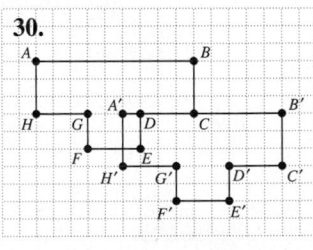

This figure contains the answers to Exercises 31 and 32.

This figure contains the answers to Exercises 33 and 34.

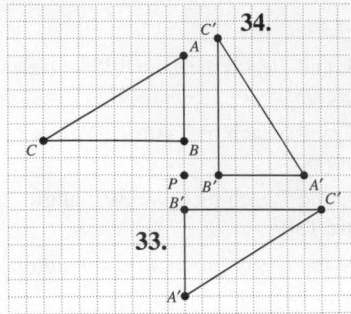

This figure contains the answers to Exercises 35 and 36.

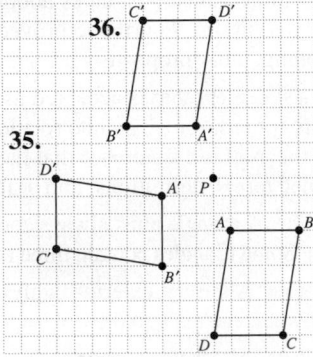

This figure contains the answers to Exercises 37 and 38.

This figure contains the answers to Exercises 39 and 40.

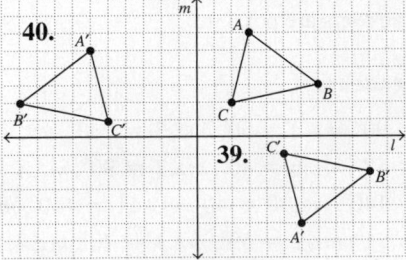

This figure contains the answers to Exercises 41 and 42.

This figure contains the answers to Exercises 43 and 44.

This figure contains the answers to Exercises 45 and 46.

47. a)

48. a)

49. a)

50. a)

51. a) **d)**

52. a) **d)**

53. a)–c)

54. a)

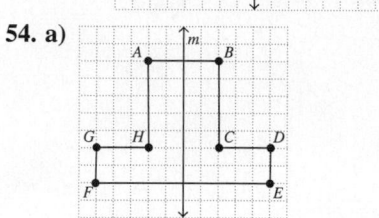

b) No. Any reflection about any horizontal line will result in the figure being in a different position than the starting position.

55. a) and b)

d) The order in which the translation and the reflection are performed is important. The figure obtained in part (a) is the glide reflection.

59. A regular pentagon cannot be used as a tessellating shape.

60. Although answers will vary depending on the font, the following capital letters have reflective symmetry about a horizontal line drawn through the center of the letter: B, C, D, E, H, I, K, O, X.

61. Although answers will vary depending on the font, the following capital letters have reflective symmetry about a vertical line drawn through the center of the letter: A, H, I, M, O, T, U, V, W, X, Y.

62. Although answers will vary depending on the font, the following capital letters have 180° rotational symmetry about a point in the center of the letter: H, I, N, O, S, X, Z.

SECTION 9.7, PAGE 556

9.
10.
11.
12.

13. a)

Start

Step 1

Step 2

14. a)

Step	Perimeter
1	3
2	4
3	$\frac{16}{3}$
4	$\frac{64}{9}$
5	$\frac{256}{27}$
6	$\frac{1024}{81}$

REVIEW EXERCISES, PAGE 560

13. $m\angle 1 = 45°, m\angle 2 = 110°, m\angle 3 = 110°, m\angle 4 = 65°,$
$m\angle 5 = 115°, m\angle 6 = 65°$

This figure contains the answers for Exercises 32 and 33.

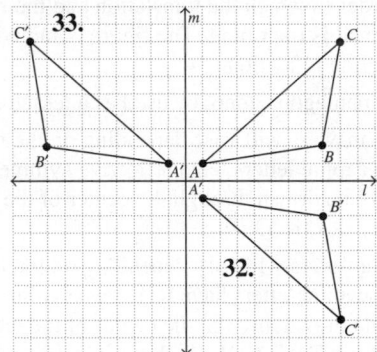

This figure contains the answers for Exercises 34 and 35.

This figure contains the answers for Exercises 36–38.

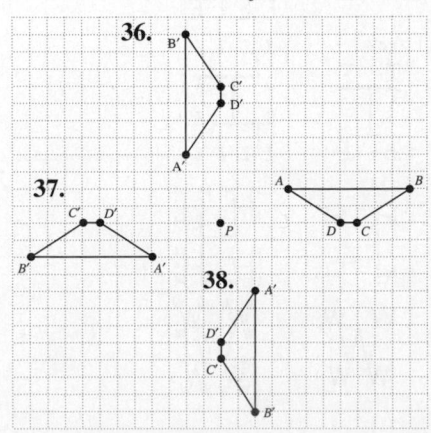

This figure contains the answers for Exercises 39 and 40.

48. Euclidean: Given a line and a point not on the line, one and only one line can be drawn parallel to the given line through the given point. Elliptical: Given a line and a point not on the line, no line can be drawn through the given point parallel to the given line. Hyperbolic: Given a line and a point not on the line, two or more lines can be drawn through the given point parallel to the given line.

49.

50.

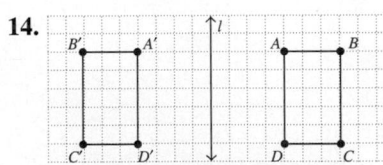

CHAPTER TEST, PAGE 563

14.

15.

16.

17.

Chapter 10

SECTION 10.1, PAGE 573

21. $(6 - 4) - 1 \neq 6 - (4 - 1)$
$$2 - 1 \neq 6 - 3$$
$$1 \neq 3$$

SECTION 10.2, PAGE 581

15. Yes; C is the identity element since the row next to C is identical to the top row, and the column under C is identical to the left-hand column.

17. a) The inverse of A is B since $A \oslash B = B \oslash A = C.$
b) The inverse of B is A since $B \oslash A = A \oslash B = C.$
c) The inverse of C is C since $C \oslash C = C.$

18. a) The inverse of A is A since $A \divideontimes A = C.$
b) The inverse of B is B since $B \divideontimes B = C.$
c) The inverse of C is C since $C \divideontimes C = C.$

41.

+	1	2	3	4	5	6
1	2	3	4	5	6	1
2	3	4	5	6	1	2
3	4	5	6	1	2	3
4	5	6	1	2	3	4
5	6	1	2	3	4	5
6	1	2	3	4	5	6

51.

+	1	2	3	4	5	6	7
1	2	3	4	5	6	7	1
2	3	4	5	6	7	1	2
3	4	5	6	7	1	2	3
4	5	6	7	1	2	3	4
5	6	7	1	2	3	4	5
6	7	1	2	3	4	5	6
7	1	2	3	4	5	6	7

65. a) $\{*, 5, L\}$ **b)** $\$$ **c)** Yes **d)** Yes, L
e) Yes, $* - 5, 5 - *, L - L$ **f)** $(* \$ 5) \$ 5 = * \$ (5 \$ 5)$
g) Yes, $L \$ * = * \$ L$ **h)** Yes

66. a) $\{3, 5, 8, 4\}$ **b)** $\overset{\circ}{X}$ **c)** Yes **d)** Yes, 4
e) Yes, 3–8, 5–5, 8–3, 4–4
f) $(5 \overset{\circ}{X} 8) \overset{\circ}{X} 4 = 5 \overset{\circ}{X} (8 \overset{\circ}{X} 4)$
g) Yes, $8 \overset{\circ}{X} 3 = 3 \overset{\circ}{X} 8$ **h)** Yes

68. b) $(1 \overset{\frown}{W} 3) \overset{\frown}{W} 4 \neq 1 \overset{\frown}{W} (3 \overset{\frown}{W} 4)$

70. Not associative:
$$\left(M \otimes \overset{\triangle}{\bigtriangleup}\right) \otimes M \neq M \otimes \left(\overset{\triangle}{\bigtriangleup} \otimes M\right);$$
not commutative: $\overset{\triangle}{\bigtriangleup} \otimes M \neq M \otimes \overset{\triangle}{\bigtriangleup}$

75. a)

+	E	O
E	E	O
O	O	E

76. a)

×	E	O
E	E	E
O	E	O

77. a) Is closed; identity element is 6; inverses: 1–5, 2–2, 3–3, 4–4, 5–1, 6–6; is associative; for example,
$$(2 \infty 5) \infty 3 = 2 \infty (5 \infty 3)$$
$$3 \infty 3 = 2 \infty 2$$
$$6 = 6$$
b) $3 \infty 1 \neq 1 \infty 3$
$$2 \neq 4$$

78. a) It is closed; identity element is F; inverses: A–E, B–B, C–C, D–D, E–A, F–F; is associative; for example,
$$(C \ominus D) \ominus A = C \ominus (D \ominus A)$$
$$E \ominus A = C \ominus C$$
$$F = F$$
b) $B \ominus C \neq C \ominus B$
$$E \neq A$$

79. a)

*	R	S	T	U	V	I
R	V	T	U	S	I	R
S	U	I	V	R	T	S
T	S	R	I	V	U	T
U	T	V	R	I	S	U
V	I	U	S	T	R	V
I	R	S	T	U	V	I

b) Yes. It is closed; identity element is I; inverses R–V, S–S, T–T, U–U, V–R, I–I; and the associative property will hold.

81.

+	0	1	2	3	4
0	0	1	2	3	4
1	1	2	3	4	0
2	2	3	4	0	1
3	3	4	0	1	2
4	4	0	1	2	3

82.

+	0	1	2	3	4	5
0	0	1	2	3	4	5
1	1	2	3	4	5	0
2	2	3	4	5	0	1
3	3	4	5	0	1	2
4	4	5	0	1	2	3
5	5	0	1	2	3	4

SECTION 10.3, PAGE 592

75. a)

+	0	1	2
0	0	1	2
1	1	2	0
2	2	0	1

76. a)

+	0	1	2	3	4	5	6	7
0	0	1	2	3	4	5	6	7
1	1	2	3	4	5	6	7	0
2	2	3	4	5	6	7	0	1
3	3	4	5	6	7	0	1	2
4	4	5	6	7	0	1	2	3
5	5	6	7	0	1	2	3	4
6	6	7	0	1	2	3	4	5
7	7	0	1	2	3	4	5	6

b) Yes   **c)** Yes, 0
d) Yes;
   0–0, 1–7, 2–6, 3–5, 4–4, 5–3, 6–2, 7–1
e) $(1 + 2) + 5 = 1 + (2 + 5)$
$$3 + 5 = 1 + 7$$
$$0 = 0$$
f) Yes; $2 + 4 = 4 + 2$
$$6 = 6$$
g) Yes. All five properties are satisfied.   **h)** Yes

77. a)

×	0	1	2	3
0	0	0	0	0
1	0	1	2	3
2	0	2	0	2
3	0	3	2	1

78. a)

×	0	1	2	3	4	5	6
0	0	0	0	0	0	0	0
1	0	1	2	3	4	5	6
2	0	2	4	6	1	3	5
3	0	3	6	2	5	1	4
4	0	4	1	5	2	6	3
5	0	5	3	1	6	4	2
6	0	6	5	4	3	2	1

b) Yes   **c)** Yes; 1
d) No; the element 0 does not have an inverse.
e) $(1 \times 2) \times 4 = 1 \times (2 \times 4)$
$$2 \times 4 = 1 \times 1$$
$$1 = 1$$
f) Yes; $2 \times 3 = 3 \times 2$
$$6 = 6$$
g) No; 0 does not have an inverse.

REVIEW EXERCISES, PAGE 596

41.

+	0	1	2	3	4	5
0	0	1	2	3	4	5
1	1	2	3	4	5	0
2	2	3	4	5	0	1
3	3	4	5	0	1	2
4	4	5	0	1	2	3
5	5	0	1	2	3	4

Yes, it is a commutative group.

42.

+	0	1	2	3
0	0	0	0	0
1	0	1	2	3
2	0	2	0	2
3	0	3	2	1

No; no inverse for 0 or 2

CHAPTER TEST, PAGE 597

5.

+	1	2	3	4	5
1	2	3	4	5	1
2	3	4	5	1	2
3	4	5	1	2	3
4	5	1	2	3	4
5	1	2	3	4	5

20. a)

×	0	1	2	3	4
0	0	0	0	0	0
1	0	1	2	3	4
2	0	2	4	1	3
3	0	3	1	4	2
4	0	4	3	2	1

Chapter 11

SECTION 11.2, PAGE 618

43. $2017.03   **44.** $3583.58   **45.** $1459.33   **46.** $4498.91
47. $5278.99   **48.** $712.45   **49.** $850.64   **50.** $3533.18
51. $6086.82   **52.** $7371.73

SECTION 11.3, PAGE 627

49. The simple interest is $20,000. The compound interest is $22,138.58. The compound interest is greater by $2,138.58.

SECTION 11.4, PAGE 641

31. d) The interest charged using the average daily balance method is $0.04 less than the interest charged using the previous balance method.
32. d) The interest charged using the average daily balance method is $0.38 less than the interest charged using the previous balance method.

SECTION 11.5, PAGE 654

27. b)

Payment Number	Interest	Principal	Balance of Loan
1	$750.00	$54.62	$99,945.38
2	$749.59	$55.03	$99,890.35
3	$749.18	$55.44	$99,834.91

d)

Payment Number	Interest	Principal	Balance of Loan
4	$780.38	$24.24	$99,810.67
5	$780.19	$24.43	$99,786.24
6	$780.00	$24.62	$99,761.62

Chapter 12

SECTION 12.1, PAGE 679

15. a) $\dfrac{13,674}{153,468}$, or ≈ 0.0891 **b)** $\dfrac{27,362}{153,468}$, or ≈ 0.1783

c) $\dfrac{11,140}{153,468}$, or ≈ 0.0726

16. a) $\dfrac{15,000,000}{101,250,000}$, or ≈ 0.1481

b) $\dfrac{23,000,000}{101,250,000}$, or ≈ 0.2272

c) $\dfrac{24,000,000}{101,250,000}$, or ≈ 0.2370

17. a) $\dfrac{16,600,000}{66,950,000}$, ≈ 0.2479

b) $\dfrac{8,870,000}{66,950,000}$, or ≈ 0.1325

c) $\dfrac{18,880,000}{66,950,000}$, or ≈ 0.2820

21. a) $\dfrac{6}{20} = \dfrac{3}{10}$ **d)** $\dfrac{2}{20} = \dfrac{1}{10}$

23. a) 0 **b)** $\dfrac{50}{250} = 0.2$ **c)** 1

25. a) $\dfrac{224}{929} \approx 0.2411$ **b)** $\dfrac{705}{929} \approx 0.7589$

26. a) $\dfrac{787}{1064} \approx 0.7397$ **b)** $\dfrac{277}{1064} \approx 0.2603$

27. No, it means that if a coin was flipped many times, about $\dfrac{1}{2}$ of the tosses would land heads up.

SECTION 12.2, PAGE 687

25. a) $\dfrac{1}{4}$ **b)** $\dfrac{1}{2}$ **c)** $\dfrac{1}{4}$ **d)** 0

26. a) $\dfrac{1}{2}$ **b)** $\dfrac{1}{4}$ **c)** $\dfrac{1}{4}$ **d)** 0

27. a) $\dfrac{1}{2}$ **b)** $\dfrac{1}{8}$ **c)** $\dfrac{1}{8}$ **d)** $\dfrac{1}{4}$

28. a) $\dfrac{1}{3}$ **b)** $\dfrac{1}{6}$ **c)** $\dfrac{1}{3}$ **d)** $\dfrac{1}{6}$

SECTION 12.3, PAGE 694

59. Horse 2, $\dfrac{2}{9}$; Horse 3, $\dfrac{1}{3}$; Horse 4, $\dfrac{1}{16}$; Horse 5, $\dfrac{5}{12}$;

Horse 6, $\dfrac{1}{2}$

SECTION 12.5, PAGE 712

9. b)

10. b)

11. b)

12. a) 6 **b)**

c) 0 **d)** $\dfrac{1}{6}$ **e)** $\dfrac{2}{3}$

13. b)

14. b)

15. b)

16. b)

Sample Space

```
        S    CS
C       P    CP
        H    CH
        C    SC
S       P    SP
        H    SH
        C    PC
P       S    PS
        H    PH
        C    HC
H       S    HS
        P    HP
```

17. b)

Sample Space

```
      1    1 1
      2    1 2
1     3    1 3
      4    1 4
      5    1 5
      6    1 6
      1    2 1
      2    2 2
2     3    2 3
      4    2 4
      5    2 5
      6    2 6
      1    3 1
      2    3 2
3     3    3 3
      4    3 4
      5    3 5
      6    3 6
      1    4 1
      2    4 2
4     3    4 3
      4    4 4
      5    4 5
      6    4 6
      1    5 1
      2    5 2
5     3    5 3
      4    5 4
      5    5 5
      6    5 6
      1    6 1
      2    6 2
6     3    6 3
      4    6 4
      5    6 5
      6    6 6
```

18. b)

Sample Space

```
          Y    YYY
    Y     N    YYN
          A    YYA
          Y    YNY
Y   N     N    YNN
          A    YNA
          Y    YAY
    A     N    YAN
          A    YAA
          Y    NYY
    Y     N    NYN
          A    NYA
          Y    NNY
N   N     N    NNN
          A    NNA
          Y    NAY
    A     N    NAN
          A    NAA
          Y    AYY
    Y     N    AYN
          A    AYA
          Y    ANY
A   N     N    ANN
          A    ANA
          Y    AAY
    A     N    AAN
          A    AAA
```

19. b)

Sample Space

```
          R    BCR
    C     S    BCS
          L    BCL
B         R    BGR
    G     S    BGS
          L    BGL
          R    ACR
    C     S    ACS
          L    ACL
A         R    AGR
    G     S    AGS
          L    AGL
```

20. b)

Sample Space

```
          B — R    HBR
H
          R — B    HRB
          H — R    BHR
B
          R — H    BRH
          H — B    RHB
R
          B — H    RBH
```

21. b)

Sample Space

```
              F    1 1 F
        1     H    1 1 H
              B    1 1 B
    1         F    1 2 F
        2     H    1 2 H
              B    1 2 B
              F    2 1 F
        1     H    2 1 H
              B    2 1 B
    2         F    2 2 F
        2     H    2 2 H
              B    2 2 B
              F    3 1 F
        1     H    3 1 H
              B    3 1 B
    3         F    3 2 F
        2     H    3 2 H
              B    3 2 B
```

22. b)

Sample Space

```
          Y     B    LYB
                J    LYJ
L         O     B    LOB
                J    LOJ
          P     B    LPB
                J    LPJ
          Y     B    TYB
                J    TYJ
T         O     B    TOB
                J    TOJ
          P     B    TPB
                J    TPJ
          Y     B    SYB
                J    SYJ
S         O     B    SOB
                J    SOJ
          P     B    SPB
                J    SPJ
          Y     B    IYB
                J    IYJ
I         O     B    IOB
                J    IOJ
          P     B    IPB
                J    IPJ
```

23. b)

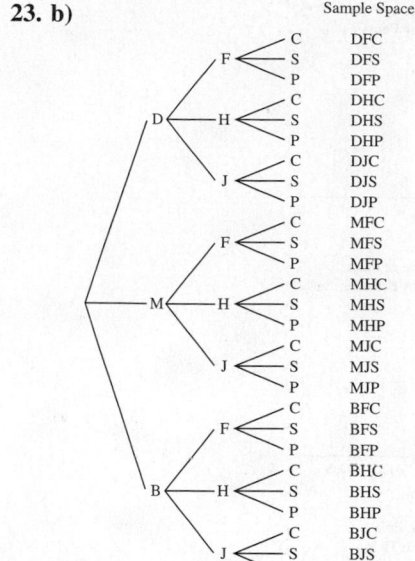

Sample Space

DFC
DFS
DFP
DHC
DHS
DHP
DJC
DJS
DJP
MFC
MFS
MFP
MHC
MHS
MHP
MJC
MJS
MJP
BFC
BFS
BFP
BHC
BHS
BHP
BJC
BJS
BJP

24. b)

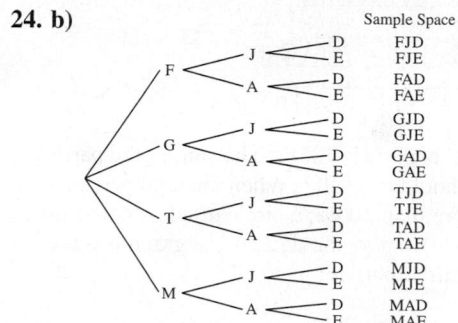

Sample Space

FJD
FJE
FAD
FAE
GJD
GJE
GAD
GAE
TJD
TJE
TAD
TAE
MJD
MJE
MAD
MAE

25. b)

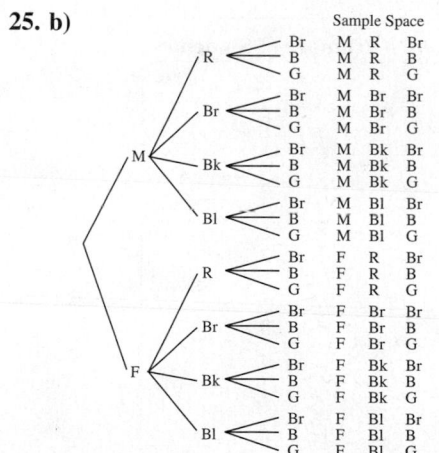

Sample Space

M R Br
M R B
M R G
M Br Br
M Br B
M Br G
M Bk Br
M Bk B
M Bk G
M Bl Br
M Bl B
M Bl G
F R Br
F R B
F R G
F Br Br
F Br B
F Br G
F Bk Br
F Bk B
F Bk G
F Bl Br
F Bl B
F Bl G

26. b)

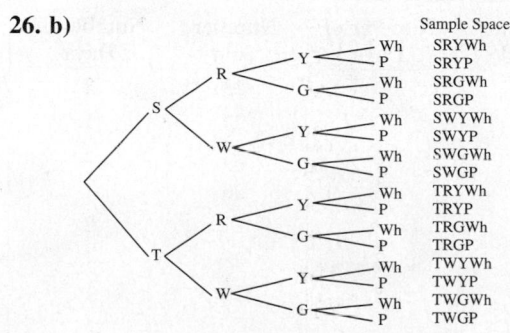

Sample Space

SRYWh
SRYP
SRGWh
SRGP
SWYWh
SWYP
SWGWh
SWGP
TRYWh
TRYP
TRGWh
TRGP
TWYWh
TWYP
TWGWh
TWGP

27. c) No, the probability of selecting a red chip is not the same as the probability of selecting a white chip.

30. 5 faces

SECTION 12.9, PAGE 749

47. a)

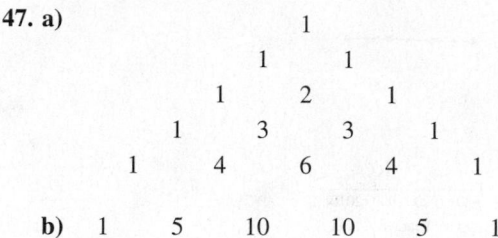

b)   1   5   10   10   5   1

REVIEW EXERCISES, PAGE 767

23. a)

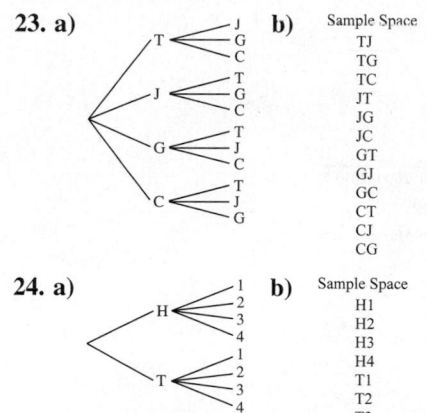

b)

Sample Space

TJ
TG
TC
JT
JG
JC
GT
GJ
GC
CT
CJ
CG

24. a)

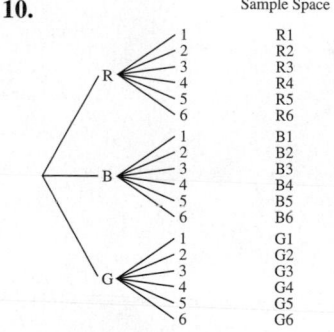

b)

Sample Space

H1
H2
H3
H4
T1
T2
T3
T4

CHAPTER TEST, PAGE 771

10.

Sample Space

R1
R2
R3
R4
R5
R6
B1
B2
B3
B4
B5
B6
G1
G2
G3
G4
G5
G6

Chapter 13

SECTION 13.2, PAGE 781

3. Mama Mia's may have more empty spaces and more cars in the parking lot than Shanghi's due to a larger parking lot or because more people may walk to Mama Mia's than to Shanghi's.

4. Although the cookies are fat free, they still contain calories. Eating many of them may still cause you to gain weight.

9. We don't know how many of each professor's students were surveyed. Perhaps more of Professor Malone's students than Professor Wagner's students were surveyed.

Also, because more students prefer a teacher does not mean that he or she is a better teacher. For example, a particular teacher may be an easier grader and that may be why that teacher is preferred.

15. a)

b)

16. a)

b)

17. a)

b)

18. a)

b)

19. a)

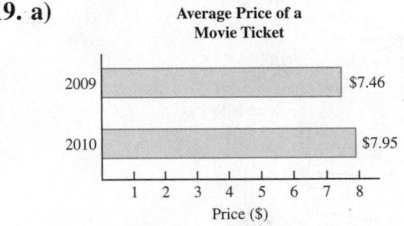

21. Yes, the sum of its parts is 121%. The sum of the parts of a circle graph should be 100%. When the total percent of responses is more than 100%, a circle graph is not an appropriate graph to display the data. A bar graph is more appropriate in this situation.

SECTION 13.3, PAGE 792

11.

Number of Visits	Number of Students
0	3
1	8
2	3
3	5
4	2
5	7
6	2
7	3
8	4
9	1
10	2

12.

Number Sold	Number of Days	Number Sold	Number of Days
15	3	23	2
16	2	24	1
17	0	25	2
18	3	26	1
19	4	27	2
20	3	28	1
21	5	29	1
22	2		

13.

Circulation (ten thousands)	Number of Magazines
173–322	33
323–472	10
473–622	1
623–772	1
773–922	1

14.

Circulation (ten thousands)	Number of Magazines
170–316	31
317–463	11
464–610	2
611–757	0
758–904	2

15.

Circulation (ten thousands)	Number of Magazines
173–272	28
273–372	10
373–472	5
473–572	1
573–672	0
673–772	1
773–872	1

16.

Circulation (ten thousands)	Number of Magazines
173–250	24
251–328	10
329–406	8
407–484	1
485–562	1
563–640	0
641–718	0
719–796	1
797–874	1

17.

Population (millions)	Number of Cities
7.0–7.9	6
8.0–8.9	4
9.0–9.9	1
10.0–10.9	3
11.0–11.9	1
12.0–12.9	2
13.0–13.9	3

18.

Population (millions)	Number of Cities
6.5–7.4	3
7.5–8.4	4
8.5–9.4	3
9.5–10.4	2
10.5–11.4	3
11.5–12.4	0
12.5–13.4	3
13.5–14.4	2

19.

Population (millions)	Number of Cities
6.5–7.5	3
7.6–8.6	4
8.7–9.7	4
9.8–10.8	3
10.9–11.9	1
12.0–13.0	3
13.1–14.1	2

20.

Population (millions)	Number of Cities
7.0–7.4	3
7.5–7.9	3
8.0–8.4	1
8.5–8.9	3
9.0–9.4	0
9.5–9.9	1
10.0–10.4	1
10.5–10.9	2
11.0–11.4	1
11.5–11.9	0
12.0–12.4	0
12.5–12.9	2
13.0–13.4	1
13.5–13.9	2

21.

Percent	Number of States
6.4–8.3	2
8.4–10.3	13
10.4–12.3	14
12.4–14.3	9
14.4–16.3	9
16.4–18.3	2
18.4–20.3	0
20.4–22.3	1

22.

Percent	Number of States
6.4–9.0	7
9.1–11.7	20
11.8–14.4	12
14.5–17.1	10
17.2–19.8	0
19.9–22.5	1

23.

Percent	Number of States
6.4–7.8	1
7.9–9.3	7
9.4–10.8	12
10.9–12.3	9
12.4–13.8	7
13.9–15.3	8
15.4–16.8	4
16.9–18.3	1
18.4–19.8	0
19.9–21.3	1

24.

Percent	Number of States
6.4–8.8	6
8.9–11.3	19
11.4–13.8	11
13.9–16.3	11
16.4–18.8	2
18.9–21.3	1

26. 1|5 represents 15

```
1 0 5 7
2 4 4
3 6 0 3
4 8 5 2 5 8
5 3 4
6 0 2 0
```

27. a)

Salaries (1000s of dollars)	Number of Social Workers
27	1
28	7
29	4
30	3
31	2
32	3
33	3
34	2

b) and c)

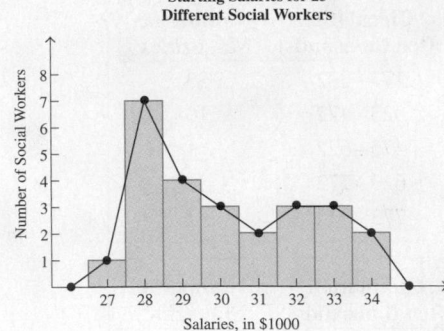

Starting Salaries for 25 Different Social Workers

c) 2|8 represents 28

```
2 7 8 8 8 8 8 8 8 9 9 9 9
3 0 0 0 1 1 2 2 2 3 3 3 4 4
```

28. a)

Age	Number of People
20–30	10
31–41	14
42–52	9
53–63	4
64–74	3

b) and c)

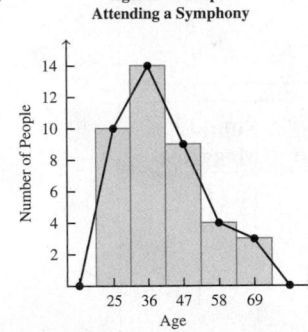

Ages of 40 People Attending a Symphony

d) 2|3 represents 23

```
2 0 0 3 3 6 6 9
3 0 0 0 1 1 2 3 4 4 5 5 7 8 9
4 0 0 0 2 5 7 9 9 9
5 0 1 1 4 7
6 2 3 6 9
7 2
```

29. a)

Total Gross (millions of dollars)	Number of Tours
80–91	12
92–103	4
104–115	3
116–127	2
128–139	3
140–151	0
152–163	1

b) and c)

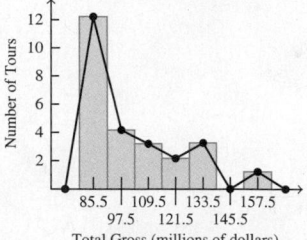

Top 25 Grossing North American
Concert Tours, 1985–2008

30. a)

Age	Number of Presidents
42–47	6
48–53	11
54–59	17
60–65	8
66–71	2

b) and c)

Ages of U.S. Presidents
at Their First Inauguration

31. e)

Number of Televisions	Number of Homes
0	2
1	4
2	8
3	6
4	4
5	3
6	1

32. e)

Price	Number of Students
625–675	2
676–726	4
727–777	6
778–828	8
829–879	7
880–930	3
931–981	0
982–1032	1

33. d)

Number of Messages	Number of People	Number of Messages	Number of People
3	2	7	3
4	3	8	8
5	7	9	6
6	4	10	3

e)

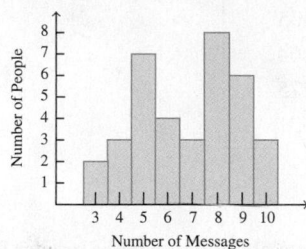

Number of E-Mail Messages Sent

34. d)

Number of Visits	Number of Families
1	4
2	2
3	8
4	8
5	6
6	11
7	9
8	3
9	0
10	1

e)

Number of Visits Selected Families
Have Made to the San Diego Zoo

35.

Tuition/Fees:	$5026.65
Room:	$5303.48
Board:	$3336.53
Computer costs:	$903.34

36.

GPS:	174
DVD player:	162
Extra cup holders:	90
Roof rack:	48
Other	126

SECTION 13.4, PAGE 802

24. Answers will vary. The National Center for Health uses the median for averages in this exercise.

25. A 79 mean average on 10 quizzes gives a total of 790 points. An 80 mean average on 10 quizzes requires a total of 800 points. Thus, Jim missed a B by 10 points, not 1 point.

53. a)

Ruth	Mantle
0.290	0.300
0.359	0.365
0.301	0.304
0.272	0.275
0.315	0.321

SECTION 13.5, PAGE 812

24. b) The spread of the data about the mean is greater for the evening class since the standard deviation is greater for the evening class.

27. d) If each number in a distribution is multiplied by n, the mean and standard deviation of the new distribution will be n times that of the original distribution.

31. a)

	East		West	
Number of Oil Changes Made	**Number of Days**		**Number of Oil Changes Made**	**Number of Days**
15–20	2		15–20	0
21–26	2		21–26	0
27–32	5		27–32	6
33–38	4		33–38	9
39–44	7		39–44	4
45–50	1		45–50	6
51–56	1		51–56	0
57–62	2		57–62	0
63–68	1		63–68	0

b)

Number of Oil Changes Made Daily at East Store

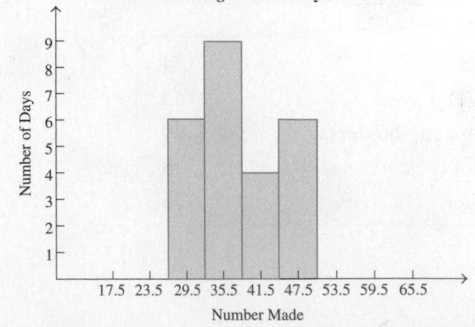

Number of Oil Changes Made Daily at West Store

SECTION 13.7, PAGE 842

23. a)   **b)** 0.981   **c)** Yes   **d)** Yes

24. a)   **b)** −0.907   **c)** Yes   **d)** No

25. a)   **b)** 0.228   **c)** No   **d)** No

26. a)   **b)** −0.883   **c)** Yes   **d)** No

27. a)   **b)** 0.999   **c)** Yes   **d)** Yes

28. a) 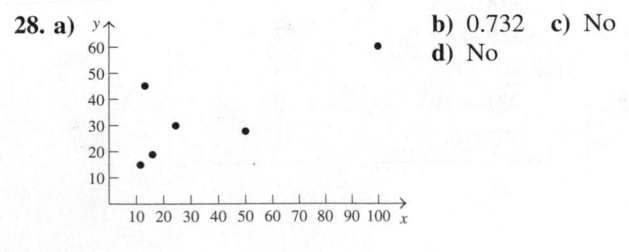   **b)** 0.732   **c)** No   **d)** No

29. a)   **b)** -0.968 **c)** Yes **d)** Yes

30. a)   **b)** 1.00 **c)** Yes **d)** Yes

49. c)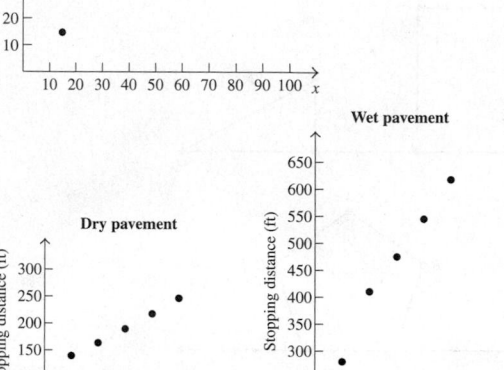

Dry pavement

Wet pavement

REVIEW EXERCISES, PAGE 848

5. a)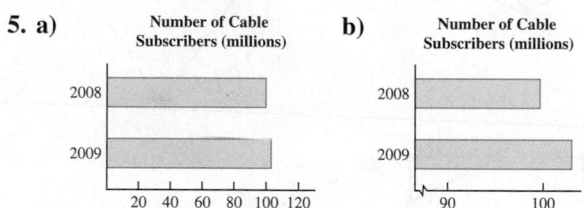

Number of Cable Subscribers (millions)

b) Number of Cable Subscribers (millions)

6. a)

Class	Frequency
35	1
36	3
37	6
38	2
39	3
40	0
41	4
42	1
43	3
44	1
45	1

b) and c)

7. a)

High Temperature	Number of Cities
58–62	1
63–67	4
68–72	9
73–77	10
78–82	11
83–87	4
88–92	1

b) and c)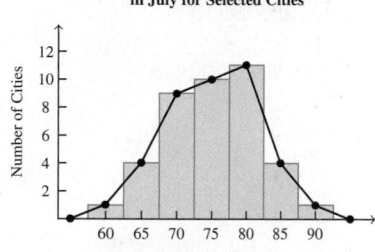

Average Monthly High Temperature in July for Selected Cities

d) 5|8 represents 58

```
5 | 8
6 | 3 6 6 7 8 8 9
7 | 0 1 1 1 2 2 3 3 3 4 5 5 5 6 6 7 9 9 9
8 | 0 0 0 0 1 2 2 2 3 4 4 7
9 | 1
```

29. a)

Bear Sightings

30. a)

Daily Sales

45.

Number of children	Number of Presidents
0–1	8
2–3	16
4–5	10
6–7	6
8–9	1
10–11	1
12–13	0
14–15	1

46. and 47.

Number of Children of U.S. Presidents

CHAPTER TEST, PAGE 851

7.

Class	Frequency
25–30	7
31–36	5
37–42	1
43–48	7
49–54	5
55–60	3
61–66	2

8.

9.

20. a)

Hourly Minimum Wage in the U.S.

Chapter 14

SECTION 14.1, PAGE 860

9. **10.**

11. **12.**

13.

14.

21. **22.**

23.

24.

25.

26.

27. **28.**

29.

30.

31.

32.

43. d) The sum of the degrees is equal to twice the number of edges, which is true since each edge must connect two vertices. Each edge then contributes two to the sum of the degrees.

44.

Other answers are possible.

SECTION 14.2, PAGE 872

27. a)

28. a)

29. a)

30. a)

31. a)

32. a)

33. a)

34. a)

35. a)

36. a)

55. b) California, Nevada, and Louisiana (and others) have an odd number of states bordering them. Since a graph of the United States would have more than two odd vertices, no Euler path and no Euler circuit exist.

57. a)   **b)**   **c)**

SECTION 14.3, PAGE 884

19.   **20.**

25. a)   **26. a)**

27. a)   **28. a)**

29. a)

30. a)

31. a)

32. a)

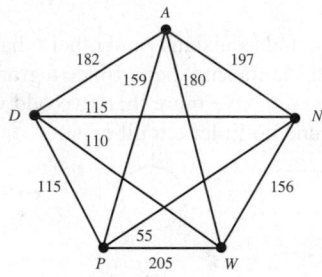

34. a) 2, 1; 2 · 1 = 2! = 2 This result is the same as the number of Hamilton circuits in a complete graph with three vertices.

  c) 4, 3, 2, 1: 4 · 3 · 2 · 1 = 4! = 24; 5, 4, 3, 2, 1: 5 · 4 · 3 · 2 · 1 = 5! = 120. These results are the same as the numbers of Hamilton circuits in complete graphs with five and six vertices, respectively.

  d) When starting at a vertex in a complete graph with n vertices, you have $n - 1$ choices. At your second vertex, you have one less choice, or $n - 2$ choices. This process continues until you only have one vertex from which to choose.

SECTION 14.4, PAGE 895

7.

8.

9.

10.

11.

Other answers are possible.

12.

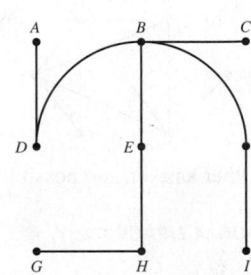

Other answers are possible.

13.

Other answers are possible.

14.

Other answers are possible.

15.

Other answers are possible.

16.

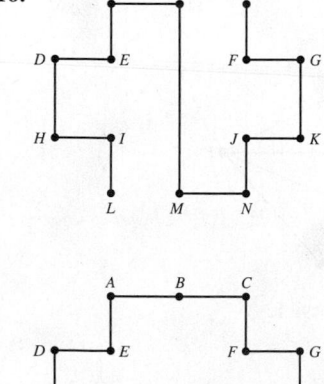

Other answers are possible.

17.

Other answers are possible.

18.

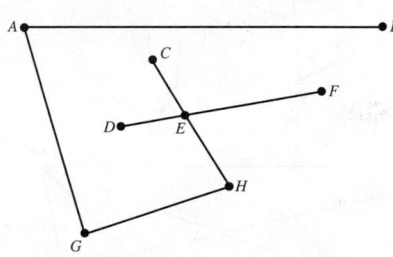

Other answers are possible.

19.

20.

21.

22.

23.

24.

25.

26.

27. a)

Other answers are possible.

b)

28. a)

Other answers are possible.

b)

29. a)

30. a)

31. a)

Other answers are possible.

b)

32. a)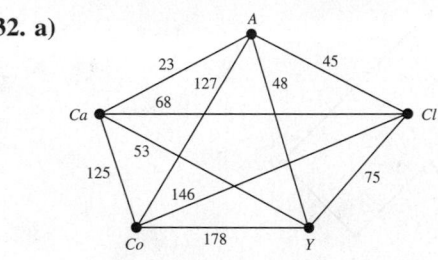

Other answers are possible.

b)

33. a) **b)**

34. a)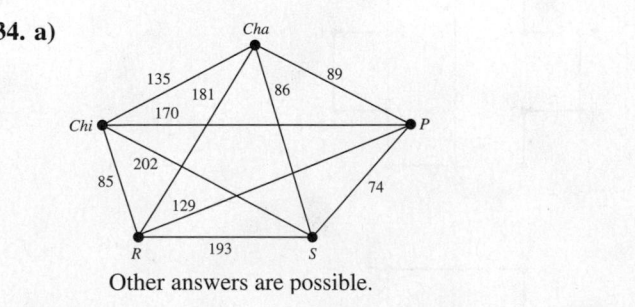

Other answers are possible.

b)

REVIEW EXERCISES, PAGE 901

1.

Other answers are possible.

2.

Other answers are possible.

5.

6.

14. a)

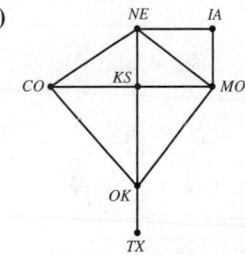

b) Yes. *CO, NE, IA, MO, NE, KS, MO, OK, CO, KS, OK, TX*; other answers are possible.

15. a)

21.

23. a)

b) *P, D, M, C, P* or *P, C, M, D, P*   **c)** $2088

24. a)

25.

26.

Other answers are possible.

27.

28. a)

b)

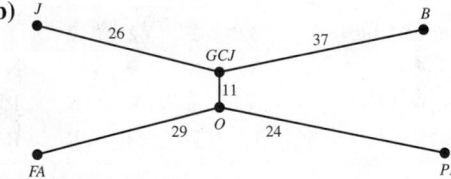

CHAPTER TEST, PAGE 904

1.

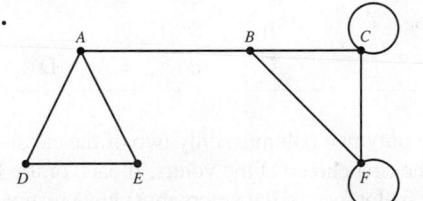

Other answers are possible.

2.

3.

4. One example:

11.

13.

16.

17.

Other answers are possible.

18.

19.

Chapter 15

SECTION 15.1, PAGE 921

11.

Number of Votes	3	1	2	2	1
First	R	N	P	P	N
Second	N	R	R	N	P
Third	P	P	N	R	R

12.

Number of Votes	2	3	2	1
First	D	C	B	C
Second	B	D	D	B
Third	C	B	C	D

43. a) If there were only two columns, only two of the candidates were the first choice of the voters. If each of the 15 voters cast a ballot, one of the voters must have received a majority of votes because 15 cannot be split evenly.

  b) An odd number cannot be divided evenly, so one of the two first-choice candidates must receive more than half of the votes.

49. One possible answer is:

Number of Votes	5	5	2
First	A	B	C
Second	B	A	B
Third	C	C	A

SECTION 15.2, PAGE 934

15. No. C wins by plurality with elimination, but A is preferred over each of the other candidates using head-to-head comparisons.

21. No. C wins by plurality with elimination. If the voters change their preference, B wins by plurality with elimination.

22. No. B wins by plurality with elimination. If the voters change their preference, A wins by plurality with elimination.

23. No. D wins by pairwise comparison. If the voters change their preference, B wins by pairwise comparison.

24. No. A wins by the Borda count method. If the voters change their preference, B wins by the Borda count method.

25. No. B wins by pairwise comparison. If A, C, and E drop out, D wins by pairwise comparison.

SECTION 15.3, PAGE 952

48. Answers will vary. One possible answer is A: 3,250,000, B: 1,750,000, C: 2,265,000, D: 2,735,000

SECTION 15.4, PAGE 961

8. b) Yes. Office B loses a chair, whereas offices C and D gains a chair if the number of chairs is increased.

13. b) Yes. Division B loses an internship to division A even though the population of division B grew faster than the population of division A.

15. b) Yes. The apportionment is now 9, 39, 7, and group B loses a manager.

REVIEW EXERCISES, PAGE 964

3.

Number of Votes	3	2	1	1	3
First	B	A	D	D	C
Second	A	C	C	A	B
Third	C	D	A	B	A
Fourth	D	B	B	C	D

4.

Number of Votes	2	2	2	1
First	C	A	B	C
Second	A	C	A	B
Third	B	B	C	A

21. No. B wins by the Borda count method, but A is preferred over each of the other candidates using head-to-head comparisons.

22. c) No. If B drops out, A is the winner by plurality with elimination. Therefore, the irrelevant alternatives criterion is not satisfied.

23. f) Plurality method, Borda count method, and plurality with elimination method all violate the head-to-head criterion.

Credits

PHOTO CREDITS

Page 01, David R. Frazier/Photolibrary/Alamy; Page 02, Flynavyjp/Dreamstime; Page 03, Michael Dwyer/Alamy; Page 04, Johnson Space Center/NASA; Page 08, OJO Images Ltd/Alamy; Page 09, Imagebroker/Alamy; Page 10, David Epperson/Photodisc/Getty Images; Page 11, Natali Glado/Shutterstock; Page 13, Courtesy of Allen Angel; Page 14, Courtesy of Allen Angel; Page 15, ex. 25, Stockbyte/Getty Images; Page 15, ex. 29, Evan Meyer/Shutterstock; Page 17, ex. 39, Courtesy of Allen Angel; Page 17, ex. 40, Michael C. Gray/Shutterstock; Page 18, ex. 47, Courtesy of Allen Angel; Page 18, ex. 48, Nick Stubbs/Shutterstock; Page 20, Anatoliy Kosolapov/Shutterstock; Page 22, box, AP Images; Page 22, margin, Christopher Eng-Wong Photography/Shutterstock; Page 23, Classic Image/Alamy; Page 25, ImageState/Alamy; Page 26, Norman Jung/Corbis; Page 31, Blend Images/Alamy; Page 37, Ron Buskirk/Alamy; Page 39, *Still Life: Vase With Twelve Sunflowers* (1888), Vincent Van Gogh. Oil on canvas. Neue Pinakothek, Munich, Germany/Bridgeman Art Library/SuperStock; Page 42, BananaStock/Thinkstock; Page 43, margin, Interfoto/Alamy; Page 43, box, Bill Bachmann/Alamy; Page 45, Jorge Salcedo/Shutterstock; Page 48, Johnson Space Center/NASA; Page 49, ex. 54, Pictorial Press, Ltd./Alamy; Page 49, ex. 58, Interfoto/Alamy; Page 51, ex. 87, Pete Whittle/Splash News/Newscom; Page 51, margin, Frank Tozier/Alamy; Page 53, BlueOrange Studio/Shutterstock; Page 54, Blend Images/Alamy; Page 55, George Doyle/Stockbyte/Thinkstock; Page 56, Courtesy of Allen Angel; Page 57, Jeff Greenberg/Alamy; Page 64, Courtesy of Allen Angel; Page 65, California California/Alamy; Page 67, ex. 102, Jeff Greenberg/Alamy; Page 67, Purestock/Getty Images; Page 68, Beth Anderson/Pearson; Page 73, Photos 12/Alamy; Page 75, Creatas/Thinkstock; Page 77, Vicki Beaver/Alamy; Page 79, Beth Anderson/Pearson; Page 80, Greg Probst/Danita Delimont/Alamy; Page 81, Stockbyte/Thinkstock; Page 82, ex. 12, JupiterImages/liquidlibrary/Thinkstock; Page 82, ex. 15, Melissa Brandes/Shutterstock; Page 83, Interfoto/Alamy; Page 85, AKG Images/Newscom; Page 89, Michael Wick/Shutterstock; Page 90, Jason DeCrow/AP Iimages; Page 91, Teekaygee/Shutterstock; Page 93, Goodluz/Shutterstock; Page 94, Daniel Hurst/Stock Connection Worldwide/Newscom; Page 95, Thinkstock; Page 96, Pictorial Press, Ltd./Alamy; Page 98, Library of Congress Prints and Photographs Division [LC-USZ62-61664]; Page 99, Andy Dean Photography/Shutterstock; Page 100, top, Beth Anderson/Pearson; Page 100, bottom, Gunter Marx/Alamy; Page 101, Lykovata/Shutterstock; Page 102, ex. 9, Exactostock/SuperStock; Page 102, ex. 13, Danylchenko Iaroslav/Shutterstock; Page 102, ex. 19, Specta/Shutterstock; Page 102, ex. 27, Joe Gough/Shutterstock; Page 103, Mlorenz/Shutterstock; Page 104, Tom Maelsa/AFP/Getty Images/Newscom; Page 105, British Retail Photography/Alamy; Page 108, Peter Nadolski/Shutterstock; Page 114, Violetkaipa/Shutterstock; Page 115, ex. 19, Lionel Hahn/Lionel Hahn/AbacaUsa/Newscom; Page 115, ex. 41, DFree/Shutterstock; Page 116, ex. 44, Jun Mu/Shutterstock; Page 116, ex. 48, EditorialByDarrellYoung/Alamy; Page 117, Digital Vision/Valueline/Thinkstock; Page 118, Cohen/Ostrow/Digital Vision/Getty Images; Page 121, Natalia Bratslavsky/Shutterstock; Page 125, ex. 28, Sonya Etchison/Shutterstock; Page 125, ex. 57, iStockphoto; Page 127, Dennis Runde; Page 130, box/top, Library of Congress Prints and Photographs Division [LC-USZ62-70064]; Page 130, box/bottom, Photos 12/Alamy; Page 131, top, Debby Wong/Shutterstock; Page 131, box, Mary Evans Picture Library/Alamy; Page 132, Ritu Manoj Jethani/Shutterstock; Page 133, Thefinalmiracle/Shutterstock; Page 135, Yuri Arcurs/Shutterstock; Page 137, ex. 41, Beth Anderson/Pearson; Page 137, ex. 54, Noel Powell, Schaumburg/Shutterstock; Page 138, ex. 62, Krivosheev Vitaly/Shutterstock; Page 138, ex. 66, Diane Macdonald/Stockbyte/Getty Images; Page 138, ex. 69, Charles T. Bennett/Shutterstock; Page 139, ex. 73, Beth Anderson/Pearson; Page 139, ex. 81, Paul Radenfeld/Digital Vision/Getty images; Page 140, Rob Hobson/UPI/Newscom; Page 142, margin/top, Bryan Busovicki/Shutterstock; Page 142, margin/bottom, Lane Ericcson-Photolink/Newscom; Page 144, James Steidl/Shutterstock; Page 146, Anthony Berenyi/Shutterstock; Page 148, ex. 33, Stockbyte/Getty Images; Page 148, ex. 43, FloridaStock/Shutterstock; Page 149, Shebeko/Shutterstock; Page 150, Helga Esteb/Shutterstock; Page 151, Interfoto/Alamy; Page 153, Pincasso/Shutterstock; Page 155, Olga_i/Shutterstock; Page 155, James Coleman/Shutterstock; Page 155, Wilfried Krecichwost/Getty Images; Page 156, Samson Yury/Shutterstock; Page 164, Motorlife/Alamy; Page 165, Steven Milne/Alamy; Page 166, NASA; Page 167, Jet Propulsion Laboratory/NASA; Page 169, Monkey Business/ Fotolia; Page 170, MCT/Newscom; Page 172, Sylvie Bouchard/Shutterstock; Page 173, Courtesy of Denise Schmandt-Besserat; Page 174, Courtesy of Allen Angel; Page 174, Courtesy of Allen Angel; Page 178, ex. 84, Digital Vision; Page 178, margin, Mark Davis/CBS/Newscom; Page 180, Andy Crawford/Dorling Kindersley, Ltd.; Page 181, Morgan Lane Photography/Shutterstock; Page 183, Olinchuk/Shutterstock; Page 185, David J. Green/Alamy; Page 186, Andersen Ross/Blend Images/Getty Images; Page 187, Darren Brode/Shutterstock; Page 188, James Hardy/PhotoAlto Agency RF Collections/Getty Images; Page 189, Khoroshunova Olga/Shutterstock; Page 192, margin, Tyler Olson/ Fotolia; Page 192, ex. 70, GM/Wieck/Newscom; Page 195, BW Folsom/Shutterstock; Page 200, margin, JupiterImages/Thinkstock; Page 200, ex. 72, Ryan McVay/Photodisc/Getty Images; Page 201, PhotoDisc Vol. 41; Page 203, Interfoto/Alamy; Page 209, H. Mark Weidman Photography/Alamy; Page 210, Svetlana Mihailova/Shutterstock; Page 211, Interfoto/Alamy; Page 212, M. Favareille/Musée des Arts et Métiers.Cnam, Paris; Page 214, SPL/Photo Researchers, Inc.; Page 216, Nan728/Shutterstock; Page 219, ex. 65, Corbis Flirt/Alamy; Page 219, ex. 68, Aurora Photos/Alamy; Page 221, Bigchen/Shutterstock; Page 224, Dorling Kindersley, Ltd.; Page 228, ex. 71, General Dynamics Electric Boat/U.S. Navy; Page 228, ex. 75, Olinchuk/Shutterstock; Page 229, Elena Elisseeva/Shutterstock; Page 230, Jeff Greenberg/Alamy; Page 237, Mikhail/Shutterstock; Page 240, Ocean/Corbis; Page 241, 2399 2009/Shutterstock; Page 243, David Stluka/AP Images; Page 245, The Art Archive/Alamy; Page 251, ex. 85, Dyoma/Shutterstock; Page 251, ex. 86, Bradcalkins/Dreamstime; Page 252, margin, Digital Vision/Getty Images; Page 252, box, Robert D. Pinna/Shutterstock; Page 253, Colin McPherson/Corbis; Page 258, Gemenacom/Shutterstock; Page 259, Scott Camazine/Alamy; Page 262, Konstantin Mironov/Shutterstock; Page 263, box/left, Collections artistiques de l'Université de Liège; Page 263, box/right, Courtesy of MRA; Page 264, April Saul/Newscom; Page 265, Library of Congress Prints and Photographs Division [LC-USZC4-8886]; Page 268, ex. 95, Whitechild/Shutterstock; Page 268, ex. 98, Pablo Fonseca Q./La Nacion de Costa Rica/Newscom; Page 268, ex. 99, Aivolie/Shutterstock; Page 270, ex. 111, Carles O'Rear/Corbis; Page 270, margin, Deco Images II/Alamy; Page 271, Bilwissedition Ltd. & Co. KG/Alamy; Page 273, Christos Georghiou/Shutterstock; Page 274, Rob Marmion/Shutterstock; Page 276, ex. 78, Denise Kappa/Shutterstock; Page 276, ex. 79, Digital Vision/Thinkstock; Page 277, Bettmann/Corbis; Page 278, margin, lidiatt/Shutterstock; Page 278, box, David Lyons/Alamy; Page 279, Vasily Topko/Shutterstock; Page 280, margin/top, Sculpies/Shutterstock; Page 280, margin/bottom, Polartern/Shutterstock; Page 280, figure 5.14, Mircea Bezergheanu/Shutterstock; Page 281, *Fibonacci's Garden* (1995), Caryl Bryer Fallert. Hand-dyed and painted, machine pieced and quilted 100% cotton fabric; batting: 80% cotton, 20% polyester; 71 × 54 in.; Page 281, *Circus Sideshow* (1887–1888), Georges Seurat. Oil on canvas, 39 1/4 × 59 in. (99.7 × 149.9 cm). Metropolitan Museum of Art, Bequest of Stephen C. Clark, 1960. [61.101.17]/SuperStock; Page 286, Visions of America, LLC./Alamy; Page 287, Ryan McVay/Thinkstock; Page 288, Goddard Space Flight Center/NASA; Page 291, Blend Images/Shutterstock; Page 292, David R. Frazier/Photolibrary, Inc./Alamy; Page 293, Steve Vidler/Alamy; Page 294, Alfonso Vicente/Alamy; Page 296, A. T. Willett/Alamy; Page 297, Gina Smith/Shutterstock; Page 298, Library of Congress Prints and Photographs Division [LC-USZ62-62123]; Page 305, Robert Harding Picture Library, Ltd./Alamy; Page 307, ex. 65, Orange Line Media/Shutterstock; Page 307, ex. 69, Courtesy of Allen Angel; Page 308, Exactostock/SuperStock; Page 310, World History Archive/Newscom; Page 311, The Art Gallery Collection/Alamy; Page 313, Iofoto/Shutterstock; Page 314, Iofoto/Shutterstock; Page 315, Monkey Business Images/Shutterstock; Page 317, Marnie Greenhut/Pearson; Page 318, ex. 31, Radius Images/Alamy; Page 318, ex. 38, Worachat Sodsri/Shutterstock; Page 319, Lindsey Stock/Dorling Kindersley, Ltd.; Page 319, Lichtmeister/Shutterstock; Page 320, Dueselder/Caro/Alamy; Page 322, Oleg Gerasymenko/Fotolia, LLC.; Page 324, Courtesy of Christine Abbott; Page 326, David P. Lewis/Shutterstock; Page 327, ex. 41, Liviu

FIGURE CREDITS

General Interest

Index

commas in, 437
conversion to/from, 464–468
conversion within, 437–440
cubic units in, 447
as decimal system, 436–437
European Union and, 459
history of, 435
length in, 436, 443–444, 466
mass in, 436, 454–459, 467, 468
in medicine, 448, 449
nonadopters of, 456, 469
prefixes for, 436–437
spaces in, 437
square units in, 445–446
temperature in, 436, 457–459
terminology of, 436
volume in, 436, 446–449, 466, 467, 468
Metric tonne, 455
micro, 437
Midpoint of class, 786
Midrange, 798–799, 800
Mihailescu, Preda, 263
milli, 436
Milligram, 455
Milliliter, 446–447
Millimeter, 443–444
Minimum-cost spanning tree, 891–895
Minuet, Peter Du, 623
Mixed numbers, 230–232
Möbius, August Ferdinand, 543
Möbius strip, 543–544, 546
   Klein bottle and, 544–545
Modal class, of frequency distribution, 786
Mode, 797–800, 799, 800
   in normal distribution, 818–828
Models. *See* Mathematical models
Modified divisor, 943–946, 947
Modular arithmetic, 585–592
   applications of, 589–590
   congruence in, 586–588
   in cryptography, 587
   groups and, 590–592
   multiplication in, 588–590
   subtraction in, 588
Modulo *m* systems, 585–590
Modulor, 280
Modus ponens, 141–142
Modus tollens, 143
Monotonicity criterion, 929–930
Morain, François, 217
Mortality statistics, 776
Mortgages, 646–657
   adjustable-rate, 646, 652–654
   adjusted monthly income and, 647
   amortization schedule for, 652
   closing and, 646
   conventional, 646, 647–652
   down payment and, 646
   FHA, 653
   monthly payment calculation for, 647–649
   payment caps for, 653
   points and, 646–647
   qualifying for, 647–648
   rate caps for, 653

second, 652
VA, 653
Motion
   parabolic, 368
   of projectile, 368
   quadratic equation for, 358
   rigid, 525–535
      definition of, 525
      reflections, 525–526
      symmetry, 532–535
      translations (glides), 528
Movies
   audience quadrants for, 336
   computer-generated, 336, 417, 492
Mozart, Wolfgang Amadeus, 730
Multiplication
   in additive systems, 171
   in algebra, 292
   associative property of, 254, 256
   in Babylonian system, 179
   in base conversion, 180, 183
   in base systems, 196–197
   of binomials, 352–353
   with calculator, 265
   in Chinese system, 173–174
   commutative property of, 253–254, 256
   cross, 304–305
   distributive property of, 254–255, 256
   in Egyptian system, 171
   in factoring, 352–356
   FOIL method of, 352
   of fractions, 235–236
   in Hindu-Arabic system, 179
   of integers, 224–225
   in Ionic Greek system, 176
   of irrational numbers, 246
   lattice, 201–202
   of matrices, 406–410
   in modular arithmetic, 588–590
   with Napier's rods, 202–203
   by negative numbers, 330
   of prime numbers. *See* Prime factorization
   product in
      of even numbers, 2
      factors of, 210
   of quaternions, 881
   Russian peasant, 200
   in scientific notation, 264
   in solving inequalities, 330
   teaching of, 201
Multiplication formula, 720–723
Multiplication property of equality, 299
Multiplicative identity element, 569, 570
Multiplicative identity matrices, 409, 414, 416
Multiplicative inverses, 409, 414
Multiplicative systems, 173–175
Music
   acoustics and, 810
   Fibonacci numbers in, 281–282
   mathematics in, 237
   probability and, 730
   rational numbers in, 237

Mutual funds, 661
Mutually exclusive events, 718–719
MySpace, 855

nano, 437
Napier's rods, 202–203
National debt, 265
Natural exponential equation, 370–372
Natural exponential growth or decay formula, 370
Natural exponential growth or decay function, 370–373
Natural numbers, 2, 43, 210
   closure of, 253
   factors of, 210
   sets of, 84–85. *See also* Set(s)
   vs. whole numbers, 221
Navigation, base 60 system in, 181
Nearest neighbor method, 880, 882–883
Negations (*not* statements), 95–96, 99, 131
   of conditional statements, 132
   definition of, 95–96
   neither-nor statements, 99
   symbol for, 97, 98, 107
   truth tables for, 105, 107. *See also* Truth tables
Negative exponent rule, 261
Negative integers, 221. *See also* Integers
Negative numbers, 301
   division by, 330–331
   multiplication by, 330
neither-nor statements, 99. *See also* Negations (*not* statements)
Nested parentheses, 109
Net worth, average, 800
New-states paradox, 958–960
Newton, Isaac, 246, 298
Nielsen ratings, 775
Nine Chapters on the Mathematical Art, 416
Noether, Amalie Emmy, 591
Nonabelian groups, 577
Noncommutative groups, 577
Non-Euclidean geometry, 550–553
   fifth axiom of, 551–553
Normal distributions, 818–828
   areas of, 821–828
   bimodal, 817
   empirical rule for, 819
   J-shaped, 816
   properties of, 818
   z-scores and, 310, 820–828
not statements. *See* Negations (*not* statements)
Notation
   decimal, 263–264
   scientific, 262–266. *See also* Scientific notation
   set-builder (set-generator), 44
Null sets, 47
   as subsets, 53
Number(s)
   for abstract quantities, 294